NELSON

Science 10

Unit 1
Bob Ritter

Unit 2
Donald Plumb

Unit 3
Frank Jenkins
Hans van Kessel

Unit 4
Alan J. Hirsch

NELSON
™
THOMSON LEARNING

Australia • Canada • Mexico • Singapore • Spain • United Kingdom • United States

NELSON

THOMSON LEARNING™

Nelson Science 10

Bob Ritter
Donald Plumb
Frank Jenkins
Hans van Kessel
Alan J. Hirsch

Nelson Science 10 Project Team:
Elaine Andrews
Julie Bedford
Marnie Benedict
Colin Bisset
Susan Calverley
Angela Cluer
Maureen de Sousa
Zenaida Diores
Erich Falkenberg
Peggy Ferguson
Anna Garnham
Anne Goodes
Susan Green
Julie Greener
Alicja Jamorski
Geraldine Kikuta
Monica Kompter

Julia Lee
Sharon Latta Paterson
Kevin Martindale
Riça Night
Linda O'Neill
Peter Papayanakis
Ruth Peckover
Suzanne Peden
Ken Phipps
Matthew Roberts
Sarah Robertson
Betty Robinson
Rosalyn Steiner
Katherine Strain
Karen Taylor
Rosemary Tanner

Cover Design:
Linda O'Neill

Illustrators:
Andrew Breithaupt
Steven Corrigan
Deborah Crowle
Margo Davis Leclair
John Fraser
Irma Ikonen
Norman Lanting
Dave Mazierski
Dave McKay
Jack McMaster
Linda O'Neill
Ken Phipps

Printer:
Transcontinental Printing Inc.

Canadian Cataloguing in Publication Data

Nelson science 10
Ontario ed.
Includes index.
ISBN 0-17-607501-1

1. Science–Juvenile literature.
2. Science–Experiments–Juvenile literature.
I. Ritter, Bob, 1950–   .
II Title: Science 10.

Q161.2.N46 2000   500
C00–930962–4

Reviewers

Contents

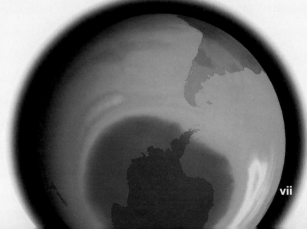

Sustaining Ecosystems

On the United Nations survey of the most desirable places to live, Canada is always ranked at or near the top. Our vast country, rich in natural resources, has benefited in the past from a relatively small human population and peoples who understood the importance of sustaining natural ecosystems. However, as our population grows, the pressure we are putting on Canadian ecosystems is also growing.

Some of that pressure arises out of our ideas, many of which have been linked with environmental problems. "Progress is the production of more goods," "science and technology will solve our problems," "all of nature was placed on Earth for our use," "resources are infinite," "humans have the knowledge to manage our planet" — all of these must be questioned. More than at any time in history, we must challenge our assumptions about the way the natural world works, and what our place is in that world.

Overall Expectations

In this unit, you will be able to

- understand how ecosystems change and how they are sustained;
- investigate factors that affect ecosystems; and
- analyze issues that affect the sustainability of ecosystems.

Chapter 1
Diversity in Ecosystems

Every living thing is part of a complex web of relationships that we call an ecosystem. Every species has a role — if even one species is removed, the ecosystem may change.

In this chapter, you will be able to

- examine the factors (natural and external) that affect the survival of species such as frogs and eagles, and that affect the balance of ecosystems;
- create a database of endangered Canadian species;
- investigate how abiotic factors, such as sunlight and moisture, affect a nonnatural ecosystem (a park) and a natural system (a meadow), and suggest ways of assuring the continuation of those ecosystems;
- examine how abiotic factors affect the survival and location of populations.

Chapter 2
Change and Stability in Ecosystems

Ecosystems often appear unchanging. An untouched forest or pond may look much the same now as it did 40 or 50 years ago. Underneath that surface stability, though, great changes are taking place as matter cycles and energy flows through the system.

In this chapter, you will be able to

- describe how carbon, oxygen, nitrogen, and phosphorus cycle through ecosystems;
- explain how pesticides move through food webs in the Great Lakes, on the Prairies, and in the forests of Atlantic Canada, and assess how the pesticides affect organisms in those food webs;
- analyze how the growth of populations (such as deer, wolves, or humans) is limited by available resources and other factors;
- analyze the benefits and risks of spraying pesticides to control caterpillars.

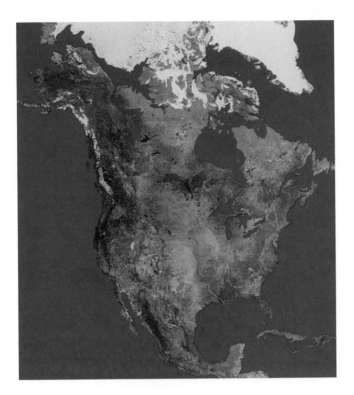

Chapter 3
Sustaining Terrestrial Ecosystems

From tundra to desert, from mixed forest to grassland, Canada supports a wide range of biomes. Many factors, both abiotic and biotic, affect which species live where.

In this chapter, you will be able to

- analyze the climate, vegetation, and physical geography of Canadian biomes, and present the information using spreadsheets, tables, graphs, and diagrams;
- assess the impact on ecosystems of change caused by natural events, and by the technologies of agriculture, forestry, and industry;
- explain how the fertility of soil can be altered and the consequences of such changes;
- research the effects of potato farming and propose a course of action that takes into account human and environmental needs;
- identify and analyze major threats to ecosystems worldwide;
- design and conduct an investigation into the effects of acid rain.

Chapter 4
Sustaining Aquatic Ecosystems

Canada's variety extends also to our aquatic ecosystems. Canadians are struggling now with initiatives to maintain those ecosystems and to produce sustainable harvests.

In this chapter, you will be able to

- explain why aquatic ecosystems respond differently to short-term stresses and long-term changes;
- analyze fish populations and explain how different factors affect the population size;
- identify and evaluate Canadian initiatives to protect the Great Lakes;
- describe and investigate the physical and chemical processes involved in cleaning up contamination in the Great Lakes and in the oceans;
- describe how the relationships between organisms and their ecosystems are viewed by various cultures.

Seeking a New Way

Viewing humans as an integral part of the biosphere allows us to begin thinking not just about how science and technology can change natural ecosystems, but also about how those changes will in turn impact us as a species. It allows us to start from the assumption that any change in the environment will ultimately affect humans, because all living things are interconnected with each other.

In the middle of the 20th century we first saw our planet as a whole, in photographs from space. Satellite images now routinely reveal scars such as forests that have been cleared for wood products or agriculture, and lakes overgrown with algae because of fertilizers and sewage. Changes from fertile farmland to desert, fluctuations in the ozone layer, and declines in fish populations can all be monitored by technology. However, this dramatic increase in the information available about the health of the environment has led us to a contradiction: the more we learn about our environment, the more we realize how little we understand about environmental change and how ecosystems are sustained.

Working on your Challenge allows you to examine real problems and assess the environmental impact of the solutions that you propose. Because you will be conducting research in environmental change, it's not likely you will find any single correct answer. Each solution comes with its own set of risks and benefits.

Challenge

Assessing the Environmental Effects of Human Communities

As you learn about ecosystems and how they are sustained, you will learn how to assess the effects of human activities on ecosystems. You will also be able to demonstrate your learning by completing a Challenge. For more information on the Challenges, see page 158.

1 A Golf Course

Golf is a rapidly growing sport. Near most towns and cities new courses are appearing in what was farmland or forest. Plan a golf course that will have minimum impact on local ecosystems.

2 Community Water Quality

We use water to drink, to wash, to build, to make chemicals, and to transport goods and raw materials. All of these activities affect the environment. Monitor indicators of water quality to assess the environmental impact of your community on a local body of water.

3 Educational Game

Create an educational boardgame that will help players learn about ecosystems and how they can be sustained.

Record your ideas for your Challenge as you progress through this unit and when you see

 # Challenge

Diversity in Ecosystems

HAVE YOU EVER THOUGHT OF OUR PLANET AS A SPACESHIP?
Travelling around the Sun in a slightly elliptical orbit, the Earth carries
with it the only known forms of life in the universe. It is a closed system.
There is no outside source for life-sustaining raw materials, nor any
interplanetary garbage dump to store wastes. Life is totally dependent
on solar energy and the matter available aboard the spaceship Earth.

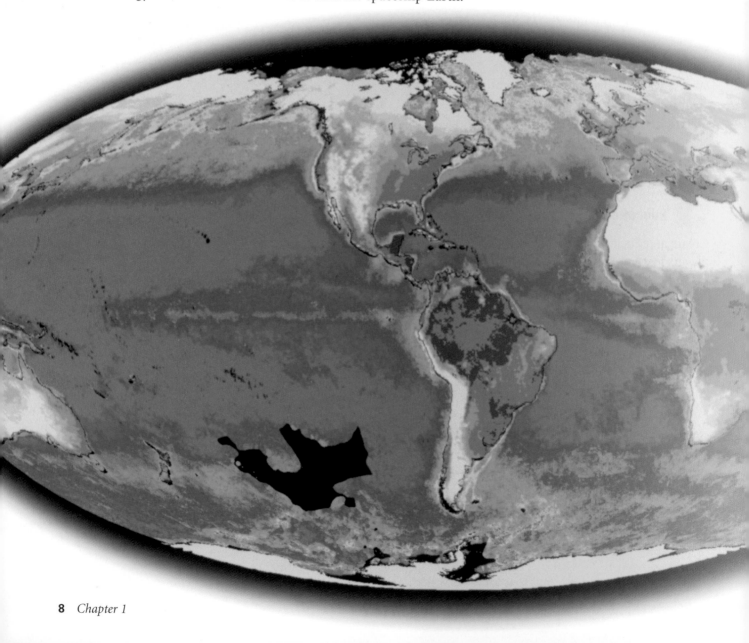

There is, however, one big difference between a spaceship and the Earth. On a spaceship, the temperature and other conditions are much the same throughout, and all of the astronauts have equal access to the ship's resources. On Earth, it is hot in some places, and cold in others. At the equator Earth's inhabitants receive sunlight for about half of each day, but those who live in the far north go months without ever seeing the Sun. The wind blows dry in some areas, and wet in others. For living things, there is no equal access to resources, and there may be wildly different conditions, all depending on where they live.

These differences affect the diversity of living things across our planet. **Figure 1** shows how the amount of plant life varies on Earth. Since animals depend on plants to survive, the number and variety of plants in any area also affect the number and variety (the diversity) of animals.

Figure 1
This satellite image was produced by combining three years of data obtained from a satellite orbiting Earth. It shows the number of plants that are found in each area of our planet.

Land
many plants   few plants

Ocean, Seas, and Lakes
many plants   few plants

Reflect on your Learning

1. As you study **Figure 1**, you can see that plant life seems dense in some areas, but much thinner in others.

   (a) Explain the distribution of plant life.

   (b) Based on the plant life, where in this photo would you expect to find many animals, and where would you expect only a few? How does this match what you know about these regions?

2. We cannot really "throw things away," because everything we discard stays on Earth. On spaceship Earth we cannot go to a "refuelling station" to take on supplies. In that way, Earth is more closed than even a spaceship. And of course on Earth, most of the inhabitants are not human. Spaceships have rules for behaviour that help astronauts to avoid fouling the air and overusing vital water and food supplies and that help them get along with each other.

   (a) Suggest a set of rules for human passengers on spaceship Earth.

   (b) How closely do we follow those rules now? Suggest some behaviours that we should consider changing.

   (c) How might these human practices and behaviours affect the diversity of living things?

Throughout this chapter, note any changes in your ideas as you learn new concepts and develop your skills.

Try This
Activity   Earth Under a Microscope

You can investigate how living things interact in a closed system, on a small and simple scale, by observing microscopic organisms.

Materials: gloves, apron, tap water, medicine dropper, microscope slides, microscope, cultures of yeast, *paramecium*, and *didinium*

🛑 Use gloves while making and observing your slides. Dispose of slides and gloves as directed by your teacher. Wash your hands before leaving the lab.

• Using a medicine dropper, prepare separate wet mounts from each of the three cultures. Examine each slide under a light microscope.

(a) How many different kinds of living things do you see for each slide?

(b) Sketch and describe the organism.

(c) Describe the behaviour of the organism.

• Combine the living things to study how they interact. Prepare the following wet mounts:
1 drop *paramecium* culture + 1 drop yeast culture
1 drop *paramecium* culture + 1 drop *didinium* culture

(d) Describe the interactions between the organisms.

(e) How would an ecosystem that contained all three organisms be different from one that contained only *paramecium*?

The Silence of the Frogs

Imagine a silent pond. No croaks, no peeps, no "ribbits," no noisy frogs. If the number of amphibians like frogs continues to decline, you will not need to use your imagination. All ponds will be silent. Biologists have recently become aware of the gradual disappearance of frogs, toads, and salamanders, which seem to be dying at unprecedented rates. About 30% of North America's frogs and toads are in trouble.

Amphibians have been around for more than 400 million years. When most animals and plants died out about 250 million years ago, amphibians survived. Frogs skipped right by the catastrophe that killed all the dinosaurs 65 million years ago. Frogs and their relatives have adapted to ice ages and extended periods of global warming without missing a beat. These timid amphibians can withstand drought, flood, and winter ice. They can be found in most ecosystems that include water. (**Ecosystem** is a term used to describe the relationships among the many species living in an environment and the relationships among those organisms and the non-living components of the environment.) Amphibians live on the peaks of the Canadian Rockies, in the city parks of Toronto, and in the swamps of Newfoundland. They have even done well dealing with the growth of the human population — at least until recently.

Why Are Scientists Concerned?

Other than those who enjoy eating frogs' legs, why would scientists care about amphibians? Many believe that the health of amphibians indicates the health of the ecosystems they live in.

The word amphibian is a clue as to why frogs and toads can be used to diagnose the health of ecosystems. The word comes from two Greek words, *amphi* ("on both sides") and *bios* ("life"). Amphibians literally have two lives (**Figure 1**). Frogs begin as eggs and grow to tadpoles in ponds, and then enter their second life as adults in forest and grassland areas. This means they are exposed to hazards in both ecosystems, instead of only one. Any decline in the health of either of the two ecosystems in which they live will have an impact on frogs.

Not only do frogs occupy two different ecosystems, they are also parts of two very different food chains. A **food chain** is a step-by-step sequence linking organisms that feed on each other, starting with a food source such as plants (**producers**), and continuing with animals and other living things that feed on the plants and on each other (**consumers**).

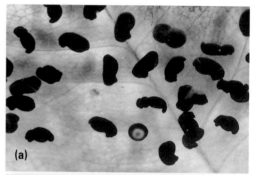

(a)

(b)

(c)

(d)

Figure 1

The northern leopard frog, native to Ontario, is one of the threatened amphibian species. **(a)** Leopard frogs lay their eggs in ponds. **(b)** Tadpoles develop. **(c)** Tadpoles grow into immature frogs. **(d)** Adult leopard frogs live in fields and around ponds.

Frogs in Their Ecosystems

Adult frogs eat mostly insects, although they may also eat some small fish. In turn, large fish, predatory birds, reptiles, and small mammals eat frogs. This makes the adult frog a member of a food chain (**Figure 2**) that includes producers (plants), **herbivores** (animals that eat plants) and **carnivores** (animals, like the frog, that feed on other animals). Animals that eat both plants and animals, such as humans, raccoons, and bears, are called **omnivores**.

If frogs were completely wiped out, insect populations would most certainly soar. This has already happened in Bangladesh, where frog populations have been decimated to supply restaurants with delicacies. The result is a rise in the number of mosquitoes, and a dramatic rise in cases of malaria among humans. Malaria is a disease that is transmitted by mosquitoes, which are eaten by frogs. The increase in malaria can be traced back to the disappearance of frogs from the local ecosystems.

Tadpoles eat large amounts of algae (small plant-like organisms), both living and dead. The tadpole is a herbivore, not a carnivore, and is part of a much different food chain (**Figure 3**). In this food chain there are two food sources — producers (the algae) and **detritus** (waste from plants and animals, including their dead remains). Detritus food chains are critical in the recycling of matter in ecosystems. They include **decomposers**, organisms that break down detritus to get nutrients for their own use, but in the process also release nutrients to the soil and water. Plants and algae use those nutrients to grow.

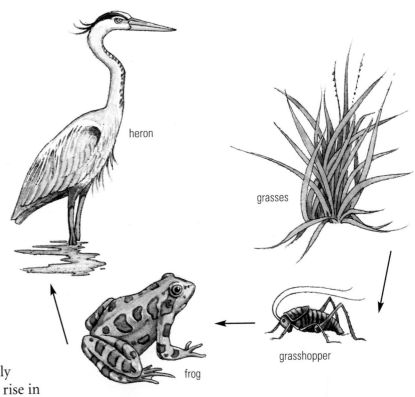

Figure 2

The adult frog is part of a food chain that includes producers (plants) that make the food and consumers (animals and fungi) that feed either directly or indirectly on the plants.

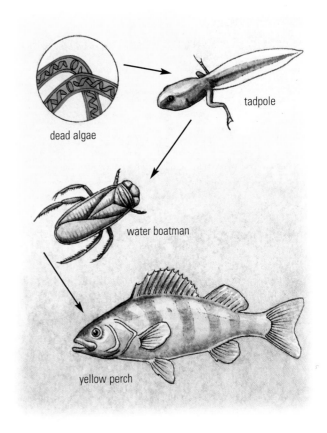

Figure 3

Waste is recycled within a detritus food chain. Organisms in the chain include fungi, bacteria, insects and other invertebrates, and, in ponds, tadpoles.

Why Are Frogs Disappearing?

The worldwide disappearance of frogs is a bit of a puzzle. In some areas, scientists don't really know what is causing the problem. In other areas, they have identified some probable causes.

Loss of Habitat

In Canada, frogs in more heavily populated areas, such as southern Ontario, seem to be in great danger. The loss of **habitat**, places where a species can live, is most often mentioned as the main cause. Frogs need wetlands, ponds, or lakes with clean water so they can breed and lay their eggs. As adults they need a place such as a forest or a field, where they can catch insects. They also need a safe path between the two. The growth of cities and other human activities, such as farming and industry, takes away all of these things. Humans drain wetlands, cut down trees, build on fields, and build roads between ponds and woods.

A highway separating a woodlot from a pond or lake can claim the lives of many frogs as they move between their feeding and breeding areas. Cutting down some of the trees that surround a lake creates problems for amphibians by exposing them to predators as they make their way between the water and the denser trees farther from the lake.

From 1984 to 1986 scientists studied an area where a swamp and a forest were separated by a road (**Figure 4**). When trees bordering the road were cut in 1986, researchers noticed a huge decline in the number of frogs and other amphibians.

Air and Water Quality

A second cause for the decline in frog numbers is pollution. This is because frog skin is thin and it is not protected by feathers, fur, or scales. Frogs have lungs, but they also breathe through their skin, which must be thin to allow oxygen through. Pollutants can also pass through their thin, moist skin. Acid rain, caused mostly by pollutants released by vehicles and industry, is just one example.

Acidity also affects frogs' ability to reproduce. Researchers have noted that if the water is even slightly acidic, it reduces the mobility of frog sperm cells. This makes it less likely that eggs will be fertilized. Even if

Changing Population of Amphibians

Figure 4

In the first year of the study, researchers counted 716 amphibians, of which 493 were frogs. After the trees were cut in 1986, they found very few.

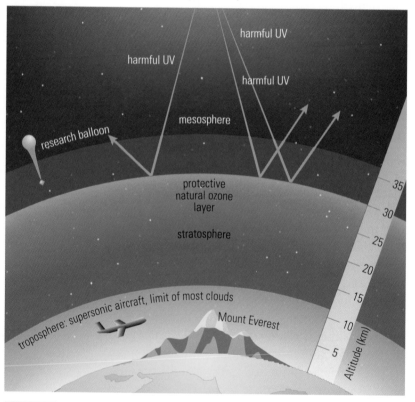

Figure 5

A thin layer of ozone (O_3) blocks harmful solar radiation. The layer is getting thinner. Atmospheric scientists believe that chlorofluorocarbons (CFCs), which were widely used in spray cans and refrigerators, are at least partly responsible for the thinning.

mating is successful, acid affects the frog's development. Embryos, if they develop at all, grow slowly in acidic water. In some locations, this means that the pond they are in will dry up before tadpoles can become adult frogs, and the tadpoles die. Acidic water can cause other problems. For example, embryos may develop deformed limbs. Tadpoles with such limbs do not survive for very long.

Ultraviolet Radiation

The thin skin of the frog is also susceptible to ultraviolet (UV) radiation. This invisible radiation from the Sun causes sunburns, but it has also been linked with more serious cell damage. The amount of UV radiation reaching Earth's surface is increasing because of damage to the protective ozone layer surrounding our planet (**Figure 5**).

Frogs at higher altitudes, where the problem of UV is greater, seem to be the ones that are most endangered. Many highland species are used to dealing with UV radiation (they lay black eggs and have developed a black covering that lines their internal organs for protection), but biologists speculate that these adaptations cannot keep pace with changes in the ozone layer.

The frog is not the only animal whose skin is exposed to UV radiation. Humans also have a delicate skin and are affected by the increase in UV rays. The fact that the rate of human skin cancer is rising all over the world underscores the importance of studying the frog as a "bioindicator" of the health of the planet.

Climate Change

Human activities that are causing a change in climate have also been linked to the disappearance of frogs. There is evidence of a global warming trend. One hypothesis links increasing global temperatures with the increased use of fossil fuels such as coal, oil, and gasoline. Climate changes can cause important changes in local ecosystems. For example, if the climate becomes drier, frogs will suffer. No frog can stay in the sun too long or completely separate itself from fresh water.

⬤ Challenge

1,2 Frogs can be used as indicator species for the health of ecosystems. What other plants and animals could be used as indicators in your Challenge? Record your thoughts as you progress through this unit.

Understanding Concepts

1. A decline in the number of frogs would affect other species. Using the term food chain, explain how the decline would affect

    (a) insects

    (b) algae

2. Classify each of the organisms in **Figures 2** and **3** as herbivore, carnivore, or omnivore. Explain your classifications.

3. In a paragraph, explain the difference between the two food chains to which the frog belongs. Explain the role of the frog in each chain.

4. **(a)** Explain why the life cycle and skin of the frog make it a good indicator animal if you want to determine the health of local ecosystems.

    (b) Construct a concept map that links the decline in the (Y) number of frogs to factors that may cause the decline.

    (c) Choose one of the possible causes and, using your own words, explain how it affects frogs.

Making Connections

5. Make a list of things that you could do, or avoid doing, that might help frogs to survive.

Exploring

6. **(a)** Design a scientific experiment that would assess the impact of acid rain on one species of frog.

    (b) If you actually carried out such an experiment, what (K) would happen to the animals you experimented on? From an ethical perspective, discuss your experimental design.

Reflecting

7. In question 5 you made a list of things you could do or avoid doing to help frogs. Identify the things that would be easy for you, and those that would demand sacrifices. Would you be willing to do the hard things to save frogs? Explain your answer.

🖑 Work the Web

Research the disappearance of the northern cricket frog (*Acris crepitani*) from southwestern Ontario and produce a report. Visit www.science.nelson.com and follow the links from Science 10, 1.1 to help in your research.

Canada's Endangered Species

The first bald eagle born and raised on the shores of Lake Erie in nearly 30 years took flight in 1983. Wildlife officers had moved the parent birds to Long Point peninsula in an attempt to re-introduce the birds to the natural ecosystem in the lower Great Lakes.

During the 1700s and 1800s the bald eagle was common along the northern shores of Lake Erie. By the early 1900s, biologists had started to note a decline in their numbers. Early settlers and farmers regarded the bird as a threat to livestock and were only too ready to kill them. (Bald eagles eat mostly fish, but they will take chickens and other small animals.) A second, and even more deadly threat, followed. Toxic chemical waste, produced by the many industrial plants that lined the Great Lakes, entered the eagles' food chain. The high levels of toxins caused eggshells of the bald eagle and some other birds, such as the double-crested cormorant and the herring gull, to become unusually thin. Eggs broke more easily, and many eagles were born with abnormalities.

The health of top-level carnivores like eagles indicates whether toxins are entering an ecosystem. Eagles depend directly or indirectly on all of the other members of their food chain (**Figure 1**).

Classifying Species at Risk

Amphibians are not the only wildlife that is disappearing. In Canada there are more than 250 species of plants and animals at various degrees of risk (**Table 1**).

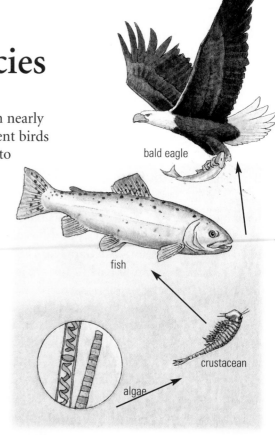

bald eagle

fish

crustacean

algae

Figure 1

The bald eagle has been re-introduced to the shores of Lake Erie, in an attempt to re-establish a natural ecosystem.

wolverine (vulnerable)

YUKON TERRITORY

NORTHWEST TERRITORIES

Pacific giant salamander (vulnerable)

BRITISH COLUMBIA

ALBERTA   SA

pitcher's thistle (endangered)

Table 1	**Classification System for At-Risk Species**	
Classification	**Description**	**Example**
extinct	a species that is no longer found anywhere	blue walleye (the last fish of this species was taken from Lake Erie in 1965)
endangered	a species that is close to extinction in all parts of Canada or in a significantly large location	eastern cougar (sightings of this large cat are very rare)
extirpated	any species that no longer exists in one part of Canada, but can be found in others	grizzly bear (no longer found in Manitoba and Saskatchewan, but still found in the mountains of Alberta and British Columbia)
threatened	any species that is likely to become endangered if factors that make it vulnerable are not reversed	wood bison (their number is small, and recently tuberculosis has become a problem)
vulnerable	any species that is at risk because of low or declining numbers at the fringe of its range or in some restricted area	grey fox (is beginning to return to southern Ontario, but needs woodlands)

Understanding Concepts

1. **(a)** In your own words, describe the classification system for at-risk species.

   (b) Why is a classification system like this useful?

2. Using the criteria in **Table 1**, classify each of the following species as extinct, endangered, extirpated, threatened, or vulnerable. Explain your classification.

   (a) The wood turtle is found in pockets throughout southern Ontario, southern Quebec, New Brunswick, and Nova Scotia. The number of wood turtles in Canada seems to be stable, but in the United States their numbers are decreasing as many are being taken from the wild into homes as pets.

   (b) Furbish's lousewort is a tall herb that grows on riverbanks. In Canada, it grows only on a 200-km stretch of the Saint John River in New Brunswick. Forestry, farming, and flooding caused by hydroelectric dams all affect the area in which it lives.

   (c) The greater prairie chicken has not been seen in Ontario, Manitoba, or Alberta for many years. It was last seen in Saskatchewan in 1977. It can still be found in the prairie states of the U.S.

3. Choose one of the species listed in **Table 1** or **Figure 2** for further research. Why is the species at risk? Are there any initiatives underway to improve the status of the species? ⓘ What could you do to help? Report on the results of your ⓡ research.

Making Connections

4. **(a)** Predict which area of Canada has the greatest number of organisms at risk. Provide a hypothesis that explains why wildlife in this area would have more problems.

   (b) Do national and provincial parks help alleviate this problem? Explain.

Reflecting

5. The bald eagle is not listed as at risk in Canada. Should resources be used to help restore this bird around Lake Erie?

🖑 Work the Web

The peregrine falcon was once considered endangered. Research Canadian efforts to restore this predator and report on their success. To do your research, visit www.science.nelson.com and follow the links from Science 10, 1.2.

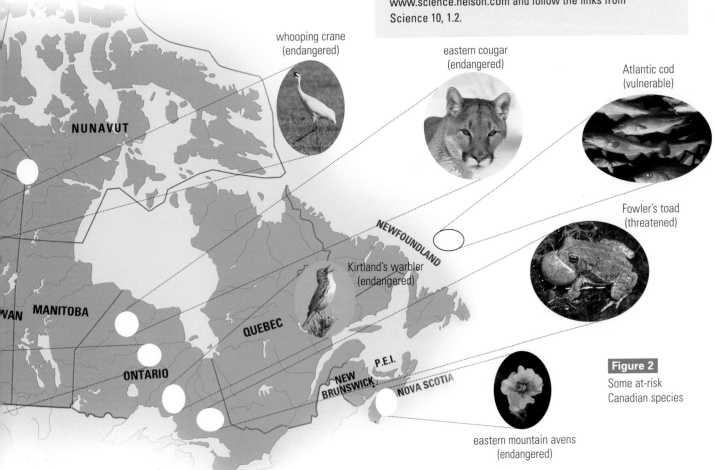

whooping crane (endangered)

eastern cougar (endangered)

Atlantic cod (vulnerable)

NUNAVUT

Fowler's toad (threatened)

NEWFOUNDLAND

Kirtland's warbler (endangered)

MANITOBA

QUEBEC

VAN

ONTARIO

P.E.I.

NEW BRUNSWICK

NOVA SCOTIA

Figure 2

Some at-risk Canadian species

eastern mountain avens (endangered)

Extinction in the Modern World

In the 1850s, flocks of passenger pigeons (**Figure 1**) would darken the sky as they migrated south for the winter. Alexander Wilson, a scientist who studied birds, once saw a flock that he estimated contained nearly 2 billion birds. By 1914, there wasn't a single passenger pigeon anywhere on Earth. The species was extinct.

How could such a successful species suddenly become extinct? Massive commercial hunting and the clearing of forests, which destroyed habitat and food for the pigeons, were both part of the reason. Passenger pigeons were curious animals, and easy to kill. A common practice was to tie a captured bird to a perch. As other pigeons flew by during their migration, they would stop to see what was going on. When a flock landed, they were slaughtered. The perch was known as a "stool," and the practice has given us the name "stool pigeon."

Figure 1
The extinction of the passenger pigeon is just one example of the growing influence of humans.

Humans and the Rate of Extinction

The extinction of the passenger pigeon was sudden, but it is not an isolated event. Humans, a recent addition to the planet, have had a profound effect on other organisms. Species extinction rates are increasing dramatically as the human population grows. Between 8000 B.C. and A.D. 1600 the species extinction rate is estimated at one species every 1000 years. Between 1600 and 1900 the estimate is that one species went extinct every four years. In modern times, the rate is soaring (**Figure 2**). In the early years of the 21st century, the projection is that one species will become extinct every 30 minutes. Although the majority of threatened species can be found in tropical rainforests, the problem also exists in Canada. The number of species at risk of extinction is growing, at the rate of about 80 species per year.

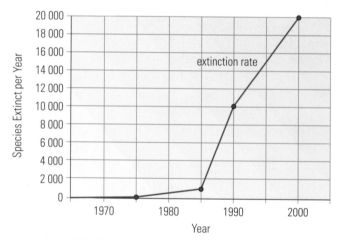

Estimated Extinction Rate

extinction rate

Species Extinct per Year

Year

Figure 2
The rate of extinction is increasing rapidly. Human activities are the major cause.

A Brief History of Extinction

The history of our planet, recorded in rocks and fossils, reveals several large-scale disasters that have destroyed huge numbers of species (**Figure 3**). Approximately 438 million years ago the first mass extinction of marine organisms took place. Another mass extinction of marine organisms happened nearly 360 million years ago. Possibly the largest mass extinction occurred about 245 million years ago. That catastrophe, in which about 80% of all species perished, was followed by another mass extinction 208 million years ago. This event marked the beginning of the age of dinosaurs. It may well have removed the competition, ensuring the success of the early reptiles, which were then no larger than a small dog. The most famous mass extinction, even though it was not as disastrous as some of the earlier ones, happened about 65 million years ago, and it marked the end of the age of dinosaurs.

Mass extinctions occurred before humans existed, but scientists believe the causes were much different from those of the modern era. The most promising theories involve asteroids crashing into Earth (**Figure 4**). A collision would raise tremendous amounts of dust, blocking light from the Sun, and set off many volcanoes, quickly altering environmental conditions. There is evidence that an asteroid hit Earth about 65 million years ago. The crater, just off the Yucatan Peninsula of Mexico, is 9.6 km deep and 300 km wide.

Other Causes of Extinction

It is estimated that nearly 500 million different species have inhabited the planet. Of these, more than 90% have either become extinct or have evolved into new species. The mass extinctions, probably caused by single catastrophes, are not the only reasons for these losses.

Climate changes and the pressure of competition from other species force organisms to adapt or die. If a new species enters an area, species that eat the same food must compete with it. A species that is better at finding food, reproducing, or defending its territory could force competing species into extinction. If one species disappears, even if only from part of its range, it can affect other species that rely on it for food.

Over the long term, hundreds of millions of years, all species eventually encounter conditions to which they cannot adapt, and they become extinct.

In modern times, however, human activities are the major causes of extinction.

The Banff longnose dace (**Figure 5**), a small minnow, was recently declared extinct. It was unable to compete with the guppies, swordtails, and other tropical fish released accidentally into warm marsh waters below the hot springs in Banff National Park.

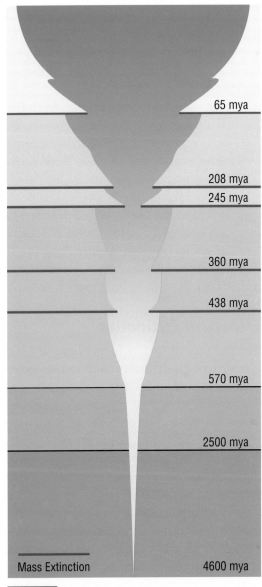

65 mya

208 mya
245 mya

360 mya

438 mya

570 mya

2500 mya

4600 mya

Mass Extinction

Figure 3
Fossil evidence shows that many species suddenly disappeared in several episodes over the last 500 million years.

Figure 4
This large circular lake in Manicouagan, Quebec, is actually a crater formed when an object from space collided with Earth.

Figure 5
The Banff longnose dace lost a competition with exotic fish.

In Canada's Arctic, climate change has been blamed for the demise of the Peary caribou (**Figure 6**). Changes in snow cover, caused by global warming, have caused changes in local plant communities. Lichens and mosses, the preferred food of the caribou, are being replaced by plants that previously grew farther south.

In fir, pine, and spruce forests from British Columbia to Newfoundland, logging, oil exploration, and expanding cities have reduced the size of ecosystems, endangering forest-dwelling species such as spotted owls, woodland bison, and woodland caribou.

The expansion of agriculture has also been identified as a major contributing factor in extinction. The decline of the monarch butterfly has been linked to the use of herbicides used to control milkweed, the monarch caterpillar's only source of food.

The burrowing owl (**Figure 7**), which lives on the prairies, is threatened because the burrows it nests in have been plowed under and rodents, its food, have been exterminated.

Figure 6

The Peary caribou was a victim of climate change.

Effects of Extinction

The number of species in an ecosystem is described as the biological diversity or **biodiversity** of the ecosystem. Because every organism in an ecosystem is connected to all the other organisms, the reduction in biodiversity caused by the extinction of a single species can cause a "domino effect." The removal of one part from an ecosystem, like the removal of a moving part from a car, can cause the collapse of an entire food chain. When the threatened species acts as a predator, it keeps the population of its prey in check; when it acts as prey, it provides an important food source.

For example, overhunting of sea otters (**Figure 8**) along the Pacific coasts of Asia and North America removed the main predator of the sea urchin. Predictably, the number of sea urchins grew rapidly. Sea urchins eat kelp, a form of seaweed. As the number of sea urchins grew, the amount of kelp declined, and so did the fish that relied on the kelp bed ecosystem for habitat and food.

Sea otters very nearly became extinct due to hunting pressure. From the point of view of humans, killing sea otters for their fur resulted in the decline of a valuable fishery. Where the sea otter has been reintroduced, sea urchin populations have fallen, kelp beds are being re-established, and the number of fish is increasing.

Figure 7

The burrowing owl is at risk of extinction due to pressures created by agricultural practices.

Restoring the Balance

The reintroduction of the sea otter to the Pacific northwest is an example of an attempt to restore a natural balance. It is not always easy to do.

The whooping crane (**Figure 9**) may be a success story — or it may not. In spring, whooping cranes fly north to live in the marshes and swamps of the prairies and the Canadian north, where they eat crayfish, fish, small mammals, insects, roots, and berries. Efforts by Canadian and U.S. conservationists over the past three decades have helped increase the population from a low of 14 individuals in 1940 to 183 in 1999. Chemical pesticides were the original human threat to the crane, but it was already

Figure 8

A sea otter eats a sea urchin. The removal of the sea otter caused a major change in the ocean ecosystems of the Pacific coast.

Figure 9

The efforts of wildlife biologists are preventing the whooping crane from becoming extinct. Some young birds are being hand-raised but, to prevent the chicks from associating humans with safety, the caregivers disguise themselves as adult cranes!

struggling. Cranes must fly a long way between their summer homes in the north and their winter homes on the Gulf of Mexico. Along the way they are vulnerable to hunting and accidents. In addition, the whooping crane reproduces very slowly. Each year females produce two eggs; however, only one will mature. The first fledgling to emerge from its egg kills its brother or sister. This ensures there will be enough food for the survivor, but it also means that once the number of whooping cranes is small, it is very difficult for the species to increase its numbers.

We do not fully understand all the relationships between species in many ecosystems, so we cannot predict reliably what will happen to an ecosystem if its biodiversity is reduced, even by one species. Allowing or forcing just one species to become extinct could possibly be disastrous, and we would not know the extent of the disaster until later.

Challenge

1 Why would a golf course have less biodiversity than a natural ecosystem? How might the lower biodiversity affect surrounding ecosystems?

Understanding Concepts

1. **(a)** Explain why the passenger pigeon became extinct.

   (b) Speculate about which animals might benefit if the passenger pigeon had not become extinct.

   (c) Compare the extinction of the passenger pigeon to the near extinction of the sea otter.

2. Explain how each of the following factors could lead to the extinction of a species. With each explanation include an example of a threatened species.

   (a) Poor reproductive success

   (b) Competition from a species newly introduced into an ecosystem

   (c) Change in climate

   (d) Hunting by humans

3. **(a)** In your own words define the term "biodiversity."

   (b) Explain why diversity is important for ecosystems.

   (c) Give two examples of ecosystems that have high biodiversity, and two that have low biodiversity. Explain your classification.

Making Connections

4. The common cockroach is not at risk of extinction. In fact, it is one of the species that have benefited from human activities.

   (a) Hypothesize about which human activities benefit the cockroach.

   (b) If a chemical company invented a spray that could kill all cockroaches, would it be acceptable to use the spray to make the cockroach extinct? Explain your position in a letter to the chemical company.

Exploring

5. The passenger pigeon is not the only bird that has become extinct due to human hunting. Research and prepare a report on the great auk or the dodo.

Work the Web

Canadian wildlife biologists have been attempting to preserve the whooping crane. Are they succeeding? In a short essay, evaluate the success of their program. To research the whooping crane program, visit www.science.nelson.com and follow the links from Science 10, 1.3.

DECISION-MAKING SKILLS
- Define the Issue
- ○ Identify Alternatives
- Research
- Analyze the Issue
- ○ Defend a Decision
- ○ Evaluate

What Is the Value of Wolves?

Once an ecosystem has been damaged by extirpation, should it be "fixed" by restoring the species that was removed? Do we "own" wildlife? The case of the wolves of Yellowstone National Park (**Figure 1**) can help us think about this issue.

Few animals stir as many emotions as the wolf. Some Native North American peoples saw the wolf as a traveller, a guide, and a teacher capable of appearing and disappearing at will. Admiration for the tireless predators, who work together to bring down much larger and more powerful prey, is easy to understand. People saw many similarities to humans in the way wolves cooperate.

The image of the wolf held by early settlers from Europe was also influenced by folklore. The wolf of European stories chased three little pigs, disguised itself in the fleece of a lamb, and ate the grandmother of Little Red Riding Hood. Unlike the Native Peoples of the Plains, Europeans held an image of the wolf as a sharp-toothed villain, that preyed on livestock and people.

Figure 1

In 1996 wolf packs were relocated from Alberta to Yellowstone National Park in an attempt to restore an ecological balance.

The Decline of the Wolf

When European settlers reached central North America, and found plains covered in bison, they were not willing to compete with the wolf for valuable hides. Thousands of wolves died after they ate poisoned bison carcasses that had been laid out as bait.

After the bison hunters left, having killed most of the bison, there was a break of a few years before the killing of wolves was revived again by ranchers in the 1880s and 1890s. Wolves killed cattle, and it was also widely believed that they killed people, despite the lack of evidence to support that belief. In both the United States and Canada, anyone bringing a wolf skin to a local government office would be paid. In 1910 the bounty for each adult wolf was $400 — a large amount at the time. In Montana alone, more than 80 000 wolves were destroyed between 1883 and 1918. The bounty is no longer in place in Midwestern states, and the wolf is considered an endangered animal, protected from hunting.

However, the effects of the removal of the wolves were dramatic. The disappearance of the wolf was followed by a dramatic increase in the population of the next dominant predator, the coyote. The coyote, a close relative of the wolf, is smaller and rarely forms packs. Bison and elk are much too large for single coyotes to hunt. The coyote eats mostly small mammals, such as mice, voles, and ground squirrels, and the eggs and fledglings of ground-nesting birds. It competes with foxes, badgers, and martens, who eat similar things. As the number of coyotes grew, the numbers of these smaller predators declined.

Wolves frequently left remains from their kills. These leftovers were taken by scavengers such as magpies, ravens, and vultures. Without the wolf, these species began to decline. Even grizzly bears, who frequently scavenge wolf kills, were deprived of an easy source of food.

Work the Web

Explore the controversy over wolves in Yellowstone National Park by visiting www.science.nelson.com and following the links from Science 10, 1.4.

Meanwhile, large herbivores such as the elk were safe. No predator, except for an occasional bear, could kill them, and they began to multiply. The population of elk in the highlands grew so large that they stripped the hills of plants. Diseases spread rapidly within their large herds.

The Return of the Wolf

The wildlife managers of Yellowstone saw all these signs and recognized that something was seriously wrong. In 1987 they put together a plan: they were going to import wolves from Canada.

Despite continuing resistance from local ranchers, who feared for their sheep and cattle, 35 wolves were transplanted from Alberta in 1996. More have since been added. Signs of change are already evident. Where wolves have been introduced, elk have moved from open fields (where they are more vulnerable), and now stick to tree-covered areas. Vegetation is recovering, and the number of small predators, such as the kit fox, is increasing. As ranchers feared, some of the new wolves have killed livestock. Five cows and 53 sheep were killed by wolves in Idaho in the spring of 1997. Ranchers are compensated for losses to wolves, but they are not happy about the reintroduction of wolves, which add to their problems.

Understanding the Issue

1. Classify the at-risk status of the wolf in and around Yellowstone National Park

   (a) before European settlers arrived.

   (b) during the bison hunt.

   (c) after ranchers arrived.

   (d) in 1996.

2. First Nations hunters lived on bison long before European hunters arrived. When they killed a bison, they would use the entire animal for food, clothing, and medicines. Many European hunters killed only for the animal's skin. How might the views of First Nations people about hunting the wolf lead them to treat wolves differently than European settlers and hunters?

3. Make a concept map showing how the removal of the
   (Y) wolf caused problems in the local ecosystem.

Take a Stand — Perspectives on the Value of Wolves

Below are three views on what should have been done about wolves in Yellowstone Park.

The Frontier View: To feed ourselves and the hungry of the world, we must open up, clear, and claim wilderness areas for ranching and other forms of agriculture. Wolves endanger that effort. They kill cattle and sheep. They must be removed wherever they interfere with farming and ranching, and they should not be reintroduced once they have been extirpated.

The Stewardship View: Humans are the most intelligent animals on the planet. It is our duty to take care of other species and preserve our world. Once we recognize that we have damaged an ecosystem, we must try to repair the damage using whatever resources are available to us. Wolves must be preserved in all ecosystems where they are now found, and reintroduced to ecosystems where they once lived.

The Ownership View: Canadians do not own wild animals or plants just because they live in Canada. We have no right to move them around whenever we feel like it. It may have been a mistake to kill the wolves of Yellowstone, but we have no right to take Alberta wolves and move them to a place they've never been before. It is better to let the ecosystem in the park find a new balance. Perhaps one day wolves will find their own way to the park.

Taking a Position

1. Should we have captured wolves in Alberta and
   (F) shipped them to Yellowstone National Park? After a group discussion, decide which views you support, or develop an alternative view.

2. Using libraries, the Web, and CD-ROMs,
   (J) research to find information that will support your position and write a report on the results of your research.

Ecology

Have you ever been stung by a wasp? The unpleasant experience is not soon to be forgotten! Organisms that cause problems for humans, like wasps, are often categorized as **pests** (**Figure 1**). Why don't scientists work to eliminate pests rather than just control their numbers?

Imagine a world without biting flies, mosquitoes, termites, caterpillars, or weeds. At first thought that world might seem very appealing, but consider how other organisms might be affected. For example, some fish and amphibians rely on mosquito larvae for food. The elimination of mosquitoes would have a devastating effect on lakes. In addition, adult mosquitoes are an important food source for swallows, robins, and other small birds.

Some other insect "pests" are needed by plants. Most plants rely on insects for pollination. Plants also benefit from insects like the wasp that help decompose tissues of dead plants and animals, returning nutrients to the soil. Many of the insects we call pests also dig around plants, loosening the soil and allowing more oxygen to get to plant roots.

Even garden weeds like crab grass serve an important purpose. Outside the garden these rapidly growing plants are an important source of food for many animals. Eliminate wild grasses and cattle, sheep, and other grazing mammals would soon become extinct. The long and fibrous roots of these hardy, fast-growing plants also pump nutrients back to the soil's surface, where they can be used by more delicate domestic plants. The greatest benefit of these plants might be their ability to grow along cliffs and in other precarious locations. Here they anchor the soil, preventing erosion.

Figure 1
Humans categorize mosquitoes as pests, but some birds and other insects would categorize them as food.

Figure 2
In the ecotone between the pond and the field, species from both ecosystems meet.

Organisms Interact Within Ecosystems

To better understand living things, scientists must put aside the idea of the pest, and examine organisms within their natural setting. Ernst Haeckel, a German biologist, first coined the word **ecology** in 1866 to describe the study of how organisms interact with each other. Ecology combines the Greek words *oikos*, meaning "the place where one lives," with *logos*, meaning "study of."

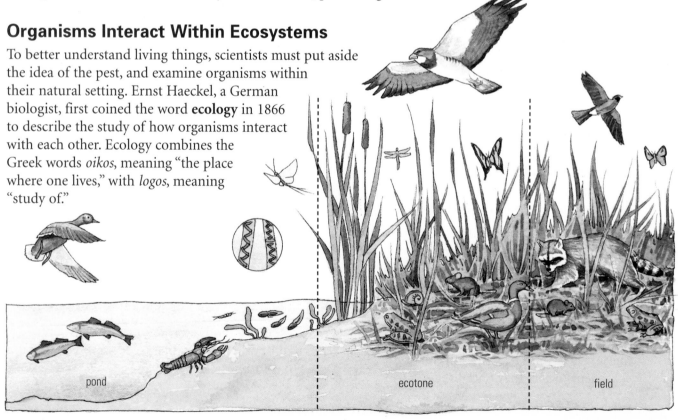

pond   ecotone   field

Ecological studies can begin at the level of a single organism. Investigations might be designed to determine how the individual interacts with its environment, and how factors in the environment affect its growth, feeding habits, and reproduction. Non-living factors or influences on organisms, such as amount of sunlight, temperature, and strength and direction of wind are called **abiotic**. Factors caused by the presence and roles of other living things are called **biotic**.

Organisms do not live in isolation. Organisms usually group with others of the same species. All of the members of the same species, living in the same ecosystem or habitat, are referred to as a **population**. For example, all the pike in a lake form a population.

Since there is usually more than one species in an ecosystem, there is also more than one population. The collection of all the populations of all the species in an ecosystem or habitat is called the **community** of organisms. The community in the lake might include populations of pike, perch, tadpoles, mosquito larvae, and algae, among others.

When studying a community, an ecologist would study how biotic factors affect each population. For example, an ecologist studying a forest community might examine the interactions between different types of plants and animals in the area.

Ecologists can extend their study beyond the community of organisms to the physical environment. When they do so they begin investigating ecosystems. An ecosystem includes the community of living things and its physical environment. For example, in studying a forest ecosystem, an ecologist could examine how much sunlight reaches the forest floor, and what affect it has on the plants and animals that live in the ecosystem.

Ecotones and Biodiversity

Ecosystems rarely have sharp boundaries, and organisms can move back and forth from one ecosystem to another. There is often a grey area between ecosystems where organisms from both ecosystems interact with each other. These transition areas or **ecotones** (Figure 2) contain species from both bordering ecosystems, so they often contain greater biodiversity (more species) than either ecosystem.

Ecosystems with greater biodiversity tend to be less fragile. For example, if a predator has to rely on a single species as a food source, its very existence is tied to the survival of the prey. In ecotones and other diverse areas there are more species, and a predator may have an alternative if something happens to the population of its main prey. It should come as no surprise that the ecotones, by providing alternative food sources, guard against extinction.

Understanding Concepts

1. In your own words, define the term "ecology."

2. List four biotic and four abiotic factors in:

   (a) a freshwater ecosystem, such as a lake

   (b) a terrestrial ecosystem, such as a forest

3. Describe how a population differs from a community, using your own examples.

4. Describe how an ecosystem differs from a community, using your own examples.

5. Predict whether you would find more species in a forest, an open field, or the forest-grassland ecotone between them. Explain your prediction.

6. **Figure 3** shows changes in the size of the populations of *paramecia* (single-cell organisms) placed in three different beakers.

   (a) Compare the growth of Species 1 in Beaker A with the growth of Species 2 in Beaker B.

   (b) What evidence suggests that the populations of *paramecia* affect each other?

   (c) Suggest a conclusion that can be drawn from the population changes in Beaker C.

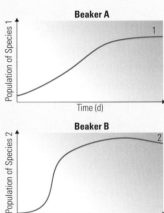
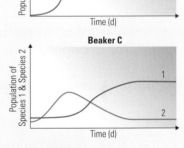

Figure 3
Graphs showing changes in populations of *paramecia* in three beakers

Challenge

1 An understanding of how abiotic factors affect communities is a good basis for understanding ecosystems. What abiotic factors must be controlled to ensure ideal playing conditions for golfers?

INQUIRY SKILLS MENU

○ Questioning   ○ Planning   ● Analyzing
● Hypothesizing   ● Conducting   ● Evaluating
● Predicting   ● Recording   ● Communicating

A Schoolyard Ecosystem

To gain a better understanding of the impact of environmental change on living things within ecosystems, you do not have to go far. You can begin by investigating your schoolyard, and how living things there respond to local biotic and abiotic factors (**Figure 1**).

Question

How do abiotic factors affect the distribution of weeds?

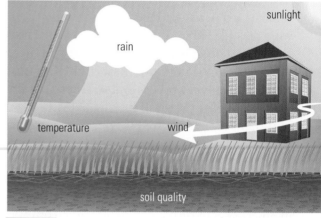

Figure 1

Some of the abiotic factors that affect living things in a schoolyard

Hypothesis/Prediction

Abiotic factors play an important role in determining which plants can succeed in a given area. In this investigation you will study sites on the north and south sides of your school building.

(a) Predict which site will contain the most weeds. Explain your prediction.
(b) Write a hypothesis to explain your prediction.

Design

This investigation is an exploration of how location affects the distribution of common weeds. A weed is any plant the human caretaker does not want (**Figure 2**). Do more weeds grow on the north side of a building or the south side of the building? You will measure abiotic factors in each location.

(c) Identify the abiotic factors being studied in Part 2.
(d) You will have to choose two study sites. Before beginning, suggest some controls you could identify to make sure the sites are as similar as possible, except in the abiotic factors being studied.

Part 1: Distribution of Weeds

Materials

- string
- metre stick or measuring tape
- 8 Popsicle sticks
- notebook

(Note: If you have access to a computer with a spreadsheet program it will help you analyze your observations.)

dandelion

crabgrass

ragweed

thistle

bindweed

plantain

Figure 2

Common weeds

Procedure

1 Set up equal study sites on the north and south sides of the school. Using string and 4 Popsicle sticks mark off each study site as shown in **Figure 3**. Make sure you push the Popsicle sticks completely into the ground. Calculate and record the area of each study site.

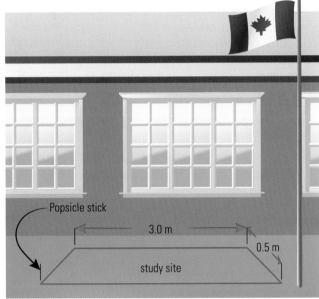

Popsicle stick

3.0 m

0.5 m

study site

Figure 3

2 Survey each study site by counting and recording the number and type of weeds in each site. Use the photos in **Figure 2** as references. Record your data in a table such as **Table 1**.

Table 1   **Incidence of Weeds in North Study Site**

Type of weed	Number of plants	Diameter of plant (cm)	Area covered (cm²)
dandelion			
plantain			

3 Within each of the study sites, record the coverage by each type of weed. Use a measuring tape or a metre stick to measure the diameter of each of the larger weeds in the study area. Record your measurements in your table.

4 Calculate the area covered by each weed using the formula

$$\text{area} = \frac{\pi d^2}{4}$$

For small weeds such as crabgrass, you can measure the entire area covered by a grouping of weeds rather than the area covered by each individual plant.

Part 2: Measuring Abiotic Factors

Materials

- plastic bottle cap
- light meter
- thermometer
- thread
- tape
- Ping-Pong ball
- protractor

Procedure

5 Toss a plastic bottle cap into a study site. Using the light meter, determine the amount of light reaching the soil next to the bottle cap. Repeat the procedure at least twice more. Record your observations in a table similar to **Table 2**.

(e) Why was the bottle cap tossed before light readings were taken?

Table 2   **Light Readings**

Measurement	North study site (lux)	South study site (lux)
1		
2		
3		
mean		

6 Repeat the light measurements in the second study area. Calculate the mean for each set of measurements.

7 Using a thermometer, measure soil temperatures in the north and south study sites. Throw the bottle cap, as in Step 5, to choose measurement locations. Record your observations in a table such as **Table 3**.

Table 3   **Soil Temperature**

Measurement	North study site (°C)	South study site (°C)
1		
2		
3		
mean		

8 Construct an anemometer (a device to measure wind speed), as shown in **Figure 4**.

Figure 4
An anemometer

9 Make sure you are not blocking the wind. Point the thin edge of the anemometer into the wind. To measure wind speed, record how many degrees from vertical the thread is at the edge of the protractor. Take three readings in each study site and record them in a table as in **Table 4**.

Table 4   **Anemometer Readings**

Measurement	North study site (°)	South study site (°)	Wind speed (km/h)
1			
2			
3			
mean			

10 Using the conversion scale in **Table 5**, convert the degree readings to wind speeds.

Table 5   **Conversion from Degrees to Wind Speed**

Angle (°)	90	85	80	75	70	65	60
Wind speed (km/h)	0	9	13	16	19	21	24
Angle (°)	55	50	45	40	35	30	25
Wind speed (km/h)	26	29	32	35	38	42	46

Analysis and Evaluation

(f) Calculate the density of each kind of weed in the north and south study sites using the following formula:

$$\text{Density} = \frac{\text{Number of weeds}}{\text{Area of the study site}}$$

(g) Determine the total number of weeds in each study site.

(h) Calculate the area covered by weeds in each study site.

(i) Was your prediction correct? Explain why, or why not, based on your observations.

(j) Which abiotic factor do you think is most (K3) important for the growth of dandelions? Use your observations to create a hypothesis, and design an experiment that would allow you to test your hypothesis.

Understanding Concepts

1. You may have noticed that there are more weeds close to a building than in the open field. How would wind help explain that difference?

2. How would the light meter help explain differences in weed distribution between the two study areas? Based on this investigation, could you tell if light or soil temperature is more important?

3. Explain why unfavourable growing conditions for grass could increase the number of weeds in a study area.

4. In which of the two study sites would you expect to find a larger animal population? Explain your answer.

Making Connections

5. How do humans affect the distribution of weeds in your study areas?

6. Examine a map of a new housing development. Provide some reasons that help explain the difference in selling price between two lots that are the same size, but on different sides of the street.

Exploring

7. One biotic factor that affects distribution of plants is competition between plants. Design an experiment that would determine how competition from other plants affects the area covered by dandelions.

Reflecting

8. You made several measurements and calculations in this investigation, including the density of each type of weed. Why would it be important for an ecologist to calculate the density of plants in an ecosystem?

Challenge

1,2 In this investigation you created biotic maps and collected data on abiotic factors. How would a map of your study area help in your Challenge?

SKILLS HANDBOOK: (K3) Developing the Prediction and Hypothesis

Karin Banerd

Science Teacher

Karin Banerd does not promote a traditional approach to life. For her, life is about making exciting choices and helping her students realize that there are many different paths people can take to find fulfillment.

Karin has always loved animals and nature. While she was growing up, her parents encouraged these interests by allowing her to keep many pets, including fish, birds, hamsters, gerbils, and a rabbit!

She also liked science and math, although she sometimes struggled with them. Her parents were supportive of these interests, even when her math grades were a little low. She appreciates their support for her interest, since it helped her to keep believing in herself, rather than giving up on something she enjoyed.

When she finished high school, she entered the three-year forestry program at Sault College, eventually focusing on fish and wildlife technology. Karin spent her summers working in unspoiled areas such as Foleyet, Chapleau, and Kapuskasing. She fondly remembers the experience of trekking through the Northern Ontario bush.

She eventually wanted a career that didn't require wearing insect repellent everyday but that still enabled her to follow her interests. As a result, Karin took part-time courses at Algoma University College (Nipissing University) in Sault Ste. Marie and correspondence courses from the University of Waterloo. She acquired a liberal science degree, then went to teacher's college at Ottawa University.

Now a high school teacher for grades 9, 10, and 11, Karin wants to share her love of science and math, especially when she remembers how she and other women were discouraged from taking these subjects in the past.

Karin considers her teaching job an interpretive one, in which she translates the information in textbooks so that students can best understand it. She sets up labs and activities to spark students' interest in different aspects of science and wants to impress upon them the fact that science is all around us. Karin feels that "there is a lot of science misinformation, and if students could leave high school thinking critically about all the information that is out there…" her job would be well done.

When she sets up labs, Karin mixes chemicals ahead of time, testing the experiments to make certain that they are effective. She shares ideas and expertise with other teachers, learning from them in those areas where her background is not strong.

She uses her science background in other aspects of her life, too. Not only does she breed canaries, finches, and parrots, but she also writes magazine articles about them. Karin's is a pretty convincing case for flexibility in building a career path.

Making Connections

1. What other experiences might lead to teacher's college?
2. Choose an area of study (e.g., insects) and investigate three different kinds of jobs that are related.

ᐃᔐ Work the Web

Research the schools Karin attended by visiting www.science.nelson.com and follow the links from Science 10, 1.7. Report on what kinds of specialized learning are offered at each school.

Comparing Ecosystems

Your schoolyard, local parks, farms, and managed forests are artificial ecosystems. An **artificial ecosystem** is planned or maintained by humans. Lakes, rivers, forests, deserts, and meadows can all be classified as natural ecosystems. In a **natural ecosystem**, the living community is free to interact with the physical and chemical environment. However, this does not mean that the area is untouched by humans: humans are a natural part of many ecosystems. Natural ecosystems haven't been planned or maintained by humans. In this case study, you will compare a meadow (natural) and a park (artificial).

Change within a park is limited because of human interference. Although the trees grow, most parks look somewhat the same from year to year. Humans manage change. Natural ecosystems undergo subtle changes as one plant or animal species gradually replaces another. In natural ecosystems, only plants suited for the environment flourish. In an artificial ecosystem, plants selected by humans have an advantage.

(a) List some reasons humans would select one plant over another in a park.

Weeds and Artificial Ecosystems

Plants can be classified in many different ways. Ecologists classify them based on structure. However, gardeners and park workers have an overall classification: weeds and nonweeds. This is a subjective grouping — the classification is not based on structure, size, or reproductive capacity. Weeds are naturally occurring plants that have fallen out of favour with humans.

(b) Suggest some reasons a plant might be categorized as a weed.

Figure 1
A meadow

Figure 2
A park

Comparing Biotic Factors

Study **Figures 1** and **2**.

(c) What human activities prevent the artificial ecosystem of the city park from changing?

(d) Which ecosystem demonstrates the greater biodiversity? Explain your conclusion.

(e) Speculate about why grasshopper sparrows, found in the meadow, are less likely to be found in a city park.

(f) Speculate about why coyotes are not common in city parks.

Comparing Environmental Factors

Table 1 provides data collected from a city park and a meadow. All measurements were taken on the same day at the same times.

Relative humidity is a measure of the percentage of water vapour in a mass of air, compared with the maximum amount of vapour that could be held at that temperature.

Evaporation rate measures the volume of water lost from soil in one day. Soil litter is a measure of the mass of decomposing organic matter found above the ground. Fallen leaves, twigs, and dead grass make up most of the soil litter.

(g) Why is it important to take measurements on the same day and at the same time?

(h) Speculate about why the wind velocity at ground level differs in the two ecosystems.

(i) Speculate about why temperatures tend to be higher in the park than in the meadow.

(j) Present an explanation that accounts for differences in the evaporation rate in the two ecosystems.

Understanding Concepts

1. (a) List abiotic factors of the city park and meadow.

   (b) Explain how human interference influences each of the factors.

2. Which of the two ecosystems, the meadow or the park, would provide a better habitat for a fox? Give reasons for your answer.

3. Not all natural ecosystems have more biodiversity than all artificial ecosystems. Give two examples of an artificial ecosystem that might have more biodiversity than a natural ecosystem. Provide an explanation of each example.

4. **Tables 1** and **2** provide some data on two ecosystems. What additional data would be useful in making a comparison of an artificial and a natural ecosystem?

Exploring

5. Some animals, such as the raccoon and the tree squirrel, do very well in artificial ecosystems. What special adaptations or behaviours make these two animals successful in human-dominated environments? Report on the results of your research.

Table 2 provides detailed counts for some species in the two ecosystems.

(k) Speculate about why goldenrod is found in the meadow but not the city park.

(l) Provide a hypothesis that explains why more earthworms are in the meadow than the park.

(m) Why are more spiders found in the meadow?

Table 1   Abiotic and Biotic Factors in Two Ecosystems

Abiotic factors	City park	Meadow
temperature (maximum)	28°C	26°C
temperature (minimum)	12°C	10°C
wind speed at ground	22 km/h	15 km/h
evaporation rate	10 L/day	3.5 L/day
relative humidity	85%	64%
light at ground (% of sunlight available)	95%	91%
soil nitrogen rating	very high	low
soil phosphorus rating	high	low
Biotic factor		
soil litter	56 g/m²	275 g/m²

Table 2   Inventory of Species in 10 m x 10 m Study Areas

Types of organism	City park		Meadow	
	Number of species	Population of all species	Number of species	Population of all species
grass	1	100 000/m²	3	40 000/m²
goldenrod	0	0	1	51
weeds	3	6	17	459
earthworms	1	25	8	210
beetles	4	7	22	39
spiders	1	2	2	13
birds	3	10	11	39
rodents	0	0	3	45

INQUIRY SKILLS MENU
○ Questioning   ○ Planning   ● Analyzing
○ Hypothesizing ● Conducting ● Evaluating
● Predicting   ● Recording   ● Communicating

A Natural Ecosystem

Lakes, rivers, forests, deserts, and meadows can be classified as natural ecosystems. Natural ecosystems are places that haven't been planned or maintained by humans, although humans may live in them. Natural ecosystems do not need to be large, but they do need to hold a community of living things. A very small ecosystem is called a microecosystem.

Question

How does the top of a fallen log differ from the bottom of the log?

Hypothesis/Prediction

If the abiotic factors on top of a fallen log differ from those below the log, then the community in the top of the log will differ from the community in the bottom of the log.

(a) Predict what differences you will find between
(K3) top and bottom when you examine a log. Explain your prediction.

Design

You will explore the relationships between the abiotic environment and living things in a fallen log.

Materials

- gloves
- several fallen logs at various stages of decay (one per group)
- hand lens or dissecting microscope
- field guide to insects/arthropods
- field guide to fungi
- metal spoon
- plastic bags or small jars with screw caps
- tweezers
- labels
- spade

Procedure

1 Use **Table 1** to describe the stage of decomposition of your group's log.

Table 1   Ratings Chart for Decomposing Logs

A rating:	Log is firm. Bark remains on log even when pressure is applied to the log.
B rating:	Log is less firm. Bark is easily pulled away when pressure is applied, but log maintains shape.
C rating:	Log feels spongy. The log breaks when pressure is applied. Wood begins to crumble.
D rating:	The last stage of decomposition. Log shows evidence of crumbling even before any pressure is applied.

2 Observe the outer surface of your log for signs that animals have burrowed into or out of the log. Record your observations.

(b) What kind of animals do you think made the marks or holes in your log?

3 Examine the outside of the bark for mosses and
(M1) other plants. Look also for fungi. (White or yellow threads also indicate the presence of fungi.) **Figure 1** may help you with your identification. Draw a diagram of the outer surface of the log, indicating the position of the organisms you identify.

(a) moss   **(b)** bracket fungi

Figure 1
Some plants and fungi commonly found on logs

SKILLS HANDBOOK: (K3) Developing the Prediction and Hypothesis (M1) Qualitative Evidence

4 Using a spoon, remove a small section of the bark and look for insect larvae and eggs, centipedes, millipedes, ants, and wood-boring beetles. Record your observations. You may wish to take a small sample of the bark back to the laboratory for later study, using tweezers and a plastic bag or a jar. Be sure to label each bag with the location from which the sample was taken.

5 Using a spade as a lever, carefully roll the log over. Feel the underside. Compare the amount of moisture on top and underneath the log. Record your observations.

6 Repeat steps 3, 4, and 5 for the underside of the log. Record your observations.

7 Return the log to its original position.

8 Wash your hands.

Analysis and Evaluation

(c) Using a table such as **Table 2**, compare the abiotic factors that influence life on the top and the bottom of the log you studied.

Table 2 **Abiotic Factors**

Abiotic factor	Top of log	Bottom of log
1. sunlight		
2. moisture		
3. wind		
4. temperature		

(d) Using a table similar to **Table 3**, categorize the members of the biotic communities you studied.

Table 3

Biotic community	Top of log	Bottom of log
1. producer		
2. consumers		
a. carnivores		
b. herbivores		
3. decomposers		

(e) Prepare a report for this investigation. In your report, include a conclusion about the hypothesis and your prediction — were there really two microecosystems and two communities in your log?

(c) mushrooms

(d) puff balls

(e) lichen

(f) mould

Understanding Concepts

1. Provide a hypothesis that explains why bracket fungi are often found on top of a log, but mould is more common under a log.

2. In what ways are the microecosystems under a log and inside a running shoe similar?

3. Based on your observations, explain why fallen trees are important in the ecosystem of the forest.

Exploring

4. Use the observations collected by other groups to compare logs at different stages of decay. Examine the drawings and the samples taken from the other logs and compare the microecosystems. For example, which log has the greatest number of fungi? On the basis of your class observations, create diagrams showing how the community in a log changes as it decays. Accompany your presentation with explanations for the changes in the community.

Reflecting

5. In this investigation you worked in a group to collect data. Explain some advantages of working in a group.

Energy in Ecosystems

The source of all energy for ecosystems is the Sun. It lights and warms the surface of our planet. It gives the energy needed to evaporate water from the oceans and lakes, to form rain and snow. Sunlight also provides the energy used by green plants to make the compounds that maintain their lives and serve as food for all other organisms.

The Sun acts like a distant nuclear fusion reactor, radiating energy out into space. Of the energy released by the Sun only about one billionth reaches Earth — after a journey of about 150 million kilometres. Much of the energy that reaches Earth's atmosphere is filtered out before it reaches the surface. Harmful high-energy cosmic rays, gamma rays, X rays, and ultraviolet radiation are all either reflected or absorbed by chemicals in the atmosphere.

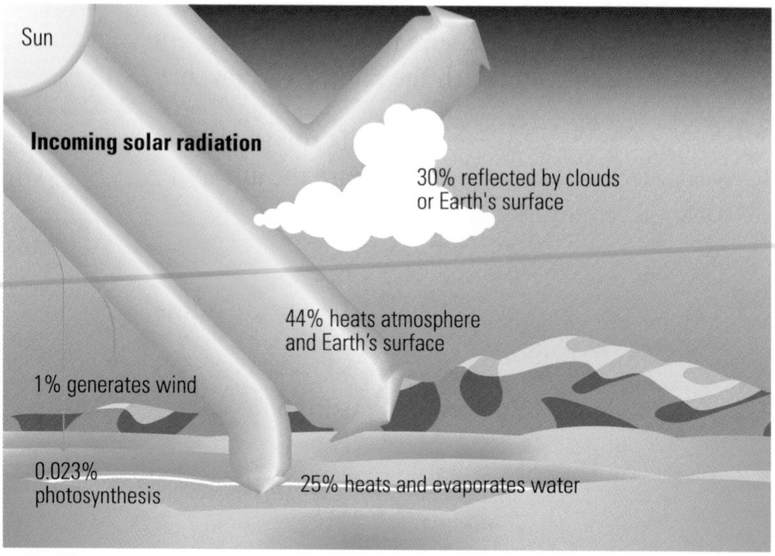

Of the energy that penetrates into the lower atmosphere, 30% is reflected by clouds or the Earth's surface. The remaining 70% warms the surface of the planet, causing water to evaporate, and generating the water cycle and weather. Only a tiny portion, approximately 0.023%, is actually used by green plants for photosynthesis (**Figure 1**). **Photosynthesis** is the process by which green plants use sunlight energy to produce carbohydrates (sugars).

Many gases found in the atmosphere actually trap thermal energy rising from the surface and direct it back to Earth. These gases permit energy from the Sun into Earth's ecosystems, but act as a barrier preventing the energy from leaving.

The Albedo Effect

When sunlight strikes an object, some of the energy is absorbed, and some is reflected. Some materials reflect sunlight better than others. **Albedo** is a measurement of the percentage of light that an object reflects. The higher the albedo, the greater the object's ability to reflect sunlight. For the Earth, the higher its overall albedo, the less energy will be absorbed and available for maintaining the global

Sun

Incoming solar radiation

30% reflected by clouds or Earth's surface

44% heats atmosphere and Earth's surface

1% generates wind

0.023% photosynthesis

25% heats and evaporates water

Figure 1

A model of the flow of energy from the Sun, to Earth, and back into space.

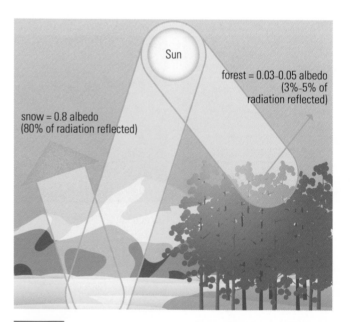

snow = 0.8 albedo (80% of radiation reflected)

Sun

forest = 0.03–0.05 albedo (3%–5% of radiation reflected)

Figure 2

Most of the radiation that reaches snow is reflected, and cannot be used to warm the surrounding air. Forests have a much lower albedo. Most of the radiation that falls on dark green leaves is absorbed, and can be used to warm the surrounding air.

temperature. For example, you've probably noticed how bright snow is when sunlight is falling on it — snow has a high albedo (**Figure 2**). Snow contributes to the low temperatures of winter by reflecting energy from the Sun back into space. Snow also delays warming in the spring. Other light-coloured (high-albedo) areas of the Earth's surface, such as sand, pale rocks, and areas without forest, have a similar effect.

Cloud cover also increases the albedo of the Earth. If there is more water vapour, or more dust for water vapour to condense on, there will be more cloud. Higher temperatures cause more water to evaporate. Industrial activities release dust.

Understanding Concepts

1. Why is sunlight important for the biosphere?

2. Make a pie graph showing what happens to the energy from the Sun that penetrates into Earth's atmosphere. Label each piece of the pie.

3. In your own words, describe the albedo effect.

4. **Table 1** provides data collected following the eruption of four volcanoes. The average summer temperature declined following each eruption.

Table 1   **Volcanoes and Lower Temperatures**

Volcano	Year of eruption	Period of low average temperature
Mt. Asama (Japan)	1783	1784–91
Mt. Tamboro (Indonesia)	1815	1816–20
Mt. Krakatoa (Indonesia)	1883	1884–90
Mt. St. Helens (United States)	1980	1981–82

(a) Write a hypothesis that explains why temperatures become lower following a volcanic eruption. (K3)

(b) Design a controlled experiment that could test this hypothesis. In your description, include the independent and dependent variables. (K4)

(c) On the basis of the data, predict which was the largest eruption. Explain your prediction.

(d) At most times, a volcano is erupting or about to erupt somewhere on Earth. If no more volcanic activity occurred, predict how world temperatures would be affected. Explain your prediction.

5. Albedo is not the only factor that determines temperature. **Table 2** includes data collected from grassland and forest ecosystems in Ontario. Air temperatures were measured simultaneously at the two study sites, which were in the same general area.

Table 2   **Soil Temperature vs. Depth**

Distance above the surface of the soil (cm)	Temperature in field (°C)	Temperature in forest (°C)
200	24	22
100	25	22
50	26	22
25	27	22
0	29	21
−10	23	18
−20	14	9
−30	10	9

(a) Use data in the table to plot a graph showing the relationship between temperature and distance from the surface of the earth. (V)

(b) List biotic and abiotic factors that might explain the difference in the data gathered from the two study sites.

(c) Explain why the difference between above-ground and surface temperatures is greater in the open field.

(d) For each site, explain the pattern in changes of temperature below the surface.

(e) Using only the information presented within the study, explain why more burrowing animals are found in grassland ecosystems than forest ecosystems.

Making Connections

6. Describe low-albedo and high-albedo areas around your school or home. What could you do to make the high-albedo areas absorb more sunlight? What could you do to make low-albedo areas absorb less sunlight?

Following Energy Movement in Ecosystems

You can begin to understand energy flows by categorizing living things by their **trophic level** in their ecosystem, according to how they gain their energy. The term "trophic" comes from a Greek word meaning "feeder."

Organisms that can make their own food from basic nutrients and sunlight or some other non-living energy source are placed in the first trophic level (**Figure 1**). Not surprisingly, these organisms are also referred to as producers or **autotrophs** (from Greek words meaning "self-feeders"). Plants, algae, and some types of bacteria are in the first trophic level.

The second trophic level contains organisms that feed on the producers. These organisms are referred to as **primary consumers**. Primary consumers rely on autotrophs directly for their source of energy.

Secondary consumers are animals in the third trophic level. They rely on primary consumers for their source of energy, but they are still dependent on the autotrophs in the first trophic level. Although a wolf eats other animals, it still relies indirectly on the photosynthesis of plants for energy. The deer the wolf eats has eaten the buds of a spruce tree or grass.

Consumers, at whatever trophic level, are sometimes called **heterotrophs**. Heterotrophs cannot make their own food, and so must obtain their food and energy from autotrophs or other heterotrophs. Human beings are heterotrophs.

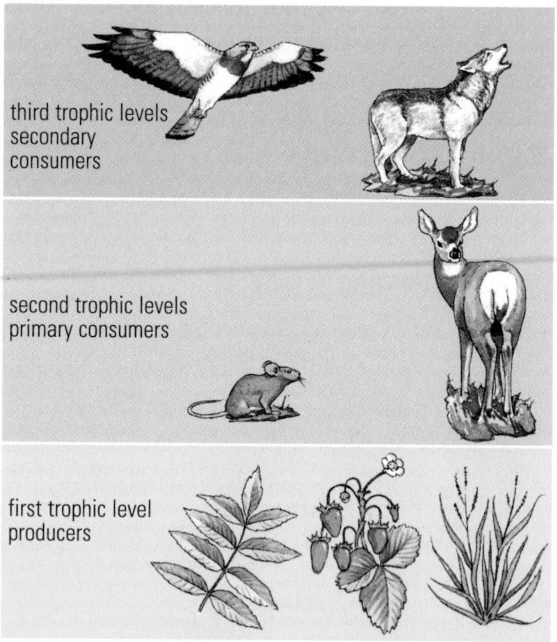

Figure 1

Trophic levels, showing producers and consumers. An ecosystem may contain more than three trophic levels.

Energy and Food Chains

Every organism within an ecosystem provides energy for other organisms. Food chains are a way of showing a step-by-step sequence of who eats whom in an ecosystem. The sequence in **Figure 2** shows a one-way flow of energy in a simple food chain from producer to secondary consumer. The deer does not make its own energy; instead it relies on the spruce tree. The deer is a heterotroph. Since the deer receives its energy two steps away from the original source (sunlight) it is in the second trophic level. Using the same reasoning, the wolf, also a heterotroph, is a member of the third trophic level.

Consumers are placed in categories based on their trophic level in a food chain. A carnivore directly feeding on a primary consumer is a secondary consumer. However, if the carnivore eats a secondary consumer (another carnivore), it is now a tertiary consumer — it is at the fourth trophic level. The final carnivore in any food chain is called a top carnivore. Top carnivores are not eaten by other animals (at least, while they are alive). In the example above, the wolf is both a secondary consumer and a top carnivore, since it obtains its energy from the deer and no other animal eats the wolf.

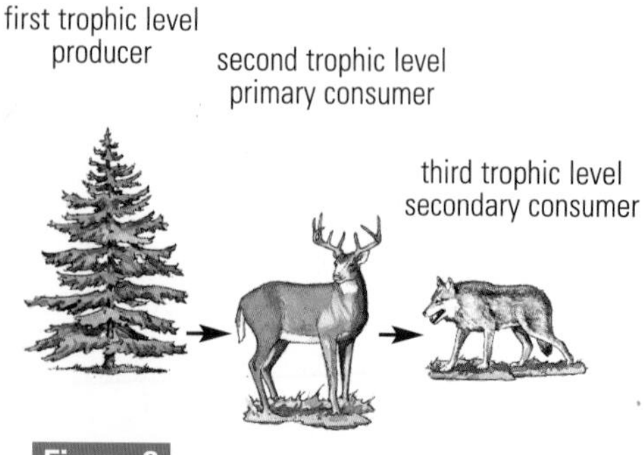

Figure 2

In this food chain, energy flows from a producer (the spruce tree) to a primary consumer (the deer), to a secondary consumer (the wolf).

Food Webs

Consider what would happen if the deer in **Figure 2** depended exclusively on the buds of spruce trees. Now imagine what would happen if a new animal were introduced. Spruce budworms also eat the buds of spruce trees. What would happen to the deer if spruce budworms ate most of the spruce buds in a forest? And how would the wolves, in turn, be affected? You might expect that the deer, deprived of food, would die, and so would the wolves. But such dramatic cause-and-effect relationship are rare in natural ecosystems.

Deer also eat buds, stems, and bark of a variety of trees and shrubs, as well as certain grasses. The wolf includes in its diet many different animals, such as rabbits, ground-nesting birds and their eggs, beavers, and muskrats. In reality, each individual organism in an ecosystem is involved in many food chains. They all interlock with each other to form a feeding relationship called a **food web** (**Figure 3**).

The most stable ecosystems, those with the greatest biodiversity, have such complex and well-developed food webs that the reduction in numbers or even the complete removal of one type of organism may have only a small effect on the overall web. If spruce budworms eat most of the spruce buds, deer will switch to another tree or grass, and wolves will not be much affected. However, where abiotic factors limit the number of organisms, the webs begin to look more like food chains.

This is particularly true in the Arctic, where the number of producers is small. Because there is less energy available from the Sun and temperatures are often low, producers in the Arctic can't photosynthesize as rapidly as they do in the south. Less energy is available, so fewer organisms can live in that ecosystem. The limited number of organisms means that their relationships with each other are more direct. In these situations, the loss of any one member will have a profound effect on all the remaining organisms. The lower the biodiversity of an ecosystem, the simpler the food web, and the more vulnerable each organism is.

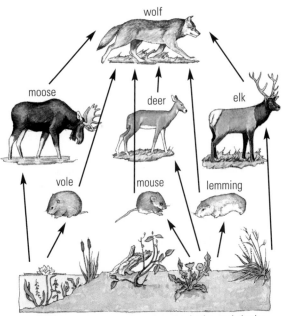

Figure 3

A simplified food web shows the wolf as the top carnivore and plants as producers. Notice that both the vole and the deer belong in the second trophic level of this web. Of course, in a real ecosystem that contained these organisms, there would also be many more other organisms, and the food web would be much more complicated.

Limits on Energy Transfer

Producers use energy from sunlight and basic nutrients to make molecules of sugar. Sugar molecules contain the chemical energy that drives ecosystems. Photosynthesis provides the energy required by the entire ecosystem. Without photosynthesis, energy would not move from the abiotic environment to living things. Solar energy must be converted into chemical energy before it can be used by living things.

Every time energy is transferred within an ecosystem, some of the energy changes form. For example, some of the energy from the Sun is converted into chemical energy by plants as they photosynthesize. Animals, in turn, rely on the chemical energy (food) produced by plants to sustain their lives. However, not all of the chemical energy that a plant creates can reach the animal that eats it. The plant uses most of that energy to stay alive and to manufacture the chemicals it needs to grow. Once an animal takes chemical energy from a plant, it doesn't store it all.

Most of that energy is used to move its limbs, pump blood, keep its body warm, and manufacture the chemicals it needs to carry out its own life processes.

For example, a mouse that has eaten grass seeds cannot store all the energy from the seeds. It must use some to stay warm, to keep its cells and organs functioning, to move around, to feed its young, and so on. Once the energy has been used, it is not available to be transferred. When an animal such as a fox eats the mouse, only a small fraction of the energy that was stored by the grass reaches the fox. It is true of all food chains that the farther up the chain you travel, the less energy is available. In every ecosystem, there is less energy available to secondary consumers than there is to primary consumers.

Thermodynamics

There is another limitation. The energy flowing from the Sun through ecosystems must obey basic scientific principles known as the laws of thermodynamics. **Thermodynamics** is the study of energy transformations.

- The **first law of thermodynamics** states that although energy can be transformed (changed) from one form to another, it cannot be created or destroyed (**Figure 4**).

- The **second law of thermodynamics** states that during any energy transformation, some of the energy is converted into an unusable form, mostly thermal energy (heat) that cannot be passed on. Each time energy is transformed, some energy is lost from the system. As a result, the amount of energy available in each step of a chain of transformations is always less than the amount of energy available at the previous step. This applies to all systems, including food chains (**Figure 5**).

Limits on Energy Transfers and the Number of Trophic Levels

Let's return to the simple spruce —> deer —> wolf food chain. If you follow the energy flow, you can see that there are several factors that reduce the available energy at each transfer.

A deer grazing on spruce may eat only the buds, not the whole tree. Not all of the bud is digested by the deer. Some is eliminated in the deer's wastes (feces). Energy is lost to waste heat during the chemical transformation of digestion. Some of the remainder is used to fuel the deer's cells, resulting in loss of energy as waste heat is generated in the process. Some of this heat is used to maintain the deer's body temperature, but it is all lost eventually to the surrounding air. As a result, only about 10% of the energy of the plant that was transferred to the deer becomes available to the wolf.

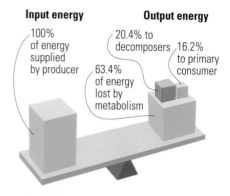

Figure 4

In any system, the energy input must equal the energy output. Most of the energy transformed from light to chemical energy by a plant is used to maintain the plant and to grow. Every time the plant uses some of its energy store, it also loses energy as heat. As a result, when the plant is eaten, only a small amount of energy is available for the primary consumer and decomposers. (Bacteria and fungi acquire 20.4% of the energy found in the producers during decomposition after the plant dies.)

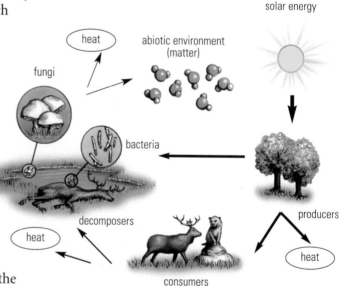

Figure 5

Because of the second law of thermodynamics, energy is lost each time energy is transferred from one organism to another, and inside each organism as it uses the energy to survive.

By not consuming parts of the deer, such as its bones, hooves, skin, and fur, the wolf uses only a portion of the energy stored in the total deer tissue. And like the deer, it loses energy in digestion and body maintenance.

In general, the overall loss of energy at each step sets a limit on the number of trophic levels in a food chain at about five. In most ecosystems, there wouldn't be enough energy to support a higher-level consumer.

Graphing Energy in Ecosystems: Ecological Pyramids

Graphs called pyramids can be used to represent energy flow in food chains and food webs or the populations of organisms in a food chain. These graphs help the ecologist visualize more clearly the relationships in an ecosystem and to compare ecosystems.

Pyramid of Energy

It is possible to measure the amount of energy available at each trophic level.

Creating a pyramid graph allows us to understand the relationships and energy flow better (**Figure 6**). The comparatively larger mass of the individual tertiary consumers and the vast amount of energy that they expend while hunting limits the number of individuals that can be supported at the top position of the pyramid.

Pyramid of Numbers

A pyramid of numbers can be drawn by counting the number of organisms at each trophic level in an ecosystem. When these numbers are then represented on a vertical graph, with the volume of each level representing the number of organisms at that level, the graph sometimes takes on the general shape of a pyramid (**Figure 7**). Ecologists have found that there are many exceptions because of the physical size of the members of a food chain. For example, many tiny aphids (an insect that feeds by sucking sap from plants) may be found feeding off a single plant (**Figure 8**).

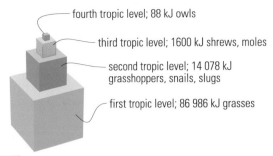

Figure 6

A pyramid of energy for a grassland ecosystem. At each level, the energy found in the bodies of the organisms is graphed. The larger the volume of the level, the greater the energy at that level. As you can see, only about one-thousandth of the chemical energy from photosynthesis stored in the producers in this food web actually reaches the top predator (the owl) at the fourth trophic level. Energy is measured using joules (1000 joules (J) = 1 kilojoule (kJ)).

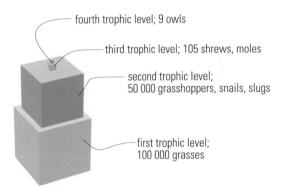

Figure 7

A pyramid of numbers for a grassland ecosystem. In this ecosystem, the number of producers is greater than the number of primary consumers.

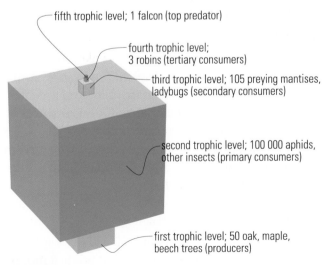

Figure 8

A pyramid of numbers for a deciduous forest ecosystem. Because an aphid is much smaller than a tree, a single plant may provide food for thousands of aphids.

Pyramid of Biomass

Another useful way to represent an ecosystem is through a pyramid of **biomass**. To make such a pyramid, the dry mass (after water has been removed) of the dry tissue in the plants or animals is measured and graphed (**Figure 9**). Occasionally, a graph of biomass is not a regular pyramid. Such ecosystems, however, are rare.

The Energy Budget

Regardless of the pyramid used to illustrate a food chain or web, each shows that the end result is the same. The energy available to maintain a food chain inevitably runs out unless the original energy, sunlight, is continuously fed into the system. Also, in every ecosystem there is a limit to how much energy is available. It is obvious that primary consumers have access to the most energy. This finding has very real implications for humans as the world population continues its dramatic rise.

Cultural Change: The Human Use of Energy in Ecosystems

Although the planet is an estimated 4.6 billion years old, the impact of humans is relatively recent. Researchers believe that modern humans have been part of worldwide ecosystems for somewhere between 60 000 and 90 000 years. Until about 12 000 years ago, however, the influence of humans on ecosystems was very small. Since that time there have been two major shifts: the agricultural revolution and the industrial revolution. Each of these cultural changes has placed increasing demands on ecosystems for energy and reduced the amount of energy available to other organisms.

By increasing the food supply, improving health, and increasing the lifespan for humans, each of these cultural changes was followed by an increase in the human population. Recently, the increase has accelerated, threatening the ability of ecosystems to sustain themselves. The increasing rate of extinction and the loss of entire ecosystems provides evidence of the strain caused by the growing human population.

Hunting and Gathering

Humans were hunters and gatherers for most of our history. Our ancestors survived by collecting edible plants and eating animals that they caught or dead animals that they found or stole from predators. They lived in small groups that moved to a new area if local resources became depleted.

The energy demands made on the ecosystem were limited to two sources: wood for fuel and food (chemical energy) obtained from plants and animals. Because of limited food resources, human populations grew very slowly or were stable.

Agriculture

Somewhere between 10 000 and 12 000 years ago, a cultural shift known as the agricultural revolution began. The gradual movement from a nomadic existence to the farm was made possible by a change in climate. The planting of crops and domestication of animals allowed people to remain in one place. Trees were cut and the lumber was used to make permanent housing.

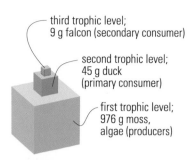

third trophic level;
9 g falcon (secondary consumer)

second trophic level;
45 g duck
(primary consumer)

first trophic level;
976 g moss,
algae (producers)

Figure 9

A pyramid of biomass for a Newfoundland peat bog. The numbers represent the dry mass (g) for all organisms at that trophic level found in 1 m^2. As you can see, there is less biomass at each trophic level.

Wetlands were drained and forests were cut so the land could be cultivated.

Farms produced more food energy for humans, and allowed the population to grow, but they also made greater demands on local ecosystems. The additional energy needed to sustain a farming community must be supplied by the ecosystem. In effect, humans began to take a larger share of the energy budget for the ecosystems they inhabited.

Industry

With the invention of technological devices to perform work, the demand on the energy of ecosystems grew. Energy from ecosystems was used to power machines. The products helped to increase food production and improve the health of humans. Although each industrial improvement allowed the local ecosystem to support a greater population of humans, an increasing population places greater demands on the ecosystem (**Figure 10**).

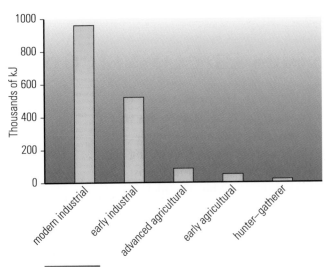

Figure 10

The amount of energy people use each day depends on the type of society they live in.

 Challenge

1,2,3 One way of understanding an ecosystem is through the study of energy transfers. What energy transfers would need to be considered in your Challenge?

Understanding Concepts

1. In your own words, explain what is meant by the term "trophic level."

2. Why are producer organisms called autotrophs?

3. How does a heterotroph differ from an autotroph?

4. What type of food would be consumed by a secondary consumer? Explain your answer.

5. In your own words, explain what is meant by the term "top carnivore." Give three examples of a top carnivore, including the ecosystem in which you would find each one.

6. Distinguish between a food chain and a food web using examples for each.

7. Explain why an Arctic ecosystem would be more fragile than a southern forest ecosystem.

8. In your own words, explain the first and second laws of thermodynamics.

9. Explain why only about 20% of the energy available in a plant is transferred to the primary consumer.

10. Using the example of a cat and a mouse, explain the factors that account for the loss of energy in the transfer from mouse to cat.

11. What data would you need to collect to create an ecological pyramid of numbers?

12. What problem might you encounter if you tried to show energy flow through an ecosystem using a pyramid of numbers?

13. How might a pyramid of energy for a grassland community differ from summer to winter? Speculate about the effects of the differing abiotic conditions by drawing an ecological pyramid of energy for each season. Include an explanation for any differences.

14. **Figure 11** shows pyramids of biomass and numbers for a deciduous forest. Explain why the two are different.

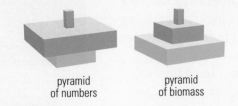

pyramid
of numbers

pyramid
of biomass

Figure 11

Reflecting

15. Despite warnings about future shortages and the pollutants released, we continue to burn oil and coal for energy. What evidence, if any, suggests attitudes toward conservation are changing? Are they changing quickly enough?

Roles in Ecosystems

Each organism has its own place within an ecosystem. The organism's place in the food web, its habitat, breeding area, and the time of day that it is most active is its **ecological niche**. The niche an organism fills in an ecosystem includes everything it does to survive and reproduce.

Each species in an ecosystem tends to have a different niche, a different role to play. This helps reduce competition between species for the same territory and resources.

Owls and hawks (**Figure 1**) feed on many of the same organisms, but they occupy distinctly different niches. The owl, with its short, broad wings is well adapted to hunt down prey within forests. The longer wings of the hawk are ideal for soaring above grasslands and open fields, but present problems for flight through dense brush. Owls are active during dusk and at night, while hawks hunt by daylight. Although the two birds do prey on some of the same species, different animals are active during the night and the day.

To support their roles, owls and hawks have different adaptations. In addition to their different wing shapes,

Figure 1
Even though the red-tailed hawk and the screech owl eat some of the same food, they are not in competition because they have different ecological niches.

they also differ in their senses, particularly their eyes. Hawk eyes are excellent at detecting changes in colour patterns, which helps them see rodents even when they are well hidden by their camouflage. Owl eyes are poor with colour, but excellent at detecting motion, even in the dark. Owls also have excellent hearing, so they can detect the tiniest rustling noises of mice and other rodents as they move.

Competition is further reduced because owls and hawks nest in different areas. Many owls seek the deep cover of trees; hawks nest near the tops of the taller tree of a forest, overlooking grassland.

The different species of warblers that inhabitant forests of Atlantic and Central Canada make up one of the best examples of how species reduce competition by occupying different niches. Each species of insect-eating bird feeds in a different part of the tree (**Figure 2**). Even though all warblers eat insects, they don't compete much with each other because different species of insects are found in their different feeding areas.

Competition for Niches

When a new species enters an ecosystem, it causes a disturbance because it will come into competition for a niche with one or more of the species already in the ecosystem. The introduction of new species (often called "exotic species" because they are not native to the ecosystem) happens naturally. Animals are mobile, and can move from one ecosystem to another. Plant seeds can be carried by the wind or animals and take root in new areas. Sometimes a completely new route to an area is opened up, allowing organisms that were separated from each other to mix.

Sometimes the results are dramatic. For example, when North and South America came together about 5 million years ago, animals could move freely from north to south. The result was devastating in South America, where many of the native species came into competition with invaders from the north, and lost. Only a few animals from the south managed to cross over to northern ecosystems and find a niche, the opossum (**Figure 3**) being one of them.

Figure 3

The opossum, once native to South America, can now be found in North America. It competed for, and established, its own niche in forest ecosystems.

Figure 2

Competition is reduced because each species of warbler prefers to feed in different sections of the tree.

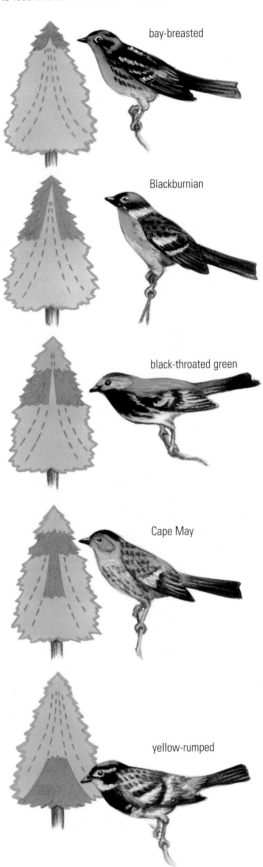

bay-breasted

Blackburnian

black-throated green

Cape May

yellow-rumped

Humans and Exotic Species

Humans constantly bring ecosystems into contact with each other, as they tend to take organisms with them when they travel, often with serious consequences. One of the best examples comes from Brazil, where in 1957 honey producers introduced wild African bees (**Figure 4**). It was believed that the more aggressive African bees would increase honey production. Although the imports do produce more honey, they also displaced native species and led to an overall decline in honey production.

The African bees are usually referred to as "killer bees" because they tend to swarm and attack animals they see as a threat to their hive. Cattle, dogs, and humans have all been killed by the bees. Unchecked by natural predators, their population grew and they began to spread. By 1986, the bees had moved north through South America, across Central America and into Mexico, claiming the lives of more than 150 people. By 1994, killer bee colonies had established themselves in Texas, Arizona, and New Mexico. Although the bees continue to move northward, coming into competition with local bees as they advance, most biologists believe that Canada is safe. Killer bees don't do well in colder climates.

Figure 4

The "killer bees" are an exotic species, introduced into the Americas by humans. So far they are winning the competition with native honey bees for an ecological niche in the ecosystems they have invaded.

The Zebra Mussel: An Exotic Species

The identification of the zebra mussel (**Figure 5**) in Lake Erie in the early 1990s set off a series of alarms that captured the attention of news media for nearly eight years. Biologists believe that this tiny bivalve, a native of the Caspian Sea in western Asia, entered the Great Lakes from bilge water discharged from ships. In the Great Lakes, this exotic species found lots of food and so spread quickly.

In 1991 there were extensive colonies of zebra mussels in Lake Ontario and small groups could be found in Georgian Bay on Lake Huron. By 1994, the zebra mussel was common in the Rideau Canal and throughout the Trent-Severn Waterway. By 1995, the invading mussels had moved through the Ohio River to the Mississippi, and could be found all the way to the Gulf of Mexico.

The mussel attaches to almost any hard object standing in water. The mussels blocked water intake pipes from the Great Lakes, choking hydroelectric plants and freshwater supplies for a number of industries. Ontario Hydro, municipalities, and the Ontario Ministry of the Environment all undertook massive campaigns to prevent the mussels from moving up intake pipes into generating stations, water treatment plants, and industrial plants. These efforts may also have diverted attention and resources away from pollution issues in the Great Lakes.

Figure 5

When the zebra mussel first arrived in the Great Lakes, there were predictions of catastrophe for the ecosystem. Some of those early predictions were overstated, but the exotic species has changed the ecology of the Great Lakes and the long-term effects are still in question.

Ecology and the Zebra Mussel

Speculations about what this rapidly reproducing organism might do to the food webs of the lake ecosystems were even more alarming. For example, ecologists noted that the pearly mussel, a natural inhabitant of most of Ontario's freshwater lakes, had difficulty competing with the zebra mussel. In every place that zebra mussels invaded, a decline in the number of pearly mussels followed. Zebra mussels and pearly mussels should not compete for the same niche: pearly mussels burrow into mud along the shores of freshwater lakes, while zebra mussels attach themselves to hard surfaces. However, the shells of the pearly mussels are a hard surface — layers of zebra mussels form on top of pearly mussels.

Mussels are filter feeders. They put out small threads covered with a sticky mucous, and comb the water to remove small organisms for food. Bacteria, algae, and very tiny animals are taken into the mollusk for food. If many zebra mussels attach to the shells of the pearly mussels, little food filters down to the pearly mussels. Also, the zebra mussels attached to their shells prevent them from moving to a more favourable location.

The introduction of zebra mussels has not been detrimental to other species (**Figure 6**). Ducks, especially the lesser scaup, and other aquatic birds feed on the mussel. The discarded shells of the zebra mussel also provide underwater shelter for snails, aquatic insects, small crustaceans, and water mites. Hydra (a small freshwater relative of the jellyfish) also benefits: the larvae of the zebra mussel provide a ready source of food.

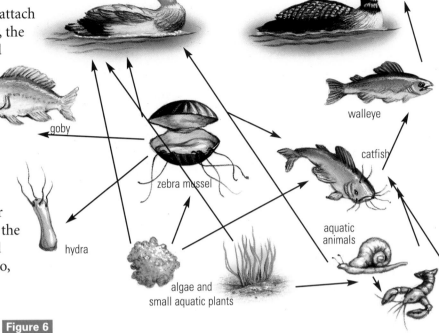

Figure 6

The zebra mussel has become part of the food web of the Great Lakes, as animals found ways to eat it and live with it. The zebra mussel has found an ecological niche, although it is still in competition with the native pearly mussel.

The invading mussels have indeed caused problems, but the Great Lakes ecosystem has not been devastated. Zebra mussels do not cover the shoreline, nor have they eliminated competing species. One study, of yellow perch in western Lake Erie, indicates that they do not interfere with the spawning of fish. In fact, they may even help yellow perch by creating a more favourable habitat for small crustaceans, such as crayfish, that feed on the mussel. Perch eat crustaceans.

Some studies even credit the zebra mussel with long-term benefits. The number of algae had been increasing greatly owing to fertilizers and other human pollutants that were carried into the Great Lakes with the spring runoff. The growth in algae was affecting aquatic plants, as the algae were blocking light from the Sun. Mussels eat algae, and now aquatic plants are thriving once again.

The mussels not only reduced the amount of algae in the Great Lakes, but they also removed pollutants from the water. Each adult mussel draws in as much as 1.5 L of water daily, retaining the pollutants and expelling the water. So much water is filtered that Lake Erie is now 60% clearer than it was before the arrival of the mussel.

However, all of this filtering of pollutants does not come without a cost. The pollutants stored in the zebra mussels are passed on to predators, for whom they can be toxic.

Ecologists are also speculating about the negative effects of reducing the algae population, because algae are the most important producers in the lakes, and so are important in the food web. Even clearer water may pose a threat. More sunlight would penetrate the water, causing greater warming. Because warm water holds less oxygen, fish such as trout, which require higher levels of oxygen, could suffer.

As you can see, assessing the impact of the zebra mussel is a complicated business, and it has recently become more complicated. Another exotic species, the goby (**Figure 7**), was found in the Welland Canal in 1996. The stowaway likely entered the Great Lakes from ballast water held in a freighter that had visited the Black Sea. Gobies eat zebra mussels, but they also have other effects — we cannot rely on them to restore the original ecosystem. The goby chases other fish away from their spawning grounds and feeds on the eggs of native fish such as walleye, perch, and small-mouth bass.

Economics and the Zebra Mussel

The predicted human disaster of clogged pipes, resulting in multi-billion-dollar clean-up bills, has proven to be slightly exaggerated. Evidence seems to indicate that chlorine has prevented the zebra mussel from choking off water intake systems. However, controlling the mussels has not come without financial cost. One estimate for Ontario Hydro has pegged the cost of the initial control efforts at $20 million, with an annual cost of as much as $1 million for maintenance. Commercial fishing has survived the influx of the invading mussel, but only barely. The industry, which generated $600 million before the zebra mussel, now generates only $200 million.

Figure 7
Another exotic introduction to the Great Lakes will also cause changes in the ecology. The goby chases less aggressive species from their spawning territory.

🖑 Work the Web

Find out more about one of the following exotic species that have been introduced into ecosystems in the Western Hemisphere: eelgrass; starlings; Russian thistle. Write a report on your findings. Visit www.science.nelson.com and follow the links from Science 10, 1.12 to conduct your research.

Understanding Concepts

1. In your own words, define the term "ecological niche."

2. Give examples illustrating the problems that can be created when a new species is introduced into an ecosystem.

3. Make a chart listing the positive and negative effects of the introduction of the zebra mussel to the Great Lakes.

4. Describe your ecological niche. Consider your habitat and your place in food webs.

Exploring

5. For many years, ecologists have argued about whether all niches within ecosystems are occupied. Present examples that support both sides of the argument.

6. Do lions and tigers occupy the same niche? Research and give reasons for your answer.

 ## Challenge

1 What exotic species might be introduced with the building of a golf course?

3 In constructing your board game, how will you show how introduction of exotic species affects ecosystems?

Chapter 1 Summary

Key Expectations

Throughout this chapter, you have had opportunities to do the following:

- Examine the factors (natural and external) that affect the survival of populations. (1.1, 1.2, 1.3, 1.12)
- Identify and evaluate Canadian initiatives in protecting Canada's ecosystems. (1.2)
- Form and defend a position in written form. (1.4)
- Describe some ways in which the relationships between organisms and their ecosystems are viewed by different cultures. (1.4)
- Examine how abiotic factors affect the survival and location of populations. (1.5, 1.6, 1.8, 1.9, 1.10)
- Compare a natural and a disturbed (artificial) ecosystem. (1.8)
- Describe a career that involves knowledge of ecology or environmental technologies and use the Internet to find out more about related careers. (1.7)
- Assess the impact of the introduction of exotic species. (1.12)

Key Terms

abiotic	food chain
albedo	food web
artificial ecosystem	habitat
autotroph	herbivore
biodiversity	heterotroph
biomass	natural ecosystem
biotic	omnivore
carnivore	pest
community	photosynthesis
consumer	population
decomposer	primary consumer
detritus	producer
ecological niche	secondary consumer
ecology	thermodynamics
ecosystem	first law
ecotone	second law
endangered	threatened
extinct	trophic level
extirpated	vulnerable

Make a Summary

In this chapter you have studied biodiversity and the abiotic and biotic factors that affect biodiversity in ecosystems.

- To summarize your learning, create a concept map with biodiversity and the factors that affect it as the central thoughts.
- Try to use as many of the terms in the Key Terms list as possible in your map.
- When you have finished your map, identify as many of the factors in your map as you can as either biotic or abiotic.

The concept map below is just one example of how a biodiversity map could be started.

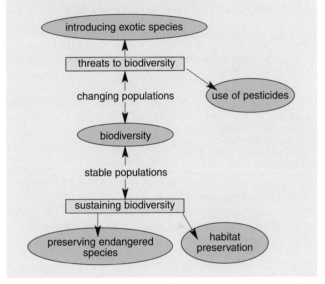

Reflect on your Learning

Revisit your answers to the Reflect on your Learning questions, page 9, in the Getting Started.

- How has your thinking changed?
- What new questions do you have?

Chapter 1 Review

Understanding Concepts

1. Explain why identifying a reason for the disappearance of frogs has been difficult.

2. The frog has been described as an indicator species for the health of an environment. In your own words, define the term "indicator species."

3. Human interference often causes ecosystems to change.
   (a) Provide an example of how human interference has caused an increase in the population of a species.
   (b) Provide an example of how human interference has caused a decrease in the population of a species.
   (c) Provide an example of how the rapid increase in a species has affected another species.

4. Why might a species be classified as endangered?

5. Provide three examples of species that can be classified as
   (a) endangered
   (b) extirpated
   (c) threatened
   (d) vulnerable

6. Use **Figure 1**, a Venn diagram showing species overlapping between a pond and a grassland, to answer the following questions.

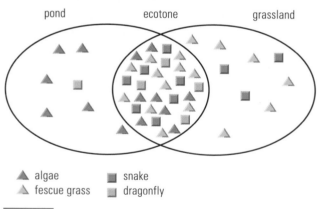

pond   ecotone   grassland

▲ algae   ■ snake
△ fescue grass ▧ dragonfly

Figure 1

   (a) Identify producers within the ecosystem.
   (b) Describe the abiotic conditions that are likely in the ecotone between the pond and the grassland.
   (c) Why is the greatest number of species found in the ecotone?
   (d) Speculate about how pollution of the ecotone might affect the grassland and pond ecosystems.

7. Use **Figure 2** to answer the following questions.

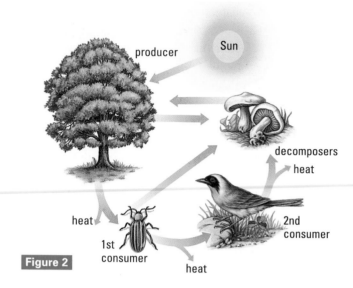

Figure 2

   (a) Explain the first and second laws of thermodynamics.
   (b) Predict an ecological pyramid of numbers using the organisms.
   (c) Predict an ecological pyramid of energy.

8. Define the term "food web." Draw a food web showing the organisms you would expect to find in a rotting log.

9. Indicate whether each of the four ecosystems listed in Table 1 can be sustained. A ✔ indicates that type of organism is present. Write a paragraph to defend each answer.

Table 1	Four Ecosystems		
System	Autotrophs	Heterotrophs	Decomposers
a	✔		
b		✔	✔
c	✔		✔
d	✔	✔	

Applying Inquiry Skills

10. Yellow-headed blackbirds are common in marshes from the Great Lakes to the Pacific Ocean. **Table 2** indicates the yellow-headed blackbird population and the amount of rainfall in two marshes from 1992 to 1999.
    (a) Graph the changes in the blackbird population.
    (b) According to the evidence, one study site consistently had more birds. Provide a possible reason.
    (c) Based on the evidence, create a hypothesis that explains the changes in population of the blackbird.

(d) Speculate some other factors that might be involved in population changes for these birds. With those factors in mind, how could you test your hypothesis?

Table 2 — Yellow-Headed Blackbird Populations

Year	Number of birds (site 1)	Number of birds (site 2)	Amount of rainfall (cm)
1992	24	28	13
1993	80	88	38
1994	75	86	35
1995	55	74	30
1996	70	98	43
1997	105	186	62
1998	90	130	50
1999	21	22	16

11. Biotic and abiotic factors were being studied in a grassland that bordered on a mixed forest. Between the two ecosystems was an area where shrubs grew. The evidence in **Table 3** was collected from plots in the three different areas.

Table 3 — A Comparison of Abiotic and Biotic Factors

Measurement	Grassland	Shrub area	Mixed forest
average daily temperature (°C)	28 (max.) 12 (min.)	25 (max.) 15 (min.)	22 (max.) 18 (min.)
relative humidity (%)	55	70	85
evaporation rate (mL/d)	60	40	17
average wind speed (km/h)	15	5	0
light (percent of ground open)	100	40	5
soil litter (g/m²)	250	370	700
soil acidity (pH)	6.9	6.8	6.0 (coniferous) 6.6 (deciduous)
earthworms (no./m²)	110	120	10 (coniferous) 200 (deciduous)
plants (no. of each type and % of ground covered)	grass: 76–100 clover: 51–75 goldenrod: 6–25 dandelion: 6–25	grass: 76–100 saskatoon: 26–51 pin cherry: 26–51 goldenrod: 6–25 wild rose: 6–25 sow thistle: 6–25	grass: 26–50 chokecherry: 26–50 pin cherry: 26–50 spruce: 6–25 aspen: 51–75

(a) What factors could help explain differences in wind speed between the three areas?

(b) What factors could help explain differences in relative humidity between the three areas?

(c) Create a hypothesis to explain how soil acidity might affect earthworms. Design an experiment to test your hypothesis.

(d) Speculate on the relationship between mass of soil litter and moisture, temperature, and number of organisms in the soil.

Making Connections

12. A study by Environment Canada showed variations in the number of prairie ponds in the 30 years from 1955 to 1984 (**Figure 3**). Graph A shows the number of ponds found each year of the study. Graph B shows the total population of ducks each year. Scientists conducting the study say the decline was caused by draining ponds to expand agricultural land.

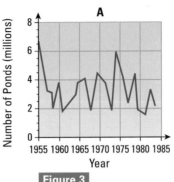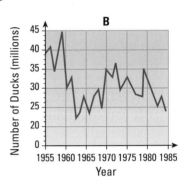

Figure 3

(a) Farming is not the only cause of changes in the number of ponds. Speculate about what abiotic factor might cause the number of ponds to fluctuate from year to year.

(b) In which year was the fewest number of ponds found?

(c) A hunters' group says that prairie ponds should be protected, to increase the number of ducks. Identify the hunters' hypothesis and restate it. Does the evidence in **Figure 3** support their hypothesis?

(d) If the number of ducks declines, what other populations might be affected? Explain your answer.

(e) Protecting ponds makes both aquatic and ecotone habitats available for wildlife but reduces the area of land on which a farmer can grow crops. Write a letter to a grain farmer, expressing your opinion about whether ponds on farmland should be protected or filled in.

13. Around the world, habitats available for wild animals have become smaller and smaller as the human population grows.

(a) Using an energy flow argument, explain why this shrinkage would affect animals in the highest trophic levels more severely than those in lower levels.

(b) Suggest a way to protect wild habitat. How would your solution affect humans?

2 Change and Stability in Ecosystems

Getting Started

WHY DO ECOSYSTEMS APPEAR TO BE SO STABLE?
If you could find an area of Ontario that hadn't been logged, and could take a ride in a time machine back to 1700, you would find that the forest then looked much like the forest does today.

From your own experience, you would probably say that the lakes and rivers you know change little. Even artificial ecosystems, such as lawns, appear stable.

However, that impression of a lack of change is anything but true. In a forest ecosystem, trees continuously die and are replaced by new trees. Lakes change greatly in temperature, oxygen levels, and kinds of organisms that live in them throughout the year. Ecosystems undergo continuous renewal to remain in that "unchanging" state we observe. By changing constantly, they remain the same — in a state we call equilibrium (balance).

However, sometimes ecosystems cannot maintain their equilibrium. Large changes in abiotic or biotic factors, such as those linked with humans, may cause a shift in the balance of the ecosystem. The diversion of a stream to create a freeway or the flooding of a valley after the construction of a dam are two examples of permanent changes caused by humans. In addition, ecosystems can change quickly if a new organism is introduced. The balances between predators and prey and those between living things that compete for space, food, or other resources within an ecosystem are in constant tension. Change a single factor and a new balance must be re-established.

Human interference in ecosystems is often described as harmful. For example, pollutants from industrial processes kill or injure some organisms. This in turn alters food webs and changes relationships within ecosystems. The harmful impacts of humans on an ecosystem dominate discussion so much that often we forget that we are part of the ecosystem — not merely agents of change. Things that change ecosystems also affect humans.

Figure 1
If left here, this truck will slowly disappear, leaving no trace.

Change and Recovery

Ecosystems can recover, even after major human intervention, but it takes many years or even centuries. The rusting truck in **Figure 1** reminds us that ecosystems respond to change. Plants will cover the body of the car. In time, the small weeds growing around the car will be replaced by shrubs, which in turn will be replaced by mature trees. Pieces of the truck will fall off and be buried under detritus. Eventually, even the iron atoms in the frame of the truck will return to the soil. A hiker returning to the forest in 200 years would see no sign that a vehicle had ever been there.

It would be hard to find a better example of the resilience of large ecosystems than the Great Lakes. During the 1950s and 1960s, some ecologists predicted the complete collapse of food webs in Lake Erie and Lake Ontario, the most polluted of the lakes. Toxic wastes, raw sewage, and acid rain mixed into the lakes to create a poisonous soup. Dying fish floated to the surface, desperately struggling for oxygen. The carcasses of birds dotted the shoreline. One river feeding Lake Erie was so polluted with oil that it actually burst into flames. Today, ecologists have gathered evidence that the Great Lakes are recovering. Pollutants are being drawn from the water and soil by microorganisms and by burial in sediment. As long as the pollutants remain buried, they are out of the food chain and no longer pose a danger. But if the sediments are stirred up by ship or wave action, pollutants again become a hazard to the ecosystem.

Reflect on your Learning

1. One throw-away car in a forest probably won't do much damage. As you have seen, the ecosystem will adjust and regain its original balance. But humans produce far more than one waste car every few centuries. Speculate about how large amounts of waste might affect an ecosystem.

2. Europeans, and their descendants in North America, often describe humans as being at the centre of change. Not only do humans cause environmental changes, but they are also responsible for those changes. In this worldview, the ideal human acts as a steward or protector for an ecosystem. In contrast, First Nations peoples often describe humans as belonging to an ecosystem. In this worldview, the ideal human lives in harmony with the ecosystem. How would the two worldviews differ in describing what has happened to the Great Lakes and the forest ecosystems of Ontario over the last century?

Throughout this chapter, note any changes in your ideas as you learn new concepts and develop your skills.

Try This Activity   Competition Between Plants

Changes in the biotic or abiotic factors within an ecosystem often cause one plant community to replace another. In turn, changes in the plant community are accompanied by changes in the animal community. In this activity, you will determine which plant species has an advantage under certain conditions. Each research group within the class can study a different set of variables.

Materials: apron, milk containers (cut in half), various kinds of vegetable or flower seeds, potting soil, water

🖐 Always wash your hands after handling soil.

K4 • As a class, decide how you will control the mix of seeds in each container.
• Fill milk containers with moist potting soil.
• Plant seeds from various species according to the instructions on the packets (**Figure 2**). Water each of the milk cartons with the same amount of water every second day. Record the amount of water used.

• Once seeds start to germinate, store each of the milk cartons in a different environment. You might want to use temperature, amount of light, or amount of water as variables.
• Measure the growth of each of the plants daily.

(a) Does one type of plant begin to dominate the community? Is it the same type of plant in all containers?

(b) Speculate about why one plant might be better adapted for a specific environment than another.

Figure 2

Cycling of Matter in Ecosystems

To understand how matter cycles through ecosystems, we must also understand the cycling of organic substances within living things.

Organic substances always contain atoms of carbon and hydrogen, and often contain oxygen and nitrogen atoms. Proteins, sugars, and fats, the important chemicals that make up your body, are all organic (**Figure 1**). Matter that doesn't contain a combination of carbon and hydrogen atoms is called **inorganic**. For example, carbon dioxide (CO_2), water (H_2O), and ammonia (NH_3) are considered to be inorganic.

Organic chemicals undergo changes within living things and within ecosystems. Their complex structures are broken and rebuilt in a continuous cycling of matter.

Cycling of Organic Matter

The materials used in building the bodies of living organisms are limited to the atoms and molecules that make up the planet. There is no alternative source of matter. Therefore, to maintain life on Earth, matter must be recycled.

Incredible as it may sound, every carbon atom is recycled time and time again into new life forms. Because of this cycling, it is likely that somewhere in your body are atoms that once made up a *Tyrannosaurus rex*, one of the giant carnivorous dinosaurs that lived 70 million years ago. You probably also contain atoms that made up one of the plants it stomped on.

Food is organic matter. Every time you eat, organic matter that was once part of other living things passes into your body. Through the process of digestion, complex organic molecules are broken down into simpler molecules. Cells use these simple molecules to build complex molecules, which become part of your own structure.

Another process involved in the cycling of matter is decay. Organic materials are held temporarily in the bodies of living organisms, but after death decomposer organisms make the materials available to other living things. Decomposers (**Figure 2**) break down the organic matter in dead bodies and feces into small, inorganic molecules. These small molecules pass into the soil or water, where they can become part of the living world at some future time (**Figure 3**).

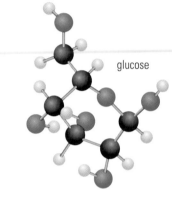

(a) alanine, an amino acid. Amino acids are used to build proteins, which regulate the chemistry of the cell and make up most of its structures.

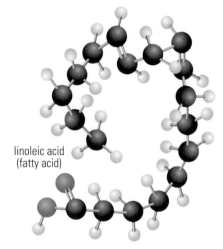

(b) glucose, a sugar. Sugars are used to store energy.

linoleic acid (fatty acid)

(c) linoleic acid, a fatty acid. Fatty acids are combined to form fats, which are used to store energy and to build cell membranes.

Figure 1

Three organic molecules. Note that they all contain carbon and hydrogen atoms. Some organic molecules are extremely complex, containing hundreds of thousands of atoms.

Figure 2

(a) Bacteria Several different types of bacteria decompose organic matter. This bacterium lives in the soil.

(b) Bracket fungi These decomposers feed on dead and living trees, breaking down complex organic molecules into simple ones.

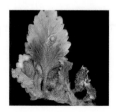

(c) Mould Another form of fungi. These decomposers feed on organic matter, returning nutrients to ecosystems.

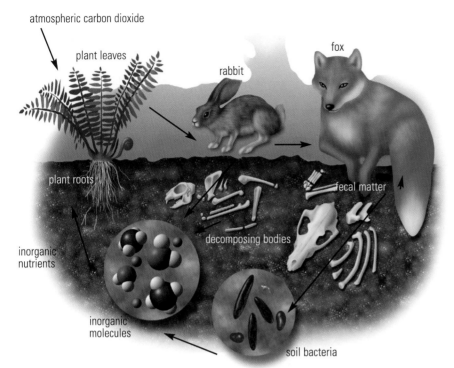

atmospheric carbon dioxide

plant leaves

rabbit

fox

plant roots

fecal matter

decomposing bodies

inorganic nutrients

inorganic molecules

soil bacteria

Decomposers break down complex organic molecules into inorganic matter, which may be used by plants. Plants reassemble these inorganic substances (also called nutrients) to make food for themselves. In turn, animals may eat the plants, continuing the cycling of matter.

Understanding Concepts

1. **(a)** Explain the difference between organic and inorganic chemicals.

   (b) Give some examples of each.

2. Using diagrams, show two different ways that a carbon atom that was once in a cell in a grass leaf could become part of a cell in your ear.

3. In a few paragraphs, explain the diagram in **Figure 4**.

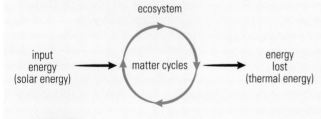

ecosystem

input energy (solar energy) → matter cycles → energy lost (thermal energy)

Figure 4

4. When space probes were sent to the Moon and Mars, soil samples were collected and analyzed for organic compounds. Why would scientists want to know if organic matter was present in these soil samples?

Making Connections

5. Predict what might happen if forest decomposers, such as soil bacteria and fungi, were destroyed by a pollutant.

6. Fire is a decomposer. It turns complex organic molecules into inorganic nutrients. Fire can be used to release inorganic nutrients from the stalks remaining after grain is harvested. This process is faster than normal decomposition, but much of the carbon in the stalks escapes to the air as carbon dioxide. Should fire be used to return nutrients to the soil? Identify both benefits and risks.

Exploring

7. Natural and genetically engineered bacteria and fungi can
   Ⓘ be used to either destroy toxic chemicals or convert them to
   Ⓙ harmless forms. The process, referred to as bioremediation, mimics nature by using decomposers to recycle matter. Research how bioremediation is used to clean up various pollutants, and report on your findings.

Reflecting

8. Cells are very complicated. Scientists continue to struggle to explain why chemical reactions in cells don't seem to work out the way they do in test tubes. There are questions about cells that are still unanswered. What questions do you have about the ideas you have encountered in this section?

Pesticides

There is no better way to understand the flow of matter through an ecosystem than to study food webs. This is true of both natural organic matter and toxins (poisons) introduced by humans. In this case study, you will investigate the impact of pesticides on living things and ecosystems. **Pesticides** are chemicals designed to kill pests. A **pest** is an organism that people consider harmful or inconvenient, such as weeds, insects, fungi, and rodents. In many situations, pesticides are used to protect species that are beneficial to humans from a competitor or predator that is less useful.

(a) Decide under what circumstances, if any, each organism in **Figure 1** could be considered a pest.

(b) Speculate about how the removal of one of the pests might affect the food web.

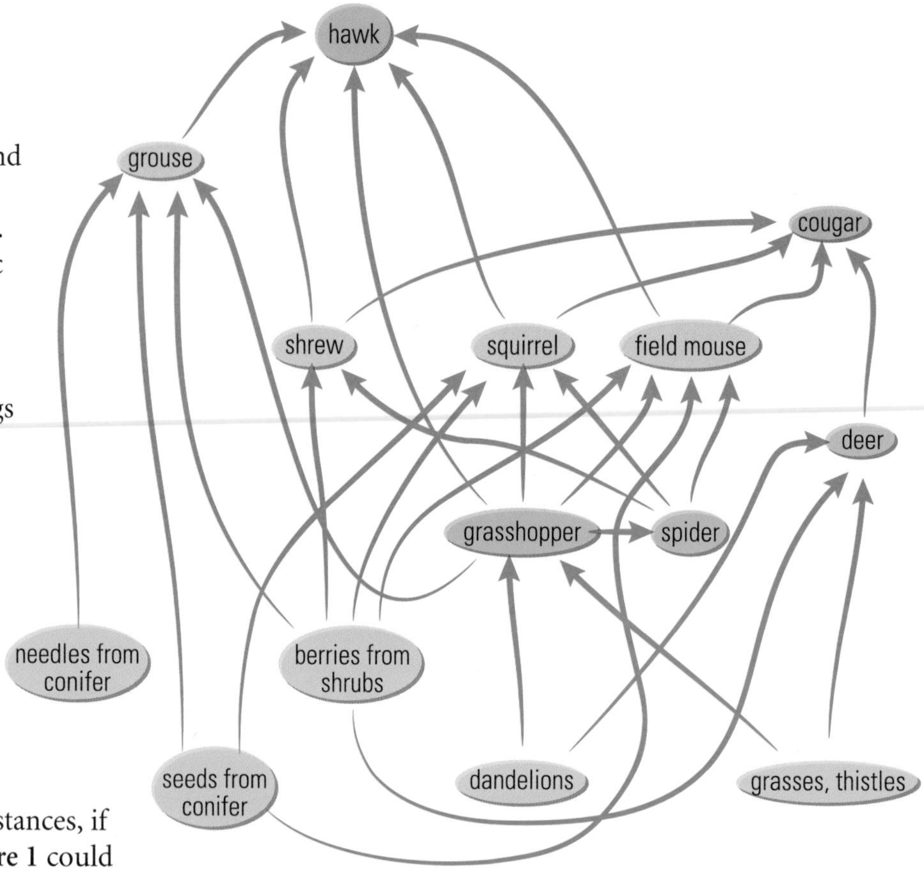

Figure 1

A food web showing relationships among organisms living at the edge of a forest ecosystem.

Why Use Pesticides?

One estimate suggests that as much as 30% of the annual crop in Canada is lost to pests such as weeds, rusts and moulds (both forms of fungi), insects, birds, and small mammals. The cost to consumers can be staggering. For example, in 1954 three million tonnes of wheat from the Prairies was destroyed by stem rust (**Figure 2**), a fungus that grows inside the leaves and stems of the wheat plant, feeding on the plant's stores of food.

The anopheles mosquito, found in tropical areas, often carries a microbe that enters the circulatory system while the mosquito is sucking the victim's blood. The microbe produces malaria. Malaria causes fever and can lead to death. As late as 1955, malaria affected more than 200 million people. Today, because of pest control measures, the incidence of malaria has been drastically reduced, although it is still a major killer in some countries.

(c) List three possible short-term benefits of using pesticides.

Figure 2
Stem rust, a fungus, is a consumer. In a wheatfield it is also a pest.

Did You Know?

We associate malaria with tropical climates, but it was once a serious problem in Canada. A malaria outbreak occurred during the building of Ontario's Rideau Canal in the 1830s.

First-Generation Pesticides

Our attempts to control pests extend back to about 500 B.C., when sulfur was first used to repel insects. During the 15th century arsenic, lead, and mercury were applied to crops as insecticides. As many farmers eventually discovered, these substances were not only deadly for insects, but also highly poisonous for people. By the 1920s, farmers had become fully aware of the hazardous effects and the practice was abandoned. Unfortunately, these dangerous substances still show up in some vegetables if they are grown in soils that were treated with the metals for a great number of years.

In 1763, French gardeners began using nicotine sulfate, a chemical extracted from the tobacco plant, to kill aphids (**Figure 3**). By the mid-1800s, two more plant extracts had been developed in the battle against insects — one from the head of the chrysanthemum and the other from the roots of a tropical legume. (Legumes are plants that bear their seeds in pods, like peas, beans, and locust trees.) Many plants have developed chemical defences against animals. Insects and other animals that try to eat the leaves or seeds of the plants die or become very ill. They learn to avoid the plant in future. Borrowing those chemicals from plants seemed to make sense.

(d) Why might chemicals taken from plants create a much lower risk for humans and ecosystems?

Figure 3
Aphids suck sap from the leaves and soft stems of plants.

Second-Generation Pesticides

Second-generation pesticides are chemicals made in a laboratory. In 1939 Paul Mueller found that *d*ichloro*d*iphenyl*t*richloroethane (DDT), a chemical known since 1874, was a potent insecticide. This discovery forever changed the practice of chemical control. It sent researchers looking for more such chemicals, which were developed to protect troops fighting in the tropical jungles of Asia and the Pacific during the Second World War.

Thousands of pesticides have since been developed. More than 500 chemical pesticides are registered for use in Canada alone. Worldwide approximately 2.3 million tonnes of pesticides are used yearly, or about 0.4 kg for every person on Earth. About 75% of these chemicals are used in developed countries, and they are not used only in agriculture. Pesticides are added to shampoos, carpets, mattresses, paints, and even the wax on produce. More than 25% of pesticides are used to get rid of pests in homes, gardens, and parks.

Pesticides can be grouped into four different categories (**Table 1**). As you can see, some pesticides decompose fairly rapidly, but others stay in the ecosystem for many years.

Table 1 **Classification of Pesticides**

Type of Pesticide	Target	Examples	Persistence
insecticide	insects	DDT	high (2–15 years)
		Malathion	moderate (1–12 weeks)
herbicide	weeds	2,4-D, Silvex, Roundup	mostly low (days to weeks)
fungicide	moulds and other fungi	Captan	low (days)
bactericides	bacteria	penicillin, vancomycin	mostly low

Bioamplification

Pesticides that contain chlorine, such as DDT and Dieldrin, are soluble in fat but not in water. As a result, these toxins cannot be released in urine or sweat, so they accumulate in the fatty tissues of animals. When there is a small amount of the pesticide in the environment, it will enter the bodies of animals that are low in the food chain. That's where the problem begins, but it gets much worse as the toxin moves up a food chain into higher trophic levels.

Even though there is only a small amount of the toxin in each of the prey animals that a secondary consumer eats, the amount of the toxin in its body will be larger because each predator eats many prey. When the secondary consumer is eaten, the higher-level predator gets all of its toxins, plus those of all the other prey it eats. At each stage of the food chain the concentration becomes greater. The higher the trophic level, the greater the concentration of toxins. This process is referred to as **bioamplification** (Figure 4).

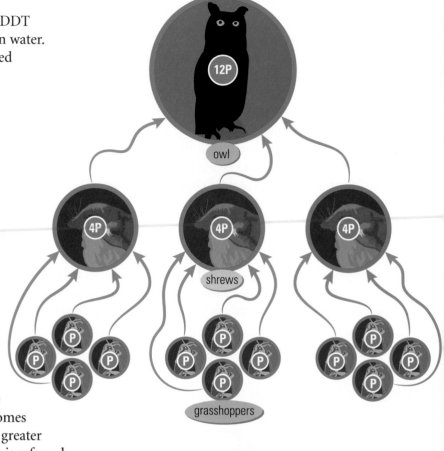

Figure 4

Bioamplification. The concentration of a fat-soluble pesticide (P) increases as you move up a food chain. The pesticide is present in only small concentrations in grasshoppers (primary consumers), higher concentrations in shrews (secondary consumers), and much higher concentration in owls (tertiary consumers). The greater the number of trophic levels, the greater the amplification in the top level.

(e) How would a chart showing the concentration of toxins differ from a biological pyramid of biomass for the same food chain?

(f) Vultures and some species of beetles feed on the dead bodies of animals from several trophic levels. Predict how these animals might be affected by bioamplification.

Effects on Humans

The irony of the insecticide is that although insecticides were developed to rid the world of harmful insects, they have had a much greater effect on humans. Like other top predators, humans are subject to bioamplification. Evidence that DDT was beginning to accumulate in humans was collected in the 1950s and 1960s.

DDT levels became especially high in humans who lived where DDT was sprayed on crops. However, anyone who ate crops from these areas or ate animals that had fed on the crops was exposed to DDT.

Concern about this growing threat was so great that use of DDT was banned in Canada in 1971 and in the United States in 1972. The ban hasn't totally eliminated the problem. Migratory birds like the mallard duck, Canada goose, and peregrine falcon winter in Central America and Mexico, where DDT is still used. Fish living in the Atlantic and Pacific oceans also migrate up and down the coasts.

(g) Why is the fact that other countries have not banned DDT of concern to Canadians?

(h) Breast milk contains fat. Speculate about how breast-feeding might affect the concentration of DDT in a mother and in her baby.

Modern Chemical Pesticides

Unlike DDT and other chlorine-based insecticides, the newer chemicals are not stored in fat tissue; they are soluble in water. Animals can remove them from their bodies by breaking them down in their livers and excreting them. They can also be broken down within the soil. These new compounds operate like nerve gases, which act by preventing electrical messages from travelling from the brain to the muscles that control breathing or the limbs. This either kills the animal directly or makes it vulnerable to predators.

Although somewhat safer than the older chemicals, the newer insecticides are not without their problems. First, they break down quickly in the soil, and so must be applied to crops more often. Second, these new chemicals are not selective. Because the nerve action of most larger animals is very similar, these insecticides are capable of killing mammals, birds, reptiles, amphibians, and fish. Unintended changes to the food web are difficult to predict. Third, animals that have died or been weakened by the toxin put any other animal that eats them at risk through bioamplification. Large dosages of the toxin can still cause death.

(i) Why are the new pesticides less harmful to ecosystems than DDT and related compounds used in the 1950 and 1960s?

The Pests Fight Back

It seems that chemical pesticides have a natural shelf life, because the pests they are supposed to kill gradually become resistant. This is particularly true of bactericides and insecticides, because of the pests' high rates of reproduction.

If the first application of a chemical kills 90% of the insects, that still leaves 10% that survive. Some of those insects have genes that helped them survive application of the pesticide (**Figure 5**). With every generation of insects, the pesticide removes those that are susceptible, and leaves those that are not. In addition, because the pesticide removes so many of the insects, the survivors have the benefit of less competition for food. After several generations of this selection process, most of the insects carry genes that will help them survive an application of the pesticide. Eventually the pesticide becomes useless, and pesticide chemists must search for a new poison.

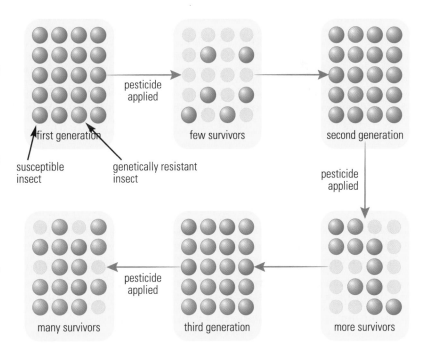

Figure 5

Continued applications of the same pesticide allow insects to gradually become resistant. Each application kills most of the susceptible insects, but not those that have genes that protect them from the insecticide.

(j) Speculate about how less competition for food helps increase the reproductive success of the remaining insects after a pesticide is applied.

(k) According to **Figure 6**, in which decade was there the greatest increase in the number of species that became resistant to pesticides? What might account for the dramatic increase?

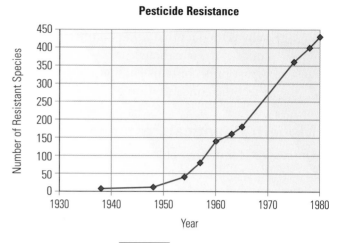

Figure 6

The number of insects resistant to at least one pesticide has increased rapidly.

Atlantic Canada and the Spruce Budworm

Throughout Canada chemical pesticides are used to control pests that threaten agriculture, forestry, and the home or garden, but due to the economic importance of spruce in pulp and paper and construction, few pests have created as much concern as the spruce budworm (**Figure 7**). Adult moths emerge in late June or July and lay eggs on spruce or fir tree. Within 10 days the eggs hatch and the larvae move into the interior of the tree. Here each worm-shaped larva spins a web and enters a dormant phase for the winter. The larvae awaken in May and begin feeding on the old needles, unopened buds and the male flowers of the trees. Eventually, the voracious larvae work their way out on the branches to the new shoots.

Often during periods of high population, the larvae eat all the new shoots early in the season, reducing growth of the trees. The removal of needles weakens the trees, making them more susceptible to infections and other insects. Successive infestations year after year could kill the tree.

The efforts to control this pest with insecticide show up in the statistics for insecticide use in Atlantic Canada (**Figure 8**).

Figure 7

The spruce budworm is a wasteful eater. It rarely eats a whole needle, rather it just bites them off at the base. Masses of dried, red-brown needles are left hanging from the ends of branches.

New Brunswick and the Budworm

From 1986 to 1990 New Brunswick dispensed about 170 000 kg of chemicals over 443 000 ha each year as it attempted to maintain control over the spruce budworm. The longest-running pesticide program in the world has protected New Brunswick forests for nearly 40 years, but it hasn't eliminated the pest. The objective of the program is to maintain acceptably low levels of the pest. Eliminating the program would likely cause the population of spruce budworms to explode, resulting in the devastation of a valuable industry.

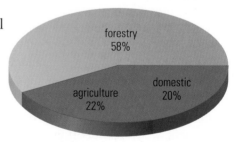

Pesticide Use in Atlantic Canada

Figure 8

The influence of the spruce budworm spraying campaign is shown in the amount of pesticides used in forestry.

(l) Speculate about why the spruce budworm hasn't been eliminated after 40 years of spraying.

(m) Why wouldn't biologists just use extremely high concentrations of insecticides to kill all of the spruce budworms?

(n) Identify groups who have benefited from the New Brunswick spraying program.

Cape Breton and the Budworm

On Cape Breton Island, authorities allowed the spruce budworm infestation to run its course. By the time the budworm population had stopped increasing, approximately 50% of the island's softwoods (spruce, fir, and pine) were lost. When assessing the economics of this decision, the cost of losing the valuable trees must be balanced against the fact that spraying is not needed to control the spruce budworm in Cape Breton.

(o) Identify groups of people who might have suffered as a result of the decision not to spray.

(p) What are the benefits of not spraying?

Pesticides and the Great Lakes

When ice and snow melt in spring, pesticides from the land are often carried into streams and lakes. Once in the aquatic ecosystems, the pesticides are absorbed into the tissues of aquatic insects and the small fish that eat these insects. At each step of the food chain, the level of toxins can become magnified.

(q) Explain why insecticides such as DDT would pose a greater threat to freshwater ecosystems than the newer, water-soluble pesticides.

The Bald Eagle

One of the animals most affected is the bald eagle (**Figure 9**), which eats mostly fish — both live fish that it catches and dead fish that it finds. Prey include large predatory fish such as trout, salmon, and pike; smaller fish; amphibians; small mammals; and birds. Once common throughout North America, the eagle began to disappear as European settlers arrived. The destruction of the large trees the eagle used for nesting, combined with human hunting of a bird that could kill young livestock, began to take its toll. However, the greatest threat to the bald eagle population was industrialization and the subsequent release of toxins into the ecosystem. Like most top carnivores, the bald eagle accumulates fat-soluble toxins from the entire food chain. Because eagles can live for as long as 25 years, they can accumulate a tremendous amount of toxins. Once in the eagles' bodies, the fat-soluble toxins are not released except through the laying of eggs.

Figure 9

Because of restoration efforts by conservationists, the bald eagle is slowly returning to the shores of Lake Erie.

(r) Why would female eagles have slightly lower levels of toxins than male eagles? Compare egg-laying in eagles with breast-feeding in humans.

(s) Draw a food web, showing the movement of pesticides in a lake from aquatic insects to the bald eagle.

Understanding Concepts

1. In your own words, define the terms "pesticide" and "pest."

2. Using your own diagram, explain bioamplification.

3. It is often said that technology can work as a double-edged sword, creating a new problem as it solves an old one. The new problem often arises because the solution to the original problem was flawed.

   (a) During the 15th century, arsenic, lead, and mercury were applied to crops as insecticides. What was wrong with this technological solution?

   (b) In 1939, Paul Mueller found that DDT was a potent insecticide and could be used to kill pests such as mosquitoes. What was wrong with this technological solution?

   (c) Modern insecticides are easily broken down in the body and the soil and do not accumulate in fat tissues; however, these new chemicals do not provide a perfect solution. What dangers were created by this most recent technological solution?

4. List at least two advantages and two disadvantages of a pesticide that is low in toxicity and breaks downs quickly.

5. Explain why farmers might wish to use pesticides that are soluble in water and remain active for an extended time. Why do those properties also make the pesticide dangerous?

6. Explain why humans can't adapt to toxic pesticides as quickly as insects.

7. A 1991 report by Environment Canada showed some contamination by DDT and other pesticides in shellfish, crustaceans, and fish on the Atlantic coast. Chemical pesticides have also been found in shore birds and marine mammals, particularly along the Bay of Fundy and the coast of Newfoundland. The report indicated that although the levels of pesticides are declining in most marine animals, there was still cause for concern. The porpoises in the lower Bay of Fundy still had unacceptably high levels of DDT, at 500 ppm.

   (a) Explain how DDT could enter a marine ecosystem.

   (b) DDT has been banned in Canada for decades. Explain why animals still carry this toxin in their bodies.

   (c) Speculate about why the levels of DDT fall more slowly in porpoises than in other animals in the ecosystem.

Making Connections

8. In Atlantic Canada, synthetic pesticides called pyrethroids were used to control two pests in apple orchards — the winter moth and leaf miners. Unfortunately, the chemicals killed more insects than intended, including those that preyed on red mites and apple mites. After spraying, the mite population rose quickly, causing damage to the trees and reducing the yield of apples. What recommendations would you make to anyone considering using a new pesticide?

9. The ideal pesticide has four characteristics. Explain why each of the characteristics is important and what the consequences are when the pesticide fails to meet each test. The pesticide should:

   • kill only the intended pest;

   • disappear into something harmless after it works on the pest;

   • not create a stock of resistant pests;

   • be cheap to produce and use.

Reflecting

10. During the 1950s and 1960s, DDT and similar chemicals were inexpensive and easy to apply. However, the environmental problems they caused created a backlash. Pesticide use is now more strictly regulated. In some countries malaria has increased once again. Have we gone too far in reducing the use of pesticides? Are there other explanations for the increase? What information would you need to collect to answer these questions?

 Challenge

1 Golfers do not like mosquitoes, but some of the most challenging golf courses border bodies of still water—the favourite breeding ground of mosquitoes. How can you provide a golf course with water hazards, control mosquitoes, and yet minimize disturbance to the environment?

2 Pesticides are carried into rivers with rain and melting snow. Herbicides can kill aquatic plants. Insecticides can kill or weaken small aquatic organisms. How will pesticides affect water quality in your area?

3 How will you include the uses and effects of pesticides in your game?

Mary Bishop

Planner

Mary Bishop has alphabet soup after her name: an honours B.Sc. degree from Dalhousie, and a Master's degree in urban and regional planning. Academic training in land use, communications, ecology, statistics, and chemistry can be added to Mary's work experience in municipal planning, environmental assessment, and socio-economic development research. She has worked with the governments in both Newfoundland and Nova Scotia. But she is not unusual in a profession that combines aspects of engineering, law, architecture, public health, and the social sciences as well as ecology and biology. Planners, she says, are the ultimate multitaskers.

Mary has been involved in research, policy planning and decision making in several key areas of Newfoundland's economic development since 1985. The project she finds most representative of her work in the field is the consultation she did with the city of Gander. Gander has a stewardship agreement with the provincial government of Newfoundland and Labrador to protect its waterfowl habitat, and Mary was called in to reconcile Gander's growing human population with the needs of the protected waterfowl. During her evaluation, she consulted all levels of government, concerned citizens' associations, local businesses, environmental activists, and a whole lot of numbers.

Understanding numbers, especially population statistics, is absolutely key to doing her job as a planner, Mary says. Statistical analysis allows the planner to balance the requirements of the individuals and the immediate community with the needs of the greater population.

Of course, adds Mary, you also need an interest in geography and the environment, as well as good teamwork skills (planners rarely work alone, but in a group of other planners, architects, engineers, and politicians) and a flair for presenting projects or proposals. After all, a planner's audience can include everyone from a schoolchild to a federal politician, and every person needs to be able to understand what is said.

Mary Bishop went into science because she was intensely curious about the world around her and how it worked. When she graduated, she decided that the world would shrink to the size of a slide on a microscope if she pursued the "traditional path" of laboratory science. "I basically fell into planning," she says gleefully, "because I wanted science to apply to the real world."

Making Connections

1. What sort of education path would you follow if you decided right now to become a planner?
2. Find out what postsecondary institutions offer a Master's degree in urban and regional planning.
3. Find five different job titles for urban and regional planners. What sort of projects might each undertake?

👆 Work the Web

Go to a search engine and do a search with the keywords "urban," "career," and "planning." How would you refine your search to find job postings in this field?

Use your results to find a development project in your geographic area on which a planner worked. Research the issues and final outcome of the project, and give a short presentation to your class.

The Interaction of Living Things

On September 26, 1991, four men and four women entered a gigantic dome near Tucson, Arizona, that contained 3800 species of plants and animals. The dome was sealed after they entered. They were to live there for a year. Nothing was to be brought in; nothing, and no one, would be allowed out. All raw materials and waste products were to be recycled by humans, animals, and plants living together.

Named Biosphere 2 (**Figure 1**), the dome was the largest, and most expensive, artificial ecosystem ever created. Texas billionaire Ed Bass, the architect behind the plan, had raised private funding to study a model of Earth's ecosystems. He was hoping to create an artificial ecosystem that could be used in space exploration. In taking a chance on this huge experiment, he was supporting scientific research into how living things interact with each other.

The experiment demonstrated in a fairly short time that we don't know everything we need to know about ecosystems. Despite careful advanced planning to ensure the right numbers of plants and animals, and the use of computer simulations and electronic monitoring devices, the amount of carbon dioxide in the air inside the dome kept increasing. Scientists were not able to establish a workable balance between the number of plants and animals. On November 12, the team running the experiment gave up and pumped purified air in from the outside.

(a) How would the environment of Biosphere 2 differ from that of a large apartment complex?

(b) Make a list of things that must be considered to create and maintain an artificial ecosystem.

Figure 1
Biosphere 2 is still being maintained in an effort to improve our understanding of all the interactions that take place in an ecosystem.

Priestley's First Experiment

Understanding the complexity of ecosystems may be one of science's greatest challenges. The first step toward understanding was made when early scientists began to investigate the relationships between plants and animals.

Joseph Priestley, an 18th-century clergyman with a strong interest in science, performed an experiment with candles, a mint plant, and two sealed glass jars (**Figure 2**).

(c) Why do you think that the candle went out in jar A?

(d) Write a hypothesis that explains why the candle with the mint plant burned for a longer time.

(e) What gas is produced as a candle burns?

(f) Would the time of burning be changed by changing the size of the candle or the size of the plant? Give reasons for your answer.

A   B

Figure 2
Priestley's first experiment. The candle in jar A burned for 3 min. The candle in jar B burned for 5 min.

Priestley's Second Experiment

Once again, Priestley used heavy glass jars to create a sealed environment (**Figure 3**) and then carefully recorded his observations.

(g) Why do you think the mouse in jar D died first?

(h) After some time the plant in jar C began to appear wilted and sickly. Provide a possible explanation for this observation. How could you test your hypothesis?

(i) The mouse in jar E lived longer and the plant appeared healthier. Provide an explanation for this observation.

Figure 3
Priestley's second experiment. Both mice eventually died, but the mouse in jar E lived longer.

Photosynthesis and Cellular Respiration

Priestley's second experiment showed that plants and animals do help each other. Scientists later discovered that plants use carbon dioxide (a gas) and water to make sugars. Oxygen (also a gas) is released as the sugars are made. The reaction below summarizes this process, known as **photosynthesis:**

$$\text{carbon dioxide} + \text{water} \rightarrow \text{sugars} + \text{oxygen}$$

Most living things, including the mice that Priestley used, use oxygen to break down sugars, their source of energy. Carbon dioxide and water are released as the sugars are broken down. The reaction below summarizes this process, known as **cellular respiration:**

$$\text{sugars} + \text{oxygen} \rightarrow \text{carbon dioxide} + \text{water}$$

(j) Identify the raw materials and products of the chemical reaction of photosynthesis.

(k) Identify the raw materials and products for the chemical reaction of cellular respiration.

Respiration is not exclusive to animals. Any organism that requires energy will undergo some form of respiration. Therefore, plants also undergo respiration. This might lead you to assume that plants could maintain the balance between oxygen and carbon dioxide by themselves. However, plants produce about nine times as much oxygen by photosynthesis as they use in cellular respiration.

Maintaining a Balance

Within the biosphere a balance of oxygen and carbon dioxide is maintained because the plants provide oxygen and sugars, while animals provide carbon dioxide and water. The processes of photosynthesis and cellular respiration are said to be complementary, which means that they support one another.

Understanding Concepts

(K3) **1.** Write a hypothesis for Priestley's first experiment.

2. In what ways are the candle in Priestley's first experiment and the mouse in his second experiment alike?

3. Explain why algae have been taken aboard space stations.

4. The scientists running Biosphere 2 hypothesized that if they put a certain mix of plants, animals, fungi, and bacteria in a dome, the ecosystem created would be self-sustaining indefinitely.

(a) Evaluate their hypothesis.

(b) Biosphere 2 was not a self-sustaining ecosystem, but can we call the experiment a failure? In a paragraph, comment on the outcome of the Biosphere 2 experiment.

5. Examine **Figure 2**.

(a) How would you test for the presence of oxygen in jar B?

(b) How would you test for the presence of carbon dioxide in jar A?

Making Connections

6. Both Priestley and modern scientists have used living organisms in experiments to discover how living things and their ecosystems work. Is this use of living things ethical? Is there a difference between using humans, mice, mint plants, or bacteria in this way? Write a set of rules that you would impose on scientists who wished to use living things in experiments.

The Carbon Cycle

Carbon is the key element for living things. Carbon can be found in the atmosphere and dissolved in the oceans as part of the inorganic carbon dioxide (CO_2) molecule. Each year, about 50 to 70 billion tonnes of carbon from inorganic carbon dioxide are recycled into more complex organic substances. This is done through photosynthesis.

During photosynthesis, plants use light energy to combine carbon dioxide from the atmosphere and water from the soil. Photosynthesis actually happens in a chain of reactions, but it can be summed up in the equation below:

$$6CO_2 + 6H_2O + \text{light} \rightarrow C_6H_{12}O_6 + 6O_2$$

carbon dioxide + water + light energy → sugar (glucose)+ oxygen

Some of the organic carbon is released back to the environment through cellular respiration as carbon dioxide. Once again, this process actually requires a long chain of reactions, but can be summed up in the simplified equation below.

$$C_6H_{12}O_6 + 6O_2 \rightarrow 6H_2O + 6CO_2$$

glucose + oxygen → water + carbon dioxide

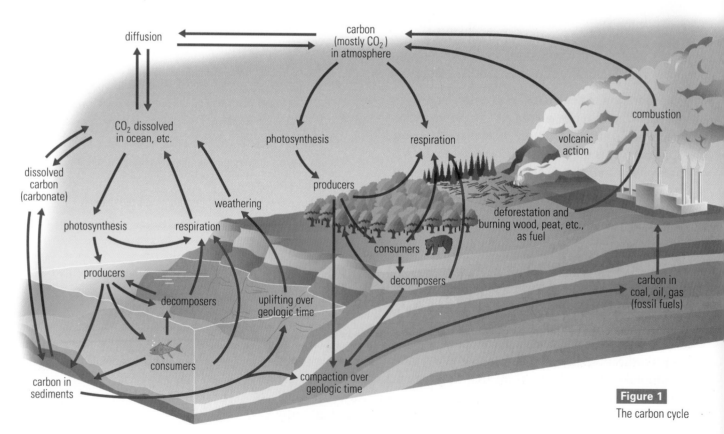

Figure 1

The carbon cycle

Because photosynthesis and cellular respiration are complementary processes, and because the carbon that they use is repeatedly cycled through both processes, this relationship is often called the **carbon cycle**. This cycle is actually much more complex than a simple exchange of carbon-as-carbon-dioxide and carbon-as-glucose (**Figure 1**). Most of the carbon that forms living organisms is returned to the atmosphere or water as carbon dioxide from body wastes and when the dead organisms decay. However, under certain conditions the decay process is delayed and the organic matter may be converted into rock or fossil fuels such as coal, petroleum, and natural gas. This carbon is then unavailable to the cycle until it is released by processes such as uplifting and weathering, or by burning as fuels. The burning process (**combustion**) releases carbon dioxide into the atmosphere.

Reservoirs for Inorganic Carbon: Delays in the Cycle

When it is not in organic form, carbon can be found in three main reservoirs (storage areas): the atmosphere, the oceans, and Earth's crust. The smallest of these reservoirs is the atmosphere. Carbon dioxide makes up a very small percentage (about 0.03%) of the gases that we breathe in. However, atmospheric carbon dioxide is easily accessed by land plants for use in photosynthesis.

A tremendous amount of inorganic carbon is held as dissolved carbon dioxide in the oceans, where it is available to algae and other water plants for photosynthesis. However, some carbon dioxide reacts with sea water to form the inorganic carbonate ion (CO_3^{2-}) and bicarbonate ion (HCO_3^-). Combined with calcium these ions become calcium carbonate ($CaCO_3$), which is used to make shells and other hard structures in living things. The carbon in carbonates can be recycled, but in the ocean much of it ends up as sediment. As layers of sediment form, the carbonates are crushed and heated and eventually become rock. Limestone is made from the discarded shells and bones of living things. And that is why by far the largest reservoir of the Earth's carbon is in sedimentary rocks. Carbon can be trapped in rock for millions of years until geological conditions bring it back to the surface. Volcanic activity can break down carbonate-containing rocks such as limestone, releasing carbon dioxide. Acid rain falling on exposed limestone will also cause the release of carbon dioxide into the atmosphere.

Figure 2 shows how long, on average, a carbon dioxide molecule will remain in each reservoir.

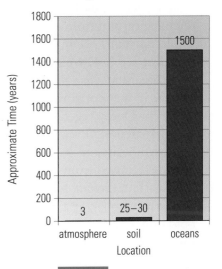

Inorganic Carbon Reservoirs

Figure 2

The average carbon atom is held in inorganic form much longer in the ocean than in the atmosphere. The time for carbon held in rocks (millions of years) would not fit well in this graph.

Reservoirs for Organic Carbon

Organic carbon is also held in reservoirs — the bodies of living things. However, all living things die, and decomposition eventually returns the carbon to the cycle in inorganic form. There is one important exception to this rule: some ecosystems, such as bogs, store huge quantities of carbon in organic form. In a bog there is very little oxygen, and under these conditions decomposition is very slow. Carbon atoms may remain locked away in dead plant matter (**peat**) for many years in a bog. Occasionally these deposits are overlain with sediment, and as more layers of sediment are piled on top, the slowly decaying organic matter can end up trapped between layers of rock. The result is the formation of a carbon-containing fossil fuel, coal (**Figure 3**).

Conditions similar to those in a bog also exist on the floors of oceans; there too organic carbon can be trapped for long periods. Oil is formed in a process similar to the formation of coal, when decaying aquatic animals and plants are trapped under sediment in a low-oxygen environment.

In the form of fossil fuels in Earth's crust, organic carbon can be held out of the carbon cycle for many millions of years.

The Human Impact on the Carbon Cycle

Humans have modified the global carbon cycle by releasing carbon from organic reservoirs faster than would normally occur, by mining and burning fossil fuels trapped in Earth's crust, and by burning forests.

Humans are also increasing the amount of carbon dioxide in the inorganic reservoir of the atmosphere by clearing away vegetation, in order to build or farm. The destruction of vegetation reduces the amount of photosynthesis, and so reduces the amount of carbon dioxide removed from the atmosphere (**Figure 4**). Most carbon dioxide released into the air eventually becomes dissolved in the oceans, but the oceans can hold only so much. The amount of carbon dioxide in the atmosphere is rising.

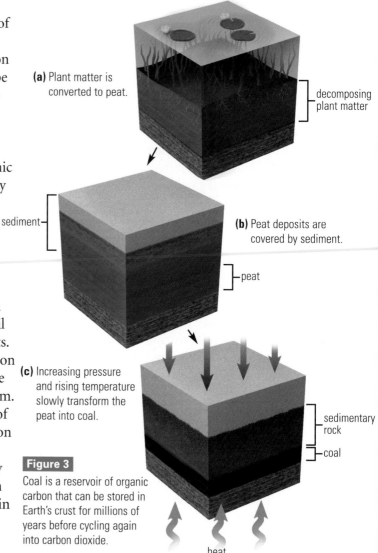

(a) Plant matter is converted to peat.

decomposing plant matter

sediment

(b) Peat deposits are covered by sediment.

peat

(c) Increasing pressure and rising temperature slowly transform the peat into coal.

sedimentary rock

coal

Figure 3

Coal is a reservoir of organic carbon that can be stored in Earth's crust for millions of years before cycling again into carbon dioxide.

heat

Try This
Activity Effect of Carbon Dioxide Levels on Photosynthesis

How do carbon dioxide levels affect photosynthesis? In this modelling experiment you can examine how a plant responds to varying levels of carbon dioxide.

Materials: apron, safety goggles, similar potted plants, plastic bags, small plastic containters, soda lime (which absorbs carbon dioxide), and baking soda (which slowly releases carbon dioxide)

🛑 Always wash your hands after handling soil.

(a) Describe a way of controlling the
(K4) experiment.

(b) Decide how you will measure the effects of changes in carbon dioxide levels on the plants.

- Set up each plant as shown in **Figure 5**.
- Observe the effects and record your observations.

(c) Use the results of your experiment to answer the initial question.

Figure 5

64 *Chapter 2*

SKILLS HANDBOOK: (K4) Creating the Design

The burning of the rainforest disrupts the balance between photosynthesis and cellular respiration. Many human activities affect the carbon cycle.

Understanding Concepts

1. In your own words, explain why photosynthesis and cellular respiration are considered to be complementary processes.

2. Explain the importance of decomposers in the carbon cycle.

3. The oceans are often described as a carbon reservoir. In what ways is carbon held within the oceans?

4. Explain how the burning of fossil fuels by humans affects the carbon cycle.

5. Carbon cycles more quickly through some ecosystems than others.

   (a) Explain why carbon is cycled more slowly in northern ecosystems than in the tropics.

   (b) Explain why carbon is cycled more rapidly in grassland communities than in peat bogs and swamps.

Making Connections

6. Scientists have expressed concerns about the burning of the rainforests to clear land for farming.

   (a) Explain how the burning of the forests could change oxygen levels in the atmosphere.

   (b) What impact would the change in oxygen levels have on living things?

7. Study **Table 1**.

   (a) Calculate the amount of carbon entering the atmosphere as carbon dioxide every year and the amount of carbon leaving the atmosphere. Is atmospheric carbon dioxide increasing or decreasing?

   (b) Draw a bar graph showing factors that increase and decrease atmospheric carbon dioxide levels.

   (c) The burning of forests contributes 2×10^{13} kg of carbon yearly, but its impact on creating a carbon imbalance is even greater than the carbon dioxide released from the burning plants. What other factor would be affected by burning plants?

Challenge

3 In many parts of the world, some of the most productive forests are being cleared for farmland. In constructing your board game, how will you show the importance of maintaining plant communities?

(d) Provide a list of suggestions that would reduce the flow of carbon dioxide into the atmosphere. How would the suggestions affect your life? Which of your suggestions do you think you could help with?

Table 1	Carbon Cycle
Carbon movement	Mass of carbon per year (10^{13} kg)
from atmosphere to plants	120
from atmosphere to oceans	107
to atmosphere from oceans	105
to atmosphere from soil	60
to atmosphere from plants	60
to atmosphere from burning of fossil fuels	5
to atmosphere from net burning of plants	2
to oceans from runoff	0.4

8. In 1998 the federal government of Canada proposed a "carbon tax" on gasoline. Some people believe such a tax would reduce the amount of carbon dioxide entering the atmosphere.

   (a) Would the tax reduce the amount of carbon dioxide entering the atmosphere? Give reasons for your answer.

   (b) What businesses would be affected by the tax? Explain how they would be affected.

   (c) What other groups or individuals would be affected by the tax? Would it apply equally and fairly to everyone?

   (d) Based on your analysis, who would you expect to oppose the tax? Who would you expect to support the tax?

The Nitrogen Cycle

Life depends on the cycling of nitrogen. Nitrogen atoms are required so that cells can make proteins. Nitrogen is also required for the synthesis of deoxyribonucleic acid or DNA, the hereditary material found in all living things. The movement of nitrogen through ecosystems, the soil, and the atmosphere is called the **nitrogen cycle**.

When you consider that nitrogen gas (N_2) composes nearly 79% of the Earth's atmosphere, you would think that access to nitrogen would not be a problem for organisms. Unfortunately, this is not the case. Nitrogen gas is a very stable molecule, and reacts only under limited conditions. To be useful to organisms nitrogen must be supplied in another form, the nitrate ion (NO_3^-).

The nitrogen cycle is exceptionally complex. The simplified description in **Figure 1** shows two ways in which atmospheric nitrogen can be converted into nitrates, in a process called **nitrogen fixation**. The first method is through lightning, and the second is through bacteria in the soil.

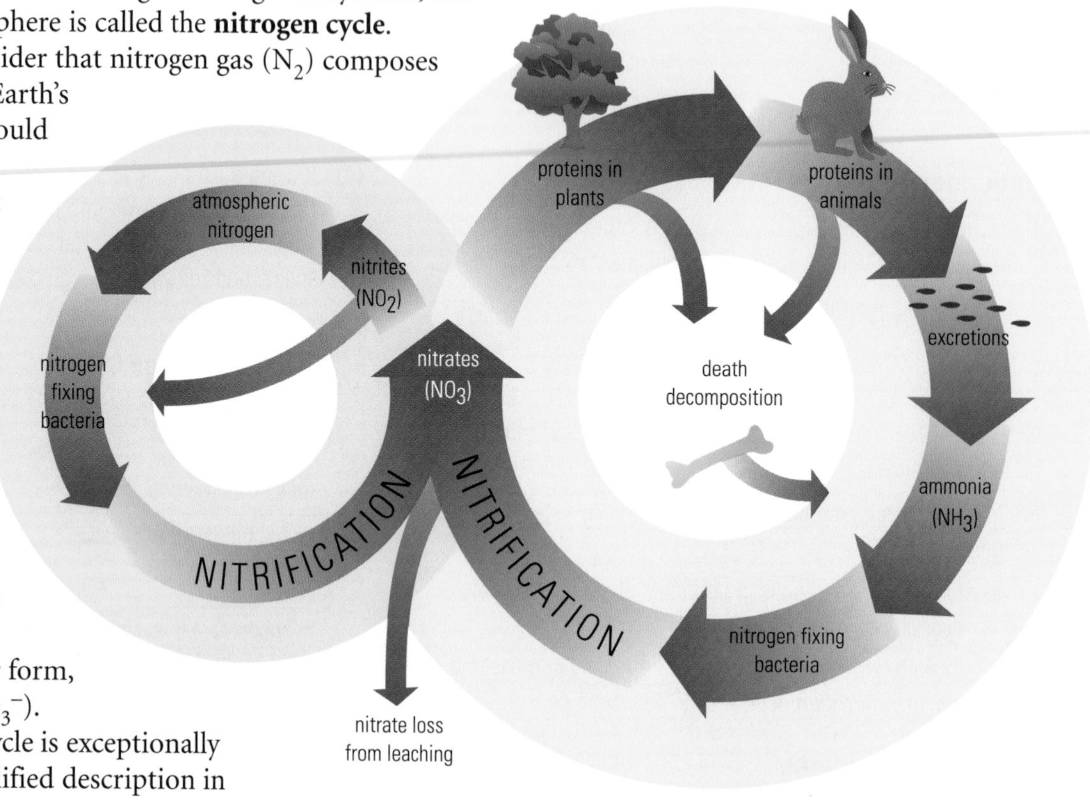

Figure 1

Like carbon, nitrogen moves in a cycle through ecosystems, passing through food chains and from living things to their environment and back again.

Nitrogen Fixation by Lightning

A small amount of nitrogen is fixed into nitrates by lightning. The energy from the lightning causes nitrogen gas to react with oxygen in the air, producing nitrates. The nitrates dissolve in rain or surface water, enter the soil, and then move into plants through their roots. Plant cells can use nitrates to make DNA, and they can convert nitrates into amino acids, which they then string together to make proteins. When a plant is consumed by animals, the animal breaks down the plant proteins into amino acids and then can use the amino acids to make the proteins it needs.

Nitrogen Fixation by Bacteria

Some bacteria are capable of fixing nitrogen. These bacteria provide the vast majority of nitrates found in ecosystems. They are found mostly in soil. Nitrogen-fixing bacteria can also be found in small lumps called nodules on the roots of legumes such as clover, soybeans, peas, and alfalfa (**Figure 2**). The bacteria provide the plant with a built-in supply of usable nitrogen, while the plant supplies the nitrogen-fixing bacteria with the sugar they need to make the nitrates. This plant-bacteria combination usually makes much more nitrate than the plant or bacteria need. The excess moves into the soil, providing a source of nitrogen for other plants.

The traditional agricultural practices of including legumes in crop rotation and mixed planting capitalize on bacterial nitrogen fixation.

Figure 2
A clover root. You can see the swollen nodules where the nitrogen-fixing bacteria do their work.

Nitrogen and Decomposers

All organisms produce wastes and eventually die. When they do, a series of decomposers break down the nitrogen-containing chemicals in the waste or body into simpler chemicals such as ammonia (NH_3). Other bacteria convert ammonia into nitrites, and still others convert the nitrites into nitrates. These bacteria all require oxygen to function. The nitrates then continue the cycle when they are absorbed by plant roots and converted into cell proteins and DNA.

Farmers and gardeners who use manure and other decaying matter take advantage of the nitrogen cycle. Soil bacteria convert the decomposing protein in the manure into nitrates. Eventually, the nitrates are absorbed by plants.

Denitrification

At various stages in the decay process, denitrifying bacteria can break down nitrates into nitrites, and then nitrites into nitrogen gas. Eventually, the nitrogen gas is released back into the atmosphere. This process, called **denitrification**, is carried out by bacteria that do not require oxygen. Denitrification ensures the balance among soil nitrates, nitrites, and atmospheric nitrogen, and completes the nitrogen cycle.

Older lawns often have many denitrifying bacteria. The fact that denitrifying bacteria grow best where there is no oxygen may help to explain why gardeners often aerate their lawns in early spring. By exposing the denitrifying bacteria to oxygen, the breakdown of nitrates into nitrogen gas is reduced. Nitrates will then remain in the soil, where they can be drawn in by grass roots and used to make proteins.

This information may also help you understand why the leaves of some plants may not be a rich green colour. Chlorophyll is a protein, and plants require nitrates to make it. The colour of a plant's leaves may tell you the nitrate content of the soil (**Figure 3**).

The denitrification process speeds up when the soil is very acid or water-logged (oxygen content is low). Bogs, for example, are well known for their lack of useful nitrogen. They can support only a few types of plants — those able to live with low levels of nitrogen. Insect-eating plants, such as sundews and pitcher plants (**Figure 4**), are commonly found in bogs. In an interesting reversal of roles, these plants obtain their nitrogen by digesting trapped animals.

Figure 3
Plants that grow in nitrogen-poor soils can form only a limited amount of chlorophyll. The yellowness of this plant's leaves indicates that the plant is starving for nitrogen.

Figure 4
Insect-eating plants like this pitcher plant, a native of Ontario, can grow in nitrogen-poor soil.

The Phosphorus Cycle

Phosphorus is a key element in cell membranes, in molecules that help release chemical energy, in the making of the long molecules of DNA, and in the calcium phosphate of bones. Phosphorus tends to cycle in two ways: a long-term cycle involving the rocks of the Earth's crust, and a short-term cycle involving living organisms (**Figure 5**).

Living things divert phosphates from the normal (long) rock cycle. Phosphorus is found in bedrock in the form of phosphate ions (PO_4^{3-}), combined with a variety of elements. Phosphates are soluble in water and so can be dissolved out of rock. While dissolved, phosphates can be absorbed by photosynthetic organisms and so pass into food chains.

Phosphates eroded from rock are also carried by water from the land to rivers, and then to the oceans. In the ocean, phosphates are absorbed by algae and other plants, where they can enter food chains. Animals use phosphates to make bones and shells. When they die, these hard remains form deposits on the ocean floor. Covered with sediment, the deposits eventually become rock, ready to be brought to the surface again. The cycle can take millions of years to complete.

In the short cycle, wastes from living things are recycled by decomposers, which break down wastes and dead tissue and release the phosphates. The short cycle is much more rapid.

Variations in Nutrient Cycling

Nitrates and phosphates are both nutrients. **Nutrients** are chemicals that are essential to living things. The rate with which nutrients cycle through an ecosystem is linked to the rate of decomposition. Organic matter decomposes relatively quickly in the tropical rain forests. Warmth, moist soil, and the vast number of diverse and specialized decomposers permit a cycle to be complete in as little as a few months. Cycling in cooler forests takes an average of between four and six years. In the even cooler tundra, nutrient cycling takes up to 50 years. In the oxygen-poor environment of most lakes, cycling may take even longer. Temperature and oxygen levels are the two most important abiotic factors regulating decomposition. Other factors, such as soil chemistry and the frequency of fire, also affect decomposition and cycling.

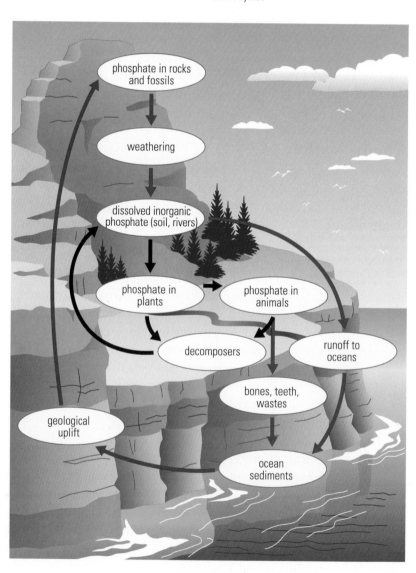

Figure 5

Phosphates cycle in both long and short cycles

Understanding Concepts

1. Explain why nitrogen is important to organisms.

2. If nearly 79% of the atmosphere is nitrogen, how could there be a shortage of nitrogen in some soils?

3. How do animals obtain usable nitrogen?

4. Nitrogen-fixing bacteria are found in the roots of bean plants. Explain how the bacteria benefit the plant and how the plant benefits the bacteria.

5. Draw a diagram of the nitrogen cycle for a farm or garden where manure is used.

6. Explain why it is a good practice to aerate lawns.

7. Explain why phosphorus is important to living things.

8. Some farmers alternate crops that require rich supplies of nitrogen, such as corn, with alfalfa. Alfalfa is usually less valuable in the marketplace than corn. Why would farmers plant a crop that provides less economic value?

9. Explain why bogs and swamps are usually low in nitrogen.

10. Speculate about why clover would begin to grow in an older lawn. How would the presence of clover benefit the lawn?

11. Nitrate levels were analyzed from living material and soil samples in three different ecosystems (grassland, temperate rain forest, and tropical rain forest) in the same month. To determine the mass of nitrates in living things, all living plant matter was collected in a study area and the levels of nitrates were determined. The same analysis was conducted for the top layer of soil. The results are listed in **Table 1**, where each ecosystem is identified by a number.

Table 1	Nitrate Content of Three Ecosystems		
Study area	Soil nitrates (kg/ha)	Biomass nitrates (kg/ha)	Soil temperature (°C)
1	30	90	25
2	10	175	19
3	2	270	30
tundra	?	?	?

(a) In which community does nitrogen cycle most rapidly? Explain your conclusion.

(b) Which ecosystem (grassland, temperate rain forest, and tropical rain forest) is study area 1, 2, and 3? Give reasons for your answers.

(c) Speculate about the data that might be collected from a tundra ecosystem (**Figure 6**). Explain your prediction.

12. The phosphorus cycle has been described as having two components — a long cycle and a short cycle. The carbon cycle can be described the same way. Draw a diagram that splits the carbon cycle into "short" and "long" components.

Making Connections

13. With each grain harvest, nitrogen is removed from the field. Farmers have traditionally rotated the crops they plant in each field. A wheat crop was often followed by a legume crop. Because legumes support nitrogen-fixing bacteria, soil nitrogen levels are replenished. The use of nitrogen-rich fertilizers has allowed farmers to abandon crop rotation.

(a) What advantages are gained from planting wheat year after year?

(b) New strains of crops have been especially bred to take up high levels of nitrogen. These strains produce more grain. Speculate about some possible long-term disadvantages that these crops might present for ecosystems.

Reflecting

14. Crop rotation is an effective way of restoring nitrogen to the soil; however, the planting of legumes is not always popular with farmers. Legume crops may provide less income, because they are more difficult to tend, more costly to plant, difficult to harvest, or worth less in the marketplace. Farmers must continually balance short-term gains and long-term results in this way. Provide some examples of how you balance short-term gains with long-term results in decisions that you make.

Figure 6

Agriculture and Nutrient Cycles

The seeds, leaves, flowers, and fruits of plants all contain valuable nutrients, which is why we eat them. However, as crops are harvested, the valuable nitrogen and phosphorus in these plants are removed and do not return to the field or orchard. This diversion of nitrates and phosphate from the local cycles would soon deplete the soil unless the farmer replaced the missing nutrients. **Fertilizers** are materials used to restore nutrients and increase production from land. Some estimates suggest that fertilizers containing nitrogen and phosphates can as much as double yields of cereal crops such as wheat and barley. However, fertilizers must be used responsibly. More is not necessarily better.

Soil bacteria convert the nitrogen content of fertilizers into nitrates, but the presence of high levels of nitrates may result in an increase in the amount of nitric acids in the soil. Changes in the levels of acidity can affect all organisms living in the soil, including decomposer bacteria.

Depending on the soil and the other chemicals in the fertilizer, a typical annual application of between 6 and 9 kg/ha of nitrogen fertilizer can in 10 years produce a soil that is 10 times more acidic. (An increase of 10 times means a drop in pH of 1, see **Figure 1**.) This can have devastating effects on food production. Most grassland soils in Canada's prairies have a pH near 7 (neutral). If the pH of the soil drops to 6, some sensitive crops like alfalfa and barley don't grow as well. The effect on agricultural land near the Great Lakes is even greater, as the local soils are more vulnerable to acids. A drop to a pH of 5 will affect almost all commercial crops. Acid rain and snow only add to the problem.

The pH Scale

		pH
Acidic	10^0 concentrated hydrochloric acid (HCl) solution	0
	10^{-1}	1
	10^{-2} stomach acid	2
	10^{-3} lemon juice / vinegar	3
	10^{-4}	4
	10^{-5}	5
	10^{-6}	6
	10^{-7} milk / pure water	7
	10^{-8} blood	8
	10^{-9} milk of magnesia	9
	10^{-10}	10
Basic	10^{-11}	11
	10^{-12} ammonia	12
	10^{-13}	13
	10^{-14} concentrated sodium hydroxide (NaOH) solution	14

(Left axis: Concentration of hydrogen ions)

Figure 1

A drop in pH from 7 to 6 is a tenfold increase in acidity. A drop in pH from 7 to 5 represents a hundredfold increase in acidity.

Fertilizer and Ecosystems

The accumulation of nitrogen and phosphate fertilizers produces an environmental problem. As spring runoff carries decaying plant matter and fertilizer-rich soil to streams and then lakes, the nutrients allow algae in the water to grow more rapidly (**Figure 2**) in what is called an algal bloom. When the algae die, bacteria use oxygen from the water to decompose them. Because decomposers flourish in an environment with such an abundant food source, oxygen levels in lakes drop quickly, so fish and other animals may begin to die. Dying animals only make the problem worse, as decomposers begin to recycle the matter from the dead fish, allowing the populations of bacteria to grow even larger, and use still more oxygen.

Nitrates present another problem. As you have seen, there are bacteria that convert nitrates into nitrites. But nitrites are dangerous to animals that have hemoglobin in their blood, such as humans and other mammals, fish, reptiles, and amphibians. Nitrites can attach to the hemoglobin in blood, reducing its ability to carry oxygen to body tissues.

The problem of nitrates in water is especially serious for young animals, including human infants. Humans and other animals usually have bacteria that convert nitrates into nitrites in their large intestines. For adults, the presence of these bacteria in the digestive system is not

Figure 2

Spring runoff of nitrogen and phosphorus fertilizers promotes the growth of algae.

harmful, because the stomach of an adult is so acidic that the bacteria cannot survive. But the stomach of an infant is much less acidic, so the bacteria can move up into the stomach, where they will convert nitrates into nitrites. The nitrites can then pass into the blood of the infant.

The question of how much nitrate should be allowed in drinking water and food is important, but we also need to know more about the nitrogen cycle in order to properly evaluate the environmental impact of nitrates.

Try This
Activity

Effects of Nitrogen on Algal Growth

Spring runoff of nitrogen fertilizers causes algae to grow rapidly in neighbouring lakes. In some lakes, a film of algae coats the entire surface of the water. This makes the lake a lot less appealing to swim in, but more importantly the resulting lack of oxygen places other organisms in the ecosystem in peril.

By passing pond water through a filter and then allowing the filter and algae to dry, you can measure the mass of algae collected.

(a) Using this technique, design a controlled
(K) investigation to measure how a fertilizer affects growth of algae.

• Have your design, safety precautions, materials, and written procedure approved by your teacher before beginning the
(M) procedure. Conduct your investigation and collect your results.

(b) Report on the results of your investigation.
(O2) Include an evaluation of your design, including suggestions for improvement.

☜Work the Web

Ploughing fields actually reduces the population of earthworms. Earthworms help decomposition and improve soil quality. Research the role of earthworms by visiting www.science.nelson.com and following the Science 10, 2.7 links. What recommendations would you make to farmers based on your research?

Challenge

1,2,3 How will you address the problem of nitrogen fertilizers in your Challenge? What problems are created as excess nitrogen is carried from the land into aquatic ecosystems? How could you measure the problems?

Understanding Concepts

1. Why do the levels of nitrogen and phosphorus in fields decline when crops are harvested?

2. Explain how excess fertilizers might affect decomposing organisms.

3. (a) Why do algal blooms usually occur in spring?

   (b) Explain how algal blooms affect other organisms in freshwater ecosystems.

4. What dangers do high levels of nitrates in the drinking water present for infants?

5. Explain why not planting a crop and then ploughing in the fall might help a farmer restore nitrogen and phosphorus levels in the soil.

Making Connections

6. Human waste contains nitrates and nitrites. Before the arrival of municipal sewers, the backyard outhouse was standard for collection of human waste. Outhouses can still be found at some cottages. Outhouses consist of a small building over a hole in the ground. Explain why outhouses pose a risk to neighbouring lakes, using information that you have gained about the nitrogen cycle.

7. To decrease the amount of carbon dioxide in the atmosphere a group of scientists has proposed adding nitrogen and phosphorus fertilizer to the oceans.

   (a) How would dumping fertilizers in the ocean help reduce carbon dioxide levels?

   (b) What environmental problems could be caused by the approach?

   (c) Suggest how an environmental modelling experiment could help determine the impact of adding fertilizers to the ocean.

Reflecting

8. Fertilizers have been with us for a long time. Explain why we must begin changing our views on the use of fertilizers so the ecosystems we live in will be sustainable. Why is it so difficult to change practices?

Effects of Deforestation on Cycling

Measurements have shown that matter cycles continuously within closed ecosystems. Based on those experiments, ecologists speculated about the impact that human activities had on the cycling of matter in the biosphere, but because they couldn't do controlled experiments, they could not demonstrate whether their speculations were accurate. Important questions, such as "How does deforestation affect nutrient cycling?" (**Figure 1**) could be answered only through environmental simulations, so the results were unreliable. In this case study you will examine a large-scale attempt at a controlled experiment in a natural ecosystem.

(a) Imagine that you were going to carry out an experiment on how
(K4) nutrient cycles in a forest are affected by logging. What would you want to measure?

Trying the Experiment

As part of a series of experiments that are still continuing, in the 1960s, Yale and Cornell universities conducted a large-scale study at Hubbard Brook Experimental Forest in New Hampshire. Researchers designed a controlled experiment to compare the flow of water and nutrients from a mature forest with the flow from one that would be logged (**Figure 2**) during the study. The mature forest would serve as a control, while the cut forest would serve as the experimental system. Concrete dams were constructed across creeks flowing out of the forests. Because the dams were anchored to bedrock, no water could slip by, and water volumes and dissolved nutrients could be measured.

(b) What advantages would be gained by conducting the experiment on a natural ecosystem, as opposed to a computer simulation?

Figure 1

It is difficult to carry out a controlled experiment on the effects of logging on matter cycles.

Figure 2

The Hubbard Brook controlled experiment

(a) The untouched, mature forest would be the control.

(b) The logged area would be the experimental system.

SKILLS HANDBOOK: (K4) Creating the Design

Setting Up

In the first part of the experiment, before cutting any trees, researchers measured the amount of water and nutrients that entered and left the forests. For several years, precipitation gauges measured water flow into the forest ecosystems. Water inflow samples were also collected to determine the amount of nutrients that entered the forests in each of the valleys. Finally, the amount of water leaving the two forest ecosystems was measured, and the water analyzed for nutrients. The nutrient inflow was found to be equal to the nutrient outflow in the two forests. In addition, scientists found that the amount of nutrients that flowed in and out was very small compared to the quantity of nutrients being cycled in the forest ecosystems.

(c) What conclusions can you draw from the initial measurements?

Experimental Logging

In the next part of the experiment, researchers disturbed the experimental ecosystem by systematically cutting down trees. The trees and shrubs were left on the ground and the soil was not disturbed any more than necessary. The cut area was then sprayed with herbicides to prevent further growth. Researchers continued to monitor water and nutrient inflow and outflow for both forests.

(d) Predict what would happen to the volume of water outflow after the trees and shrubs were cut. Explain your prediction.
(e) How would the change in runoff in the logged area affect the amount of nutrients flowing out of the forest ecosystem?

Measuring Changes

Overall, the flow of nutrients from the cut forest was four to six times greater than from the unlogged forest, but the flow of nitrates was much greater (**Figure 3**).

(f) Study the concentration of nitrates flowing from the forested system. Explain the annual peaks in the flow.
(g) Compare nitrate outflow from the mature forest and logged area from 1965 to 1971. Speculate about the reasons for the changes.

Understanding Concepts

1. Algal growth increases in valleys that have been logged. Explain why.

2. Assume that all the dead trees in the logged sites dry out. At some point, lightning strikes the area and the logs burn. How would the fire affect the flow of nutrients from the logged area?

3. Critique the experimental design used by the Hubbard Brook researchers. Identify problems for the design that were created by:

   (a) using herbicides to prevent growth of plants following the logging of the area.

   (b) leaving the trees and the shrubs that were cut on the ground in the experimental forest.

Making Connections

4. In much of Central and South America, farmers cut and burn rain forests to open land for the growing of crops.

   (a) Use a series of diagrams to show the effects of this practice on nutrient flow.

   (b) What could the farmers do instead to increase output from their current land? What effects would you expect your recommendations to have on local ecosystems?

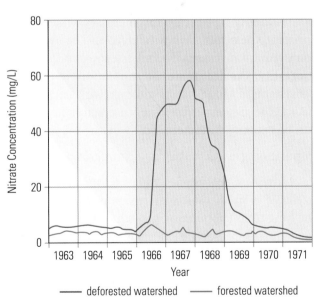

Concentration of Nitrates in the Outflow

Figure 3

Flow of nitrates from both forests

Monitoring Changes in Populations

The population of humans on the planet remained remarkably stable for thousands of years before the invention of agriculture. When a significant number of human societies switched from hunting and gathering to agriculture, the population of humans began to grow. Societies that harvest and store food for use during the winter months or during periods of drought have an advantage over those that must seek their food every day. During the centuries that followed the switch to agriculture, there was a steady rise in the human population, but no real explosion. It was not until the mid-1600s that the global human population reached about 500 million.

During the last three centuries, the global population has risen at an exponential rate (**Figure 1**). The population increased from 500 million in 1650 to 1 billion in 1850. That doubling took 200 years. The next doubling, to 2 billion people, took 80 years. From 1930 to 1975 (45 years) the population doubled again, to 4 billion. At the current annual growth rate of 1.55%, which adds about 80 million people per year, the next doubling to 8 billion will be complete by 2013, only 39 years.

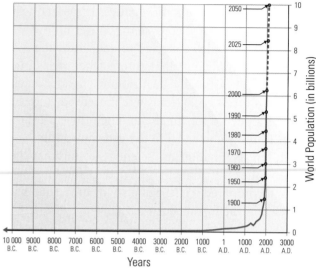

Figure 1
The global human population is growing rapidly.

Population Growth Patterns

Changes in population size in a community occur when individuals are added to or removed from a population (**Table 1**).

If **natality** (the birth rate) increases while other factors remain constant, the population will increase. The same holds true if immigration increases. The reverse effect occurs if there is an increase in **mortality** (the death rate) or emigration. In populations in natural ecosystems, all four factors interact, with natality and mortality generally having the greatest effect. The four factors involved in population growth can be expressed mathematically by the formula

Population growth = (births + immigration) − (deaths + emigration)

In mature ecosystems, where resources tend to be constant or available in predictable patterns, populations remain relatively stable over the long term (population growth = 0). Increases in natality are balanced by increases in mortality or increased emigration. This balance is referred to as dynamic equilibrium, or a steady state.

Open and Closed Populations

Ecologists classify populations as either open or closed. In most natural ecosystems all four factors (natality, mortality, immigration, and emigration) are acting on the population of each organism. These populations are said to be **open populations**. However, immigration and emigration do not happen in laboratory settings and in some game reserves,

Table 1 **Factors That Affect Population Size**

Factor	Description
natality (births)	the number of offspring of a species born in one year.
mortality (deaths)	the number of individuals of a species that die in one year.
immigration	the number of individuals of a species moving into an existing population.
emigration	the number of individuals of a species moving out of an existing population.

so populations of organisms in these situations are considered **closed populations** — only natality and mortality affect their population size.

The global population of humans or any other type of organism is also considered a closed population. People do not emigrate to other planets, and as far as we know none are immigrating either. Changes in the size of a global population result only from natality and mortality.

The current growth rate of the global human population is about 2.7 times as many births as deaths, which means that in 1996 Earth's population of 5.8 billion increased by 89.9 million people, or by 246 200 people each day. The human population is not in dynamic equilibrium.

Population Histograms

Population histograms (**Figure 2**) are useful when studying populations of long-lived organisms, such as humans. Double histograms are often used to provide a profile of age groups by sex. These histograms allow you to examine the population of an organism in terms of its age structure and the proportions of males and females at a specific instant in time.

The shape of the pyramid allows you to predict changes in the population. A pyramid with a wide base, as shown by histogram (**a**) in **Figure 2**, is characteristic of a rapidly growing population. It means that the number of births has been high recently. Another indicator of future growth is the number of individuals capable of reproduction. If this number is high, it means that a large number of births can be expected in coming years. In a human population, individuals of reproductive age would be found at the centre of the pyramid.

In contrast, histogram (**b**) in **Figure 2** represents a fairly stable population. There have been fewer births than in the A population. In addition, with infant mortality higher than the mortality of most other age groups, the population is growing very slowly. This population is approaching what is often described as zero population growth.

When the base of the pyramid is narrower than the middle section, as shown in histogram (**c**), fewer offspring are being produced. If the trend continues, this population will decline. **Figure 3** shows population histograms for three countries.

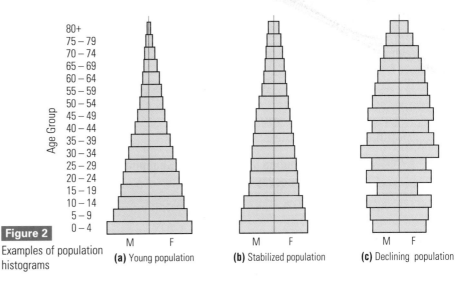

Figure 2

Examples of population histograms

(a) Young population (b) Stabilized population (c) Declining population

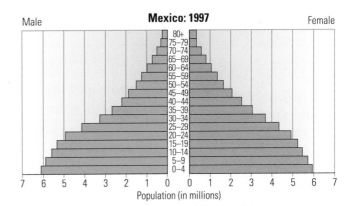

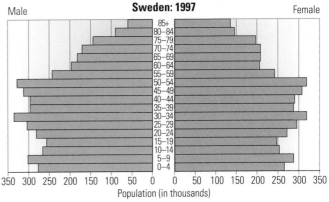

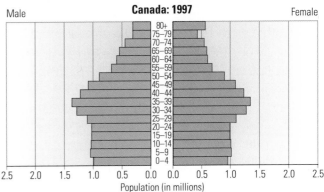

Figure 3

Mexico has a rapidly growing population, while the population in Sweden will soon start to decline. Based on the histogram, what do you predict for the future of the Canadian population?

Change and Stability in Ecosystems **75**

Try This Activity — Making a Histogram

To draw a histogram, you must start with population data (**Table 2**).

Table 2   **Age Distribution of Humans in a Shopping Mall (Wednesday at 5 p.m.)**

Ages	Female	Male
0–4	8	7
5–9	6	4
10–14	8	2
15–19	5	1
20–24	3	5
25–29	9	3

- Begin by drawing population size values along the x-axis, extending to both the right and left of the y-axis. Decide which half of the graph will represent the female population and which half will represent the male population.
- For the first category (0 to 4 years old), draw a bar for the number of females (8) on one side and a bar representing the number of males (7) on the other. Make sure to label the age distribution.
- Add a bar for each of the age categories.

(a) Complete the histogram showing age distribution from a shopping mall. What conclusion can you draw from interpreting the histogram?

(b) How might the results of the histogram differ if readings were taken at 10:00 a.m. on a Monday or 10:00 a.m. on a Saturday?

Understanding Concepts

1. In your own words, explain the difference between populations with linear and exponential growth rates. Provide examples in your answer.

2. What type of growth pattern has the human population followed? Explain your answer.

3. Four factors regulate population growth. Using an example of a nonhuman population, explain how each factor would affect the population size.

4. In your own words, explain the difference between open and closed populations and give two new examples of each.

5. Draw a population histogram that represents a population with a declining growth rate. Explain why the population you have represented will decline.

6. A single-cell organism called *paramecium* is found in pond ecosystems. In this type of ecosystem *paramecia* feed almost exclusively on algae. As the pond slowly warms, more algae grow. To answer the following questions, use the graph in **Figure 4**.

   (a) Explain why the population of *paramecia* is increasing.

   (b) Which population provides an example of a linear growth rate? Explain your answer.

   (c) Predict what might happen to the population of algae and *paramecia* after point B.

   (d) Sketch ecological pyramids of numbers for points A and B.

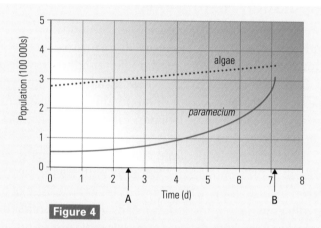

Figure 4

7. In January, 1999, the population of varying hares in a mixed woodland ecosystem was 60. During 1999, the following data on the hare population were obtained:

   births = 20   deaths = 25
   immigration = 3   emigration = 7

   (a) Calculate the population of hares in January, 2000.

   (b) Calculate the population growth as a percentage of the original population.

🖐 Work the Web

Visit www.science.nelson.com and follow the links from Science 10, 2.9. Select population data that could be represented by a histogram. Present the data first in table format and then in a histogram. Based on your histogram, make a prediction about the growth of the population.

Limits on Populations

Field mice may have litters with six or more pups, and they can reproduce every six weeks. It takes only six weeks for a mouse to become sexually mature. In 6 months, a population of 20 mice could become a population of 5120 mice. Mice have been around for millions of years, so why is it that when you look out the window you see grass and trees, birds and squirrels, and not a vast carpet of millions and millions of mice?

The reason is that there are limits on all populations, including those of the prolific mouse.

Biotic Potential

One of those limits on population is imposed by the species on itself. Species vary in their capacity to reproduce. **Biotic potential** is the maximum number of offspring that a species could produce, if resources were unlimited. You have seen how quickly field mice reproduce, but many animals have a much lower biotic potential. For example, mature female black bears give birth to one or two cubs after a gestation period of 7.5 months. Generally, bears take at least two years to mature, during which time their mother will not give birth again. Biotic potential is regulated by four important factors, shown in **Figure 1**.

 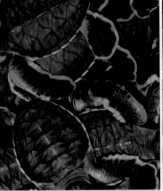  

Factor: birth potential

Description: The maximum number of offspring per birth.

Whooping crane females lay two eggs per year, and only one chick survives.

Factor: capacity for survival

Description: The number of offspring that reach reproductive age.

The female sea turtle lays many eggs, but only a few of her offspring even reach the sea, and fewer still reach maturity.

Factor: procreation

Description: The number of times that a species reproduces each year.

Elk mate only once per year, during the fall.

Factor: length of reproductive life

Description: The age of sexual maturity and the number of years the individual can reproduce.

African elephants reach sexual maturity at about 15 years of age, but may reproduce until they are 90.

Figure 1
Factors that determine biotic potential

Limiting Factors

The environment provides factors that prevent populations from attaining their biotic potential. Any resource that is in short supply is a limiting factor on a population. Food, water, territory, and the presence of pollutants and other toxic chemicals are all limiting factors, as shown in Table 1.

Table 1   Factors That Limit Populations

	Factors that cause a population to increase	Factors that cause a population to decrease
Abiotic	favourable light	too much or too little light
	favourable temperature	too cold or too warm
	favourable chemical environment	unfavourable chemical environment
Biotic	sufficient food	insufficient food
	low number or low effectiveness of predators	high number or high effectiveness of predators
	few or weak diseases and parasites	many or strong diseases and parasites
	ability to compete for resources	inability to successfully compete for resources

For example, a fern plant produces more than 50 000 spores in a single year (**Figure 2**). If all fern spores germinated, fern plants would cover all of North America within two generations of the first plant. This doesn't happen because of the limiting biotic and abiotic factors. If the weather is wetter than usual, the soil is moist, and many fern spores will germinate, so the fern population will increase. A return to drier weather will not only prevent spores from germinating, but will also kill plants in exposed areas, so the population declines. The presence of many grazing animals will reduce the population of ferns, and if there are few grazers the population will grow (**Figure 2**). Fluctuations like these, caused by one factor, can occur in natural ecosystems; however, most populations are affected by more than one factor at a time.

Figure 2
Abiotic and biotic factors limit the number of ferns in an ecosystem.

Carrying Capacity

Populations fluctuate regularly due to an interaction of the many biotic and abiotic limiting factors. However, communities do tend toward stability. Stability is achieved when an ecosystem is in equilibrium, when none of the populations exceeds the carrying capacity of the ecosystem. The **carrying capacity** is the maximum number of individuals of a species that can be supported indefinitely by an ecosystem. The carrying capacity for any species is determined by the availability of resources, such as food and water.

A population can exceed the carrying capacity of the ecosystem, but not for long. Consider the field mouse again. Imagine that the population of predators is lower than usual. Suddenly, the mouse population can grow. However, the extra mice will eat all the available food. Hungry rodents soon become sickly — making them easy prey for the hawks, owls, and foxes that are present. The mouse population will decline again, to or below the carrying capacity. Ecosystems soon re-establish equilibrium.

Did You Know?

The "lemming mass suicides" you may have seen or read about don't really happen. When Arctic lemming populations grow larger than the local carrying capacity, many of the lemmings migrate to neighbouring territories. They always try to arrive alive when they migrate.

Limits of Tolerance

You have seen that the survival and reproduction of an organism depend on the presence of nutrients and the ability of the organism to withstand the abiotic factors in the environment. This understanding has developed over many years.

In the mid-1800s, Justus von Liebig noted that certain substances must be present if plants are to grow. If any one of these substances is present in low amounts, the growth of the plant is reduced, regardless of how much of the other substances is present. This observation became known as the **law of the minimum:** the nutrient in least supply is the one that limits growth.

In 1913, Victor Shelford added to von Liebig's work by noting that too much of a factor can harm an organism. This principle is often called Shelford's **law of tolerance:** an organism can survive within (tolerate) a certain range of an abiotic factor; above and below the limit it cannot survive. The greater this range of tolerance, the greater the organism's ability to survive.

As seen in **Figure 3**, maximum population size is possible when the abiotic factor is at an optimum level within the range of tolerance. However, many abiotic factors act on a species at any given time. Most species have a broad range of tolerance for some factors, and a narrow range for others.

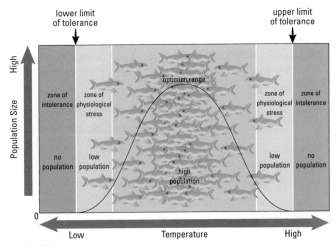

Figure 3

The population of a fish species is likely to increase as the water temperature gets closer to the optimum. None of the fish can survive if the water gets too hot or too cold.

Table 2   **Factors that Cause Changes in Populations**

Density-independent factors	Density-dependent factors
• flood • fire • spraying with pesticides • change in climate or temperature • destruction of habitat • drought	• food shortage • competition for mates, breeding areas (habitat) • disease caused by a microorganism or parasite • introduction of an exotic species • increased predation • competition for water and other resources

Density Dependent and Independent Factors

The number of organisms in an ecosystem is important when considering the effects of some abiotic and biotic factors. A population is said to be dense when there is a large number of organisms in a small area.

Density-independent factors affect members of a population regardless of population density. Fire and flood are two naturally occurring events that are density-independent. They will affect a population regardless of its size.

When the density of a population increases, other factors may limit further growth or reduce population numbers. **Density-dependent factors** affect a population *because* of the density of the population. Food supply, water quality, sunlight, disease, and territory are density-dependent factors. For example, when a tree in a dense forest becomes infected with a fungal blight, the infection will spread more quickly than it would in a forest where trees are separated by larger distances.

Similarly, individuals in more densely populated areas are more prone to starvation, as food is in lower supply. Competition for food may leave animals weak and more susceptible to predation. The density-dependent factors in **Table 2** will cause higher mortality rates, lowering the population density. When the population density is reduced, the effects of the density-dependent factors are also reduced.

 Challenge

1,2 Changes in populations of different species are often used to assess environmental impact. Species can either be counted or be measured by mass. How will you monitor changes in populations to determine environmental impact for your Challenge?

3 There are more resources in a tropical rain forest than in a tundra ecosystem, so the forest is able to support many more animals and many more different species. In designing your board game, how will you teach players how carrying capacity limits the number and type of organisms in an ecosystem?

Understanding Concepts

1. Cedar waxwings are one of the few birds that can withstand the cold and lack of available food during our winters. To ease the strains of winter, bird watchers in Barrie provide cedar waxwings with seeds during winter months.

   (a) Would the seeds alter the carrying capacity of the ecosystem? Explain.

   (b) Provide a hypothesis that explains why bird watchers have noted an increase in the falcon population in recent years.

2. **(a)** Create a table like **Table 3** and classify the following information within it.
   - Larger mammals generally live longer than smaller ones.
   - Pregnant female elephants carry their young for nearly 18 months.
   - Elephants reach sexual maturity at 15 years.
   - Elephants usually produce one offspring each birth.
   - Most elephants wait more than 5 years between births.
   - Female elephants care for their young for more than 10 years.
   - Mice often produce litters of 6 or more.
   - After about 6 weeks, mice reach sexual maturity.
   - In a natural setting, few mice are older than 2 years.
   - A pregnant female mouse will carry her young for 22 days.
   - Mice will breed every 6 weeks or less.

Table 3

Biotic potential	Elephant	Mouse
offspring per birth		
capacity for survival		
procreation		
maturity		

   (b) Refer to your table and write a paragraph comparing the biotic potentials of elephants and mice.

3. A scientist studying wolves near Kirkland Lake notices a steady decline in the population of wolves for four consecutive years.

   (a) Make a prediction about how the population of wolves will affect the population of moose. Give your reasons.

   (b) Assuming that humans are not the cause of the wolf population decline, would it be reasonable to conclude that the wolf population will continue to decline until there are no more wolves left in the area? Give your reasons.

   (c) What might cause the wolf population to begin increasing again?

   (d) Using a flow chart, explain how changes in the wolf population would affect the plant community surrounding Kirkland Lake.

Making Connections

4. In an attempt to increase the local food supply for people, humans introduced 26 reindeer (24 females and 2 males) to an island off the coast of Alaska in 1910. **Figure 4** shows how the reindeer population changed after the introduction.

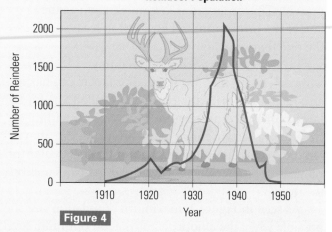

Reindeer Population

Figure 4

   (a) Speculate as to why more females were introduced than males.

   (b) By 1937 the reindeer population had soared to 2000. What evidence supports the hypothesis that the carrying capacity for reindeer had been exceeded?

   (c) Reindeer feed on slow-growing lichens and moss. Would you expect to find more food for reindeer on the island in 1931, 1935, or 1950? Explain your answer.

   (d) The introduction of a new species can cause major changes in an ecosystem. Should the reindeer have been put on the island? Explain your position.

5. Technological advances in agriculture have changed the carrying capacity for humans of most ecosystems.

   (a) Give some examples of agricultural advances and how they have affected carrying capacity.

   (b) Has the planetary carrying capacity for humans been reached, or can the human population grow larger without reaching capacity? In an essay, explain your position.

2.11 Explore an Issue

DECISION-MAKING SKILLS
- Define the Issue
- ○ Identify Alternatives
- Research
- Analyze the Issue
- Defend a Decision
- ○ Evaluate

Should We Use Pesticides to Control Pests?

For years, Ontario's tent caterpillar population will be fairly low; so low that the caterpillars can go virtually unnoticed. Then suddenly it seems that every other tree contains a caterpillar nest, and that the trees are being stripped of all their leaves (defoliated) (**Figure 1**).

The caterpillars are an example of a common phenomenon. Some species can reproduce so rapidly that they are capable of exceeding the carrying capacity of their ecosystem. Sudden spurts in one population can disturb even the most stable ecosystems. Such disturbances favour some species and hamper others (even to the point of completely eliminating them, at least temporarily). However, forces in the environment eventually cause the population to decline. A scarcity of food, an increased incidence of disease, or an increase in the predator population brings the population back into line.

The Caterpillar Problem

Tent caterpillars have one generation per year. They hatch in spring, about the same time as trees come into leaf, and begin to eat (**Figure 2**). The caterpillars reach maximum size by mid-July, at which point each one forms a pupa and begins its metamorphosis into the adult form. The adult moth emerges 10 days later and mates. Soon after mating the adults die, but not before the females lay their eggs. The life cycle continues the following spring.

Although their principal food is poplar leaves, tent caterpillars also eat the leaves of many other trees, including fruit trees. By eating a tree's leaves, the caterpillars prevent the tree from making and storing food. As a result the tree may be so badly weakened that it cannot reproduce (produce fruit). Most trees survive, but can make fewer leaves the following year.

If there is plenty of food for the caterpillars and if predators are few, many of the caterpillars become moths and reproduce. The result is a population explosion the following year. However, high populations of caterpillars mean plenty of food for predators, so the population of predators increases rapidly — their numbers will be high the following year. In addition, if there are many caterpillars,

1988

1991

1995

Figure 1

Brown areas indicate where tent caterpillars have completely defoliated trees. Trees that have lost their leaves in spring can grow new leaves later in the year, but the loss of time to gather food and the cost of growing new leaves weaken the tree.

Figure 2

Tent caterpillars spread out and eat the leaves of a tree during the day. In the evening, they all crawl into the web they make lower on the branch, where they are protected from predators.

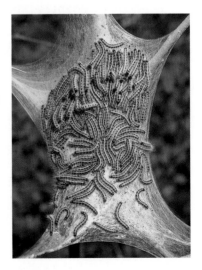

damage to trees results in less food being available the following year. Both developments result in a dramatic drop in the caterpillar population in subsequent years (**Figure 3**).

🖑 **Work the Web**

To research tent caterpillars, visit www.science.nelson.com and follow the links from Science 10, 2.11.

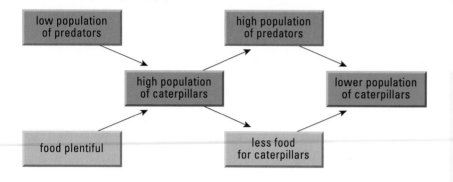

Figure 3

Factors that affect the population of tent caterpillars

Understanding the Issue

1. What factors control the population of tent caterpillars?

2. Make a list of individuals, communities, companies, and other organizations that would consider tent caterpillars a pest.

]DEBATE[Pesticides and the Tent Caterpillar

Proposition

Caterpillar infestations are part of a natural cycle of events. Pesticides are not required to control the caterpillars. We should allow nature to take its course.

Point

- If humans do nothing, the environment adjusts. Infestations of caterpillars are followed by years when they are rare, and the forest regenerates.
- Insecticides may remove the pest and its predators. Often the predators, such as birds, are harmed more by the insecticide than the insect pest. If the result is a decline in the population of predators, an important control factor on the caterpillar population is removed.

Counterpoint

- Trees in urban areas don't adjust — there are no young trees to take the place of damaged trees. Infestations could damage thousands of trees in a town or city.
- Orchards and forestry companies can't afford to wait for predators to solve their problems. It could take 20 years or more to replace lost trees. Spraying and biological controls can keep populations in check before they get out of control.

Taking a Position

- Ⓧ • In your group, discuss the proposition and the points and counterpoints above. Write down additional points and counterpoints suggested by your group.
- Ⓕ • Decide whether your group agrees or disagrees with the proposition.
- Ⓙ • Carry out research to learn more about the tent caterpillar, its economic effects, and the technologies used to control it.
- Ⓢ • Prepare to defend your group's position in a debate.

Chapter 2 Summary

Key Expectations

Throughout this chapter you will have had an opportunity to do the following:

- Describe the processes of photosynthesis and cellular respiration as they relate to the cycling of energy, carbon, and oxygen through abiotic and biotic components of an ecosystem. (2.1, 2.4, 2.5, 2.6)

- Illustrate the cycling of matter through biotic and abiotic components of an ecosystem by tracking nitrogen. (2.1, 2.6, 2.7, 2.8)

- Explain the process of bioamplification and assess its potential impact on the viability and diversity of consumers at all trophic levels. (2.2)

- Identify and evaluate Canadian initiatives in protecting Canada's ecosystems. (2.2)

- Describe careers that involve knowledge of ecology or environmental technologies, and use resources such as the Internet to determine the knowledge and skill requirements of such careers. (2.3)

- Assess the impact of technological change and natural change on an ecosystem. (2.7, 2.8)

- Examine the factors (natural and external) that affect the survival and equilibrium of populations in an ecosystem. (2.2, 2.9, 2.10, 2.11)

- Identify and research a local issue involving an ecosystem; propose a course of action; defend your position. (2.11)

Reflect on your Learning

Revisit your answers to the Reflect on your Learning questions, page 49, in the Getting Started.

- How has your thinking changed?
- What new questions do you have?

Key Terms

bioamplification	inorganic
biotic potential	law of the minimum
carbon cycle	law of tolerance
carrying capacity	mortality
cellular respiration	natality
closed population	nitrogen cycle
combustion	nitrogen fixation
denitrification	nutrient
density-dependent factor	open population
density-independent factor	organic
emigration	peat
fertilizer	pest
glucose	pesticide
immigration	photosynthesis

Make a Summary

In this chapter you learned how ecosystems change to remain vital. Matter cycles continuously through ecosystems through the birth, growth, and death of individual organisms.

- To summarize your learning select 15 of the Key Terms and write them on small file cards.

- Place the file cards on a desk and begin connecting the key terms with yarn or thread. Add key terms as required to make the connections.

- Be prepared to explain why you made each of the connections.

- View the maps made by other students in the class and ask them to explain why they made certain connections.

Chapter 2 Review

Understanding Concepts

1. Label the following organisms as producers (P), consumers (C), or decomposers (D). Some organisms could belong to more than one category.
   (a) mushroom
   (b) pine tree
   (c) soil bacteria
   (d) bread mould
   (e) cougar
   (f) algae

2. In your own words, define "matter cycle."

3. In your own words, define "bioamplification."

4. Using Joseph Priestley's experiments, explain why plants are vital for the survival of animals.

5. Copy **Table 1** and use it to compare photosynthesis with respiration. For items indicated with (?) put a check mark in the appropriate cell.

Table 1

Comparison	Photosynthesis	Respiration
raw materials		
products		
occurs in plants (?)		
occurs in animals (?)		
light is required (?)		
energy is released (?)		
energy is needed (?)		
chlorophyll needed (?)		

6. Use the ecosystem shown in **Figure 1** to answer the following questions.

Figure 1

   (a) Using the organisms in the ecosystem, explain the carbon cycle.
   (b) In a flow chart explain how nitrogen in the air reaches the caterpillar.

   (c) **Figure 1** doesn't show any bacteria, but they are always present in ecosystems. What roles do bacteria have in the ecosystem?
   (d) If DDT were used to control mosquitoes in the ecosystem, which organism would end up with the highest concentration of the insecticide in its body? Explain your answer.

7. (a) In your own words, define "nutrient."
   (b) Why do nutrients cycle faster in a tropical rainforest than on the tundra?

8. In your own words define:
   (a) nitrogen fixation
   (b) denitrifcation

9. Nitrogen is cycling through the ecosystems near your home and school. Choose a local natural wooded area and use a diagram to show how nitrogen cycles within this area.

10. Using the field mouse or the lemming as an example, explain the limits on the size of a population.

11. Calculate the change in a population of 1000 trumpeter swans after the following data were collected.
    births = 300
    deaths = 200
    immigration = 4
    emigration = 5

12. Is the human population of Ontario an open or a closed population? Explain.

13. Compare the populations in **Figure 2**:

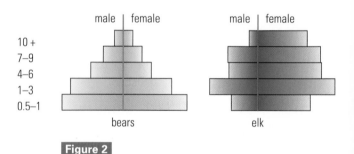

Figure 2

   (a) Which population appears to be most stable?
   (b) Identify differences in the growth patterns of elk and bears.
   (c) Which population has undergone a recent hardship? Explain.

14. What evidence have you gathered in this chapter that supports the statement that ecosystems must change to remain stable?

Applying Inquiry Skills

15. A lemming population was monitored in a study area (now in Nunavut) from 1986 to 1998. Use the data in **Table 2** to answer the following questions.

Table 2

Year	Population
1986	2200
1990	3050
1994	3200
1998	3500

(a) Graph the changes in population.
(b) Would you describe the growth pattern as exponential? Explain your answer.

16. A researcher conducts a study near Sudbury to find a possible biological control for pine bark beetles, an insect considered a pest by the forestry industry. The researcher sets up four different studies of predators and the pine bark beetle. The populations of prey and predator are monitored over many different generations. The graphs in **Figure 3** show changes in populations over time.

(a) Which species is most likely the best controlling agent? Give your reasons.
(b) Sometimes the eggs of a predator are eaten by its prey. Which predator might serve as a food source for its prey? Give your reasons.
(c) Why is the population of predator A consistently lower that that of the pine bark beetle?
(d) Predict what would happen to the population of pine bark beetles if predator species C exceeds the carrying capacity of the environment after year 9.

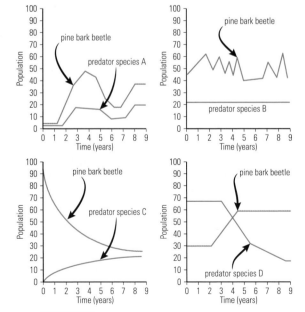

Figure 3

Making Connections

17. Using the example of pesticides and the spruce budworm, explain the impact of technological change and natural change on ecosystems.
(a) What might happen to a managed spruce and pine forest if pesticides are not used after an outbreak of budworm is noted?
(b) Outline some potential difficulties that could arise if pesticides are the only strategy used to control spruce budworms.

18. When the population of white-tailed deer becomes large, they destroy the vegetation, drastically altering the entire ecosystem and placing other populations, both plants and animals, in peril. Once food supplies decline, the deer herd becomes more prone to disease and starvation. This problem is developing on Navy Island, near Niagara Falls. Controlled hunting has been proposed as a solution. There are several different opinions on whether hunting of white-tailed deer should be allowed on Navy Island.
(a) Identify the perspective for each of the statements below.
(b) Do you agree with each statement? Give your reasons for agreeing or disagreeing.
- Once deer populations increase beyond the food supply, the herd will become ill. Some will die, and others will be taken by predators, removing the weak from the population. This will eventually strengthen the herd — only the strong remain. Generally, hunters shoot only the largest and healthiest animals. Hunting will weaken the deer.
- The beaches of Navy Island are visited regularly by the general public, and camping is allowed with a permit from the Niagara Parks Police. Hunting might create dangers for tourists.
- There are no wolves or cougars on Navy Island, and introducing natural predators to control the deer isn't an option in tourist areas. Predators large enough to kill deer also pose threats to humans, pets, and farm animals. Hunting is the best control option.
- If deer eat too much of the local vegetation, there will be no more food left and they will begin to starve. It is more humane to allow hunting than to allow the deer to starve.

19. Wolves often prey upon cattle or sheep as well as natural species, such as deer. Earlier in the century it was considered beneficial to eliminate predators. Identify and explain two harmful outcomes of this approach to managing predator populations.

3 Sustaining Terrestrial Ecosystems

Getting Started

WHAT IS THE VALUE OF AN ECOSYSTEM?
We drain wetlands to make way for more farmland to feed ourselves. We cut forests to supply wood and paper. We can place a value on farmland and timber, and we have systems to track that value. But what about the original ecosystem? What was its value, and what was the cost of changing it?

A **sustainable system** is one that survives and functions over time. In human terms, a sustainable system is one that meets the needs of present and future generations. To support a system, human societies must not sacrifice long-term benefits for short-term gains. To avoid that pitfall, we must have a clear idea of the value of ecosystems. In a sustainable society, decisions are made by taking into account socioeconomic and ecological considerations. A sustainable society manages its economy in such a way that human demands on ecosystems do not exceed the planet's ability to replenish resources, so the requirements of future generations are not compromised.

It is possible to think of the value of ecosystems just as we think about value in our own lives. Living sustainably is like living within our means and not using up our savings. In thinking about ecosystems, however, we must think not only about ourselves, not only about the next generation, but also about the many generations to come. There is a limited supply of topsoil, water, fossil fuels, and minerals on our planet. To be sure that future generations will have access to non-renewable resources such as coal, oil, copper, iron, sulfur, and aluminum, we must budget those resources. Resources that can be renewed, such as topsoil, forests, grasslands, and wildlife, must be monitored so that their use and destruction does not exceed the rate at which they are restored.

Reflect on your Learning

1. Examine the pictures that appear on these pages.

   (a) For each picture, identify problems that threaten sustainability.

   (b) Suggest some solutions to these problems.

   (c) Are any of the problems beyond a solution? Explain why or why not.

   (d) Make a list of things that you could do to maintain the environment you live in.

   Throughout this chapter, note any changes in your ideas as you learn new concepts and develop your skills.

Try This
Activity An Ecosystem on the Moon

Before we can colonize the Moon and other planets, we must learn how to create an ecosystem that can support humans and that does not rely on help from Earth. You can design a model ecosystem that could be built on the Moon. Think about the following problems while designing your ecosystem.

- How will you provide a continuous supply of oxygen?

- How will you provide a continuous supply of food and water?
- What will happen to wastes?

(a) Make a list of plants and animals that are essential to humans and must be included in your sustainable ecosystem. Explain why you think each organism is essential.

(b) List the things that are needed for the survival of each of the plants and animals on your list.

Canadian Biomes

Ecosystems can be grouped into larger categories called biomes. A **biome** is a collection of ecosystems that are similar or related to each other, usually in the type of plants they support. Canada can be organized into four major biomes (**Figure 1**).

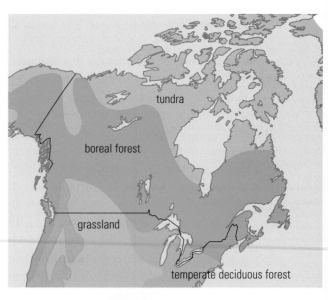

The Tundra Biome

Canada's northernmost biome, the **tundra,** is a cold desert. Like a desert, the tundra receives surprisingly little precipitation — often only 10 to 12 cm per year. (It looks as though there is more only because the small amount of snow that falls remains for months, and the harsh winds blow it around.) Also like a desert, the tundra supports only a small number of organisms.

The most important abiotic factor in tundra is the length — or more accurately the shortness — of the growing season. The short season limits the types of plants that can survive; they must be able to grow quickly, flower, and seed before winter returns. Plants must also deal with **permafrost,** a layer of soil that never thaws. Above the permafrost is another layer of soil, referred to as the **active layer,** that thaws in summer to permit the uptake of water and minerals by plant roots. Plants that grow close to the ground and have fibrous root systems that can anchor themselves in the shifting active layer of soil are best adapted to this environment. Large trees cannot grow on the tundra.

In the northernmost reaches of the tundra, where the active layer is thinnest and air temperatures are most extreme, lichens and moss dominate. Toward the south, where it is warmer, taller plants such as grasses can grow. Still farther south, where the permafrost is weakening, tall grasses, small shrubs, and even stunted coniferous trees can be found.

Although it is desertlike in terms of precipitation, the tundra does not usually lack water in the summer growing season. That is because melted snow, which cannot flow through the permafrost, is held in the active layer.

Decomposition of plant and animal matter is extremely slow in cold temperatures. The cold limits the reproduction of soil bacteria and the growth of soil fungi. As a result, there are few bacteria and fungi available in the tundra to decompose organic matter. The cycling of matter is slow and there is only a small amount of organic matter in the thin soil. The combination of pools of surface water and slow decomposition results in the formation of muskeg (bogs), which are made from moss growing on a layer of partially decomposed moss (peat) soaked with meltwater (**Figure 2**).

The lack of plant matter limits the number of other organisms on the tundra. Caribou (**Figure 3**) eat lichen and moss. The barren-ground caribou is one of the last mammals to form large, freely migrating herds.

Figure 1

Canadian terrestrial ecosystems can be grouped into four main biomes: the tundra, the boreal forest, the grasslands, and the temperate deciduous forest. Climate, soil quality, and exposure to light create environments that prevent some species from taking up residence while allowing others to flourish.

Figure 2

Because water collects near the surface and decomposition is slow, muskeg areas form on the tundra.

However, their population is in decline, having dropped from an estimated 30 million in 1906 to between 300 000 and 400 000. Some of the abiotic factors that affect communities on the tundra are listed in **Table 1**.

Table 1 **The Tundra**

Abiotic factors	Communities
• very low temperatures for most of the year • short growing season • permafrost layer beneath soil • low precipitation • poor soil quality	• rapid-flowering plants (**Figure 4**) • mosses and lichens • caribou • ptarmigan (**Figure 4**) • lemmings • arctic foxes • wolverines

Figure 3

Caribou form large herds.

The Boreal Forest Biome

Immediately south of the tundra is the boreal forest, or taiga, biome (**Figure 5**). Dominated by conifers (trees with needle-shaped leaves), the **boreal forest** is found in every province and makes up approximately 80% of the forested areas.

Figure 4

(a) Cranberries are one of the small plants found on the tundra.
(b) The rock ptarmigan is one of the few birds that live permanently in the tundra biome. It feeds on buds, leaves, and seeds of plants, such as the sedge.

The climate of the boreal forest is harsh, with rapid changes in temperature. As a result of this mixing of warm and cold air, the boreal forest receives more precipitation than the tundra. The slightly higher temperatures mean that the soil manages to thaw every summer — there is no permafrost layer. This thaw permits the growth of plants with deeper root systems. In addition, higher temperatures allow organic matter to decompose more rapidly, which provides better soil than that found on the tundra. However, the soil is also more acidic, because decay of conifer needles produces acids. Only a limited number of plants thrive in acidic soils.

The fact that conifers dominate the boreal forest is no coincidence. Conifers are especially well adapted to the extreme climate. In the boreal forest, the long days and higher temperatures of summer are countered by the short days and low temperatures of winter. Because warm air can hold more moisture than cold air, plants must be adapted to live in conditions with drastically different amount of air moisture. Each of the thin, needle-like leaves of conifers have a small surface area, and so lose little water during winter. In addition, a thick cuticle of wax covers the needles, reducing water loss and protecting against frost damage. The pyramid shape and flexible branches of conifers are adaptations that allow the trees to support the crushing weight of a heavy snowfall (**Figure 6**).

With the exception of the tamarack, conifers shed their leaves slowly throughout the year, instead of all at once, as deciduous trees do. This is another advantage conifers have when the growing season is short: when the growing season begins, they are ready to photosynthesize.

Figure 5

Where the permafrost ends, the boreal forest begins. The transition between tundra and boreal forest can be very sharp.

Although all forests in this biome may look much the same to the casual observer, they are actually a mosaic of several different species, each adapted to different local abiotic factors. For example, the roots of the black spruce and the tamarack are adapted to water-soaked soil, so they dominate lower areas with poor drainage. White spruce and jack pine are most often found on slopes, where drainage is better.

Because conifers don't shed their leaves, and because their branches and needles form a dense canopy, the floor of the boreal forest lies in almost continuous shade. Only shade-loving plants such as moss and ferns can grow on the forest floor. As a result, food sources for animals living lower in the forest are limited. The other source of food — the trees — provides cones and leaves, but only a small number of animals can eat them. For example, only about 50 species of birds are found in the boreal forest. The seed-eaters, such as white-winged crossbills (**Figure 7**), require special beaks to pry seeds out of cones or crack the cones. Only a very few birds, such as the spruce grouse (**Figure 8**), eat the needles and buds from the trees. Some of the abiotic factors that affect various communities in the boreal forest are listed in **Table 2**.

Table 2 **The Boreal Forest Biome**

Abiotic factors	Community
• warmer than tundra (no permafrost) • changeable weather • soil contains some water and is acidic • precipitation 40 cm/a or more	• coniferous trees (Figure 9) • seed-eating birds • squirrels • voles • snowshoe hares • deer • pine martens (Figure 9) • grey wolves

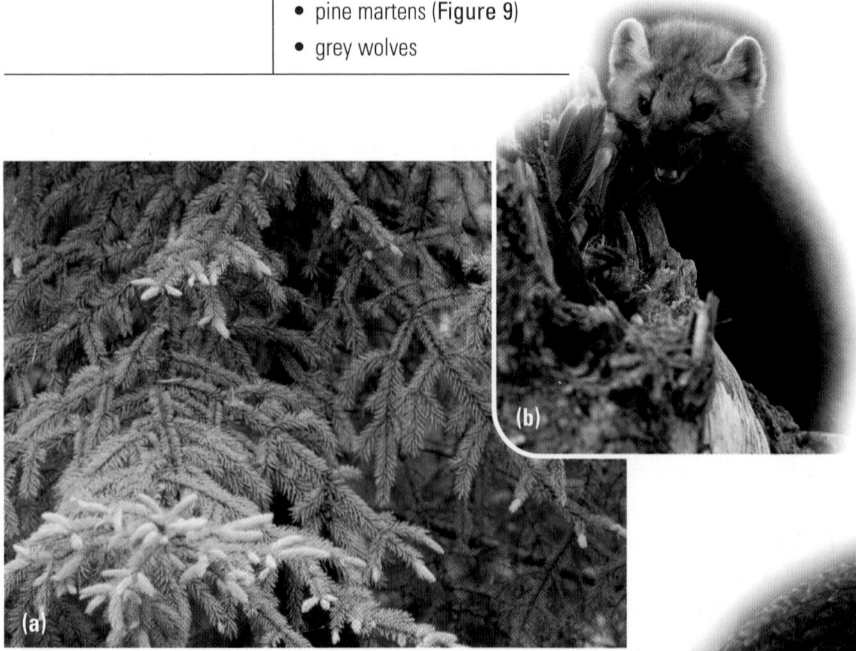

Figure 6

Snow will slide off a conifer. The flexible branches bend, causing the snow to tumble down. In contrast, many deciduous trees have rigid branches that point upward, like an inverted cone, with many branches at the top of the tree. Although this arrangement is ideal for collecting sunlight, it also makes the tree vulnerable to heavy snow and freezing rain. The great freezing rain storm of 1998 killed or damaged many deciduous trees in Quebec and eastern Ontario.

Figure 7

White-winged crossbill

Figure 8

Spruce grouse

Figure 9

(a) Conifers such as the white spruce dominate the boreal forest.
(b) The pine marten is a small carnivore of the boreal forest. It eats mostly small mammals.

The Temperate Deciduous Forest Biome

South of the boreal forest, in Eastern and Central Canada, is the **temperate deciduous forest** biome, which is dominated by deciduous trees such as maples and oaks. Unlike the obvious shift from tundra to boreal forest, the transition from boreal forest to deciduous forest produces a wide ecotone where trees native to both biomes can be found. As you move south to more moderate temperatures and less snowfall, you can see the conifers gradually giving way to deciduous trees. Within the deciduous forest there is also a shift from north to south, as the poplar, birch, and maple trees of the north are gradually replaced by the beech and oak trees of the south.

Figure 10

Among Canada's biomes, the deciduous forest contains the greatest biodiversity because it can support organisms in three different layers.

The broad leaves of deciduous trees maximize light capture for photosynthesis, which allows the trees to compete successfully with conifers. A single oak tree with a trunk diameter of about 50 cm can have over 100 000 leaves, providing a surface area greater than that of a tennis court.

Higher temperatures, which allow faster decomposition, and the organic matter available from fallen leaves provide the basis for formation of a richer soil than is found in the boreal forest. In addition, because light can reach the forest floor, more plants grow under the large trees of this biome. Although it is true that during the summer months only about 6% of the sunlight that strikes the top of the forest actually reaches the forest floor, during the early spring, most of the sunlight reaches the undergrowth. By the time the large trees have put out their leaves, the undergrowth, or understorey, is well established. This lower level of plants includes small trees, shrubs, and ferns.

Figure 11
Great crested flycatcher

The presence of so many different kinds of plant allows the deciduous forest to support many animals (**Figure 10**). The thick litter of the forest floor, made up of fallen leaves, provides an ideal environment for many different types of insects. The insects support a wide range of predators, including amphibians and lizards, birds such as flycatchers (**Figure 11**), and insect-eating mammals such as shrews (**Figure 12**).

The rich vegetation of the understorey and the lower branches of the trees provide food for large herbivores such as deer and moose. The upper levels of the trees — the canopy — support many species of birds and some mammals. Some of the abiotic factors that affect various communities in the deciduous forest are listed in **Table 3**.

Figure 12
Short-tailed shrew

Table 3 The Deciduous Forest Biome

Abiotic factors	Community
• longer growing season than boreal forest • higher temperatures than tundra or boreal forest • fertile soil • precipitation up to 100 cm/a	• deciduous trees (Figure 13) • many shrubs, ferns • tree and ground squirrels • many insects (Figure 13) • shrews, mice • deer • black bears • woodpeckers • weasels • wolves

(a) **(b)**

Figure 13

(a) The red maple is one of the trees of the temperate deciduous forest.
(b) The litter of the forest floor supports many insects, including the ground beetle.

The Grassland Biome

The **grassland** biome is found at approximately the same latitude as deciduous forests. As you move west from the Great Lakes and south from northern Saskatchewan and Alberta, the forests gradually thin, forming an ecotone between boreal forest and grassland. The grassland itself extends from eastern Manitoba to the Rocky Mountains.

Because of the similar latitude, the abiotic factors of the grassland mirror those of the deciduous forest — with one notable exception. Grasslands receive less moisture. Annual rainfall of between 25 and 75 cm means there is not enough water to support trees, except near rivers, lakes, and ponds. Also, when the area was prairie instead of mostly farmland as it is now, fires would periodically sweep through the grasslands, ensuring that trees would not grow. The fires also acted like decomposers, speeding the return of nutrients to the soil. Recognizing the importance of fire, some of the First Nations peoples of the Prairies deliberately set fires to maintain the grasslands.

The black earth of grasslands is the most fertile soil in the world. Short-lived grasses provide a great biomass for decomposition and high summer temperatures promote rapid decay, ensuring that the concentrations of nutrients and organic matter in the soil are high.

Like the forest biomes, the original grasslands were not the same everywhere. The length of the grasses was regulated by rainfall: the more rain, the longer the grass. As much of the grassland is now devoted to growing grain, there is little of the original prairie left. For example, one of the very few naturally occurring examples of tall-grass prairie can be found in a small 10-ha preserve within the city limits of Winnipeg (**Figure 14**).

Deciduous forests have three levels that support animals (the canopy, the understorey, and the litter) but grassland ecosystems have only one layer, so biodiversity is lower. The grasses of this biome once supported herds of migrating bison (**Figure 15**). Some of the abiotic factors that affect communities on the grasslands are listed in **Table 4**.

Figure 14

Only pockets of the prairie remain. This tall-grass prairie in Winnipeg has been preserved.

Figure 15

Bison feed on grass and other plants. Huge herds of bison once roamed the grasslands.

Table 4   The Grassland Biome

Abiotic factors	Community
• longer growing season than boreal forest • higher temperatures than tundra or boreal forest • rich, fertile soil • precipitation from 25 to 75 cm/a	• fescue grasses (Figure 16) • grasshoppers • bison • voles, mice • snakes (Figure 16) • hawks • wolves

Figure 16

The prairie rattlesnake is very much at home in the grasslands of Saskatchewan.

Understanding Concepts

1. Explain why tundra can be compared to a desert.

2. In your own words, define the term "permafrost."

3. Explain why soil is thin in the tundra biome and rich in the grassland biome.

4. Using diagrams, explain why few trees grow on:
   (a) the tundra.
   (b) the grasslands.

5. What adaptations make conifer trees better suited than deciduous trees for the abiotic factors of the boreal forest biome?

6. Explain why the forest near Owen Sound would be different from that near Fort Erie, even though they are in the same biome.

7. Match each of the biomass pyramids in **Figure 17** with a tundra, grassland, or temperate deciduous forest biome. Give reasons for each of your matches.

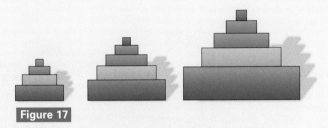

Figure 17

8. Rank the tundra, boreal forest, deciduous forest, and grassland biomes in descending order according to the following abiotic factors and explain your selections.
   (a) amount of precipitation
   (b) temperature
   (c) length of growing season
   (d) biodiversity
   (e) biomass

9. Identify an environmental problem created by people in each of the Canadian biomes.

Making Connections

10. As people move from one geographic biome to another they often bring plants that help make their new home feel more familiar.

    (a) Explain how transporting plants from one biome to another could cause environmental problems.

    (b) In Canada it is not illegal to take maple seedlings from the temperate deciduous biome of Ontario and plant them in the grasslands of Alberta. Should ecosystems be protected by laws that regulate transplantation?

11. Diamonds have been discovered near Yellowknife, NWT. Mining companies are developing the deposits.

    (a) Make a list of potential dangers to the local ecosystem that might be created by a diamond mine.

    (b) Make a list of the potential economic and social benefits that would arise from development of a diamond mine.

    (c) If you were the government official advising the Minister of the Environment, would you recommend licensing the diamond mine? Draft a letter that will go to the mining company and local citizens, explaining your decision.

Reflecting

12. Would a database of the organisms found in the different biomes of Canada be useful? How would you go about organizing such a database?

✍ Work the Web

Construct a food web for each of the Canadian biomes. To do your research, visit www.science.nelson.com and follow the links from Science 10, 3.1.

Biogeography

Why do different types of grasses grow in different parts of the prairie? Why do the types of trees change as you move south into deciduous forests? Why are there different types of forests and deserts?

To answer these questions we must begin by looking at various abiotic factors. Temperature, water, wind, and light are the major components of climate. Climate varies with latitude (distance from the equator) and altitude (elevation above sea level). In this case study you will look at temperature and precipitation (amount of rain and snow).

Latitude and Altitude

If you were to travel from the equator toward either pole, the air would get progressively cooler. You would also notice the vegetation changing as you went. Local vegetation is adapted to the local climate. A similar observation can be made as you begin to climb a mountain. **Figure 1** shows changes in vegetation according to latitude and altitude.

(a) In what ways is the mountain top similar to the tundra biome?

(b) Using plants as a clue, explain what happens to temperature as you climb a mountain.

(c) In your own words, describe the changes in vegetation you would expect to see as you travelled from southern Mexico to the Canadian Arctic.

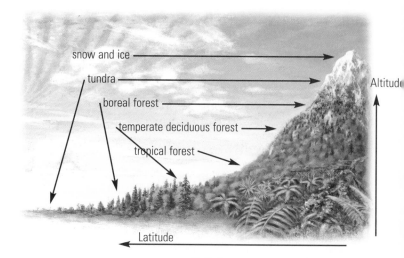

Figure 1

Climate is one factor that determines the ecosystems found at each latitude and on mountainsides.

Climatographs

As you have already discovered, the amount of precipitation (rain and snow) determines what kinds of plants can grow in an area. The influence of temperature and precipitation can be seen by constructing a climatograph — a graph of temperature and precipitation. The climatograph in **Figure 2** shows the major biomes in North America.

(d) Compare the rainfall in boreal and temperate forests.

(e) According to the climatograph, what factor accounts for the difference between a boreal forest and a temperate deciduous forest?

(f) Compare deserts with arctic tundra.

(g) What changes in climate could turn a boreal forest into a grassland?

(h) What changes in climate could turn a grassland into a desert?

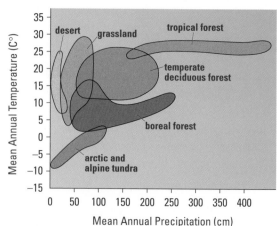

Figure 2

A climatograph shows the conditions that result in the major types of terrestrial biomes.

Variations in Climate

The climatograph in **Figure 2** doesn't provide a definitive picture of plant distribution. You will notice that there are overlaps, which makes prediction of biomes based only on mean temperature and precipitation unreliable. This limitation is borne out by the fact that in Canada areas with nearly identical mean temperatures and rainfall may support deciduous forest, coniferous forest, or grassland. Knowing mean values for temperature and precipitation is not enough. To understand variations in biomes, you must also look at variations in the patterns of temperature and rainfall within a year. For example, an area that has a dry season and a wet season could have the same total precipitation over the year as an area that receives the same amount of rain every month. The two areas would have the same mean precipitation, but you would expect to find different plant life in each area. **Figure 3** shows variations in temperature and precipitation for typical areas in some biomes.

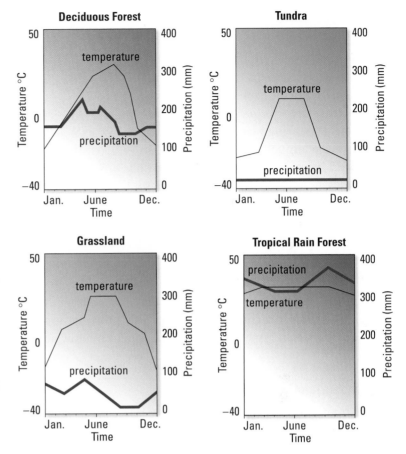

Figure 3

Mean monthly temperature (left axis) and precipitation (right axis) in four biomes

(i) Over 12 months, which biome shows the least change in precipitation? in temperature?

(j) Over 12 months, which biome shows the greatest change in precipitation? in temperature?

(k) Explain why plants that grow in a temperate deciduous forest have problems that plants in a tropical forest will not face.

Plant Adaptations

Plants exposed to the arctic climate must withstand low temperatures and must minimize water loss during the dry winter. In summer, only the top few millimetres of soil thaw, so all the water available to plants is found at the surface (**Figure 4**). Only plants that grow close to the ground can survive. By growing close to the soil, plants expose little of their structure, and they don't need elaborate water transport systems either above or below the surface.

(l) Why wouldn't tall grasses or deciduous trees be well adapted to an arctic area?

(m) Many plants do not grow in winter. Using the graphs in **Figure 3** in your answer, explain why this would be a good strategy in grassland and temperate deciduous forest, but not in tropical forest.

(n) Most coniferous trees have narrow, pointed leaves (needles), covered by a waxy coating. Explain how these leaves help them to deal with climate in the boreal forest.

Figure 4

Tundra plants stay low to the ground.

Climate and Root Systems

If you were to dig up plants and examine their roots, you would find another set of adaptations that helps them deal with climate. The plant uses its roots to draw water from the soil, and must compete with neighbouring plants for that water. Each of the annual plants shown in **Figure 5** has a specialized root system that provides an advantage in certain habitats. For example, the root system of the smartweed has branches at the top and also a tap root that runs deep into the soil. Only a constant supply of water would allow a small plant to support such a large root system.

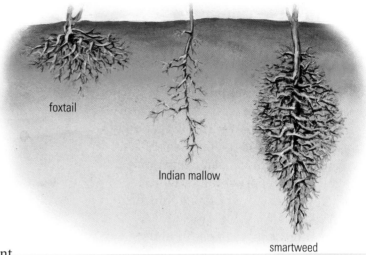

Figure 5

Some root types for small plants

(o) How does the root system of the foxtail allow it to survive in a climate that offers little precipitation?

(p) To which type of climate is the Indian mallow adapted?

Understanding Concepts

1. Make a table similar to **Table 1** and fill the blank cells.

Table 1

Abiotic and biotic factors	Biomes			
			Grassland	Temperate deciduous forest
soil	acidic soil	permafrost		rich fertile soil
vegetation	spruce trees	lichens and moss		
annual mean temperature (°C)	12 °C	−4 °C	14 °C	18 °C
annual mean precipitation (cm)	130	35	40	160

2. Explain the statement "Climbing a mountain is like travelling thousands of kilometres."

3. Explain how it is possible that two areas with identical mean annual precipitation and mean temperatures could support different vegetation.

4. Using **Figure 3** as a guide, draw a graph showing the changes you would expect in monthly temperature and precipitation for a boreal forest. Explain your graph.

5. Draw a map of your province and locate areas that can be classified as boreal forest, temperate deciduous forest, grassland, and tundra.

Making Connections

6. Plants are found in specific regions because they have proven to be highly adapted for that environment. If industrial pollutants and elevated levels of carbon dioxide gas in the atmosphere cause a rapid change in climate, many plants will die. Will the transition zones between biomes (ecotones) be more severely affected than the biomes themselves? Give reasons for your prediction.

Exploring

7. Occasionally plants are transported from one biome to another and survive. Identify a plant that is found in one of the Canadian biomes and indicate why it might survive in a totally different biome.

Reflecting

8. For many generations, the Inuit people were hunters.

   (a) Explain why a lifestyle of hunting and gathering allowed the Inuit to live sustainably within a tundra ecosystem.

   (b) Why would farming be an inappropriate lifestyle on the tundra?

Challenge

3 In constructing your board game, you could have players determine what would happen to different biomes if global warming occurred. How would global warming affect abiotic factors such as precipitation and air temperatures?

Soil and Its Formation

Soil is so familiar that its importance can go unnoticed. A thin layer of soil, rarely more than two metres thick and often much thinner, provides nutrients for all plants that grow on land. The quality and amount of soil available are crucial factors in determining the size and health of the plant community, and so the biodiversity of the local ecosystems. Entire civilizations have collapsed because topsoil was depleted or overused (**Figure 1**).

Components of Soil

Soil can be viewed as a series of layers, each of which can be identified by its distinct colour and texture. As you move downward, deeper into the soil, less organic matter can be detected.

In a forest or grassland community, the upper layer, known as the **litter**, is made up mostly of partially decomposed leaves or grasses. In many ways, the litter acts like a fluffy blanket, limiting temperature variations in the soil and reducing water loss by evaporation.

Beneath the litter is the **topsoil** layer, made up of small particles of rock mixed with decaying plant and animal matter (**humus**). Humus is black, so topsoil is often dark. Topsoil usually contains a rich supply of minerals and other nutrients that plants require for growth. Nutrients from dead and decaying matter are recycled as new plants grow. Also present in the topsoil, in the spaces between the rock particles, are air and water. For dead material to decompose completely, oxygen is needed. This is because the microbes that cause decay use oxygen for respiration. If oxygen is present in only small amounts, dead plant material decays slowly and can build up into a layer of peat.

Below the topsoil is the **subsoil**, a layer that usually contains more stones, mixed with only small amounts of organic matter. The subsoil is usually lighter in colour because of the lack of humus. Subsoil may contain relatively large amounts of minerals such as iron, aluminum, and phosphorus.

Beneath the soil lies a layer of rock, the **bedrock**, which marks the end of the soil.

Figure 1

There are many possible explanations for the disappearance of the civilization that created these statues on Easter Island. One theory is that the islanders removed too many trees, causing the topsoil of the island to erode. With their soil depleted, the people grew a lot less food.

Formation of Soil

Soil begins as bedrock. Over time the rock is attacked by rain, wind, frost, snow, and living things and broken down into smaller particles, in a process called weathering. Once a thin layer of small particles is present, small plants can grow (**Figure 2**). Plants speed up the process of weathering and add material from their bodies to enrich the topsoil, allowing still larger plants to grow. This process can take hundreds, or thousands, of years. Eastern Canada was covered by glaciers as recently as 12 000 years ago. Most of the soil you see was formed from weathered rock that was exposed when the ice receded.

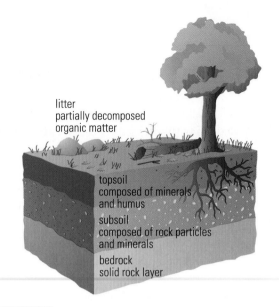

Figure 2

The soil can be divided into layers. Each layer can be identified by colour and the presence of stones. Roots from trees help break up large stones in the subsoil and the bedrock itself, helping to deepen the soil.

Water Beneath the Soil

Precipitation that collects and flows above the ground is called **surface water**. Lakes, ponds, and rivers are all surface water. Rain and melted snow run off into streams and other surface water, but also seep into the soil and porous rock below the soil. Once in the soil or rock water is called **ground water** (**Figure 3**).

Ground water, pulled by gravity, flows downward through the soil in a process called **percolation**. The larger the particles that make up the soil, the greater is the size of the spaces between the particles, and so the faster is the percolation rate. The water that percolates down through the soil eventually reaches a layer that is saturated with water. The boundary between the area where ground water is percolating down and the saturated layer is called the **water table**. The saturated layer lies above a layer that water cannot penetrate, such as impermeable bedrock or dense clay. In general, where rainfall is great, the water table will be higher (closer to the surface). However, areas where ground water cannot flow through soil and rock to bodies of surface water may also have a high water table, and elevated areas (where ground water can escape easily) may have low water tables.

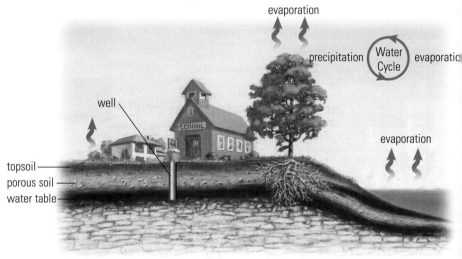

Figure 3

Ground water is part of the water cycle.

As water seeps downward, it dissolves organic matter and minerals from the soil and carries them deeper in a process called **leaching**. Leaching is a serious problem because plants require these nutrients for growth and development. In many ways, plants help to correct the problem themselves. Their branching roots extend deep into the soil and help pump minerals and other chemicals from the lower levels back to the surface.

Soil pH

Soil can be acidic, neutral, or basic. (Basic soils are often referred to as alkaline soils.) The pH of the soil is determined by the nature of the rock from which it was formed, and by the nature of the plants that grow in it. (The decomposition of organic matter from dead plants and discarded leaves can cause the accumulation of acids in the soil.)

The acidity of rain and snow, and so of the ground water that enters the soil, also plays a role. Humans, by burning fossil fuels such as coal, oil, and gasoline, have been contributing to higher levels of acidity in many soils.

The burning of fossil fuels releases sulfur doxide and nitrogen oxides into the air. These gases form acidic compounds in the atmosphere that fall to earth as **acid deposition**. (When dissolved in water, the acidic compounds form acid rain or snow.) Acidic water in the soil increases the problem of leaching by causing some nutrients held in soil particles to become dissolved in water, where they can be carried into the lower depths of the soil by percolation. Potassium, calcium, magnesium, and ammonium are nutrients affected by this process. The fertility of the soil is reduced by this removal of nutrients. Plants grow more slowly in such soil, and also become vulnerable to diseases

The pH of the soil determines which plants will grow best. For example, conifers do very poorly in strongly acidic soils, even though they are well adapted to mildly acidic soil. The removal of needed minerals from soil causes their needles to turn yellow and then brown. However, not every plant does poorly in acidic soil. Mosses often flourish in acidic soils because of decreased competition from other plants that require more nutrients. The pH of acidic soils can be raised by adding calcium or alkaline compounds.

In Canada's grasslands, acid rain does not cause the same problem. Soils in this biome, which are often formed from limestone, are usually rich in alkaline compounds and acid rain changes the pH of the soil only slightly. Once again, however, the pH of the soil has an effect on which plants can grow — many plants do not do well in alkaline soil. The ability of roots to take up important minerals such as phosphorus and zinc is reduced in alkaline soils. Prairie grasses prosper in alkaline soil, but trees, which require a much larger amount of minerals, are unable to grow. The pH of alkaline soils can be reduced by adding sulfur. The sulfur is converted into acids by soil bacteria.

Understanding Concepts

1. Distinguish between humus and peat.

2. If you were to dig a hole in local soil, what layers would you expect to see? Explain your answer.

3. In your own words, describe how soil is formed.

4. Using diagrams, show how the water table forms.

5. Describe two factors that would alter the amount of ground water in an area.

6. In a diagram, explain how minerals leach from the soil and how plants help to correct this process.

7. Gardeners faced with a layer of peat in their soil will aerate (add oxygen) to the peat. Speculate about how they might aerate peat and explain why they would do this.

8. A gardener has been trying to grow a pine tree, without success — every tree he has planted has died. He believes that his soil might be the cause. Identify possible problems, and explain how you might solve them.

 # Challenge

1 If you are going to design a golf course, a soil quality analysis is very important. Which type of grass grows best in the existing soil? Should the soil pH be changed? If so, how would the change affect the ecosystem?

Selecting Soil for a Sports Field

Baseball purists claim that artificial turf has ruined the game. The smooth carpet causes the ball to move too quickly across the infield following a bunt. Real grass slows the ball and makes for a more exciting running game. Baseball fields (and also football and soccer fields) require soil that drains quickly, but provides maximum nutrients for a lush, even lawn. If you were choosing a location for a new baseball stadium, what kind of soil would be best (**Figure 1**)? Assume the new baseball stadium will be built in an area that experiences wide ranges of temperature and precipitation throughout the baseball season, for example Southern Ontario.

clay particles (<0.002 mm diameter)

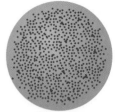
silt particles (0.002–0.02 mm diameter)

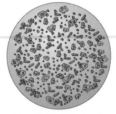
sand particles (0.02–2.0 mm diameter)

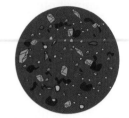
gravel particles (>2.0 mm diameter)

Figure 1

Soil is composed of rock particles of various sizes. Clay particles are the smallest, followed by silt, then sand, and finally gravel. Large particles have large spaces between them, which can be occupied by air or water. Small particles have much smaller spaces between them.

Question

Which soil sample would provide maximum drainage and still provide enough nutrients for the growth of a lush and even lawn?

Prediction

(a) Make a prediction about which of the soil (K3) samples would be best. Explain your prediction.

Design

In this investigation you will conduct tests that will help you rate each of four soil samples for qualities that provide maximum water drainage and support the growth of grass.

(b) To properly compare different samples of soil, (K4) make a list of variables that must be controlled throughout the experiment.

(c) Make a table to record your observations, measurements, and calculations.

Materials

- safety goggles
- apron
- 250 mL each of dry soil samples A, B, C, D
- 4 50-mL beakers
- tablespoon
- white paper
- hand lens
- 4 plastic jars, with lids
- water
- 2 100-mL graduated cylinders
- mass balance
- weighing boat
- hot plate
- beaker tongs

When using your nose to gather observations, wave your hand over the opening of the beaker to identify the odour. Never place your nose over the edge of the beaker and inhale.

Procedure
Part 1: Classifying Soil Particles

1 Obtain a level tablespoon of each soil sample and put it in a separate labelled beaker.

2 Compare the samples of soil, using your nose, fingers, and eyes. Record your observations in your table.

3 Place a few soil particles from each of the samples on a piece of white paper and examine them with a hand lens. Using **Figure 1** as a reference, attempt to classify the soil particles in each sample. Record your observations in your table.

SKILLS HANDBOOK: (K3) Developing the Prediction and Hypothesis   (K4) Creating the Design

Part 2: Viewing Soil Layers

4 Pour soil from sample A into a clear plastic jar, until it is about ¼ full. Add water until the jar is ¾ full. Replace the lid and shake vigorously for 2 min. Leave the jar for 2 min or until its contents settle. Record your observations in a diagram.

(d) Are larger particles found near the top or bottom of the jar?

5 Repeat step 4 for Samples B, C, and D.

(e) Observe the results from other groups. Do all samples look the same?

Part 3: Measuring Soil Density

6 Using the tablespoon, put 20 mL of soil sample A in a 100-mL graduated cylinder.

7 Using a balance, determine the mass of a weighing boat. Pour the soil from the graduated cylinder into the weighing boat. Measure the mass of the weighing boat and the soil. Calculate the mass of the sample. Record your calculation in your table

8 Using the measured mass and volume of the soil sample, calculate the density of soil sample A. Record your calculation in your table.

9 Repeat steps 6, 7, and 8 for soil samples B, C, and D.

Part 4: Measuring Air Content

10 Place 40 mL of soil sample A in a 100-mL graduated cylinder. Slowly add 40 mL of water. Observe how the water interacts with the soil.

(f) Did you notice any bubbles coming from the soil when the water was added? What does the presence of bubbles tell you?

(g) Measure the volume of the soil/water mixture. Calculate the volume of the air that was in the sample and record your calculation in your table.

Part 5: Measuring Humus Content

11 Put about four tablespoons of soil sample A into a small beaker. Using a balance, measure the mass of the beaker and soil sample. Record the mass of the beaker and soil sample in your table. Repeat for B, C, and D.

12 Ask your teacher to place the beakers on a hot plate for 4 min. Heating the soil will cause organic material in the soil to combust, forming gases that will rise out of the soil. Using beaker tongs, carefully remove the beakers from the hot plate. Allow the beakers to cool for 3 min, then measure the final mass of each beaker. Calculate the mass of the material (humus) that was lost during heating and record it in your table.

13 Clear your workspace and wash your hands thoroughly.

Analysis and Evaluation

(h) Peat is made from decomposed plant matter. Which of your senses would provide the best clues for identifying peat? Explain your answer.

(i) Which of the tests you conducted could be used to rate the drainage provided by each soil sample? Explain your answer.

(j) Which tests could be used to provide information about which soil would provide the best environment for the growth of a lawn? Explain your answer.

(k) According to your evidence, rate the four soil samples according to how appropriate they are for use in a sports field. Compare your answer to your prediction.

Understanding Concepts

1. Many plants grow best in soils that have large air spaces. Speculate about why this is the case.

2. Explain why it is more difficult to dig in clay than in sand.

3. Explain the dangers of burying toxic waste in a sandy area.

Reflecting

4. What other information would you need to gather before making a recommendation to a municipality or company that was planning to build a stadium with natural grass? Consider what other tests that you could run or experiments that you could perform.

 Challenge

1 Compare the soil requirements of a baseball field with those of a golf course. What special soil qualities would be needed for a golf course in a warm, dry climate or a cold, wet climate?

3.5 Investigation

INQUIRY SKILLS MENU
- ● Questioning
- ○ Hypothesizing
- ● Predicting
- ● Planning
- ● Conducting
- ● Recording
- ● Analyzing
- ● Evaluating
- ● Communicating

Soil Nutrients and Plant Growth

In a natural setting, plants can grow without benefit of artificial fertilizers. The continuous recycling of nutrients between decomposing matter and growing plants, together with changes in the species of plants growing in the soil, ensures that the soil remains productive. However, not all soils are equal. In this investigation, you will determine whether nutrients leached from different soils promote plant growth. Because many of these nutrients are water-soluble, they are carried downward to the lower levels of the soil by percolation.

Question

(a) Write a question for this investigation.
 K2

Hypothesis/Prediction

Because each soil has a different structure and contains different amounts of organic materials, each soil will provide different amounts of nutrients for the plants growing in it. If water is passed through soil samples, nutrients will be dissolved. By using the water that passed through the soil samples to provide nutrients to plants, you will be able to determine which soil is best for plant growth.

(b) Predict which soil sample will provide the most
K3 nutrients for plant growth.

Design

This is a controlled experiment to determine which of three soil samples yields the most dissolved nutrients. Seeds are planted in standard potting soil and watered using leachate from three soil samples.

(c) Identify the dependent and independent
K4 variables in this experiment.
(d) What control is used in the experiment? Explain your answer.
(e) Create a table to record your observations.

Materials

- safety goggles
- apron
- 250 mL clay soil (sample A)
- 250 mL silt soil (sample B)
- 250 mL sandy soil (sample C)
- potting soil
- food colander
- cheesecloth
- distilled water
- 250-mL beaker
- bucket or other large container
- 3 plastic storage bottles
- marking pen
- 4 2-L milk cartons
- pea, corn, or bean seeds (presoaked for 24 h)
- 100-mL graduated cylinder

Procedure

1 Leach the nutrients from each soil sample into a separate storage bottle by first lining a colander with cheesecloth. Place 250 mL of soil sample A in the colander. Position a large container under the colander and pour 250 mL of distilled water over the soil. Allow the water to collect in the container.

2 Repeat step 1 twice, reusing the water in the container. After the final filtering, store the filtered water in a plastic storage bottle and label it "leachate from soil sample A" (**Figure 1**).

Figure 1

3 Repeat steps 1 and 2 for soil samples B and C.

4 Create planters using the empty milk cartons. Remove the top of each milk carton. Label one milk carton "control" and the others A, B, and C.

5 Pour a 20-cm depth of potting soil into each planter (**Figure 2**).

Figure 2

6 Plant five seeds in each milk carton.

7 Using a 100-mL graduated cylinder, add 50 mL of leachate from soil sample A to the planter labelled A (**Figure 3**), from soil sample B to planter B, and from soil sample C to planter C.

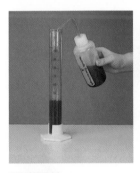 

Figure 3

8 Add 50 mL of distilled water to the seeds in the planter labelled "control."

9 Put the planters in a warm, well-lit location.

10 Each day, check the soil in the planters for moisture (the soil should be moist, but not wet). If water must be added, add the same amount of water to each planter from its leachate bottle.

11 Record the height of each plant every day. Make
(M) notes on the colour, health, and appearance of each of the plants.

12 Always wash your hands thoroughly after handling soil.

Analysis and Evaluation

(f) Calculate the mean height for the control and experimental plants each day. (If one seed in a
(W) group fails to germinate and grow, do not count it when you calculate the mean).

(g) Why is it useful to report the mean height for all five plants, rather than the height of each individual plant?

(h) Plot a line graph of the mean height over time
(V2) for the control and experimental groups.

(i) Read the comments you kept about the plants as
(03) they grew and review your growth data. Does the evidence that you collected in this experiment support or contradict your prediction? Explain your answer.

(j) This experiment was designed to demonstrate
(04) that different soils contain different amounts of nutrients. However, potting soil contains humus and inorganic fertilizers, and not all nutrients dissolve quickly and easily in water. Would these factors affect the results? Explain how you could modify the experiment to fix any flaws in the design and in the materials chosen.

Making Connections

1. Grain farmers may burn the stubble (the stalks of the grain plants) after harvest. List the advantages and disadvantages of burning stubble for

   (a) the farmer

   (b) soil organisms

   (c) neighbours

2. Suggest gardening techniques that could help reduce the amount of artificial fertilizer used in a garden.

 Challenge

3 In designing your board game, make a list of factors that can cause deterioration of the soil quality. Link these factors to environmental consequences. How will the loss of soil quality affect the sustainability of an ecosystem?

INQUIRY SKILLS MENU
○ Questioning   ● Planning   ● Analyzing
○ Hypothesizing ● Conducting   ○ Evaluating
○ Predicting   ● Recording   ● Communicating

The Animal Community in Soils

The distribution of plants determines which animals can live in a given area. In this investigation you will examine some of the smaller creatures that live in the soil and litter. **Figure 1** may help you to identify the soil organisms that you find.

Design

This is an exploratory investigation. You will observe and count the organisms you find in a local soil sample.

(a) Design a table in which to record your (K7) observations.

Materials

- disposable gloves
- apron
- sample of local litter
- sample of local soil
- newspaper
- hand lens or dissecting microscope
- spoon
- small jars with a cover
- funnel
- pinch clamp
- cheesecloth

Procedure

1 Place several sheets of newspaper on a desk and empty the bag containing the litter sample onto the newspaper. Using a spoon and a hand lens, sort through the litter, looking for organisms. Transfer larger organisms to separate collecting jars. Record your observations, including identifications and estimates or accurate counts of the number of each organism. If you cannot identify an organism, sketch it.

2 Carefully return the litter to the bag. Follow your teacher's instructions for disposing of the newspaper.

3 Repeat Steps 1 and 2 with the soil sample.

4 Set up a Baermann funnel, as shown in **Figure 2**, to find small roundworms in the soil. Place a small amount of soil in the cheesecloth, and tie the cloth into a pouch. Place the pouch in a funnel and add water until the pouch is partially submerged. Look for small worms leaving the soil through the cheesecloth as water enters.

5 Examine the roundworms with a hand lens and record the number you found in the soil sample.

6 Return the soil to the bag. Follow your teacher's directions for disposing of the newspaper.

7 Return any organisms you collected in jars to the soil or litter, and return the soil and litter to the place where it was collected.

8 Wash your hands thoroughly.

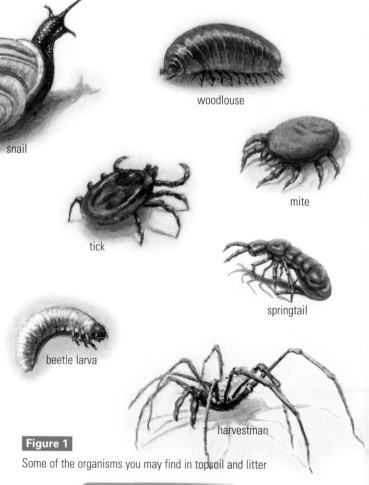

snail

woodlouse

mite

tick

springtail

beetle larva

harvestman

Figure 1
Some of the organisms you may find in topsoil and litter

SKILLS HANDBOOK: (K7) Preparing Tables of Evidence

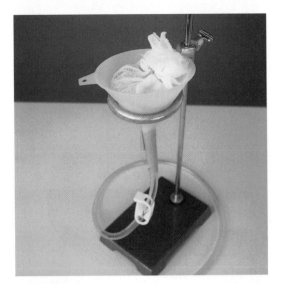

Figure 2

Analysis

(b) Compare the number of organisms you found in the litter with the number found in the soil. Explain any difference.

(c) Explain how trees could affect the animal population.

(d) Identify abiotic conditions that affect the animal population in soil or litter. Explain how two of these factors would affect specific animals.

(e) Prepare a report on the animals you found in the litter and soil samples. Include in your report comments on how abiotic conditions affect the animals and on any interactions you noticed among the animals. Include your sketches and counts of each animal.

millipede

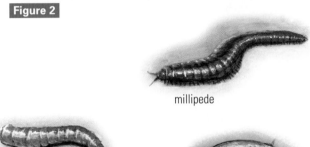

fly larva

silverfish

ant

roundworm

earthworm

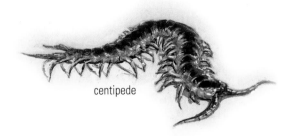

centipede

Understanding Concepts

1. Based on your observations, how do animals affect soil quality? Explain your answer.

2. The data in **Table 1** were collected from three different litter and soil samples. The study area for each of the three samples was 200 cm x 200 cm.

Table 1	Animals Found in Three Soil Samples		
	Sample 1	Sample 2	Sample 3
amount of water held by 100 g of soil (mL)	10	25	5
mass of litter above soil (g)	12.1	35.3	2.2
earthworms	2	8	0
beetles	1	3	0
centipedes	0	1	0
millipedes	2	3	0

(a) Match each soil sample to one of the following biomes: desert, grassland, deciduous forest. Give reasons for each match.

(b) What abiotic factors provide a favourable environment for earthworms in soil sample 2?

(c) What biotic factors provide a favourable environment for earthworms in sample 2?

(d) Centipedes prey on insects. Why are centipedes more likely to be found in sample 2 than in sample 3?

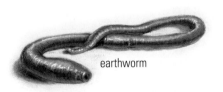

Agriculture and Food Production

More than 6 billion people inhabit the 145 000 000 km² of land on planet Earth. Estimates indicate the population will likely soar to nearly 10 billion by 2050. The most dramatic increases will occur in areas that are already crowded. Can Earth's carrying capacity for humans be stretched to allow such a large population increase? Technology has met this challenge in the past, but can that success continue?

Land and Food Production

Imagine your classroom with twice the number of students. Would everyone have a place to sit? Now imagine your lunchroom with twice as many people, but approximately the same amount of food. Without question, the lunchroom would have problems. However, the problem facing agriculture is far greater than the problem described in the lunchroom analogy.

Only about 11% of the Earth's land is suitable for growing crops, and most experts believe that new technologies are unlikely to increase that percentage. For example, unfavourable climatic conditions make tundra inappropriate for growing food for humans. **Figure 1** shows world land use.

Watering the Desert

Dry pasture land, normally used for raising cattle, sheep, or goats, could be modified to grow crops. Adding water to an arid landscape can have dramatic effects (**Figure 2**). Near-deserts can support rich plant growth, if all necessary conditions are met.

This technological solution has two requirements: an abundant source of water (which must be diverted or pumped from somewhere else, see **Figure 3**); and an irrigation system. Depending on the size of the project and the geological conditions, these two requirements may be fairly easily achieved, resulting in new productive cropland. However, large projects on challenging terrain would be very expensive, and may produce food at a price too high for most

Land Use Around the World

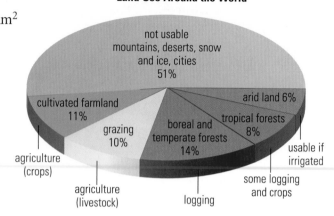

Figure 1

Food supply could be increased by cutting forests and irrigating arid land. However, converting any more land into cropland would likely lead to ecological disaster. Valuable forest resources would be destroyed, the biodiversity of ecosystems would be reduced, and water quality and quantity would decline.

Figure 2

A natural irrigation system — a desert oasis. Water allows plants to grow nearby, creating islands of green in a sea of sand.

Figure 3

Rivers that used to run into the Aral Sea in Central Asia were diverted to irrigate land. As a result, the sea is shrinking and may dry up completely.

people to afford. When does the cost of the project outweigh the benefit?

All fresh water contains a small amount of salts. During the heat of the day, some of the water being used for irrigation will evaporate from the soil, but the salt remains. Each day the flow of water brings more salt. As the concentration of salt rises, the soil eventually becomes too salty to grow crops.

Fertilizing the Soil

If we can't increase the amount of land used for crops, we must explore other approaches. The use of nitrogen, phosphorus, and potassium fertilizers dramatically increased food production during the 1960s and 1970s. Before the widespread use of fertilizers farmers had to rotate crops to ensure that nutrients were replenished, for example using a legume crop to restore nitrogen to a field that had been depleted by growing grains.

As with irrigation, the technological fix offered by spreading fertilizers on land is not without risk. The nutrients seep into groundwater, and run off into surface water, stimulating the growth of algae in lakes and rivers (**Figure 4**). Eventually, the algae die and are decomposed by bacteria that return the nutrients to the water. However, the bacteria also use up the oxygen in the water. With less oxygen available, fish and other organisms begin to die.

Figure 4

Fertilizer that runs off fields encourages growth of algae.

Try This Activity   Hydroponics

Hydroponics is a technology in which plants are grown indoors in water, with nutrients and air added. Could this technology expand the amount of land available for farming? You can make your own mini-hydroponics lab.

Materials: apron, large beaker, water, aquarium pump and tubing, small pots, plastic or metal mesh screen, vermiculite, seeds

• Set up your minihydroponics lab as shown in **Figure 5**.
• Fill the small pots with vermiculite and place them on a screen that is resting inside a large beaker. Plant seeds in the vermiculite.

(a) What nutrients should you add to the water? You may want to experiment with different mixes. Be sure to obtain the approval of your teacher before experimenting with nutrients.

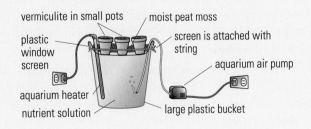

vermiculite in small pots   moist peat moss
plastic window screen   screen is attached with string
    aquarium air pump
aquarium heater
nutrient solution   large plastic bucket

Figure 5

The Threat of Monocultures

Any discussion about increasing food production for humans must take into account the damage done to ecosystems by agriculture and forestry. Attempts to produce more food or harvest more timber have involved replacing biodiverse ecosystems with artificial ecosystems that contain a single crop, a single source of food (**Figure 6**).

Environmental damage might occur on any scale. For example, to create more space for crops, a farmer might drain a marsh or remove a small stand of trees. Additional planting space means increased crop yield. However, by draining the marsh or removing the trees, the farmer is reducing the biodiversity of the land.

A wheat field is a monoculture, an ecosystem in which there is only one plant. It is designed to produce a single food. The amount of fertilizer applied, the irrigation, and the timing of harvesting can all be adjusted to make conditions in the field as close to ideal as possible for that single crop. Other species that have different nutritional requirements or needs for water can be ignored. In addition, any species that interfere with the growing and harvesting of the crop are removed. Unlike diverse natural habitats, monocultures tend to support very high populations of a limited number of species.

But monocultures are especially vulnerable to pests. In a grain field or a managed forest, the pest lives in an artificial ecosystem that may not contain many of its natural predators.

There is also a vast supply of food for the pest. The eggs of pests hatch amid a food supply that could support a huge population, if the farmer would allow it. In addition, the food attracts and supports many members of the same species from surrounding areas. A rapid rise in population is likely when animals don't have to expend much time and energy looking for food and mates. In a monoculture, pests have lots of free time and energy, and few predators to contend with. Monocultures are incubators for a few species of organisms.

Figure 6

Agriculture and forestry tend to create monocultures.
(a) Once trees were harvested from the previous mature forest, the diverse ecosystem was replanted with a single species of trees (the one that was considered most valuable by the forest company).
(b) By controlling abiotic and biotic factors so they are ideal for one species, a farmer ensures that a single crop grows in a field.

Fighting Pests in Monocultures

It follows that an important strategy for humans is to reduce the population of pests that compete with humans for food from crops. Killing insects that eat grain increases yields from cropland.

However, as you discovered earlier, the use of pesticides is not without problems, including bioamplification and the growth of resistance among pest.

Most pesticides are not target-specific: they kill insects other than the targeted pest, damaging food webs in the process. Damage to other crops may also result: insects that pollinate crops, such as bees, may be killed along with the pests.

Pesticides also affect people. Some farmers have poor equipment, and some workers are not properly educated in the use of toxic chemicals. The World Health Organization estimates that pesticides are responsible for 20 000 deaths and nearly 1 million poisonings every year.

Integrated Pest Management

In natural ecosystems, populations of all species are controlled by environmental and biological factors, including availability of habitat, availability of food, and the populations of predators and parasites. Integrated pest management combines natural controls and cultural practices with the limited use of pesticides (**Figure 7**). Examples of integrated pest management range from simple practices, such as building birdhouses that attract insect-eating birds, to much more complicated strategies involving the use of predators, parasites, and competition for food supplies. The objective is to learn as much as possible about the biology of the pest organism, and use that knowledge to reduce its population.

One effective example of integrated pest management comes from China. Instead of spraying insecticides, farmers have begun building straw huts in their rice fields during the fall. The huts provide shelter for spiders looking for a place to hibernate. More spiders survive the winter, and when spring arrives they emerge with a ravenous appetite for the insect pests that live on the rice. The estimated 30 000 species of spiders in the world kill more insects yearly than do all worldwide insecticide applications. A typical meadow can contain as many as 2 million spiders, each devouring hundreds of insects annually.

Integrating biological controls with limited applications of chemicals has several advantages over the use of only large-scale chemical sprays. The biggest advantage is that it allows the farmer to focus on the target species, and reduces the damage to other species in the ecosystem. It has been estimated than less than 2% of the insecticide used in spraying actually kills the intended pest. In sharp contrast, every spider will find specific species for food. Spiders are both selective and effective.

In Canada and the United States, spiders have been used to control spruce budworm, an insect that infests and kills spruce and fir trees. Spiders have also been used to control gypsy moths, which feed on the leaves of trees such as poplar and birch. In warmer climates, banana spiders have even been used to control cockroaches.

In Newfoundland, plastic mulches on cabbage and celery have reduced the need for weed-killing herbicides. In New Brunswick, potato growers are using a monitoring system for aphids; by treating aphids at their most vulnerable time, they can use a smaller dose of pesticide. In Nova Scotia, predator mites are being used in apple groves and strawberry farms to control pests. In Prince Edward Island, pests that eat the leaves of broccoli, cauliflower, and potato plants have been studied to determine action thresholds (situations in which pest numbers reach a critical point, resulting in the need for action). Knowing when to act and when to let the ecosystem use its natural regulatory mechanisms may be the most important factor in integrated pest management.

Other Weapons Against Pests

Another important weapon for the farmer is crop rotation, a practice that has been used less often since the invention of modern chemical fertilizers. Changing the plant in the monoculture reduces opportunities for pests. The pest larvae will emerge to discover a food supply that is not only different from the one their parents fed on but also possibly unfavourable. In

Figure 7

The ladybug eats aphids, a pest that sucks fluids from a variety of human food plants. Farmers can increase production from their land by encouraging predators like the ladybug.

addition, the new vegetation may attract different predators.

Planting times can sometimes be adjusted, so that when the insect pest emerges there are no growing plants to feed on. In Nicaragua, small patches of cotton are planted ahead of the main crop. After the parasitic boll weevil hatches, it must move to these small patches to find food. The small planting is a trap: once the weevil enters the trap crop, it can be destroyed by hand or by reduced amounts of pesticide. By the time the main crop begins to grow, the population of pests has already been much reduced.

Removing sick or infected plants can forestall a pest epidemic. Diseased plants, which are weaker and do not have their normal defences, can act as incubators for pests.

Microbes and Biological Control

One of the most successful biological controls in Canada is the bacterium *Bacillus thuringiensis*, commonly known as Bt. This microbe produces a protein that is highly toxic to caterpillars, including those of the spruce budworm. Other strains of the microbe have proven effective in the control of the Colorado potato beetle.

Concerns about the impact of Bt on food webs have been raised by the Natural History Society of P.E.I., where Bt is being used to control biting flies. The Environmental Protection Service and Canadian Wildlife Service are monitoring the P.E.I. program to determine its impact on aquatic ecosystems.

Challenge

1, 2 The source of most water pollution can be found on land. Have any of the technologies used to increase crop yields found their way into maintaining golf courses, yards, and parks? Do any of the approaches create problems for aquatic ecosystems? By answering these questions, you may be able to choose water quality testing sites.

3 In designing your board game, consider how changes in agriculture have increased the carrying capacity of our planet. How many people can be supported by the planet? At what point is the environment no longer sustainable?

Understanding Concepts

1. Briefly describe three concerns surrounding food production.

2. Why are monocultures more susceptible to pest infestations than natural ecosystems?

3. Describe three examples of how integrated pest management can increase food production.

Making Connections

4. (a) Make a list of agricultural technologies that have allowed us to produce more food. A chart like **Table 1** might prove useful.

Table 1	
Technology	**Why the technology allows production of more food**
fertilizers	

(b) Which of the technologies in your chart have created environmental problems? Describe how the technology has caused the environmental problem.

5. Each new agricultural technology increases the amount of food that can be produced. As each technology is applied, it permits a larger population of people. The population grows. Then another new technology is introduced. The population grows again. It is not likely that this cycle can be maintained indefinitely. Many ecologists are forecasting a disaster for ecosystems and a wave of human misery when the cycle fails and the carrying capacity of the planet is exceeded.

(a) Is it possible to break the cycle? Offer some suggestions, explaining how they could be implemented.

(b) Is the carrying capacity of our planet solely dependent upon food production? What other factors could limit carrying capacity?

Exploring

6. The newest technological revolution in agriculture is genetically engineered foods. By changing the genetic instructions in plants, scientists hope to create crops that have greater resistance to disease, are able to grow and reproduce at a faster rate, and provide more nutrients. Research the potential of genetically engineered foods, and why some people are concerned about them. Report on your research in an essay or poster.

SKILLS HANDBOOK: (I) General Research Tips (J) Internet Research (R) Writing for Specific Audiences

Brian Swaile

Plant Manager

Brian Swaile has been combining business with pleasure for 30 years, working for Ontario's Ministry of Natural Resources (MNR). For the last 19 years, he has worked at the Ontario Tree Seed Plant in Angus, Ontario. He has helped the Plant collect samples from over 50 different species of trees, including many that are native only to Canada.

Growing up in the central Ontario village of Coldwater, Brian fell hard — for nature. He often ventured out to visit relatives on the farm, and to "play in the bush." He chose to attend Sir Sandford Fleming College in Lindsay, Ontario, and was certified as an environmental resource technician. The school was relatively new then but is now recognized as an excellent place to combine theoretical and hands-on studies.

In his first job with the MNR, Brian worked in the bush around Minden. Then he was transferred to Darlington Provincial Park for a stint as superintendent. After leaving Darlington he became involved with the Ontario Tree Seed Plant — first as assistant superintendent, then as superintendent.

The Ontario Tree Seed Plant obtains seeds from different types of trees and then freezes and stores them. The seeds are sold to a variety of users, such as nurseries and researchers. The Plant also extracts and stores seeds for big lumber and pulp and paper companies. The forestry companies send to the Plant cones from trees they have selected.

To extract the seeds, workers at the Plant put the cones in a combination tumbler/kiln. As the cones are heated their scales release moisture. That causes them to open. The tumbling action causes the cones to release their seeds. The seeds are then collected and any debris, such as cone scales, twigs, and hollow seeds, are removed. The seeds are then conditioned and tested to make sure that when they are frozen and stored, the seeds will not lose their ability to germinate. Brian says many factors can affect a seed's ability to germinate. Insects, weather, and disease can all affect a developing seed.

Brian has almost finished his official working career, but he is not willing to give up his first love. He plans to continue his long association with nature by "educating people on proper methods of handling cones and seeds."

Over the years, he has found that it's important to keep learning. He has striven to upgrade his management skills and to better his understanding of tree and seed biology and physiology.

Making Connections

1. What qualifications are required in an occupation like Brian Swaile's?
2. Search for schools that offer programs similar to the one at Sir Sandford Fleming College. What programs do they offer for people who want to work with nature?

🖑 Work the Web

Research job opportunities by going to www.science.nelson.com and following the Science 10, 3.8 links. What jobs are available at the MNR? Report on one job at the MNR or elsewhere that interests you. What qualifications does it require? What experience would you need? Where would you work if you got the job?

DECISION-MAKING SKILLS MENU
- ● Define the Issue
- ● Identify Alternatives
- ● Research
- ● Analyze the Issue
- ○ Defend a Decision
- ○ Evaluate

How Many Potatoes Are Enough?

Is the ever-increasing popularity of potato chips and french fries placing strains on the environment (**Figure 1**)? To meet consumer demands for these fast foods, farmers have increased potato production. Nowhere in Canada is the result more evident than in Canada's smallest province, Prince Edward Island. On the Island, the amount of land devoted to growing potatoes increased by nearly 70%, from 25 688 hectares in 1986 to 43 200 hectares in 1996 (**Figure 2**).

With increased cultivation have come new jobs in processing plants and transportation. Agriculture is the largest sector of the province's economy, and the potato is the dominant crop, accounting for more than half of agricultural revenue.

As you have learned, increasing land committed to one crop is risky both for farmers and ecosystems. Environmentalists are concerned that farmers are abandoning responsible agricultural methods in an attempt to meet the demand for more potatoes. By eliminating crop rotation (which maintains soil quality) and hedgerows between fields (which decrease soil erosion), farmers may have achieved short-term economic gains by jeopardizing long-term soil quality. Scientists are researching less environmentally damaging ways of increasing potato production.

The desire to increase farmland by planting on hillsides, draining swamps, and invading forest areas is changing the ecological balance of the island. Insects, birds, and mammals that rely on these natural ecosystems must find food and habitat in the remaining untouched areas, or leave the island, if they can.

Figure 1

The demand for potatoes is growing.

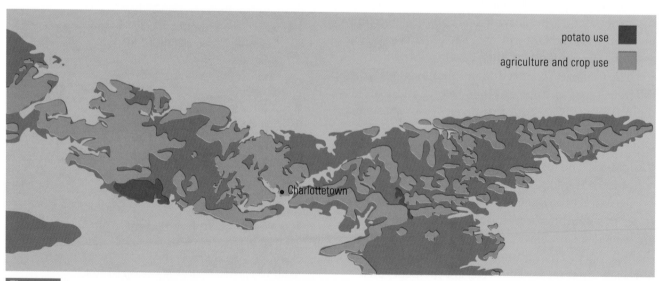

potato use

agriculture and crop use

Charlottetown

Figure 2

The amount of P.E.I. land devoted to potato farming is growing. This map shows the land use in 1998.

The impact of replacing a great number of different organisms with a monoculture is not well understood, but the potential for disaster is well documented. It takes many years for a stable ecosystem to develop. The relationships among plants, animals, and soil microbes are intricate and delicate. The loss of each species that is crowded out affects a great number of organisms directly or indirectly.

Consumer demand for potatoes has caused farmers to not only extend agricultural land but also to increase crop production on existing land. Increasing production also has a price: any increase in the number of potatoes is followed by a rise in the population of potato pests, which in turn reduce crop yield.

To regulate pests, farmers have relied more heavily on pesticides. Each year an estimated 600 t of pesticides are applied to the farming lands of Prince Edward Island. Although the pesticides are keeping potato pests in check, potato fields are not isolated from other food chains. It is feared that pesticides will leach into the groundwater or be carried into freshwater or marine ecosystems. As these pesticides find their way up food chains, a reduction in the number of trout and salmon in streams and a decline in the number of insect-eating birds are possible.

Understanding the Issue

1. What benefits do the people of Prince Edward Island gain by planting more potatoes?

2. Why do some people object to using more land to cultivate potatoes?

3. Why might an increase in potato cultivation result in the spraying of more pesticides?

Work the Web

To research the issue of increased potato farming, visit www.science.nelson.com and follow the links from Science 10, 3.9.

Take a Stand   The Potato Fracas

Proposition

The world needs more potatoes, and P.E.I. is a good place to grow them. If more land can be farmed, it should be.

Point

- Farming is a vital business. The world population in 1999 was approximately 6 billion. In 2050 it will be 10 billion. The world faces a major food shortage problem. The only way to feed people is to increase food production.

- Potato farmers will not use pesticides indiscriminately, because pesticides are expensive. They will spray just enough to control the pests, without endangering wildlife.

Counterpoint

- Sustainability must be the principal concern over the long term. We must find ways to reward farmers for preserving biodiversity, instead of only for increasing production.

- P.E.I. has two other important industries — fishing and tourism. Both are threatened by increased use of pesticides. Dead trout in streams foretell of more trouble.

Taking a Position

- **C** • Identify the perspectives of each of the opposing opinions.
- • Expand on the initial points provided. What other ways are there of looking at the issue?
- **I** • Research the issue further.
- **J** • Develop and reflect upon your opinion. What role could you play in finding a solution?
- **R** • Write a position paper to summarize your opinion.

Logging Forests

Forests are important resources. Forests regulate climate by recycling water and carbon dioxide. On hot days a large tree may absorb 5.5 t of water from the soil and release it into the atmosphere through its leaves in a process called transpiration. Between 40% and 50% of the water above a temperate rainforest comes from transpiration. In addition, the forest acts as a giant sponge, slowing runoff and holding ground water. Root systems also hold the soil, preventing erosion and reducing the amount of sediment that washes into streams.

Some areas of Canada have been forested for hundreds, even thousands of years. These forests, called old-growth forests, have many important ecological features. Old-growth forests contain an enormous number of fallen trees that slowly decompose, providing a constant source of nutrients for the soil. These forests also act as reserves for a tremendous diversity of wildlife, providing nesting sites and food for many animals.

Forestry Practices

Forest harvesting falls into two categories. **Clear-cutting** involves the removal of all trees in an area for use in timber or pulp. In Canada, this approach has traditionally been followed by replanting the dominant species, creating a monoculture.

Selective cutting is the second approach. Only certain trees are harvested from an area, usually the largest and most valuable for lumber or pulp.

Evaluating a Clear-Cut

From the point of view of the forest company, the workers it employs, and the communities they live in, a clear-cut has advantages over a selective cut. Clear-cutting is less expensive than selective cutting, which means the company can provide timber or pulp at a more competitive price. Clear-cutting is safer for the workers. Finally, when the land has been cleared, the company can choose which trees to plant — the ones that it can get the best price for when the area is logged again decades later.

From an ecological point of view, there are drawbacks. After a clear-cut, soil erosion and runoff into local streams increases. There is a surge in nitrates and other nutrients entering the water, increasing growth of algae. Also, the eroded soil forms sediment in streams, affecting spawning areas of fish. The removal of vegetation on the ground exposes the soil, increasing the warming of the area in summer and cooling in winter. Exposure also increases water loss from the soil.

A clear-cut creates completely different abiotic and biotic conditions in the area — the ecosystem must change, resulting in a wholesale change in the community. The loss of forest plants results in the loss of forest animals. They are replaced by animals that do well in the new conditions, which are more like a grassland than a forest. Ecotones are also created between the remaining forest and the newly cut area.

1600

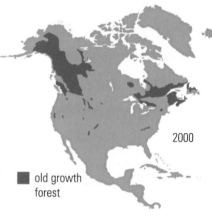
2000

■ old growth forest

Figure 1

In A.D.1600 there were approximately 6 billion ha of forest on Earth. An estimated 4 billion ha remain. Most of the difference has been used to create farmland or build cities. In Canada, approximately 60% of the original forest has been cut at least once.

SKILLS HANDBOOK: Ⓕ Analyzing the Issue

If the cut trees are replaced with seedlings of one or two species, the result is closer to a farm than a natural ecosystem. When the new forest grows, some, but not all, of the forest animals will return. There will be no food for some of the animals that lived in the more diverse forest that was logged. The new forest will have a lower biodiversity than the original forest. **Figure 2** shows how a replanted forest might be managed after a clear-cut.

(a) Two or three years after a clear-cut, herbicides are used to prevent hardwood trees from crowding out the more valuable softwood trees.

(b) At about 10 years, the underbrush is removed.

(c) At about 35 years, the trees are checked for diseases and pests, such as the spruce budworm. Monocultures are more susceptible to disease than natural forests.

Figure 2

Softwoods, such as spruce and fir, are used for pulp and paper and are often considered more valuable than hardwoods, which grow more slowly.

Understanding Concepts

1. In your own words, describe how forests affect the local water cycle.

2. In your own words, describe the two main methods for harvesting trees.

3. Does clear-cutting followed by a replanting program meet the requirements of a sustainable ecosystem? Explain your answer.

4. Selective cutting is not without problems. Identify some of the ecological problems that might occur in a temperate deciduous forest if only trees that produce the most valuable lumber, such as white oak and black walnut, are cut.

Making Connections

5. Create a chart comparing the benefits and drawbacks of clear-cut logging. Are there situations where a clear-cut would be appropriate? Explain your conclusion.

6. During a protest against the clear-cutting of an old-
(F)
(R) growth forest in the Clayoquot Sound area of Vancouver Island, environmentalists blocked a logging road, preventing workers from reaching the trees. Similar actions have been taken recently in Ontario and New Brunswick. Are such protests justified? Report on a recent environmental dispute over a forest, giving a fair summary of the positions of each side and your own opinions on how the dispute should be resolved.

Reflection

7. Logging companies, peoples of the First Nations, and
(C) environmental activists have been clashing over forests
(D) across Canada. Each group has different priorities and values, and so they come into conflict. Make a list of goals and values that would be most important to each group. Analyze your lists for differences. Which of the differences create conflict? Are any compromises possible?

🖑 Work the Web

Visit www.science.nelson.com and follow the links from Science 10, 3.10 to research disputes over Canadian forests. Report on one dispute. What evidence can you find that members of one group, or the public at large, are showing signs of a change in attitude?

Acid Deposition and Forest Ecosystems

Technology has been described as a double-edged sword, cutting through human problems with one edge while scarring the environment with the other. The technologies that contribute to acid deposition are a case in point. Coal-burning plants, cars and trucks, metal smelters, and oil refineries provide energy, transport, and materials for the industrial world, but at the same time produce oxides of sulfur and nitrogen, among the most dangerous of air pollutants.

The Problem with Combustion

When fossil fuels and metal ores containing sulfur undergo combustion, the sulfur is released in the form of sulfur dioxide (SO_2), a poisonous gas. Combustion in automobiles and in fossil-fuel-burning power plants produces various nitrogen oxides (NO_x), as does the processing of nitrogen fertilizers. When sulfur and nitrogen enter the atmosphere they may combine with water droplets to form acids (**Figure 1**). Upon entering the water cycle, the acids return to the surface of the Earth in the form of snow or rain, called **acid precipitation**.

Acid rain 40 times more acidic than normal rain has been measured. Acid precipitation kills fish, soil bacteria, and both aquatic and terrestrial plants. However, the damage is not uniform. Some areas are insulated from the worst effects of the acid by their soils. Alkaline (basic) soils neutralize the acids, minimizing their impact before runoff carries the acids to streams and lakes. Unfortunately, soils in much of southeastern Canada have a thin layer of rich soil on top of a solid granite base. This structure does not offer much protection from acid precipitation.

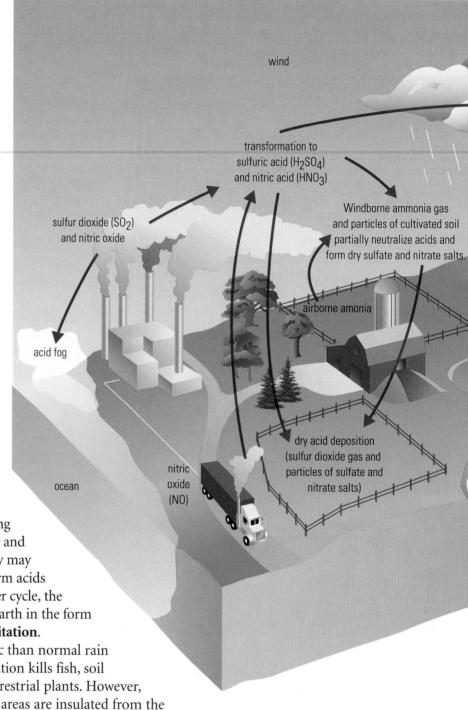

wind

transformation to sulfuric acid (H_2SO_4) and nitric acid (HNO_3)

sulfur dioxide (SO_2) and nitric oxide

Windborne ammonia gas and particles of cultivated soil partially neutralize acids and form dry sulfate and nitrate salts.

airborne amonia

acid fog

nitric oxide (NO)

ocean

dry acid deposition (sulfur dioxide gas and particles of sulfate and nitrate salts)

Sulphur and nitrogen oxides combine with water to form wet acid deposition (droplets of H_2SO_4 and HNO_3) dissolved in rain and snow.

Lakes in shallow soil low in limestone become acidic.

Lakes in deep soil high in limestone are protected.

Figure 1

Formation of acid deposits

Figure 2

This forest was devastated by long-term exposure to acid rain. Conifers are particularly susceptible to acid rain. Scarring caused by acids makes the trees vulnerable to a variety of infections.

The sulfur and nitrogen oxides released from tailpipes and smokestacks do not always enter the water cycle in the atmosphere. Depending on the weather conditions, particles of sulfur and nitrogen compounds may remain airborne and settle out in the dry state, as dry deposition (**Figure 1**). Eventually, however, dry deposition enters the water cycle, because the dry pollutants form acids when they combine with moisture. Dew on a lawn, the surface of a lake, and the water inside your respiratory tract are but a few of the potential sites where acids can form.

The Effects of Acid Precipitation

Direct effects on humans include slowly dissolving marble statues, corroding metal, car finishes that go dull, and damage to buildings. Medical effects include accelerated respiratory problems, such as asthma and bronchitis. In higher concentrations the acids can cause eyes to water, and may even irritate the skin.

Within ecosystems, acid rain places many organisms at risk. The effects are most noticeable in terrestrial ecosystems when the pH drops below 5.1. Acid deposition can damage leaves directly, but the most serious effects occur because the damaged tissues of trees become more susceptible to fungal or bacterial infections. Trees that grow in areas where the soil has little capacity to neutralize the acid, such as mountaintops, are most susceptible to damage (**Figure 2**).

As acids fall to the soil, they kill bacteria important to the nitrogen cycle. In addition, an acid soil promotes the growth of acid-loving plants, such as moss. Moss reduces the uptake of nutrients by trees by killing a fungus found growing on the tree's roots. Inside the soil acids can have another effect — they cause the release of aluminum from soil particles. The aluminum can damage roots or be carried into lakes with the spring runoff, where it kills fish and other aquatic life.

Cars and Acid Rain

The biggest acid rain threat is the automobile, and the problem may be getting worse. Although modern vehicles using modern fuels produce far less nitrogen and sulfur oxides than they used to, there are also many more millions of them on the road.

The problem is worsened by the spread of automobile use. As developing countries make economic gains, the demand for cars within those countries increases. Much as it was in industrialized countries, ownership of an automobile is a mark of success and wealth in developing nations. The increase of ownership in China alone has been phenomenal. There were about 13 million motor vehicles in China in 1998. It is estimated that the number of vehicles would be 20 million in 2000 and close to 35 million by the end of 2001. In China, which has emission standards that are different from those applied in Canada, vehicles release two to seven times more nitrogen oxides — close to the standard of emission that North American vehicles produced in the 1960s. Pollution created in China is blown over the Pacific Ocean, and can fall as acid deposition in Canada (although current amounts don't compare to the amount of acid created by Canadians).

The issue is not, however, that people in developing countries are causing acid rain. The issue is that there is a new source of pollutants for an already overloaded atmosphere. Can we in Canada really expect people in China to forego the convenience of cars, unless we act first?

Understanding Concepts

1. In your own words, explain the causes of acid rain.

2. List three sources of the pollutants that cause acid rain.

3. Describe how acid rain can kill trees.

4. In a diagram, describe problems caused by acid rain when it reaches vulnerable soil.

Making Connections

5. Motor vehicles are probably the largest source of the pollutants that cause acid rain. Suggest some ways that you could change your transportation habits that would reduce the amount of pollutants produced.

Exploring

6. Some plants, such as moss, do well in acidic soils. Design
(K) an experiment that would determine which plants do best in acidic soils. Have your procedure and safety precautions approved by your teacher before carrying out the experiment.

🖑 Work the Web

Burning gasoline is a major source of sulfur emissions. Oil companies have different strategies for reducing sulfur emissions. Is there one strategy that is better than the others? To research sulfur strategies, visit www.science.nelson.com and follow the links from Science 10, 3.11.

3.12 Investigation

INQUIRY SKILLS MENU
- Questioning
- Hypothesizing
- Predicting
- Planning
- Conducting
- Recording
- Analyzing
- Evaluating
- Communicating

Assessing the Effects of Acid Rain

You have learned that acid precipitation can have a devastating impact on ecosystems. In this investigation you will explore some of the effects of acid and design your own experiments to determine the effects of acid rain on materials and living things.

Materials

- goggles
- safety apron
- gloves
- hydronium pH paper
- lemon juice
- distilled water
- 10-mL graduated cylinder
- 2 small test tubes
- test-tube rack
- chalk or marble chips

Procedure

1 Using a small strip of pH paper, determine the pH of 1 mL of lemon juice. Using the graduated cylinder, add 9 mL of water to the lemon juice (this provides a 1/10 dilution) and determine the pH.

2 Remove 1 mL of the diluted lemon juice and add it to 9 mL of distilled water (this provides a 1/100 dilution). Using the hydronium paper, measure the pH of the solution. Copy **Table 1** and complete it.

Table 1   **pH of Diluted Lemon Juice**

Concentration of lemon juice	pH measured
concentrated	
1/10 solution	
1/100 solution	

3 Place a small piece of chalk in 10 mL of concentrated lemon juice. Record your observations.

Part 1: Abiotic Environment

K You will design an experiment that assesses the damage to marble buildings caused by various concentrations of acid rain.

Question

(a) Create a question for your experiment.

Prediction/Hypothesis

(b) Write a hypothesis for your experiment, based on the question. Using your hypothesis, predict the outcome of your experiment.

Design

Design an experiment to answer your question, and that will test your hypothesis.

(c) Identify the independent and dependent variables in your experiment.
(d) Identify the controls you have established for your experiment.
(e) Create any tables or charts you will need to record your observations.

Materials

(f) Decide which materials and equipment you will need for your experiment.
(g) Establish safety procedures for your
B experiment.

Procedure

1 Before beginning your experiment, submit to your teacher your written procedure, your safety procedures, your sample observation tables, and a diagram of any equipment setups you will use.

2 With your teacher's approval, carry out your experiment.

3 Always wash your hands once your experiment is completed for the day.

Part 2: Biotic Environment

(K) You will design an experiment that assesses the damage to germinating seedlings caused by acid rain of various concentrations.

Question

(h) Create a question for your experiment.

Prediction/Hypothesis

(i) Write a hypothesis for your experiment, based on the question. Using your hypothesis, predict the outcome of your experiment.

Design

Design an experiment to answer your question, and test your hypothesis.

(j) Identify the independent and dependent variables in your experiment.

(k) Identify the controls you have established for your experiment.

(l) Create any tables or charts you will need to record your observations.

Materials

• various seeds

(m) Decide what other materials and equipment you will need for your experiment.

(n) Establish safety procedures for your experiment.

Procedure

1 Before beginning your experiment, submit to your teacher your written procedure, your safety procedures, your sample observation tables, and a diagram of any equipment setups you will use.

2 With your teacher's approval, carry out your experiment.

3 Always wash your hands once your experiment is completed for the day.

Analysis and Evaluation

(o) Discuss the importance of controlling all variables except the dependent and independent variables in your experiment.

(p) Write a report on your experiment. Include in
(Q) your report your tables of evidence, any graphs you have drawn to help you analyze the evidence, and evaluations of the design and your hypothesis.

Making Connections

1. Use **Table 2** to explain why Ontario is more likely than Alberta to support legislation enforcing the reduction of sulfur emissions from the processing of fossil fuels.

Table 2	A Comparison of Ontario and Alberta	
Decision Factor	**Ontario**	**Alberta**
soil type	granite base, sensitive to acids	alkaline soils neutralize acids
tourism	large sports fishing industry	limited sports fishing
petrochemical industry	refining of fossil fuels	exploration, extraction, and refining of fossil fuels
geography	close to the industrialized centres of the United States	far from the industrialized centres of the United States

Key Expectations

- Examine the relationship between abiotic factors and the survival and geographical location of biotic communities, and explain why ecosystems with similar characteristics can exist in different geographical locations. (3.1, 3.2, 3.3, 3.5)

- Explain how soil composition and fertility can be altered in an ecosystem, and the possible consequences of such action. (3.3, 3.5, 3.7, 3.9, 3.11, 3.12)

- Conduct an inquiry into ecological relationships. (3.4, 3.5, 3.6)

- Analyze data and evaluate evidence, identifying flaws such as errors. (3.5, 3.12)

- Assess the impact of technological change on ecosystems. (3.7, 3.9, 3.10, 3.11, 3.12)

- Identify and evaluate Canadian initiatives in protecting Canada's ecosystems. (3.7, 3.10, 3.11)

- Describe careers that involve knowledge of ecology or environmental technologies and use resources such as the Internet to determine the knowledge and skill requirements of such careers. (3.8)

- Identify and research an issue involving an ecosystem, propose a course of action, taking into account human and environmental needs, and defend your position in written form. (3.9)

- Explain changes in popular views about the sustainability of ecosystems and humans' responsibility in preserving them. (3.9, 3.10)

- Design and conduct an investigation to examine the effects of one factor on soil composition and fertility, using instruments, apparatus, and materials safely and controlling major variables. (3.12)

Key Terms

acid deposition	litter
acid precipitation	percolation
active layer	permafrost
bedrock	selective cutting
biome	subsoil
boreal forest	surface water
clear-cutting	sustainable system
grassland	temperate deciduous forest
ground water	topsoil
humus	tundra
leaching	water table

Make a Summary

In this chapter you learned that sustainable terrestrial ecosystems maintain living things. A sustainable society manages its resources in such a way that human demands do not exceed the carrying capacity of the ecosystems we rely on.

- Construct a graphic organizer to summarize what you have learned in the chapter about sustainable ecosystems. Begin with the Key Terms for the chapter. Be prepared to add other terms to your diagram.

- You may wish to begin using the sample in **Figure 1**.

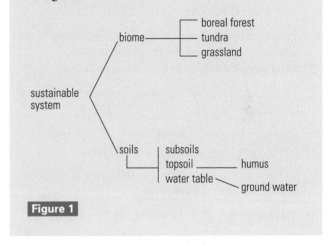

Figure 1

Reflect on your Learning

Revisit your answers to the Reflect on your Learning questions, page 87, in the Getting Started.

- How has your thinking changed?

- What new questions do you have?

Chapter 3 Review

Understanding Concepts

1. Create a table that compares Canada's four major biomes under the following categories: vegetation; animals; abiotic factors.

2. What abiotic characteristic do deserts and arctic regions share?

3. What special adaptations allow plants to grow in tundra biomes?

4. Why are tundra ecosystems more fragile than ecosystems in boreal or deciduous forests?

5. Explain why trees in a temperate deciduous forest lose their leaves during the winter, but those in a boreal forest hold their leaves all year long.

6. List some special adaptations of coniferous trees that allow them to survive in the extreme climatic conditions found in the boreal forest biome.

7. Describe changes in vegetation in Canada as latitude and altitude increase.

8. Explain why soils in a grassland tend to be more fertile than those found in a boreal forest.

9. In your own words define the following terms: litter, topsoil, humus, subsoil, peat

10. Use **Figure 1**, which shows data gathered about soil samples from three different biomes, to answer the following questions.

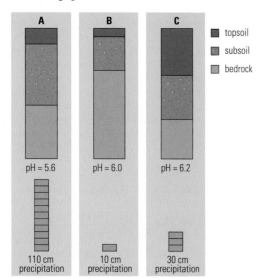

Figure 1

    (a) Identify soil profiles A, B, and C as coming from tundra, boreal forest, or grassland.
    (b) Which soil type could support more plants? Give your reasons.

11. Explain why gardeners would mix sand into soils that have high concentrations of clay.

12. Examine **Figure 2**, which shows soil profiles in five different biomes.

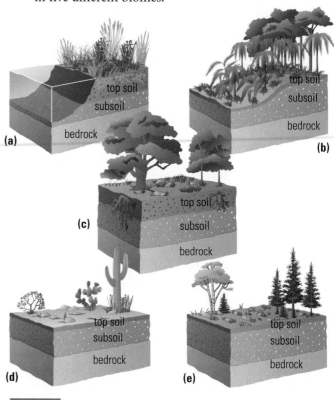

Figure 2

    (a) Identify each biome.
    (b) Which soil do you believe is best for growing crops? Give your reasons.
    (c) Trees of the tropical rain forests have been cleared to create grassland for grazing cattle. Using the information provided by the diagram, would you expect this strategy to be successful?

13. In October, 1999, the world population reached 6 billion people. List four concerns that ecologists might have about the rapidly increasing human population.

14. What environmental problems are created by growing a single crop repeatedly in the same field?

15. Explain why so many animals can be found in the forest litter.

16. What factors affect the distribution of small shrubs in a dense forest?

17. What problems could be created by clear-cutting an old-growth forest?

18. Using a diagram, explain why acid precipitation is harmful to forests.

Applying Inquiry Skills

19. To determine the percolation rates of three soil samples, students used the equipment setup shown in **Figure 3**. They followed the procedure below and recorded their observations in **Table 1**.

Figure 3

Procedure
1. Water is added to a dry soil sample.
2. The water is collected and measured in a graduated cylinder.

Table 1   **Percolation Rates of Three Soil Samples**

Soil sample	Mass of soil (g)	Volume of water added to soil (mL)	Volume of water collected (mL)	Time allowed for percolation (s)
A	40	100	30	60
B	30	100	22	40
C	23	100	5	75

(a) Examine the procedure and observations (**Table 1**) and identify and list sources of error.
(b) Rewrite the procedure to reduce the sources of error.

20. A researcher carried out an experiment in a temperate deciduous forest to determine the rate of decay of fallen leaves. Decay was measured by determining the change in mass of 200-g samples of leaves every 3 months for one year. The researcher's observations are recorded in **Table 2**.

Table 2   **Decay of Leaves of Four Species**

Type of leaf	Original mass (g)	Mass after 3 months (g)	Mass after 6 months (g)	Mass after 9 months (g)	Mass after 12 months (g)
poplar	200	185	150	110	50
willow	200	190	170	140	100
maple	200	185	155	135	75
oak	200	160	130	85	45

(a) Identify the dependent and independent variables in the experiment.
(b) Present the research data in a line graph.
(c) Which type of leaf decays most rapidly?
(d) Calculate the percentage decay for one year for each of the leaf types.
(e) How might the percentage decay be useful for researchers?
(f) Identify two abiotic and two biotic factors that would speed the rate at which leaves decay.
(g) What controls could you add to this experiment to make the comparisons of decay for each type of leaf meaningful?

Making Connections

21. (a) Describe three methods for reducing the populations of insect pests in a monoculture without using pesticides.
(b) Taking the viewpoint of a farmer, compare the methods you have suggested with using pesticide sprays. Which would you use? Why?

22. You are a landscape specialist, hired to plant trees in a stretch of river valley within a city. The river runs west-to-east. Before planting, you observe the natural growth in the valley. You note that deciduous trees are found only near the water's edge on the south shore. Higher on the south slope, conifers dominate. The north slope is largely grassland; however, there are a few shrubs near the water's edge. Despite the fact that rainfall and air temperature are similar throughout the year on both slopes, you conclude that different species of plants must be planted on each slope.
(a) What abiotic factors are creating differences in the communities on the north and south slopes of the river? In a diagram, explain the location of deciduous and coniferous trees on the south slope.
(b) In comparing the soil from both slopes, you find less water but more nutrients in the soil of the north slope. Explain why these differences exist.
(c) The city council wants you to plant trees on the north slope. What would you recommend? Explain your recommendation.
(d) A committee formed by local residents has recommended that all of the natural plants in the river valley be replaced with trees they consider more beautiful, such as oak and maple trees. Should you follow this recommendation? Give reasons for your opinion.

WHY IS EARTH CALLED THE BLUE PLANET?
Water.

Water covers more than two-thirds of our planet. Ninety-seven percent of that water is saltwater. We cannot drink saltwater, at least not without special technology, but those great reserves of ocean water are of tremendous value to all living things. The oceans to a large extent control the weather patterns on our planet. They also provide a constant supply of freshwater through evaporation.

Most freshwater is stored as snow and ice, which may not be as surprising to Canadians as to some other people. Of the rest, only a small portion is readily accessible for human use. It has been estimated that 0.0005% of our planet's available freshwater can sustain the world's human population.

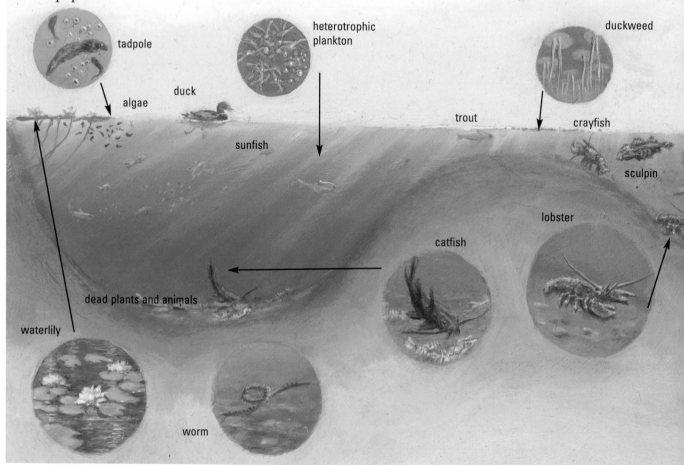

tadpole

algae

duck

sunfish

heterotrophic plankton

duckweed

trout

crayfish

sculpin

lobster

catfish

dead plants and animals

waterlily

worm

With some important exceptions, aquatic ecosystems are not as productive as terrestrial ecosystems. For example, the water in mid-ocean contains approximately one-thousandth the amount of phosphorus and nitrogen found in fertile soil. This means that, volume for volume, mid-ocean water can support only a small fraction of the life found on land. A single cubic metre of soil might produce as much as 50 kg of biomass, compared with as little as 5 kg in a cubic metre of ocean.

Plants and animals in aquatic ecosystems have adapted to abiotic conditions dramatically different from those on land. There is a lot less oxygen available, which limits activity. Water is about 800 times denser than air, making it more difficult to move through. And although sea animals can travel widely without obstruction, they are limited in how much they can move up and down — 10 m down, the pressure is roughly double what it is at the surface, and the pressure increases by one atmosphere for every 10 m of depth. The average depth of the ocean is about 4000 m. Very few animals are adapted to survive both near the surface and under the crushing pressure at the ocean bottom.

Reflect on your Learning

1. Think about lakes, ponds, rivers, and oceans (**Figure 1**). What abiotic factors make them unique?

2. Make a list of problems that Canadians have created for aquatic ecosystems.

3. Select one of the problems that you have identified and describe the efforts that have been made to solve the problem. What part could you play in solving it?

Throughout this chapter, note any changes in your ideas as you learn new concepts and develop your skills.

Try This
Activity Life in Pond Water

The most important organisms in aquatic ecosystems, just as in soil, are the very small ones. If you examine pond water under a microscope, you will discover a new and fascinating world.

Materials: pond water, microscope, slides

- Try to identify the pond organisms you see. Your teacher will provide you with a diagram of some pond organisms. Draw sketches of any you cannot identify.
- Observe the behaviour of the organisms closely. Which ones are producers? primary consumers? secondary or higher-order consumers?

(a) Make a food web that includes the organisms you can see.

🖐 Wash your hands thoroughly after handling pond water.

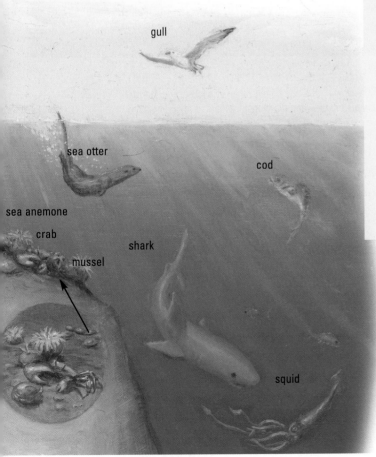

Figure 1

Conditions near the surface of lakes and oceans are much different from conditions in the depths.

Abiotic Factors in Lakes

There is considerable variation among aquatic ecosystems. Swamps, marshes, ponds, lakes, rivers, and marine ecosystems all have distinct abiotic factors that require specific adaptations by their communities. That diversity is also evident within each of the ecosystems. From the surface a lake may appear to be pretty much the same everywhere, but below the surface the amount of light available, the water temperature, and oxygen levels can all vary. Not surprisingly, the organisms you can find in each area also differ greatly.

The Structure of Lakes and Ponds

Figure 1 shows a cross section of a typical lake. The **littoral zone** is the area extending out from the lakeshore to the point where plants rooted in the bottom of the lake can no longer be found. Aquatic plants that grow to the surface, such as bulrushes and water lilies, take hold where the littoral zone is shallow. In slightly deeper areas, plants that are rooted to the bottom but completely submerged may thrive.

Beyond the littoral zone is the **limnetic zone**, the area of the open lake where there is enough light for photosynthesis to occur. The most common form of organism within the limnetic zone is called plankton. The word **plankton** is used to describe both autotrophic and heterotrophic microorganisms. Heterotrophic plankton (invertebrate animals) feed on the autotrophic plankton (tiny plants and algae). Both kinds of plankton are food for consumers in the higher trophic levels, such as fish, tadpoles, and birds.

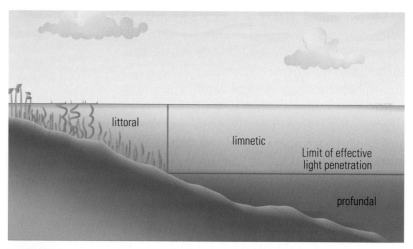

Figure 1

A cross section showing the three main zones of a lake. Note that the depth of the boundary between the limnetic zone and the profundal zone varies in each lake. Living things such as algae and undissolved solids can both block light.

The region beneath the limnetic zone, where there is not enough light for photosynthesis to occur, is called the **profundal zone**. (This zone is not found in ponds.) In most lakes, the only source of nutrients in the profundal zone is the rain of dead plants and animals that falls from the limnetic zone. This detritus is slowly broken down by bacteria or consumed by other bottom-dwelling invertebrates and fish, called detritus feeders.

The decay of this falling organic matter has important consequences for the ecosystem. Bacteria use oxygen to decompose detritus, reducing the amount of oxygen available in the water. In the absence of sunlight and plants to replenish the oxygen, oxygen levels could be reduced to very low levels. The only larger organisms that survive are those that can tolerate low oxygen levels; they include some invertebrates, and a very few fish species such as carp.

Changes in Lake Ecosystems

There are two kinds of lake.
Oligotrophic lakes are typically deep and cold. Lake Baikal in Russia (which is very deep — more than 1600 m at the deepest point — and holds more water than any other lake), and Lake Superior (much of which is over 200 m deep) are prime examples. Nutrient levels are low in such lakes, limiting the size of producer populations. Because there are limited numbers of only a few kinds of organisms, the water is usually very clear.

Eutrophic lakes are generally shallow and warmer, and have an excellent supply of nutrients. Many species of photosynthetic organisms find these abiotic conditions very favourable. As a result, the water of eutrophic lakes is often murky.

In general, oligotrophic lakes gradually become eutrophic. Eutrophic lakes become increasingly shallow, eventually filling in and becoming dry land. This evolution from oligotrophic, to eutrophic, to land is called eutrophication and may take hundreds or even thousands of years. **Figure 2** shows the eutrophication of a lake.

Humans sometimes accelerate eutrophication by adding to lakes nutrient-rich substances such as human wastes, fertilizers in the runoff from agricultural land, and other household and industrial products.

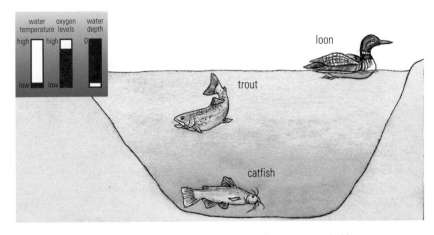

(a) An oligotrophic lake. Deeper lakes tend to be cooler. Cold water can hold more dissolved gases (including oxygen) than warm water.

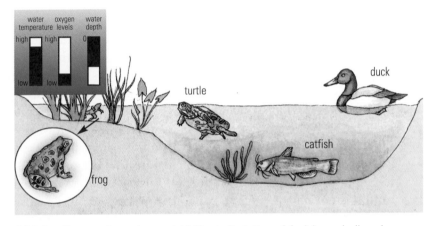

(b) Soil sediment and organic material falling to the bottom of the lake gradually make the lake shallower. As it becomes shallower, its profundal zone slowly disappears, until eventually sunlight can reach the lakebed. Lake temperatures rise and oxygen levels drop. Organisms that require higher levels of oxygen begin to disappear.

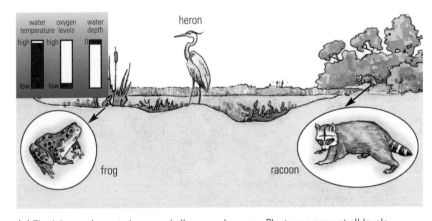

(c) The lake continues to become shallower and warmer. Plants can grow at all levels, and the warmth encourages the growth of plankton. When the plants die, decomposers return their nutrients to the lake, using oxygen in the process. Later in the eutrophication process, the lake will become a marsh and then dry land.

Figure 2

The eutrophication of a lake, as seen through changes in the community (summer conditions)

Seasonal Variations in Canadian Lakes

The unique property of water plays a crucial role in Canadian lakes. As water cools, just like other substances, it becomes more dense. However, as water cools below 4°C a strange thing happens — it starts becoming less dense (**Figure 3**). This is why ice floats, forming a layer on top of cold water, and why the lowest layer of water in a lake or in the ocean often has a temperature of 4°C. Seasonal variations in a lake are shown in **Figure 4**.

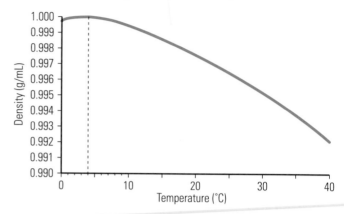

Effect of Temperature on the Density of Water

Figure 3

Unlike most substances, water becomes less dense as it cools below 4°C.

Winter

During the winter, many of our lakes are covered by ice and snow. This prevents atmospheric oxygen from dissolving in the water. Under the ice the water is arranged in layers, according to its density. The least dense water, at or slightly above 0°C, is near the surface. The densest water, at 4°C, is found at the bottom. No matter how cold the air becomes above the ice, this structure remains the same, although the ice will get thicker if the air remains cold.

If the ice is wind-blown and transparent, light can penetrate into the water, supporting photosynthesis in the liquid water below. However, if the ice freezes to a greater thickness than normal, or if the ice is covered in thick snow, light can no longer penetrate, and the organisms under the ice are in trouble. The level of dissolved oxygen in the water may drop until it is not high enough to support some organisms. Because fish are particularly sensitive to dissolved oxygen concentrations, the result could be a massive die-off of some fish species. In shallow lakes, particularly in the Arctic, ice may form right to the bottom, virtually eliminating most life forms every winter.

Spring

Spring brings storms and the melting of the ice. Oxygen can now pass from the air into the water. Wind stirs the water, creating waves that increase the surface area and so the rate at which oxygen can dissolve. As the cold surface water warms, it eventually reaches a temperature of 4°C, at which point it begins to slowly sink through the less dense water beneath it, carrying its precious supply of oxygen with it. The mixing process that results is called the spring turnover.

Summer

As surface water warms above 4°C, it will no longer sink, because it is less dense than the cooler water below. Just as in winter, layers of water are set up, with the densest water at the bottom. If you swim in a lake during summer you can experience these layers. By allowing your feet to descend slowly through the water, you will encounter colder regions.

The upper level of a lake, which warms up in summer, is called the **epilimnion**. The lower level, which remains at a low temperature, is called the **hypolimnion**. Between these two levels is the **thermocline**, a narrow zone in which the temperature drops rapidly from warm to cold.

Because the epilimnion and hypolimnion do not mix, there is little movement of oxygen from the surface to the depths during summer. Organisms living in the hypolimnion must rely on oxygen reserves brought down during the spring turnover.

The epilimnion has a different oxygen problem. The ability of water to hold dissolved gases is inversely proportional to the temperature of the water: the warmer the water, the less dissolved oxygen it can hold (**Figure 5**). During a hot spell, a lake that is fairly shallow may lose so much oxygen that some species, such as lake trout, will die.

Fall

As temperatures begin to drop in the fall, surface water begins to cool. Once again, as the surface water reaches a temperature of 4°C, it sinks down through the lake. This fall turnover renews oxygen levels at lower levels, and breaks up the summer thermal layers.

Solubility of Oxygen in Water

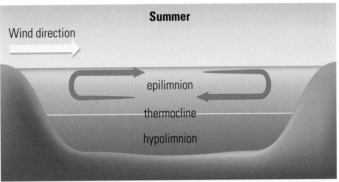

Figure 5

Solubility of oxygen in water

Figure 4

Temperature and the variable density of water both play important roles in seasonal changes in Canadian lakes.

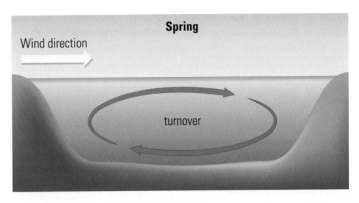

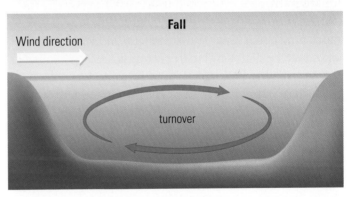

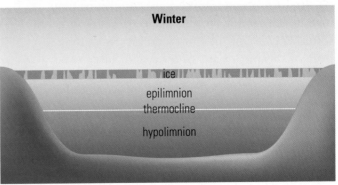

Individual Variations in Lakes

Every lake has its own special conditions (Table 1). These conditions determine which species can live in them. For example, each species of fish has a particular level of tolerance for oxygen. Trout, which require high levels of dissolved oxygen, can be found at all levels of a lake in spring and fall, but in summer are confined to regions where more oxygen is available. Unlike trout, perch can can live in shallow lakes that become warm in summer, because they can tolerate lower levels of dissolved oxygen.

The most productive part of a lake is the littoral zone, the area where algae and plants take advantage of the sunlight to carry out photosynthesis. The size of the littoral zone is determined by the depth of a lake and the slope of its lakebed, both of which are individual to each lake.

That said, there are some general similarities among lakes within geographic regions. In Central Canada, extending through Quebec and Ontario into Nunavut and the Northwest Territories, most lakes were formed when glaciers gouged out basins in the granite bedrock of the Canadian Shield. Central Canadian lakes are often deep. Because minerals in granite do not dissolve well, these lakes also tend to be low in nutrients. As a result, most are oligotrophic.

Lakes in the Atlantic region are also mostly glacial in origin, but the bedrock in this region is more varied, as it originated from rock layers in ancient mountains. As a result, some lakes have more nutrients available than others, and the lakes may be oligotrophic or eutrophic.

Lakes in the Prairie provinces were also formed by glaciers, but mostly in thick layers of gravel and sand. This varied base is richer in soluble nutrients, making the ecosystems of these lakes more productive. The lakes tend to be fairly shallow and collect sediments more rapidly than the shield lakes. They are usually classified as eutrophic.

Arctic lakes and ponds have conditions that distinguish them from the lake ecosystems of the south. Because of the low temperatures at the peak of summer, many of the Arctic lakes experience only one turnover. Some lakes may not even thaw.

Our largest lakes run in a curve from Great Bear Lake in the north to Lake Ontario in the southeast. They lie on the boundary between the glacial deposit to the south and west and the Central Canadian lakes to the north and east. They are considered to be oligotrophic, due to their depth and low water temperatures. The major exception is Lake Erie, which is fairly shallow. Agricultural and industrial pollutants

Table 1   Dissolved Oxygen in Two Lakes (Summer)

Region	Depth (m)	Dissolved oxygen (mg/L)	
		Oligotrophic	Eutrophic
epilimnion	0	8.3	7.8
epilimnion	5	7.9	7.9
thermocline	10	7.5	7.0
hypolimnion	15	7.0	5.2
hypolimnion	20	6.9	2.0
hypolimnion	25	6.8	0.2

Did You Know?

The word *rival* comes from the Latin word *rivus* (stream). The first rivals were people who lived along the same stream — and competed for the same water.

Try This
Activity   Undissolved Solids

Rain carries soil and other solids into surface water where they can remain suspended, creating turbidity (cloudiness or murkiness) that limits the penetration of sunlight and reduces photosynthesis. Solids that are deposited as sediment on the bottom of the body of water can also affect ecosystems. Large volumes can bury bottom-feeding animals and the eggs of fish. Large amounts of falling sediment also make life generally unpleasant for filter feeders such as oysters.

(a) Using filter paper and other materials, design a procedure (including safety precautions) to determine how much undissolved solid material there is in water samples from three different sources.

• Have your materials list and procedure approved by your teacher before starting. (Shake each of the samples before each test.)

(b) Present your results (including your data) in a written report.

plus human wastes have accelerated the eutrophication of Lake Erie, resulting in striking changes in the communities that inhabit the lake. Joint action by Canada and the United States appears to have slowed this process considerably.

Understanding Concepts

1. In your own words, define the terms "oligotrophic" and "eutrophic."

2. Explain why you would expect to find different organisms in the limnetic, littoral, and profundal zones of a lake. In your answer, refer to the abiotic factors in each zone.

3. Explain why a shallow lake tends to be warmer than a deep lake in summer.

4. In your own words, describe the changes that happen in a lake from summer to winter.

5. Describe what you would expect to happen to oxygen levels in the hypolimnion of a lake over the summer months.

6. Cold water holds more dissolved gas than warm water. Cold water also tends to collect in the lower levels of a lake. However, in summer oxygen levels in a lake can be highest in the warm surface water of a lake. Explain why.

7. Predict what would happen to a lake that experienced no seasonal changes in temperature. Make a diagram showing the temperature and oxygen levels in the water of the lake after many years of little change in surface air temperatures.

8. Use **Figure 2** to answer the following questions.
   (a) What happens to the depth of a lake over time?
   (b) Explain how the change in mean water temperature is related to the depth of the lake.
   (c) How would the change in lake temperatures affect the types and numbers of plants found in the area?
   (d) Describe changes in the species and populations of fish you would expect to find in a lake that progresses through the three stages of eutrophication.
   (e) Explain why turtles might be found in the second stage, but not the first.
   (f) Speculate about why loons are replaced by ducks.

9. Using the terms you've learned in this section, describe a local lake or pond.

Making Connections

10. A good fisher knows where to find fish. Catfish are less active than trout. In the summer months, which of these fishes would you expect to find in the hypolimnion and the epilimnion? Give your reasons.

11. Make diagrams showing how building a road along the shore of a lake would affect lake ecosystems. What measures could the road-builders take to reduce damage to organisms in the lake?

12. A factory is built along the shore of a lake, resulting in a gradual reduction of the number of algae in the lake. Years later, visitors notice that the lake is clearer than it used to be. Does this mean that the lake is less polluted than it once was? Explain your answer.

Exploring

13. (a) Using soda pop, beakers, water, and other materials you choose, design a demonstration (including safety precautions) that shows the relationship between water temperature and the amount of dissolved gas. Have your teacher approve your materials list and design before you begin.
    (b) How did you measure the amount of dissolved gas in the soda pop?
    (c) Present your data in a graph and interpret your findings.

Work the Web

Various groups across Canada are working to reduce the effects of pollution on water systems. Choose one such group and report on their progress in a poster. To research antipollution groups, visit www.science.nelson.com and follow the links from Science 10, 4.1.

Challenge

2 Before you can assess the quality of water, you should ask three important questions:

- What will the water be used for?
- What are possible sources of pollutants?
- What can be measured?

What would measures of the level of dissolved oxygen and undissolved solids indicate about water quality?

Sources of Water Pollution

Water pollution is any physical or chemical change in surface water or ground water that can harm living things. Biological, chemical, and physical forms of water pollution can be grouped into five categories (**Table 1**).

Indicators of Water Quality

Water quality is usually defined by its intended use. Water too polluted to drink is often considered acceptable for industrial processes or watering the lawn. Water too polluted for swimming may be considered acceptable for boating or fishing. There are three main indicators of water quality: bacteria count, the concentration of dissolved oxygen, and the biological oxygen demand.

Bacteria

The detection of disease-causing bacteria is both difficult and expensive. However, there is an indirect way to discover if these bacteria are present in water. Detecting **coliform bacteria**, a type of bacteria that occurs naturally in the intestines of humans and many other animals, is fairly easy (**Figure 1**). The presence of coliform bacteria indicates that animal wastes are polluting the water. Since many of the dangerous disease-causing bacteria are transmitted in wastes, the presence of coliform bacteria indicates that more dangerous bacteria may also be present. Some lakeside beaches are frequently closed to swimming in summer due to high counts of coliform bacteria.

Dissolved Oxygen

A second indicator of water quality is dissolved oxygen. Several different solutions can be used to test for oxygen. The solutions change colour when they react with oxygen dissolved in a water sample. Lakes that are cooler and have fewer pollutants have levels of dissolved oxygen of between 8 and 14 mg/L. As dissolved oxygen begins to drop, fewer organisms can be supported. As you can see from **Table 1**, a wide range of pollutants cause oxygen levels to fall.

Another way to determine dissolved oxygen levels is to examine the living things found in the water. Healthy trout indicate a high oxygen level; carp and catfish indicate a low level. A complete absence of fish may indicate oxygen levels are very low, but it is also possible that there are toxins in the water that kill fish.

Table 1 Categories of Pollution

Pollutant	Source	Effects
organic solid waste	human sewage, animal wastes, decaying plant life, industrial wastes (e.g., from paper mills, food processing)	Oxygen in the water is used up as organic matter is decomposed by bacteria. The decomposition may also cause a foul odour.
disease-causing organisms	human sewage and animal wastes that enter aquatic ecosystems with runoff	These organisms can trigger an outbreak of a waterborne disease, such as typhoid, cholera, infectious hepatitis, beaver fever, or dysentery.
inorganic solids and dissolved minerals	acids from combustion and refining of fossil fuels, mining	Acid rain kills soil bacteria and injures trees.
	salts from irrigation, mining, and runoff from salted roads	Salts kill freshwater organisms and make freshwater unusable for drinking and irrigation.
	fertilizers (phosphates and nitrates) from farms and gardens entering aquatic ecosystems through runoff	Fertilizers cause algal blooms. As the algae die, decomposers recycle the organic matter, using oxygen in the process.
	mineral solids from soil erosion (e.g., after trees are removed)	Inorganic solids make water murky (turbid), harming plant life. They also cause sediment formation, which affects detritus feeders
heat	electricity generating plants and other industries	Industries draw on water to cool machinery or products and then return warm water to the ecosystem. The addition of warm water decreases the solubility of oxygen in the water.
organic chemicals	oil and grease from roads	Toxic to fish and waterfowl. Oil films on water reduce the transfer of oxygen from air to water.
	pesticides and herbicides from farms, parks, and gardens	Toxic to various organisms. Some pesticides result in damage to animals at higher trophic levels through bioaccumulation.
	detergents (organic phosphates) from washing of clothes, cars, dishes, etc.	Phosphates promote the growth of algae and aquatic plants, resulting in a loss of oxygen during decomposition.

Biological Oxygen Demand

To narrow down the causes of low dissolved oxygen levels, it is possible to test the biological oxygen demand (BOD). The **BOD** is a measure of the amount of dissolved oxygen needed by decomposers (bacteria) to break down the organic matter in a sample of water over a five-day period at 20°C. The BOD indicates the amount of available organic matter in a water sample. As the number of organisms in an ecosystem increases, so does the biological oxygen demand. A cold, less productive lake with fewer organisms might have a BOD near 2 mg of oxygen per litre, while a more productive lake with many living things might have a BOD as high as 20 mg/L.

It is important to note that, as the number of organisms increases and biological demand increases, more organisms use oxygen from the water. This causes the level of dissolved oxygen to decrease.

Sewage, Decomposers, and Oxygen Levels

Too many nutrients can create problems for a lake. Consider the problems when cities release sewage into aquatic ecosystems without treatment. (Montreal releases untreated solid wastes into the St. Lawrence River. St. John's and Halifax release wastes into their harbours.) The greater the amount of decaying matter introduced into the water, the greater will be the population of decomposing bacteria. Unfortunately, both bacteria and fish use oxygen. While some species of fish have greater oxygen requirements than others, all fish eventually die if oxygen levels drop too low. Moreover, the death of fish adds detritus to the ecosystem. That detritus further promotes growth of the bacterial population. In turn, this causes oxygen levels to drop even more. To make matters even worse, human wastes act much like fertilizers by introducing nitrogen and phosphates into the ecosystem. The added nutrients promote the growth of plants and algae, which will eventually die and be decomposed. Each time organic matter is returned or added to an ecosystem, oxygen levels are further reduced.

To prevent damage to ecosystems, many municipalities have built treatment plants for sewage (**Figure 2**).

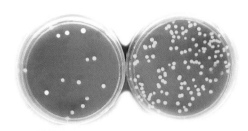

Figure 1

Agar nutrient medium, which contains minerals and a source of energy, is used to grow bacteria. Each bacterium in a water sample divides into many cells, forming colonies that can be seen on the agar plate. The greater the number of colonies, the more polluted the water sample is. Drinking water should produce less than four colonies of coliform bacteria per 100 mL to be considered safe. In contrast, swimming pools are permitted 200 colonies per 100 mL.

Figure 2

Sewage treatment plants use decomposer bacteria to reduce the amount of organic matter that is released into aquatic systems. Human wastes are broken down in special treatment ponds.

Try This Activity   Testing for Coliform Bacteria

You can measure the population of bacteria by adding a water sample to a tube that contains lactose broth (lactose is the sugar found in milk). An indicator for carbon dioxide can then be added. The amount of time it takes for the sample to turn yellow provides an indirect measurement of the population of bacteria in the water sample. The greater the population of bacteria, the faster they will produce carbon dioxide as they use up the lactose through respiration.

🖐 Wear safety glasses and an apron. Wash your hands after the activity.

• Collect a sample from water you wish to test.
• Using a clean eyedropper, add 20 drops of the water sample to the lactose broth. Add the indicator. Water that meets the acceptable standard for drinking will not cause a colour change in less than 24 h at room temperature.
• Record the amount of time needed for a colour change to occur.

(a) Is the water safe for drinking? Present your conclusions in a written report.

Thermal Pollution

As a result of thermal pollution, summerlike conditions can be maintained throughout the year in some lake ecosytems. Water removed from a lake by industry (**Figure 3**) and used as a coolant is sometimes returned warm enough to prevent freezing in winter. As a result, many organisms that would normally become dormant continue to thrive through the winter, producing more detritus, with its resultant decomposition. One potential effect is an oxygen-depleted hypolimnion, with all of its implications. Additional organic matter at the bottom of a lake results in more rapid eutrophication.

Point and Nonpoint Sources of Pollution

When monitoring pollutants, it is important to understand how the pollutants enter the water ecosystem (**Figure 4**). Some pollutants, such as sewage from a faulty treatment plant or oil discharged from a tanker, enter the water from a single source, called a point source. The pollutants enter the water in a concentrated fashion and are slowly diluted in the ecosystem. The effects at the point of entry are much more severe than they are in more distant areas, where the pollutant has been diluted. To assess the impact of these pollutants, ecologists must make decisions about where test sites should be established.

Other forms of pollution come from more widespread source. A farm (runoff of fertilizer) and a road (salts and organic chemicals) are both examples of nonpoint sources. Unlike ecosystems affected by point-source pollutants, those polluted from a nonpoint source are less likely to have a single area of extreme stress. Another difference is that nonpoint sources of pollution are likely to be variable and repeating. For example, pollutants from a road are most likely to enter an ecosystem after rainfall or snow melt.

Figure 3

This power-generating station draws cool water from Lake Ontario and returns warm water.

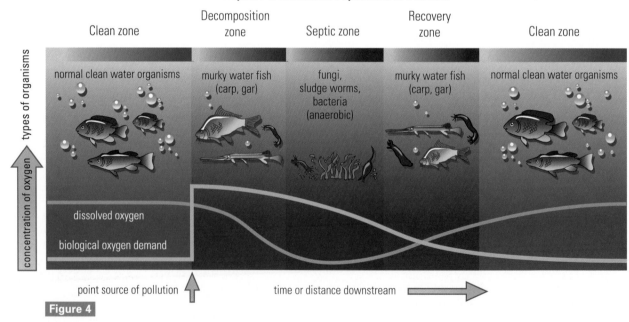

Figure 4

Pollutants such as untreated sewage can cause oxygen depletion. As you can see, as long as there is only one point source (and the amount of organic material is not too large), the stream can eventually recover downstream from the source. Oxygen re-enters the water from the air and plants.

Try This

Activity Nutrients and Algae

Garden fertilizers encourage growth of more than just vegetables. Nutrients that are carried off into freshwater ecosystems with runoff stimulate the growth of algae and weeds in lakes and ponds.

(a) Using a funnel, filter paper, and other materials you choose, design a procedure (including safety precautions) to determine how various nutrients affect the growth of algae.

(b) Make a list of variables that you will control and identify the independent and dependent variables.

• Obtain the approval of your teacher before beginning your investigation.

(c) Write a report on your results.

Understanding Concepts

1. List types of pollution that cause reduced levels of dissolved oxygen in aquatic ecosystems. For each type of pollution, explain in your own words how dissolved oxygen is affected.

2. Which would show a higher biological oxygen demand: a sample of water from a cold lake or a sample of water from a warm lake? Explain your answer.

3. After complaints were received from fishers on a river (**Figure 5**), the data in **Figure 6** were collected from three sites. Measurements of indicators and nutrients are in ppm (parts per million).

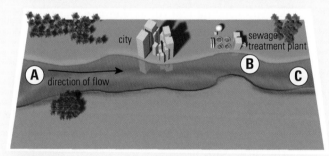

Figure 5

A polluted river, with test sites

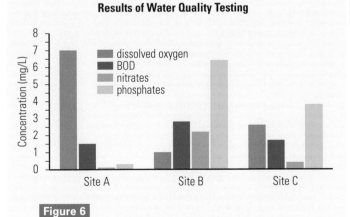

Figure 6

(a) What is the source of nitrates and phosphates?

(b) In which area of the river would you find the highest level of eutrophication? Explain your answer.

(c) Why does the BOD increase from site A to site B?

(d) Why does the BOD decrease from site B to site C?

(e) Sewage treatment plants are supposed to remove organic waste. Is the plant doing a good job?

4. In your own words, explain how thermal pollution affects fish populations.

Exploring

5. Design and conduct an investigation to determine how water temperature affects algal growth. Based on your results, how would you expect surface thermal pollution to affect dissolved oxygen levels in the epilimnion and hypolimnion of a lake? Draw diagrams illustrating your hypothesis.

🖱 Work the Web

How are Canadians doing at controlling pollution in lakes? To learn more about water pollution, visit www.science.nelson.com and follow the links from Science 10, 4.2. Report on the success or failure of a pollution control initiative in a water system near you.

◓ Challenge

2 Your choice of sites for water sampling is crucial if you are to build a true picture of the quality of water in an ecosystem. Is it possible to assess the quality of water in a lake or river by taking a water sample from only one site? What might you miss by taking only one sample? What must you consider before choosing your sample sites?

3 In designing your board game, consider how sources of pollution will affect the sustainability of an aquatic ecosystem over time.

INQUIRY SKILLS MENU
- ○ Questioning
- ● Hypothesizing
- ● Predicting
- ○ Planning
- ● Conducting
- ● Recording
- ● Analyzing
- ● Evaluating
- ○ Communicating

Phosphate Identification

Algae populations increase rapidly in response to phosphate pollution. There is quick, simple test for detecting this form of pollution. The presence of phosphates in a water sample can be detected by adding the salt magnesium sulfate. The magnesium in the compound combines with phosphates in the water to form the insoluble salt magnesium phosphate. As crystals of magnesium phosphate form, they turn the clear solution in the test tube cloudy.

Hypothesis/Prediction

Water samples that contain phosphates will turn cloudy when magnesium sulfate is added.

(a) Predict which of your water samples will contain phosphates. Explain your prediction.

Design

This is a controlled test in which water samples taken from known locations are tested for the presence of phosphates using the chemical indicator magnesium sulfate.

(b) Read the procedure. What purpose does sample A serve in this experiment?

Materials

- goggles
- safety gloves
- apron
- 4 large test tubes
- test-tube rack
- wax pencil
- distilled water (A)
- water samples (B, C, and D)
- 10-mL graduated cylinder
- medicine dropper
- dilute ammonium hydroxide solution
- magnesium sulfate solution
- watch glass
- hand lens

Procedure

1 Obtain four large test tubes and label them A, B, C, and D. Place the tubes in a test-tube rack. Using a graduated cylinder, pour 10 mL of distilled water into tube A. Pour 10 mL each of samples B, C, and D into the test tube with the corresponding letter label. Make sure that you rinse and dry the cylinder after each sample.

(c) Why is it important to rinse the cylinder?

2 Using a medicine dropper, add 25 drops of dilute ammonium hydroxide to each sample. This will ensure that the samples will be basic (have a pH greater than 7).

Figure 1

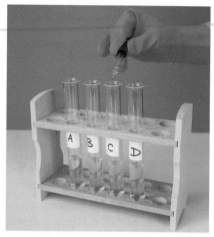

3 Using the graduated cylinder, add 2 mL of magnesium sulfate solution to each of the samples in the test tubes. Let the test tubes stand for 5 min. Record your observations over the 5 min.

4 Pour a small sample of the solution from test tube A into a clean watch glass. Using a hand lens, examine the sample for crystals. Record your observations. Repeat this step for each of the other samples.

(d) Why is it important to rinse the watch glass between tests?

5 Wash your hands, first with your gloves on and then without.

Analysis and Evaluation

(e) Based on your results, which of the samples contained phosphates?
(f) Compare your results with your prediction. Evaluate your prediction.
(g) Speculate about the source of phosphates in each of the samples that tested positive. What is the most likely source? Make a plan to determine the source of the phosphates.

Understanding Concepts

1. Describe two ways in which phosphates can get into surface water.

2. Why might a technician working at a sewage-treatment plant test water quality by monitoring phosphates?

3. The data in **Table 1** were collected from the numbered test sites (**Figure 2**). Turbidity is a measure of the number of small particles (ranging in size from 0.45 to 0.1 μm) suspended in water. These small particles can be rock or detritus from living things. Turbidity is measured in Jackson turbidity units (JTU) and indicates how far light can be expected to penetrate through the water. High numbers indicate the water is more turbid.

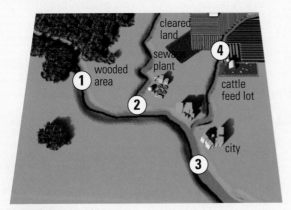

cleared land
sewage plant
4
wooded area
1
cattle feed lot
2
city
3

Figure 2

Table 1   **Test Results**

Test performed	Site 1	Site 2	Site 3	Site 4
phosphates (mg/L)	0.4	0.5	1.2	0.8
turbidity (JTU)	1.3	2.2	55.8	12.3
dissolved oxygen (mg/L)	8.9	6.8	2.3	4.5

(a) What factors contribute to the high phosphate concentration at site 3?

(b) From **Figure 2**, identify point and non-point sources of pollutants.

(c) Explain why samples from site 4 show more phosphates than those from site 1.

(d) List factors that might affect the turbidity reading at each site.

(e) What effect might an increase in algal growth have upon dissolved oxygen?

(f) What factors might cause a decline in dissolved oxygen at site 3?

(g) What indicators can be used to evaluate the effectiveness of the sewage treatment plant used by the city?

(h) Make a list of potential problems for the river that could be linked with the cattle feed lot. What modifications to the testing plan should be made to assess those problems?

(i) Compare water quality from inflow and outflow of the city.

Making Connections

4. (a) Identify aquatic systems in your own area that you would expect to contain high levels of phosphates. Explain your prediction.

(b) Take water samples from the identified systems and test for phosphates. Evaluate your prediction.

5. Small communities often discharge sewage into fields. Bacteria break down the organic wastes, releasing nutrients such as phosphates and nitrogen. Plants growing in the fields absorb the nutrients.

(a) What advice would you give a small community investigating this approach to waste treatment?

(b) Identify potential problems if the field is located in a valley that floods every spring.

6. Communities that wish to improve their treatment of sewage face a battle in finding enough money to pay for equipment, technicians, and buildings, and then to keep the treatment plants running. If you do not live in such a community, imagine that you do. Identify as many possible sources of funding for sewage treatment as possible. Assess those sources. Who should pay for sewage treatment? What should be the role of each level of government? Prepare a presentation on your ideas for a joint meeting of municipal councillors and the local MPP and MP.

Exploring

7. In this investigation you carried out a procedure that identified phosphates. Suggest a way to modify the procedure that would allow you to determine the amount of phosphate present in each sample. Why might this modification be important to an ecologist?

Reflecting

8. Testing for phosphates provides an indicator of water quality, but that single test has limitations. Why wouldn't you want to assess water quality from a single test?

 ## Challenge

2 As you are assessing water quality in your community, how will you identify sources of phosphate pollution? Once you have identified the sources, how will you decide which testing sites will provide the best information on phosphate content of local water?

INQUIRY SKILLS MENU
○ Questioning   ● Planning   ● Analyzing
● Hypothesizing   ● Conducting   ● Evaluating
● Predicting   ● Recording   ● Communicating

Oxygen Demand and Organic Pollutants

As you have seen, thermal energy and nutrients can deplete dissolved oxygen in aquatic ecosystems. As oxygen levels drop, the community that can survive in the ecosystem changes. In this investigation, you will use methylene blue indicator to detect a change in oxygen levels. The indicator turns from blue to colourless when the oxygen content of the sample drops below a threshold level.

The biological oxygen demand (BOD) is the amount of dissolved oxygen needed by decomposers to break down organic matter in the water. If more organic matter is introduced into an ecosystem, the population of decomposing bacteria will increase. This large population of bacteria requires more oxygen.

Question

How do nutrients and heat affect dissolved oxygen?

Hypothesis/Prediction

(a) Read the procedure and write a hypothesis for this investigation.

(b) Based on your hypothesis, predict which sample will have the greatest BOD.

Design

This is a partially controlled experiment with two independent variables. The indicator methylene blue will turn from blue to colourless when the oxygen level in a sample drops. The time taken for this colour change indicates the BOD.

(c) Identify the dependent and independent variables in this investigation.

(d) Identify the control for thermal pollution.

(e) Read the procedure and create a table in which to record your data.

 Always handle hot plates and heated items with care.

Materials

- safety goggles
- safety apron
- water
- 500-mL beaker
- hot plate
- thermometer
- brewer's yeast
- mass balance
- 10-mL graduated cylinder
- 2 50-mL flasks

- stirring rod
- wax pencil
- 11 mL homogenized milk
- 4 20-mL test tubes
- test-tube rack
- medicine dropper
- methylene blue indicator
- timing device
- beaker clamp

Procedure

1 Make a hot-water bath by pouring about 400 mL of water into a 500-mL beaker and placing the beaker on a hot plate. Heat the water until the temperature reaches 40°C (**Figure 1**). Using a thermometer, periodically check that the water temperature is maintained near 40°C.

Figure 1

2 Measure 5 g of brewers' yeast with a mass balance. Pour 20 mL of water into a 50-mL flask, then add the yeast. Gently stir until the yeast dissolves (**Figure 2**). Label the flask "yeast."

3 (L3) Prepare a 25% milk solution: mix 5 mL of milk and 15 mL of water in a 50-mL flask. Label the flask "25% milk solution."

Figure 2

4 Using a wax pencil, label four test tubes 1, 2, 3, or 4 and put them in the test-tube rack. Add 3 mL of 100% milk to test tubes 1 and 2. Add 3 mL of 25% milk solution to test tubes 3 and 4.

When the temperature of the hot-water bath reaches 40°C, add two drops of methylene blue indicator to each of the test tubes (**Figure 3**).

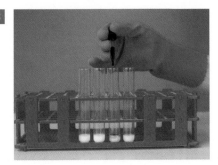

Figure 3

(f) Methylene blue indicates the presence of oxygen. Why is oxygen is present in each test tube.

6 Rinse the graduated cylinder with tap water. Add 2 mL of the yeast solution to each of the test tubes. Place test tubes 1 and 3 in the hot-water bath and leave test tubes 2 and 4 in the test-tube rack. Record the time at which you put the tubes in the bath as time 0. Note the time when the methylene blue indicator turns colourless in each tube.

7 Tidy your workspace and wash your hands.

Analysis and Evaluation

(g) Compare your initial predictions to the results that you collected. Suggest reasons for any differences.
(h) What was the source of organic matter used in this investigation?
(i) Yeast is a living organism. What purpose did the yeast serve in this investigation?
(j) A control was not used for the effect of nutrients on BOD levels. Devise such a control.
(k) Suggest some sources of error that might affect the outcome of this investigation.
(l) How does the level of nutrients affect the BOD?
(m) How does water temperature affect the BOD?

Understanding Concepts

1. Explain why an increase in the amount of organic matter in an aquatic ecosystem will reduce oxygen levels.

2. List some ways in which the amount of organic matter in an ecosystem can increase.

3. Describe the two ways in which thermal energy reduced oxygen levels in this investigation.

4. As the level of dissolved oxygen declines, fish are often the first to die. How would a large number of dead fish affect a lake?

5. Spring runoff can carry nutrients from decomposing terrestrial plants into a lake. Predict the effects of spring runoff on

   (a) BOD

   (b) dissolved oxygen

   (c) fish populations

Making Connections

6. Cities like Halifax and Toronto have an innovative approach to providing air conditioning while reducing energy use. The Toronto District Heating Corporation has plans to bring cold water from Lake Ontario into buildings for the purpose of cooling. Downtown tunnels have been dug, pipes laid, and customers identified.

   (a) Identify and explain some environmental benefits of the plant.

   (b) Identify and explain an environmental risk.

Exploring

7. During spring, organic matter from decomposing terrestrial plants is carried into rivers and lakes with melting snow. In summer, the runoff following thunderstorms also contains high levels of nutrients. Both cause a rapid increase in the population of algae. The decomposition of huge amounts of algae adds organic matter to water, and this organic matter causes an unpleasant taste in drinking water. Charcoal filters can be used to remove the organic matter. (Organic matter adsorbs (sticks to) the surface of charcoal). Design and, with your teacher's approval, carry out an experiment to test the effectiveness of the charcoal filter shown in **Figure 4**. Write a report that includes

   (a) an explanation of the method you used to demonstrate whether the filter removes organic matter;

   (b) a description of independent, dependent, and controlled variables;

   (c) suggestions for how to improve the filter so it could be used in a commercial product.

Figure 4

The Great Lakes

Spanning more than 1200 km from west to east, the Great Lakes are the largest surface freshwater system on Earth. The lakes contain a huge volume of water (about 23 000 km³) and cover an area of approximately 244 000 km².

(a) Why would pollutants from a new point source be less likely to show up quickly in the Great Lakes system than in a small lake?

(b) Explain why the Great Lakes are vulnerable to atmospheric pollutants.

Human Populations

Before the arrival of Europeans, the Great Lakes area supported an estimated 1 million people. In 2000, approximately 38 million people (including those in the United States) lived in the basin (**Figure 1**). Nearly 30% of Canada's population is found along the shores of the Great Lakes (including Lake St. Clair and the river systems between the lakes). The Great Lakes provide these people with drinking water, water for industry, transportation routes, fish, and opportunities for recreation.

(c) What problems would be created for an aquatic ecosystem when the surrounding human population increases dramatically?

(d) How were the Great Lakes used by First Nations and how are they used today? Present your comparison in a chart.

Pollution in the Great Lakes

Nearly 18% of the Earth's liquid freshwater is found in the Great Lakes. Yet, in spite of their enormous size, the Great Lakes are vulnerable to pollution. The volume of water exchange is rather low. Less than 1% of the water in the Great Lakes flows out of the St. Lawrence each year.

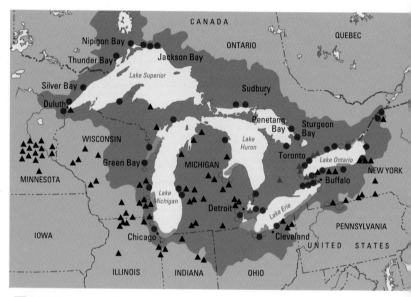

Figure 1

Some of the largest cities in North America are situated on the Great Lakes. The area is also an important industrial centre, both in Canada and the United States.

Figure 2

Pollution and its sources in the Great Lakes basin

■ Great Lakes drainage basin
□ Eutrophic areas
● Most polluted areas, according to the Great Lakes Water Quality Board
● Other "hot spots" of toxic concentrations in water and sediments
▲ U.S. Superfund hazardous waste sites (not including those added after October 1983)
▲ Canadian industrial waste sites identified by the Ontario Ministry of the Environment as "needing monitoring"

A variety of chemicals, including pesticides and fertilizers, enters the lake from runoff. These chemicals mix with the industrial outflow from chemical processing, forming a toxic mixture that poisons wildlife. The perils of water pollution came to light in the 1960s, when biologists began to note severe eutrophication, massive fish kills, and contamination by bacteria from sewage.

(e) Why would polluting a system with limited water outflow cause particularly severe environmental problems?
(f) According to the information presented in **Figure 2**, which of the Great Lakes is the most polluted?
(g) Using **Figures 1** and **2**, explain how pollution is related to human population size and industrialization.

Comparing the Lakes

Lake Superior is the largest and coldest of the Great Lakes. Lake Erie is the warmest and smallest. (Lake Ontario is smaller in surface area than Lake Erie, but it is also deeper and so contains more water.) The western end of Lake Erie, containing approximately 20% of the lake, is especially shallow, with an average depth of only 7.4 m. It frequently freezes over in winter. Lake Huron is the third-largest lake by volume. On the Canadian side, Lake Huron is used mostly for recreation.

(h) Lake Superior is considered an oligotrophic lake, and Lake Erie is regarded as eutrophic. Explain why.
(i) Which of the lakes would you predict has the lowest dissolved oxygen level? Give reasons for your prediction.
(j) By 1970, most of the fish had disappeared from Lake Erie. Suggest reasons for the disappearance.

Cottage Country

Figure 3 shows a stream flowing into Lake Huron. At one time, the stream was a prime location for boating and fishing, which made it an attractive area for development. A developer cleared the trees on both sides of the stream to make way for cottages. The trees that had once provided shade for the water in the stream were stacked up and burned.

shade provided

Lake Huron

Before

cottages built

Lake Huron

After

trees removed

trees burned

Figure 3

Development of a Lake Huron stream

Plant growth in the stream soon increased, making boating difficult. In an attempt to restore the area's appeal, the developer sprayed herbicides on the plants. Many of the plants died, but then the fishing in the stream became poor.

(k) Explain why the plant population in the stream increased.

(l) Explain how the spraying of a herbicide to kill plants could reduce the number of fish in the stream.

(m) Develop a plan for building cottages near the stream that does less damage to the aquatic ecosystem.

🖑 Work the Web

Many environmental groups are concerned about the Great Lakes. Many problems that once appeared to be beyond solution have been tackled in effective ways. Choose a group that has been working on a solution to a problem. What has the group accomplished? To do your research, visit www.science.nelson.com and follow the links from Science 10, 4.5.

Understanding Concepts

1. The data in **Table 1** were collected before and after trees were removed from the banks of a stream flowing into Lake Huron. The cut trees were burned along the shore.

Table 1 Test Results Before and After Deforestation

Test	Before removal of trees	1 year after removal of trees	5 years after removal of trees
mean June water temperature (°C)	12	15	17
mean depth (m)	1.5	1.2	1.1
mean June dissolved oxygen (ppm)	7.8	5.5	5.1
phosphates (ppm)	0.2	3.6	2.5
nitrates (ppm)	0.1	1.2	0.6
inorganic solids (g/L)	0.1	1.6	1.3

(a) The mass of inorganic solids (soil particles) is measured by filtering solids from the water. Explain why the amount of sediment changed after the removal of the trees.

(b) Why did the nitrate and phosphate levels change after the trees were removed?

(c) Explain how changes in depth, temperature, and dissolved oxygen relate to one another.

(d) Speculate about how changes in the stream might lead to changes in Lake Huron.

Making Connections

2. (a) Draw a diagram showing sources of pollution in the Great Lakes basin and how pollutants from those sources enter the lakes.

(b) According to your diagram, are you contributing to pollution in the Great Lakes? Suggest some changes that you could make in the way you live that would help to solve the problem.

3. According to some ecologists, there are too many cottages on the shores of some lakes.

(a) Outline some of the potential problems created when cottages are built along a lakefront.

(b) What interest groups would oppose a law that limited the number of cottages that could be built on a lakefront? What arguments would you expect each group to make?

4. In 1972, the Canadian and U.S. governments decided to try to clean up the Great Lakes. Great strides have been made since that time. Create a table similar to **Table 2** and fill in the blank cells.

Table 2 Great Lakes Initiatives

Initiative	Indicator of improvement	Reason for initiative
Upgrade sewage treatment plants.	decreased levels of coliform bacteria	
Ban phosphates in detergent.		Phosphates promote algae growth.
Reduce the use of chlorine-based pesticides.		
Reduce combustion of fossil fuels.		
Ban use of chlorine bleach by pulp and paper industry.		

Biological Indicators of Pollution in Streams

Many different pollutants can affect water quality. No single test can be used to assess water quality; however, an examination of the plants and animals found in the system can be used as a useful indicator of pollution in streams. Species that are active, such as trout, have high oxygen demands, while those that are less active, such as slugworms, need much less oxygen. When aquatic ecosystems contain high levels of oxygen, the active species gain the advantage in the competition for food and territory. When oxygen levels are low, however, less active species gain the advantage. Table 1 correlates oxygen level with species expected in freshwater systems.

Investigating oxygen content as an indicator of pollution has its limitations. Oxygen concentration in water is only one indicator of problems. For example, any pollution caused by heavy-metal contaminants such as mercury wouldn't be detected by monitoring oxygen. In addition, low oxygen levels aren't always linked to pollution. Bogs and swamps naturally contain a tremendous amount of organic matter that is being slowly broken down by decomposers. Because the decomposers use oxygen, we would expect lower levels of dissolved oxygen in those ecosystems.

It is also important to note that the presence of a species usually identified with low levels of oxygen, such as the slugworm, does not mean that the water is polluted or even that oxygen levels are low. Slugworms can be found in well-oxygenated waters; however, their numbers tend to be lower.

Question

Can organisms be used to indicate water quality in a stream?

Hypothesis/Prediction

If a stream contains only organisms that do well when dissolved oxygen content is low, then the amount of dissolved oxygen in the stream will be low.

(a) Examine the stream you will investigate and the territory it flows through. Predict whether dissolved oxygen levels in the water will be high or low. Explain your prediction.

Table 1   Oxygen Levels and Species

Oxygen level (mg/L)	Description	Species present
8 and above	high level of dissolved oxygen is positive for most species, resulting in high biodiversity	Fish: trout, jackfish, whitefish Invertebrates: mayfly larvae, caddis fly larvae, beetles, waterboatman
6 and above	level of dissolved oxygen sufficient for most species, although presence of active fish such as trout is less likely	Fish: perch, bottom feeders such as catfish Invertebrates: few mayfly larvae, some beetles, more worms (including leeches) slugworms.
4 and below	critical level for most fish; invertebrate populations increase	Fish: few Invertebrates: freshwater shrimp, many midge larvae, slugworms, leeches
2 and below	too low for fish	Invertebrates: some midge larvae, some slugworms, many small protozoans (amoeba)

Design

This is an exploratory investigation in which you will observe the community in a local stream.

(b) Construct a table in which to record your observations.

Materials

- field guides to birds, fish, and invertebrates
- high boots
- plankton net
- hand lens
- bottom dredger
- shovel
- pan
- bucket with lid
- forceps
- dissolved oxygen kit

Procedure

1 Before entering the stream, take a while to watch for fish and birds such as ducks and wading birds. Try to identify those you see, or record their colouring and shape for later identification.

2 Use a plankton net to take samples from the surface water. Examine the plankton with a hand lens. Record the type and population of the organisms you find (**Figure 1**).

3 Using a bottom dredger and a shovel, collect a sample from the streambed (**Figure 2**). Place the sample in a large pan and examine the organisms using the forceps and a hand lens. Be careful not to injure any organisms. Record your observations. Return the sample to the stream.

4 Use a bucket to collect a water sample from the stream. Using a dissolved oxygen kit, measure the amount of oxygen in the water (**Figure 3**).

direction of current

Figure 2

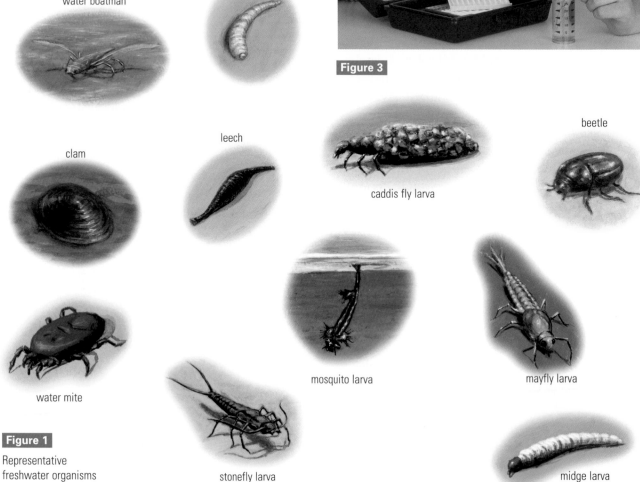

Figure 3

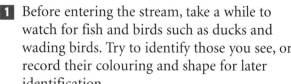

water boatman

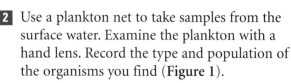

horse fly larva

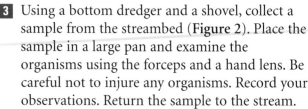

clam

leech

caddis fly larva

beetle

water mite

mosquito larva

mayfly larva

stonefly larva

midge larva

Figure 1

Representative freshwater organisms

144 *Chapter 4*

Analysis and Evaluation

(c) Was your prediction correct? How do you account for any discrepancy between your observations and your prediction?

(d) Identify potential sources of pollution for this ecosystem.

(e) Suggest a method for determining the amount of plankton collected. How could one test site be compared with another?

(f) Using **Table 1** and your observations, rate the effects of pollution on the ecosystem you analyzed.

 Challenge

2 In doing an environmental assessment you must select many potential testing sites before identifying those that are most important. One problem created by multiple sites is that it is very time-consuming and expensive to conduct all tests at every site. How would biological indicators such as the presence of particular species help with this problem?

Understanding Concepts

1. Make a food web of the organisms you found.

2. Make a pyramid of numbers for the organisms you found in the stream according to the following classification: producers; primary consumers; secondary consumers; decomposers.

Making Connections

3. Use **Figure 4** to assess the environmental impact of a sewage treatment plant.

   (a) Which organism is most tolerant of low dissolved oxygen?

   (b) Why does the dissolved oxygen decrease when the biological oxygen demand increases?

   (c) Compare the rate of recovery of the mayfly larva and shrimp.

   (d) On the basis of the data provided, assess the impact of the sewage treatment plant on the river.

   (e) What other tests would you want to conduct to provide an accurate environmental assessment of the sewage treatment plant?

   (f) On the basis of the data provided, would you recommend that anyone fish downstream from the treatment plant? Give your reasons.

   (g) If a pulp and paper company makes an application to construct a mill 5 km downstream from the sewage treatment plant, what questions must be asked before granting the permit?

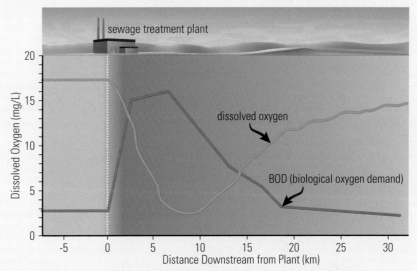

Dissolved Oxygen and BOD Near a Sewage Treatment Plant

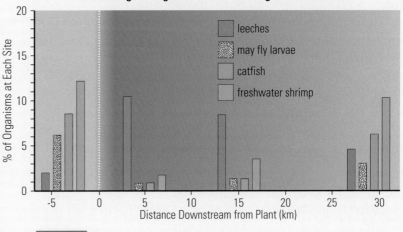

Percentage of Organisms Near a Sewage Treatment Plant

Figure 4

The sewage treatment plant is at kilometre 0.

Marine Ecosystems

Salt is the major abiotic factor that makes marine ecosystems different from freshwater ecosystems. Although the amount of salt varies greatly in different oceans and seas, the average concentration is about 3.5% (or 3.5 g of salt in every 100 g of seawater). There is another factor that is significant: oceans have tides. The tides result from the gravitational interactions of the Sun, Moon, and Earth.

Oceans have two major zones: the coastal zone and the open sea (**Figure 1**). The more productive of the two is the **coastal zone**, which consists of the relatively shallow water from the high-tide mark on land to the edge of the continental shelf. The open ocean is cooler, and contains fewer minerals and nutrients. Although the coastal zone accounts for less than 10% of the oceans' total area, it contains approximately 90% of their living things. Rich in resources such as fish, oil, and gas, the coastal zone is also more important for humans.

The coastal zone can be divided into two areas: the neritic zone and the intertidal zone.

The **intertidal zone** is defined by low and high tide. Organisms found in this area must be able to withstand the crushing and scraping forces of waves during high tide and, during low tide, periods of drying (although the tides do leave pools in rocky areas). Clams, starfish, mussels, oysters, and sea anemones are common in the intertidal area. Attachment devices such as suctionlike feet or small fibres prevent these organisms from being swept away during wave and tidal movement.

The water beyond the intertidal zone is referred to as the **neritic zone**. Its depth depends on the slope of the continental shelf, but areas below 200 m, where light cannot penetrate, are not considered part of this zone. On the eastern coast of Canada is a section of the neritic zone known as the Grand Banks. This highly productive zone is home to many species of fish, mollusks (e.g., clams, mussels), and crustaceans (e.g., crabs and lobsters).

Estuaries and Coastal Marshes

By far the most productive areas of marine ecosystems are tidal marshes (**Figure 2**) and estuaries. Tidal marshes, which are periodically flooded by high tides, are biodiverse in both plants and animals. Because marshes are shallow, there is a large area where plants can grow and photosynthesize. These plants provide consumer organisms with more energy per hectare than is found in any other aquatic ecosystem.

Estuaries exist where rivers and streams flow into the ocean. (The Gulf of St. Lawrence is the largest estuary in Eastern Canada.) Water in an estuary is a combination of saltwater from

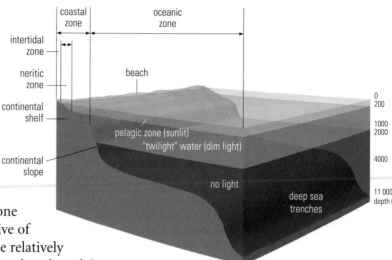

Figure 1

A cross section of the ocean

Figure 2

The most productive marine ecosystems are tidal marshes.

the ocean and nutrient-rich freshwater carrying runoff from more productive terrestrial ecosystems. The presence of these nutrients allows estuaries to be more productive than the rest of the coastal zone (**Figure 3**). However, differences in temperature, salinity, and density between freshwater and saltwater create special problems for species living in the area. Fish and other organisms must adapt to variations in the concentration of salt in the water, which rises with high tide and falls with low tide, falls during the spring melt (when the river is discharging more water) and rises in winter (when ice reduces flow from the river).

Temperature and salinity also affect density. Cold water is more dense than warm (unless it is below 4°C), and salt water is more dense than fresh. For example, in summer the freshwater is warm and free of salt, and so tends to form a layer above the colder, salty ocean water. Fish and mammals that live in estuaries must be able to adapt to both layers.

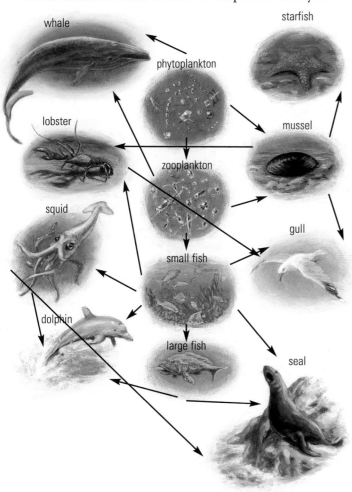

Figure 3

An estuarial food web. Estuary ecosystems benefit from the flow of nutrients from terrestrial ecosystems.

Understanding Concepts

1. Use **Figure 3** to answer the following questions.
   (a) Construct a pyramid, assigning each organism to a trophic level.
   (b) Which organisms within the food web would be directly affected by the harvesting of large numbers of fish?
   (c) Predict how the dolphins would respond if all large fish were removed from the food web. How would their response affect other organisms?
   (d) Predict how the elimination of whales would affect the populations of starfish and squid.
   (e) If the shark population increased significantly, how would other populations be affected?

2. The Gulf of St. Lawrence is home to many herons, large wading birds that feed on small fish. Heron droppings add phosphates and nitrates to the water. Eelgrass and other aquatic plants provide food for small fish. Large fish feed on small fish. There was a proposal to increase the number of large fish available to fishers by regulating (hunting) herons. Ecologists argued that reducing the heron population might also cause a decline in the population of ducks that feed on eelgrass.
   (a) Construct a food web based on this scenario.
   (b) Explain why a reduction in the number of herons might cause a decline in the duck population.
   (c) Describe two ways in which the duck population could be increased.

Making Connections

3. One answer to concerns about pollution of the oceans has always been "the oceans are so large that pollutants just naturally dilute to low levels." Is this a strong argument? Should the oceans be used to dispose of wastes? How would you go about convincing a community that discharges waste into the ocean to begin planning for a better system?

Reflecting

4. Because the human population is growing, the threat to ocean ecosystems has been increasing. Oceans don't have to suffer any more damage, however, if people become more environmentally responsible. Do you see any evidence that attitudes about the oceans are changing?

Crude Oil in Marine Ecosystems

The oceans have been described as the end of every pipe (**Figure 1**). Many pollutants from terrestrial and freshwater ecosystems are carried to the oceans, where they spread out and are diluted in the great volume of ocean water. Before pollutants can reach the open ocean, however, they must first flow through the waters that adjoin the land. The most productive areas of the ocean are also the ones where pollution levels are highest.

Nearly half of the world's population lives on the coast of bodies of saltwater, including 14 of the world's 15 most populous cities. (Mexico City, the largest city, is the exception.)

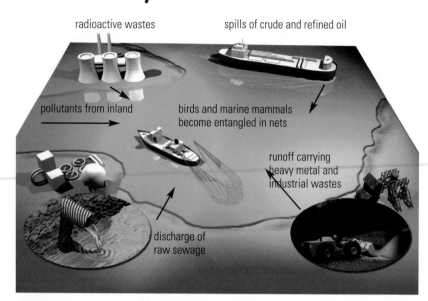

radioactive wastes   spills of crude and refined oil

pollutants from inland

birds and marine mammals become entangled in nets

runoff carrying heavy metal and industrial wastes

discharge of raw sewage

Figure 1

Sources of pollution of marine ecosystems

How Oil Enters Marine Ecosystems

Crude and refined oil pose serious ecological threats to marine ecosystems. Although oil tanker accidents receive the most publicity, more oil enters the oceans from offshore wells, daily washing of tankers, and storage leaks than from tankers. The bulk of the oil entering the oceans comes from activities on land. Most experts believe that at least 50% of the oil entering the oceans can be traced to disposal of waste oil, which enters the oceans through drainage pipes. Yearly waste oil from the cars of the 60 million motorists in the United States and Canada is equivalent to the oil spilled by 17 ships the size of the infamous *Exxon Valdez* (**Figure 2**). Another 10% of the oil entering the oceans comes from the atmosphere, mostly from oil fires (**Figure 3**).

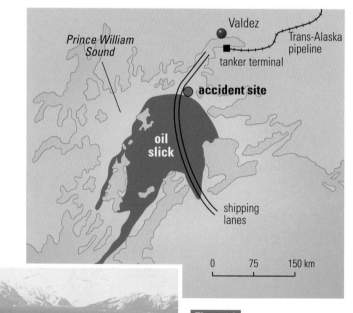

Valdez

Prince William Sound

Trans-Alaska pipeline

tanker terminal

accident site

oil slick

shipping lanes

0   75   150 km

Figure 2

One of the worst oil spills from a tanker occurred on March 24, 1989. *Exxon Valdez*, a tanker as long as three football fields, dumped enough oil to form a 1600-km-long slick in Prince William Sound off the coast of Alaska.

Ecological Effects of Oil Pollution

Lighter oils, those that float, are a direct threat to shore birds and diving birds. When the oil coats their feathers, it dissolves the natural oils that waterproof the birds. When water enters their plumage, it destroys the insulation provided by air. Without that insulation, birds can die of hypothermia in the cool marine waters. Globs of crude oil can also make their way into the respiratory tracts of birds and marine mammals, blocking breathing.

Heavy oil components that sink to the bottom of the ocean also create a problem. The sludge forms a suffocating blanket that covers bottom-dwelling organisms such as mussels, crabs, and oysters. As those bottom dwellers became part of the food chain, the oil finds its way into the bodies of consumers such as fish, birds, and mammals, including humans.

Cleaning an Oil Spill

Although Exxon spent more than $2.2 billion cleaning up the oil spill after the *Exxon Valdez* accident, ecologists are now suggesting that the cleanup may have caused even more problems than the original spill. High-pressure hoses sprayed hot water to clean oil off the shoreline. The damage done by the hot water was so devastating that sites that had not been cleaned recovered more rapidly than the washed sites.

Floating sponges were used to sop up some of the oil before it reached shore, however, this activity required many people. The crush of the equipment and the booted feet walking though delicate intertidal zones killed many of the animals that survived the clogging sludge.

If cleaning up can be so damaging, what is the alternative? Sometimes waiting and letting nature clean up is better. Marine bacteria will eventually break down the sludge, but it takes years. Recent research indicates that ecosystems come close to full recovery after a crude oil spill within three years; however, recovery from a spill of refined oil may take more than 10 years.

Figure 3

Oil fires — accidental or deliberately set — are another major source of oil pollution in marine ecosystems.

Understanding Concepts

1. Why are coastal areas usually the most polluted areas of an ocean?

2. In your own words, describe the ways that oil can enter a marine ecosystem.

3. List the problems caused by oil spills.

4. Predict what would happen if an oil spill was not cleaned up.

5. Speculate about why oil pollution in the Arctic would be especially dangerous to marine ecosystems.

Making Connections

6. The places where oil is discovered are often far away from the places where oil is used, forcing transportation. Imagine that oil producers are faced with a choice of shipping oil overland through above-ground pipes or by sea in oil tankers. Prepare a chart outlining the risks and benefits of each route. Which route would you recommend?

7. Oil tanker accidents get headlines, but when a motorist pours a litre of used oil down the drain, or when a poorly maintained car leaks oil onto the road, no one notices. There are a lot more spills by motorists than by tankers. Make a list of suggestions for the maintenance of vehicles and proper disposal of used oil.

Reflecting

8. The process used to clean up after the *Exxon Valdez* spill was not appropriate, in that it did more damage than it fixed. But standing by and waiting while nature cleans up our messes is not a satisfying option to many people. Imagine what the response might have been if Exxon had suggested that nothing be done about the spill, and no money be spent! What do you suggest would have been the appropriate response to the oil spill?

👆 Work the Web

The natural impulse of those desperately trying to clean up an oil spill is to try to help the birds caught in the spill by washing off the oil that coats them. But is that impulse wise? Research this question by visiting www.science.nelson.com and following the links to Science 10, 4.8. Make a presentation to your class on the results of your research.

Managing Fish Populations

Although fish are potentially a renewable resource, we must leave enough stock every year to ensure that the population is renewed for the following year. A **sustainable yield** is achieved when the size of the catch is balanced by the birth rate and survival rate of fish the following year. The number of fish removed from the oceans must be no greater than the number of new fish that reach reproductive age.

Scientists estimate that the sustainable yield of the world's marine fisheries is about 100 million t (approximately 87% of the annual catch of fish and shellfish comes from saltwater). About 99% of the marine catch comes from the coastal zone, but the coastal zone is being polluted at an alarming rate. Examine **Figure 1**.

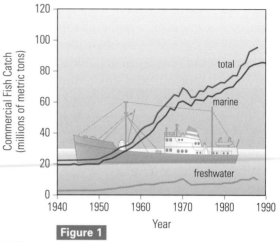

Figure 1

Worldwide catch of fish, 1940 to 1990

(a) Compare changes in the freshwater fish harvest to those in the marine fish harvest.
(b) In which decade did the harvest of marine fish begin to grow rapidly?
(c) What was the peak year for the freshwater fish harvest?
(d) According to the graph, when did marine fishing reach its maximum sustainable yield?
(e) If the scientists are right, and the maximum sustainable yield is 100 million t, what is happening to populations of fish? Predict what will happen to the yield in future years.

Catching Down

The increases in worldwide catch shown in **Figure 1** do not tell the whole story. In some areas, the catch has been declining for years (**Figure 2**). The harvest in the North Atlantic, for example, may well have reached and exceeded the maximum sustainable yield in the early 1970s. Since then the catch has declined 50%. What makes the decline especially disturbing is that the North Atlantic includes what were once the world's most

Figure 2

Fish catches are in decline in most regions of the world. The percentages show the change in catch between the peak year (indicated) and 1992. A negative number means a decrease in catch.

productive waters, the Grand Banks and Georges Bank of eastern North America (**Figure 2**).

(f) Which ocean is suffering the most from over fishing?

(g) Which of Canada's fisheries is in the greatest danger?

(h) Which areas of the world have not yet reached the peak total catch?

The Need to Fish

On average, people get 30% of their protein requirements from fish and shellfish. Although the total number of fish caught per year has increased, largely due to increasingly efficient fishing technologies, the amount of fish caught per person has declined in recent years (**Figure 3**).

(i) In what year did the per capita fish catch reach its peak?

(j) How is it possible for the per capita fish catch to decline when the number and mass of fish caught every year continues to climb?

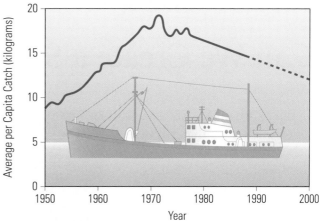

Figure 3
The decline in the per capita fish catch appears to be a long-term trend.

 Challenge

3 In constructing your board game, consider how to present the idea of overfishing. Humans are part of ocean ecosystems, and so their population cannot exceed the carrying capacity of those ecosystems. What happens when overfishing depletes fish stocks?

Understanding Concepts

1. Use the data provided in **Figure 2** to complete a bar graph showing changes in fish harvests.

2. Study the data in **Table 1**. (We recommend using a spreadsheet to complete the following questions.)

Table 1 **Commercial Landings in Atlantic Canada by Year, Species, and Province**

Year/ Species	NS	NB	PEI	NF	Total
1990 cod	112 612	10 371	4 103	245 896	372 982
haddock	20 193	15	1	1 938	22 147
halibut	1 810	47	1	303	2 161
total					
1994 cod	19 015	576	473	2 292	22 356
haddock	6 912	21	0	22	6 955
halibut	1 031	9	0	63	1 103
total					
1998 cod	11 872	812	259	21 936	34 879
haddock	11 438	85	0	198	11 721
halibut	824	19	1	263	1 107
total					

(a) Calculate the total production for each of the species for each year. What conclusions can you draw?

(b) Calculate the total fish production for province for each year. What conclusions can you draw?

(c) Using a line graph, present the number of tonnes of cod caught between 1990 and 1998 in each of the provinces.

(d) Calculate the percentage change in the cod harvest in Newfoundland from 1990 to 1998.

Making Connections

3. Drift nets often catch animals other than food fish. In 1990, drift nets accidentally entangled 42 million animals, including sea birds and marine mammals. The United Nations has proposed that shorter drift nets be used. It has banned nets longer than 2.5 km. Italy, France, and Ireland are among the countries that have ignored the ban. Should nations be allowed to ignore international rulings? In an essay, explain your position.

Reflecting

4. The data on overfishing presented here tells only part of the story. Make a list of questions you have that weren't answered here. What important research needs to be done to provide a more complete picture of the health of ocean ecosystems?

4.10 Explore an Issue

DECISION-MAKING SKILLS MENU
- Define the Issue
- Identify Alternatives
- Research
- Analyze the Issue
- Defend a Decision
- Evaluate

Can We Create a Sustainable Fishery?

In the 1970s, it become increasingly clear that cod were being overfished in the northwest Atlantic Ocean. For years Canada accused European fishing boats, especially Spanish and Portuguese vessels, of taking too many fish. The Europeans responded by pointing the finger back at Canada. In an attempt to protect its lucrative cod fishery, Canada extended its territorial boundaries from 160 km to 320 km, putting most of the richest cod feeding grounds in the world — the Grand Banks — inside Canada's borders (**Figure 1**). However, the nose and tail of the Grand Banks are outside Canada's 200-km limit. There is still significant international fishing activity in those areas.

Figure 1

Not all foreign ships respected Canada's claim to the Grand Banks. This Spanish vessel was seized for fishing in Canadian waters in 1995. Brian Tobin was the federal Fisheries Minister at the time.

In 1986, with the cod catch dwindling, Canada closed its ports to European fishing boats. The catch continued to decline. In May 1992, Newfoundland's northern cod fishery was closed for two years, in the hope that a ban on fishing would allow cod populations to recover. In 1995, with little sign of improvement in sight, the Canadian government declared a three-year moratorium on all cod fishing. The collapse of a fishery that had been abundant for centuries was a catastrophe for Maritime Canadians. Some 50 000 Canadian fishers and fish-plant workers were left unemployed.

Fish populations respond to predators much like those of other prey organisms. When the needs of the predators exceed the capacity of the prey animals to replenish themselves, the population of the prey must fall. Shortly thereafter, the population of the predators must also decline, unless they find another food source. Humans are the predators, and we are running out of new food sources.

To avoid a worldwide crash in the population of fish, humans must not take more than the maximum sustainable yield from any fishery. But the population of people is increasing, and they must eat. In this environment, what can we do to guarantee that there will always be fish to feed the world? What does a sustainable system look like in a world where nations compete with each other for fish?

Understanding the Issue

1. Has there been any international cooperation in the attempt to protect the cod fishery?

2. Suggest some reasons why fishers might feel they must continue to fish, even though the fish population they rely on is declining.

☜ Work the Web

To research fishing practices of large fishing nations visit www.science.nelson.com and follow the links from Science 10, 4.10.

Role Play   The Fish Conference

UN Statement

The goal of the United Nations Subcommitee on Oceans and Coastal Areas (SOCA) is to promote the sustainable use and conservation of marine living resources, both on the high seas and in coastal areas under national jurisdiction. SOCA is concerned that national fishing regulations and international treaties are often ignored. The Subcommittee is therefore organizing a conference to establish worldwide rules for fishing and to decide on penalties for nations that ignore these rules. The following countries are invited to send representatives to the conference:

- Canada
- United States
- Spain
- Norway
- Japan
- India
- Peru
- Russia

In this activity you will form groups representing the fishing nations that have been invited to the conference. The representatives will gather at the conference to propose and vote on resolutions that will result in a sustainable international commercial fishery.

- Each group will prepare for the Fish Conference by researching the practices of its nation. What is important to that nation? What can it give up, and what would it need from an international agreement?
- Each group will also research the other nations. What practices do they follow that threaten a sustainable fishery?
- Each nation will brief a delegate to the conference. The delegate will present that nation's position. Once a nation has made its presentation, delegates of other nations may ask questions and challenge statements. Only delegates can speak at the conference, but everything a delegate says must be approved by the rest of the delegate's group.
- After the presentations are finished, delegates can make proposals that will be voted on. The conference will arrive at the final plan democratically. Nations are allowed to speak on motions publicly through their delegates, but they are also allowed to negotiate privately with other nations before each vote.
- After the Fish Conference, evaluate the performance of your group. Do you feel you were well prepared for the conference? Was your presentation well received? How successful was your group in negotiation and discussion? Did the final resolutions give your group what it wanted?

Clynt King

Great Lakes Activist

Clynt King has an original approach to saving the environment. Born in 1964 to the Bear clan of the Anishinabe tribe (also known as the Ojibwa), he has lived his entire life as part of the Mississauga New Credit First Nations near Hagersville, Ontario. Clynt studies environmental and pollution problems in the Great Lakes area using a blend of Western scientific method and his indigenous cultural knowledge.

Clynt was initially inspired to help the environment when he saw his older brother at work planting trees and maintaining woodlots. After taking everything from environmental science to calculus to typing in high school (Clynt still considers typing the most useful subject he studied, or at least the most used), he studied forestry at Lakehead University. When he went to work for Environment Canada, he also took courses in meteorology, waste management, environmental law, and waste-water treatment plants. Asked for advice on pursuing a career as an environmental activist, Clynt recommends a degree or diploma in geography, which provides the basic foundation for specialization in every field of environmental studies.

Studying and protecting the environment is a vocation that brings together almost every branch of science. The chemistry of water pollutants, from zinc to hydrogen sulfide, affects the biological interactions of the organisms that depend on the water.

Clynt learns daily in his "outdoor" classroom on and above the ground. An aerial view of the Great Lakes area shows a large green rectangular patch between Lake Ontario and Lake Erie — unusual in Ontario, which was clearcut long ago. That patch exists because the New Credit and Six Nations First Nations have maintained the trees and natural areas on their land; their indigenous cultural values and beliefs have saved a healthy and biologically diverse section of Ontario's old-growth forest. Unfortunately, this preservation area is under pressure from rapid population growth. He argues that since First Nations values and beliefs protected the area in the first place, they should be strengthened and supported to continue the protection. This is the main thrust of Clynt's activism, which now includes coordinating the First Nations Environmental Network (FNEN) for the Great Lakes region and working with environmental nongovernmental organizations (ENGOs). With these activities, combined with grass roots initiatives, Clynt believes we can make that little patch of green the rule rather than the exception.

Making Connections

1. What sort of ENGOs exist, and what do they do? How do you go to work for them? Research the application process and draft a cover letter applying for an internship at one of the major organizations.

🖑 Work the Web

What does the First Nations Environmental Network do where you live? Look FNEN up on the Web and find the representative in your area. Write a report for your school or neighbourhood newspaper.

Key Expectations

Throughout the chapter, you have had opportunities to do the following things:

- Examine how abiotic factors affect the survival and geographical location of biotic communities. (4.1, 4.2, 4.3, 4.4, 4.5, 4.6, 4.7)
- Examine the factors (natural and external) that affect the survival and equilibrium of populations in an ecosystem. (4.1, 4.2, 4.5, 4.6, 4.7, 4.8, 4.9)
- Identify and evaluate Canadian initiatives in protecting Canada's ecosystems. (4.1, 4.5, 4.10)
- Assess the impact of technological change on an ecosytem. (4.2, 4.4, 4.5, 4.6, 4.8, 4.9)
- Compare a natural and a disturbed ecosystem and suggest ways of assuring their sustainability. (4.2, 4.5, 4.8)
- Demonstrate the skills required to plan and conduct an inquiry into ecological relationships, using instruments, apparatus, and materials safely and accurately, and controlling major variables and adapting or extending procedures where required. (4.4, 4.6)
- Analyse data and information and evaluate evidence and sources of information, identifying flaws such as errors and bias. (4.3, 4.4, 4.10)
- Explain changes in popular views about the sustainability of ecosystems and humans' responsibility in preserving them. (4.5, 4.8, 4.9, 4.10)
- Explain why different ecosystems respond differently to short-term stresses and long-term changes. (4.2, 4.5, 4.9)
- Describe ways in which the relationships between living organisms and their ecosystems are viewed by other cultures. (4.10)
- Describe the physical and chemical processes involved in the methods used to clean up a contaminated site. (4.8)
- Formulate scientific questions about observed ecological relationships, ideas, problems, and issues. (4.9)
- Select and integrate information from various sources, including electronic and print resources, community resources, and personally collected data, to answer scientific questions. (4.10)
- Describe careers that involve knowledge of ecology or environmental technologies, and use resources such as the Internet to determine the knowledge and skill requirements of such careers. (4.11)

Key Terms

biological oxygen demand (BOD)

coastal zone

coliform bacteria

epilimnion

eutrophic

hypolimnion

intertidal zone

limnetic zone

littoral zone

neritic zone

oligotrophic

plankton

profundal zone

sustainable yield

thermocline

water pollution

Reflect on your Learning

Revisit your answers to the Reflect on your Learning questions, page 125, in the Getting Started.

- How has your thinking changed?
- What new questions do you have?

Make a Summary

In this chapter you learned that sustainable aquatic ecosystems are those that maintain living things. Human societies are more likely to maintain sustainable ecosystems if they are careful not to sacrifice long-term benefits for the sake of short-term gains.

- Construct a table that examines the impact of humans on aquatic ecosystems.
- Start by examining some of the Key Terms used in the chapter. The table below may help you get started.

Environmental problem	Short-term gain	Potential long-term problem
acid deposition		
overfishing		
using rivers and lakes to dilute pollutants		
nutrients (eg., nitrogen fertilizers) enter lakes		

Chapter 4 Review

Understanding Concepts

1. Draw a diagram of a lake and label the following zones: limnetic, littoral, and profundal.

2. Make a chart that compares abiotic factors in oligotrophic and eutrophic lakes.

3. Compare dissolved oxygen and light intensity in the epilimnion and hypolimnion of eutrophic and oligotrophic lakes.

4. A biologist notes that a lake that was once filled with algae is now crystal clear. Does the clear water provide conclusive proof the water quality has improved?

5. (a) Describe the spring and fall turnovers as they occur in most Canadian lakes.
   (b) Costa Rica is a Central American country that is much closer to the Equator than Canada. Explain how the process of turnover in a deep lake in Costa Rica differ might differ from that in a deep lake in Canada.

6. Predict how increased algal growth in a lake would affect the following factors. Give reasons for your predictions.
   (a) the depth of the limnetic zone
   (b) dissolved oxygen
   (c) BOD
   (d) the mass of organic matter found at the bottom of the lakes

7. Explain how oxygen levels in a lake are affected by the
   (a) amount of organic matter in a lake.
   (b) rate of decomposition of organic matter.

8. A lake contains high amounts of undissolved solids. Suggest two possible sources of the solids.

9. Make a sketch showing food webs in a lake as the lake changes from oligotrophic to eutrophic.

10. Predict how thermal pollution of a lake would affect the following factors. Give reasons for your predictions.
    (a) BOD
    (b) dissolved oxygen
    (c) coliform bacteria
    (d) algae population
    (e) light penetration
    (f) undissolved solids

11. Why is the use of phosphate detergents discouraged in Canada?

12. How can coliform bacteria be used as indicators of river health?

13. Construct a chart to compare abiotic factors in marine and freshwater ecosystems.

14. Construct rough graphs that show the relationship between algae growth and
    (a) nutrients such as phosphates and nitrogen in lake.
    (b) water temperature.

15. Outline two problems facing ecosystems in the Great Lakes area that have been caused by humans. Indicate potential solutions for each of the problems.

16. Make a table like **Table 1** comparing abiotic and biotic factors in Lake Superior and Lake Erie. Indicate in which lake you would expect each factor to be greater.

Table 1

Factor	Lake Superior	Lake Erie
temperature		
mean depth		
BOD		
dissolved oxygen		
population of slugworms/1000 m^3		
population of trout/1000 m^3		
biomass of algae kg/1000 m^3		

17. Explain why ecologists monitor the populations of edible fish in oceans.

18. Describe how oil spills and their aftermath can affect marine ecosystems.

Applying Inquiry Skills

19. Use the data in **Table 2**, which were collected from two lakes in summer, to answer the following questions.

Table 2

Depth (m)	Oxygen concentration (mg/L)	
	Lake X	Lake Y
0 m (surface)	8.3	7.8
5 m	7.9	7.9
thermocline	7.5	7.0
15 m	7.0	5.2
20 m	6.9	2.0
25 m	6.8	0.2

(a) Classify each lake as eutrophic or oligotrophic.
(b) Explain the large change in oxygen levels below the thermocline in Lake Y.
(c) Present the data in a graph.
(d) On your graph, show how oxygen levels would change in the fall.

20. Design an animal that is well adapted to the intertidal zone of the North Atlantic Ocean. Explain how each of the animal's features would help it to survive.

21. Levels of nutrients, algae, and light penetration were measured throughout the year in the limnetic zone of a Northern Ontario lake, producing the patterns shown in **Figure 1**.

Seasonal Changes in a Lake

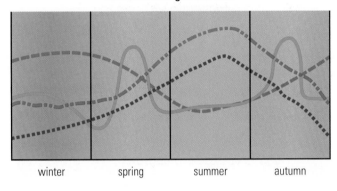

winter   spring   summer   autumn

——— algae   ---- nutrients   --·--· light   ········ temperature

Figure 1

(a) At which times of the year is the population of algae highest?
(b) Explain the changes in algae population.
(c) Explain the changes in temperature.
(d) Why do nutrient levels in the lake rise in winter but fall in summer?
(e) Explain fluctuations in light penetration.
(f) Using a similar diagram, show changes you would expect to see in dissolved oxygen in the same lake.
(g) Using a similar diagram, show changes you would expect to see in BOD in the same lake.
(h) Explain how the patterns would change if sewage began to be dumped into the lake.

22. In an attempt to compare the amount of undissolved solids at two different sites in a lake, the following procedure was followed at each site.

Procedure
- The mass of a cheesecloth is measured using a triple-beam balance.
- The cheesecloth is placed over the opening of a kitchen sieve.
- The sieve is moved back and forth in water for 5 minutes.

- The cheesecloth is removed from the sieve and the mass of the cheesecloth is measured using the triple-beam balance.
(a) Identify potential sources of error in the procedure described above.
(b) Provide suggestions to improve the procedure.

Making Connections

23. Use the food web from the marine ecosystem in **Figure 2** to answer the following questions.
(a) How would the removal of sharks by hunting affect the food web?
(b) Some ecologists worry about an increase in the seal population because seals eat cod. Studies show that increases in the seal population coincide with declines in the cod population. What other factors would have to be considered before coming to the conclusion that seals were responsible for a decline in cod populations?
(c) Some ecologists have expressed concerns about the number of lobsters being trapped by fishers. Explain how removing too many lobsters could affect other species.

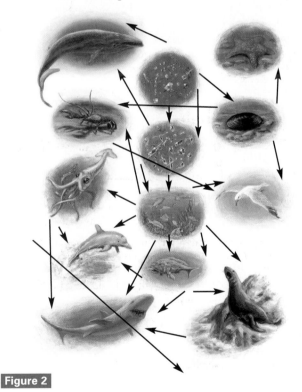

Figure 2

24. Aquaculture (fish farming) has been suggested as an alternative to taking wild fish from the oceans. It has been claimed that more use of aquaculture will increase the amount of food available for humans while reducing pressure on natural marine ecosystems. Research aquaculture and indicate some benefits and limitations of this technology in solving the problem of overfishing.

Assessing the Environmental Effects of Human Communities

A sustainable system is maintained when the effects of population growth, use of resources, and the build-up of wastes do not exceed the capacity of the environment to regenerate.

The influence of humans can create imbalances in ecosystems, leading to environmental problems. Each of these Challenges allows you to examine the impact of humans on natural ecosystems.

1 Design a Golf Course

Golf courses affect neighbouring natural ecosystems. Some of the effects are caused by the desire to provide clear, lush fairways and smooth greens for golfers; some are caused by the design and placement of the course. Your task is to design a golf course that would be attractive to golfers, and yet have minimal impact on local ecosystems.

In designing your golf course, you should

- select an area in your own community where a golf course could be developed;
- create a scale model or diagram showing the location of the proposed golf course and its surroundings;
- identify any environmental problems that could be created by the construction and maintenance of the golf course;
- identify tests that could be conducted before and after construction to assess the environmental impact of the golf course;
- prepare a presentation for the local community in which you explain the benefits of your course design and strategies that will be used to minimize environmental problems.

2 Assess Community Water Quality

We use water to drink, to wash, to build, to make chemicals, and to transport goods and raw materials. All, or most, of these activities affect the aquatic ecosystems in and near your community. You can't study the effects of them all, but you can monitor the effects of one or two potential problems as a start to assessing the environmental impact of your community. Your task is to produce an environmental impact assessment of local sources of pollution.

In conducting your assessment of water quality, you should

- identify potential sources of pollution;
- identify tests that will measure the effects the pollution might have on water quality;
- set up testing sites;
- measure the effects of pollution and identify its sources;
- write a report that assesses water quality and the impact of the pollution sources you identified.

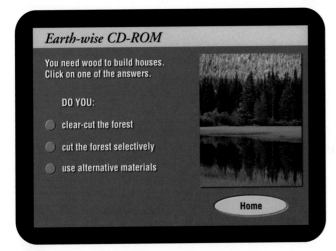

Earth-wise CD-ROM

You need wood to build houses.
Click on one of the answers.

DO YOU:

○ clear-cut the forest

○ cut the forest selectively

○ use alternative materials

Home

3 Educating Through Play

The pressures humans place on the environment are growing, but many people don't realize the effects of their actions. Through education, they can be alerted to how ecosystems are harmed, and how they can be sustained. Play is often an effective form of education. Your task is to create a game or simulation that will entertain players, but also educate them so that they understand better how humans affect ecosystems, and how alternative practices could help sustain ecosystems.

In making your game or simulation, you should

- identify actions and behaviours causing environmental problems that threaten the sustainability of ecosystems;
- identify alternatives to the harmful practices that ensure the long-term survival of ecosystems;
- create a game or simulation that demonstrates to players how environmental problems arise and how the alternatives can avoid or reduce problems;
- create a quiz that tests players to determine how much they have learned about sustainability.

 Assessment

Your completed Challenge will be assessed according to the following:

Process

- understand the specific challenge
- develop a plan
- choose and safely use appropriate tools, equipment, materials, and computer software
- analyze the results

Communication

- prepare an appropriate presentation of the task
- use correct terms, symbols, and SI units
- incorporate information technology

Product

- meet established criteria
- show understanding of the concepts, principles, laws, and theories
- show effective use of materials
- address the identified situation/ problem

 When preparing to use a chemical test, carry out an experiment, or to build or test a device, be sure to have your plan approved by your teacher before you begin.

Unit 1 Review

Understanding Concepts

1. In your notebook write the word(s) needed to complete each of the sentences.
   (a) The area of Canada with limited precipitation, few large plants, permafrost, and cold winters is called the _____ biome.
   (b) The original source of energy for most ecosystems on earth is _____.
   (c) Within a food web, plants are classified as _____ and animals as _____
   (d) In a food web, organisms that break down organic matter, returning nutrients to the ecosystem for further growth, can be classified as _____ .
   (e) A group of animals of the same species, and living in the same area, is called a _____
   (f) An area in which organisms interact with the physical environment is called an _____ .
   (g) _____ factors, such as sunlight, water temperature, and wind, influence organisms within an ecosystem.
   (h) Ecological _____ are graphs that can be used to represent energy flow in food chains and food webs.
   (i) The _____ is the largest population of a species that an ecosystem can support.
   (j) The increasing concentration of a toxin in organisms as you move up a food chain is referred to as _____ .
   (k) At various stages in the decay process, bacteria break down nitrates to nitrites, and then to nitrogen gas in a process called _____.

2. Indicate whether each of the statements is true or false. If you think that the statement is false, rewrite it to make it true.
   (a) A hawk and and an owl occupy the same ecological niche.
   (b) Decomposers break down nitrogen-containing chemicals in animal waste into simpler chemicals such as ammonia (NH_3), then other decomposing bacteria convert ammonia into nitrites, and eventually to nitrates.
   (c) Because the denitrification process speeds up when the soil is very acid or water-logged, bogs often lack useful nitrogen.
   (d) If fertilizers are carried from the land to an aquatic ecosystem with spring runoff, the population of algae will decrease quickly.
   (e) A rapid increase in the deer population always indicates the ecosystem is healthy.
   (f) If the birth rate increases while death rate and immigration remain constant, the population will increase.

   (g) Biotic potential is the minimum number of offspring that a species could produce, if resources were unlimited.
   (h) Boreal forests receive less precipitation than tundra.
   (i) In general, warmer biomes have greater biological diversity.
   (j) The change in vegetation as you move in latitude from southern Ontario northward is similar if you climb a mountain.
   (k) Removing plants from an area will increase the fertility of the soil.
   (l) Lakes that are covered by a thick layer of ice contain more oxygen than open lakes during the winter months.

3. A step-by-step sequence showing how organisms feed on each other is referred to as:
   (a) an ecosystem (c) a population
   (b) a food chain   (d) an ecological pyramid

4. Bracket fungi, mushrooms, and bread mould are all:
   (a) producers   (c) carnivores
   (b) herbivores   (d) decomposers

5. An example of an endangered Canadian species is:
   (a) passenger pigeon   (c) Atlantic cod
   (b) eastern cougar   (d) grizzly bear

6. There are 2000 white-tailed deer in 100 km² of a forest. This description is of a deer:
   (a) community   (c) biome
   (b) population   (d) species

7. Which of the following describes abiotic factors in an ecosystem?
   (a) competition between species
   (b) predator-prey relationships
   (c) amount of sunlight
   (d) birth rate

Use **Figure 1**, which shows a food chain, to answer questions 8–11.

Figure 1

8. Which organism would be classified as the producer?
   (a) maple tree (c) spider
   (b) beetle   (d) sparrow

9. Which organism would be part of a population that would have the least biomass?
   (a) beetle (c) sparrow
   (b) spider (d) hawk

10. Which organism would have the greatest population?
    (a) maple tree (c) spider
    (b) beetle   (d) sparrow

11. Which level of organism has the least energy available to it?
    (a) beetle (c) sparrow
    (b) spider (d) hawk

The temperature of the air, the litter, the topsoil (10 cm below the surface) and the subsoil (30 cm below the surface) were monitored in one location in a temperate deciduous forest through the day. Use the data in **Figure 2** to answer questions 12 and 13.

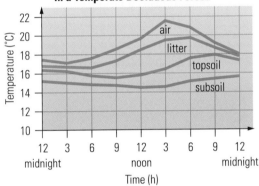

Temperature Readings Taken Over a 24-Hour Period in a Temperate Deciduous Forest

Figure 2

12. In which area of the forest did the greatest variation in temperature occur?
    (a) air   (c) topsoil
    (b) litter (d) subsoil

13. What abiotic factor would account for the greatest difference in temperature readings in the litter?
    (a) wind
    (b) exposure to sunlight
    (c) moisture of the soil
    (d) thickness of the blanket of leaves

14. Green plant are referred to as autotrophs. Autotrophs:
    (a) convert ammonia into nitrates.
    (b) carry out photosynthesis.
    (c) feed on primary consumers.
    (d) occupy the top of the food pyramid.

15. Use the Great Lakes food web in **Figure 3** to construct an ecological pyramid of numbers.

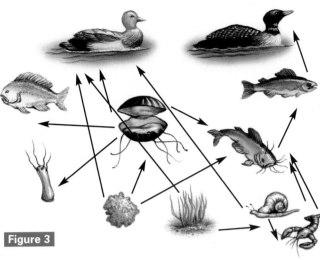

Figure 3

16. Data for **Table 1** were collected in four different locations.
    (a) Match each location with a Canadian biome.
    (b) On a map of Ontario indicate where you would find areas that match two of the locations.

Table 1

	Location 1	Location 2	Location 3	Location 4
community	grass, beetles, snakes, antelope	moss, lichens, blackflies, ptarmigan	spruce and fir trees, moss, ruffed grouse, grizzly bear	poplar, birch, and maple trees, heron, moose
soil type	thick topsoil with lots of humus	thin topsoil, permafrost below	thin, acidic topsoil layer	thick topsoil with lots of humus
annual precip. (cm)	10	4	40	102

Applying Inquiry Skills

Use **Figure 4** to answer questions 17-19. The conversion of ammonia to nitrates was measured in four soil samples, each with a different water content.

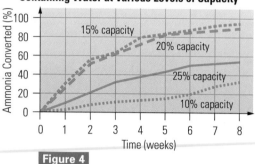

Figure 4

17. The amount of ammonia converted to nitrates after 4 weeks was approximately
    (a) 80% in the soil sample that contained 15% of its water capacity.
    (b) 80% in the soil sample that contained 10% of its water capacity.
    (c) 20% in the soil sample that contained 20% of its water capacity.
    (d) 20% in the soil sample that contained 25% of its water capacity.

18. According to the data presented, the best amount of water within the soils for conversion of ammonia to nitrates is
    (a) 10% capacity.   (c) 20% capacity.
    (b) 15% capacity.   (d) 25% capacity.

19. Develop a hypothesis that explains why conversion of ammonia to nitrates is so slow when the amount of water in the soil is only 10% of its capacity.

20. When carbon dioxide gas is dissolved in water, some of the gas reacts to form carbonic acid.
    Bromothymol blue indicator turns yellow in the presence of acids. **Figure 5** describes an experiment in which bromothymol blue indicator was added to

each of four test tubes. All of the test tubes were stored near a window and at the same temperature. The test tubes were observed at the beginning of the experiment and after two weeks. Observations from the experiment are recorded in **Table 2**.

Table 2

Test tube	Initial colour of water plus indicator	Final colour of water plus indicator
1	Dark blue	Dark blue
2	Dark blue	Dark blue
3	Dark blue	Yellow
4	Dark blue	Light blue

(a) What was the purpose of test tube 1?
(b) Using the carbon cycle as the basis for your answer, explain why test tube 3 changed color, but test tube 2 did not.
(c) Why is there little change in colour in test tube 4?
(d) Predict how the results of the experiment would change if the test tubes had been placed in a dark cupboard instead of in a window. Give your reasons.

Use the information provided in the graph in **Figure 6** to answer questions 21 and 22.

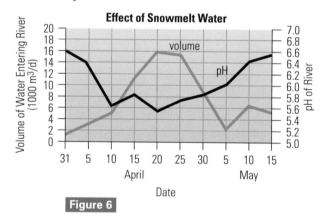

Figure 6

21. Describe and explain the data presented. Include specific dates and measurements in your summary.

22. Propose a hypothesis to account for the observations.

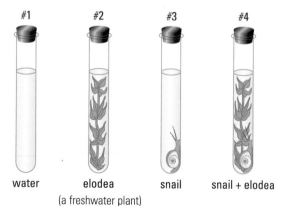

#1 water   #2 elodea (a freshwater plant)   #3 snail   #4 snail + elodea

Figure 5

Table 3

Year	Water depth (m)	Surface temperature (mean midday, July, °C)	Bottom temperature (mean midday, July, °C)
1885	25	25	10
1955	20	29	20
2000	14	30	25

Table 4

Year	Population of trout (per 1000 m³)	Population of perch (per 1000 m³)	Population of catfish (per 1000m³)
1885	12	22	14
1955	7	23	15
2000	1	12	16

Table 5   **Solubility of Carbon Dioxide and Oxygen in Water**

Temperature (°C)	CO₂ solubility (mg/L)	O₂ solubility (mg/L)
0	1.0	14.6
5	0.8	12.7
10	0.7	11.3
15	0.6	10.1
20	0.5	9.1
25	0.4	8.3
30	0.4	7.5

Making Connections

23. Scientists studying the same lake in an extended project collected the data in **Tables 3** and **4**.
    (a) According to the observations, what has been happening to the lake?
    (b) List factors that might explain why the lake becomes shallower.
    (c) It is projected that average summer temperatures will rise in this area. Using the data from the tables, predict long-term consequences of prolonged warming.
    (d) List factors that would contribute to an increase in the amount of dissolved carbon dioxide in Ontario lakes in winter.
    (e) Account for changes in the fish populations of the lake over time.
    (g) Identify two human activities that can accelerate the eutrophication of a lake and explain the environmental impact of these activities.
    (h) What can be done to reduce the impact of the human activities you identified?

24. The worldwide disappearance of frogs is a puzzle. In some areas, scientists don't really know what is causing the problem. Provide examples that support each of the following hypotheses as a possible explanation for the disappearance of frogs. Suggest things that the average citizen could do to remedy the problem implied in each hypothesis.
    (a) Hypothesis: loss of habitat
    (b) Hypothesis: falling quality of air and water
    (c) Hypothesis: increase in ultraviolet radiation
    (d) Hypothesis: climate change

25. Different cultures often look at the relationship between living organisms and their ecosystem differently.
    (a) Using the wolf as an example, explain how the worldviews of First Nations people and early European settlers were different.
    (b) Attitudes change over time. What evidence do you have that the attitude of modern Canadians towards ecosystems is different from that of early European settlers?
    (c) What further change in Canadian attitudes would you recommend?

26. The water entering the ocean from the river in **Figure 7** is polluted with nitrates. A group of

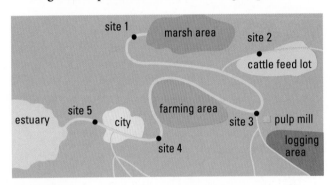

Figure 7

scientists decided to identify the sources of nitrogen pollution. They chose five different testing sites to measure nitrate concentration in the water.
    (a) Choose two sites and explain why these two sites might show a local source of nitrates.
    (b) Describe two effects of severe nitrate pollution.
    (c) Choose one site and describe how the level of nitrates in the water could be reduced.

27. The removal of all trees from a forest is called clear-cutting. After they are cut, the trees are separated by type and the wood is used to make many different products. Many of these products are sold to other countries; for example, Canada exports paper products to the United States.
    (a) Identify reasons why clear-cutting could be defended by businesses, governments, and forestry workers.
    (b) Identify some of the ecological problems associated with clear-cutting.
    (c) Identify and explain the roles of industry, government, and individuals in management of forest ecosystems in a way that ensures sustainability.

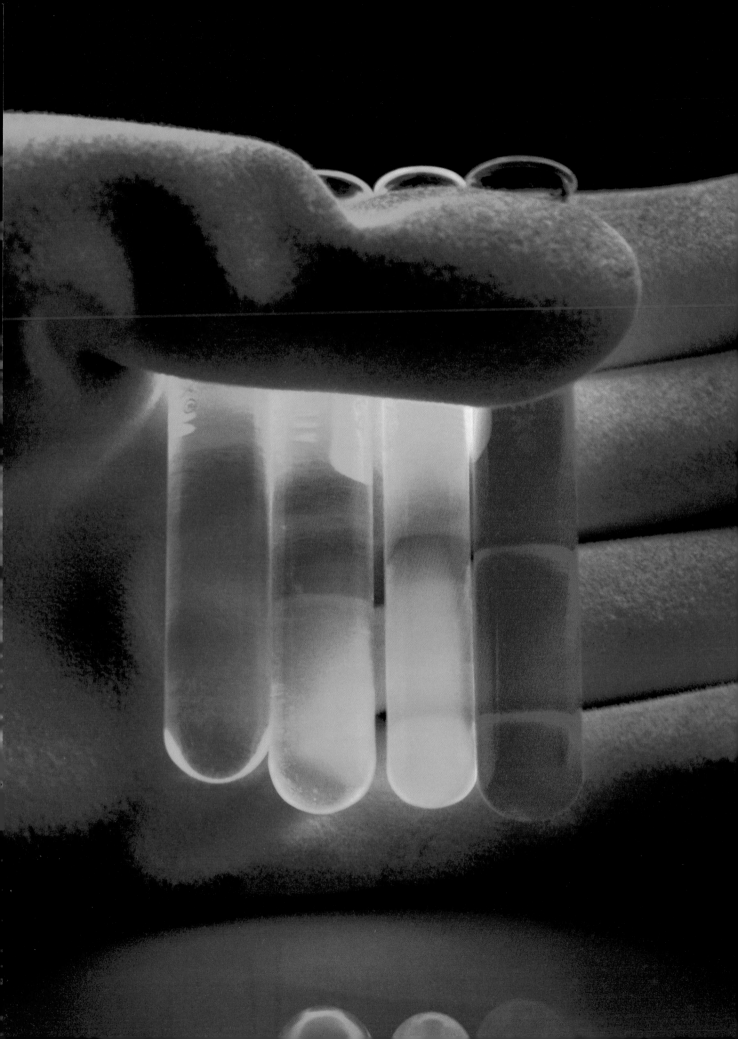

Chemical Processes

Chemical processes have a role in almost every aspect of everyday life. The clothes we wear, the food we eat, and the places where we live, work, and learn all contain the products of chemical reactions. The chemical industry that makes these products is a major driving force in our economy. Understanding chemical compounds and the reactions that they can undergo is key to developing new products and solutions to social and environmental problems.

Unit 2 Overview

Overall Expectations

In this unit, you will be able to

- describe chemical reactions and the symbolic systems used to describe them;
- investigate types of reactions and the factors that control their rates;
- develop an awareness of societal issues related to chemical compounds and their reactions.

Chapter 5
Chemicals in Action

Chemical compounds can be classified as ionic or molecular. These compounds can be represented with chemical formulas and naming systems. Both ionic and molecular compounds include naturally occurring and synthetic materials that can be used in a variety of products.

In this chapter, you will be able to

- recognize the relationships among chemical formulas, composition, and names;
- write the chemical formulas for ionic and molecular compounds, and name these compounds using appropriate vocabulary;
- perform chemical tests, including those to identify common gases, safely and accurately.

Chapter 6
Understanding Chemical Reactions

Chemical reactions can be classified according to the types of reactants involved. These reactions can be represented using word and balanced chemical equations. Chemical reactions can produce useful new products, but can also produce toxic substances that may affect the environment.

In this chapter, you will be able to

- apply the Law of Conservation of Mass to balance chemical equations;
- recognize and predict the products of different types of chemical equations;
- represent chemical reactions using word equations and balanced chemical equations;
- obtain qualitative and quantitative data to analyze patterns in chemical reactions, to compare theoretical and empirical values, and to calculate experimental errors;
- describe how an understanding of chemical reactions has led to the production of new consumer products and technological processes.

Chapter 7
Controlling Chemical Reactions

The speed or rate of chemical reactions can be affected by several factors, including temperature and concentration of reactants. Factors that affect rates of reaction can apply to laboratory experiments, to the production of chemicals in industry, and to common reactions around the home.

In this chapter, you will be able to

- explain how factors affect rates of chemical reaction;
- design and perform controlled experiments to gather experimental data and to investigate variables that affect rates of chemical reactions;
- identify everyday examples of ways in which rates of reaction are controlled.

Chapter 8
Acids and Bases

Acids and bases are compounds of particular interest because of their reactivity. They can be produced through the reaction of metals and nonmetals with oxygen and the reaction of their oxides with water. Acids and bases are important in many industrial reactions that produce both useful materials and pollutants.

In this chapter, you will be able to

- describe and experimentally investigate the relationships among metals, nonmetals, acidic oxides, basic oxides, acids, bases, and salts;
- describe acid-base neutralization and how the pH scale relates to the acidity of a solution;
- conduct experiments to identify the relative acidity or pH of common substances;
- explain how environmental challenges, such as acid rain, can be understood and addressed through a knowledge of acids and bases.

Chemistry and Society

Chemistry is the study of substances and their reactions. An understanding of chemical reactions allows us to invent new materials that have properties not dreamed of only a few decades ago. But understanding brings with it a responsibility to use these materials wisely.

You can practise chemistry by simply performing laboratory experiments; that way you will learn how chemicals interact. But the effects of science extend beyond the school walls. Learning about chemistry involves not only mixing substances in test tubes and researching specific topics, but also applying and extending the depth of your knowledge. As you learn about chemical processes, you will become more aware of the ways in which chemistry-related issues affect people's lives and our society as a whole.

As a citizen, you make personal choices and influence public decisions. Your growing knowledge of chemical processes will help you make informed decisions about issues that affect you in your home and community: Which products are most appropriate for a given use? Should tax dollars be spent on pollution control? Should the use of some chemicals be banned because of their effects on the environment? Should we be burning fossil fuels when these same fuels can be used to manufacture plastics? As a "chemistry-literate" citizen, you have the opportunity to help make better decisions as an individual and as a member of society.

As you work on one of the Challenges in this unit, you will learn in greater depth how our use and understanding of chemical processes benefit us, and how they require us to take responsibility for our actions.

Challenge

Assessing the Effects of Chemical Processes

As you learn about chemical processes, you will develop an awareness of the ways in which they may be applied and their impact on society.

1 Making a Consumer Product

The consumer products that we use today are made of a much wider variety of synthetic substances than those of 40 years ago. Choose a product and identify the materials that it is made of. Find out where the raw materials come from, and identify the chemical processes used to transform the raw materials into the product. Finally, assess the effects these processes have on society.

2 Marketing Alternative Fuels

Chemical reactions are used to propel most of our vehicles, even battery-powered toys. Research the substances and chemical processes that are used to power vehicles today. Then research alternative sources of chemical energy, such as hydrogen power, fuel cells, or more efficient batteries. Choose one of these sources and prepare a marketing proposal in which you promote your choice as the fuel of the future.

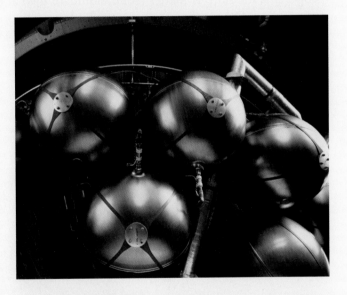

3 Acid Rain Action Plan

Acid rain is a product of our lifestyles. The demand for electricity and, in particular, our consumption of fossil fuels create huge amounts of air pollutants. Create an education plan that explains to people how their lifestyle decisions affect the production of acid rain. Then develop an action plan that could be used in your school or community to change people's attitudes and encourage them to adopt more "environment-friendly" habits.

Record your ideas for your Challenge as you progress through this unit, and when you see

Challenge

WHAT IS CHEMISTRY?

Chemistry is the study of matter, its properties, and its changes or transformations. **Matter** is anything that has mass and takes up space. All types of matter have physical and chemical properties. One physical property is the state of matter (solid, liquid, or gas) at room temperature. Other physical properties include colour, odour, lustre, solubility, and melting and boiling points. A piece of solid granite found on a shoreline may be grey, hard, and crystalline. Hand lotions are opaque, white liquids at room temperature. The carbon dioxide gas that we exhale with every breath is colourless and odourless. Every day we use hundreds of different types of matter.

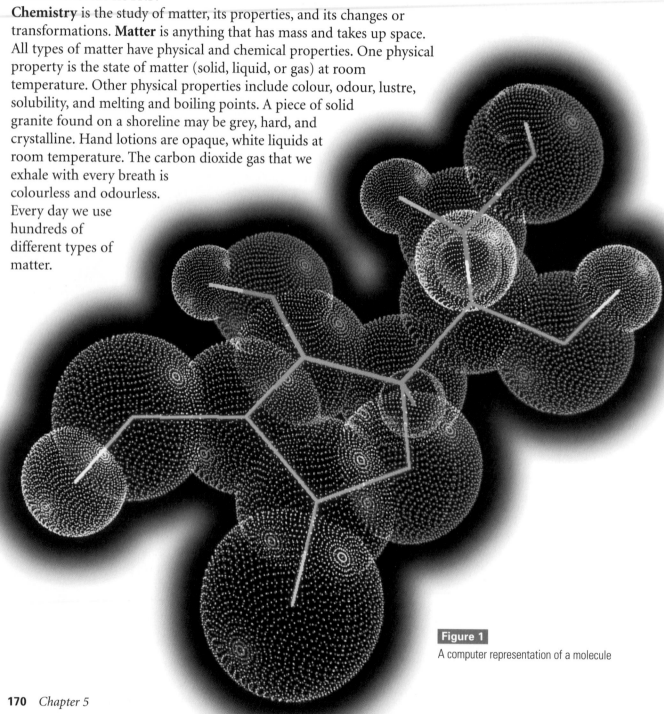

Figure 1

A computer representation of a molecule

Why are some chemicals safe and others dangerous to use? Chemists are trained to work safely with a variety of substances. Corrosive acids, reactive metals, and poisonous powders must all be used and disposed of safely. More importantly, everybody needs to understand the chemical properties of substances because they determine the changes or transformations that substances may undergo. Some substances, such as salt, simply dissolve when added to water. Other substances, such as household cleaners contain "active ingredients" that cause chemical reactions and should be used with caution.

How does chemistry affect our everyday life? Everything in the world involves chemistry because everything in the world is made of matter. Water, sand, and the oxygen in the air are substances that have always existed. Other molecules, such as DNA, have always existed, but have only been recently understood. Still other substances have been created in the last few years by chemists. "Bucky-balls" and "super-magnetic" ceramics have existed for only a few years. Scientists are constantly developing new drugs that fight cancer and other diseases.

Reflect on your Learning

1. Make a list of what you think are the 10 most important examples of matter that you encounter in a typical day.

2. What are five examples of substances that you might encounter in and around the home that need to be treated with care?

3. Make a table with two columns. In the first column, list chemical substances that you think have always existed; in the second column, list substances that you think have been developed and produced by people in the past 50 years.

Try This
Activity   Household Substances

We live in a world full of chemicals, and many of those chemicals are found in the home. The labels on household products, including foods and cleaners, often provide important information.

- With an adult's permission, find 5 to 10 household products that have labels. (Do not open the containers.) The information presented on the label can be qualitative (a list of ingredients) or quantitative (the percentage concentration of an ingredient). Note that product labels list the most abundant material first and the least abundant last.
- Make a table that summarizes the information, using the following questions as a guide:

(a) Describe the products you chose. Was there an "active ingredient" in each product? If the label listed a number of substances, what was the major ingredient?

(b) Was any quantitative information provided? For example, was the percentage concentration of an ingredient given?

(c) List any safety information or safety symbols that the labels provided. For example, was there a reference to daily use if the substance was a food? Were there any warnings, such as suggestions not to add the product to certain other materials?

(d) Describe any patterns in the amount and type of information that you noticed in certain groups of products: for example, were there similarities in the cleaning products?

Chemicals and Chemical Change

How can we make sense of the different types of matter that make up our world? Scientists classify matter either as pure substances or as mixtures (**Figure 1**). **Figure 2** shows the classification of matter.

Classifying Pure Substances

How do we know that a sample of matter is a pure substance? You have studied John Dalton's atomic model, which proposed that all matter is made up of particles. A **pure substance** is one in which all the particles that make up the substance are the same. As a result, the substance has constant properties. For example, pure water is a clear, colourless substance that freezes at exactly 0°C and boils at 100°C.

Chemists tend to classify pure substances on the basis of the particles of which they are made. In this system, pure substances are classified as elements or compounds. **Elements** are pure substances that cannot be broken down into simpler substances. Oxygen, hydrogen, iron, and mercury are elements because each contains only one kind of atom.

Figure 1

A pizza and a soft drink are examples of mixtures of pure substances. Mixtures can be either solutions (homogeneous mixtures) or heterogeneous mixtures. Which one is a solution, and which one is a heterogeneous mixture?

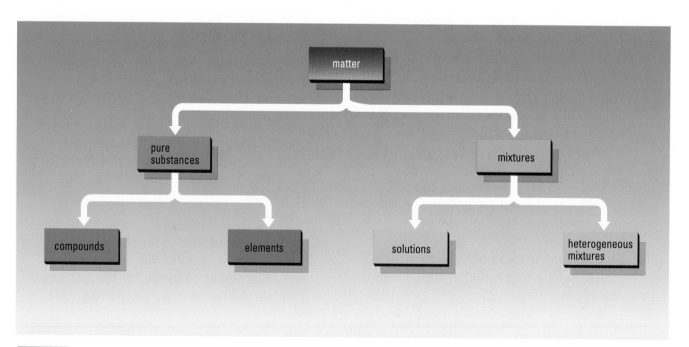

Figure 2

The classification of matter. Mixtures contain two or more pure substances. Solutions have only one visible component. Heterogeneous mixtures contain two or more visible components.

Elements can be identified with a chemical symbol. Pure gold (symbol Au) is completely made up of atoms of gold. All elements are listed in the periodic table (shown at the back of this text). Some elements consist of molecules, which are formed when two or more atoms join together; for example, the element oxygen (O) occurs in nature as pairs of oxygen atoms, or molecules of oxygen (O_2).

Compounds are pure substances that contain two or more different elements in a fixed proportion. Compounds can be identified with chemical formulas. For example, carbon dioxide (formula CO_2) is a compound. Each molecule of carbon dioxide is composed of one carbon atom and two oxygen atoms (**Figure 3**). Water (H_2O), carbon monoxide (CO), sodium chloride (NaCl or salt), and calcium carbonate ($CaCO_3$) are also compounds.

Figure 3

Each particle in dry ice, or solid carbon dioxide, is a molecule made up of one carbon atom and two oxygen atoms. It has the formula CO_2.

Properties of Matter

All matter has physical and chemical properties. The state of matter at room temperature, hardness, melting and boiling points, odour, solubility, and colour are all physical properties. A **physical property** is a characteristic of a substance. For example, baking soda is a pure substance that has a number of physical properties. It is a white, crystalline solid at room temperature that dissolves readily in water to form a solution. A change (such as dissolving or melting) in the size or form of a substance, which does not change the chemical properties of the substance, is called a **physical change**.

A **chemical property** is a characteristic behaviour that occurs when a substance changes to a new substance. The change itself is called a **chemical change** (**Figure 4**). For example, when baking soda is added to acid, a new substance, carbon dioxide gas, is formed. This reaction with acid is a chemical property of baking soda. When an iron nail is left out in the rain, it undergoes a chemical change: the iron combines with the oxygen in the air to form a new substance, iron(III) oxide (rust). The starting materials in such a change are called **reactants**, and the new materials produced are called **products**. For example, iron and oxygen are reactants and iron(III) oxide is a product.

A new colour appears.   Heat or light is given off.

Bubbles of gas are formed.   A solid material (called a precipitate) forms in a liquid.   The change is difficult to reverse.

Figure 4

Clues that a chemical change has happened

Chemical Tests

How are chemical changes useful? Chemical changes can be used to make new substances. They can also be used to identify unknown substances. For example, a geologist can add an acid to an unknown sample of rock. If bubbles of carbon dioxide gas are formed, the rock is probably limestone. As you work through this unit, you will encounter chemical reactions that can also be used to identify gases. For example, suppose that

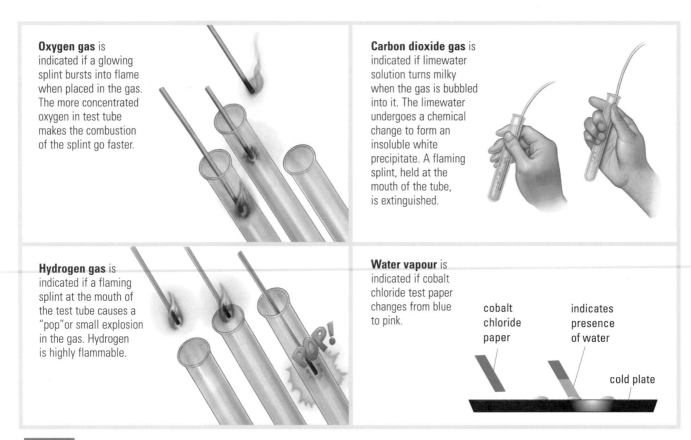

Oxygen gas is indicated if a glowing splint bursts into flame when placed in the gas. The more concentrated oxygen in test tube makes the combustion of the splint go faster.

Carbon dioxide gas is indicated if limewater solution turns milky when the gas is bubbled into it. The limewater undergoes a chemical change to form an insoluble white precipitate. A flaming splint, held at the mouth of the tube, is extinguished.

Hydrogen gas is indicated if a flaming splint at the mouth of the test tube causes a "pop" or small explosion in the gas. Hydrogen is highly flammable.

Water vapour is indicated if cobalt chloride test paper changes from blue to pink.

cobalt chloride paper

indicates presence of water

cold plate

POP!

Figure 5

Testing for gases

you did an experiment in which an odourless, colourless gas was produced. How would you know what the gas was? Oxygen, hydrogen, carbon dioxide, and water vapour are all odourless, colourless gases. However, they differ in the ways they interact with other chemicals. Chemists can use **chemical tests**, or distinctive chemical reactions, to identify unknown gases or other substances (**Figure 5**).

Chemicals and Safety

Imagine that you plan to work with a chemical in the school lab, at home, or in the workplace. How do you know what its properties are? How do you know what chemical reactions may occur if you mix the chemical with another substance? You may not have time to perform chemical tests to find out. Is there a way to predict a chemical's properties before opening the container?

Many chemicals can be hazardous to human health or to the environment if they are not handled safely. There are a variety of symbols that are used to identify hazardous chemicals. Many household products are labelled with Hazardous Household Product Symbols (HHPS). Dangerous materials in the workplace are labelled using the Workplace Hazardous Materials Information System (WHMIS). Every chemical that is ordered for use in your school arrives with a Materials Safety Data Sheet (MSDS). This sheet describes the hazards that are associated with the chemical, the protective clothing that should be worn when handling the chemical, and steps that should be taken if the chemical is spilled.

Challenge

1 What are the names of the chemical compounds that make up your consumer product?

Understanding Concepts

1. Classify each of the following as a pure substance or a mixture. Explain your choices.

   (a) soapy water

   (b) hydrogen gas

   (c) sodium chloride

2. Classify each of the following as an element or a compound. Explain your choices.

   (a) hydrogen

   (b) potassium carbonate

   (c) water

   (d) Mg

3. Draw sketches to represent 10 particles of the following:

   (a) an element

   (b) a compound

   (c) a mixture

4. Classify each of the following as a physical property or a chemical property. Explain your choices.

   (a) Gasoline is a clear pink solution.

   (b) Gasoline burns in air.

   (c) Water boils at 100°C.

   (d) Electric current can split water into hydrogen and oxygen gases.

5. When aluminum metal is added to hydrobromic acid, hydrogen gas and an aluminum bromide solution are formed.

   (a) What kind of change has occurred? Explain.

   (b) Which substances are the reactants and which are the products?

6. In your own words describe the chemical tests that can be used to identify the following gases:

   (a) hydrogen

   (b) oxygen

   (c) carbon dioxide

   (d) water vapour

7. When sodium carbonate is added to water, the sodium carbonate dissolves. When hydrochloric acid is added to the solution, the solution fizzes. What kinds of changes have occurred? Explain.

8. **(a)** Why does a glowing splint burst into flame when oxygen gas is tested?

   (b) When you test for hydrogen gas, another gas is involved as a reactant. What is this gas?

Making Connections

9. Two bottles of materials, as shown in **Figure 6**, are found in a laboratory.

Substance 1   Substance 2

Figure 6

   (a) What hazard is indicated on each bottle?

   (b) What safety precautions would you take if handling these materials?

10. Obtain a sample MSDS sheet from your teacher. Use the sheet to answer the following questions:

   (a) Write the name and formula of the substance.

   (b) Describe one physical property of the substance.

   (c) What fire or explosion hazard data are provided?

   (d) What health hazards are associated with the substance?

Reflecting

11. Which of the two hazard warning systems do you think is more effective: HHPS or WHMIS? Explain.

12. Discuss why it is necessary to have a system like WHMIS in the workplace. How does it benefit the employee or employer?

Try This Activity   A Lab Safety Concept Map

Make a laboratory safety concept map to place at the front of your notebook.

(a) Write "Lab Safety" in the middle of a sheet of Ⓑ paper. Draw lines out from the centre and, at the end of each line, write a word or phrase that summarizes a lab safety idea.

(b) Draw a map of your science classroom Ⓐ indicating the location of safety equipment.

Hazardous Household Chemicals

In Section 5.1 you reviewed how to use properties to classify substances. You also learned how symbols can be used to identify hazardous materials. How can you apply your knowledge to chemicals that you encounter in your home?

Household products, like everything else in the world, are made of substances that have their own particular properties. Many of these products are unreactive. You would not want a plastic container to react with the food inside it. Nor would you want an aluminum pan to catch on fire or react with food while you were making dinner! The less reactive many household products are, the better.

(a) Name five household products that are not reactive.
(b) For each product, describe the properties that make it useful.

Other household products are useful because they do interact with other materials. For example, some cleaning solutions dissolve grease in a physical change. Other cleaners contain bleach, which actually reacts with a stain in a chemical change to remove its colour. Household products can be toxic (poisonous), flammable, explosive, or corrosive (reactive). Product labels often identify these hazards using the Hazardous Household Product Symbols. Hazardous products must be used safely, and any waste must be disposed of properly so as not to damage the environment. Household products can be categorized according to where they are used: the garage, the kitchen and bathroom, the walls, and the garden.

(c) Give an example of a household product that works using a physical change and an example of a product that works using a chemical change.
(d) What are the four categories of Hazardous
ⒶHousehold Product Symbols that might be on a label?

Chemicals in the Garage

Automobiles use many different chemicals in various engine components. Gasoline, a mixture of molecules called hydrocarbons, burns in the engine and produces mainly carbon dioxide and water vapour, but also pollutants. Many other products used in cars contain hazardous chemicals and produce hazardous waste materials (**Figure 1**, and **Table 1**).

Figure 1

Car maintenance requires chemicals. Antifreeze, oil, and transmission fluids contain hazardous chemicals.

Table 1   **Automobile Products**

Chemical product	Hazardous ingredient(s)	Hazard
antifreeze	ethylene glycol	☠
transmission fluids	hydrocarbons	🔥 ☠
brake fluids	glycol ethers	🔥 ☠
used oils	hydrocarbons	🔥 ☠
batteries	sulfuric acid, lead	🜂 ☠

SKILLS HANDBOOK: Ⓐ Safety Conventions and Symbols

Concerns about the environment have led to the development of two approaches to dealing with chemicals in the garage. One possibility is finding alternative products to use. For automobile products, the main alternative to the use of chemicals is to not use the car at all! The second possibility is to improve waste management by finding safe ways of disposing of or recycling products used in cars. Service stations use such large amounts of these materials that they have systems for recycling most automobile products.

(e) What are some alternatives to using a car?
(f) Which waste product would you expect to be produced in greater quantities in Canada compared to warmer parts of the world? Explain.

Chemicals in the Kitchen and Bathroom

Cleaning products are used throughout the home (**Figure 2**). However, the greatest quantities of cleaners are used in the kitchen and bathroom. These products generally work in one of two ways. Many contain solvents (substances that can dissolve other substances) or detergents that dissolve grease and dirt (a physical change). Others contain substances that chemically react with dirt and stains. Many cleaners contain hazardous chemicals (**Table 2**).

There are numerous alternatives to using cleaning products that contain toxic chemicals. Blocked drains can be cleared using boiling water and plungers. Dissolving either baking soda or vinegar in water makes an effective cleaning solution, and borax dissolved in water is a practical disinfectant. A mixture of lemon juice and vegetable oil can be used as furniture polish.

The disposal of cleaners can create a hazard to the environment. The best approach to disposing of waste cleaners is to use up as much of the substance as possible so that there is a minimum of waste.

(g) What are the main hazards associated with cleaners?
(h) What safety precautions should you take when handling these substances?

Chemicals on the Walls

Have you ever felt dizzy when working with paints in an enclosed space? Paints and solvents make you feel this way because they contain hazardous chemicals

Figure 2
Cleaners contain a wide range of chemicals.

Table 2 **Cleaning and Related Products**

Chemical product	Hazardous ingredient(s)	Hazard
abrasive cleaners	trisodium phosphate	
window cleaner	ammonia	
mothballs	naphthalene	
bleach cleaners	hydrogen peroxide, sodium hypochlorite	
floor/furniture polishes	petroleum distillates	
rug cleaners	perchloroethylene, oxalic acid	
drain cleaners	sodium hydroxide, sulfuric acid	
disinfectants	diethylene glycol	
toilet cleaners	oxalic acid, calcium hypochlorite	
oven cleaners	sodium hydroxide, ammonia	

(**Figure 3**). All paints contain pigments (for colour), resin (for stickiness), and solvents (to dissolve the components of the mixture). Some of the substances in paint and related products are described in **Table 3**.

(i) Which type of hazard is most prevalent in these products?

Alternatives to paints are limited, although water-based products are less hazardous. Waste management includes fully using the products, storing any unused materials in tightly sealed containers, and straining solid waste through mesh to save any solvents. There are also often municipal programs for recycling paints and solvents.

Chemicals in the Garden

Chemicals used for lawns and gardens include fertilizers and pesticides. Fertilizers are generally not a major concern as long as they are used in appropriate amounts and properly stored. The compounds in pesticides and other yard products are extremely poisonous (**Table 4** and **Figure 4**). Pesticides are discussed in detail in Chapter 2.

(j) Which type of hazard is most prevalent in these products?

Alternatives to pesticides include the use of insecticidal soaps, predator insects such as ladybugs, and insect and mouse traps, as well as the removal of debris from gardens.

Waste management is important due to the toxicity of these products. Pesticides should be disposed of properly. Some communities hold special curbside collection days when pesticides and other hazardous wastes are collected.

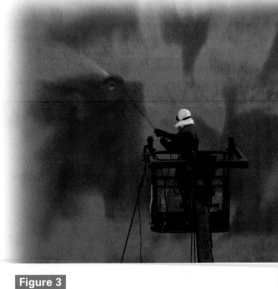

Figure 3

Paint products are a major source of hazardous household waste.

Table 3   Paint Products

Chemical product	Hazardous ingredient(s)	Hazard
oil-based paints	pigments, hydrocarbons	
water-based paints	pigments, resins, glycol ethers	
thinners and solvents	acetone, petroleum distillates	
wood preservatives	chlorinated phenols, creosote	
stains, finishes	halogenated hydrocarbons, mineral spirits	

Table 4   Pesticides and Other Yard Products

Chemical product	Hazardous ingredient(s)	Hazard
fungicides	captan, folpet	
insecticides	malathion	
general pesticides	pyrethrins, aldrin	
pet flea collars	carbamates, pyrethrins	
roach and ant killers	carbamates, pyrethrins	
rat and mouse poison	coumarins	
herbicides	2,4-D, prometon	
pool chemicals	hydrochloric acid, sodium hypochlorite	

Figure 4

Appropriate protective gear should be worn when using pesticides.

Understanding Concepts

1. **(a)** In what ways are household wastes hazardous?

   (b) Which type of hazard is posed by the largest number of products?

2. Give an example of a hazardous substance that might be found

   (a) in the garage

   (b) in the kitchen

   (c) in the bathroom

   (d) in the garden

3. Give two examples each of the physical changes and the chemical changes involved in the use of household products.

4. Where in the house do you find the highest concentration of hazardous compounds? Why do you think this is so?

5. Find five household products that have suggestions for first-aid treatment on the labels. What general suggestions are made?

Making Connections

6. Which automobile products does your local service station recycle? Which products do they dispose of? What government regulations apply to this process? Phone your nearest service station to find out the answers to these questions.

7. How does your local greenhouse or plant nursery deal with hazardous waste? Phone your nearest garden centre to find out the answer to this question.

8. Disposing of chemical products, whether hazardous or not, can cause problems. Research and report on the meanings of the following terms and how they relate to the disposal of chemical wastes:

   (a) nonbiodegradable

   (b) landfill

   (c) runoff

   (d) incinerator

5.3 Investigation

INQUIRY SKILLS MENU
○ Questioning   ○ Planning   ● Analyzing
○ Hypothesizing   ● Conducting   ○ Evaluating
○ Predicting   ● Recording   ● Communicating

Testing Properties of Substances

How can you investigate a chemical substance in the laboratory? As you have seen, labels, WHMIS symbols, and the MSDS can provide some information about the physical and chemical properties of substances. You can also use chemical tests to investigate the properties of a substance.

Physical properties that can be tested for in the laboratory include solubility in water and the ability to conduct an electrical current. An **electrolyte** is a substance whose water solution can conduct electricity. A nonelectrolyte is a substance whose water solution does not conduct electricity.

Chemical properties can also be investigated in the laboratory. For example, the characteristic chemical reaction of a substance with an acid is a chemical property because it results in the production of a new substance, usually a gas. Often, the gas itself can be identified through observation of its properties. In this investigation, you will have the opportunity to review some basic lab skills as you investigate the properties of substances.

Question

How can the physical and chemical properties of substances be determined?

Design

In this investigation, you will test the solubility and electrical conductivity of several substances. You will also investigate the reactions of some substances with acid, and use chemical tests to determine the identity of gases formed as products.

(a) Read the Procedure and make a table to record
(K7) your observations. For Parts 1 and 2, possible headings could be *Substance tested*, *Solubility in water*, and *Conductivity of solution*. For Part 3, possible headings could be *Starting materials*, *Observations during change*, and *Observations during gas test*.

Materials

- apron
- safety goggles
- sodium chloride (salt)
- sodium bicarbonate (baking soda)
- calcium carbonate powder (chalk)
- potassium bromide
- calcium chloride
- copper(II) sulfate
- glucose
- sucrose (table sugar)
- scoopula or toothpicks
- large-well "comboplate" microtray or 11 50-mL beakers
- distilled water
- tap water
- vegetable oil
- conductivity apparatus
- mossy zinc
- hydrochloric acid solution (10% or 1.0 mol/L)
- 3 small test tubes
- test tube holder
- wooden splints
- limewater (calcium hydroxide) solution (0.02 mol/L)
- rubber stopper or cork

 Copper(II) sulfate and potassium bromide are poisonous and are irritants. Report any spills to your teacher.

 Hydrochloric acid is corrosive. Any spills on the skin, in the eyes, or on clothing should be washed immediately with plenty of cold water. Report any spills to your teacher.

SKILLS HANDBOOK: (K7) Preparing Tables of Evidence

Procedure

Part 1: Solubility in Water

1 Put on your apron and safety goggles (**Figure 1**).

Figure 1

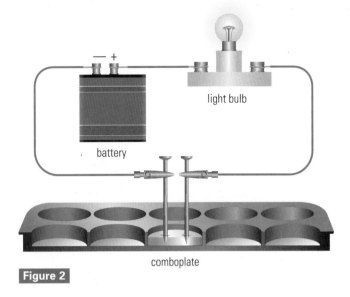

Figure 2

2 Obtain small samples of each of the following solids: sodium chloride, sodium bicarbonate, calcium carbonate, potassium bromide, calcium chloride, copper(II) sulfate, glucose, and sucrose.

3 Number eleven microtray wells or beakers. Each well or beaker will hold a different set of substances. Half-fill each of eight microtray wells with distilled water.

4 Add a small amount (enough to cover the tip of the scoopula) of sodium chloride to well 1. Stir the mixture to see whether the solid will dissolve. Save the mixture for Part 2. Record your observations.

5 Repeat step 4 with the seven other solids (one in each of wells 2 through 8). Record your observations.

Part 2: Conductivity

6 Half-fill three more microtray wells with distilled water (well 9), tap water (well 10), and vegetable oil (well 11).

7 Assemble the conductivity apparatus, as shown in **Figure 2**. Insert the two nails into the well containing distilled water (well 9). If the lamp glows, the liquid conducts electricity. If the lamp does not glow, the liquid does not conduct electricity. Rinse and dry the nails. Record your observations.

8 Insert the conductivity apparatus into the well containing tap water (well 10). After testing for conductivity, rinse and dry off the nails. Record your observations.

9 Insert the conductivity apparatus into the vegetable oil (well 11). After testing for conductivity, dry off the nails to remove any oil coating, rinse them with water, and dry them again. Record your observations.

10 Insert the conductivity apparatus into each of the mixtures in the remaining eight wells in turn (i.e., wells 1 through 8), cleaning the nails between trials. If the lamp glows, the solid is an electrolyte. If the lamp does not glow, the solid is a nonelectrolyte. Record your observations.

Part 3: Reaction with Acid

11 Obtain a small amount of zinc. Place hydrochloric acid solution to a depth of 2 cm in a small test tube.

12 Add the zinc to the hydrochloric acid. When the reaction has proceeded for about 30 s, light a wooden splint and bring it to the mouth of the test tube (**Figure 3**). Record your observations.

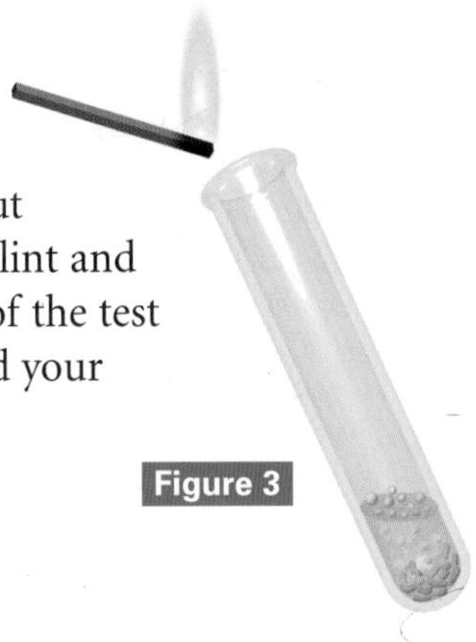

Figure 3

13 Place hydrochloric acid to a depth of about 0.5 cm in a test tube. Add about three times the volume of water to make a more dilute hydrochloric acid solution. In another test tube, place limewater to a depth of about 2 cm.

14 Obtain a small amount of calcium carbonate powder (enough to cover a fingernail). Add the calcium carbonate to the dilute hydrochloric acid. When the reaction has proceeded for about 30 s, carefully pour the product gas from the reaction into the limewater solution (**Figure 4**).

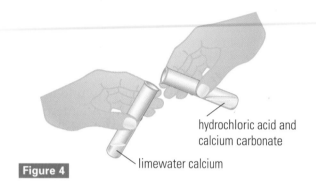

hydrochloric acid and calcium carbonate

limewater calcium

Figure 4

Do not allow any of the liquid to pour from the reaction tube. Insert a rubber stopper or cork into the limewater tube and shake the tube to dissolve the gas. Record your observations.

15 Dispose of the mixtures in your test tubes and microtrays as instructed by your teacher. Clean up your work station. Wash your hands.

Analysis

(b) Which substances were soluble in water? Which were insoluble?

(c) Which soluble substances were electrolytes? Which were nonelectrolytes?

(d) What gas was produced when zinc and hydrochloric acid were mixed?

(e) What gas was produced when calcium carbonate was added to hydrochloric acid solution?

(f) Write up your investigation as a formal
(Q) lab report.

Understanding Concepts

1. Which properties in this investigation were physical and which were chemical? Explain.

2. What gases were tested for in this activity? What chemical test was used for each gas?

3. (a) What do the substances whose water solutions conduct electricity have in common? For example, what kinds of elements are they composed of?

   (b) Sucrose and glucose contain the elements carbon, oxygen, and hydrogen. What kinds of elements are these?

   (c) What conclusions can you make about substances that conduct or cannot conduct electricity when dissolved in water?

Making Connections

4. What safety precautions did you follow in this investigation?

Exploring

5. Carbon dioxide is naturally present in air and can be produced using common household materials.

   (a) Plan a way to test air for the presence of carbon dioxide.

   (b) Plan methods of testing whether carbon dioxide is
   (K) present when

      (i) a seltzer tablet is placed in water

      (ii) a can of pop is opened

      (iii) vinegar is added to baking soda

   Check all procedures with your teacher. Try the methods, observing all safety measures, and write a brief report on the ways in which carbon dioxide is produced.

Reflecting

6. Complete the following statement: "Something that captured my attention in this investigation was ... ."

Lynn Walker

Chemical Engineer

Lynn Walker has always wanted to apply her science interests and training to challenging, real-world problems. She discovered that she could accomplish all this as a chemical engineer.

Lynn earned a degree in chemical engineering from the University of Waterloo in 1998. She took a five-year co-op program alternating four months of class study with four months of work in the field. During those co-op terms, she worked in the paint department of a car-manufacturing plant, for Environment Canada, and at Petro-Canada.

Lynn enjoyed her Petro-Canada experience and now is a process engineer in the company's Oakville refinery. She works in a team that solves problems arising in the refinery's day-to day operations and also makes sure that all oil-processing systems are operating at peak efficiency. A big focus of her work is ensuring that environmental regulations are met. To address these efficiency and environmental goals, chemical engineers have to be innovative.

"You need to be creative in your thinking. Part of being a process engineer is getting your coveralls on and going out into the plant to obtain physical measurements, which sometimes requires climbing tall distillation towers. You also must talk to a range of refinery personnel from tradespeople, to other engineers, and to senior management," Lynn says.

During high school, Lynn excelled at science and math, but was also strong in English. According to Lynn, good communication skills are a necessity in chemical engineering.

She became interested in engineering during her senior year of high school. Lynn admits that when choosing a career, she was influenced by her father's career choice (an electrical engineer). She was able to see firsthand that engineering is an applied science, mixing theory and practice.

While the academic training of Lynn's chemical engineering degree gave her the background needed in the petroleum industry, much of her learning has been acquired on the job. And there's a lot to know, given the different chemical distillation processes involved in creating the many products made from crude oil: gasoline, diesel, jet fuel, home heating oil, asphalt for roads, materials used to manufacture plastics, and sulfur, a by-product sold to make sulfuric acid.

Asked what she most enjoys about her work, Lynn replies, "It's hands-on and applied. You can see direct results of the work you do, and you're always learning. The field never stays still."

Making Connections

1. Lynn emphasizes the importance of good communication skills in her work. Interview an engineer to find out what communication tools or techniques are used.

Work the Web

Visit www.science.nelson.com and follow the links from Science 10, 5.4 to help you answer the questions below.

(a) How does an engineer qualify to have P. Eng. after his or her name?

(b) List industries and other places where a chemical engineer might work.

Elements and the Periodic Table

In Investigation 5.3, you discovered that some substances are electrolytes—their water solutions conduct electricity. Such substances as sodium chloride, potassium bromide, lithium fluoride, and calcium chloride all produce solutions that are electrical conductors. What makes these compounds electrolytes?

Substances such as vegetable oil and sugar are nonconductors, or insulators, when they are dissolved in water. They are nonelectrolytes. What makes these compounds different from electrolytes? We can answer these questions by looking at the types of elements that make up these compounds.

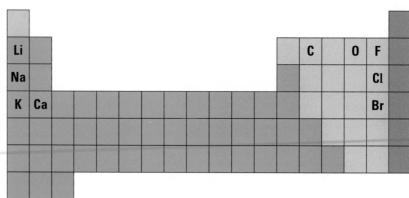

Figure 1
The position of elements in the periodic table provides hints about the types of compounds they form.

The Periodic Table

You have already learned that all the elements can be organized into a **periodic table** — a structured arrangement of elements that helps us to explain and predict physical and chemical properties. You will see a more detailed periodic table at the back of this text, but **Figure 1** shows a periodic table with only certain elements highlighted.

Elements such as sodium (Na) and potassium (K) were combined with other elements, such as chlorine (Cl) and bromine (Br) to form the compounds you encountered in Investigation 5.3. Note that sodium chloride, potassium bromide, lithium fluoride, and calcium chloride all involve pairs of elements that are on opposite sides of the periodic table. Something about the structure of these compounds results in the formation of conducting solutions.

Sugar and methyl alcohol contain carbon (C) and oxygen (O), which are both on the right side of the table. Even when these substances dissolve in water, they are nonelectrolytes. How does the arrangement of elements in the table reflect the types of compounds that elements form?

The periodic table is generally arranged with metals toward the left side of the table. Sodium, potassium, lithium (Li), and calcium (Ca) are all metals (**Figure 2**). Nonmetals are generally found on the right side of the

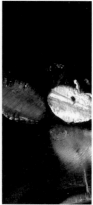

Figure 2
Metals are generally shiny solids.

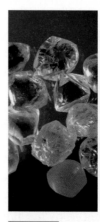

Figure 3
Nonmetals exist in all three states of matter at room temperature.

table. Carbon, oxygen, fluorine (F), and chlorine are all nonmetals (**Figure 3**). One exception is the lightest element, hydrogen (H). Although it is located in the top left corner of the periodic table, it behaves mostly as a nonmetal.

Metals and nonmetals have quite different physical and chemical properties, as **Table 1** shows. These properties can be explained by considering the structure of the atoms that make up these elements.

Table 1	Properties of Metals and Nonmetals	
Property	**Metals**	**Nonmetals**
lustre	shiny	dull
malleability	malleable	brittle
conductivity	conductors	mostly insulators
reactivity with acid	mostly yes	no
state at room temperature	mostly solids	solids, liquids, and gases

Chemical Families

Elements in the periodic table can be grouped into families. **Chemical families** are groups of elements in the same vertical column of the periodic table. They tend to have similar physical and chemical properties. For example, the elements in the far left column of the periodic table are called **alkali metals**. These elements, also called Group 1 elements, include lithium, sodium, and potassium, and are all shiny, silvery metals. They form compounds that are mostly white solids and are very soluble in water. Group 2 elements, also known as **alkaline earth metals**, include magnesium (Mg), calcium, and barium (Ba). These elements are also shiny, silvery metals, but they form compounds that are often insoluble in water.

The elements in the far right column of the periodic table are called the **noble gases**. Noble gases include such elements as helium (He) and neon (Ne). Generally, noble gases do not form compounds.

The elements in the second column from the right are called **halogens**. These nonmetallic elements, also called Group 17 elements, include fluorine, chlorine, and bromine. Halogens are all poisonous elements that react readily with sodium and other alkali metals.

Elements and Atomic Structure

What are atoms made of? The Bohr-Rutherford model of the atom (**Figure 4**) suggests that atoms are composed of three types of subatomic particles: protons, neutrons, and electrons. **Protons** are heavy positively charged particles that are found in a dense positive core of the atom called the nucleus. The number of protons in an atom is equal to the element's atomic number. **Neutrons** are neutral particles that have about the same mass as protons and are also found in the nucleus. **Electrons** are negatively charged particles with almost no mass that "circle" the nucleus at different energy levels, also called orbits or shells. Since atoms are electrically neutral, the number of electrons in an atom equals the number of protons.

The key to understanding the formation of compounds is understanding the arrangement of the electrons about the nucleus.

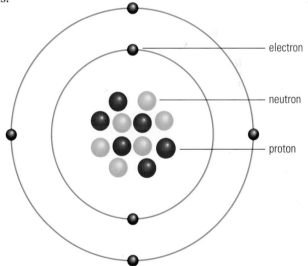

electron

neutron

proton

Figure 4

In the Bohr-Rutherford model of the atom, electrons travel in orbits about a positively charged nucleus. This is a model of a carbon atom (not to scale).

The farther away an electron is from the nucleus, the greater is its energy and the more likely it is to be involved in a chemical change. Thus, the electrons in the outer orbit are involved in bonding. We can use **Bohr diagrams** to represent the arrangement of electrons in various orbits. Each orbit has a definite number of electrons. The first orbit can have a maximum of two electrons. The second orbit can have no more than eight electrons and, for elements with up to twenty electrons, the third orbit can also have no more than eight electrons. **Figure 5** shows Bohr diagrams for several elements.

The noble gases do not easily form compounds because their arrangements of electrons are particularly stable. The electron arrangements for the first three noble gases are shown in **Figure 6**.

When elements form compounds, changes occur in the arrangement of electrons. In some compounds, electrons are transferred from one atom to another (or to several others) so that the atoms can have the stable electron arrangements of the closest noble gases.

Consider what might happen to the electrons in a metal such as lithium. As you can see in **Figure 5**, lithium has two electrons in the first orbit and one in the second orbit. If lithium loses the electron in its outer orbit, it has the same stable electron arrangement as helium: two electrons in the first orbit. But the lithium atom no longer has a neutral electric charge. It has formed an **ion**, a charged atom in which the number of electrons is different from the number of protons. The **ionic charge** is the numerical value of the electric charge with a plus or minus sign. For example, the lithium ion has an ionic charge of 1+, because it has three positive protons in the nucleus and only two negative electrons (see **Figure 7**). The lithium atom has become a positive lithium ion, Li^{1+} which is commonly written as Li^+.

A similar electron transfer happens to calcium when it forms compounds. Calcium, as shown in **Figure 5**, has two electrons in the first orbit, eight in the second orbit, eight in the third orbit, and two in the fourth orbit. If calcium loses two electrons, it has the same electron arrangement as the noble gas argon. The result is a Ca^{2+} ion (because it has twenty protons, but only eighteen electrons). Metals tend to have one, two, or three electrons in their outer orbits. They tend to lose these electrons when they combine with other elements to form positive ions.

What happens to the electrons in nonmetals such as fluorine or sulfur (S)? Consider the electron arrangement in fluorine as shown in **Figure 5**. Fluorine has two electrons in the first orbit and seven electrons in the second. If it gains one electron, it will have the stable electron arrangement of neon. The fluorine atom becomes a stable fluorine ion, F^-. When nonmetals gain electrons to form ions, the name of the ion changes its ending to "ide." Thus, a F^- ion is called a fluoride ion.

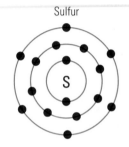

Figure 5

Bohr diagrams for lithium (element 3), fluorine (element 9), sulfur (element 16), and calcium (element 20).

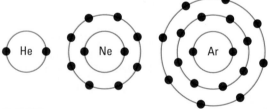

Figure 6

Helium (element 2), neon (element 10), and argon (element 18) have stable electron arrangements, and do not readily form compounds.

Similarly, sulfur has sixteen protons in its nucleus and sixteen electrons arranged in three orbits (**Figure 5**). If it gains two electrons to become an ion, it will have the stable electron arrangement of argon. The sulfur atom becomes a stable sulfide ion, S^{2-}. Nonmetals tend to have five, six, or seven electrons in their outer orbits. They all tend to gain electrons when they combine with metals to form compounds.

	Lithium	Calcium	Fluorine	Sulfur
protons	+3	+20	+9	+16
electrons	−2	−18	−10	−18
	+1	+2	−1	−2

Figure 7

Lithium, calcium, fluorine, and sulfur either gain or lose electrons to form stable ions. Protons are positive and electrons are negative.

Did You Know?

Positive ions are also called cations, and negative ions are also called anions. An easy way to remember these terms is that a**n**ions are **n**egative and ca**+**ions are **+**ve.

Understanding Concepts

1. Set up a chart to compare metals and nonmetals with respect to the following:
   - **(a)** lustre
   - **(b)** conductivity
   - **(c)** location in the periodic table
   - **(d)** state at room temperature
   - **(e)** numbers of electrons in the outer orbit
   - **(f)** tendency to gain or lose electrons
   - **(g)** charges of ions formed
   - **(h)** other properties
   - **(i)** examples
2. What element is located in the metallic area of the periodic table, but has mainly nonmetallic properties?
3. How many electrons are found in each of the first three orbits for the first twenty elements?
4. Draw Bohr diagrams for the following:
   - **(a)** a boron atom
   - **(b)** a chlorine atom
   - **(c)** a nitrogen atom
   - **(d)** a beryllium atom
5. What kind of arrangement of electrons in the outer orbit does a stable ion have?
6. **(a)** Draw Bohr diagrams for the stable ion formed by each of the atoms in question 4.
   - **(b)** State the number of electrons gained or lost to form each ion.
   - **(c)** State the ionic charge on each of the ions.
   - **(d)** Name the noble gas that has the same number of electrons as each ion.
7. A new element, ontarium (On), has been formed. We know that it is a halogen.
   - **(a)** How many electrons does it have in its outer orbit?
   - **(b)** What will be the name of the compound it forms with sodium?
   - **(c)** What will be the name of the compound it forms with calcium?
   - **(d)** Predict the formulas of the compounds named in (b) and (c).
8. Atoms and ions are described as isoelectronic if they have the same number of electrons. Name the noble gas that is isoelectronic with each of the following stable ions:
   - **(a)** Li^+
   - **(b)** F^-
   - **(c)** Ca^{2+}
   - **(d)** S^{2-}
   - **(e)** Br^-
   - **(f)** Rb^+

How Elements Form Compounds

The model you have just learned of, with atoms losing or gaining electrons to become stable, explains how some compounds are formed. For example, both sodium and chlorine are highly reactive. Atoms of these elements combine by transferring electrons from one to another as shown in **Figure 1**. Sodium chloride is a relatively harmless compound because the sodium and chlorine atoms have formed stable ions. The compound formed is called an **ionic compound** because it is made up of positive and negative ions that have resulted from the transfer of electrons from a metal to a nonmetal. The positive and negative ions are attracted to each other because they have opposite charges. **Figure 2** shows some common ionic compounds.

Consider a slightly more complicated example. Calcium and fluorine react to form calcium fluoride, an ionic compound. Each calcium atom has two electrons in its outer orbit that it tends to lose to become more stable. Each fluorine atom has seven electrons in its outer orbit and needs to gain only one more electron to become stable. How can this mismatch of electrons be solved? The solution is that one calcium atom requires two fluorine atoms to form the compound calcium fluoride (**Figure 3**).

Sodium burns rapidly in chlorine gas to form the compound sodium chloride, a compound so harmless that you sprinkle it as salt onto your French fries. This reaction is too dangerous to carry out in a classroom. Each atom of sodium loses an electron to an atom of chlorine.

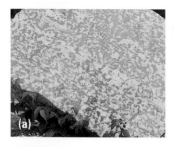
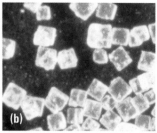

Figure 2

(a) Limestone ($CaCO_3$), **(b)** sodium chloride (table salt), **(c)** road salt (calcium chloride), and **(d)** copper(II) sulfate (algaecide) are all examples of ionic compounds.

Figure 3

The calcium atom transfers one electron to each of the two fluorine atoms. The result is one calcium ion, Ca^{2+}, and two fluoride ions, F^-. The overall charge of the compound is zero because the positive charge on the calcium ion balances the negative charges on the two fluoride ions. The compound is calcium fluoride (CaF_2).

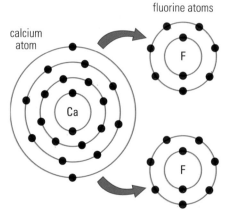
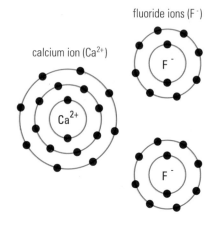

Chemical Formulas and Composition of Compounds

A chemical formula is a combination of symbols that represents a particular compound. As you have seen, ionic compounds can be represented by such formulas. The formula $MgCl_2$ (magnesium chloride) describes a compound in which the combining ratio of magnesium ions to chloride ions is one magnesium ion to two chloride ions. Similarly, the formula AlF_3 (aluminum fluoride) describes a compound in which the combining ratio of aluminum ions to fluoride ions is one aluminum ion to three fluoride ions.

Ionic compounds dissolve in water to form solutions that conduct electricity because they are made up of charged ions. When the substances are dissolved in water, the ions separate from one another and are now free to move and carry electric current (**Figure 4**).

In Investigation 5.3, you found that compounds such as distilled water (H_2O), glucose ($C_6H_{12}O_6$), and sucrose ($C_{12}H_{22}O_{11}$) were non-electrolytes. Such compounds, called **molecular compounds**, are formed when nonmetals combine with other nonmetals. You will learn about molecular compounds in lesson 5.11.

Figure 4
When ionic compounds are placed in water, the ions separate and are surrounded by water molecules. They are electrolytes.

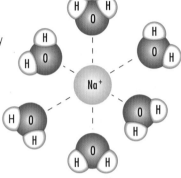

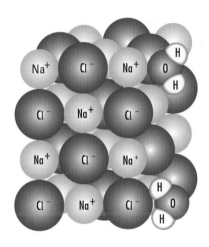

$$NaCl_{(s)} \longrightarrow Na^+_{(aq)} + Cl^-_{(aq)}$$

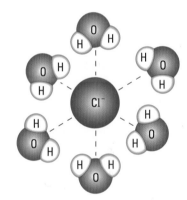

Understanding Concepts

1. **(a)** How do metals form ionic compounds with nonmetals?

   (b) Describe the process with an example.

2. Beryllium and fluorine react to form an ionic compound.

   (a) Which element is the metal and which is the nonmetal?

   (b) Draw Bohr diagrams of beryllium and fluorine.

   (c) How many electrons must each element gain or lose to form stable ions?

   (d) Draw sketches to show how this compound forms by transfer of electrons.

   (e) Indicate the ionic charges on the ions.

   (f) What is the overall charge on the compound?

   (g) What is the chemical formula of the compound?

3. Repeat question 2 for the compound formed by aluminum and fluorine.

4. What part of the atom is involved in making chemical bonds?

5. Look at your observations from Investigation 5.3.

   (a) Which substances conducted electricity?

   (b) What ions did they form when they dissolved in water?

Ionic Charges and Chemical Families

In section 5.5 you reviewed the structure of the atom and learned how some atoms can form stable ions by gaining or losing electrons. You have also learned that the periodic table is a useful organizing tool for understanding and predicting the behaviour of substances. Elements in the same vertical column of the periodic table are described as members of the same chemical family or group. **Figure 1** shows some of these chemical families. For example, lithium, sodium, potassium, and other Group 1 metals are all members of a family called the alkali metals. Beryllium, magnesium, and other Group 2 metals are members of a family called the alkaline earth metals. And fluorine, chlorine, and other nonmetals are members of the halogen family.

How is an element's position in the periodic table related to the types and formulas of the compounds that it forms? In this activity, you will investigate and summarize the information that will enable you to write your own chemical formulas.

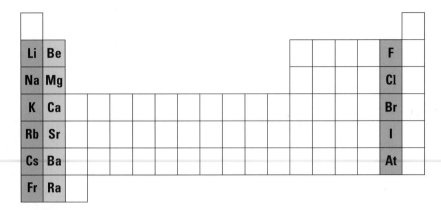

Figure 1

The location of the alkali metals (dark green), the alkaline earth metals (light green), and the halogens (red) in the periodic table.

Procedure

1 Construct a table titled "Alkali Metals" that includes the following information:

- the names of the alkali metals (remember that hydrogen is a special element with special properties and is not a member of this family);
- the symbols of the alkali metals;
- Bohr diagrams for the first three alkali metals;
- Bohr diagrams for the stable ions that the alkali metals will form;
- the ionic charge for the alkali metal ions.

2 Construct a table titled "Alkaline Earth Metals" that includes the following information:

- the names of the alkaline earth metals;
- the symbols of the alkaline earth metals;
- Bohr diagrams for the first three alkaline earth metals;
- Bohr diagrams for the stable ions that the alkaline earth metals will form;
- the ionic charge for the alkaline earth metal ions.

3 Construct a table titled "Halogens" that includes the following information:

- the names of the halogens;
- the symbols of the halogens;
- Bohr diagrams for the first three halogens;
- Bohr diagrams for the stable ions that the halogens will form;
- the ionic charge for the halogen ions;
- the name of each ion.

Analysis

(a) For the alkali metals (**Figure 2**), what connections can you draw from the data in your tables (names, symbols, ionic charges, symbols for the ions, and electrons in the outer orbit)?

(b) For the alkaline earth metals, what connections can you draw from the data in your tables (names, symbols, ionic charges, symbols for the ions, and electrons in the outer orbit)?

(c) For the halogens, what connections can you draw from the data in your tables (names, symbols, ionic charges, symbols for the ions, and electrons in the outer orbit)?

Figure 2
Sodium, like all alkali metals, reacts vigourously in water.

Understanding Concepts

1. For the metallic elements sodium, magnesium, and aluminum, answer the following questions:

   (a) Draw a Bohr diagram for each element. How many electrons are in their outer orbits?

   (b) Do these metallic elements tend to gain or lose electrons? Give reasons for your answer.

   (c) What is the charge on each of the metal ions? (Include the ion symbol.)

2. For the nonmetallic elements nitrogen, oxygen, and fluorine, answer the following questions:

   (a) Draw a Bohr diagram for each element. How many electrons are in their outer orbits?

   (b) Do these nonmetallic elements tend to gain or lose electrons? Give reasons for your answer.

   (c) What is the charge on each of the nonmetal ions? (Include the ion symbol.)

Exploring

3. Predict the names and charges of the ions that cesium, barium, and bromine might form.

Reflecting

4. This activity did not involve the family of elements on the far right side of the table. Why?

5. This activity omitted the family of elements that includes carbon (element 6) and silicon (element 14). The compounds that these elements form will be discussed in lesson 5.11.

   (a) Draw Bohr diagrams for carbon and silicon.

   (b) Do you think that these elements tend to gain or lose electrons? Give reasons for your answer.

Ionic Compounds

There are over one hundred elements in the periodic table, and thousands of different compounds are formed when these elements combine. How can we name these compounds? How can we write formulas to represent them?

In section 5.7, you saw that the periodic table and a knowledge of electronic structure could be used to predict the ionic charges of elements. Elements in the same families tend to form ions with similar ionic charges. Such an ionic charge may also be called the **valence**, or combining capacity, of an element. **Figure 1** shows the ionic charges of selected elements. Some elements with more than 20 electrons are included, although their electronic structure is more complicated than the model we have discussed so far.

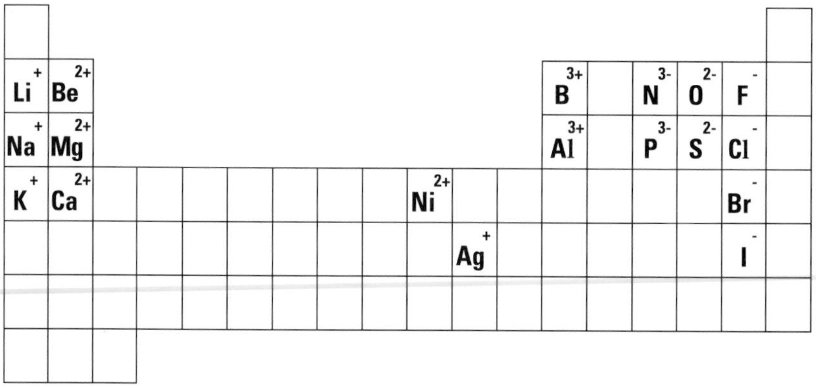

Metals and nonmetals combine to form ionic compounds by transferring electrons. The metal atoms lose electrons to form positive ions, and the nonmetal atoms gain those electrons to form negative ions. The result is a compound that is electrically neutral. The sum of the charges on the positive ions equals the sum of the charges on the negative ions.

Consider the compound aluminum chloride ($AlCl_3$). As you can see in **Figure 1**, the ionic charge of the aluminum ion is 3+ and the ionic charge of each chloride ion is 1–. Since the compound contains a ratio of one Al^{3+} ion to three Cl^- ions, the total ionic charge is described by the following expression:

$$(3+) + 3(1-) = 0$$

The positive and negative ions attract each other to make a stable compound. Another way to look at the process is to think of the aluminum atom as losing three electrons, one to each of three chlorine atoms (**Figure 2**).

Figure 1

Ionic charges (or valences) of some elements in the periodic table.

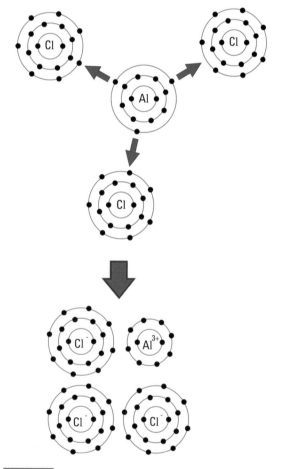

Figure 2

An aluminum atom transfers electrons to three chlorine atoms to form a stable compound of aluminum chloride.

Writing Formulas for Ionic Compounds

How can you write formulas for ionic compounds? You could randomly try different numbers of positive and negative ions until you obtained a neutral compound. However, a more logical approach involves a series of steps, as shown in the following example.

What is the formula for the ionic compound formed by calcium and iodine?

Step 1. *Write the symbols, with the metal first.*
   Ca   I

Step 2. *Write the ionic charge above each symbol to indicate the stable ion that each element forms.*
   $2+$ $1-$
   Ca   I

Step 3. *Determine how many ions of each type you need so that the total ionic charge is zero.*
   One Ca^{2+} ion will balance the charge of two I^- ions.

Step 4. *Write the formula using subscripts to indicate the number of ions of each type.*
   The formula is Ca_1I_2 or CaI_2. The subscript "1" is unnecessary because the symbol itself represents one atom or ion.
   The total ionic charge is $(2+) + 2(1-) = 0$

Consider a second example in which the above steps are described as rules.

What is the formula for the ionic compound formed by aluminum and sulfur?

Rule 1: Write the symbols of the elements.
   Al   S

Rule 2: Write the ionic charges.
   $3+$ $2-$
   Al   S

Rule 3: Choose the number of ions to balance the charge.
   The total ionic charge is $(3+) + (2-) = 1+$
   Therefore, to balance the ionic charge,
$$2(3+) + 3(2-) = 0$$
   Two Al^{3+} ions will balance the charge of three S^{2-} ions.

Rule 4: Write the formula using subscripts.
   The formula is Al_2S_3.

There is another simple way to obtain the formula of a compound, called the "crisscross" rule, which replaces Rules 2, 3, and 4.

What is the formula for the ionic compound formed by aluminum and sulfur?

Crisscross Rule: Write the ionic charges above the symbols. Then crisscross the numbers, using them as subscripts.

$$3+ \quad\quad 2-$$
$$Al \quad\quad S$$

The formula is Al_2S_3.
The total ionic charge is $2(3+) + 3(2-) = 0$

Consider a final example, in which the "crisscross" rule is modified.

What is the formula for the ionic compound formed by nickel and oxygen?

Rule 1: Write the symbols of the elements.
Ni   O

Crisscross Rule: Write the ionic charges above the symbols and crisscross them.

$$2+ \quad\quad 2-$$
$$Ni \quad\quad O$$

The formula is Ni_2O_2.
However, the formula must have the lowest number of ions that will produce an electrically neutral compound. Dividing by the common factor (in this case, 2), we find that the correct formula must be NiO.
The total ionic charge is $(2+) + (2-) = 0$

In the same way, the compound formed by tin ions (Sn^{4+}) and oxide ions (O^{2-}) would seem to have the formula Sn_2O_4. However, this formula can be reduced to SnO_2.

Naming Ionic Compounds

In many cases, the names of ionic compounds are quite straightforward. Just as in the chemical formula, the name of the metal is first, followed by the name of the nonmetal. However, the *ending* of the name of the nonmetal changes to "ide." For example, the compound formed by calcium and iodine is called calcium iodide. The compound formed by aluminum and sulfur is called aluminum sulfide. **Table 1** gives the names of some nonmetals in ionic compounds.

Table 1	Names and Ionic Charges of Some Nonmetals		
Name of element	**Symbol**	**Ionic charge**	**Name in compound**
fluorine	F	1–	fluoride
chlorine	Cl	1–	chloride
bromine	Br	1–	bromide
iodine	I	1–	iodide
oxygen	O	2–	oxide
sulfur	S	2–	sulfide
nitrogen	N	3–	nitride
phosphorus	P	3–	phosphide

Names and Formulas for Atoms with More Than One Ionic Charge

Some metals are able to form more than one kind of ion. For example, the element copper forms two completely different compounds when it reacts with chlorine. One of the compounds is white; the other is yellow. Chemists have found that the ionic charge on the copper in the white compound is 1+. Its chemical formula is CuCl, since the ionic charge of chlorine is always 1−. The ionic charge on the copper in the yellow compound is 2+. Its formula is therefore $CuCl_2$. **Table 2** shows the names and ionic charges of some metals that have more than one ionic charge.

These compounds are named in the same way as other ionic compounds, except that a Roman numeral (as shown in **Table 2**) is added in round brackets after the metal to indicate its ionic charge. For example, CuCl is called copper(I) chloride because the ionic charge on the copper is 1+. $CuCl_2$ is called copper(II) chloride because the ionic charge on the copper is 2+. Remember that you have to use the Roman numeral system only when naming the ions of metals that can have more than one ionic charge.

Table 2	Names and Multiple Ionic Charges of Some Metals		
Name of element	**Symbol**	**Ionic charges**	**Roman numeral**
copper	Cu	1+, 2+	I, II
iron	Fe	2+, 3+	II, III
lead	Pb	2+, 4+	II, IV
tin	Sn	2+, 4+	II, IV

 **Challenge**

1 Are there any ionic compounds in your product? What are their names?

Understanding Concepts

1. **(a)** How does the sum of the charges on the positive ions compare to the sum of the charges on the negative ions in ionic compounds?

   (b) Calculate the sum of the ionic charges in the compound Al_2O_3. Show your calculation.

2. Draw a Bohr diagram to show the electron transfer that occurs when magnesium and fluorine form the compound magnesium fluoride.

3. Write the formulas for the compounds formed by the following combinations of elements:

   (a) lithium and fluorine

   (b) calcium and bromine

   (c) sodium and nitrogen

   (d) aluminum and nitrogen

4. Name each of the compounds in question 3.

5. Write the formulas for the following compounds:

   (a) sodium iodide

   (b) beryllium fluoride

   (c) magnesium oxide

   (d) aluminum sulfide

6. Write the names for the following compounds:

   (a) KCl

   (b) Na_3P

   (c) CaF_2

7. Write the formulas for the following compounds:

   (a) copper(I) bromide

   (b) copper(II) bromide

   (c) iron(II) sulfide

8. Write the names for the following compounds:

   (a) $SnCl_2$

   (b) $SnCl_4$

   (c) $PbBr_2$

9. Write the formula and name of the compound formed by each of the following combinations of ions. (Note that some of these ions will require the use of Roman numerals in the names.)

   (a) Fe^{3+} and O^{2-}

   (b) Ca^{2+} and F^-

   (c) Cu^+ and S^{2-}

10. In mining, some minerals are referred to as ferrous. What metallic element is present in these compounds? (Hint: Look at the letters that begin the word.)

Polyatomic Compounds

You have investigated such compounds as calcium carbonate, sodium bicarbonate, calcium hydroxide, and copper(II) sulfate. These names do not seem to fit the naming pattern we have been examining so far. What are these compounds?

Such compounds are pure substances that involve combinations of metals with polyatomic ions (**Table 1**). **Polyatomic ions** are groups of atoms that tend to stay together and carry an overall ionic charge. An example of a polyatomic ion is the nitrate ion (**Figure 1**). When a compound containing this ion is dissolved in water, the positive metal ion and the nitrate ion separate from each other, but the nitrate ion itself stays together as a unit surrounded by water molecules.

Table 1	Common Polyatomic Compounds	
Compound	**Formula**	**Use or source**
calcium carbonate	$CaCO_3$	chalk and building materials
magnesium hydroxide	$Mg(OH)_2$	stomach antacids
sulfuric acid	H_2SO_4	car battery acid
sodium hypochlorite	$NaClO$	clothing bleach
copper(II) sulfate	$CuSO_4$	fungicide
sodium carbonate	Na_2CO_3	laundry detergents
ammonium nitrate	NH_4NO_3	fertilizer

Writing Formulas for Polyatomic Compounds

The ionic charges of polyatomic ions make it possible for them to form ionic compounds. **Table 2** lists some common polyatomic ions and their ionic charges.

When a polyatomic ion such as nitrate or sulfate combines with other elements, we follow the same rules for writing formulas that we learned in section 5.8, just as if it were an individual nonmetal ion. Consider the following example.

What is the formula for the ionic compound formed by sodium and a sulfate ion?

Rule 1: Write the symbols of the metal and of the polyatomic group.
   Na SO_4

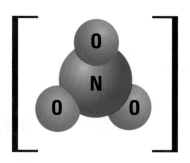

Figure 1
The nitrate ion contains one nitrogen atom tightly bonded to three oxygen atoms. The overall ionic charge on the ion is 1–.

Table 2	Common Polyatomic Ions and Their Ionic Charges	
Name of polyatomic ion	**Ion formula**	**Ionic charge**
nitrate	NO_3^-	1–
hydroxide	OH^-	1–
bicarbonate (hydrogen carbonate)	HCO_3^-	1–
chlorate	ClO_3^-	1–
carbonate	CO_3^{2-}	2–
sulfate	SO_4^{2-}	2–
phosphate	PO_4^{3-}	3–

Did You Know?

Acid spills in the laboratory can be safely neutralized by sprinkling solid sodium bicarbonate ($NaHCO_3$, or baking soda) on them. The bicarbonate ion (HCO_3^-) combines with the acid to form harmless carbon dioxide gas and water.

Rule 2: Write the ionic charges.

$$1+ \qquad 2-$$
$$\text{Na} \qquad \text{SO}_4$$

Rule 3: Choose the number of ions to balance the charge.
Two Na^+ ions will balance the charge
of one SO_4^{2-} ion.

Rule 4: Write the formula using subscripts.
The formula is Na_2SO_4.
The total ionic charge is $2(1+) + (2-) = 0$

As an alternative, you can use the "crisscross" rule.

Rule 1: Write the symbols of the metal and of the polyatomic group.
Na SO_4

Crisscross Rule: Write the ionic charges above the symbols and crisscross them.

$$1+ \qquad\qquad 2-$$
$$\text{Na} \qquad\quad \text{SO}_4$$

The formula is Na_2SO_4.
Note that polyatomic ions do not "reduce." For example, the
formula Na_2SO_4 cannot be simplified to Na_1SO_2 because the SO_4
is a group.

Naming Polyatomic Compounds

The name of the ionic compound in the previous
example is simply sodium sulfate. This stable
compound is shown in **Figure 2**. The names for
polyatomic compounds are relatively straightforward.
The name is simply a combination of the name of
the metal and the name of the polyatomic ion.

For example, the compound formed by a
carbonate ion (CO_3^{2-}) and a potassium ion (K^+) has
the formula K_2CO_3 and its name is potassium
carbonate. You will note that the positive part of the
compound is always written first in both the formula
and the name. Ammonium (NH_4^+) and nitrate
(NO_3^-) combine to form ammonium nitrate
(NH_4NO_3).

Polyatomic ions make it possible to have an even wider range of ionic
compounds, especially when they combine with metals that may have
more than one ionic charge.

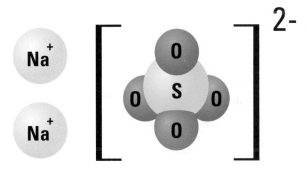

Figure 2
Sodium sulfate is made up of two sodium ions (each with an ionic
charge of 1+) combined with a sulfate ion (one sulfur atom tightly
bonded to four oxygen atoms, with a total ionic charge of 2-). The
overall compound is neutral.

Consider the following example.

What is the formula of lead(IV) carbonate? Note that lead has two different valences, but the Roman numeral tells you which one to use.

Rule 1: Write the symbols of the metal and of the polyatomic group.
    Pb CO_3

Crisscross Rule: Write the ionic charges above the symbols and crisscross them.

$$\overset{4+}{Pb} \diagdown \diagup \overset{2-}{CO_3}$$

The formula is $Pb_2(CO_3)_4$, which must be reduced to $Pb(CO_3)_2$. Note that parentheses are included in the formula to show the number of CO_3 ions in the formula.

Oxyacids

There are many types of polyatomic ions, but one special group should be mentioned. **Oxyacids** are compounds formed when hydrogen combines with polyatomic ions that contain oxygen. The hydrogen has an ionic charge of 1+ in these compounds. **Table 3** describes and names some common oxyacids.

Table 3	Common Oxyacids			
Ion name	Ion formula	Ionic charge	Oxyacid formula	Oxyacid name
nitrate	NO_3^-	1–	HNO_3	nitric acid
nitrite	NO_2^-	1–	HNO_2	nitrous acid
chlorate	ClO_3^-	1–	$HClO_3$	chloric acid
carbonate	CO_3^{2-}	2–	H_2CO_3	carbonic acid
sulfate	SO_4^{2-}	2–	H_2SO_4	sulfuric acid
sulfite	SO_3^{2-}	2–	H_2SO_3	sulfurous acid
phosphate	PO_4^{3-}	3–	H_3PO_4	phosphoric acid

Understanding Concepts

1. In your own words, explain what is meant by the term "polyatomic ion." Give two examples.

2. What happens to the ions in the compound sodium nitrate when it dissolves in water?

3. Write the formulas for the following compounds:
   (a) sodium phosphate
   (b) calcium sulfate
   (c) potassium chlorate
   (d) aluminum hydroxide
   (e) beryllium nitrate
   (f) magnesium hydrogen carbonate (magnesium bicarbonate)
   (g) nickel carbonate

4. Write the names for the following compounds:
   (a) K_2CO_3
   (b) Na_2SO_4
   (c) $Al(HCO_3)_3$
   (d) $AgNO_3$

5. **(a)** What pattern do you see in the formulas of the oxyacids and the original ionic charge of the polyatomic ion? Explain, with two examples.
   (b) Why does this pattern make sense?

6. Why is ammonium nitrate (NH_4NO_3) not written as $N_2H_4O_3$?

7. Some polyatomic ions have a positive charge. The ammonium ion (NH_4^+) is an example. Give the names and formulas of the compounds formed by this ion with:
   (a) a chloride ion
   (b) a sulfate ion

INQUIRY SKILLS MENU
- ○ Questioning
- ○ Hypothesizing
- ○ Predicting
- ○ Planning
- ● Conducting
- ● Recording
- ● Analyzing
- ● Evaluating
- ● Communicating

Testing for Ions

What kinds of substances are present in a glass of water? We know that there are molecules of water (H_2O) present, but are there other substances as well? People often say that water from a different area has a different taste. Could there be small amounts of substances dissolved in a water sample from one area that gives it a different composition from another sample of water?

In fact, drinking water does contain many different substances (**Figure 1**). Some are added deliberately during the process of water purification. But many substances in water occur naturally. As rainwater passes through the ground, minerals dissolve into the water. These minerals are ionic compounds that may contain ions such as calcium (Ca^{2+}), magnesium (Mg^{2+}), iron (Fe^{3+}), chloride (Cl^-), nitrate (NO_3^-), or sulfate (SO_4^{2-}).

One method of detecting these ions is to use chemical tests. Such tests can also be used to identify unknown ions. A **positive test** for a substance is one that clearly indicates the substance is present. A positive test for a dissolved ion may produce an insoluble precipitate or it may produce a coloured product. In this investigation, you will use chemical tests to investigate the ions that are dissolved in water.

Question

How can samples of water be tested for the presence of chloride ions (Cl^-), sulfate ions (SO_4^{2-}), and iron ions (Fe^{3+})?

Design

In this investigation you will test solutions containing three known ions with various testing solutions. You will then test some unknown solutions with the same testing solutions and compare your observations to determine which ions are present in the unknown solutions.

(a) Plan a table to record your observations. Write the names of the testing solutions along the top and the names of the known solutions and the codes for the unknown ones on the side.

Figure 1
Water quality technicians test water for dissolved substances.

Materials

- apron
- safety goggles
- testing solutions:
  - silver nitrate solution (0.5% or 0.03 mol/L)
  - barium chloride solution (2% or 0.1 mol/L)
  - potassium thiocyanate solution (1% or 0.1 mol/L)
- sample solutions:
  - potassium chloride solution (3% or 0.4 mol/L)
  - sodium sulfate solution (3% or 0.2 mol/L)
  - iron(III) nitrate solution (3% or 0.1 mol/L)
- unknown solutions:
  - teacher-provided solutions containing one or more ions
  - samples of water from various sources (tap water, bottled waters, etc.)
- labelled microdroppers
- microtrays

 Silver nitrate solution is toxic and can stain skin and clothing. Barium chloride and potassium thiocyanate are toxic. Iron (III) nitrate is an irritant. Any spills on the skin, in the eyes, or on clothing should be washed immediately with cold water.

Part 1: Testing Known Solutions
Procedure

1 Put on your apron and safety goggles.

2 Obtain a microdropper containing potassium chloride solution (source of chloride ion) and a second microdropper containing silver nitrate solution.

3 Add one or two drops of the first solution to one of the wells on the microtray. Add one or two drops of the second solution to the same well (**Figure 2**). Record your observations, particularly noting the appearance and colour of both starting materials and any product.

4 Obtain a microdropper containing sodium sulfate solution (source of sulfate ion) and a microdropper containing barium chloride solution. Repeat step 3 in another well on the microtray. Record your observations.

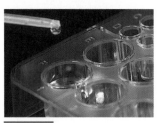

Figure 2

 Avoid cross-contamination of micro-droppers and solutions; let solutions "free-fall" into the microtray wells rather than touching the dropper to the microtray.

5 Obtain a microdropper containing iron(III) nitrate solution (a source of iron(III) ions) and a microdropper containing potassium thiocyanate solution. Repeat step 3 in another well on the microtray. Record your observations.

Part 2: Testing Unknown Solutions

6 Obtain a microdropper containing one of the unknown solutions provided by your teacher. Use the testing solutions in separate microtray cells to determine whether chloride, sulfate, or iron(III) ions are present in the solution. Record your observations.

7 Repeat step 6 for other unknown solutions.

8 Dispose of the mixtures and put away your materials as directed by your teacher. Clean up your work station. Wash your hands.

Analysis

(b) Make a table to summarize the observations that indicate a positive test for chloride, sulfate, and iron(III) ions. Possible headings could be: *Type of ion, Reagent solution added,* and *Observation for positive test.*

(c) Make a table to summarize your analyses of the unknown solutions.

Understanding Concepts

1. **(a)** Explain what is meant by a positive test for an ion.

   (b) Describe two types of changes that demonstrate a positive test.

2. Write chemical formulas for the following substances:

   (a) silver nitrate

   (b) barium chloride

   (c) sodium sulfate

   (d) iron(III) nitrate

3. Why do you think chemical tests, similar to the tests used in this investigation, are called qualitative analyses?

4. If a silver nitrate solution is added to a potassium chloride solution and a precipitate forms, what are the names and formulas of the possible products?

Exploring

5. Suppose that you were asked to determine whether an ion was present in a solution and how much ion was present.

   (a) Compare the amounts of precipitate that you would expect if you added barium chloride to two solutions that contained different amounts of sulfate ion.

   (b) Compare the colour intensity that you would expect if you added potassium thiocyanate to two solutions that contained different amounts of iron(III) ion.

   (c) Design an experiment to compare the amount of
   (K4) chloride, sulfate, or iron(III) ion present in a solution.

Molecular Compounds

Imagine that you find an unlabelled container of solid white crystals in the kitchen. You are sure that the crystals are either salt or sugar. A simple taste test will tell you what the crystals are. But imagine that you find the same crystals in the lab. A taste test is too dangerous, so you dissolve the crystals in water and test for conductivity. If the solution conducts electricity, the compound must contain ions. Salt, or sodium chloride, is an ionic compound. In ionic compounds, metals with one, two, or three electrons in their outer shell lose electrons to nonmetals, which often have five, six, or seven electrons in their outer shell. If the solution does not conduct electricity, it must be a different kind of compound.

Most of the compounds you encounter every day do not contain ions. Rather, they contain neutral groups of atoms called molecules. Sugar is a molecular compound. It is made up of molecules in which nonmetal atoms, such as hydrogen and oxygen, share electrons to form stable arrangements. Water and carbon dioxide are also molecular compounds, whether in a gas, a liquid, or a solid state. The particles in ionic and molecular compounds are different, as shown in **Figure 1**.

Hydrogen gas is a molecule formed when two hydrogen atoms combine. Each hydrogen atom has one electron. Helium is the nearest noble gas with a stable electron arrangement — it has two electrons in the first orbit. For the two hydrogen atoms to become stable, both must gain an electron. They do this by sharing a pair of electrons, one from each atom, as shown in **Figure 2**.

The result is a **covalent bond** — a shared pair of electrons held between two nonmetal atoms that holds the atoms together in a molecule. Many nonmetals form molecules in this way. For example, chlorine gas is a molecule that consists of two chlorine atoms held together with a covalent bond. Each chlorine atom has seven electrons in its outer orbit and needs to gain one electron to become stable. The atoms share electrons to form a

Figure 1

Salt (NaCl) is an example of an ionic compound made up of ions of opposite charge. Ice (H_2O) is an example of a molecular compound made up of neutral molecules.

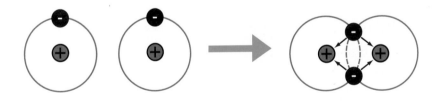

Figure 2

Two hydrogen atoms share a pair of electrons to form a covalent bond. Both negative electrons are attracted by the positive nuclei of both atoms.

stable arrangement, as shown in **Figure 3**.

Many nonmetallic elements exist as covalently bonded molecules. **Table 1** lists elements that form diatomic molecules (molecules made of two atoms). This table includes only molecules made up of two identical atoms, but atoms of different elements can also form covalent bonds.

Molecular compounds are all around us (**Figure 4**). A bottle of soda pop contains water molecules, sugar molecules (usually compounds called sucrose, glucose, or fructose), and other molecules that provide flavour and colour. All of these molecular compounds are made up of nonmetal elements that are sharing electrons. The models and electronic structure of some simple molecular compounds are shown in **Figure 5**.

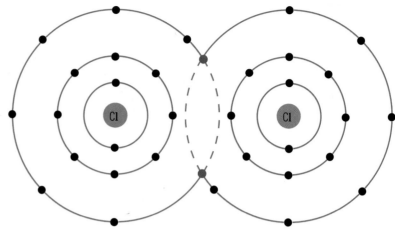

Figure 3

Two chlorine atoms share a pair of electrons to form a covalent bond. Each chlorine atom now has eight electrons in its outer orbit.

Table 1   **Elements That Form Diatomic Molecules**

Name of element	Chemical symbol	Formula (and state at room temperature)
hydrogen	H	H_2 (gas)
oxygen	O	O_2 (gas)
nitrogen	N	N_2 (gas)
fluorine	F	F_2 (gas)
chlorine	Cl	Cl_2 (gas)
bromine	Br	Br_2 (liquid)
iodine	I	I_2 (solid)

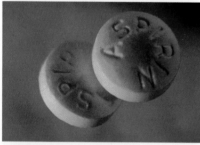

Figure 4

Sugar, Aspirin, and gasoline are all examples of molecular compounds.

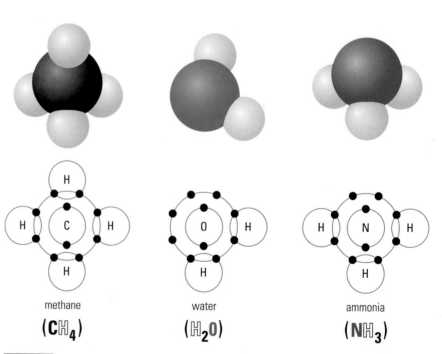

methane

(CH_4)

water

(H_2O)

ammonia

(NH_3)

Figure 5

Methane, water, and ammonia are all covalently bonded molecules.

Writing Formulas for Molecular Compounds

The formulas of many molecular compounds can be predicted using a method similar to the one you used for ionic compounds. The number of electrons that metals and nonmetals transfer to become stable ions can be a clue to the formula of an ionic compound. Similarly, the number of electrons that a nonmetal needs to share to become stable is a clue to the number of covalent bonds it can form. The **combining capacity** of a nonmetal is a measure of the number of covalent bonds that it will need to form a stable molecule. These combining capacities are listed in **Table 2**.

Carbon (element 6) has four electrons in its outer (or valence) orbit. If it lost four electrons, it would have the electron arrangement of helium (element 2) and would form a positive ion. If it gained four electrons, it would have the electron arrangement of neon (element 10) and would form a negative ion. It turns out that carbon cannot form either ion. Instead it "gains" four electrons by sharing; carbon has a combining capacity of four. For example, when carbon shares one of its outer orbit electrons with each of four different hydrogen atoms, as shown in **Figure 5**, the result is methane (CH_4), the major component of natural gas. As a result of forming covalent bonds through sharing electrons, the atoms end up with a stable electron arrangement in their outer orbit similar to that of a noble gas.

You can use the combining capacity to write the formulas of molecular compounds without having to consider electronic structure. Consider the following example.

How would you write the formula for a compound formed between carbon and sulfur?

Rule 1: Write the symbols, with the left-hand element from **Table 2** *first, with the combining capacities.*
    4   2
    C   S

Rule 2: Crisscross the combining capacities to produce subscripts.

    4   ╳   2
    C   S

The formula is C_2S_4.

Rule 3: Reduce the subscripts if possible.
    The formula C_2S_4 can be reduced to C_1S_2.

Rule 4: Any "1" subscript is not needed.
    The correct formula is CS_2.

Naming Molecular Compounds

Many molecular compounds have simple names. The compound H_2S is called hydrogen sulfide, much as if it were ionic. Other molecular compounds have names that are familiar to us, even though they do not follow a system.

Table 2	Combining Capacities of Nonmetal Atoms		
4	**3**	**2**	**1**
			H
C	N	O	F
Si	P	S	Cl
	As	Se	Br
			I

Common names have been used for centuries for water (H_2O); ammonia (NH_3), which is used in many cleaning products; hydrogen peroxide (H_2O_2), used in antiseptic solutions; and methane (CH_4), found in natural gas.

The names of molecular compounds often contain prefixes. These prefixes are used to count the number of atoms when the same two elements form different combinations. For example, the gas that you exhale is carbon dioxide (CO_2), while the poisonous combination of carbon and oxygen that can be formed in automobile engines is carbon monoxide (CO). The prefixes "di" and "mono" differentiate between the two molecules. When there is only one atom of the first element in the molecular compound, the prefix "mono" is not necessary. The prefixes that you will commonly encounter in molecular compounds are listed in Table 3.

Table 3   **Prefixes in Molecular Compounds**

Prefix	Number	Example (formula)
mon(o)-	1	carbon monoxide (CO)
di-	2	carbon disulfide (CS_2)
tri-	3	sulfur trioxide (SO_3)
tetra-	4	carbon tetrafluoride (CF_4)
pent(a)-	5	phosphorus pentabromide (PBr_5)

Challenge

1 Are there any molecular compounds in your product? What are their names?

Understanding Concepts

1. How can you tell the difference between an ionic compound and a molecular compound?

2. (a) What kinds of atoms form molecular compounds?

   (b) How do the atoms in molecular compounds form stable electron arrangements?

   (c) What type of bond holds atoms together in molecules?

3. (a) How many valence electrons are there in a fluorine atom?

   (b) How many electrons does a fluorine atom need to share to become stable?

   (c) Draw a sketch to show how two fluorine atoms could form a stable molecule.

4. Some elements exist in the form of diatomic molecules. Where are these elements generally located in the periodic table?

5. Name the following compounds (use prefixes):

   (a) CBr_4

   (b) NI_3

   (c) OF_2

   (d) $SiCl_4$

6. Write chemical formulas for and name the molecular compounds formed by the following pairs of elements:

   (a) silicon and oxygen

   (b) nitrogen and hydrogen

   (c) phosphorus and chlorine

   (d) sulfur and bromine

   (e) oxygen and fluorine

   (f) carbon and chlorine

Making Connections

7. Sugars were described as molecular compounds.

   (a) Name three sugar molecules.

   (b) What do you notice about the names of these substances?

   (c) Find five foods that contain different types of sugar molecules and examine the labels to name the types of sugar molecules.

8. (a) Chlorine has a combining capacity of one. How many electrons does it need to share to have the same electron arrangement as the nearest noble gas?

   (b) What is the combining capacity of oxygen? How many electrons does it need to share in order to have the same electron arrangement as the nearest noble gas?

   (c) Investigate the relationship between combining capacity and the number of electrons needed for stability in a number of other nonmetals.

   (d) Make a general statement to summarize your findings.

Reflecting

9. Could a pair of metal atoms form a covalent bond? Explain.

Hydrocarbons: A Special Group of Molecules

What do gasoline, dynamite, a plastic toy, aspirin pain reliever, and sugar have in common? They are all substances that are made of organic molecules. **Organic compounds** are molecular substances that contain carbon atoms as basic building blocks. The simplest organic compound is methane (chemical formula CH_4), and there are literally tens of thousands of different organic compounds.

In fact, carbon is contained in more compounds than all of the other elements put together. Why are there so many organic compounds? The answer is the remarkable combining capacity of carbon, which has a combining capacity of four. It has the ability to combine with other nonmetals, especially hydrogen, oxygen, and nitrogen, to form very stable compounds. Most of the food that we eat, whether from plants or animals, is made up of organic compounds. For example, table sugar (**Figure 1**) is an organic molecule. It is not surprising that food is organic because most of the human body is organic as well. Another important source of organic compounds is through chemical changes. Chemists use chemical reactions to make new substances from existing organic molecules. For example, plastics are made from crude oil.

Figure 1

Table sugar, or sucrose, is an example of an organic compound. Its chemical formula is $C_{12}H_{22}O_{11}$. In the molecular model, black carbon atoms form the core of the molecule, with red oxygen and white hydrogen atoms attached.

Sources of Organic Compounds

Where do naturally occurring organic compounds come from? Many are produced by plants during the process of photosynthesis. Plants take in carbon dioxide from the air and water from the ground, and then build organic molecules — sugars, carbohydrates, proteins, and fats. Animals consume these organic molecules and make new molecules in more chemical reactions. Humans consume plants and animals, and the carbon-containing molecules are eventually recycled into the soil.

Another major source of organic molecules also has its origin in photosynthesis. In this case, though, the photosynthesis occurred millions of years ago. Crude oil petroleum and natural gas are obtained from under the ground, as shown in **Figure 2**. The main components in these mixtures are **hydrocarbons**, which are compounds of hydrogen and

> **Did You Know?**
>
> All food contains organic molecules. Plants and animals must all take in nutrients from their environment. However, some people use the term "organic" to describe food that has been grown without having any pesticides or other chemicals deliberately added by the farmer. Ironically, pesticides are organic molecules.

Figure 2

Oil wells produce oil and natural gas, which are mixtures of hundreds of different organic molecules.

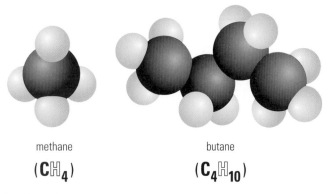

methane
(CH₄)

butane
(C₄H₁₀)

carbon found in various combinations. These mixtures of organic molecules were produced over millions of years as once-living plants and animals decayed and were changed by heat and pressure under the surface of Earth. These substances are also called **fossil fuels** because of their origin in living matter. Some examples of hydrocarbons are shown in **Figure 3**.

Petroleum and natural gas are transported across North America and around the world. Petroleum is generally moved by rail, road, or ship in tankers (**Figure 5**). Natural gas is transported across North America by pipeline and overseas by tanker as LNG (liquefied natural gas).

Crude oil and natural gas have become very important materials to people. For example, the energy released from burning these natural fuels is used to heat homes, produce electricity, and power automobiles and other machines. To the industrial chemist, however, crude oil and natural gas are more than just sources of fuel. The different types of molecules, or petrochemicals, present in these mixtures can be used to make industrial chemicals and consumer products, including plastics, synthetic fibres, and pharmaceuticals (**Figure 6**). The manufacture of chemical products consumes about 16% of the total petrochemical production.

Did You Know?

Gasoline mixtures are tested for their "octane rating." A higher-octane gasoline burns more efficiently and produces less engine "knock." Pure isooctane is given a rating of 100. Other fuel mixtures are assigned numbers by comparison with this standard.

The crude oil that comes out of the ground is a thick black "soup" of molecules. To make useful mixtures, the liquid crude oil and natural gas mixtures are separated into their components in a process called fractional distillation: the mixture passes into a distillation tower (**Figure 4**) that separates the components according to their boiling points.

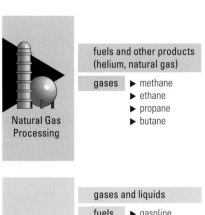

Natural Gas Processing

fuels and other products (helium, natural gas)

gases
▶ methane
▶ ethane
▶ propane
▶ butane

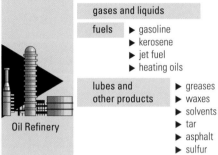

Oil Refinery

gases and liquids

fuels
▶ gasoline
▶ kerosene
▶ jet fuel
▶ heating oils

lubes and other products
▶ greases
▶ waxes
▶ solvents
▶ tar
▶ asphalt
▶ sulfur

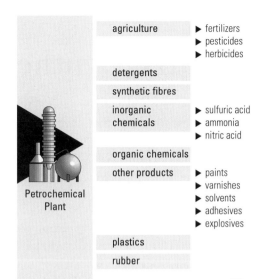

Petrochemical Plant

agriculture
▶ fertilizers
▶ pesticides
▶ herbicides

detergents

synthetic fibres

inorganic chemicals
▶ sulfuric acid
▶ ammonia
▶ nitric acid

organic chemicals

other products
▶ paints
▶ varnishes
▶ solvents
▶ adhesives
▶ explosives

plastics

rubber

Figure 6

Some of the hundreds of substances obtained from crude oil and natural gas

 Challenge

2,3 Most fuels are hydrocarbons. What are the names and formulas of these molecules?

3 What pollutants are produced when fossil fuels burn?

Try This
Activity Teacher Demo

Organic compounds, such as table sugar or sucrose ($C_{12}H_{22}O_{11}$) contain considerable amounts of stored energy. What would happen if the "H_2O" was removed from the sugar?

• Place about 1 cm depth of sugar in a 250-mL beaker.

• Add about 30 mL of concentrated sulfuric acid to the sugar. Wait and observe.

This demonstration should be done under a fume hood. Concentrated sulfuric acid is very dangerous. Wear safety goggles and stand back from the reaction. Be careful in cleaning up the products. Use sulfuric acid only in a well-ventilated area.

Understanding Concepts

1. **(a)** What are organic compounds?

   (b) What are the most common elements present in organic compounds?

   (c) What is the combining capacity of carbon?

   (d) Why is carbon called the backbone of organic molecules?

2. What are two sources of different kinds of organic compounds?

3. **(a)** What elements are present in hydrocarbon molecules?

   (b) How are hydrocarbons produced naturally?

4. **(a)** What is meant by the term "fossil fuel"?

   (b) Name three examples of fossil fuels.

5. Give five uses for natural gas and petroleum products.

Exploring

6. Research the mixture of substances found in gasoline. List each molecular compound.

7. Find out about the geological process through which petroleum and natural gas are formed as plants and animals decay. Report on your reserarch in a series of diagrams.

Chemical Wizardry: Synthetic Substances

Every hour of every day, people buy or use products that have become part of their way of living. Few people think about how these products have been produced using the application of chemistry. These substances include the fabrics in clothing, detergents for cleaning, plastics used to wrap food, and paints that decorate homes. Some chemicals prevent moisture loss and decay, and are used as preservatives in foods. Other substances give cosmetics their colours and textures. All of these are the products of applied chemistry and most of them are produced from hydrocarbons.

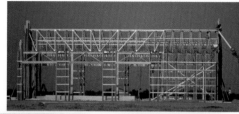

Natural or Synthetic?

What do we mean when we describe a product as natural? **Natural products** are obtained from natural sources — animals, plants, or minerals (**Figure 1**). For example, leather and wool come from animals. Cotton, rubber, and wood are derived from plants. Mineral sources provide hydrocarbon fuels, metals, fertilizers, and cement. Many of these materials may be mixed with other substances or reshaped, but they all come from natural sources.

Figure 1
What natural substances are in these products?

Many other products are made of **synthetic**, or artificially made, materials that have been manufactured in the chemical industry. Chemical changes are used to make these new substances with new properties. For example, natural crude rubber is obtained from the sap of trees; it is made up of molecules that are long and springy. This rubber stretches easily, but tends to become sticky when warm, and brittle when cold. Over a century ago, Charles Goodyear discovered a process he called vulcanization. In this process, natural rubber reacts with sulfur to form a new synthetic product called "vulcanized rubber." This substance is neither too hard nor too soft when the temperature changes. Today, car tires are made from completely synthetic molecules that are manufactured from petroleum (**Figure 2**). Such synthetic rubber is more resistant to acids and other chemicals, including gasoline.

Synthetic substances are used in most areas of daily life, as shown in **Table 1**. They are normally manufactured from petrochemicals. For example, polyethylene, used to make plastic bottles, is formed from ethene (C_2H_4), which has been separated from other hydrocarbon molecules in crude oil. Pharmaceutical chemists manufacture synthetic drugs, such as Aspirin. Other industrial chemists develop synthetic materials that are used to make products ranging from clothing to videotapes to computer chips.

Figure 2
The vulcanized rubber used in the tires on antique cars was an early example of a synthetic substance. Today's car tires are composites, or mixtures, of synthetic molecules. The composition of tires can be adjusted to make tires that perform better on wet roads or even high-speed racetracks.

Table 1	Some Synthetic Substances Made from Petrochemicals	
Substance	**Chemical name**	**Use**
PVC	polyvinyl chloride	plastic pipe for plumbing
Teflon	polytetrafluoroethylene	coatings for frying pans
BHA	butylated hydroxyanisole	food additive
polypropylene	polypropene	carpet fibres
Aspirin (ASA)	acetylsalicylic acid	pain killer
vinyl	polyvinyl chloride	upholstery
TNT	trinitrotoluene	explosive
Plexiglas	polymethylmethacrylate	transparent car reflectors
PABA	para-aminobenzoic acid	sunscreen
Styrofoam	polystyrene	insulation
neoprene	polybutadiene	synthetic "rubber" hoses

Did You Know?

Polymers are not only produced in the chemical industry. Some polymers are naturally produced in living organisms. Starch, found in potatoes and other foods, is a natural polymer made up of hundreds of sugar molecules joined together in a long chain. Digestion breaks the polymer apart.

Polymers

Many synthetic substances, like polyethylene and Kevlar (**Figure 3**), are formed when tens or hundreds of smaller molecules link together to form long, thin molecules called **polymers**, shown in **Figure 4**. These polymers have very different properties from the reactants. For example, small styrene molecules are colourless, strong-smelling, and liquid at room temperature. They react to form the polymer polystyrene, which is used as insulation (Styrofoam).

Polymers that are shaped by flow at some point in their manufacture are called **plastics**. For example, a plastic spoon is formed by melting the polymer material into a mould and allowing it to cool in the desired shape. Fibres are made by drawing out the polymer into a thread as it forms.

Figure 3

Kevlar is an extremely strong, flexible polymer that is used in applications from ropes to skis to bulletproof vests.

 ## Challenge

1 What are the names and formulas of the synthetic substances in your product?

Figure 4

Polymers are long-chain molecules formed when hundreds of smaller molecules link together. Polyethylene plastic is made from synthetic polymers.

Did You Know?

Synthetic polymers can be formed into different types of plastics. Thermoplastic polymers, such as those used to make plastic cutlery, may be remelted with heat and reshaped. Thermosetting polymers become hard when they are heated and cannot be reheated and reshaped. They are baked in moulds to produce car battery and telephone casings, and electrical switches and fittings.

Fibres and Fabrics

Fibres are thin, hairlike strands of material that can be spun into thread or yarn. There are synthetic fibres and natural fibres (**Figure 5**). Fabrics are made when fibres are woven together.

Natural fibres have been used for thousands of years, and have many advantages over synthetic fibres. The structure of the natural fibre gives the fabric special properties. For example, wool fibres readily trap air when spun or woven. The trapped air pockets make wool a good heat insulator, even when wet. Silk fibres are like long, smooth tubes which give the silk fabric its satiny texture. Cotton fabrics allow good air circulation and absorb moisture, and are therefore excellent for hot weather use. By contrast, synthetic fibres generally do not "breathe" as well as natural fibres and tend to lose their insulating ability when wet. Moreover, natural fibres come from renewable sources — plants and animals that can produce more raw materials each year. Synthetic fibres, on the other hand, come from nonrenewable petroleum resources.

Synthetic fibres do have some advantages over natural fibres. Synthetics like polyester and nylon are becoming less and less expensive as the technology for making them from petrochemicals improves. The synthetic fibres used to make the fleece used in winter clothing are sometimes even made from recycled pop bottles! Research chemists are constantly working to produce new synthetic molecules with new properties. As a result, today there is a much greater variety of synthetic fibres from which to choose.

Figure 5
Which fabrics are made from natural fibres and which are made from synthetic fibres?

Did You Know?

Linen is one of the oldest and strongest natural fibres used in making fabrics. Egyptian mummies have been discovered still wrapped in linen thousands of years old.

Understanding Concepts

1. Name five natural materials found in the home. List two products that contain each material (e.g., cement: basement floor, sidewalk).

2. Name five synthetic substances found in the home. List two products that contain each material (e.g., nylon: windbreaker, socks).

3. Give two examples of useful properties of synthetic materials.

4. What are the raw materials used to make many synthetic substances?

5. (a) What is a polymer?

   (b) What are three examples of polymers?

   (c) What is the difference between a polymer and a plastic?

6. Examine the chemical names of the substances in **Table 1**. Which of the substances do you think are polymers?

7. (a) What are the advantages of synthetic fibres as compared to natural fibres?

   (b) What are the disadvantages of synthetic fibres as compared to natural fibres?

Making Connections

8. The tag on an article of clothing describes it as 65% polyester and 35% cotton. Suggest reasons why this blend of fibres might have been used.

9. Find examples of as many different fibres as possible at home. (Hint: Clothing tags and washing machine instructions will be useful.) Make a table to summarize the following:

   (a) name of fibre (e.g., cotton)

   (b) type of fibre (e.g., natural)

   (c) example of application (e.g., rug)

   (d) washing instructions

   What differences do you see in washing instructions for various fibres?

Reflecting

10. Research and report on synthetic fibres used in athletic clothing. Investigate the advantages and disadvantages of these fibres. For example, consider their ability to stretch, washability, and resistance to bleaching by chemicals or light.

11. Can you think of any examples of synthetic materials that have changed how people live? Explain.

SKILLS HANDBOOK: (I) General Research

5.14 Explore an Issue

DECISION-MAKING SKILLS
- ● Define the Issue
- ○ Identify Alternatives
- ● Research
- ● Analyze the Issue
- ● Defend a Decision
- ○ Evaluate

Is "Natural" Better than Synthetic?

What types of chemical substances should people be using? You have already looked at some of the differences between natural and synthetic substances. In particular, you compared the advantages and disadvantages of synthetic and natural fibres, such as those used in clothing. But comparisons of synthetic and natural substances go far beyond fibres and clothing.

Some people believe that our society has become too dependent on synthetic materials over the last 50 years. As much as they can, they try to use natural products made from plants and animals, rather than synthetic products, which have been made by the chemical industry. But is it really better to use natural products than synthetic ones? Natural products often come from animals or plants raised with the assistance of chemicals. And land must be cleared for farms. On the other hand, natural products are more likely than synthetic products to be biodegradable.

After researching this question, two groups of students came up with the following lists of reasons for favouring either the "prosynthetic" (**Figure 1**) or the "pronatural" (**Figure 2**) position.

1. Synthetic antibiotics save thousands of lives every year. They are more effective and faster to produce than natural products. Without synthetic antibiotics, there would be worldwide epidemics.
2. Styrofoam coffee cups actually use up fewer resources than cardboard cups when you consider the trees that are cut down to make cardboard. Disposable cups may even be more environmentally friendly than china cups, when you consider the large amounts of hot water and detergent needed to clean china cups after each use.
3. Synthetic vitamins are cheaper, more convenient, and more effective than natural vitamins. Many people eat processed foods, which may have lost many of the minerals and vitamins necessary for health.
4. Synthetic diapers are better than cotton because they keep the baby's skin drier. They contain a super-absorbent polymer that effectively absorbs the moisture. They are also more convenient to use, and do not require hot water for washing.
5. Plastics are used in almost every kind of transportation. Synthetic canoes and other boats are lighter, more durable, and easier to repair than any craft made out of wood. Parts of snowmobiles are made out of plastic.
6. Synthetic fertilizers can be made to exact specifications for particular crops. They can be delivered in precise amounts more easily than natural fertilizers, and there is less waste.
7. Development of synthetic materials has allowed us to invent new devices. Artificial limbs and prosthetic devices, computers, and cellular phones are all made out of plastics and other synthetic materials.
8. The use of synthetic materials saves our forests. Trees are a renewable resource; however it takes decades for a tree to be replaced. Clearcutting of forests to meet our demand for wood and paper products is destroying our environment.
9. Sports equipment made of synthetics is superior to that made from natural products. Aluminum baseball bats, graphite composite tennis racquets, and metal-alloy golf clubs are all superior to their wooden counterparts.
10. The production of items using natural materials damages the environment. The production of leather requires the death of the animal, and the production of wool, cotton, and linen requires the use of large amounts of land that could otherwise be used for recreation or food crops.

Figure 1
"Prosynthetic" Viewpoint

1. Natural drugs, such as herbal extracts, are safer and often more effective than synthetic drugs. As a society, we consume too many drugs. The overprescription of antibiotics is producing "super bugs" that may eventually cause epidemics.
2. Cardboard containers, such as those used in fast food restaurants, do not use up valuable petroleum resources. They are made from trees, a renewable resource.
3. Losing weight by simply cutting back on food is healthier than taking synthetic diet pills. Diet pills are expensive and may cause long-term health problems.
4. Cotton diapers are better than synthetic diapers, because they are reusable and do not take up valuable space in landfills. If people have concerns over the time required for cleaning, they can use a diaper service that picks up and delivers.
5. Natural foods contain the nutrients that our bodies need. A well-balanced diet provides all the vitamins and other molecules needed for health.
6. Organic fertilizers, such as manure, allow farmers to recycle animal wastes and provide crops with a natural source of nutrients. Synthetic fertilizers are expensive, and crops become dependent on them.
7. Paper products are better than plastics because paper is easier to recycle. There are so many different kinds of synthetic plastics that they have to be sorted before they can be recycled — a process that is expensive and time-consuming.
8. Wood frames for houses are superior to metal or plastic frames. Wood is biodegradable, reusable, and recyclable. Natural cellulose insulation in houses is superior to fibreglass because it is a better insulator and does not irritate the skin.
9. Natural materials are safer to produce. They do not require huge chemical factories that generate large amounts of toxic air and water pollutants.
10. Natural wool carpets stabilize the relative humidity in a house by absorbing or releasing atmospheric moisture.

Figure 2
"Pronatural" Viewpoint

DEBATE: Natural Products are Better than Synthetic

Proposition

Natural products are made from renewable resources and are therefore better than synthetic products.

- (C) (E) Your teacher will place you in a group of four students. One pair of students will be assigned the "pronatural" position, and the other pair will be assigned the "prosynthetic" position. Whichever your assigned position (and regardless of your own personal opinion), conduct further research to support that position. Remember to investigate the issue from a variety of perspectives. Keep notes as you research and form your evidence into supportive arguments.
- Share your findings with your partner and decide who will present which points.
- (S) Carry out a debate, with the two "pronatural" speakers presenting first.
- After all four students have spoken for 2 min each, reverse your positions: the "prosynthetic" students now take the "pronatural" position, and vice versa. Argue your new viewpoint for 2 min each.
- Finally, in your group of four, discuss the issue and arrive at a position. Produce a 20- to 50-word statement that summarizes your group's feelings on the issue. The group must all show your agreement by signing this consensus statement.

Work the Web

Synthetic materials tend to be extremely durable and long-lived. This is an advantage when we are using them, but a problem when we want to get rid of them. What are chemists doing to try to reduce this problem? Visit www.science.nelson.com and follow the links from Science 10, 5.14 to investigate the development of biodegradable plastics.

Understanding the Issue

1. What is the source of most natural products?
2. Write a paragraph outlining the arguments for and against using disposable diapers.
3. List two pronatural and two prosynthetic arguments (D) made from an ecological perspective.

 SKILLS HANDBOOK: (C) Defining the Issue (E) Researching Alternatives (S) Oral Presentations (D) Identifying Alternatives

Chapter 5 Summary

Key Expectations

Throughout the chapter, you have had opportunities to do the following things:

- Recognize the relationships between chemical formulas, composition, and names. (all)
- Use appropriate apparatus and apply WHMIS safety procedures for handling, storage, disposal, and recycling of materials in the lab. (5.1, 5.3, 5.10)
- Select and integrate information from many sources including electronic, print, and community resources, and personally collected data. (5.2, 5.13, 5.14)
- Explain how environmental challenges can be addressed through an understanding of chemical substances. (5.2)
- Conduct chemical tests to identify common gases (oxygen, hydrogen, carbon dioxide). (5.3)
- Analyze experimental data, evaluate evidence and sources of information, and identify errors and bias. (5.3, 5.10, 5.12, 5.14)
- Write lab reports. (5.3, 5.10)
- Explore careers based on technologies that use chemical reactions. (5.4)
- Write the names and formulas for common ionic, polyatomic, and molecular compounds using the periodic table. (5.7, 5.8, 5.9, 5.11)
- Ask questions about practical problems and issues involving chemical processes. (5.10, 5.14)
- Describe how an understanding of chemical reactions has led to new consumer products and technological processes. (5.12, 5.13, 5.14)

Key Terms

alkali metals
alkaline earth metal
Bohr diagram
chemical change
chemical family
chemical property
chemical test
chemistry
combining capacity
compound
covalent bond
electrolyte
electron
element
fossil fuel
halogens
hydrocarbon
ion
ionic charge
ionic compound
matter
molecular compound
natural product
neutron
noble gases
organic compound
oxyacid
periodic table
physical change
physical property
plastics
polyatomic ion
polymers
positive test
product
proton
pure substance
reactant
synthetic
valence
valence shell

Make a Summary

Make a concept map to summarize the material that you have studied in this chapter. Start with the word "chemicals" and try to use as many of the terms in the Key Term list as possible in your map.

Reflect on your Learning

Revisit your answers to the Reflect on your Learning questions, page 171, in the Getting Started.

- How has your thinking changed?
- What new questions do you have?

Chapter 5 Review

Understanding Concepts

1. Explain the difference between the following pairs of terms. Give an example for each term:
   (a) physical property and chemical property
   (b) element and compound
   (c) metal and nonmetal
   (d) ionic compound and molecular compound
   (e) natural substance and synthetic substance

2. For each of the following, replace the description with one or two words:
   (a) a sample of matter that contains only one kind of atom;
   (b) a characteristic of matter that involves the formation of a new substance;
   (c) the starting material in a chemical reaction;
   (d) a family of elements that includes sodium and potassium;
   (e) the positively charged particle in the atom;
   (f) an electrically charged atom;
   (g) artificially made.

3. The sentences below contain errors or are incomplete. Write complete, correct versions.
   (a) Elements and solutions are examples of pure substances.
   (b) The melting point of a substance is an example of a chemical property.
   (c) The chemical test for hydrogen gas is to use a glowing splint.
   (d) Fluorine, chlorine, and iodine are members of the alkaline earth metals family.
   (e) Negative particles called neutrons circle the nucleus of the atom.
   (f) An atom with more electrons than protons will be a positive ion.
   (g) A molecular compound is held together with ionic bonds.
   (h) The chloride ion is an example of a polyatomic ion.
   (j) Cotton, leather, and wool are examples of synthetic substances.

4. Use the periodic table at the back of this book to determine the atomic numbers and to draw Bohr diagrams for the following elements:
   (a) aluminum
   (b) fluorine
   (c) magnesium
   (d) phosphorus

5. For each of the elements in question 4:
   (a) Draw a Bohr diagram of the stable ion that it would form.
   (b) Write the symbol and ionic charge of the stable ion.

6. Write the name of the compound that would be formed by combining each of the following pairs of elements:
   (a) magnesium and chlorine
   (b) sodium and bromine
   (c) magnesium and oxygen
   (d) aluminum and phosphorus
   (e) aluminum and sulfur

7. Write the formula for each of the compounds in question 6.

8. Examine the Bohr diagram in **Figure 1**. This diagram could represent the electronic structure of a noble gas or a stable ion. What would be the chemical symbol and ionic charge if the nucleus of the atom contained:

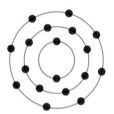

Figure 1

   (a) 16 protons
   (b) 18 protons
   (c) 19 protons

9. For each of the following compounds that involve elements with more than one ionic charge, write the corresponding name or chemical formula:
   (a) CuCl
   (b) FeI_2
   (c) tin(IV) oxide
   (d) lead(II) bromide

10. For each of the following compounds that involve polyatomic ions, write the corresponding name or chemical formula:
    (a) $CuCO_3$
    (b) $FeSO_4$
    (c) tin(IV) phosphate
    (d) lead(II) nitrate

11. For each of the following molecular compounds, write the corresponding name or chemical formula:
   (a) carbon monoxide
   (b) nitrogen triiodide
   (c) SCl_2
   (d) CCl_4

Applying Inquiry Skills

12. Describe four safety procedures that you followed during your investigations.

13. A student performs an experiment in which a solid white substance is added to a solution and produces a gas. When a sample of the gas is tested with limewater, the solution turns cloudy.
   (a) What is the name and chemical formula of the gas?
   (b) What would be the effect of the gas on a glowing or blazing splint?
   (c) Suggest a reasonable possible formula for the original white solid.

14. A group of students performs an investigation to test an unknown solid. They dissolve the solid in water and then, using small samples of this solution, do separate tests for the presence of ions. **Figure 2** shows their experimental results.

Procedure	Observations
• examined original solution	• solution was clear and very pale yellow
• added some silver nitrate solution	• solution turned milky white
• added some barium nitrate solution	• no change in solution
• added some potassium thiocyanate	• solution turned reddish brown

Figure 2

   (a) What ion(s) were present in the solution? Explain.
   (b) What ion(s) were not present in the solution? Explain.
   (c) Give a possible name and formula for the unknown solid.

15. An unknown element X forms an oxide with the formula X_2O_3.
   (a) What is the ionic charge or valence of element X? Explain.
   (b) What would be the formula of the compound that element X would form with chlorine?

16. Natural and synthetic fibres have different properties (see **Figure 3**). Design and perform a controlled experiment to compare the characteristics of various natural and synthetic fibres. Some possible areas of study might be
   (a) the effect of heating the fibres with an iron;
   (b) the fibres' solubility in solvents (e.g., acetone);
   (c) the fibres' ability to absorb moisture;
   (d) the effect of bleach on the fibres;
   (e) the fibres' insulating ability.

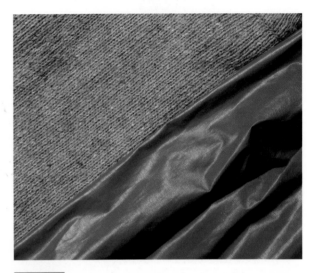

Figure 3

Making Connections

17. Choose a category of household hazardous products and design a poster to be displayed in your home to encourage people to handle and dispose of these materials safely. Include HHPS or WHMIS symbols.

18. Research and report on environmentally friendly alternatives to hazardous household products.

19. Contact an oil company to obtain information about gasoline. Report on (a) the types of molecules present in unleaded and leaded gasoline; or (b) octane-rating and "knocking."

20. What natural and synthetic materials are used in modern tires? Contact a company that makes tires, and report on the substances that they use.

6 Understanding Chemical Reactions

WHAT CHEMICAL REACTIONS DO YOU CONDUCT EVERY MORNING?
Brushing your teeth, eating breakfast, and getting a ride all qualify as chemical
reactions. The fluoride compounds in your toothpaste react with compounds
in your teeth to produce new, harder compounds that can resist decay. Acids
and other chemicals in your digestive system react with food to produce the
nutrients that your body needs. Hydrocarbons in the fuel that powers the
family car react with oxygen from the air to produce new gas molecules and
energy.

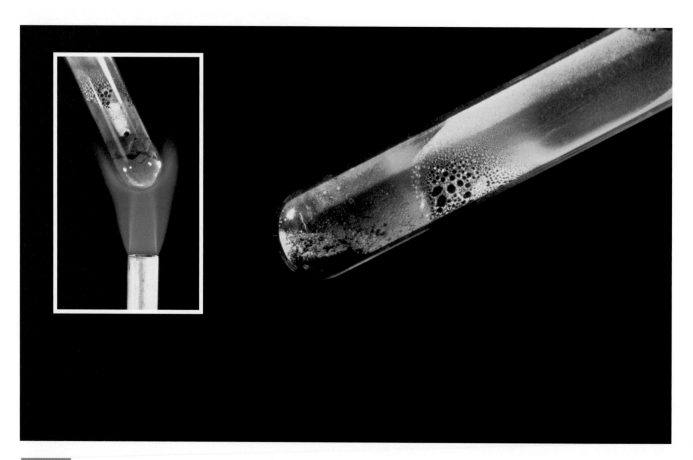

Figure 1

Mercury oxide produces a liquid and a gas (inset) when heated by a flame. This is a
decomposition reaction. What are the products of this reaction?

Chemical reactions are also used to make many of the chemical compounds that are part of our lives. The plastic containers that hold your lunch and the synthetic fibres used to make some of your clothes have been made by the chemical industry. When you get a bacterial infection, the antibiotics that the doctor may prescribe are the products of the pharmaceutical chemical industry. Children's toys, whether dolls or plastic miniblocks or in-line skates, are almost all made of synthetic products. But chemical reactions may have negative effects as well. The combustion of gasoline gives us the freedom to travel large distances, but produces polluting gases that can cause respiratory and other health problems.

How do chemical reactions happen? How do chemists categorize the thousands of different chemical reactions? In Chapter 5, you saw patterns in how chemical compounds can be categorized as ionic or molecular. Using your understanding of these patterns, you were able to name different chemical compounds. In this chapter, you will learn to recognize patterns that will help you understand and predict different types of chemical reactions.

Reflect on your Learning

1. What happens to matter in chemical changes?

2. How can we represent chemical reactions?

3. How can chemical reactions be classified or grouped?

4. What are some examples of different types of chemical reactions?

Throughout this chapter, note any changes in your ideas as you learn new concepts and develop your skills.

Try This
Activity   Looking at a Chemical Reaction

Can you classify the changes that occur during a chemical reaction?

- Put on goggles and an apron.
- Obtain a piece of magnesium metal and a beaker containing 10 mL of vinegar from your teacher. Note that vinegar is a solution of the compound acetic acid in water.
- Examine and describe the starting materials.

(a) How could you classify the starting materials according to their physical properties?

(b) How could you classify the starting materials according to their structure or formula, or type of matter?

- Think about laboratory safety procedures and how you can use your five senses to make observations. Note that the sense of smell must be used with caution.

(c) How can you safely test the odour of a substance?

(d) Which sense should you never use in a laboratory?

- Add the magnesium to the vinegar and observe the changes that occur. Use three of your senses to make your observations.

(e) How could you classify the products according to their physical properties?

(f) How could you classify the products according to their structures or formulas?

(g) Describe some other chemical changes. How would you classify these changes?

- Dispose of the materials as instructed by your teacher.
- Wash your hands.

Word Equations

Chemical reactions may involve sophisticated chemicals, as in the explosive reaction of dynamite, or simple household materials, as in the reaction of a bathroom cleaner with a stain. They may occur constantly, as in the growth of your body, or occasionally, as in the changing colour of leaves in the fall. How can you describe such a wide range of reactions? For convenience, chemists use a word equation. A **word equation** is one way of representing a chemical reaction: it tells you what reacts and what is produced. Word equations are an efficient way to describe chemical changes, to help chemists recognize patterns, and to predict the products of a chemical reaction.

Writing Word Equations

Word equations are written in a particular format. The left side of a word equation lists the names of all the reactants (the substances present initially), and the right side lists the names of all the products (the substances present at the end). An arrow points from the reactants to the products:

all the reactants → all the products

The reactants, as well as the products, are separated by a plus sign (+):

reactant 1 + reactant 2 → product 1 + product 2

Word Equations for Some Chemical Reactions

You know that the rusting of iron is a slow process — it takes a car a long time to rust. However, when hot steel wool (iron) is plunged into a bottle of oxygen, a spectacular chemical reaction occurs (**Figure 1**). The reactants are iron and oxygen, and the product is iron(III) oxide. The word equation for this reaction is written as

iron + oxygen → iron(III) oxide

The reaction that occurs when a coil of copper wire is placed in a beaker of colourless silver nitrate solution is shown in **Figure 2.** The word equation for this chemical reaction is

copper + silver nitrate → silver + copper(II) nitrate

In Chapter 5, you investigated several chemical reactions. These reactions can be described using word equations. For example, when zinc metal is added to a hydrochloric acid solution, a flammable gas and a colourless solution result:

zinc + hydrochloric acid → hydrogen + zinc chloride

In the chemical test for hydrogen, the gas "pops" as it reacts explosively with oxygen from the air:

hydrogen + oxygen → water vapour

Figure 1

Iron(III) oxide forms when steel wool and oxygen react.

Challenge

1,2,3 What word equations represent the reactions in your Challenge?

Figure 2

When a coil of copper is dipped in silver nitrate solution, a furry deposit of silver metal forms on the coil. The solution also turns blue as a copper(II) nitrate solution forms.

Try This
Activity Completing Word Equations

Chemists use word equations to summarize what they observe. Copy and complete the word equations that describe the following observations.

(a) Aluminum resists corrosion because it reacts with a gas found in air to form a protective coating of aluminum oxide.

$$\text{aluminum} + ? \rightarrow \text{aluminum oxide}$$

(b) Zinc metal, used as a coating in galvanized iron, also reacts with air to form a coating that resists further corrosion.

$$\text{zinc} + \text{oxygen} \rightarrow ?$$

(c) When aluminum foil is placed in a solution of copper(II) chloride, copper metal and another solution are formed.

$$\text{aluminum} + \text{copper(II) chloride} \rightarrow \text{copper} + ?$$

(d) When sodium sulfate and calcium chloride solutions are mixed, a precipitate of calcium sulfate and another substance is formed.

$$\text{sodium sulfate} + \text{calcium chloride} \rightarrow \text{calcium sulfate} + ?$$

Understanding Concepts

1. What is the purpose of writing a word equation?

2. Examine the following word equation:

$$\text{propane} + \text{oxygen} \rightarrow \text{carbon dioxide} + \text{water}$$

(a) List all the reactants in this reaction.

(b) List all the products in this reaction.

(c) What is the purpose of the arrow in the word equation?

3. Write word equations for the following reactions:

(a) $CaCl_2$ and Na_2SO_4 react to form $CaSO_4$ and $NaCl$.

(b) $BaCO_3$ reacts when heated to produce BaO and CO_2.

(c) $AgNO_3$ reacts with KCl to produce $AgCl$ and KNO_3.

4. Write word equations to represent the following chemical reactions:

(a) Carbon dioxide and water are produced in human cell respiration. The reactants are sugar and an important gas that humans need to survive.

(b) Stalactites form in caves when calcium bicarbonate reacts to form calcium carbonate, water, and carbon dioxide gas.

Reflecting

5. Write your own word equation for the production of a peanut butter sandwich.

6. How would you classify the reactions you see in the Try This?

INQUIRY SKILLS MENU
- ○ Questioning
- ○ Planning
- ○ Analyzing
- ● Hypothesizing
- ● Conducting
- ● Evaluating
- ● Predicting
- ● Recording
- ● Communicating

Measuring Masses in Chemical Changes

You know how to represent the changes that occur when elements and compounds undergo chemical changes. But what happens to the quantities of these substances in a chemical reaction? When matter changes, does the mass of matter also change? For example, if two solutions are mixed together to form a solid, does the mass increase? In this investigation, you will measure the masses of reactants and products to find out.

Question

Does the mass of a substance change when it undergoes a chemical reaction?

Hypothesis

In a group, discuss how a chemical reaction might affect the total mass of reactants and products.

(a) Write a hypothesis explaining whether the mass (K3) should increase, decrease, or stay the same.

Design

In this investigation, you will work in a group to test your hypothesis by measuring the masses of substances in a closed system (a stoppered flask).

(b) Make a data chart as shown in **Table 1** and be prepared to record the group's data on a class chart.

Table 1 **Measuring Masses in a Chemical Reaction**

Total mass of reactants and apparatus (g)	Predicted mass of products and apparatus (g)	Measured mass of products and apparatus (g)	Qualitative observations of reactants and products

Materials

- apron
- safety goggles
- small test tube
- 250-mL Erlenmeyer flask
- stopper for the flask
- iron(III) chloride solution (3% or 0.2 mol/L)
- graduated cylinder
- sodium hydroxide solution (3% or 0.8 mol/L)
- paper towel
- balance

Procedure

 Put on your apron and safety goggles.

 Check that your test tube is the correct size for your flask (see **Figure 1**).

3 Remove the test tube from the flask. Pour about 10–15 mL of iron(III) chloride solution into the flask.

Figure 1

Iron(III) chloride is a strong irritant, corrosive, and toxic. Any spills on the skin, in the eyes, or on clothing should be washed immediately with cold water. Report any spills to your teacher.

4 Fill your test tube about one-half full with sodium hydroxide solution. Carefully dry off the outside of the test tube with a paper towel. Gently place the test tube in the flask, being careful not to spill the solutions.

(c) Describe the properties of the starting materials.

Sodium hydroxide is corrosive. Any spills on the skin, in the eyes, or on clothing should be washed immediately with cold water. Report any spills to your teacher.

 Put the stopper firmly in the flask. Check that the outside of the flask is dry. If it is not, dry it off with a paper towel.

6 Determine the total mass of the reactants, the
L3 test tube, and the flask. Record your
measurement.

(d) Record your prediction of what the final
mass will be in the data table.

7 Holding the stopper firmly in place, gently
invert the flask. This will mix the iron(III)
chloride solution from the flask with the
sodium hydroxide from the test tube (**Figure 2**).

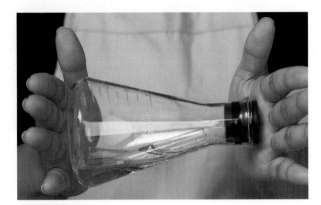

Figure 2

8 Observe the reaction that occurs.

9 Measure the mass of the flask and its contents
using the same balance you used for the first
measurements. Record your measurements.
Record your qualitative observations, such as
the appearance of any products if or when a
reaction occurs.

10 Dispose of the contents of your flask and clean
and put away your materials as directed by your
teacher. Clean up your work station. Wash your
hands.

Analysis and Evaluation

(e) Compare your group's results with those of the
rest of your class.

(f) Total the mass changes from each group, and
calculate the average mass change.

(g) How do you think the procedure in this
experiment could have been improved?

(h) Answer the initial question.

Q (i) Communicate your findings in a lab report.

Understanding Concepts

1. Write a general statement to summarize the results of
this investigation.

2. What evidence do you have that a chemical reaction
occurred in your flask?

3. **(a)** The products of the reaction are iron(III) hydroxide
and sodium chloride. Write a word equation for this
reaction.

   (b) Write the same equation again using the correct
chemical formula for each chemical compound.

4. Which product(s) could you see in the flask after the
reaction? Explain your answer.

5. Explain why the measurement of the mass of the
products might differ for each group. Does this indicate
that any of the groups made a mistake?

6. Explain why an average change in mass was calculated
and used in (e).

Exploring

7. Repeat this investigation using a different pair of
reactants: sodium carbonate solution and calcium
chloride solution. Before you begin, predict the products
of this reaction and write its word equation.

Reflecting

8. **(a)** List possible factors that might explain why the
mass of the products is not equal to the mass of
the reactants in some student investigations.

   (b) What effect would each of these factors have on
the observed results? For example, would the
spilling of some solution produce a higher or lower
value in the final mass?

6.3

Conserving Mass

In Investigation 6.2, you saw that when two solutions react to form a solid precipitate, the mass stays the same. Is the mass constant for other types of reactions? Are there any reactions where mass is gained or lost?

In some chemical reactions, matter may appear to be destroyed. For example, you might think that the burning of a forest destroys matter, reducing the trees to a mere handful of ashes (**Figure 1**). What happens in a chemical reaction when one or more of the reactants or products is a gas?

For more than 200 years, scientists tried to devise methods to trap the gases that were used or produced in reactions, and to find ways to measure their masses. After years of experimenting, scientists agreed that mass is neither gained nor lost in any chemical reaction. This conclusion is stated as a law. A **scientific law** is a general statement that sums up the conclusions of many experiments, or a statement that summarizes an observed pattern in nature.

Figure 1
The biomass in trees seems to "disappear" when a forest fire destroys a forest.

The Law of Conservation of Mass

The Law of Conservation of Mass states that, in a chemical reaction, the total mass of the reactants is always equal to the total mass of the products.
Since the mass of the products is always the same as the mass of the reactants, what does this tell us about the atoms that make up the reactants and products?

Experiments have shown that atoms in a chemical reaction are not changed — the number of each kind of atom is the same before and after a reaction. In chemical reactions, the atoms of the reactants are simply rearranged. Molecules may be broken apart and new molecules may be formed, but the atoms in the products are the same atoms that were in the reactants.

For example, look at the burning of methane or natural gas (**Figure 2**). The word equation for this reaction is

methane + oxygen → water + carbon dioxide

The reactants are two molecules of oxygen gas (O_2) and one molecule of methane (CH_4), as shown in **Figure 3**. As the molecules collide, a chemical reaction occurs that produces two molecules of

Figure 2
When natural gas burns, it reacts with oxygen in the air. The mass of every gas must be taken into account when calculating the final mass of a chemical reaction.

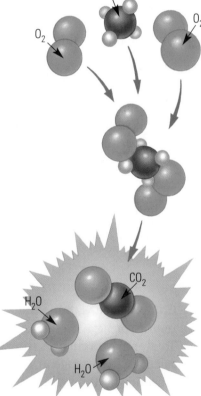

Figure 3
Atoms are not destroyed in a chemical reaction, just rearranged.

water (H_2O), one molecule of carbon dioxide (CO_2), heat, and light.

As you can see in **Figure 3**, all the atoms present at the beginning of a chemical reaction are present after the reaction. Thus, the total mass of the atoms in the reactants remains equal to the total mass of the atoms in the products; the atoms in the reactants recombine to form new molecules.

An Environmental View

The Law of Conservation of Mass has implications far beyond the laboratory. Think about engines that use fuels as a source of energy. When cars burn gasoline, energy is released during the chemical reaction of combustion. However, since mass is conserved, all of the mass of the fuel is still present in some form after combustion occurs (**Figure 4**).

Figure 4
Every kilogram of fuel mixed with oxygen in an internal combustion engine produces 3 to 4 kg of water vapour and carbon dioxide gas, as well as pollutant gases such as nitrogen oxides and unburned hydrocarbons.

 Challenge

3 How does the Law of Conservation of Mass relate to your Challenge?

🖑 Work the Web

What is being done to reduce the amounts of pollutants in vehicle exhausts? Visit www.science.nelson.com and follow the links from Science 10, 6.3 to research this issue.

Understanding Concepts

1. State the Law of Conservation of Mass. How is this law explained in terms of atoms?

2. When a log burns in a fire, the ashes have a much lower mass than the log. Explain.

3. **(a)** Make a table with three columns and four rows as follows:

Number of atoms	Reactants	Products
carbon		
oxygen		
hydrogen		

   (b) Using **Figure 3**, count the number of atoms of each type in the reactants and record them in the table. Count the number of atoms of each type in the products and record them in the table.

   (c) What do your results suggest about the Law of Conservation of Mass?

4. A solid has a mass of 35 g. When it is mixed with a solution, a chemical reaction occurs. If the final total mass of products is 85 g, what was the mass of the solution?

5. Solution A has a mass of 60 g. Solution B has a mass of 40 g. When they are mixed, a chemical reaction occurs in which gas is produced. If the mass of the final mixture is 85 g, what mass of gas was produced?

6. Have you ever noticed that if you weigh yourself immediately before bed and immediately after getting up in the morning, you weigh less in the morning? Does this mean that the Law of Conservation of Mass is not true? Suggest an explanation for the difference in mass.

7. Why does bread rise when it is baked? How do you think the mass of the bread would compare to the original total mass of the ingredients in the recipe?

Exploring

8. Design an apparatus that would allow you to compare the mass of reactants with the mass of products when a small amount of wood burns.

Reflecting

9. How have your ideas about matter and mass changed? Did you know that gases had mass? Did you know that matter could not be created or destroyed? Write a short paragraph describing how your ideas may have changed.

Finding the Missing Mass

In Investigation 6.2, you investigated the masses of reactants and products for a chemical change in which a precipitate (solid) was formed from two solutions. What happens when gases are produced in chemical reactions? Like any other type of matter, gases are made of atoms and molecules, and have mass. But they can easily escape from a container used for a reaction. In this investigation, you will compare the mass of reactants with the mass of products in a reaction that produces a gas.

Question

Can the Law of Conservation of Mass be applied to a chemical reaction in which a gas is produced?

Prediction

(a) Write a prediction, describing how the mass of
(K3) the products will compare to the mass of the reactants.

Design

You will measure the total mass of reactants and total mass of products, and compare them.

(b) Make a table to record your observations of masses during the investigation. Include a column in your table for your qualitative observations.

Materials

- apron
- safety goggles
- test tube
- 250-mL beaker
- hydrochloric acid solution (3% or 0.4 mol/L)
- graduated cylinder
- sodium bicarbonate (baking soda)
- 2-mL measuring scoop
- balance

 Hydrochloric acid is corrosive. Any spills on the skin, in the eyes, or on clothing should be washed immediately with plenty of cold water. Report any spills to your teacher.

Procedure

1 Put on your apron and safety goggles.

2 Be sure that the test tube and beaker are clean and dry before you begin. Pour 10 to 15 mL of hydrochloric acid into the test tube (**Figure 1**).

Figure 1

3 Put one scoop (about 2 g) of sodium
(L3) bicarbonate into the beaker. Place the test tube in the beaker. Measure the total mass of the beaker, test tube, and reactants (**Figure 2**). Record your measurement.

Figure 2

SKILLS HANDBOOK: (K3) Developing the Prediction and Hypothesis (L3) Using a Mass Balance

Remove the beaker from the balance. Slowly pour the acid from the test tube into the beaker (**Figure 3**). Record your qualitative observations.

Figure 3

5 Put the test tube back into the beaker. Measure and record the total mass of the beaker, test tube, and products.

6 Dispose of the contents of your beaker and clean and put away your materials as directed by your teacher. Clean up your work station. Wash your hands.

Analysis and Evaluation

(c) What were the names of the reactants?

(d) What was the difference in mass between the reactants and the products?

(e) What might account for any difference in mass you observed?

(f) Why does the glassware have to be dry?

(g) What improvements could you suggest in the experimental design?

(Q) (h) Write up your findings in a lab report.

Understanding Concepts

1. What evidence do you have that a chemical change took place after you poured the dilute acid into the beaker?

2. **(a)** What were the three products of this reaction?

   (b) Which of these products remained in the beaker? Explain.

   (c) Write a word equation to represent the chemical reaction.

   (d) Write the same equation again, but replace each word with a correct chemical formula, using your knowledge of naming chemical compounds.

3. Suggest why you were told to remove the beaker from the balance before mixing the two reactants.

4. A senior science student carried out an experiment to examine the burning of magnesium. She determined the mass of a piece of magnesium ribbon. Then she burned it, being careful to collect all the pieces of white ash. Finally, she determined the mass of the ash. Look at her results in **Table 1** and explain them. Write a word equation for the reaction. There are two reactants and one product.

Table 1	Burning of Magnesium
mass of magnesium	3.0 g
mass of ash	5.0 g
difference	2.0 g

Exploring

5. **(a)** Suppose that you wanted to use the acid–baking soda reaction to prove the Law of Conservation of Mass. How would you modify your procedure and apparatus?

   (b) How might this modification be dangerous?

   (c) What property of which product causes the potential danger?

🖑 Work the Web

Some people think that gases have no mass or even that gases have negative mass. They look at hot air balloons rising into the air and say that the gas inside a balloon makes it weigh less. How can you explain this observation? Visit the Nelson web site at www.science.nelson.com and follow the Science 10, 6.4 links to conduct your research.

Balancing Chemical Equations

How do scientists in different countries, speaking different languages, communicate the results of their experiments to each other (**Figure 1**)? How do they represent information about elements, compounds, and chemical equations? You have learned that chemical substances can be represented with names and formulas. You have also learned that chemical reactions can be represented by word equations. Can we describe chemical reactions in symbolic form?

A **skeleton equation** is a representation of a chemical reaction in which the formulas of the reactants are connected to the formulas of the products by an arrow. Consider the example of the burning of methane. We can describe this reaction in a word equation as follows:

La réaction du méthane, brulant avec l'oxygène, produit de l'eau et du gaz de dioxyde de carbone.

$$CH_4 + 2O_2 \rightarrow 2H_2O + CO_2$$

Methane burns in air by reacting with oxygen to produce water and carbon dioxide gases.

$$CH_4 + 2O_2 \rightarrow 2H_2O + CO_2$$

甲烷在空氣中燃燒是因爲甲烷和氧反應產生水和二氧化碳。

$$CH_4 + 2O_2 \rightarrow 2H_2O + CO_2$$

Figure 1

A chemical equation is written the same way in any language, making it universally understandable.

methane + oxygen → carbon dioxide + water

We can then write a skeleton equation by replacing each name with a formula:

$$CH_4 + O_2 \rightarrow CO_2 + H_2O$$

However, there is a problem. The Law of Conservation of Mass states that the mass of the reactants equals the mass of the products. In other words, atoms can be neither created nor destroyed in a chemical change. If we look at the reactants and products, we can record the numbers of atoms of each type in a table like **Table 1**.

There is an apparent imbalance between the numbers of atoms in the reactants and the numbers of atoms in the products. We have seemingly created an oxygen atom and destroyed two hydrogen atoms (**Figure 2**).

We cannot change the types or formulas of the molecules. So how can we solve this imbalance?

Table 1 **Combustion of Methane**

Type of atom	Reactants	Products
C	1	1
H	4	2
O	2	2 + 1 = 3

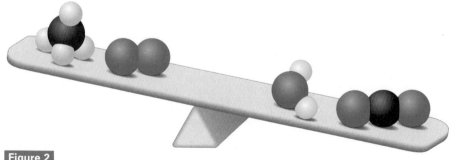

Figure 2

The numbers of atoms of reactants and products are out of balance. The total masses of reactants and products are also out of balance. The see-saw tilts to the product side because of the greater mass.

The answer is to change the numbers of molecules rather than their formulas. If we add an oxygen molecule to the reactants and a water molecule to the products, this balances the equation (**Figure 3**).

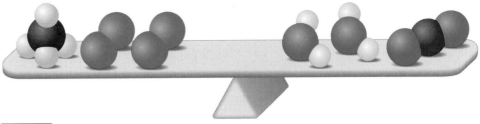

Figure 3

The numbers of atoms are now in balance. The mass of the reactants also equals the mass of the products.

$$CH_4 + O_2 + O_2 \rightarrow CO_2 + H_2O + H_2O$$

An equation in which the reactants and the products contain equal numbers of atoms of each type is a **balanced chemical equation**. The usual way to write a balanced equation is to use coefficients. A **coefficient** is a number written in front of a chemical symbol or formula. It indicates the number of atoms or molecules of that substance. The coefficients are shown in red in the following equation.

$$CH_4 + 2O_2 \rightarrow CO_2 + 2H_2O$$

Note that by balancing an equation, the mass of the reactants will be equal to the mass of the products.

How to Balance an Equation

Let's look at an example to see how an equation can be balanced. Iron reacts with oxygen to form magnetic iron oxide (Fe_3O_4) (**Figure 4**). What is the balanced chemical equation for this reaction?

Step 1. Write the word equation for the reaction.

iron + oxygen $\rightarrow$ magnetic iron oxide

Did You Know?

When iron reacts with oxygen, it forms two oxides. Magnetic iron oxide is an equal mixture of iron(II) oxide (FeO) and iron(III) oxide (Fe_2O_3). Add up the atoms to get the formula Fe_3O_4.

Figure 4

Iron reacts with oxygen to form rust or magnetic iron oxide.

Step 2. Write the skeleton equation by replacing each name with a correct formula.

$$Fe + O_2 \rightarrow Fe_3O_4$$

Step 3. Count the numbers of atoms of each type in reactants and products.

The numbers of atoms may be recorded in a table (**Table 2**).

Table 2   **Rusting of Iron**

Type of atom	Reactants	Products
Fe	1	3
O	2	4

Step 4. Multiply each of the formulas by the appropriate coefficients to balance the numbers of atoms.

To balance the three iron atoms on the right side, multiply the iron atoms on the left side by 3. To balance the four oxygen atoms on the right side, multiply the oxygen atoms on the left side by 2. Check that the atoms on each side are balanced.

$$3Fe + 2O_2 \rightarrow Fe_3O_4$$

A balanced chemical equation has been written. The formulas are unchanged, and the numbers of atoms are balanced.

The same steps are used to balance equations that involve more complex molecules. For example, what is the balanced chemical equation for the reaction of magnesium metal with nitric acid?

Step 1. Write the word equation for the reaction.

magnesium + nitric acid → hydrogen + magnesium nitrate

Step 2. Write the skeleton equation by replacing each name with a correct formula.

$$Mg + HNO_{3(aq)} \rightarrow H_2 + Mg(NO_3)_2$$

The following subscripts are used to indicate the state of each substance: (s) indicates a solid; (l) indicates a liquid; (g) indicates a gas; and (aq) indicates an aqueous solution (in water).

Try This
Activity   **Equation Balancing for "Smarties"**

Use candies to represent the process of balancing equations. For example, consider the balanced chemical equation for the combustion of methane in oxygen to produce carbon dioxide and water:

$$CH_4 + 2O_2 \rightarrow CO_2 + 2H_2O$$

- Start with one black (or brown) candy, four yellow candies, and four red candies. Arrange the candies to represent the reactants. For example, methane could be a black candy with four yellow candies just touching it, and the two oxygen molecules could each be two red candies just touching.

- You can represent the chemical reaction by mixing all the candies together.
- The products could then be represented with a carbon dioxide molecule (one black candy with two red candies) and two water molecules (each molecule is one red candy with two yellow candies).
- Use the candies to represent other chemical reactions that you have encountered in this chapter. For a challenge, try to represent the burning of ethane (C_2H_6) in oxygen gas to produce carbon dioxide and water.

Step 3. Count the numbers of atoms of each type in reactants and products. This example is complicated by the polyatomic nitrate ion.

The compound magnesium nitrate contains a total of six oxygen atoms because there are two NO_3 groups, each of which has three oxygen atoms. The numbers of atoms may be recorded in a table (**Table 3**).

Table 3 **Magnesium Reacts with Nitric Acid**

Type of atom	Reactants	Products
Mg	1	1
H	1	2
N	1	2
O	3	6

Step 4. Multiply each of the formulas by the appropriate coefficients to balance the numbers of atoms.

To balance the number of hydrogen atoms, the coefficient 2 is placed in front of the HNO_3 molecule. Note that this coefficient affects the number of nitrogen and oxygen atoms as well.

$$Mg + 2HNO_{3(aq)} \rightarrow H_2 + Mg(NO_3)_2$$

The equation is now balanced.

Challenge

1,2,3 What balanced chemical equations represent the reactions in your Challenge?

Work the Web

Visit www.science.nelson.com and follow the Science 10, 6.5 links to web sites that show how to balance chemical equations. Choose a reaction and show it as a word equation, a skeleton equation, and as a balanced equation.

Understanding Concepts

1. **(a)** Why is the following equation not balanced?

   $$N_2 + H_2 \rightarrow NH_3$$

   (b) The following is an attempt to balance the above equation. What is wrong with the way that the equation is balanced?

   $$N_2 + H_3 \rightarrow N_2H_3$$

2. Copy the following skeleton equations into your notebook. Then balance the equations:

   (a) $Na + Cl_2 \rightarrow NaCl$

   (b) $K + O_2 \rightarrow K_2O$

   (c) $H_2 + O_2 \rightarrow H_2O$

   (d) $H_2 + Cl_2 \rightarrow HCl$

   (e) $N_2 + H_2 \rightarrow NH_3$

   (f) $CO + O_2 \rightarrow CO_2$

   (g) $Al + Br_2 \rightarrow AlBr_3$

   (h) $N_2H_4 + O_2 \rightarrow H_2O + N_2$

   (i) $CH_4 + O_2 \rightarrow CO_2 + H_2O$

3. For each of the following, write the correct skeleton equation, and then balance it to form a chemical equation:

   (a) copper(II) oxide + hydrogen $\rightarrow$ copper + water

   (b) lead(II) nitrate + potassium iodide $\rightarrow$ lead(II) iodide + potassium nitrate

   (c) calcium + water $\rightarrow$ calcium hydroxide + hydrogen gas

   (d) lead(II) sulfide + oxygen $\rightarrow$ lead + sulfur dioxide

   (e) hydrogen sulfide $\rightarrow$ hydrogen + sulfur

4. Imagine that you are an engineer trying to determine how much air had to be supplied to burn gasoline in a car engine. Assuming that gasoline is heptane (C_7H_{16}), the word equation is

   heptane + oxygen $\rightarrow$ carbon dioxide + water vapour

   (a) Write the skeleton equation for the reaction.

   (b) Balance the equation by adding coefficients as necessary.

   (c) How many molecules of oxygen are required for every molecule of heptane that burns?

Making Connections

5. Nitrogen oxides are a group of air pollutants produced by internal combustion engines in automobiles. These pollutants are formed by the reaction of atmospheric nitrogen (N_2) and oxygen (O_2) to form various combinations, including NO, NO_2, N_2O_4, N_2O_3, and N_2O_5. Write balanced chemical equations to represent the production of each of these substances.

Combustion

What chemical reactions are involved when you strike a match? What further reactions happen when the match is brought close to a candle and the wax burns? Chemists use their knowledge of types of reactions to decide on the chemical composition of matches and to explain how these chemicals react (**Figure 1**).

There are different categories of chemical reactions. One possible category is combustion. **Combustion** is the very rapid reaction of a substance with oxygen to produce compounds called oxides. We often call this process burning. One way to represent combustion is using the following word equation:

fuel + oxygen → oxides + energy

The energy produced is mainly in the form of heat and light. The fuel can be a variety of elements and compounds.

The most important fuels that we burn are hydrocarbons. Gasoline in our automobiles, natural gas in our home furnaces, kerosene in jet airplanes, and even the candles on a birthday cake are all made of hydrocarbons (**Figure 2**). When these fuels burn, the products are carbon dioxide and water. The word equation for the combustion of a hydrocarbon can be represented as

hydrocarbon + oxygen → carbon dioxide + water vapour + energy

The complete combustion of hydrocarbon fuels results in the production of millions of tonnes of water and carbon dioxide, which are released into the atmosphere. The carbon dioxide that we produce as a society is a significant contributor to the greenhouse effect discussed in Chapter 16. An example of the combustion of hydrocarbons is the burning of butane in a lighter. Butane (C_4H_{10}) is a gas at room temperature, but it is a liquid under pressure.

Figure 1

A match provides the heat to start the combustion of the wax in the candle.

Figure 2

Jet aircraft engines burn hydrocarbons to produce energy.

When butane is allowed to escape the lighter through a valve and a spark ignites it, the following reaction occurs:

butane + oxygen → carbon dioxide + water + energy

$$2C_4H_{10} + 13O_2 \rightarrow 8CO_2 + 10H_2O$$

Incomplete Combustion

Hydrocarbons can also undergo a chemical reaction called **incomplete combustion**. Incomplete combustion occurs when there is not enough oxygen available. Instead of two products, four products are produced: carbon monoxide (CO), carbon (C), carbon dioxide, and water. Carbon monoxide is an odourless, colourless gas that is extremely poisonous. It combines with hemoglobin in the blood to starve the body of oxygen and cause death. The carbon sometimes produced in incomplete combustion is responsible for the black coating (soot) you observe in fireplaces.

Matches and Their Reactions

What reactions occur when a match ignites? The wood of the matchstick itself undergoes combustion to produce carbon dioxide and water vapour. But what reactions happen in the head of the match?

Matches are a complex mixture of chemicals (**Figure 3**). The head of a wooden match is dipped first in paraffin wax (a hydrocarbon) and then into a mixture of glue, colouring, a fuel, and a compound that is a source of oxygen. The fuel is sulfur (S), and the source of oxygen is potassium chlorate ($KClO_3$). Finally, the tip or striking surface is made by dipping the head into another mixture, which consists of more glue, another fuel — called tetraphosphorus trisulfide (P_4S_3) — and powdered glass. The match is ready to strike!

The process that makes matches burn is actually a series of connected reactions that start at the outside of the match and work their way in. Some matches are called "strike-anywhere" matches because that is exactly what you do to light them. When the tip of such a match is rubbed on any rough surface, the frictional heat produced by the powdered glass and glue is enough to ignite the tetraphosphorus trisulfide fuel as it reacts with oxygen from the air in the following reaction:

(1) $P_4S_3 + 6O_2 \rightarrow P_4O_6 + 3SO_2 + heat$

The heat that is produced causes the potassium chlorate in the next layer to break apart to form smaller molecules:

(2) $2KClO_3 \rightarrow 2KCl + 3O_2$

This oxygen gas, in combination with the heat from the first reaction, causes the sulfur to catch fire:

(3) $S + O_2 \rightarrow SO_2 + heat$

The heat from this reaction ignites the paraffin wax, which is a mixture of hydrocarbons:

(4) hydrocarbons + $O_2 \rightarrow CO_2 + H_2O + heat$

The burning paraffin sets the wood of the match on fire in a remarkable series of reactions. No wonder the match lights!

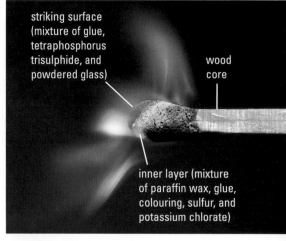

striking surface (mixture of glue, tetraphosphorus trisulphide, and powdered glass)

wood core

inner layer (mixture of paraffin wax, glue, colouring, sulfur, and potassium chlorate)

Figure 3

Matches are made in a series of layers of chemical mixtures

Safety matches are similar to "strike-anywhere" matches, except that the match must be struck on the matchbook cover (**Figure 4**). The inner layers of the safety match are similar to those of the "strike-anywhere" match, except that cardboard is used instead of wood for the core of the match. The striking surface is a layer of red phosphorus, powdered glass, and glue. The frictional heat produced by rubbing the match on the matchbook surface changes the red phosphorus to a different form of phosphorus, called white phosphorus, which then ignites spontaneously in air:

(5) P_4 (red) $\rightarrow$ P_4 (white)

(6) P_4 (white) $+ 5O_2 \rightarrow P_4O_{10} +$ heat

This heat is sufficient to set the rest of the match on fire.

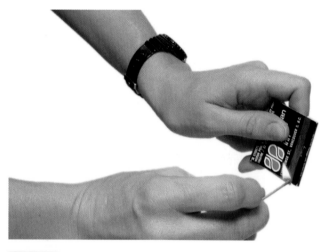

Figure 4
Safety matches can be struck only on the matchbook surface.

Challenge

2,3 How are complete and incomplete combustion involved in your Challenge?

Understanding Concepts

1. What is the meaning of the term "combustion"?

2. Describe the series of steps that result in the ignition of a match in a flow chart. Make sure you include heat and all the various materials in the appropriate steps.

3. Write word equations to represent the complete and incomplete combustion of propane, a fuel used in stoves and home heating.

4. Write balanced chemical equations for the reactions in question 3, given that the chemical formula of propane is C_3H_8.

5. **(a)** How are complete and incomplete combustion different?

   (b) Explain how both complete and incomplete combustion can pose environmental hazards.

6. Why should automobiles and gas barbecues never be operated in enclosed spaces like garages?

7. Canoeists going on long trips in the wilderness depend on matches for campfires. Some of them specially treat their matches by dipping the whole match in liquid paraffin, which hardens to a solid waxy coating. Why do they do this? Do you think it is an effective method? Explain.

8. One of the ways to understand chemical reactions is to categorize reactions that have similarities.

   (a) Why might you group reactions (3) and (6) together?

   (b) In what way is reaction (2) the opposite of reactions (3) and (6)?

Making Connections

9. Draw a labelled diagram showing how burning fossil fuels might lead to global warming.

Work the Web

Where do the chemicals used in matches come from? Are there any significant environmental concerns around match production? Research and report on match production by visiting www.science.nelson.com and following the Science 10, 6.6 links.

Types of Chemical Reactions: Synthesis and Decomposition

Imagine that you are baking some cookies at home and have decided to modify a recipe for oatmeal raisin cookies. You know that there are patterns in the ways that certain ingredients go together so you make a new recipe by substituting dried cranberries for raisins and cornmeal for oatmeal (**Figure 1**).

Just as a cook knows how ingredients will work together in a recipe, so a chemist knows that elements and compounds undergo particular types of chemical reactions. You know that elements can be classified into different chemical families. All members of a chemical family react in a similar way. For example, alkali metals behave in similar ways in chemical reactions. Compounds can also be classified as ionic or molecular, and have definite patterns of chemical properties.

Chemists use these patterns to classify groups of chemical changes. Most chemical reactions can be grouped into four categories:
- synthesis
- decomposition
- single displacement
- double displacement

Knowledge of these types of reactions is useful for two reasons. Firstly, we can better understand experimental observations of the behaviour of substances in chemical changes. Secondly, we can predict the products of unknown reactions.

Look at the reactants represented in **Figure 2**. Which reaction involves elements as reactants? Which reaction involves compounds as reactants? Recognizing the types of reactants is the key to identifying the reaction type. First we will look at two of the reaction types: synthesis and decomposition.

Figure 1

Baking cookies involves mixing a number of ingredients.

synthesis reaction

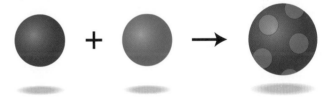

decomposition reaction

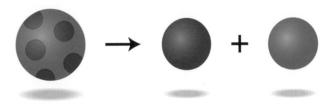

Figure 2

A synthesis reaction involves the combination of smaller molecules. A decomposition reaction involves the breaking apart of larger molecules.

Synthesis Reactions

Synthesis reactions involve the combination of smaller atoms and/or molecules into larger molecules. These reactions are also called **combination reactions**. Often the reactants are elements that combine chemically to form compounds. Synthesis reactions have the following general formula:

$$A + B \rightarrow AB$$

If you see two elements as reactants, you know the reaction has to be a synthesis reaction. Most of these elements are represented as single atoms, but some elements occur naturally as diatomic molecules (**Table 1**). For example, when hydrogen and oxygen gases react, the product is the compound water. This reaction can be represented as word, skeleton, and chemical equations:

$$\text{hydrogen} + \text{oxygen} \rightarrow \text{water}$$
$$H_2 + O_2 \rightarrow H_2O$$
$$2H_2 + O_2 \rightarrow 2H_2O$$

Synthesis reactions can also involve combinations of small molecules. For example, when ammonia and hydrogen chloride vapours combine, they form a white smoke as solid particles of ammonium chloride are formed (**Figure 3**):

$$\text{hydrogen chloride} + \text{ammonia} \rightarrow \text{ammonium chloride}$$
$$HCl + NH_3 \rightarrow NH_4Cl$$

Similarly, the combination of water and carbon dioxide molecules to form carbonic acid is a synthesis reaction. The chemical equation for this reaction is

$$CO_2 + H_2O \rightarrow H_2CO_{3(aq)}$$

Normal rainwater is acidic because of this reaction (**Figure 4**). Acids will be discussed in more detail in Chapter 8.

Decomposition Reactions

Decomposition reactions involve the splitting of a large molecule into elements or smaller molecules. Decomposition reactions have the following general formula:

$$AB \rightarrow A + B$$

If you see a binary compound (one made up of only two elements) as the only reactant, you know that the reaction has to be a decomposition reaction that produces two elements as products. For example, the electrolysis of water uses electricity to split water molecules into their elements. This reaction can be represented as word, skeleton, and chemical equations:

$$\text{water} \rightarrow \text{hydrogen} + \text{oxygen}$$
$$H_2O \rightarrow H_2 + O_2$$
$$2H_2O \rightarrow 2H_2 + O_2$$

Table 1	Elements That Occur as Diatomic Molecules
Element	**Diatomic molecule**
hydrogen	H_2
oxygen	O_2
nitrogen	N_2
fluorine	F_2
chlorine	Cl_2
bromine	Br_2
iodine	I_2

Figure 3

Ammonia and hydrogen chloride vapours combine in a synthesis reaction.

Figure 4

Normal rainwater contains carbonic acid because of the synthesis reaction between carbon dioxide and water.

Sometimes decomposition reactions can involve large amounts of energy (**Figure 5**). Nitrogen triiodide decomposes rapidly to form the elements nitrogen and iodine. This decomposition reaction can be represented by the following word, skeleton, and chemical equations:

nitrogen triiodide $\rightarrow$ nitrogen + iodine
$$NI_3 \rightarrow N_2 + I_2$$
$$2NI_3 \rightarrow N_2 + 3I_2$$

Decomposition reactions can also involve the production of two small molecules from a large molecule. For example, when ammonium nitrate is heated to above 250°C, it decomposes explosively to form nitrous oxide and water molecules. This reaction can be written as the following word, skeleton, and chemical equations:

ammonium nitrate $\rightarrow$ nitrous oxide + water
$$NH_4NO_3 \rightarrow N_2O + H_2O$$
$$NH_4NO_3 \rightarrow N_2O + 2H_2O$$

Figure 5

Nitroglycerine, the active chemical in dynamite, is an unstable compound. Its decomposition reaction is violent and results in the formation of carbon dioxide, water vapour, and molecular nitrogen and oxygen.

✍ Work the Web

Visit the Nelson web site at www.science.nelson.com. Follow the Science 10, 6.7 links to web sites that show examples of synthesis and decomposition reactions. Report on three reactions, including balanced chemical equations.

 Challenge

1 What synthesis or decomposition reactions are involved in the production of your consumer product?

Understanding Concepts

1. Why are synthesis and decomposition reactions sometimes described as opposite reactions? Explain with an example.

2. Classify each of the following reactions as either a synthesis reaction or a decomposition reaction:

   (a) iron + oxygen $\rightarrow$ iron(III) oxide

   (b) sodium iodide $\rightarrow$ sodium + iodine

   (c) hydrogen + oxygen $\rightarrow$ water vapour

   (d) zinc carbonate $\rightarrow$ zinc oxide + carbon dioxide

3. Write skeleton equations for each of the equations in question 2.

4. Balance each of the skeleton equations in question 3.

5. When water is electrolyzed, two gases are produced. As indicated in the chemical equation, twice the volume of one gas is produced compared to the other.

   (a) Which gas is produced in larger quantities? Explain.

   (b) How would you test the gases to confirm your choice?

6. Polymers are long-chain molecules that are made up of many smaller repeating units called monomers. For example, polyethylene is made up of hundreds of ethylene molecules linked together. What kind of reaction is polymerization? Explain, and write a word equation to illustrate.

Putting Things Together

A synthesis reaction involves the direct combination of two substances to produce one new substance. In this investigation, you will have the opportunity to observe synthesis (combination) reactions. Some synthesis reactions will involve elements, while others will involve small molecules combining to make a larger molecule. For example, one of the compounds that you will produce is a hydrate. A **hydrate** is a solid compound in which water molecules are part of the solid crystalline structure. For example, the formula of cobalt chloride dihydrate is $CoCl_2 \cdot 2H_2O$. The crystalline form of cobalt chloride that does not contain these water molecules is called anhydrous cobalt chloride and has the formula $CoCl_2$. Another example of a hydrate is copper(II) sulfate pentahydrate, or $CuSO_4 \cdot 5H_2O$.

Question

What are some examples of synthesis reactions?

Prediction

(a) Write word equations for the expected reactions in air of magnesium and copper.

(b) What would you expect to happen when water combines with anhydrous copper(II) sulfate?

Design

You will react various elements and compounds in air to form new compounds.

(c) Make a table to record all your observations. There should be four columns: *Starting material, Appearance of starting material, Observations during change,* and *Appearance of products.*

Materials

- apron
- safety goggles
- steel wool
- tongs
- magnesium ribbon (approximately 5 cm)
- large beaker
- anhydrous copper(II) sulfate
- eyedropper
- copper wire (approximately 5 cm, 1 mm in diameter)
- Bunsen burner
- watch glass
- water
- copper(II) sulfate pentahydrate (bluestone)

Procedure

1 Put on your apron and safety goggles.

2 Polish a 5-cm piece of copper wire (Cu) with a small piece of steel wool. Examine the wire carefully and record your observations. Hold one end of the wire with tongs, and place the wire in the hottest part of the Bunsen burner flame (**Figure 1**). Remove the wire after 20 s and note any changes that you observe. Your teacher may ask you to set the wire aside for use in Investigation 6.9. Record your observations in the data table.

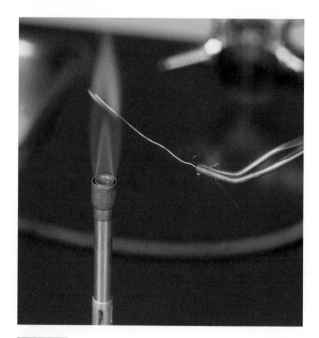

Figure 1

3 Repeat step 2 using a piece of magnesium ribbon (Mg), but remove the ribbon from the flame as soon as the reaction starts (**Figure 2**) and move the magnesium to a large empty beaker. Record your observations.

🛑 This demonstration should take place under a fume hood. Long hair should be tied back and loose clothing should be avoided when burning metals. Do not look directly at the piece of magnesium when it reacts.

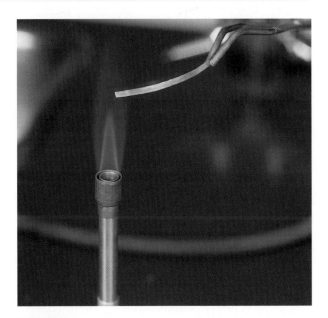

Figure 2

4 Place about 1 g of anhydrous copper(II) sulfate ($CuSO_4$) on a watch glass. Using an eyedropper, add a single drop of water to the powder. Compare the product to a small sample of copper(II) sulfate pentahydrate (bluestone) that your teacher may make available. Record your observations.

Ⓣ Copper(II) sulfate is poisonous and is an irritant. Report any spills to your teacher.

Analysis
(d) For each reaction, what evidence is there that a chemical change occurred?
(e) For each reaction, what evidence did you have that a synthesis reaction occurred?
(f) When the copper was heated, what gas did it combine with? Suggest a name for the product.
(g) When the magnesium burned, what gas did it combine with? Suggest a name for the product.
(h) What evidence was there that a synthesis reaction occurred when water was added to the anhydrous copper(II) sulfate?
(i) Summarize the three reactions as sentences, as word equations, and as balanced chemical equations.

Understanding Concepts
1. In your own words, explain what is meant by synthesis.
2. **(a)** What is another name for synthesis reactions that involve oxygen?
   (b) What are the names of the kinds of compounds that are produced in these reactions?
3. Was it appropriate to label your table's first two columns *Starting material* and *Appearance of starting material*? Suggest better headings for these columns.
4. Examine the reactions described in section 6.6. Which of these reactions could clearly be described as synthesis reactions? Explain.

Reflecting
5. Write a few sentences to complete the following phrase: "A question that this activity raised in my mind was...."

🖰 Work the Web

Visit www.science.nelson.com and follow the Science 10, 6.8 links to web sites that deal with fuel cells. Classify the reactions that occur in fuel cells by their type.

INQUIRY SKILLS MENU
○ Questioning   ○ Planning   ● Analyzing
○ Hypothesizing   ● Conducting   ● Evaluating
● Predicting   ● Recording   ○ Communicating

Taking Things Apart

A decomposition reaction involves the breaking up of a compound into simpler substances. It is exactly the reverse of a synthesis reaction. In this investigation, you will observe the decomposition of compounds to form smaller molecules, including some common gases. For example, when cobalt chloride dihydrate ($CoCl_2 \cdot 2H_2O$) is heated, the water molecules are lost and the product is anhydrous cobalt chloride ($CoCl_2$).

Question

What are the products of the decomposition of some compounds?

Prediction

(a) What gases would you expect to be produced when hydrogen peroxide (H_2O_2), copper(II) carbonate ($CuCO_3$), and copper(II) sulfate pentahydrate ($CuSO_4 \cdot 5H_2O$) decompose.

(b) What tests would you perform to test for these gases?

Design

You will decompose some compounds using heat, electricity, or another chemical substance.

(c) Make a table to record all your observations. For each reaction, there should be four columns.

Materials

- apron
- safety goggles
- scoopula
- copper(II) carbonate
- 4 test tubes (25 × 200 mm)
- test-tube holder
- test-tube rack
- Bunsen burner
- retort stand
- limewater (calcium hydroxide) solution
- anhydrous copper(II) sulfate

- wooden splint
- rubber stopper to fit test tube
- previously heated piece of copper wire from Investigation 6.8
- copper(II) sulfate pentahydrate (bluestone)
- cobalt chloride test paper
- 3% hydrogen peroxide solution
- manganese dioxide

Procedure

Part 1: Decomposition of a Carbonate

1 Put on your apron and safety goggles.

2 Using a scoopula, add one or two scoops of copper(II) carbonate to a test tube. Make certain that the copper(II) carbonate lies along the side of the large-angled test tube and does not remain at the bottom. Assemble the equipment as shown in **Figure 1**. The test tube should be mounted about 20° above horizontal.

Figure 1

3 Gently heat the test tube, making sure to distribute the heat evenly along the side of the tube underneath the copper(II) carbonate. Record your observations.

4 Obtain a second test tube roughly half-full of limewater solution. As you start to see changes in the copper(II) carbonate, position the second test tube so that any gas produced in the reaction can "flow" into the second tube. After about 60 s, stopper the test tube and shake its contents. Record your observations.

5 Continue heating for several minutes, and observe the contents of the test tube. Compare the appearance of the product in the test tube with a previously heated piece of copper wire. Record your observations.

Part 2: Decomposition of a Hydrate

6 Repeat step 2 using copper(II) sulfate pentahydrate (bluestone).

> (T) Copper(II) sulfate pentahydrate (bluestone) is toxic if ingested and is an irritant.
> Copper(II) carbonate, anhydrous copper(II) sulfate, and manganese dioxide are toxic. Report any spills to your teacher.

7 Gently heat the test tube, making sure to distribute the heat evenly along the side of the test tube underneath the bluestone until a change occurs. Compare the product to a small sample of anhydrous copper(II) sulfate. If you see droplets of liquid near the top of the test tube, test them with cobalt chloride test paper. Record your observations.

Part 3: Decomposition of Hydrogen Peroxide

8 Place a test tube in a test-tube rack. Pour 3% hydrogen peroxide solution into the test tube to a depth of about 3 cm.

> (T) Hydrogen peroxide is poisonous and a strong irritant. Report any spills to your teacher.

9 Add a small amount of manganese dioxide (enough to cover the tip of a wooden splint) to the test tube. Note any changes that occur. Put a glowing (not flaming) splint into the mouth of the test tube to test the gas produced. Record your observations.

10 Dispose of the mixtures in the test tubes and put away your materials as instructed by your teacher. Clean up your work station. Wash your hands.

Analysis and Evaluation

(d) For each reaction, what evidence is there that a chemical change occurred?

(e) For each reaction, what evidence did you have that a decomposition reaction occurred?

(f) What solid ionic compound was formed when copper(II) carbonate was heated? What gaseous molecular compound was formed at the same time?

(g) What ionic compound was formed when bluestone was heated? What molecular compound was produced at the same time?

(h) What gas was produced when manganese dioxide was added to hydrogen peroxide solution?

(i) What gases did you test for in this investigation? How successful were the tests?

(j) Suggest ways to improve the design of this investigation.

(k) Summarize the three reactions as sentences, as word equations, and as balanced chemical equations.

Understanding Concepts

1. Some chemical reactions can be reversed. Give an example of a reversible chemical reaction that you encountered in the past two investigations.

2. Sometimes a substance can be used to speed up a reaction without itself being consumed. Name the substance that performed this function in this investigation.

3. When hydrogen peroxide antiseptic is tightly capped and left on the shelf for a long period of time, the bottle is observed to swell. When opened, it "hisses" noticeably. Explain these observations. Is the antiseptic likely to be as effective?

4. Suggest a reason why hydrogen peroxide is not sold in clear bottles, and why it should be stored in a cool place.

Reflecting

5. Write a few sentences to complete the following phrase: "Something that captured my attention in this investigation was...."

Types of Chemical Reactions: Single and Double Displacement

You have investigated synthesis reactions, in which elements were "put together." You have also looked at some decomposition reactions where a compound was "taken apart." What happens when an element and a compound combine in a chemical reaction? What happens when two ionic compounds react with each other? In this lesson, you will learn to recognize displacement reactions and to predict the products that they form in chemical changes. The general pattern of displacement reactions is shown in **Figure 1**. In each type of displacement reaction, atoms are recombined to form new compounds.

single displacement reaction

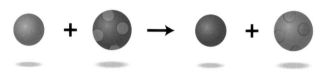

double displacement reaction

Figure 1

In single displacement reactions, an element takes the place of another element in a compound. In double displacement reactions, elements in two compounds "change partners."

Single Displacement Reactions

Single displacement reactions are chemical changes that involve an element and a compound as reactants. One element displaces or replaces another element from a compound. For example, consider the reaction that occurs when a coil of magnesium ribbon is placed in a solution of silver nitrate (**Figure 2**). This reaction can be represented as the following word, skeleton, and chemical equations:

magnesium + silver nitrate → silver + magnesium nitrate
$$Mg + AgNO_3 \rightarrow Ag + Mg(NO_3)_2$$
$$Mg + 2AgNO_3 \rightarrow 2Ag + Mg(NO_3)_2$$

Consider another reaction — one that occurs when the element bromine is added to a solution of calcium iodide. We say that bromine displaces (or takes the place of) the iodide ion. Remember that elements such as bromine and iodine exist as diatomic molecules (refer to section 6.7, **Table 1**). The word and chemical equations for this reaction are

bromine + calcium iodide → iodine + calcium bromide
$$Br_2 + CaI_2 \rightarrow I_2 + CaBr_2$$

Single displacement reactions have the following general formula:

$$Z + AB \rightarrow ZB + A$$

However, this general formula can also be written as follows:

$$Y + AB \rightarrow AY + B$$

In the first case, the metal Z has taken the place of element A. In the second case, the nonmetal Y has taken the place of element B.

Figure 2

Magnesium ribbon placed in a solution of silver nitrate rapidly displaces the silver because it combines with the nitrate group to form magnesium nitrate. The deposit formed is metallic silver.

⌨ Work the Web

One way that displacement reactions may be applied is in the process of refining metals such as aluminum and copper from their minerals. Visit the Nelson web site at www.science.nelson.com. Follow the Science 10, 6.10 links to find out more about this process.

How do we decide which element is displaced? Our knowledge of the periodic properties and naming of compounds can help. Metals are found on the left and centre of the periodic table. Nonmetals are found on the right side of the periodic table. In deciding which element is replaced, we use the general rule of metal replacing metal and nonmetal replacing nonmetal.

In the first example reaction, silver and magnesium are both metals and have positive ionic charges, or valences. The magnesium displaces the silver and forms a compound of magnesium nitrate, which remains dissolved in solution as the solid silver appears. In the second example reaction, bromine and iodine are both nonmetals in the same chemical family. They also have negative ionic charges, or valences, when they form compounds. Thus, bromine displaces iodine rather than the metal calcium.

Figure 3

When lead(II) nitrate and potassium iodide solutions are mixed, a yellow precipitate of lead(II) iodide forms.

Double Displacement Reactions

Double displacement reactions occur when elements in different compounds displace each other or exchange places. For example, the reaction of solutions of lead(II) nitrate and potassium iodide is shown in **Figure 3**. This reaction can be represented in the following word, skeleton, and chemical equations:

lead(II) nitrate + potassium iodide → lead(II) iodide + potassium nitrate

$$Pb(NO_3)_2 + KI \rightarrow PbI_2 + KNO_3$$
$$Pb(NO_3)_2 + 2KI \rightarrow PbI_2 + 2KNO_3$$

Both lead(II) nitrate and potassium iodide are ionic solids, and both are very soluble in water. When lead(II) nitrate is dissolved, it forms lead and nitrate ions. When potassium iodide is dissolved in water, it separates into potassium and iodide ions. When the two solutions are combined, lead ions from the lead(II) nitrate solution and iodide ions from the potassium iodide solution form the solid lead(II) iodide precipitate. Lead(II) iodide remains a solid because it will not dissolve in water. The potassium and nitrate ions will remain in solution as long as water is present because the compound potassium nitrate is highly soluble in water. As a result, this double displacement reaction is sometimes written as

$$Pb(NO_3)_{2(aq)} + 2KI_{(aq)} \rightarrow PbI_{2(s)} + 2KNO_{3(aq)}$$

where (aq) represents an aqueous (or water) solution, and (s) represents a solid.

Double displacement reactions have the following general formula:

$$AB + XY \rightarrow AY + XB$$

where A and X are metallic elements and B and Y are nonmetallic elements. During the reaction, B and Y (or A and X) exchange places.

 **Challenge**

1 What displacement reactions are involved in the production of your product?

Understanding Concepts

1. Consider the four types of reactions you have learned about so far. They all involve elements and compounds as reactants. Which type of reaction has as reactant(s)
   (a) two compounds?
   (b) one element and one compound?
   (c) two elements?
   (d) one compound?

2. Classify each of the following reactions:
   (a) copper + silver nitrate → silver + copper(II) nitrate
   (b) zinc + hydrochloric acid → hydrogen + zinc chloride
   (c) calcium carbonate + hydrochloric acid → carbonic acid + calcium chloride
   (d) aluminum + copper(II) chloride → copper + aluminum chloride

3. Write a skeleton equation and a balanced equation for each reaction in question 2.

Making Connections

4. You work for a company with a large quantity of silver nitrate solution. It wants to recover and sell the silver metal. Design a process to recover the silver metal from solution.

Single Displacement Reactions

In a single displacement reaction, one element replaces another element in a compound. Generally, metals replace other metals, or nonmetals replace other nonmetals. For example, the metal zinc replaces the metal silver from silver nitrate, and fluorine replaces bromine from sodium bromide. A single displacement reaction is also referred to as a substitution reaction. In this investigation, you will observe reactions in which one element takes the place of another element in a compound. The compounds, which may also be referred to as salts, will generally be dissolved in water.

Question

What are the products when an element reacts with a compound that has been dissolved in a solvent?

Prediction

Write word equations predicting the products of the following reactions:

(a) magnesium reacts with sulfuric acid,
(b) magnesium reacts with zinc chloride,
(c) magnesium reacts with copper(II) chloride,
(d) chlorine reacts with potassium bromide, and
(e) chlorine reacts with potassium iodide.

(*Hint*: Think of sulfuric acid as hydrogen sulfate when trying to predict the name of one of the products.)

Design

You will react a metal with an acid and a metal with two solutions of salts.

(f) Make a table to record all your observations. For each reaction, there should be three columns: *Appearance of starting materials, Observations during change,* and *Appearance of products.*

Materials

- apron
- safety goggles
- 3 test tubes
- test-tube rack
- sulfuric acid solution (5% or 1.0 mol/L)
- magnesium pieces (turnings)
- wooden splint
- magnesium ribbon
- steel wool or sandpaper
- microtray
- zinc chloride solution (2% or 0.2 mol/L)
- copper(II) chloride solution (2% or 0.2 mol/L)

Ⓣ The chemicals in this investigation are toxic. Some are also irritants.
Sulfuric acid is corrosive. There is risk of eye and skin damage.

Ⓢ Any spills on the skin, in the eyes, or on clothing should be washed immediately with cold water. Report any spills to your teacher.

Procedure

Part 1: Metals and Acid

1 Put on your apron and safety goggles.

2 Add sulfuric acid to a test tube to a depth of about 2 cm.

Add a 2- to 3-cm piece of magnesium to the test tube. Observe the reaction and test the gas produced with a burning splint (**Figure 1**). Record your observations in the data table.

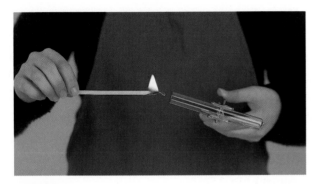

Figure 1

 When testing for gases, point the mouth of the test tube away from yourself and other people.

Part 2: Metals and Salt Solutions

4 Clean two strips of magnesium ribbon, approximately 2 cm in length, with steel wool (or sandpaper) until shiny. Half-fill a microtray well with zinc chloride solution. Place one strip of magnesium in the well, as shown in **Figure 2**. Observe the reaction for several minutes then record your observations.

Figure 2

5 Repeat step 4, adding the second piece of magnesium to a well containing copper(II) chloride solution. Observe for several minutes and record your observations in the data table.

6 Dispose of the mixtures and put away your materials as instructed by your teacher. Clean up your work station. Wash your hands.

Analysis and Evaluation

(g) For each reaction, what evidence is there that a chemical change occurred?

(h) What gas was produced when magnesium and sulfuric acid reacted?

(i) What metals were produced when magnesium was added to the salt solutions?

(j) Look back at your predictions. Do you think they were correct? Make any necessary corrections.

(k) What are some sources of error in this investigation?

Understanding Concepts

1. What are single displacement reactions?

2. What happens when a metal is added to the solution of an ionic compound? Explain with an example.

3. Write word equations for all the reactions that occurred.

4. Write balanced chemical equations for all the reactions that occurred.

5. Predict the products of the single displacement reactions that occur when

   (a) magnesium is added to hydrochloric acid (HCl);

   (b) zinc is added to copper(II) sulfate solution; and

   (c) bromine is added to sodium iodide solution.

6. Write word equations to represent the reactions in question 5.

7. Write balanced chemical equations for the reactions in question 5.

Reflecting

8. Write a short paragraph to complete the following phrase: "What I learned from doing this lab was...."

INQUIRY SKILLS MENU
○ Questioning   ○ Planning   ● Analyzing
● Hypothesizing   ● Conducting   ● Evaluating
● Predicting   ● Recording   ○ Communicating

Double Displacement Reactions

A double displacement reaction, sometimes called a double decomposition reaction, involves the reaction of two compounds to form two new compounds. In effect, the compounds change partners with each other. Sometimes, if the reactions occur in solution, an insoluble product called a precipitate may form (**Figure 1**).

Figure 1

When lead(II) nitrate and sodium sulfide solutions are mixed, a precipitate of lead(II) sulfide is formed. Sodium nitrate remains dissolved in the water.

Question

What are the products when pairs of compounds react in double displacement reactions?

Prediction

Write word equations for the predicted products of the following reactions:

(a) sodium chloride and silver nitrate,
(b) silver nitrate and potassium iodide,
(c) iron(III) chloride and sodium hydroxide,
(d) sodium chloride and potassium nitrate, and
(e) sodium carbonate and calcium chloride.

Design

You will use microdroppers and a microtray to combine clear solutions of various compounds. If a precipitate forms in a solution, you will have evidence that a double replacement reaction has occurred.

(f) Make a table to record your observations.

Materials

- apron
- safety goggles
- microtray
- 8 labelled microdroppers
- sodium chloride solution (1% or 0.1 mol/L)
- silver nitrate solution (1% or 0.1 mol/L)
- potassium iodide solution (1% or 0.1 mol/L)
- iron(III) chloride solution (1% or 0.1 mol/L)
- sodium hydroxide solution (1% or 0.1 mol/L)
- potassium nitrate solution (1% or 0.1 mol/L)
- sodium carbonate solution (1% or 0.1 mol/L)
- calcium chloride solution (1% or 0.1 mol/L)

 Silver nitrate solution is toxic and can stain skin and clothing. Any spills on the skin, in the eyes, or on clothing should be washed immediately with cold water.

   Iron(III) chloride is a strong irritant, corrosive, and toxic. Any spills on the skin, in the eyes, or on clothing should be washed immediately with cold water. Report any spills to your teacher.

Sodium hydroxide is corrosive. Any spills on the skin, in the eyes, or on clothing should be washed immediately with cold water. Report any spills to your teacher.

Procedure

1 Put on your apron and safety goggles.

2 Add two or three drops of sodium chloride to one of the wells on the microtray using the labelled microdropper. Add two or three drops of silver nitrate solution to the same well, using a second labelled microdropper (**Figure 2**). Record your observations, noting the appearance and colour of any product.

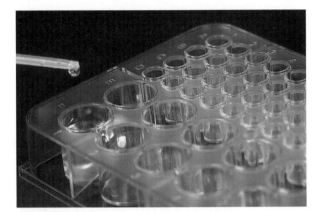

Figure 2

⊘ Avoid cross-contamination of microdroppers and solutions; let solutions "free-fall" into the microtray wells rather than touching the dropper to the microtray.

3 Repeat step 2 using the other labelled microdroppers and solutions as follows: silver nitrate and potassium iodide; iron(III) chloride and sodium hydroxide; sodium chloride and potassium nitrate; and sodium carbonate and calcium chloride.

4 Dispose of the mixtures in the microtrays, and clean and put away your materials as instructed by your teacher. Clean up your work station. Wash your hands.

Analysis and Evaluation

(g) What evidence was there that a chemical reaction occurred? Did a reaction occur in every combination of solutions? Explain.

(h) What were some sources of error in this experiment?

(i) One of the combinations of solutions did not produce any visible change. Can we conclude that no reaction occurred? Explain.

(j) Look back at your predictions and make any necessary changes.

Understanding Concepts

1. **(a)** What is a double displacement reaction?

   (b) How is it different from a single displacement reaction?

2. Write word equations for all the reactions that occurred in this investigation.

3. Use your knowledge of ionic charges to write a skeleton equation for each of the reactions in question 2.

4. Write balanced chemical equations for each of the skeleton equations in question 3.

Exploring

5. Hard water contains calcium, magnesium, and iron ions that can be removed by precipitation. Find out how water can be softened and write a report to explain the process. Include any significant health concerns regarding chemically softened water.

6. Many of the reactions that you observed in this investigation formed precipitates in solution. How could you decide which of the two possible products was the precipitate? Design an experimental procedure to answer this question. Most chemistry textbooks have "solubility tables" that may help you with this process.

Putting It All Together

You have learned that chemical reactions can be grouped into various categories. The system we have used looks at the reactants. Are they elements or compounds? Are they metals or nonmetals? In this activity, you will make a graphic organizer to summarize your knowledge of the types of chemical reactions.

Materials

- scissors
- paper
- coloured markers
- glue stick

Procedure

1 Your teacher will put you into cooperative
X groups. Your teacher may also decide to assign you specific roles, such as Writer, Textbook Resource, or Materials Manager.

2 Cut out 30 small pieces of paper, each roughly a 2-cm × 4-cm rectangle. Write the following words on the rectangles, using your choice of appropriate coloured markers:

- "element" on 6 rectangles
- "compound" on 12 rectangles
- "smaller compound" on 4 rectangles
- "larger compound" on 2 rectangles
- "metal" on 2 rectangles
- "nonmetal" on 4 rectangles

(a) What are the meanings of the terms "element" and "compound"?

(b) What are several examples of elements and compounds?

(c) What are the meanings of the terms "metal" and "nonmetal"?

(d) What are several examples of metals and nonmetals?

3 Cut out 8 smaller rectangles, and draw an arrow on each rectangle. This arrow links reactants and products in chemical equations. Cut out 12 to 15 very small squares on which you can write a plus (+) sign to use in building some equations.

4 Review the four types of chemical reactions that you have encountered in this chapter. Cut out 4 large rectangles; on each of these rectangles, write in block capitals the name of one type of reaction (Synthesis, Decomposition, Single Displacement, or Double Displacement).

5 Write the heading "Types of Chemical Reactions" on a piece of paper. Place the labels for the types of reactions in different areas of the sheet. For example, below the "Synthesis" label, place words in different combinations that summarize the information you have learned about synthesis reactions (**Figure 1**). Make sure you leave some space underneath each of the labels.

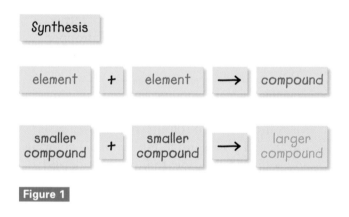

Figure 1

Repeat step 5 for the other three types of reactions, using the remaining words. Feel free to organize the words as you choose and to make other labels if they seem appropriate.

7 Underneath or beside each set of labels, add other information that may help you to summarize what you know about these reactions. For example, **Figure 2** shows some additional possible information about synthesis reactions.

8 Organize the labels so that they provide the most efficient summary of what you know about these types of reactions. Glue the rectangles in place.

9 Save this chart for later use.

Understanding Concepts

1. What do synthesis and single displacement reactions have in common?

2. What do decomposition and double displacement reactions have in common?

3. Which two types of reactions seem to be opposites? Explain.

4. Identify each of the following reactions as one of the four types of reactions:

   (a) barium + sulfur → barium sulfide

   (b) bromine + sodium iodide → iodine + sodium bromide

   (c) barium nitrate + sodium sulfide → barium sulfide + sodium nitrate

   (d) lithium carbonate → carbon dioxide + lithium oxide

   (e) lead(II) oxide → lead + oxygen

   (f) calcium + water → hydrogen + calcium hydroxide

   (g) sulfur trioxide + water → sulfuric acid

5. Write skeleton and balanced chemical equations for each of the reactions in question 4.

6. Where would you put combustion reactions in your chart? Explain.

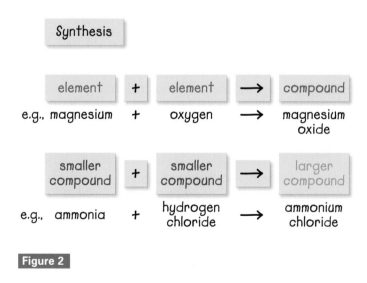

Figure 2

DECISION MAKING SKILLS
● Define the Issue   ● Analyze the Issue
○ Identify Alternatives ● Defend a Decision
● Research   ○ Evaluate

Is Pollution Necessary?

Have you ever considered how your lifestyle may affect the environment? When you or your family buys a product, whether it is a durable product such as a computer or a disposable product such as a magazine, what you buy affects the environment. Heating your house, running your computer, and travelling in a car all require energy. What kind of balance should exist between your lifestyle and concerns about the environment?

Canadians enjoy a high standard of living. However, maintaining such a high quality of life has negative effects on the environment. Using energy to power appliances or automobiles, buying products, and disposing of packaging and useless or worn goods are all individual choices that produce pollution.

Energy production and use are the major sources of air pollution. Canadians use more energy per person than people in most other countries. There are several reasons for this: Canada has a cold climate, a large industrial base that consumes 31% of the energy produced, and a large land area over which to transport goods and people. Almost 70% of Canadian energy requirements are supplied by burning fossil fuels. The burning of fossil fuels releases air pollutants, such as carbon dioxide, nitrogen oxides, and sulfur dioxide. Toxic air pollutants, such as benzene, are released during the handling and storage of fossil fuels.

Consumer products and packaging create wastes. It is estimated that over 300 kg of household waste is produced per person each year. Our choices of products, such as batteries, paints, and pesticides, contribute to hazardous wastes. The typical Canadian household produces 6.8 kg of hazardous waste per year.

However, consumer products are important. Buying products is important to the economy; manufacturing industries provide jobs (**Figure 1**). Appliances, such as microwave ovens and dishwashers, make our lives easier and more time-efficient. Materials can be reused, recycled, or repaired. Transportation of products around Canada ensures that everyone has access to the products.

Figure 1

Factories may produce pollution, but they also provide jobs and make useful products.

Understanding the Issue

1. Suggest some sources of pollution that are related to our high standard of living.

2. How do Ontario's geography and climate affect our consumption of energy?

3. What types of products could you choose that would help reduce the effects of pollution?

🖑 Work the Web

Explore the effects of pollution on the environment by following the Science 10, 6.14 links at www.science.nelson.com.

SKILLS HANDBOOK: Ⓨ Graphic Organizers

Economist Says Pollution No Problem

Alex Leroy, an internationally known economist, spoke to the Chamber of Commerce yesterday on the need for a growing economy.

"The manufacturing sector is a powerful economic force, creating products that people need, and providing economic growth, jobs, and income. Consumer products are necessary for an expanding population. Without gasoline-powered vehicles, our economy would literally grind to a halt.

"I believe that pollution is not a problem. Some pollution is unavoidable, but controls are in place to keep this pollution to a minimum. In fact, the environment is improving. Proper disposal of hazardous wastes can minimize the effect these materials have on the environment. Packaging foods not only protects the product and preserves freshness, but ensures that only 2% of food is wasted before reaching the customer. And recycling is working: approximately 50% of all

iron and steel produced in Canada comes from recycled iron and steel scrap. In a way, pollution even stimulates the economy by directly providing jobs through its cleanup. New technologies have led to the development of more energy-efficient appliances. Industries, logging, mining, construction, agriculture, and transportation all are vital to our standard of living, and are controlled to limit their environmental impact."

Figure 2

Environmentalist Says Quality of Life Threatened

Sandy Green, spokesperson for the "Save Our World" group, spoke at a rally at City Hall yesterday.

"We need to change our attitudes about progress and growth in the economy. People think that 'standard of living' means how big their car is or how many televisions they own. But a good standard of living includes having clean air, soil, and water. Pollution is threatening our quality of life.

Industries pump poisonous gases into the air. We consume and waste

energy at an alarming rate. Cars are a major source of air pollution: in Canada, there is approximately one car for every two people. Nuclear power plants produce nuclear wastes, that we can't dispose of, and fossil fuel-burning power plants contaminate the air with pollutants that contribute to global warming and acid rain. The excess packaging of products consumes materials such as glass, cardboard, and metals, uses energy in production, and creates waste.

"There are many alternatives. We should be reducing our levels of energy consumption, recycling materials, and reusing products. We should be using natural materials rather than synthetics. We should be using public transportation, rather than driving everywhere. Did you know that one bus replaces about 44 cars? We should be carefully thinking about the goods that we buy and how our choices can save the environment."

Figure 3

Take a Stand Perspectives on Pollution and the Standard of Living

The issue of pollution and our standard of living is a complex one. Newspapers, magazines, and other media usually present definite points of view. Some articles may be "pro-business," while others may be "pro-environment." Read the views presented in **Figures 2** and **3**.

1. Working in a group, brainstorm as many (Y) (D) ideas about the issue as possible and record your ideas in a P-M-I graphic organizer. The newspaper articles will give you some hints, but use your own knowledge and imagination to add your own ideas. Plus (P) comments describe benefits and positive effects of

processes that produce pollution. Minus (M) comments describe problems and negative effects of pollution. Interesting Questions (I) describe what the group would like to know about the topic to help make a decision. As a group, decide which view you support.

2. Using libraries, the Internet, and CD (E) references, research to find information that will further support both sides of the issue.

3. Write a short play in which a group of friends is discussing what they choose to buy with their part-time wages. If possible, stage your play.

Ann Tran

Hospital Pharmacist

When a patient is connected to several IV (intravenous) drips in a hospital, the last thing on her mind is whether the various chemicals are going to do something nasty in her body. Ann Tran's job is to make sure that doesn't happen. "If you're not careful," she says, "you can put a patient on two drips that will react to form a precipitate. The chemicals then will not have the effect intended, and the precipitate may very well be poisonous." Certainly not what the doctor ordered!

Ann is a hospital pharmacist. She emigrated to Canada from Vietnam at the age of 2 with her mother (a teacher) and her father (a mechanical engineer at the Riverdale Hospital in Toronto). Ann worked weekends as a teenager in her aunt's pharmacy and as a summer student at the Riverdale hospital. Despite her aunt's reassurance that pharmacy is a great career "because most pharmacists keep regular hours," Ann found herself drawn to a practice in hospital pharmacy, where the hours are anything but regular, but the reward comes from the thrill of observing treatment firsthand.

Ann graduated from the University of Toronto with a Bachelor of Science in pharmacy and promptly did a clinical pharmacy residency at the Sunnybrook and Women's College Health Sciences Centre.

In her capacity as staff pharmacist in general surgery at Sunnybrook, Ann monitors and studies the actions, reactions, and interactions of drugs and the human body, which is also made of chemicals, and all react with each other in normal or abnormal ways, depending on the health of the patient.

Even though the chemistry of the human body is relatively constant around the world (some blood types are more prevalent in certain areas of the world, sickle-cell anemia is more common in tropical climates, and simple things like hydration levels differ from place to place), laws regulating drugs change from country to country, and, within Canada, from province to province. This requires a pharmacist to learn constantly, as new drugs with new effects and interactions come on the market. Ann attends conferences, works on task forces, reads as many journals as she can find time for, and generally works hard keeping up-to-date with the effects and benefits of all the latest drugs.

Making Connections

1. The pharmacy program in many universities is a "second-level entry program," which means that you must complete a year of university before applying. Find out what courses would be necessary in your first year of university to gain admission to a pharmacy program.

🖱 Work the Web

Chemicals (drugs or medicines) that react to each other or to certain medical conditions in a harmful way are called "contraindicated." Aspirin (acetylsalicylic acid), for example, is contraindicated for hemophiliacs. Visit www.science.nelson.com and follow the links from Science 10, 6.15 to find some contraindicated medicines. Report on two contraindicated situations.

Key Expectations

Throughout the chapter, you have had opportunities to do the following things:

- Use the Law of Conservation of Mass as a rationale for balancing equations. (6.1, 6.2, 6.3, 6.4, 6.5)

- Represent chemical reactions using models, word equations, and balanced chemical equations. (6.1, 6.5, 6.7, 6.9, 6.10, 6.11, 6.12)

- Use appropriate apparatus and apply WHMIS safety procedures for handling, storage, disposal, and recycling of materials in the lab. (6.2, 6.4, 6.8, 6.9, 6.11, 6.12, 6.13)

- Formulate questions about practical problems and issues involving chemical processes. (6.2, 6.4, 6.8, 6.9, 6.11, 6.12, 6.14)

- Analyze data and information, evaluate evidence and sources of information, and identify errors and bias. (6.2, 6.4, 6.13, 6.14)

- Describe experimental procedures in the form of a laboratory report. (6.2, 6.4, 6.8, 6.9, 6.11, 6.12)

- Use appropriate vocabulary, SI units, tables, and descriptions of procedures using the scientific method. (6.2, 6.4)

- Compare theoretical and empirical values, and account for discrepancies in conservation of mass experiments. (6.2, 6.4)

- Describe from observations the reactants and products of a variety of chemical reactions, including synthesis, decomposition, and displacement reactions. (6.6, 6.7, 6.8, 6.9, 6.10, 6.11, 6.12, 6.13)

- Describe how an understanding of chemical reactions has led to new consumer products and technological processes. (6.6)

- Conduct chemical tests to identify common gases. (6.9, 6.11)

- Select and integrate information from many sources including electronic, print, and community resources, and personally collected data. (6.14)

- Explain how environmental challenges can be addressed through an understanding of chemical substances. (6.14)

- Explore careers based on technologies that use chemical reactions. (6.15)

Key Terms

balanced chemical equation

coefficient

combination reaction

combustion

decomposition reaction

double displacement reaction

hydrate

incomplete combustion

Law of Conservation of Mass

scientific law

single displacement reaction

skeleton equation

synthesis reaction

word equation

Make a Summary

Ⓨ Use a "fishbone" graphic organizer to summarize what you have learned in this chapter (**Figure 1**).

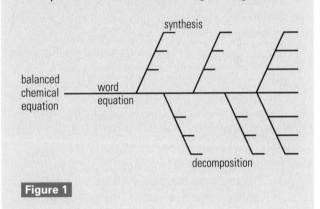

Figure 1

Reflect on your Learning

Revisit your answers to the Reflect on your Learning questions, page 217, in the Getting Started.

- How has your thinking changed?

- What new questions do you have?

Chapter 6 Review

Understanding Concepts

1. (a) State the Law of Conservation of Mass.
   (b) How does this law explain why we balance chemical equations?

2. For each of the following, replace the description with one or two words:
   (a) a reaction that involves the combination of two elements;
   (b) a solid compound that contains water molecules;
   (c) an unbalanced equation that describes formulas of substances;
   (d) the breaking apart of a larger molecule into smaller molecules;
   (e) the number placed in front of a formula in a balanced equation.

3. The sentences below contain errors or are incomplete. Write complete, correct versions.
   (a) A word equation contains words to represent compounds.
   (b) The total mass of products equals the total mass of reactants unless a gas is produced.
   (c) A scientific law is a theory used to explain experimental observations.
   (d) Atoms may be destroyed in some chemical changes.
   (e) Compounds are broken down in synthesis reactions.
   (f) Elements and compounds react in double displacement reactions.
   (g) Elements combine in single displacement reactions.
   (h) The products of the combustion of a hydrocarbon are carbon dioxide and oxygen.

4. Write word equations to represent the following changes and identify each of them as a synthesis, decomposition, single displacement, double displacement, or combustion reaction:
   (a) A welder's torch combines acetylene and oxygen gases to form carbon dioxide and water.
   (b) A piece of zinc metal added to silver nitrate produces zinc nitrate and silver.
   (c) When zinc carbonate is heated, zinc oxide and carbon dioxide are produced.
   (d) Nitrogen and oxygen gases react in automobile engines to produce poisonous nitrogen dioxide.
   (e) Potassium hydroxide and phosphoric acid react to produce water and potassium phosphate.
   (f) Hydrogen and nitrogen gases react to make ammonia used in fertilizer.

5. Determine whether the following equations are balanced as written. Balance the equation if necessary.
   (a) $CO + O_2 \rightarrow CO_2$
   (b) $Cl_2 + KBr \rightarrow Br_2 + KCl$
   (c) $4NH_3 + 3O_2 \rightarrow 2N_2 + 6H_2O$

6. Balance the following equations.
   (a) $Ca + HBr \rightarrow CaBr_2 + H_2$
   (b) $Al + O_2 \rightarrow Al_2O_3$
   (c) $KNO_3 + HBr \rightarrow KBr + HNO_3$
   (d) $Ba + H_3PO_4 \rightarrow Ba_3(PO_4)_2 + H_2$
   (e) $CaCl_2 + Al_2(SO_4)_3 \rightarrow CaSO_4 + AlCl_3$
   (f) $C_3H_8 + O_2 \rightarrow CO_2 + H_2O$

7. Write the corresponding word or skeleton equations and balanced chemical questions for each of the following.
   (a) $BaCl_2$ and Na_2SO_4 react to form $BaSO_4$ and NaCl.
   (b) When sulfuric acid and sodium hydroxide react, the products are sodium sulfate and the most important liquid on earth.
   (c) Potassium chlorate produces potassium chloride and a gas that causes a glowing splint to burst into flame.

8. You may have noticed that a silver utensil will tarnish or turn black over time (**Figure 1**).

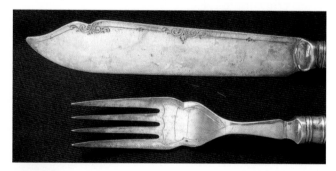

Figure 1

   (a) What do you think the mass of the tarnished fork is compared to its original silver condition? Explain.
   (b) What do you think happens to the mass of the fork when the black tarnish is removed with a silver cleaner?

9. In an experiment, 24 g of magnesium react with 73 g of hydrogen chloride to produce a gas and 95 g of magnesium chloride.
   (a) Do these results prove the Law of Conservation of Mass? Explain your answer.
   (b) What gas do you think was produced? How much of the gas do you think was produced?

10. When methane (CH_4) burns in oxygen gas (O_2), it produces water (H_2O) and carbon dioxide (CO_2).
    (a) Write a skeleton equation for the reaction.
    (b) Draw a sketch to represent each of the molecules. For example, methane might be a black circle (carbon atom) attached to four white circles (hydrogen atoms).
    (c) According to the Law of Conservation of Mass, what relationship is there between the numbers of atoms in reactants and products?
    (d) Draw sketches to represent the numbers of molecules of each type necessary to balance the equation.
    (e) Write the balanced chemical equation for the reaction.

Applying Inquiry Skills

11. When baking soda and vinegar are mixed together, a chemical reaction occurs that produces carbon dioxide gas. Baking soda is $Na(HCO_3)$ and vinegar is a solution of acetic acid $H(C_2H_3O_2)$. (The brackets have been included here only to assist you.)
    (a) What kind of reaction involves two compounds as reactants?
    (b) Write a skeleton equation to represent the reactants and possible products.
    (c) One of the products is a soluble sodium compound and the other is an acid which can undergo a second reaction that produces water and a gas. Write a balanced chemical equation for this second reaction.

12. A student performs a reaction in which a metal is added to an acid solution and a gas is produced. The following results are obtained:
    mass of magnesium   = 3.4 g
    mass of acid   = 102.5 g
    mass of product solution = 105.6 g
    Calculate the mass of the gas produced.

13. Design an experiment to confirm the Law of Conservation of Mass. Check your design with your teacher before proceeding. Report on your findings.

14. When a car burns gasoline, it produces carbon dioxide and water vapour. Assuming that gasoline is octane, the skeleton equation for this reaction is
    $$C_8H_{18} + O_2 \rightarrow CO_2 + H_2O$$
    (a) What type of reaction is this?
    (b) Write a balanced equation for this reaction.
    (c) When a car burns one litre of gasoline, it produces about 2.5 kg of carbon dioxide. Make a rough calculation of the number of litres of gasoline that your family car burns in an average week. How many kilograms of carbon dioxide are produced at the same time?

(d) Why is carbon dioxide an environmental concern?
(e) What steps do you think people should take to deal with this environmental issue?

Making Connections

15. An important industrial process is the refining of iron ore in a blast furnace (**Figure 2**). In the reaction, carbon displaces iron metal from impure iron(III) oxide. The word and skeleton equations for this reaction are
    carbon + iron(III) oxide → iron + carbon dioxide
    $$C + Fe_2O_3 \rightarrow Fe + CO_2$$

Figure 2

    (a) Write a balanced chemical equation for this reaction.
    (b) What type of reaction is this?
    (c) What element displaces the iron?
    (d) What type of element is carbon?
    (e) How is this reaction different from the pattern of reactions that you learned about in this chapter?

16. Cyclopropane (C_3H_6) is a hydrocarbon that was once used as an anaesthetic. Its properties, however, made it a safety concern.
    (a) What type of chemical reaction could cyclo-propane undergo?
    (b) Write word, skeleton, and balanced chemical equations for this reaction.
    (c) What types of safety precautions do you think medical personnel would have had to follow to prevent this reaction?

17. Survey newspaper articles about pollution and/or industrial processes for a week. Build a scrapbook of articles that support a pro-industry or a pro-environmental viewpoint. Analyze the point of view of the newspaper. Which point of view does it seem to support, either in editorials, in amount of coverage, or in the tone of the articles?

Controlling Chemical Reactions

Getting Started

WHY ARE SOME REACTIONS MUCH FASTER THAN OTHERS? When a hiker lights a campfire, the wood reacts quickly in air to produce heat and light, and carbon dioxide and water vapour. You have learned that this process is called combustion. Other substances react with air or oxygen in chemical processes that are much slower. For example, the rusting of a steel garden tool is a slow reaction of iron with oxygen.

All reactions take place at different speeds. The speed at which a reaction occurs is called its **rate of reaction**. The rate at which reactions occur varies considerably. When a cook bakes a cake, the ingredients are mixed together at room temperature. When baking soda is mixed with cream of tartar, the substances react together to produce bubbles of gas that cause the cake to expand, or rise. This reaction occurs quite slowly at room temperature, but occurs quickly in a hot oven.

Without thinking about it, both the hiker lighting a campfire and the cook baking a cake are controlling chemical reactions. They are changing factors, or variables, to make chemical reactions occur at different rates. In this chapter, you will investigate the factors that control rates of reaction.

Reflect on your Learning

1. What are some examples of chemical reactions that happen slowly?

2. What are some reactions that happen quickly?

3. What are some examples of household chemical reactions that happen quickly or slowly depending on the conditions?

4. How can you make chemical reactions go faster?

5. Can you think of a way to slow down reactions?

Throughout this chapter, note any changes in your ideas as you learn new concepts and develop your skills.

Try This
Activity A "Speedy" K-W-L Organizer

Ⓨ Think about the answers to the Reflect on your Learning questions as you do the following activity.

- Working alone or in a small group, obtain a blank sheet of paper and divide it into three sections. Write the letter *K* at the top of the first section. Write the letters *W* and *L* in the other two sections.

- When your teacher directs you to start, think of everything you *know* about rates of reactions. Write these facts or ideas down in the *K* section without evaluating them. Your teacher will specify the number of minutes that you have for this brainstorming process.

- When the teacher calls time, think of everything you *want to know* about rates of reactions. Write these down in the *W* section. Again, you will have a specified number of minutes for this brainstorming process.

- When the teacher calls time, present all the *K* and *W* ideas to the class. The *L* section of the page will remain blank for now.

In the Review section of this chapter, you will have an opportunity to report on what you have *learned* about the rates of reactions.

Figure 1

Lighting a campfire involves controlling the rate of the reaction. The hiker chooses specific types of dry wood and starts the fire with small pieces of wood — factors that make the combustion of the wood happen faster.

INQUIRY SKILLS MENU
- Questioning
- Hypothesizing
- Predicting
- Planning
- Conducting
- Recording
- Analyzing
- Evaluating
- Communicating

Temperature and Rate

Why does wood burn quickly when it is put on a fire that is already blazing? Why do we use stoves and microwave ovens to prepare food? The answer to both these questions involves temperature and its effect on the rate of a reaction. The rate of a reaction is the speed at which a chemical change occurs. It can be measured by how quickly (or slowly) a reactant is consumed or a product is produced. The greater the rate of reaction, the less time the reaction will take.

Question

How does temperature affect the rate of a reaction?

Prediction

(a) How do you think increasing the temperature will affect the rate of a reaction (i.e., will the rate increase or decrease)?

Design

In this investigation, you will measure the time taken to dissolve an Alka-Seltzer tablet in water at different temperatures. You will then analyze your results graphically.

(b) Make a table to record all your observations. Your table should have three columns: *Temperature (°C)*, *Time (s)*, and *Qualitative observations*.

Materials

- apron
- safety goggles
- 4 250-mL beakers
- ice
- cool water
- stopwatch or timer
- hot water (from the tap)
- very hot water (from a kettle)
- thermometer
- 4 Alka-Seltzer tablets

 Boiling water can cause burns. Handle with care.

Procedure

1 Put on your apron and safety goggles.

2 Fill a beaker with ice and water. Fill three other beakers with cool water, hot water, and very hot water (from a kettle), respectively.

3 (M) Use the thermometer to measure the temperature of the water in each of the four beakers. Record these temperatures in your data table.

4 Obtain four Alka-Seltzer tablets of similar mass.

5 (L1) Set your stopwatch or timer to zero. Before the water has a chance to change temperature, drop one Alka-Seltzer tablet into each beaker at the same time (**Figure 1**). Record how long it takes for each tablet to completely dissolve and any other qualitative observations. Your teacher may also ask you to record your results in a class data table or on a class graph on the overhead projector.

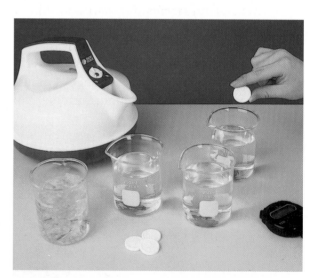

Figure 1
Measure the time it takes an Alka-Seltzer tablet to dissolve in water.

SKILLS HANDBOOK: (M) Observing and Recording (L1) Using Timing Devices

6 Dispose of the mixtures, and clean and put away your materials as instructed by your teacher. Clean up your work station. Wash your hands.

Analysis and Evaluation

(c) Plot a graph of time vs. temperature, using your results and/or the class results as instructed by your teacher. If there is more than one result at a particular temperature, calculate and use an average value. Title the graph and make sure it has all the required components of a good graph.

(d) Use your graph to draw conclusions about the effect of temperature on reaction rate.

(e) Compare your conclusions in (d) with your initial prediction in (a).

(f) What happened to the Alka-Seltzer tablets when you put them into the water?

(g) What evidence do you have that a chemical reaction occurred?

(h) What effect did a 10°C increase in temperature have on the rate of the reaction? A 20°C increase?

(i) What were some sources of experimental error in this investigation?

(j) It is important in experiments to control all of the variables except the one under study. What variables were controlled in this investigation? What was the independent variable? What was the dependent variable?

Understanding Concepts

1. Describe, qualitatively, the effect increasing the temperature has on the rate of reaction.

2. The kinetic molecular theory suggests that particles are constantly moving and that they move more quickly at higher temperatures. Use this theory to explain your results in this investigation.

3. Use your graph to predict the amount of time this reaction would take at 40°C and at 60°C.

4. Compare your data to the class data. In what ways are the graphed results different from yours? In what way are the graphed results the same?

5. Answer the two questions posed in the introduction to this investigation.

6. List and explain three other examples of reactions in which temperature is altered to increase or decrease the rate of a reaction.

Making Connections

7. **(a)** Why does the Alka-Seltzer tablet react only after it is placed in water?

   (b) Explain why it is packaged as it is.

Exploring

8. Measure the mass of a typical Alka-Seltzer tablet. Calculate a numerical value for the rate of reaction at 20°C, 30°C, and 40°C by applying the following formula:

$$\text{rate} = \frac{\text{mass of tablet (g) dissolved}}{\text{time (s)}}$$

The rate will be expressed in units of g/s.

Reflecting

9. What are the advantages of using a larger set of class results rather than just your own?

Try This
Activity   The Expanding Balloon

You can investigate the effect of temperature on the reaction between an Alka-Seltzer tablet and water in a different way.

• Place an Alka-Seltzer tablet in a large balloon, and then stretch the balloon over the top of an Erlenmeyer flask containing water.

• Set up three other flasks in the same way, but containing water at different temperatures.

• Flip the balloons up so that the tablets fall into the flasks at the same time.

(a) Record and analyze the rate of change that occurs in the volume of the balloons.

Concentration and Rate

You know that substances that burn relatively quickly in air burn very rapidly in pure oxygen. The speed at which substances, such as sulfur (**Figure 1**) burn depends on the concentration of oxygen. The concentration of a solution is the amount of solute dissolved in a certain volume of solution. For a gas, the concentration is the number of gas molecules in a given volume. A **concentrated solution** is a solution that has a large amount of solute compared to solvent. A **dilute solution** is a solution that has a small amount of solute compared to solvent.

Figure 1
Sulfur burns rapidly in pure oxygen.

The concentration of a solution can be described quantitatively. For example, in a solution that is 20% hydrochloric acid by mass, 20 g of hydrochloric acid have been dissolved in enough water to form 100 g of solution. A more dilute solution can be made either by dissolving less acid in the same amount of solvent (water) or by adding more water to increase the volume of the solution.

In this investigation, you will look at the rate of the reaction of zinc with different concentrations of hydrochloric acid. When zinc is added to hydrochloric acid, the zinc is completely consumed as hydrogen gas and a solution of zinc chloride are formed. The rate of reaction can be measured as the rate at which the zinc is consumed. It is important in experiments to control all of the variables except those under study: in this case, the concentration of hydrochloric acid and the rate of the reaction.

Question

How does an increase in the concentration of one of the reactants change the rate of a chemical reaction?

Hypothesis/Prediction

(a) Write a hypothesis giving a general rule for the
(K3) effect of concentration on rates of reaction.
(b) Write a statement predicting the effect of doubling the concentration of hydrochloric acid on the time required for all of the zinc to be consumed.

Design

In this investigation, you will react zinc metal with hydrochloric acid solutions of different concentrations. The time required for all of the zinc to react will be measured. A shorter time indicates a faster reaction.

(c) What are the independent, dependent, and controlled variables?
(d) Make a table to record your quantitative and qualitative observations.

Materials

- apron
- safety goggles
- 4 zinc pieces (each 5 mm square)
- 10-mL graduated cylinder
- 4 labelled test tubes
- test-tube rack
- hydrochloric acid solution (4% or 0.5 mol/L)
- hydrochloric acid solution (8% or 1.0 mol/L)
- hydrochloric acid solution (12% or 1.5 mol/L)
- hydrochloric acid solution (16% or 2.0 mol/L)
- solution of a weak base (e.g., sodium bicarbonate solution)
- stopwatch or timer

Procedure

1 Put on your apron and safety goggles.

2 Collect four equal-sized pieces of zinc metal.

3 Transfer 10 mL of 16% hydrochloric acid into a labelled test tube (**Figure 2**).

Hydrochloric acid is corrosive. Any spills on the skin, in the eyes, or on clothing should be washed immediately with plenty of cold water. Report any spills to your teacher.

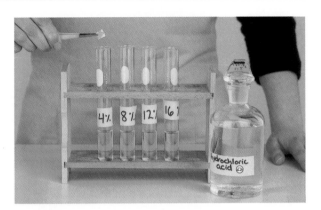

Figure 2

4 Carefully add one piece of zinc to the hydrochloric acid and start the stopwatch. Measure and record the time required for all of the zinc to react. Record your qualitative and quantitative observations in your data table.

5 Repeat steps 3 and 4 using 4%, 8%, and 12% hydrochloric acid in separate labelled test tubes. Record your observations. Your teacher may also ask you to record your results in a class data table or on a class graph on the overhead projector.

6 Neutralize the acid with a solution of a weak base, and pour it down the drain with large amounts of water. Clean and put away your materials as instructed by your teacher. Clean up your work station. Wash your hands.

Analysis and Evaluation

(e) Plot a graph with concentration of acid on the horizontal axis and time of reaction on the vertical axis. Draw a "best-fit" curve or line through the data points. Your teacher may ask you to calculate mean class values and plot them on the same graph.

(f) As the concentration of acid increased, what was the general effect on the time taken for the zinc to be consumed?

(g) Compare your data to the class data. What were some sources of experimental error?

(h) Evaluate your hypothesis. Modify it, if necessary, including explanations.

(Q) (i) Prepare a lab report for this investigation.

Understanding Concepts

1. How are the time of reaction and the rate of reaction related?

Making Connections

2. What is the standard safety procedure followed whenever an acid spill occurs? How is this practice consistent with your clean-up procedure?

3. (a) What were the names and chemical formulas of the reactants used in this investigation?

(b) What type of chemical reaction occurred?

(c) Write a word equation for the reaction.

(d) Write a balanced chemical equation for the reaction.

Exploring

4. (a) Explain how you could calculate numerical values for the rate of a reaction at different concentrations of acid. (See the calculation in Investigation 7.1.)

(b) Determine the relationship between the rate of reaction and concentration.

5. Find a recipe for making muffins that uses baking soda or baking powder. Design an experiment to test the effect of concentration of baking soda in the recipe. Make sure that you clearly identify the independent, dependent, and controlled variables and the method that you will use to vary concentration and measure results.

6. What are some other examples of reactions in which concentration is altered to increase or decrease the rate of reaction?

Reflecting

7. Complete the following statement: "In this investigation, something that captured my attention was...."

Factors that Affect Rates of Reaction

Have you noticed that some reactions occur quickly, while others occur slowly? A match burns almost immediately, but the epoxy glue used to repair a toy may take a day to completely harden (**Figure 1**). What factors affect the rate of reaction, and how can we explain these effects?

There are four factors that affect the rate of reaction. You have seen the effects of temperature and concentration on the rate of reaction in Investigations 7.1 and 7.2. Other factors that affect rates of reaction are surface area and the presence of catalysts. How do these factors affect the rate of reaction?

Changing the Rate of a Reaction

Imagine that you are on a canoe camping trip and have just finished a long day. You want to build a campfire to cook your meal and to provide warmth (**Figure 2**). What materials will you choose to burn? Why? How will you arrange those materials? How will you work with the fire to make it burn more quickly? How will you put the fire out before you go into your tent to sleep?

You must first decide how to set up the fire pit and what to burn. Rocks can be used to surround and contain the fire because they do not burn. All wood is flammable, but some kinds of wood burn faster than others. You will need to find dry wood because you need a high temperature to get the fire burning; wet wood uses much of this heat to evaporate the water. If you start your fire with paper or small pieces of wood, you can gradually add larger pieces as the fire gets going. To make your fire burn more quickly, you can blow on it or fan it. In building this fire, what factors are you changing to control the reaction? Before we answer this question, let's review a model that might help our understanding of why reactions occur.

The Kinetic Molecular Theory: A Collision Model

In previous grades, you used the particle theory of matter to explain changes of state. For example, as a solid is heated, the molecules move more quickly until they break apart from one another to form the liquid state. The kinetic molecular theory states that particles are constantly moving and that they move more quickly at higher temperatures. Can the particle theory and the kinetic molecular theory also be used to explain how various factors affect the rate of a reaction?

As particles, or molecules, move about, they hit or collide with each other. If the molecules are moving slowly or if they are very stable, the colliding molecules just bounce off one another, and no reaction occurs. But if the molecules move more quickly and hit harder, there is a chance

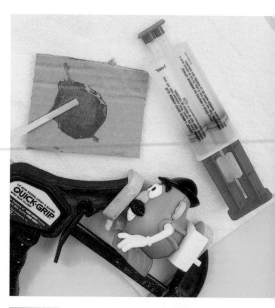

Figure 1
The two ingredients in epoxy glue combine and harden in a chemical reaction that occurs at a definite rate.

Figure 2
A number of factors control how fast a campfire burns.

Did You Know?

When you blow air on a fire, you are exhaling oxygen. The process of respiration produces carbon dioxide gas, but we also breathe out a considerable fraction of the oxygen that we breathe in.

that the molecules may come apart and the atoms may combine to form new molecules. Most collisions just result in the molecules bouncing off one another, with no change. But a small fraction of collisions are effective: they cause chemical bonds to break and re-form to make new molecules (**Figure 3**).

The **collision model** states that the rate of reaction is affected by the number of collisions of reactant molecules. Molecules in a gas or a liquid are constantly colliding with each other. If all the collisions between molecules were effective, then reactions would occur instantaneously. According to the collision model, there are two ways to make a reaction go faster:

- increase the number of collisions;
- increase the fraction of collisions that are effective.

We can use the collision model to help us understand how temperature, concentration, surface area, and catalysts affect the rate of a reaction.

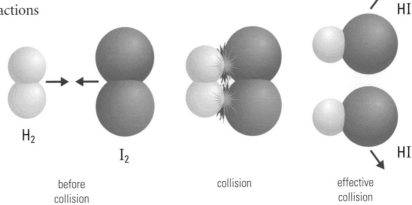

before collision   collision   effective collision

Figure 3

Effective collisions between molecules can cause the formation of new molecules.

Temperature

How does temperature affect the rate at which a reaction occurs? You know that sugar dissolves faster in hot water than in cold. Broiled burgers and French fries at your local hamburger restaurant are products of chemical reactions that occur faster at higher temperatures. Most reactions occur faster at higher temperatures.

Of course, temperature can also be used to slow reactions down. The refrigerator and freezer at home are used to reduce the rate of natural decay reactions that occur in foods. At low temperatures, "cold-blooded" animals become less active (**Figure 4**).

Temperature is the most important factor in making a reaction go faster. An increase in temperature of only 5°C or 10°C is enough to double the rate of many reactions. Why does this happen? As the temperature increases, the average speed of the molecules increases. As the molecules move faster around the container, they encounter and collide with more molecules. Although there are still some molecules that move slowly, there is a larger fraction of "quick" molecules. These molecules may hit each other hard enough for chemical bonds to break and new molecules to form. An increase in temperature makes the molecules collide more often and more effectively. No wonder it has such a dramatic effect on the rate of a reaction!

Figure 4

The temperature of a cold-blooded animal depends on the temperature of its surroundings. As its environment cools, this toad's body temperature drops, the reactions taking place in its body slow down, and the animal becomes sluggish.

Concentration

What happens to the rate of a reaction when the concentrations of the reactants increase? Concentrated hydrochloric acid reacts vigorously with metals (**Figure 5**) and other substances, but the same molecule is in your stomach right now! The hydrochloric acid that digests your food is much less concentrated because it is dissolved in water. As you learned in Investigation 7.2, increasing the concentration of a reactant increases the rate of the reaction.

How can we use the collision model to explain the increase in the rate of reaction as the concentration of reactants increases? When more molecules are packed into a smaller space, they are more likely to collide with each other. As an analogy, imagine that you are measuring the number of times that you meet your friends by chance in the hallway during a typical school day. If you increase the number of friends you have at school, you will likely encounter more friends during the day. If you and your friends were to move to a much smaller school, you would also be more likely to meet more friends in a given day. Increasing the concentration of the reactants in a container increases the number of collisions between the molecules.

Figure 5
Concentrated acids are very corrosive and must be treated with care.

Surface Area

The rate of a reaction is affected by surface area. **Surface area** is the amount of area of a sample of matter that is visible and able to react. For example, the surface area of a whole orange is the outer peel; more surface area is exposed if we cut the orange in half.

When reactants are present in different phases — for example, a solid and a gas — the area of contact, or surface area, determines the rate of reaction. The surface area can be increased by decreasing the sizes of the pieces of the reactant. For example, a pile of flour does not react quickly with oxygen from the air, even when a flame is directed onto it. But when a cloud of flour particles is puffed through a flame (**Figure 6**), the reaction happens much more quickly as the flour and oxygen combine. Such dust explosions have destroyed grain elevators and caused fatal accidents (**Figure 7**).

Figure 7
Grain elevators are used to store wheat and other grains. Care must be taken not to have open flames where dust particles might be suspended in the air and able to react with oxygen.

Figure 6
Increasing the surface area of a solid increases the rate of reaction.

How can we use the collision model to explain the increase in rate of reaction as the surface area of the reactants increases? Reactions occur more quickly as the number of collisions between molecules increases. A reaction between a solid and a liquid or gas can occur only where the solid particles are in contact with the other phase. Increasing the number of solid particles that are available to react allows more molecules of the second phase to collide with them. Increasing the surface area increases the number of collisions between molecules and therefore the rate of reaction.

Catalysts

What happens to the rate of a reaction when a catalyst is used? A **catalyst** is a substance that increases the rate of a chemical reaction without being consumed by the reaction. Thus, a catalyst is not a reactant. Catalysts are used in many industrial processes, including oil refining (**Figure 8**). As you may know, catalysts are also very important in controlling reactions in biological systems.

To understand how a catalyst works, think of a chemical reaction as being similar to a car trip into the mountains. Imagine that you are travelling from

Figure 8

A catalytic cracking unit at an oil refinery. Catalysts are used to crack hydrocarbons into smaller fragments that can be re-formed into components of gasoline.

DESCRIBING THE RATE OF REACTION QUANTITATIVELY

How can we calculate the rate of reaction? The rate of reaction may be described by a simple equation:

$$\text{rate of reaction} = \frac{\text{quantity of product produced}}{\text{time required}}$$

Thus, a process has a greater rate of reaction if more product is produced in a given time. For example, imagine a car factory. Suppose that the workers produce 20 cars in a day. Thus,

$$\text{rate of reaction} = \frac{20 \text{ cars}}{1 \text{ day}} = 20 \text{ cars/day}$$

If the workers produce more cars in the same time (for example, 30 cars in a day) then the rate of reaction increases.

$$\text{rate of reaction} = \frac{30 \text{ cars}}{1 \text{ day}} = 30 \text{ cars/day}$$

The rate of reaction may also be higher if the same number of cars is produced in a shorter time (for example, 20 cars in half a day).

$$\text{rate of reaction} = \frac{20 \text{ cars}}{0.5 \text{ day}} = 40 \text{ cars/day}$$

 # Challenge

1 You have now learned how various factors affect the rates of reactions. During the manufacturing process of your product, can you determine what, if any, factors are used to increase the rate of reactions?

☝ Work the Web

Visit the Nelson web site at www.science.nelson.com. Follow the Science 10, 7.3 links to web sites that show reactions that occur at different rates.

Alphaville to Betaville (**Figure 9**). To get to Betaville, you could travel over a mountain through Gammaville. But if you take the road through Deltaville (representing a catalyst), you still arrive at the same place and you have an easier trip.

A catalyst provides an easier way for a chemical reaction to occur. It does this by decreasing the amount of collision energy that molecules need to break bonds and form new molecules. Instead of one molecule in a thousand being able to react, perhaps one molecule in ten can react. A catalyst increases the fraction of collisions that are effective. You will learn more about catalysts later in this chapter.

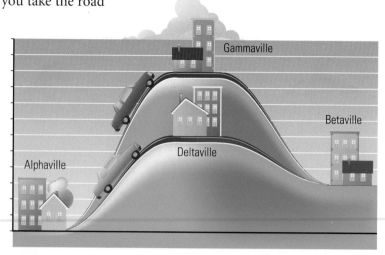

Figure 9

A catalyst provides an easier path for a reaction to follow.

Understanding Concepts

1. Make a chart to summarize the four factors that affect the rate of reaction. For each factor,

   (a) describe how it affects rate;

   (b) give an example; and

   (c) draw a sketch to show, on a molecular level, how it makes a reaction go faster.

2. Explain how you would use your knowledge of factors that affect the rate of reaction to cook a steak as quickly as possible.

3. Consider a reaction in Container A in which 1000 collisions occur per second, and 100 of these collisions are effective — that is, they break chemical bonds to make a product.

   (a) What fraction of the collisions are effective?

   (b) Consider Container B, in which more reactants are packed into the same space, so that 3000 collisions occur per second. How many effective collisions will now occur per second?

   (c) Suppose a catalyst is added to Container A so that twice the fraction of collisions are effective. How many effective collisions will now occur per second?

4. What effect on the rate of reaction of a metal with 20 mL of dilute acid at room temperature would you expect if

   (a) the acid was cooled to 10°C?

   (b) 2 mL of concentrated acid was added?

   (c) the metal was ground into powder before addition to the acid?

Making Connections

5. Imagine that a factory is assembling cars. An efficiency expert is hired to try to analyze factors that affect how quickly cars are being assembled. On Monday, she divides the jobs so that different groups are working on different parts of the car at the same time. On Tuesday, she turns down the temperature in the factory. On Wednesday, she finds a worker who has invented a new-and-improved way to bolt together the vehicle's parts. On Thursday, she hires more workers to work in the factory.

   (a) Which "rate factor" is being investigated each day?

   (b) What effect do you think would be observed each day on the rate of production of the cars?

   (c) Which factor do you think would be most effective?

   (d) How is this analogy not quite the same as the rate of reaction in a chemical system?

6. Look back at Investigation 6.9. What substance was used as a catalyst in that activity?

7. Why do photographers and technicians often store film and batteries in the refrigerator?

8. When you chew crackers, it is possible that three factors affect the rate of breakdown of carbohydrates. Explain.

9. Would ground meat or a steak spoil more quickly? Explain, using the collision model.

10. Which factors that affect the rate of reaction are involved in making a campfire? Explain.

Explosives and Air Bags

You have learned that chemical reactions occur at different rates and that various factors control these rates. But some reactions seem absolutely uncontrollable. Imagine trying to do a controlled experiment with dynamite (**Figure 1**)!

Some reactions occur so quickly that we call them explosions. Usually, these reactions involve the production of large amounts of hot gases, which expand and exert force on the surroundings. For example, when gunpowder is heated, it reacts to produce large amounts of nitrogen and carbon dioxide gases.

(a) How are explosions different from other chemical reactions?

(b) Explain how a cannonball is fired from a cannon.

Many explosions are quite useful. To be useful, an explosive must have four properties:
- It must produce heat when it reacts.
- It must produce gases as products.
- It must react very quickly.
- It must be stable enough so that it can be exploded in a controlled manner.

Explosive chemicals or charges can demolish a building that would otherwise take months to take apart (**Figure 2**). The reactions that take place inside internal combustion engines are explosive reactions of gasoline or diesel fuel with oxygen. Other explosive reactions are used in military weapons.

(c) What are some other examples of useful or harmful explosive reactions?

How does our collision model explain explosions? The bonds that hold the molecules together in explosives are generally weak enough that most collisions between reactant molecules are effective and lead to the formation of products. Explosive mixtures are often made by forcing the reactants together in a confined space to increase their concentrations. Each reaction produces energy, so that the temperature of the reacting mixture rises. This increase in temperature makes the molecules move even faster, and the rate of reaction increases rapidly.

Figure 1
The explosion of dynamite is a rapid reaction of fuel with oxygen.

Figure 2
Carefully placed explosive charges can be used to demolish buildings.

Figure 3
A 1917 explosion in Halifax devastated the city and shattered windows in Truro, 100 km away.

(d) Endothermic reactions require energy; exothermic reactions release energy. Are explosive reactions likely to be endothermic or exothermic? Explain.

A Canadian Explosion

On December 6, 1917, a series of human errors led to a devastating explosion in Halifax, Nova Scotia (**Figure 3**). Almost 2000 people were killed, and 9000 people were injured. During World War I, Halifax was a major port: many ships were docked in its harbour that day, loading and unloading military materials. The *Mont Blanc* was carrying three powerful explosives—trinitrotoluene (TNT), picric acid, and guncotton—along with benzene, an extremely flammable liquid. Disaster struck when a relief vessel, the *Imo*, collided with the *Mont Blanc* in the narrowest part of the harbour. The drums of benzene, which had been tied down to the *Mont Blanc*'s decks, broke apart. Sparks generated during the collision ignited the benzene. The benzene started to drip onto the explosive cargo held on the ship's lower decks. The resulting explosion almost completely obliterated the *Mont Blanc*. A half-melted cannon and a piece of the anchor were the only recognizable parts that were ever found.

> ### Did You Know?
> Sodium azide is a very toxic compound. Apart from its use in air bags, it is also used as a preservative in laboratory chemicals and as a herbicide.

(e) Explain, using the collision model, why the reactions started after the *Mont Blanc*'s collision with the *Imo*.

Fertilizer or Explosive?

One of the most important industrial compounds in North America is ammonium nitrate (NH_4NO_3), which is used in fertilizer as a concentrated source of nitrogen. Ammonium nitrate is also a powerful explosive that can react in two ways. At 250°C, it decomposes to form nitrous oxide (N_2O), water, and heat:

ammonium nitrate → nitrous oxide + water + heat

At 300°C, it decomposes in a different reaction—one that produces nitrogen gas (N_2), water, oxygen gas (O_2), and even larger amounts of heat:

ammonium nitrate → nitrogen + water + oxygen + heat

 **Challenge**

2 Are any explosive reactions involved in your Challenge?

When the ammonium nitrate is mixed with specific organic compounds, their combined combustion releases even larger amounts of energy. Ammonium nitrate is such an effective explosive that it is the most widely used explosive in road building and in mining. Scientists are trying to find compounds that could be added to fertilizers that contain ammonium nitrate to prevent their use as part of an explosive mixture.

(f) What kinds of substances or reactions might scientists be looking at in their efforts to make fertilizers less explosive?

An Explosion That Saves Lives

Another remarkable explosive is sodium azide (NaN_3). This compound is used in air bags in automobiles. An air bag contains a sodium azide pellet. If the automobile hits something or is hit, the impact triggers the decomposition of the pellet to produce sodium, nitrogen gas (N_2), and heat:

sodium azide $\rightarrow$ sodium + nitrogen + heat

The reaction occurs so quickly and generates such high temperatures that roughly 100 g of sodium azide can produce 60 L of nitrogen gas in a fraction of a second. The gas fills the bag in less than a tenth of a second to create a "gas cushion" that protects the driver or passenger (**Figure 4**).

The pellet also contains iron(III) oxide, which almost immediately reacts to consume the sodium as follows:

sodium + iron(III) oxide $\rightarrow$ sodium oxide + iron

The sodium oxide reacts with atmospheric carbon dioxide and water:

sodium oxide + carbon dioxide + water $\rightarrow$
                        sodium hydrogen carbonate

All of these reactions happen within a fraction of a second. The reaction's explosive force is so intense that it can injure children and small adults who are seated in the front seat of the vehicle.

(g) Classify each of these three reactions.

(h) Why is iron(III) oxide incorporated into the airbag's pellet?

Air bags inflate within a fraction of a second when a vehicle collides with a barrier.

Understanding Concepts

1. What four properties must an explosive reaction have to be useful?

2. Explain, in terms of molecules and chemical bonds, why some substances react explosively.

3. Describe in your own words the sequence of events that occur when a car with an air bag collides with another vehicle.

4. Write balanced chemical equations for the word equations used in this lesson.

Making Connections

5. Research the safety recommendations regarding where
(J) children and small adults should sit in vehicles that are equipped with air bags.

6. Semtex is an odourless plastic explosive. Its manufacturers now mix another chemical with the Semtex during manufacture to give it a strong odour. Why do you think they do this?

7. Scientists are sometimes placed in situations where
(C) they have to make ethical decisions. Imagine that you
(F) were working for a company and had just discovered a powerful new explosive. How would you feel about your discovery? Would you have any reservations about the use of your discovery? Explain.

ᗑ Work the Web

What do the Nobel Peace Prize and dynamite have in common? To find out, visit www.science.nelson.com and follow the Science 10, 7.4 links. Report on your discoveries.

INQUIRY SKILLS MENU
- Questioning
- Planning
- Analyzing
- Hypothesizing
- Conducting
- Evaluating
- Predicting
- Recording
- Communicating

Surface Area and Rate of Reaction

For two substances to react, their molecules must come into contact with each other. Solutions of liquids and gases are mixtures that are so well mixed that almost all of the particles come into contact. But in a mixture of a solid and a liquid, contact can occur only on the outer surface of the solid (**Figure 1**). You have learned that changes in surface area affect the number of collisions per second and, thus, the rate at which a reaction occurs. In this investigation, you will observe the effect of surface area on the rate of reaction.

Figure 1
When sodium metal is added to water, the reaction can occur only on the outer surface of the sodium metal, which is in contact with the water.

Question

(a) Write a question about surface area and rate of reaction.

Hypothesis

(b) Write a hypothesis outlining a general rule for the effect of surface area on reaction rates.

Prediction

Make predictions by completing the following statements:

(c) When a cube is divided into eight smaller cubes, the surface area will....

(d) Increasing the surface area of a solid in a chemical reaction will....

Design

You will investigate the surface area of a cube and the surface area of the same cube divided into smaller cubes. You will then design an experiment to test your hypothesis experimentally by considering the reaction between calcium carbonate (chalk) and hydrochloric acid solution:

$$\text{calcium carbonate}_{(s)} + \text{hydrochloric acid}_{(aq)} \rightarrow$$
$$\text{carbon dioxide}_{(g)} + \text{water}_{(l)} + \text{calcium chloride}_{(aq)}$$

Materials

- set of 8 1-cm cubes (optional)
- apron
- safety goggles
- mortar and pestle
- calcium carbonate (chalk)
- hydrochloric acid solution (3% or 0.4 mol/L)
- stopwatch or timer
- test tubes and test-tube rack
- wooden splint

Hydrochloric acid is corrosive. Any spills on the skin, in the eyes, or on clothing should be washed immediately with plenty of cold water. Report any spills to your teacher.

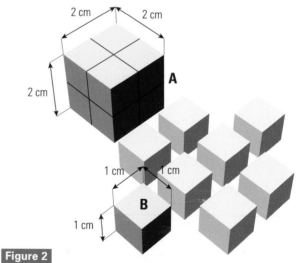

Figure 2
By what factor does the surface area change when the large cube (A) is cut into eight smaller cubes (B)?

SKILLS HANDBOOK: (K3) Developing the Prediction and Hypothesis

broken down to provide energy. A large number of enzymes are also found in the blood to promote clotting. This is essential to limit bleeding after injury, but the enzymes are absent in people suffering from a disease called hemophilia.

The importance of enzymes becomes particularly apparent when a person's body is unable to make a particular enzyme. For example, some people cannot produce an enzyme that digests lactose — a sugar found in dairy products. Although lactose intolerance causes bloating and diarrhea, these symptoms can be prevented through careful food choices or by taking enzyme supplements.

Enzymes are found naturally in many foods. For example, pineapple and papaya both contain natural enzymes that break down proteins. However, many enzymes are heat sensitive: when heated, they break down, becoming ineffective as catalysts. For example, recipes for gelatin desserts (**Figure 3**) often specify the use of cooked canned pineapple rather than fresh pineapple. Gelatin is a protein that dissolves in warm water and then "sets" into a solid solution as it cools. The active enzymes in fresh pineapple decompose the gelatin protein molecules and prevent the dessert from setting properly.

Figure 3
Pineapple and some other fruits contain enzymes that digest proteins.

Understanding Concepts

1. List four examples of catalysts and their effects.

2. **(a)** What is the difference between an enzyme and a catalyst?

   (b) Describe two examples of enzymes and their effects.

3. Increasing the temperature of a reaction generally increases its rate. However, increasing the temperature of a reaction that is catalyzed by an enzyme may actually slow it down. Explain using an example.

Making Connections

4. **(a)** Explain how ozone depletion is an example of the action of a catalyst.

   (b) Why is ozone depletion still an issue, even though CFC use has been largely banned?

5. Some laundry cleaning products are advertised as containing enzymes.

   (a) What purpose do you think the enzymes would serve?

   (b) Why do you think the instructions often suggest soaking the garment in laundry detergent at room temperature before putting it into a hot wash?

Exploring

6. Turnip contains another substance that catalyzes the decomposition of hydrogen peroxide. Design and perform an experiment to investigate the catalytic action of turnip.

7. Research the role of enzymes in blood clotting and how a (I) lack of these enzymes can run in families.

Try This
Activity Investigating an Enzyme

Liver contains an enzyme called peroxidase that catalyzes the breakdown of hydrogen peroxide to form oxygen gas. Many enzymes are destroyed by cooking. Observing all necessary safety precautions, perform the following experiment to investigate the action of an enzyme.

• Obtain a few small pieces of liver and hydrogen peroxide solution (a 3% solution is a commonly used antiseptic found in pharmacies). Add a small piece of liver to a

few millilitres of hydrogen peroxide.

• Repeat the process with a piece of cooked liver. Record your observations.

(a) How was the liver cooked? Did you use a (K) microwave or a frying pan? How long did you cook the liver? Investigate the effects of these variables on enzyme action.

• When you have finished the activity, wash your hands.

INQUIRY SKILLS MENU
○ Questioning   ● Planning   ● Analyzing
● Hypothesizing   ● Conducting   ● Evaluating
● Predicting   ● Recording   ● Communicating

Catalyst or Reactant?

How do you know that a substance is a catalyst? The decomposition of hydrogen peroxide is normally very slow. But the rate of reaction is much greater when certain substances, such as blood or manganese dioxide, are added (**Figure 1**). Are these substances truly catalysts, or are they reactants that are consumed during the reaction?

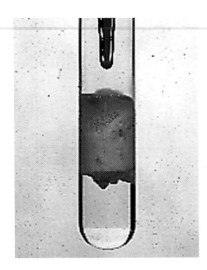

Figure 1
Blood contains an enzyme called peroxidase. Adding peroxidase to hydrogen peroxide solution causes the normal decomposition of hydrogen peroxide to speed up.

Recall that a catalyst is defined as a substance that speeds up a chemical reaction without being consumed. The mass of the catalyst should not change during the reaction: it should have the same mass at the end of the reaction that it had at the beginning of the reaction. If a substance is a reactant, its mass steadily decreases as the reaction proceeds.

Question

How can you determine whether manganese dioxide is a catalyst or a reactant?

Hypothesis/Prediction

(a) Complete the following statement: Manganese
 dioxide is a _____ in the decomposition reaction of hydrogen peroxide.
(b) Write a prediction: a testable form of your hypothesis.

Design

In this investigation, you will determine the mass of a quantity of manganese dioxide and then react it with hydrogen peroxide solution. You will then reweigh the manganese dioxide to determine whether any was consumed during the reaction.

(c) Design a table to record your qualitative and
 quantitative observations.

Materials

- apron
- retort stand
- funnel
- fine filter paper
- balance
- water
- graduated cylinder
- stirring rod

- safety goggles
- ring clamp
- 2 beakers
- manganese dioxide powder
- 3% hydrogen peroxide solution

> ⓣ Hydrogen peroxide is poisonous and a strong irritant. Report any spills to your teacher.
>
> ⓣ Manganese dioxide is toxic. Report any spills to your teacher.

Procedure

1 Put on your apron and safety goggles.

2 Set up a retort stand, a ring clamp, a funnel, and a beaker. Prepare the filter paper by folding it once in half and then a second time, almost in quarters (**Figure 2**), forming a small pocket and a large pocket.

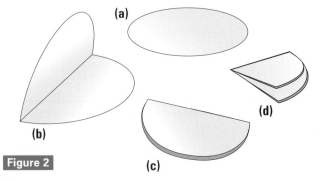

Figure 2

SKILLS HANDBOOK: (K3) Developing the Prediction and Hypothesis (K7) Preparing Tables of Evidence

3 Put about 0.5 g of manganese dioxide powder into the bottom of the large pocket of the filter paper. Determine the mass of the filter paper and chemical, being careful not to spill any powder. Record your observations.

4 Wet the funnel with water and fit the cone of the filter paper into it, taking care not to lose any powder. Wetting the funnel will help the filter paper stick to it.

5 Obtain about 20 mL of hydrogen peroxide solution in a beaker. Pour the solution through the manganese dioxide in the filter paper, into a second beaker, as shown in **Figure 3**. Record your observations.

Figure 3

6 If the filter paper is too coarse, some black material may come through with the filtrate. If this happens, place the first beaker under the funnel. Pour the filtrate in the second beaker back through the filter paper as before. Swirl a small amount of water around in this beaker, and then filter this liquid to make sure that all black material remains in the filter. Repeat this process until the filtrate is completely clear and no further gas is produced.

7 When you are finished, discard the filtrate and clean and put away your materials as instructed by your teacher. Clean up your work station. Wash your hands.

8 As instructed by your teacher, allow the filter paper and the solid filter residue to dry overnight. Reweigh the filter paper and residue. Record your observations.

Analysis and Evaluation

(d) What evidence was there that a chemical reaction occurred?

(e) Compare the masses of the filter paper and contents before and after the reaction. Calculate the difference.

(f) What were some sources of experimental error?

(g) Suggest some ways to improve the experimental design.

(h) Calculate the percentage error in your results using the formula

$$\text{percentage error} = \frac{|\text{expected mass} - \text{observed mass}|}{\text{expected mass}} \times 100\%$$

(i) Based on your percentage error, evaluate your hypothesis.

Understanding Concepts

1. Write the word equation and the balanced chemical equation for the decomposition of hydrogen peroxide.

2. **(a)** How can you decide whether a substance is a reactant or a catalyst in a chemical reaction? Explain using an example.

   (b) What evidence was there that manganese dioxide is a catalyst?

Making Connections

3. Why was it perfectly safe to pour the filtrate from this investigation down the drain when the reaction was complete?

4. A geologist finds two rocks. She thinks one is limestone. To test this idea, she adds it to hydrochloric acid. Vigorous bubbling occurs, and the stone weighs less after the reaction. The other rock is a dense steel-grey substance that she thinks is pyrolusite. When this mineral is dropped into a hydrogen peroxide solution, vigorous bubbling occurs, but the mass of the rock remains unchanged.

   (a) Which of the substances in the two reactions are reactants?

   (b) Which of the substances is a catalyst?

   (c) Find the chemical formula of pyrolusite.

Exploring

5. Find out why blood contains peroxidase enzymes. What would be the effects if these enzymes were missing?

Reflecting

6. Complete the following statement: "In this investigation, something that surprised me was...."

DECISION MAKING SKILLS
- ○ Define the Issue
- ● Identify Alternatives
- ● Research
- ● Analyze the Issue
- ○ Defend a Decision
- ○ Evaluate

Rates and Automobiles

When people talk about rates and automobiles, they are usually talking about how quickly the car moves — that is, its speed. But many chemical reactions are involved in an automobile's production and performance. Each of these reactions occurs at a specific rate.

The most obvious chemical reaction is the explosive combination of hydrocarbon fuel and oxygen in the engine (**Figure 1**). What factors that affect the rates of reaction are involved in this process? Engineers design engines so that the concentrations of the gasoline and oxygen molecules in the fuel injector are made as large as possible. Temperature is a key factor because the reaction occurs at a very high temperature. Surface area would be a factor if liquid gasoline and oxygen gas were reacting, but the car is engineered to evaporate the gasoline as it mixes with exactly the right amount of air in the fuel injector.

Catalytic Converters

Cars' exhaust systems contain catalytic converters, which reduce automobile emissions. A **catalytic converter** is a device that converts polluting exhaust gases into safer molecules. When an engine burns hydrocarbons, the two main products are carbon dioxide and water vapour. But the high temperatures and pressures in the engine cylinders also result in the production of pollutants including carbon monoxide, nitrogen dioxide, and unburned hydrocarbon gases. To reduce the amount of these pollutants, exhaust gases are passed from the engine through catalytic converters before being released into the air (**Figure 2**).

Gases passing through the converter are in contact with the catalyst for a fraction of a second. In that time:
- over 95% of the hydrocarbons produced are converted to carbon dioxide and water;
- over 95% of the carbon monoxide produced is converted to carbon dioxide; and
- over 75% of the nitrogen dioxide produced is converted to nitrogen gas.

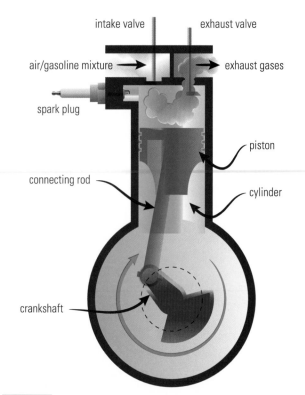

Figure 1

A cross section of an engine cylinder. The reaction of gasoline with air drives the piston down in the cylinder, and this motion is eventually converted to turning motion in the wheels of the car.

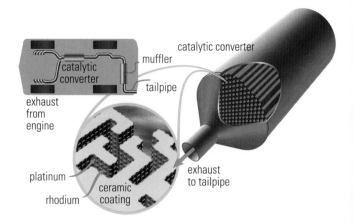

Figure 2

Exhaust gases pass through the catalytic converter. The inside surface of a catalytic converter is a honeycomb or beadlike structure so that the surface area is as large as possible. The catalyst is "painted" on the surface. The actual chemicals used as catalysts include platinum, rhodium, and chromium oxide.

]DEBATE[The Sale and Use of Cars Should Be Restricted

Proposition

Cars are major users of nonrenewable natural resources and producers of air pollution. To reduce the environmental impact of their production and use, there should be a limit to the number of cars sold.

Point

- Earth has a finite amount of minerals and hydrocarbons that are used to produce and power automobiles. Limiting car use would protect these resources.

- People buy unreasonable numbers of vehicles. Restricting the number of vehicles produced would discourage people from buying new cars.

- Cars produce huge amounts of carbon dioxide, which contributes to the greenhouse effect and global warming. The effects on our world's environment may be catastrophic.

- Cars produce large amounts of air pollutants, such as ground-level ozone and nitrogen oxides that damage lung tissue and cause respitory problems. Fewer cars would mean less pollution.

Counterpoint

- People need cars as part of their everyday life. Public transit and carpools are not convenient alternatives.

- The industrial production of automobiles creates jobs. The auto industry is a key component of our economy.

- Catalytic converters and other technology, including fuel cells, are making emissions from automobiles safe.

- Restricting a person's freedom to purchase vehicles would be too much government interference.

Taking a Position

- In a group, discuss the proposition, and the points and counterpoints. Write down additional
(D) points and counterpoints that your group generates.
- Decide whether your group agrees or disagrees with the proposition.
- Research to find more information to support your position. Remember to look at the issue from
(E) a variety of perspectives.
- Assemble your findings into a logical order and organize them into an oral presentation.
- Present and defend your group's position in a debate. Try to answer your opposition's arguments
(S) logically, suggesting realistic alternatives.

🖑 Work the Web

What is being done to reduce the environmental impact of cars? Visit www.science.nelson.com and follow the Science 10, 7.8 links to discover more about different engine designs, and the possibility of eliminating engines altogether!

Understanding the Issue

1. What features of engine design affect the rate of gasoline combustion?

2. Briefly describe the purpose and structure of a catalytic converter.

Challenge

2, 3 How are the rates of reaction controlled in the production of pollutants by automobiles? How can you interpret this information within your Challenge?

Blast Off!

You have learned that a number of factors can affect the rate of a chemical reaction. Temperature, concentration, surface area, and the presence of a catalyst are all factors that affect how quickly a reaction can occur. You will be given a film canister with a lid and chemicals that will produce a gas when mixed together. You will then apply your knowledge of rates of reaction and the process of science to design a way to blow the lid off the canister in a specified number of seconds.

Question

How can a chemical reaction be controlled so that an event occurs at a specific time?

Design

You will design an experiment to test several variables that affect the buildup of gas in the closed canister. You will then apply your findings to blow the lid off the canister in a target time specified by your teacher (**Figure 1**).

(a) In your group, discuss and decide on all the
(K) variables that you think might affect the time
(X) taken for the lid to come off. Record your decisions.
(b) Plan a series of experiments to investigate the effects of several variables on the time taken for the lid to come off. Include all necessary safety precautions. Set up an observation chart to record your variables and times.
(c) Have your experimental design approved by your teacher.

Figure 1

Materials

• apron
• safety goggles
• 2 Alka-Seltzer tablets
• plastic film canister and lid
• water
• stopwatch or timer
• graduated cylinder

Procedure

1 Put on your apron and safety goggles. Collect your materials. You may not have more than two tablets, so should plan accordingly. Save a sufficient amount of Alka-Seltzer for the final "blast off."

2 Carry out your planned experiments. Measure and record your variables.

🛑 The canister lid can come off at a high speed. Wear goggles and make sure the canister is sitting upright on the desk during all trials. Everyone should stand well back from the canisters.

3 Analyze your results and decide on a final "recipe" that you will use for the final "blast off."

4 Join the other groups at the front of the room for the "blast off." At the signal for zero time, drop a piece of tablet into the canister, put the lid on, and **step back** (**Figure 2**). As the teacher or timer counts up from zero, record the time at which each of the lids comes off. The winning team is the one whose lid "blasts off" closest to the target time.

5 Dispose of the mixtures down the sink with plenty of water, and put away your materials as instructed by your teacher. Clean up your work station. Wash your hands.

Analysis and Evaluation

(d) What variables affected the time for blast off?

(e) Which variables had the greatest effect? Explain. Which variables had little or no effect?

(f) Hold a class discussion comparing the various "recipes" used. Which was most successful in the "blast off"? Why?

(g) How would you have improved your experimental design if you had been given more time and more materials?

✍Work the Web

Investigate how gases are used in the operation of one of the following devices: rocket launchers, jet engines, and jet skis. Visit www.science.nelson.com and follow the links from Science 10, 7.9.

Understanding Concepts

1. What evidence was there that a chemical reaction occurred?

2. Which of the four variables that affect rate of reaction were investigated in this activity? Which were not?

Making Connections

3. Alka-Seltzer tablets contain two dry compounds that react when dissolved in water.

   (a) What type of chemical reaction must occur when they react?

   (b) What gas do you think is produced?

Exploring

4. How do you think this reaction could be used to make a "pop-bottle racer," given a 1-L pop bottle, a cork, a set of wheels, duct tape, and the same chemicals or their equivalents? Design and with your teacher's approval, test your own racer. Make sure you follow all safety procedures.

Reflecting

5. How well do you think your group functioned? What changes do you think you might have made to operate better as a team?

Figure 2

Food Preservation

When you make supper, you try to speed up the cooking process by chopping up vegetables to increase surface area, cooking the ingredients at a high temperature, and using a meat tenderizer that contains a catalyst. But sometimes people want to slow down the reactions that happen in food, especially the natural process of decay or spoilage. What is food spoilage? How does our understanding of rates of reaction explain the techniques that people use to preserve food?

Food spoilage is the natural breakdown of food that occurs over time. It may be caused by physical or chemical changes in the food itself, or by the action of microorganisms such as bacteria or fungi. The ripening of fruit is an example of food spoilage (**Figure 1**). Preservation methods have been used for centuries by people who wanted their food to last longer, and new methods are being found every year (**Table 1**). Historically, people worked with the substances they had readily available. Salt, vinegar, and sugar were common substances, and because microorganisms do not grow well in their solutions, pickling and sugaring were used to preserve vegetables and fruit (**Figure 2**). Other methods, such as canning, worked by killing microorganisms and then sealing the food to prevent further contamination.

(a) Describe three methods of food preservation that might have been used in the 19th century and those preferred today.

Figure 1

Unripe bananas are shipped to Canada from tropical countries. Ethylene gas is used to stimulate the ripening of the fruit before it is sold.

Figure 2

Salt, sugar, and vinegar are common preservatives.

Table 1 **Methods for Preserving Food**

Method	Technique	Example
freezing or chilling	lower the temperature	frozen fish and vegetables
canning	cook and seal in cans	canned soups and meats
drying	dry in sun or freeze-dry	dried fruits and vegetables
pickling	soak food in vinegar	pickles
chemical preservatives	add chemicals to food	most packaged foods
salting or curing	soak food in salt solution	bacon
sugar preserves	keep food in a strong sugar solution	jam, jellies
vacuum packing	remove air from food	meat
coating	cover food with wax or other coating	apples

How can other preservation methods be explained by looking at the factors that affect the rates of reaction? The most obvious example is chilling or freezing food (**Figure 3**). Lowering the temperature reduces the rate of all reactions, including those involved in decay. At low temperatures, the particles move more slowly and undergo fewer collisions that lead to reaction. The lower the temperature, the slower the reaction, so we put foods that we want to keep for a long time, such as meat and ice cream, in the freezer. We put other foods that we will use sooner, such as milk and vegetables, in the refrigerator.

(b) Explain, using the collision model, why putting food in the freezer is a good way to preserve it.

Reducing the concentration of reactants is another way to slow reactions. Many decay processes involve the reaction of food with oxygen from the air. Vacuum-sealing food packages, using resealable plastic bags, and coating the food with wax to keep air away from the food effectively reduce the concentration of oxygen that can react. Similarly, storing food in large pieces slows the rate of decay by reducing the surface area available to react. Drying food removes water that would allow the reactants to come into contact more easily (**Figure 4**).

(c) Explain how storing food in a vacuum-sealed bag prevents food spoilage.

Antioxidants

If you look at the label on a bag of potato chips (**Figure 5**), you may see such ingredients as BHA (butylated hydroxyanisole) or BHT (butylated hydroxytoluene) listed. These substances are **antioxidants** —substances that act as preservatives by slowing down the rate of oxidation, or decay, of molecules in food, particularly fats. BHA and BHT are inhibitors because they slow down, rather than speed up, chemical reactions. These substances greatly increase the shelf life of products in grocery stores. Products can stay on the shelves for months and still be sold safely to customers.

A combination of techniques that has recently been tried to preserve some foods is to coat the food with biodegradable films and coatings that contain antioxidants. The coatings may be edible, like the wax that is used to coat apples imported from

Figure 3
Keeping food cool slows down the rate of decay.

Figure 4
Dried fruit and freeze-dried meals are often used by hikers and canoeists.

Figure 5
BHA and BHT are antioxidants, or inhibitors.

overseas (**Figure 6**). There is some concern that food preservatives, like any food additive, may have negative effects on people's health. Some people have allergic reactions to chemicals that are added to foods.

(d) Describe what is meant by the term "antioxidant," with an example. Compare antioxidants to catalysts.

(e) Suggest reasons why some people are concerned about the long-term health effects of food additives, such as antioxidants.

Figure 6
The shelf life of apples may be extended by coating them with edible wax to prevent air from reaching the skin.

Understanding Concepts

1. Make a chart to summarize how the factors that affect the rate of a chemical reaction can be applied to different methods of food preservation. Chart headings could be *Factor*, *Example*, and *Explanation*.

Making Connections

2. Carrots that have been cut into pieces have a shorter shelf life than whole carrots. Explain this observation using what you know about factors that affect rate of reaction.

3. Some food is preserved by removing the air and replacing it with a different gas, such as nitrogen. Explain how this technique might preserve the food.

4. Fruit can be preserved to some extent by keeping it in a dark, cool place. Suggest why this technique might work.

Exploring

5. A controversial method proposed for preserving food is irradiation. This approach involves using a radioactive source to bombard food and kill microorganisms that might cause decay. Research and report on how this technique works and why it is controversial. Try the key words "food + irradiation" in an Internet search.

6. Either look in your own cupboard at home or visit your local supermarket and make a list of as many different methods of food preservation as possible (with examples of foods that use each method). Make a chart to summarize your observations.

Reflecting

7. Imagine that you were going on a two-month voyage on a sailboat. What food would you take? How would you preserve the food for your trip? Make a chart to list the foods and how you would store them.

🖑 Work the Web

Visit www.science.nelson.com and follow the Science 10, 7.10 links to web sites that describe food preservation.

7.11 Investigation

INQUIRY SKILLS MENU
○ Questioning   ○ Planning   ● Analyzing
○ Hypothesizing   ● Conducting   ○ Evaluating
● Predicting   ● Recording   ● Communicating

Exothermic and Endothermic Reactions

Why do some reactions seem to speed up as they proceed? Wood burns slowly at first, but the rate of reaction increases as more wood becomes involved. Eventually, the result can be an uncontrolled forest fire (**Figure 1**). One of the reasons for this acceleration of the reaction is the heat released when the reaction occurs. You have seen that temperature affects the rate of a reaction. In the case of the burning of wood, the reaction releases heat, which causes the temperature of the surroundings to increase. As the temperature rises, the rate of burning increases.

The explosion of dynamite, the freezing of water, and the burning of wood are all processes in which heat is given out to the surroundings. For example, dynamite explodes in a chemical change that releases large amounts of heat and light. Changes that release energy are said to be **exothermic**. Many chemical changes are accompanied by the release of heat to their surroundings. For example, the combustion of gasoline can be represented by the following word equation:

gasoline + oxygen → carbon dioxide + water + heat

Some physical changes are also exothermic. For example, when sulfuric acid dissolves in water, the process can be represented as:

$$\text{sulfuric acid}_{(l)} \rightarrow \text{sulfuric acid}_{(aq)} + \text{heat}$$

This reaction is so exothermic that it can be quite dangerous. Chemists must always be careful to add acid to water, not the other way around, so that the heat is absorbed by the larger volume of water.

Water, changing from the liquid to the solid phase (freezing), releases heat as its molecules slow down. This is, of course, a physical change. Other physical and chemical changes take place only when heat is continuously supplied to the reactants. Such changes do not speed up as they occur because the temperature of the surroundings decreases as the reactants absorb heat. Reactions that absorb heat from the surroundings are **endothermic** (**Figure 2**). For example, the melting of ice can be represented by the word equation:

$$\text{water}_{(s)} + \text{heat} \rightarrow \text{water}_{(l)}$$

Figure 1
A forest fire starts with a spark and builds to a rapid chemical reaction that can cause the destruction of hectares of trees.

Figure 2
Athletic cold packs contain chemicals which interact in a process that absorbs heat from an injured area.

As a general rule, when bonds within substances are broken, energy is absorbed (endothermic). When bonds are formed, energy is released (exothermic) .

Question

Which of the following systems undergo exothermic reactions and which undergo endothermic reactions? How can you represent the changes?

Prediction

(a) Read through the following experiments and predict whether the changes will be endothermic or exothermic.

Design

You will mix together several combinations of substances that will undergo physical or chemical changes, releasing or absorbing heat in the process. The heat involved will be measured using a thermometer.

(b) Make a table to record all your observations.

Materials

- apron
- steel wool
- narrow-mouth glass jar or flask
- thermometer
- 2 Styrofoam cups
- water
- 250-mL beaker
- ammonium thiocyanate
- stirring rod

- safety goggles
- dilute hydrochloric acid solution (1% or 0.1 mol/L)
- thermometer fitted into one-holed stopper to fit jar or flask
- ammonium chloride
- Drano cleaner (crystal form)
- wooden block
- barium hydroxide octahydrate

Procedure

Part 1: Steel Wool and Oxygen

1 Put on your apron and safety goggles.

2 Clean a roll of steel wool by immersing it in dilute hydrochloric acid solution. Rinse the steel wool with water, and put it in a glass jar or flask. Using the thermometer fitted into a one-holed stopper, place the bulb of the thermometer in the middle of the steel wool. Stopper the jar or flask (**Figure 3**).

 Hydrochloric acid is corrosive. Any spills on the skin, in the eyes, or on clothing should be washed immediately with plenty of cold water. Report any spills to your teacher.

3 Observe the temperature every 5 min as the reaction with oxygen in the air proceeds. Record the time and temperature data in your table. As this reaction progresses, you may continue with the other parts of the investigation.

Part 2: Ammonium Chloride and Water

4 Fill a Styrofoam cup with water, and carefully measure the temperature of the water. Dissolve about 2 g of ammonium chloride in the water, and measure the temperature of the solution. Record the initial temperature and the highest temperature reached in your data table.

 Ammonium chloride is toxic.

Part 3: Drano and Water

5 Half-fill a Styrofoam cup with water, and measure the temperature of the water. Dissolve 5 g of Drano cleaner in the water, and measure the temperature again. Record the initial temperature and the highest temperature reached in your data table.

 Drano cleaner contains sodium hydroxide, which is highly corrosive and must not contact skin or eyes. If accidental contact occurs, flush immediately with large quantities of water. Report any such incidents to your teacher.

6 Dispose of the mixtures and clean and put away your materials as instructed by your teacher. Clean up your work station. Wash your hands.

Part 4: Ammonium Thiocyanate and Barium Hydroxide Octahydrate

Teacher Demonstration

7 Place a 250-mL beaker on a wet wooden block in a fume hood (**Figure 4**).

Figure 4

8 Add about 16 g of solid ammonium thiocyanate to the beaker. Add about 32 g of barium hydroxide octahydrate, and mix with a stirring rod. Quickly insert a thermometer. Record the temperature at regular intervals in your data table.

Ammonium thiocyanate and barium hydroxide octahydrate are poisonous. Do not breathe the gases produced. Use a fume hood.

9 After a few minutes, gently try to lift the beaker off the block.

Analysis and Evaluation

(c) Which of the changes were physical changes? Explain.
(d) Which of the changes were chemical changes? Explain.
(e) Classify each change as endothermic or exothermic.
(f) Answer the initial questions with explanations.
(g) Revisit your predictions. Were they correct?

 Challenge

2 Is the combustion of a fuel always exothermic? When fuel cells or batteries operate, are these changes exothermic? How can you use this information in your Challenge?

Understanding Concepts

1. Which of these reactions would you expect to happen faster as the reaction proceeded? Explain.

2. Steel wool is mainly iron. When it reacts with oxygen, the product is iron(III) oxide. Write a word equation for the reaction in Part 1, and make sure your equation includes the word "heat."

3. Write a word equation for the reaction in Part 2, again including the word "heat."

4. Drano cleaner is mainly sodium hydroxide. Write a word equation for the reaction in Part 3, once again including the word "heat."

Making Connections

5. When you put alcohol on your skin, the alcohol feels cold. Why?

6. Plumbers use either concentrated sodium hydroxide or sulfuric acid to clear drains. The reaction of both these substances with water is very exothermic. Why do you think plumbers choose these types of reactions?

7. Design a device that could be used to heat a can of soup when camping without using a campfire or stove.

8. For what other practical purpose(s) could exothermic or endothermic reactions be used?

Exploring

9. The chemical reaction in Part 4 was quite complex. The chemical change was a double displacement in which one of the products then decomposed to produce a pungent gas and a common liquid. Use chemistry texts or other resources to find out what changes are occurring. Write word equations for the chemical change and physical change that occurred in this demonstration. Include a heat term in each equation.

Mark Argent

Explosives Expert

The term "reaction rate" has two separate meanings for former Canadian Forces Sergeant Mark Argent, now a field expert for the Canadian Association for Mine and Explosive Ordnance Security. The term could refer to the rate at which the given chemicals react to produce an explosion. But for explosive ordinance disposal (EOD) experts such as Mark, the term also means the speed at which an EOD expert responds to an explosive. The scale runs from "A" bombs (immediate danger of explosion, where a life is threatened) when you act quickly with the materials available and evacuate people as fast as possible, to "D" explosives (no immediate threat — the bombs or mines are in an uninhabited, untravelled place).

Mark always had an interest in explosives. When he graduated from high school in Sudbury, Ontario, he applied directly to the Canadian Armed Forces to be a field engineer — the person who places the explosives. After much field experience (he spent time teaching Afghan refugees to defuse Russian land mines after the occupation ended and was one of two Canadian EOD experts assigned to the "clean-up" in Kuwait and Iraq after the 1991 Gulf War), he was released from the army. Now he teaches others how to dispose of explosives, although he still gets his hands dirty on a regular basis.

Along with the practical experience, of course, goes lots of theoretical training. Explosions are chemical reactions in which a small quantity of solid material is transformed almost instantaneously (sometimes controlled by a fuse — a chemical or physical delay mechanism) into a much larger volume of hot gases. The solid explosive reacts with carbon, hydrogen, and oxygen, and breaks down chemically. The amount of oxygen available to the solid explosive is very important — the more oxygen there is, the larger, more powerful, and faster the explosion will

be. This chemical knowledge is drummed into EOD experts by nongovernmental organizations, scientists, and especially the armed forces. Mark estimates that he took every training course the army offered. He also emphasizes that there is no "short" route to becoming an EOD expert — you have to enlist in the military and train your way to the top.

Explosives are often used for peaceful purposes. Mining, quarrying, fireworks, breaking up ice jams for ships, projecting life-lines onto roofs of burning buildings, even the production of industrial-grade diamonds — all use basic chemical explosions. However, when explosives are put in the way of innocent civilians, there will be people like Mark to make sure nothing goes wrong.

Making Connections

1. Mark notes that the best way to become an EOD expert is to enlist in the armed forces. Can you think of any other training path, from high school onward, that could provide you with a similar level of knowledge? Research your results and draw a flow chart of the path.
2. What are some of the peaceful uses for explosives? Can these uses also be dangerous? Explain.

🖑 Work the Web

Canada has been active in the worldwide movement to ban land mines. Visit www.science.nelson.com and follow the links from Science 10, 7.12 to find out why. Present a short report to the class, explaining the ways in which students can support the effort to make land mines illegal.

Chapter 7 Summary

Key Expectations

Throughout the chapter, you have had opportunities to do the following things:

- Describe and explain qualitatively how factors such as temperature, concentration, and surface area affect the rates of reaction. (7.1, 7.2, 7.3, 7.5, 7.6, 7.7, 7.8, 7.9, 7.10, 7.11)

- Use appropriate apparatus and apply WHMIS safety procedures for handling, storage, disposal, and recycling of materials in the lab. (7.1, 7.2, 7.5, 7.7, 7.9, 7.11)

- Analyze data and information, evaluate evidence and sources of information, and identify errors and bias. (7.1, 7.2, 7.5, 7.7, 7.8, 7.9, 7.11)

- Describe experimental procedures in the form of a laboratory report. (7.1, 7.2, 7.5, 7.7, 7.9, 7.11)

- Identify everyday examples where the rates of chemical reactions are modified. (7.1, 7.2, 7.3, 7.6, 7.8, 7.10)

- Formulate questions about practical problems and issues involving chemical processes. (7.2, 7.4, 7.5, 7.8, 7.9, 7.10, 7.11)

- Recognize the relationships between chemical formulas, composition, and names. (7.4)

- Represent chemical reactions using word equations. (7.4)

- Describe how an understanding of chemical reactions has led to new consumer products, technological processes, and ways of addressing environmental challenges. (7.4, 7.8, 7.10)

- Plan and conduct an inquiry into chemical processes using a range of tools, controlling variables, and adapting or extending procedures where required. (7.5, 7.9)

- Use appropriate vocabulary, SI units, tables, descriptions of procedures using the scientific method. (7.5, 7.7, 7.9, 7.11)

- Design, plan, and conduct an experiment to determine qualitatively the factors that influence the rate of reaction. (7.5, 7.9)

- Select and integrate information from many sources including electronic, print, and community resources. (7.8, 7.10)

- Explain how environmental challenges can be addressed through an understanding of chemical substances. (7.8)

- Explore careers based on technologies that use chemical reactions. (7.12)

Key Terms

antioxidant

catalyst

catalytic converter

collision model

concentrated solution

dilute solution

endothermic

enzyme

exothermic

rate of reaction

surface area

Make a Summary

In this chapter you have studied chemical reactions and how to control them. Revisit the Try This on page 255 in the Getting Started. Working alone or in your group, brainstorm as many ideas as possible that you have *learned* about rates of reactions. Write down all your ideas in the *L* section. Prepare to present your ideas to the class.

Reflect on your Learning

Revisit your answers to the Reflect on your Learning questions, page 255, in the Getting Started.

- How has your thinking changed?

- What new questions do you have?

Chapter 7 Review

Understanding Concepts

1. Make a chart to summarize the factors that affect rate of reaction. Headings could be: *Factor, Effect on rate,* and *Example.*

2. For each of the following, replace the description with one or two words:
   (a) producing heat
   (b) removes polluting gases from automobile exhausts
   (c) containing a large amount of solute
   (d) speeds up a reaction
   (e) reaction with oxygen
   (f) slows down a reaction
   (g) prevents decay in foods

3. The sentences below contain errors or are incomplete. Write complete, correct versions.
   (a) Increasing the temperature decreases the number of collisions per second.
   (b) Another word for biological catalyst is inhibitor.
   (c) Adding water to a solution makes the solution more concentrated.
   (d) A single block of a solid should react more quickly than the same solid in powder form.
   (e) As the rate of reaction increases, the time taken for the reaction increases.
   (f) An inhibitor makes a chemical reaction follow an easier path.
   (g) Explosive reactions are endothermic.
   (h) The "air bag" reaction produces oxygen gas.
   (i) The catalyst used in the decomposition of hydrogen peroxide is manganese disulfide.
   (j) The element in CFCs that is responsible for the depletion of the ozone layer is iodine.

4. The decomposition of hydrogen peroxide produces oxygen gas.
   (a) Describe three ways in which this reaction can be made to go faster.
   (b) Which common factor used to increase rate of reaction does not apply to this system.

5. Describe three chemical reactions in your daily life in which you might want to control the rate of reaction.

6. Use the collision model to explain why each of the following factors increases the rate of reaction:
   (a) temperature
   (b) concentration
   (c) surface area
   (d) catalyst

7. "Explosives are both necessary and dangerous."
   (a) Explain this statement, with examples to support your argument.
   (b) What four properties make a substance explosive?

8. Explain the following in terms of factors that affect rates of reaction:
   (a) Perfume and cologne can be stored in the refrigerator to extend their useful life.
   (b) Wheat dust is more flammable than pieces of grain.
   (c) Stomach acid is the same acid that is used to etch concrete.
   (d) A few drops of copper(II) sulfate make the reaction of zinc and sulfuric acid go faster (**Figure 1**).

Figure 1

9. Imagine that a 4 cm × 4 cm × 4 cm cube of calcium metal is placed in water and takes 240 s to be completely consumed.
   (a) Calculate the surface area of the cube.
   (b) Imagine that a cube of exactly the same size is cut into eight 2 cm × 2 cm × 2 cm cubes. Calculate the surface area of the set of cubes.
   (c) Estimate the time that it would take for the set of eight cubes to be completely reacted if they were all placed in water at the same time.

10. (a) What are catalysts?
    (b) What do we call biological catalysts? What are some examples of these substances?
    (c) An inhibitor is sometimes called a negative catalyst. Explain, with an example.

11. Endothermic reactions must be continually supplied with heat from the surroundings as they react. Once started, many exothermic reactions occur quickly and need no further energy from the surroundings. Explain.

Applying Inquiry Skills

12. When you cut an apple or banana, it gradually turns brown and spoils. What factors affect this chemical reaction? Design an experiment to investigate the factors that affect the rate of this reaction. Try to test as many variables as possible. You might try lemon juice or ascorbic acid (Vitamin C) as possible inhibitors.

13. An experiment was performed to investigate the reaction of calcium carbonate in sulfuric acid. In the first trial A, a 1-g cube of solid calcium carbonate was added to 5% sulfuric acid at room temperature, and the amount of time taken for the cube to disappear completely was measured. The results shown in **Table 1** were obtained when the variables were changed.

Table 1 **Student Data for Calcium Carbonate— Acid Reaction**

Trial	Calcium carbonate	Temperature (°C)	Acid concentration (%)	Time (s)
A	1 g cube	20	5	60
B	1 g cube	30	5	30
C	1 g cube	20	10	30
D	1 g powder	20	5	10
E	1 g cube	10	5	?
F	1 g cube	30	10	?

(a) Describe the factors that affected the time of reaction in each of Trials B, C, and D compared to A.

(b) Which factor was not tested in this activity?

(c) Predict a reasonable time of reaction for Trial E. Explain your reasoning.

(d) Predict a reasonable time of reaction for Trial F. Explain your reasoning.

(e) Write word and balanced chemical equations for the reaction.

14. You have already used Alka-Seltzer tablets to investigate the effect of temperature on rate of reaction. How would you modify the procedure to investigate the effects of another factor on rate of reaction? Which factor(s) would be difficult to investigate using this system? Explain.

15. Recipes for gelatin desserts often include pineapple, which contains enzymes that affect the hardening of gelatin desserts. Many enzymes are destroyed by cooking. Design and after obtaining your teacher's approval, perform an experiment to investigate the effect of heating on the action of these enzymes. You may want to include different types of heating (e.g., stove or microwave) and time of heating as variables. Handle hot objects with care.

Making Connections

16. Scientists have evidence that the depletion of the ozone layer is caused by chlorofluorocarbons (CFCs) that have been released through human activities into the atmosphere. Research and report on this issue in order to answer the following questions:

(a) What are CFCs and what are their sources?

(b) How are CFCs believed to catalyze the destruction of ozone molecules?

(c) What alternatives are now used to replace these chemicals?

17. Irradiation of food, using radioisotopes, is a recent and controversial approach to food preservation. Research and prepare a report to describe:

(a) how this technique works,

(b) advantages and disadvantages of the technique, and

(c) your opinion on whether it should be used.

18. The burning of gasoline is a major contributor to environmental pollution.

(a) What factors affect the fuel efficiency of an automobile? Investigate this question and write a report to summarize your research.

(b) Some people believe that a "carbon tax" should be imposed on gasoline to reduce consumption and to encourage people to use more fuel-efficient vehicles. Other people believe that gas is already overtaxed. State your opinion, with reasons to support it.

Acids and Bases

WHAT ARE ACIDS AND BASES?
What do lemon juice, dry ice in water, and vinegar have in common? Why would chemists consider them to be opposites of drain cleaner, baking soda, and ammonia? These substances can all be classified as either acids or bases. Chemists use classification systems to make sense of matter. So far in this unit, you have learned about the classification of mixtures and pure substances, elements and compounds, and metals and nonmetals. Acids and bases are types of compounds that have characteristic formulas and similar chemical behaviours, especially when they are dissolved in water (**Figure 1**).

Figure 1

Stalagmites and stalactites, seen in limestone caverns, are formed when the limestone dissolves in water that contains carbonic acid. Carbonic acid is formed when carbon dioxide dissolves in water.

In Chapter 5, you learned how to name oxy-acids. In Chapter 6, you looked at different types of reactions of acids. Acids and bases are important reactants and catalysts used in the chemical industry to make such products as pharmaceutical drugs and plastics. We encounter acids and bases everyday: common acids include lemon juice, vitamin C, and vinegar. Common bases include antacids, ammonia, and baking soda.

Problems have been associated with acids and bases. The safe handling of acids and bases is a definite concern whether at school, at home, or in the workplace. Concentrated solutions of acids and bases can cause severe burns, so spills must be dealt with immediately. Acid precipitation is a serious environmental concern in eastern Canada.

Reflect on your Learning

1. What are acids and bases?

2. What methods can we use to identify them?

3. What are some examples of acids and bases?

4. What are some chemical formulas of acids and bases?

Throughout this chapter, note any changes in your ideas as you learn new concepts and develop your skills.

Try This
Activity Introducing Acid–Base Reactions

Remember to think about the answers to the Reflect on your Learning questions as you do this activity. Wear safety goggles and an apron, and make careful observations at each step.

- Find some frozen cranberry or grape juice concentrate. Mix about 10 mL of concentrate with an equal volume of water to make a small amount of juice solution. Divide the juice solution into two small clear glasses.
- Put about 5 mL of water into a third clear glass. Use the flat end of a toothpick to add a small amount of baking soda powder to the water. Swirl to dissolve. Put about 5 mL of vinegar into a fourth clear glass.
- Pour the vinegar into one of the glasses of juice solution.

(a) What happens? Record your observations.

- Pour the baking soda solution into the other glass of juice solution.

(b) Explain why the result is different.

(c) Predict what will happen when the two mixed solutions are put together. Try it.

- Add a small amount of baking soda powder to the final mixture. You should see something different.

(d) Which combinations of reactants cause colour changes?

(e) Which combinations of reactants seem to produce a gas? What is this gas? (The labels on the containers may provide some clues.)

INQUIRY SKILLS MENU

○ Questioning	● Planning	● Analyzing
○ Hypothesizing	● Conducting	● Evaluating
● Predicting	● Recording	● Communicating

Recognizing Acids and Bases

What makes a substance acidic or basic? Why do we classify lemon juice and vinegar as acids, and drain cleaner and ammonia window cleaner as bases? Acids and bases are common chemical compounds that can be grouped according to their physical and chemical properties (**Figure 1**).

You have observed some of the properties of acids and bases, including their reactions with metals. Another property is their effect on **indicators,** which are substances that turn different colours in acids and bases. Litmus is one example of an indicator. In acid solutions, blue litmus paper turns red; in basic solutions, red litmus paper turns blue. Indicators can be obtained from many sources, including plants (**Figure 2**). In this investigation, you will prepare some indicators and you will react the indicators with some acids and bases. You will also look at some properties of acids and bases.

Figure 1

Acids and bases are found in many household substances.

Figure 2

Strawberries and red cabbage both contain pigments called anthocyanins, which are indicators. The molecular structure of anthocyanins changes when the pigment is combined with an acid or a base. This change affects their ability to interact with light, and thus, their colour. These pigments are used as colours in some soft drinks.

Question

What are some characteristic properties of acids and bases?

Prediction

(a) Predict what you will observe when acids and bases react with indicators.

Design

In the first part of the investigation you will make some natural indicators. In the second part of the investigation, you will design a procedure to compare the properties of water, acids, and bases.

(b) Make a data table to record your observations. Some useful headings for your table may include *Test, Observations with water, Observations with acid*, and *Observations with base*.

Materials

- apron
- safety goggles
- red cabbage
- tea bag
- plant materials (blueberries, beets, cranberries or cranberry juice, grape juice, geranium leaves, or rose petals — not white or yellow)
- red and blue litmus paper
- knife or shredder
- 2 large pots or large beakers
- hot water kettle or hot plate
- wire sieve or tea strainer
- 6 small beakers or jars
- microtray
- microdroppers
- calcium carbonate (chalk)
- sodium bicarbonate (baking soda)
- small pieces of magnesium ribbon
- small pieces of aluminum foil
- hydrochloric acid test solution (1% or 0.1 mol/L)
- sodium hydroxide test solution (1% or 0.1 mol/L)
- distilled water test solution

Procedure

Part 1: Making Natural Indicators

1 Your teacher may divide the class into groups to make different indicator solutions from red cabbage, tea, or other plant materials. These solutions can be shared with other groups.

2 Put on your apron and safety goggles.

3 To make red cabbage indicator: Chop up or shred about a quarter of a red cabbage. Put the pieces into a large pot and add some boiling water — enough to cover the cabbage — as shown in **Figure 3.** Stir the mixture, and then leave the pieces to soak for at least 15 min.

Figure 3

Figure 4

5 To make tea indicator: Half-fill a small beaker or jar with hot water. Place a tea bag in the beaker and stir occasionally for 5 min. Discard the tea bag. Label the container and put the solution aside for use in Part 2.

6 To make other plant indicators: Use steps 2 to 4 as a guide. Make solutions of some of the following substances in water: blueberries, beets, cranberries or cranberry juice, grape juice, geranium leaves, and rose petals. Put the solutions aside in labelled containers for use in Part 2.

Part 2: Testing Acids and Bases

7 Note the list of substances in the Materials
K4 section.

(c) Design a procedure to compare the properties of acids, bases, and water when they are combined with various reactants, including chalk, baking soda, pieces of metal, and indicator solutions.

Hydrochloric acid and sodium hydroxide are corrosive. Any spills on the skin, in the eyes, or on clothing should be washed immediately with plenty of cold water. Report any spills to your teacher.

Handle the knife or shredder carefully. When carrying pointed items, make sure the pointed end is toward the floor.

Hot liquids can cause severe burns. Check with your teacher about safety precautions when handling a hot kettle or hot liquids.

4 Pour the cabbage water through a wire sieve or tea strainer into a second pot, as shown in **Figure 4.** Discard the cabbage. Put the cabbage water in a labelled beaker or jar for use in Part 2.

(d) Design a data table in which to record your observations. Have your teacher check both your procedure and your data table before you proceed.

8 Test small samples of the acid test solution, base test solution, and water using the microdroppers and microtray (**Figure 5**). Record your observations in your data table.

 Avoid cross-contamination of the microdroppers and solutions. Use only the droppers that have been assigned to particular solutions. Let the drops "free-fall" into the microtray wells rather than touching the dropper to the microtray.

Figure 5

9 Dispose of the mixtures, and clean and put away your materials as instructed by your teacher. Save unused indicator solutions for later investigations. These solutions should be refrigerated. Clean up your work station. Wash your hands.

Analysis and Evaluation

(e) Answer the initial Question by comparing the properties of acids, bases, and water in a chart.

(f) Why do you think that you needed to use both red and blue litmus paper?

(g) Which indicator(s) made the clearest distinction between an acid and a base? Explain.

(h) How would you improve the design of this experiment?

Ⓠ (i) Write up Part B in a lab report.

Understanding Concepts

1. What atom or part of a chemical formula is found in
   (a) acids?
   (b) bases?
   (*Hint*: You may want to review section 5.9.)

2. What was the purpose of testing water as well as samples of an acid and a base?

3. Explain in your own words what is meant by the term "indicator."

4. Lemon juice and vinegar are both acids. What does this suggest about the taste of acids?

Making Connections

5. Think about the types of reactions you learned about in Chapter 6. What gases were produced when acids reacted with
   (a) a metal?
   (b) a carbonate compound?
   (c) a hydrogen carbonate compound?

6. Why are metal pop cans lined with a plastic coating?

Exploring

7. What do you think would happen if you tested solutions of acids and bases with mixtures of indicators? Try this with your teacher's permission.

8. Some gases were produced in this investigation. How would you test for these gases?

Reflecting

9. Why do you think there are so many different kinds of indicators (e.g., paper, liquid, different substances)?

Properties of Acids and Bases

You have seen that acids and bases have characteristic reactions with indicators. What are some other properties of these substances? Can we look at the name or formula of a substance and decide whether it will behave as an acid or base?

Acids are sour-tasting, water-soluble substances that are found in many common products (**Table 1**). They are so reactive that they can combine with many other substances (**Figure 1**). For example, acids react with some metals to produce hydrogen gas. For example,

$$\text{zinc}_{(s)} + \text{hydrochloric acid}_{(aq)} \rightarrow \text{hydrogen}_{(g)} + \text{zinc chloride}_{(aq)}$$

Acids also react with compounds that contain carbonate and hydrogen carbonate groups. For example,

$$\text{hydrochloric acid}_{(aq)} + \text{calcium carbonate}_{(s)} \rightarrow$$
$$\text{carbon dioxide}_{(g)} + \text{water}_{(l)} + \text{calcium chloride}_{(aq)}$$

Another characteristic property of acid solutions is that they are good conductors of electricity. All acids contain hydrogen atoms in combined form. When acids are dissolved in water, they release hydrogen ions (H^+). For example, hydrochloric acid ($HCl_{(aq)}$) consists of hydrogen ions and chloride ions (Cl^-) dissolved in water:

$$HCl_{(aq)} \rightarrow H^+_{(aq)} + Cl^-_{(aq)}$$

Acids are also important in the chemical industry (see Case Study 8.12). The most important industrial chemical in North America is sulfuric acid. It is so reactive that it can combine with thousands of other compounds and can act either as a starting material or as a catalyst in chemical reactions. It is used in such varied processes as manufacturing fertilizers and explosives, refining oil, and electroplating metals.

Acids must be treated with care. For example, sulfuric acid and hydrochloric acid are both very corrosive. Sulfuric and nitric acids released into the environment can cause serious damage, as you will learn in Case Study 8.7.

Figure 1

Nitric acid reacts quickly with copper metal. This reaction can be used to produce works of art.

Did You Know?

The taste of sour milk is caused by lactic acid, the same molecule that accumulates and causes pain in your muscles when you exercise.

Did You Know?

Stomach acid is a solution of hydrochloric acid. The inside lining of the stomach is acid-resistant. However, if this lining is damaged, the acid can attack the stomach wall and cause ulcers to form.

Table 1   **Examples of Some Common Acids**

Common name	Formula	Source or use
vinegar (acetic acid)	$HC_2H_3O_{2(aq)}$	salad dressing
citric acid	$HC_6H_7O_{7(aq)}$	oranges, lemons
ascorbic acid	$HC_6H_7O_{6(aq)}$	Vitamin C
lactic acid	$HC_3H_5O_{3(aq)}$	sour milk
carbonic acid	$H_2CO_{3(aq)}$	carbonated drinks
acetylsalicylic acid (ASA)	$HC_9H_7O_{4(aq)}$	Aspirin
sulfuric acid	$H_2SO_{4(aq)}$	car batteries

Bases are bitter-tasting, water-soluble substances that feel slippery when in aqueous solution. Bases are good conductors of electricity because they release hydroxide ions (OH^-) when they dissolve in water. For example, sodium hydroxide (NaOH) produces sodium ions (Na^+) and hydroxide ions when it dissolves in water:

$$NaOH_{(aq)} \rightarrow Na^+_{(aq)} + OH^-_{(aq)}$$

Common bases are shown in **Table 2**. Substances that are described as bases may also be described as **alkaline.** Bases react with proteins to break them down into smaller molecules. A hair-clogged drain may be cleared by treating it with a drain cleaner that contains sodium hydroxide because the sodium hydroxide breaks down the protein in the hair. Precautions must be taken to avoid getting sodium hydroxide in your eyes because it will react with protein molecules in the eye and cause blindness if untreated.

In Investigation 8.1, you found that acids and bases are most easily recognized by their effects on indicators. Chemists use a great variety of indicators, depending on the types of solutions that they want to investigate (**Figure 2**).

Table 2   **Examples of Some Common Bases**

Common name	Formula	Use
sodium hydroxide	$NaOH_{(aq)}$	drain cleaner
potassium hydroxide	$KOH_{(aq)}$	soap, cosmetics
aluminum hydroxide	$Al(OH)_{3(aq)}$	antacids
ammonium hydroxide	$NH_4OH_{(aq)}$	ammonia window cleaner
sodium bicarbonate	$NaHCO_{3(aq)}$	baking soda
potassium sulfite	$K_2SO_{3(aq)}$	food preservative

Figure 2

Acids and bases show a range of colours in different indicators.

Try This
Activity   Tasting Acids and Bases

If you have ever bitten into a lemon, you know that acids taste sour. Bases, on the other hand, taste bitter. What chemical reactions are involved in these sensations? The sense of taste depends on the chemical reactions that occur when molecules contact the taste buds on the tongue. There are four different types of taste buds: sour, bitter, sweet, and salty (**Figure 3**). Make a solution of baking soda in a glass, and dip a cotton swab into the solution. Test different areas of the tongue for taste. Repeat the process with another cotton swab dipped in vinegar solution. How do your findings compare to **Figure 3**?

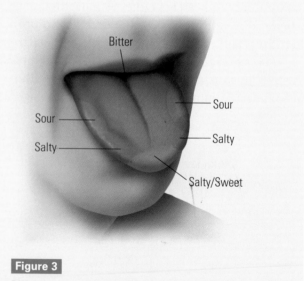

Figure 3

Different areas of the tongue detect specific tastes.

Formulas for Acids and Bases

Earlier in this unit, you learned how to name some chemical compounds. How can you recognize acids and bases from their chemical formulas?

Common acids are easily recognized because their formulas begin with a hydrogen. For example, sulfuric acid is H_2SO_4, carbonic acid is H_2CO_3, and phosphoric acid is H_3PO_4. As you can see in **Figure 4,** both sulfuric acid and hydrochloric acid have hydrogen atoms that are available to react.

Deciding whether a substance is a base from its formula is more complicated. Most bases are compounds that contain the hydroxide ion (OH^-) (**Figure 5**). When you see the hydroxide group in an ionic compound, you know that the compound is a base. For example, sodium hydroxide has the formula NaOH. But some bases are more difficult to recognize. Substances that contain the bicarbonate, or hydrogen carbonate, (HCO_3^-) group, for example, are bases because they react with water to form hydroxide ions. Baking soda is sodium bicarbonate, or sodium hydrogen carbonate, ($NaHCO_3$), a base commonly used in cooking.

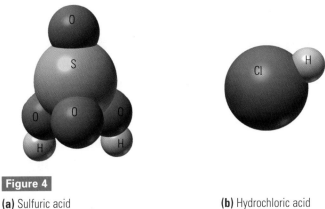

Figure 4

(a) Sulfuric acid   **(b)** Hydrochloric acid

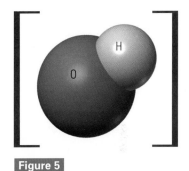

Figure 5

Bases produce hydroxide ions in solution.

Understanding Concepts

1. Make a table or a web diagram to summarize what you (Y) know about acids and bases. The headings could include: *Physical properties, Chemical properties,* and *Examples.*

2. **(a)** Describe three chemical reactions that involve acids.

   (b) Write a word equation to represent each reaction.

   (c) Write a balanced chemical equation for each reaction.

3. Identify each of the following substances as an acid, a base, or neither:

   (a) potassium hydroxide

   (b) $HClO_3$

   (c) $Mg(OH)_2$

   (d) HNO_3

   (e) potassium bicarbonate

4. Write the corresponding name or formula for each of the substances in question 3.

Making Connections

5. What is meant by the term "acid indigestion"? Research and report on the acids that are present in the stomach and the ways in which this problem may be treated.

6. If you found a solid substance in your kitchen cupboard, how would you test it to decide whether it was an acid or a base? Remember you should never test unknown substances by tasting.

Exploring

7. What types of WHMIS or Hazardous Household Product (A) safety symbols would you expect to find on acids and bases? Visit your local hardware store or (with your teacher's permission) look around your school laboratory to find examples of acids and bases, and report on the safety symbols that they display.

The pH Scale

Concentrated acids and bases are very hazardous. For example, concentrated hydrochloric acid is so corrosive that it will burn through clothing. A concentrated base is also highly corrosive. However, hydrochloric acid is also found in your stomach, and baking soda is safe enough to put in the food that you eat. A dilute solution of hydrochloric acid is less acidic and less likely to react than a concentrated solution. How can we determine how acidic or basic a substance is?

Chemists use the **pH scale** to represent how acidic or basic a solution is. Most acids and bases can be ranked on this scale. A very acidic solution has a very low pH value. A neutral solution, like pure water, has a pH of 7. A very basic (or alkaline) solution has a very high pH value. The pH values for a variety of common substances are shown in **Figure 1.**

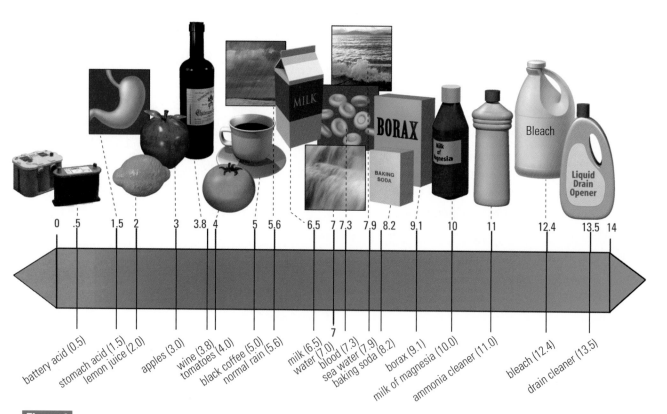

Figure 1

The pH scale was developed in 1909 to allow scientists to compare the concentration of hydrogen ions in various solutions.

pH: A Logarithmic Scale

The pH scale is a logarithmic scale (**Figure 2**), which means that every change of one unit on the scale represents a tenfold effect on the concentration of the solution. For example, an increase of one on the scale represents dividing the concentration by 10 (or 10^1), and a decrease of two represents multiplying the concentration by 100 (or 10^2).

As the pH decreases, the solution becomes more acidic. A solution with a pH of 3 is 10 times more acidic than a solution with a pH of 4 and 100 times more acidic than a solution with a pH of 5. As the pH increases, the solution becomes more basic. Thus, a solution with a pH of 13 is 10 times more basic than a solution with a pH of 12 and 100 times more basic than a solution with a pH of 11.

The pH is defined according to the following formula:

$$pH = -\log_{10} [H^+]$$

where the square brackets around the H^+ ion represent the "concentration of hydrogen ions in solution." The units of concentration are mol/L (read as "moles per litre").

Figure 2

The Richter scale is a logarithmic scale. An increase of three units on the scale represents an earthquake that is 1000 times worse. The 1989 earthquake that caused serious damage in parts of California measured 7.1 on the Richter scale.

Try This Activity   Dilution and pH

If your school lab is equipped with a pH meter that gives digital readouts of pH, you could use it to investigate the effects of dilution on pH.

- Put on safety goggles and an apron.
- Obtain 10 mL of a solution with a pH of 1. (A 1% hydrochloric acid solution would be appropriate.) Measure the exact pH of the solution using the meter.
- Dilute the solution by a factor of 10. For example, place 10 mL of the acid in a graduated cylinder and add 90 mL of water to make 100 mL of solution. Measure the pH of this dilute solution.
- Repeat the process with successive dilutions of acid. Record and analyze your results using a table and graph.

(a) Explain your results.

- Repeat the process using a solution with a pH of 13. (A 0.5% solution of sodium hydroxide would be appropriate.)

(b) Explain your results.

Sodium hydroxide is corrosive. Any spills on the skin, in the eyes, or on clothing should be washed immediately with cold water. Report any spills to your teacher.

Hydrochloric acid is corrosive. Any spills on the skin, in the eyes, or on clothing should be washed immediately with cold water. Report any spills to your teacher.

pH and Soil

Have you ever seen someone adding lime to soil? Lime (CaO) can be added to acidic soil to make the soil more basic. As you learned in Chapter 3, the pH of soil determines the fertility of the soil. Plants differ in their preference for soil acidity. For example, many leguminous crops prefer neutral to slightly alkaline soils (pH of 7 to 10); corn and small grains prefer slightly acidic soil (pH of 5 to 6); and potatoes and blueberries prefer acidic soils (pH of less than 5). The sources of soil acidity include organic matter decay, naturally occurring acids, and acid precipitation. The correct management of soil pH is important for providing optimal growing conditions for plants, maintaining optimal levels of nutrients, and using fertilizers efficiently.

pH and Cosmetics

Have you ever heard pH mentioned in advertisements for skin and hair products? Many products advertise that they are "pH balanced" or that they "restore your hair's natural pH" (**Figure 3**). Should you believe such claims? What do they mean?

The acidity of a shampoo can have a definite effect on hair. The clear outer protein layer of hair is called the cuticle. Very basic (high-pH) shampoos cause the inner hair shaft to swell and push apart the cuticle. The harsh bases used in hair permanents and hair colouring have even stronger effects. They can dissolve the cuticle and damage the hair, making it dull and dry.

Acidic (low-pH) shampoos shrink the inner shaft, causing the cuticle to lie flat and restoring the hair's original flexibility and shine. However, low-pH shampoos are not for everyone. People with thick, curly hair who would prefer their hair to be straighter can benefit from more alkaline (higher-pH) shampoos, which soften and straighten the hair.

The pH of soaps and other cosmetic products can also affect skin cells. The pH of skin normally ranges between 5 and 6. Using basic (high-pH) products can remove the outer layer of dead skin cells, which contain protein molecules. The skin will look brighter and clearer. But frequent use of basic products may remove too many layers of cells. Moreover, the top layer of the skin contains natural acids that protect the skin from infection. Too much use of very basic soaps can remove these protective acids.

Figure 3

Some cosmetic products advertise their pH.

 ## Challenge

1 Some personal care products have a particular pH. Does the pH of the product you have chosen have any effect on its marketability or its usefulness?

Try This
Activity Red Tornado

Put on your apron and safety goggles.

Add red cabbage juice to a tall clear container. Add a small amount of vinegar until you get a red colour. Stir the mixture with a spoon until it swirls like a tornado. Drop an Alka-Seltzer tablet into the mixture. Describe and explain what you observe.

Understanding Concepts

1. In your own words, explain the meaning of the term "pH."

2. What would you expect as an approximate pH value for each of the following:
   (a) a very concentrated base;
   (b) a dilute basic solution;
   (c) a very concentrated acid;
   (b) a dilute acid solution;
   (e) tap water.

3. How much more acidic is a solution with a pH of 4.5 than a solution with a pH of
   (a) 5.5?
   (b) 6.5?

4. How much more basic is a solution with a pH of 12.5 than a solution with a pH of
   (a) 10.5?
   (b) 8.5?

5. Look at **Figure 1**. Roughly how much more acidic is
   (a) stomach acid than tomatoes?
   (b) lemon juice than apples?

6. Look at **Figure 1**. Roughly how much more basic is
   (a) borax than baking soda?
   (b) bleach than blood?

7. What happens to the pH of an acid when water is added to it?

8. Look in your bathroom at home or in the local pharmacy to find some examples of products that include information about pH levels. Record your observations in a table with the headings: *Product*, *pH*, and *Use*. What connections can you see between a product's pH and its use?

9. Toothpastes are usually slightly basic (alkaline). Why does this make sense? (Hint: Consider the types of compounds in our mouths that may damage teeth.)

Exploring

10. Use the pH formula to calculate the pH of solutions in which the hydrogen ion concentration (in mol/L) is
    (a) 0.1
    (b) 0.01
    (c) 0.001
    (d) 1×10^{-5}
    (e) 1×10^{-4}

11. Summarize your calculations in question 10 as
    (a) a table
    (b) a graph
    (c) a statement describing the relationship between concentration of hydrogen ions and pH.

12. You can investigate another way of looking at the acidity of solutions using the following equation:

    $[H^+] = 10^{-pH}$

    Calculate the concentrations of hydrogen ion for the following pH values: 1.0, 2.0, 2.5, 3.0, and 5.0.

INQUIRY SKILLS MENU
- ○ Questioning
- ○ Hypothesizing
- ● Predicting
- ○ Planning
- ● Conducting
- ● Recording
- ● Analyzing
- ● Evaluating
- ● Communicating

Household Products and pH

You saw in Investigation 8.1 that indicators can be used to determine whether a substance is acidic or basic. But how can you determine the exact pH of a substance? One way is to test the substance with a series of different indicators. Different indicators change colour at different pH values.

Another technique is to use a universal indicator. A **universal indicator** is a substance that turns different colours in solutions with different pH values. In this investigation, you will use universal indicators to determine the pH of some products commonly found around the home.

Question

How does a universal indicator compare to the natural indicators that you made in Investigation 8.1? How can you determine the pH of some common household substances?

Prediction

(a) Predict the pH of various household substances.

Design

You will compare the colours of a commercial universal indicator with the colours of some natural indicators. You will then measure the pH of some common household substances.

(b) Make a table to record all your observations.

Materials

- apron
- safety goggles
- microtray
- microdroppers
- samples of products with roughly known pH values, such as Fantastik household cleaner, ammonia window cleaner, baking soda, pure water, vinegar, and 1% hydrochloric acid
- universal indicator solution or wide-range pH paper (including colour chart)
- samples of natural indicators (including red cabbage) from Investigation 8.1
- samples of household or other products

Hydrochloric acid and many household cleaners are corrosive. Any spills on the skin, in the eyes, or on clothing should be washed immediately with cold water. Report any spills to your teacher.

Procedure

Part 1: Comparing Universal and Natural Indicators

1 Put on your apron and safety goggles. Your teacher may organize you into groups to test particular indicators.

2 Use labelled microdroppers to put a few drops of each of the six products with roughly known pH values into specific wells of a microtray (**Figure 1**). Organize your microtray by devoting one row of the microtray to each product.

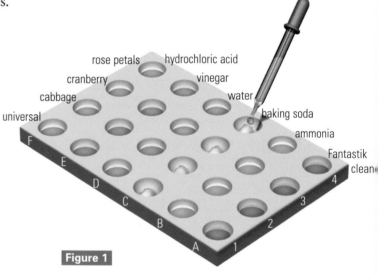

rose petals — hydrochloric acid
cranberry — vinegar
cabbage — water
universal — baking soda — ammonia — Fantastik cleaner

Figure 1

Avoid cross-contamination of the microdroppers and solutions. Use only the droppers that have been assigned to particular solutions. Let the drops "free-fall" into the microtray wells rather than touching the dropper to the microtray.

3 Add a drop of universal indicator to one well of each of the household products. Use the colour chart supplied with the universal indicator to determine the exact pH of each of the six products.

4 Add a drop of red cabbage indicator to each of the six wells in the second column. Record the colour of the red cabbage in each of the six solutions.

5 Repeat step 4 using the other natural indicators you have chosen and record your results in your data table.

6 Dispose of the mixtures in the microtray as instructed by your teacher.

Part 2: Testing the pH of Household Products

7 Your teacher may organize you into groups to test specific household products or to use particular indicators.

8 Repeat steps 2 and 3 for as many household products as you have time to test. You may decide to test each solution with a drop of one of your natural indicators as well. Record your observations.

9 Dispose of the mixtures in the microtray, and clean and put away your materials as instructed by your teacher. Clean up your work station. Wash your hands.

Analysis and Evaluation

(c) How closely did the rough pH values for the first set of products compare to the actual pH values as measured with the universal indicator?

(d) Make a pH diagram similar to **Figure 1** in section 8.3. Label your diagram to record and summarize your experimental results.

(e) Which natural indicators do you think would be most useful? Explain.

(f) How accurate were your predictions? Explain.

Understanding Concepts

1. In general, which types of products were acids? Which products were bases?

2. What advantages or disadvantages do commercial universal indicators have over natural indicators?

3. When ammonia is sprayed on some shades of bright yellow (called goldenrod) paper, the paper turns red. Explain what is happening. How might this affect the cleaning instructions provided for photocopiers?

4. What practical use could indicators have? Describe an invention that uses indicators.

5. What do you think would happen if you tested bleach with an indicator?

Exploring

6. If your school lab is equipped with a pH meter that gives a digital readout of pH, use it to determine the pH values for the solutions in this investigation. Record your values in a data table, and compare them to the pH values obtained using indicators.

7. Design and, with your teacher's approval, test your own universal indicator. Choose different combinations of natural indicators until you find a combination that gives a range of colours for different pH values. Report on your findings.

Making Acids and Bases

Acids and bases have characteristic properties that allow us to identify them. You have investigated their effects on various indicators, including litmus and universal indicators. In this investigation, you will look at how acids and bases are formed.

One way of forming acids and bases is by reacting elements with oxygen to form oxides, and then reacting those oxides with water:

element + oxygen → oxide (acidic or basic)

oxide + water → acid or base

The products of these reactions can be identified using indicators.

Question

What patterns can we see in the ways that elements react with oxygen and water to form acids or bases?

Design

You will burn a number of metals and nonmetals in oxygen to form oxides. You will then react the oxides with water to form solutions, and use indicators to test these solutions for acidity and basicity.

(a) For Part 1, make a table to summarize your observations of the colours of different indicators in an acid, a base, and water.

(b) For Part 2, make a full-page data table with the following headings: *Element name and symbol, Physical properties of element, Observations during burning, Properties of oxide,* and *Effects of aqueous solution on indicators.*

Materials

- apron
- safety goggles
- test tubes
- test-tube rack
- hydrochloric acid solution (1% or 0.1 mol/L)
- sodium hydroxide solution (1% or 0.1 mol/L)
- distilled water
- bromthymol blue indicator
- red and blue litmus paper
- phenolphthalein indicator
- 5 gas bottles
- magnesium ribbon
- iron (steel wool)
- sulfur
- pneumatic trough
- 5 glass plates
- tongs
- 400-mL beaker
- sodium
- carbon (charcoal)
- oxygen cylinder and delivery hose
- pencil
- Bunsen burner
- deflagrating spoon

Procedure

Teacher Demonstration with Student Assistance

Part 1: Checking Indicators

1 Your teacher may assign you to help with various parts of this investigation. If you are to be involved in the demonstration, put on your apron and safety goggles.

2 Place about 1 cm depth of hydrochloric acid solution, sodium hydroxide solution, and distilled water into three separate test tubes in a rack. Add two or three drops of bromthymol blue to each test tube. Save the test tubes for colour comparisons. Record your observations in your data table.

 Hydrochloric and sodium hydrochloride are corrosive. Any spills on the skin, in the eyes, or on clothing should be washed immediately with plenty of cold water. Report any spills to your teacher.

3 Repeat step 2 using small pieces of red and blue litmus paper instead of bromthymol blue.

4 Repeat step 2 using phenolphthalein indicator.

Phenolphthalein indicator is flammable. Keep it away from sparks and flames.

Part 2: Preparing for Burning

Label a gas bottle for each of the elements to be studied (Mg, Na, Fe, C, and S). Examine the samples of elements to be burned.

(c) What common properties do you see in magnesium, sodium, and iron?

(d) What common properties do you see in carbon and sulfur?

6 Fill each of the gas bottles with oxygen (**Figure 1**) and cover with a glass plate. Leave about 3 cm of water in the bottom of each bottle.

Figure 1

Part 3: Burning Magnesium, Sodium, and Iron

> ✋ The following steps should only be performed by a teacher, and should take place under a fume hood.

7 Wrap a 5-cm piece of magnesium ribbon around a pencil so that when you remove the pencil, the ribbon forms a spiral shape. Using tongs to hold the magnesium, ignite it in the Bunsen burner flame. Gently lower the burning magnesium into a gas bottle. Take care to avoid touching the bottle with the burning metal. Keep the gas bottle partly covered with the glass plate. Allow the ash to drop into the bottle. When the combustion is complete, withdraw the tongs.

> ✋ Touching the burning metal to the glass may cause the glass to crack.

> ✋ The flame is very intense. Do not look at it directly.

8 Cover the gas bottle with the glass plate. Hold the glass plate on the top of the bottle, and shake the bottle vigorously. Divide the solution into three test tubes. Add two or three drops of bromthymol blue indicator to one test tube, two or three drops of phenolphthalein indicator to the second test tube, and pieces of red and blue litmus paper to the third test tube.

(e) Complete the data table for this element.

9 Place a small piece of sodium (approximately 3 mm in diameter) into a clean, dry deflagrating spoon (**Figure 2**). Hold the spoon in the edge of a Bunsen burner flame until the sodium ignites. Immediately lower the spoon into a gas bottle. Keep the gas bottle partly covered with the glass plate. When combustion is complete, briefly immerse the spoon in the water and then remove it.

Figure 2

> ✋ Touching the hot spoon to the glass may cause the glass to crack.

10 Repeat step 8 for the gas bottle in which the sodium was burned.

11 Hold a small piece of steel wool with tongs in the edge of a Bunsen burner flame until it ignites. Lower it into a gas bottle. Take care to avoid touching the bottle with the burning metal. Keep the gas bottle partly covered with the glass plate. When combustion is complete, allow any residue to drop into the water and remove the tongs.

12 Repeat step 8 for the gas bottle in which the steel wool was burned.

Part 4: Burning Carbon and Sulfur

13 Hold a small piece of charcoal (carbon) in a deflagrating spoon in the edge of a Bunsen burner flame until it glows red-hot. Lower the glowing charcoal into a gas bottle. Keep the gas bottle partly covered with the glass plate. Do not remove the spoon until the charcoal stops glowing. Cover the gas bottle with the glass plate.

14 Repeat step 8 for the gas bottle in which the charcoal was combusted.

☠ The following procedure produces a very toxic gas, so the procedure must be performed in a fume hood by a teacher.

15 Obtain a very small quantity of sulfur in a clean deflagrating spoon. Place a beaker of water next to a gas bottle. Ignite the sulfur in the Bunsen burner flame. Quickly insert the spoon into the gas bottle. After observing for a few seconds, remove the spoon and plunge it quickly into the beaker of water to extinguish the flame. Cover the bottle.

16 Repeat step 8 for the gas bottle in which the sulfur was burned.

17 Dispose of the mixtures in the test tubes as instructed by your teacher. Wash your hands.

Analysis and Evaluation

(f) What kinds of elements are magnesium, sodium, and iron?

(g) When magnesium, sodium, and iron reacted in oxygen, what was the state of the oxides formed?

(h) When the oxides of magnesium and sodium reacted in water, what kind of solution was formed?

(i) Which oxide(s) was (were) not soluble in water?

(j) What kinds of elements are carbon and sulfur?

(k) When carbon and sulfur reacted in oxygen, what was the state of the oxides formed?

(l) When the oxides of carbon and sulfur reacted in water, what kind of solution was formed?

(m) Write a statement to answer the initial Question.

(n) Which of the indicators were most useful for detecting acids and bases? Explain.

Understanding Concepts

1. Make a general statement about the type of:
   (a) oxides formed when metals react with oxygen;
   (b) solutions formed when basic oxides react with water;
   (c) oxides formed when nonmetals react with oxygen;
   (d) the types of solutions formed when acidic oxides react with water.

2. What were the names and formulas of the oxides formed by magnesium, sodium, and iron?

3. What were the names and formulas of the bases formed by magnesium and sodium oxides?

4. Write word and balanced chemical equations for:
   (a) the synthesis reactions of magnesium, sodium, and iron with oxygen gas (O_2);
   (b) the reactions of their oxides with water.

5. The oxides formed by carbon and sulfur were carbon dioxide and sulfur dioxide. Write their formulas.

6. Write word and balanced chemical equations for:
   (a) the reactions of carbon and sulfur with oxygen gas (O_2);
   (b) the reactions of their oxides with water to form carbonic acid (H_2CO_3) and sulfurous acid (H_2SO_3).

7. Compare the reactions of the elements in air to their reactions in pure oxygen. Use your knowledge of rates of reaction to explain their behaviour.

Making Connections

8. Milk of magnesia is a common antacid used to treat stomach problems. It is a white, milky water suspension of a substance that you made in this investigation. What are the name and formula of this substance?

8.6

Elements and Oxides

You are familiar with acids such as hydrochloric acid, nitric acid, and sulfuric acid. You have performed activities in which you have made bases such as sodium hydroxide and magnesium hydroxide. In Chapter 5 you saw that you can use the periodic table to predict the physical and chemical properties of an element. How does an element's position in the periodic table affect the element's ability to form acids and bases?

Reactions of Metals

Generally, metals are found on the left side of the periodic table and nonmetals are found toward the right side. As you learned in Chapter 5, metals have some common physical properties. They are generally shiny, malleable, and ductile, and they tend to be good conductors of heat and electricity. With the exception of mercury, most metals are solids at room temperature. Metals generally follow certain patterns of chemical behaviour:

- They react in oxygen to form **metal oxides.**
- Metal oxides are always solids.
- Metal oxides react in water to form bases.

Figure 1

Potassium metal reacts with water to form hydrogen gas and potassium hydroxide, a base.

Metal oxides can also be called **basic oxides,** or basic anhydrides. They are useful substances because they are stable compounds that can produce bases when dissolved in water. For example, consider some synthesis reactions of potassium, a member of the alkali metals (Group 1). Potassium burns in oxygen to produce potassium oxide:

$$4K_{(s)} + O_{2(g)} \rightarrow 2K_2O_{(s)}$$

The potassium oxide then reacts with water to form potassium hydroxide:

$$K_2O_{(s)} + H_2O_{(l)} \rightarrow 2KOH_{(aq)}$$

Potassium hydroxide is used in making soap, liquid fertilizer, paint removers, and cosmetics. It is a typical base that turns red litmus blue and colourless phenolphthalein indicator pink. Potassium hydroxide can be formed directly by adding potassium to water (**Figure 1**). The reaction also produces hydrogen gas:

$$2K_{(s)} + 2H_2O_{(l)} \rightarrow 2KOH_{(aq)} + H_{2(g)}$$

Less-reactive metals show similar behaviours. Calcium is a member of the alkaline earth metals. Its reactions in oxygen and water follow a pattern similar to those of alkali metals:

$$2Ca_{(s)} + O_{2(g)} \rightarrow 2CaO_{(s)}$$
$$CaO_{(s)} + H_2O_{(l)} \rightarrow Ca(OH)_{2(aq)}$$

Acids and Bases **305**

Calcium oxide is used to enrich the soil and make it possible for new plants to grow (**Figure 2**). Calcium hydroxide is used to make brick mortar and plasters, and as a food additive.

Reactions of Nonmetals

Nonmetals are generally dull and brittle, and tend to be poor conductors. Nonmetals have a variety of states at room temperature and can also take part in a wide variety of chemical changes, including reactions with oxygen. Nonmetals also follow certain patterns of chemical behaviour:

Figure 2

Some plants grow better in basic (alkaline) soil conditions. Calcium oxide, more commonly called lime, is a metal oxide that can be used to make soil more basic.

- They react in oxygen to form **nonmetal oxides.**
- Nonmetal oxides are often gases or liquids.
- Nonmetal oxides react in water to form acids.

Nonmetal oxides are also known as **acidic oxides,** because they form acids in water. For example, consider some reactions of nitrogen. Nitrogen can be made to react with oxygen to produce nitrogen dioxide in the following reaction:

$$N_{2(g)} + 2O_{2(g)} \rightarrow 2NO_{2(g)}$$

The nitrogen dioxide then reacts with water to form nitric acid:

$$3NO_{2(g)} + H_2O_{(l)} \rightarrow 2HNO_{3(aq)} + NO_{(g)}$$

Nitric acid is used in many industrial reactions and is a key contributor to air pollution. You will look more closely at air pollution in Case Study 8.7.

Other nonmetals show similar behaviours. Phosphorus is a nonmetal found in two different forms: white phosphorus and red phosphorus. It reacts with oxygen to form phosphorus pentoxide (**Figure 3**).

$$4P_{(s)} + 5O_{2(g)} \rightarrow 2P_2O_{5(s)}$$

The phosphorus pentoxide reacts with water to form phosphoric acid:

$$P_2O_{5(s)} + 3H_2O_{(l)} \rightarrow 2H_3PO_{4(aq)}$$

Most of the phosphoric acid produced is used to make fertilizers. It is also found in soft drinks.

Figure 3

Phosphate fertilizers are produced in large quantities.

The most familiar nonmetal oxide is carbon dioxide (CO_2). When carbon dioxide reacts with water, it forms carbonic acid.

$$CO_{2(g)} + H_2O_{(l)} \rightarrow H_2CO_{3(aq)}$$

Carbonic acid is the basis of most soft drinks and contributes to their slightly sour taste as well as the bubbles that are released when the cap is removed from the bottle (**Figure 4**).

Understanding Concepts

1. Make a chart summarizing the similarities and differences between metal and nonmetal oxides.

2. Write word equations for the reactions that occur when the following elements react with oxygen:
   (a) barium
   (b) chromium
   (c) chlorine

3. Predict what kind of solution would be formed when each of the following oxides reacts with water:
   (a) bromine monoxide
   (b) nickel(II) oxide
   (c) potassium oxide

4. Write balanced chemical reactions to represent the following reactions:
   (a) lithium + oxygen → lithium oxide
   (b) lithium oxide + water → lithium hydroxide
   (c) barium oxide + water → barium hydroxide

Making Connections

5. Lime is a good substance to add to soil to make the soil more basic because it is not very soluble in water. Why would this property be an advantage in its use as a soil additive?

Exploring

6. Visit a local plant store or nursery to find out what substances are used to make soil more acidic. What kinds of plants grow better in acidic soil? What kinds of plants prefer basic soil? Research and report on your findings.

Try This Activity   A Chalk Reaction

Put on your apron and safety goggles, and observe all safety procedures.

Calcium carbonate (chalk) is very insoluble in water.
- Try dipping a piece of chalk in a solution of phenolphthalein indicator.
- Heat the piece of chalk in a Bunsen burner flame for several minutes. Allow the chalk to cool and then dip it in the solution again. What do you observe?

(a) What type of reaction takes place when the chalk is heated?

(b) Use your knowledge of types of oxides to identify the product of the reaction. What gas must have been given off? Support your prediction with chemical equations.

Air Pollution and Acid Precipitation

When you step outside your home on a rainy day, do you ever notice the air that you breathe, or do you ever think about what makes up the rain falling from the sky? Both the atmosphere and the precipitation are complex mixtures of chemical substances. Many of these substances are acidic oxides.

The most common acidic oxide in the air is carbon dioxide, which reacts with water to make carbonic acid (**Figure 1**). Carbon dioxide is naturally produced by all living creatures, including plants. Carbon dioxide is also produced by automobiles and industries. One car produces three and a half times its weight every year in carbon dioxide emissions. So much carbon dioxide is being produced that there is growing concern over its contribution to the greenhouse effect and global warming.

Figure 1

Normal rainwater is slightly acidic because it contains carbonic acid; it has a pH of 5.6, the pH of carbon dioxide in distilled water.

(a) Why is normal rainfall slightly acidic?

(b) What do you predict would be the effect of increasing the amount of carbon dioxide in the air? Explain.

Carbon dioxide is not the only chemical substance in the air. Many chemicals in the air cause harm to living things or to the environment. These chemicals are called **pollutants**. Air pollutants can cause problems in many people, including asthma, headaches, and irritations of the eyes, nose, and throat. Air pollutants can also aggravate heart and lung conditions.

> **Did You Know?**
>
> Acid rain with a pH of 2.4 fell during a storm in New England. That's the same pH as vinegar! The pH of rain in Ontario's Muskoka–Haliburton area ranges between 3.9 and 4.4.

(c) What negative effects do pollutants have on people? Speculate how pollutants might cause each of these effects.

Air pollutants are produced in two ways: naturally and by people. Natural sources of air pollution include forest fires, volcanoes, and the decay of vegetation. But more often, air pollution is caused by people. For example, the deliberate burning of wood to clear land and the burning of wastes are both sources of air pollution. When fossil fuels are burned, large amounts of carbon dioxide and water vapour are produced, along with carbon monoxide (CO), nitrogen oxides (NO, NO_2, and other oxides), sulfur oxides (SO_2 and SO_3), and hydrocarbons. The major sources of these pollutants are shown in **Figure 2**. Note that carbon monoxide, nitrogen oxides, and sulfur oxides are all acidic oxides.

(d) What are two ways in which pollution is produced? Do you think both ways have always existed?

(e) What are five different types of air pollutants? Predict the effect of each.

Carbon Dioxide

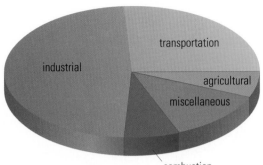

(a) Human-made sources of carbon dioxide. Carbon dioxide is an odourless, invisible gas produced when wood or fossil fuels are burned. It is the major greenhouse gas that may cause global warming.

Carbon Monoxide

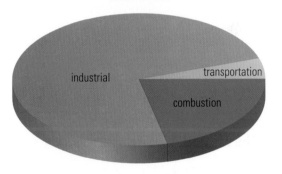

(b) Sources of carbon monoxide. Carbon monoxide is an odourless, invisible gas produced when fuel is not completely burned in vehicle engines. It can make you feel sleepy or give you a headache; it can even cause death.

Nitrogen Oxides

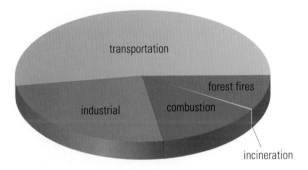

(c) Sources of nitrogen oxides. Nitrogen oxides are produced when fuels burn at high temperatures. They cause the brownish haze seen during rush hour in cities. Nitrogen oxides also contribute to acid precipitation. Nitrogen oxides react with water in a synthesis reaction to form nitric acid (HNO_3).

Sulfur Oxides

(d) Sources of sulfur oxides. Sulfur oxides form when coal that contains sulfur is burned and when ore that contains sulfur is smelted. Sulfur dioxide is the main cause of acid precipitation. This gas combines in the atmosphere with oxygen gas to form sulfur trioxide (SO_3), which reacts with water to form sulfuric acid (H_2SO_4).

Hydrocarbon Pollutants

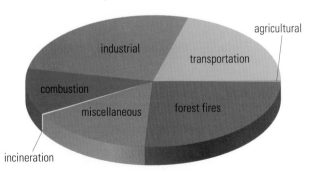

(e) Sources of hydrocarbon pollutants. Hydrocarbons (or volatile organic compounds) are substances contained in solvents, oil-based paints, and fossil fuels. They undergo chemical changes to form gas pollutants that cause breathing problems.

Figure 2

Sources of air pollutants (adapted from Environment Canada, 1995)

Acid Precipitation

Acid precipitation describes any precipitation that has a pH of less than 5.6 (the pH of normal rainwater). The main causes of acid precipitation, which includes acid rain, acid fog, acid dew, and acid snow, are sulfur dioxide and nitrogen oxides. Acid precipitation affects forests (**Figure 3**) and aquatic ecosystems (**Table 1, Figure 4**), and is related to respiratory problems in children and people with asthma. Acid precipitation causes damages estimated at about $1 billion in Canada every year.

(f) Why is acid precipitation a more accurate term than acid rain?

(g) What are the major contributors to acid precipitation?

Figure 3

Acid precipitation can seriously harm forests by washing away the nutrients from the soil. Acid precipitation also inhibits plant germination and affects the protective waxy surface of leaves, which lowers a tree's disease resistance.

Preventing Acid Rain

There are several possible strategies for reducing sulfur oxide and nitrogen oxide emissions (**Table 2**). However it is accomplished, reducing emissions in both Canada and the United States is essential. More than half of the

Table 1	The Effect of pH on Aquatic Life
pH level	**Effect**
6	Crustaceans, insects, and some plankton species begin to disappear.
5	Less-desirable species of mosses and plankton appear.
	The progressive loss of some fish populations begins.
	Fish cannot reproduce.
	Deformed adult fish appear because of lack of nutrients.
<5	All species of fish disappear.
	No decay of material occurs.
	Near-shore areas become dominated by mosses.
	Lake-bottom plants and mosses, and blackfly larvae, thrive.

Figure 4

Caddis flies are considered to be biological indicators of water quality. When water quality declines, their population drops.

Table 2	Industrial Strategies for Reducing Levels of Sulfur Dioxide and Nitrogen Oxides	
Strategy	**Method**	**How it works**
reduce SO_2	coal cleaning	reduces the amount of sulfur in coal
reduce SO_2	burning low-sulfur coal	burns coal that contains low amounts of sulfur
reduce SO_2	fluidized bed combustion (FBC)	limestone reacts with SO_2 during combustion
reduce SO_2	scrubbing	flue gas containing SO_2 enters a scrubber that consists of limestone, lime, or sodium hydroxide; the scrubber removes the SO_2 from the gas
reduce NO_2	catalytic reduction system	ammonia gas reacts with nitrogen oxides to produce nitrogen gas
reduce NO_2	catalytic converters	reactions convert nitrogen oxides, carbon dioxide, and unburned hydrocarbons to harmless gases

Figure 5

Industry and power plants are major producers of sulfur dioxide. Industries that have scrubbers have been able to decrease their sulfur dioxide emission levels significantly.

acid precipitation received in Canada originates from the United States. The Eastern Canada Acid Rain program, initiated in 1985, has seen a 54% reduction from 1980 levels of SO_2 (**Figure 5**). Nitrogen oxide levels are also slightly decreasing because of programs that target vehicles and encourage retrofits at fossil-fuelled power plants. Reductions in levels of sulfur dioxide and nitrogen oxides have also been seen in the United States.

(h) What steps can you take to reduce sulfur dioxide and nitrogen oxide emissions? Think about how you use energy in your home and when travelling around your community.

 Challenge

3 How are the pollutants that cause acid precipitation produced? From the information given in this lesson, what recommendations could you suggest to help reduce acid precipitation in your area?

3 On February 23, 2000, the residents of Bogota, Colombia left their cars at home to take public transportation, walk, or ride their bicycles as part of a car-free day. Include in your action plan on acid rain how feasible it would be to encourage your community to participate in a car-free day.

Understanding Concepts

1. Make a table to summarize the information presented in **Figure 2**. Useful headings could be *Name of the pollutant*, *Problems it can cause*, and *Source(s) of the pollutant*.

2. Consider the different types of pollutants. What is the greatest single source of all these pollutants?

3. What natural processes are involved in the production of carbon dioxide?

4. What type of air pollution

   (a) can make you sleepy?

   (b) can cause a brownish haze in the air?

   (c) produces gases that cause breathing problems?

5. Describe three industrial strategies for reducing sulfur dioxide and nitrogen oxide emissions.

6. What nonmetal oxide is produced from the ashes of trees burned in a forest fire?

Making Connections

7. What are three human activities that cause air pollution? Suggest some ways the amount of pollution produced in these activities could be reduced. Refer to your answer to (h) and prepare an action plan.

INQUIRY SKILLS MENU
- Questioning
- Hypothesizing
- Predicting
- Planning
- Conducting
- Recording
- Analyzing
- Evaluating
- Communicating

Acid Precipitation and Buildings

You have learned that acid precipitation can have damaging effects on trees and fish. But acid precipitation also accelerates the corrosion and discoloration of buildings and statues. Metals, limestone, and sandstone are examples of materials used in many buildings that are affected by acid precipitation.

Acids are very reactive substances. For example, some metals react with sulfuric acid to produce hydrogen gas:

iron + sulfuric acid → iron sulfate + hydrogen

Since the iron sulfate is water-soluble, the metal tends to wear away.

Acids also attack some carbonate compounds. For example, sulfuric acid can be shown in the laboratory to react with barium carbonate crystals to produce barium sulfate and carbonic acid:

sulfuric acid + barium carbonate →
barium sulfate + carbonic acid

The barium sulfate is insoluble in water, so it forms a solid in the cracks and pores of the crystals. As the solid barium sulfate forms, it expands, making the cracks even wider. As a result, bits break off and the crystals crumble away. Do acids have the same effect on carbonate compounds, such as calcium carbonate (limestone), that are used in building materials (**Figure 1**)?

Figure 1
Did acid precipitation damage this limestone gargoyle?

In this investigation, you will be presented with a scenario that involves looking at how acid precipitation may affect a carbonate compound used in building materials. Your teacher will organize you into teams to perform either Part 1 or Part 2. Read the scenario provided. Decide on an appropriate name for your group.

Part 1: The Consulting Firm

You are part of a consulting firm that has been hired by your local town council to determine whether some apparent damage to municipal buildings has been caused by environmental pollution — in particular, acid precipitation. The buildings are made of limestone, and you know that calcium carbonate ($CaCO_3$) is a mineral that exists in the form of limestone, marble, and chalk.

Question

Does acid precipitation have any effect on the limestone used in building materials? Does the concentration of the acid matter?

Hypothesis

(a) Write a hypothesis to address the Questions.

Design

(b) Design an experiment, using the materials
(K) provided or using materials of your choice, to test your hypothesis.
(c) Construct a data table in which to record your observations.

Materials

- apron
- safety goggles
- beakers
- pieces of calcium carbonate (chalk)
- vinegar
- hydrochloric acid solution (5% or 0.5 mol/L)
- graduated cylinder
- storage bottles
- additional materials of your choice, such as paints, lacquers, cleaning agents, bases, and other chemicals

SKILLS HANDBOOK: (K) Planning an Investigation

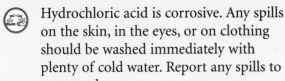 Hydrochloric acid is corrosive. Any spills on the skin, in the eyes, or on clothing should be washed immediately with plenty of cold water. Report any spills to your teacher.

Many paints and laquers are toxic and flammable, and should only be handled with caution in a well-ventilated area. Many household cleaning agents are also toxic and corrosive. Check the labels and follow all necessary safety precautions.

Procedure

1 Obtain your teacher's approval of your design, and conduct your experiment, observing all proper safety procedures. Record your observations.

Analysis and Evaluation

(d) Use your observations to answer the initial

Ⓝ Questions.

(e) Do your observations support your hypothesis? Explain.

(f) Write a report to the town council summarizing

Ⓡ your group's findings. Include an introduction, results, conclusions, and recommendations. If possible, prepare your report as a series of flipchart sheets or computer presentation slides that you could present to the council.

Part 2: The Engineering Pilot Team

You are part of an engineering team that has been hired by your local town council to do a pilot project to determine ways to protect the municipal buildings from further damage from acid precipitation. Your research team has been asked to investigate the effectiveness of various treatments that might be applied to the buildings to stop their deterioration.

Question

(g) Write a question for your team to answer.

Prediction

(h) Make a prediction about the effectiveness of an anti-corrosion treatment.

Design

(i) Design an experiment to test your prediction.

(j) Construct an observation table.

Materials

(k) Create a list of the materials you will require.

Procedure

1 When you have your teacher's approval of your materials and design, assemble the necessary materials and conduct your experiment, observing all proper safety procedures. Record your observations.

Analysis and Evaluation

(l) How did you design your experiment to make sure that only one variable was tested at a time? What controls did you use?

(m) How would you modify your experimental

Ⓞ design if you were to do it again?

(n) Write a report to the town council summarizing your findings. Be sure to state and answer your Question, and explain the accuracy of your prediction.

Understanding Concepts

1. Think about the types of reactions that you studied in Chapter 6. What kind of chemical change is the reaction between

   (a) iron and sulfuric acid?

   (b) barium carbonate and sulfuric acid?

   (c) calcium carbonate and hydrochloric acid?

2. Write balanced chemical equations for the changes in question 1.

Making Connections

3. Consider the cost of protecting building materials on a large scale. How practical is such protection?

Reflecting

4. Review the scientific inquiry process outlined in the Skills

Ⓚ Handbook.

   (a) Which steps did you follow in this investigation?

   (b) Which steps were easiest, and which were most challenging? Explain why.

5. How did you organize your team? How successful were you? Evaluate the effectiveness of your team.

INQUIRY SKILLS MENU
- ○ Questioning
- ● Hypothesizing
- ● Predicting
- ○ Planning
- ● Conducting
- ● Recording
- ● Analyzing
- ● Evaluating
- ● Communicating

Reacting Acids and Bases

What happens when acids and bases are mixed with each other? Such reactions between acids and bases are called **neutralization** reactions. The products of these reactions are often solutions of new compounds in water. For example, the reaction between hydrobromic acid and sodium hydroxide produces water and sodium bromide (a salt):

$$HBr_{(aq)} + NaOH_{(aq)} \rightarrow H_2O_{(l)} + NaBr_{(aq)}$$

As an acid is added to a basic solution, the base is gradually consumed. When all the base has reacted, the result is a neutral solution of a salt and water; the solution is neither acidic nor basic. (A **salt** is a compound made up of positive and negative ions.) Any additional acid will make the solution acidic. These changes can be observed using a universal indicator that changes through many colours as the pH changes. Alternatively, an indicator that changes colour as soon as the base is completely consumed — for example, litmus — can be used.

Qualitative neutralization involves mixing approximate amounts of an acid and a base. For example, baking soda (a base) may be sprinkled onto the floor to react with a sulfuric acid spill. The amount of baking soda does not really matter, as long as the acid is completely neutralized.

Sometimes a chemist wants to mix exact amounts of an acid and a base. Such a quantitative neutralization of an acid and a base is called **titration**. In this investigation, you will observe both qualitative and quantitative neutralizations.

Question

What happens when an acid reacts with a base? How can we detect when an acid has just neutralized a base?

Prediction

(a) Predict answers to the Questions above.

Hypothesis

(b) Write a hypothesis to address the Questions.

Design

You will observe the reaction between an acid and a base. You will then quantitatively neutralize a base by adding an acid.

(c) Make a table to record all your observations.

Materials

- apron
- safety goggles
- sodium bicarbonate (baking soda)
- citric acid powder
- red cabbage juice
- graduated cylinder
- large sealable (zipper-lock) plastic bag
- small sealable (zipper-lock) plastic bag
- 2 test tubes
- sodium hydroxide solution (2% or 0.5 mol/L)
- hydrochloric acid solution (4% or 0.5 mol/L)
- 3 microdroppers
- evaporating dish
- phenolphthalein indicator
- stirring rod
- water
- drying oven or hot plate
- conductivity apparatus (optional)

 Phenolphthalein indicator is flammable. Keep it away from sparks and flames.

Procedure

Part 1: Qualitative Neutralization

1 Put on your apron and safety goggles.

2 Put about 3 g of baking soda and 5 g of citric acid powder into a large sealable plastic bag.

3 Put about 10 mL of red cabbage juice into a small sealable plastic bag. Seal this bag and put it into the large bag (**Figure 1**).

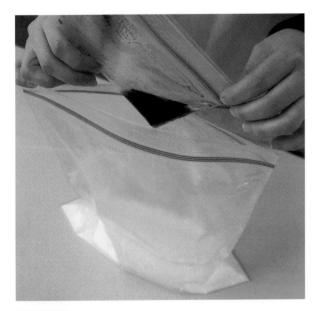

Figure 1

4 Seal the large bag.

5 Open the smaller bag without opening the large bag. Turn the smaller bag over so that the liquid spills out and mixes with the dry powder. Observe what happens in the bag, using as many of your senses as possible, and record your observations.

Part 2: Quantitative Neutralization

6 Obtain a test tube containing about 5 mL of sodium hydroxide solution. With a microdropper, measure 20 drops of the sodium hydroxide solution into an evaporating dish. Using another microdropper, add a drop of phenolphthalein indicator. Record the physical properties of the solutions, along with any changes you observe.

Both sodium hydroxide and hydrochloric acid solutions are corrosive. Any spills on the skin, in the eyes, or on clothing should be washed immediately with plenty of cold water. Report any spills to your teacher.

7 Obtain a test tube containing about 5 mL of hydrochloric acid. Using a fresh microdropper, add the hydrochloric acid, one drop at a time, to the sodium hydroxide–phenolphthalein solution (**Figure 2**). Stir the solution with the stirring rod after each addition. Keep track of the number of drops you add. Continue to add the acid, drop by drop, until the colour change is complete. Record the physical properties of the solutions and any changes you observe, as well as the total number of drops added.

Figure 2

8 Allow the liquid in the dish to evaporate using whatever method your teacher recommends.

If a hot plate is used, the solution will tend to spatter out of the evaporating dish. Care must therefore be taken to prevent the solution from landing on skin, eyes, or clothing.

9 Examine the solid residue.

(d) In your notebook, describe and sketch the residue.

10 Dissolve the solid residue in water. If conductivity apparatus is available, test the solution for conductivity.

11 Dispose of the mixtures, and clean and put away your materials as instructed by your teacher. Clean up your work station. Wash your hands.

Analysis and Evaluation

(e) Answer the initial Questions by writing a summary paragraph of your observations and your explanation for those observations for Part 1.

(f) In Part 1, why did no reaction happen until the liquid mixed with the powders?

(g) In Part 2, why did a colour change occur?

(h) How did the numbers of drops of acid and base compare to each other?

(i) What were some sources of error in this experiment? How do you think you could have improved your results?

Understanding Concepts

1. What was the identity of the gas in Part 1? Explain your reasoning.

2. What do the heat changes in Part 1 suggest about the reaction between citric acid and baking soda?

3. Write a word equation for the reaction in Part 1.

4. In Part 2, what was the purpose of the phenolphthalein?

5. (a) How many drops of acid would you have had to add to the base if the concentration of the base had been twice as large?

   (b) How many drops would you have had to add if the concentration of the acid had been twice as large?

6. (a) What was the identity of the solid produced in the evaporating dish? Explain your answer using the appropriate equations.

   (b) What was the name of the other material produced in the reaction?

7. Given the results of the conductivity test, what type of substance must have been produced in the reaction?

Exploring

8. Repeat Part 2 using milk of magnesia instead of sodium hydroxide with the hydrochloric acid. Observe all necessary safety precautions. You will get the same reaction that occurs in your stomach when you take milk of magnesia for acid indigestion (**Figure 3**). Analyze the acid-neutralizing ability of milk of magnesia compared to the standard sodium hydroxide solution that you used in Part 2.

Figure 3

Try This

Activity Antacid Effectiveness

Antacids are used to react with excess stomach acid. To test the relative effectiveness of antacid tablets, try the following activity.

- Put on your safety goggles and apron, and observe all necessary safety precautions. Wash your hands after completing the activity.

- Obtain three or four sealable (zipper-lock) plastic bags. Into each bag, put about 5 mL of vinegar, 10 mL of water, and enough red cabbage indicator to give the solution a definite colour.

- Add a different antacid tablet to each bag, squeeze out any excess air, seal each bag, and carefully pinch each tablet to break it up. When the reaction has stopped, note the colours and estimate the pH based on your past experience of this indicator's colours at different pH values.

(a) Explain your observations.

Neutralization Reactions

What kind of reaction occurs when acid precipitation attacks a limestone statue? Why are stomach remedies called antacids? Why is a gas produced when baking soda is added to vinegar? All of these changes are examples of acid–base, or neutralization, reactions.

As you saw in Investigation 8.9, the products of a neutralization reaction are a salt (**Figure 1**) and often water. Neutralization reactions are a special case of the double displacement reactions that you studied in Chapter 6. For example, the reaction between hydrochloric acid and sodium hydroxide involves an "exchange" of atoms:

$$HCl_{(aq)} + NaOH_{(aq)} \rightarrow H_2O_{(l)} + NaCl_{(aq)}$$

Another example of a double displacement reaction occurs between sulfuric acid and potassium hydroxide:

$$H_2SO_{4(aq)} + 2KOH_{(aq)} \rightarrow 2H_2O_{(l)} + K_2SO_{4(aq)}$$

During a neutralization reaction, the hydrogen ion from the acid reacts with the hydroxide ion from the base:

$$H^+ + OH^- \rightarrow HOH \text{ or } H_2O$$

There are many ways to use acid–base reactions. For example, a hairdresser uses acids and bases to make permanent waves or curls. The hair-curling solution is a base that breaks some of the links between molecules and softens the hair so that it can take the shape of the curlers (**Figure 2**). After soaking the hair in the base solution for the required time, the hairdresser stops the curling process by squirting on a "neutralizer" solution. This solution contains an acid that reacts with and uses up the base. Links between molecules re-form, and the hair retains its new shape.

Acids and bases also react in soda–acid fire extinguishers. When a fire extinguisher is activated, sulfuric acid and sodium bicarbonate (sodium hydrogen carbonate) react according to the following equation:

$$H_2SO_{4(aq)} + 2NaHCO_{3(s)} \rightarrow Na_2SO_{4(aq)} + 2CO_{2(g)} + 2H_2O_{(l)}$$

The reaction produces large quantities of a foamy mixture of carbon dioxide bubbles, which smother the flames.

A neutralization reaction is also useful for cleaning up acid spills. You may have a container of sodium bicarbonate in your lab available for such spills. A sodium bicarbonate solution can

Figure 1

Sodium chloride deposits occur both above and below ground. These salt flats are in Death Valley, California. Where do you think the salt in this deposit came from? Why has it not been washed away by rain?

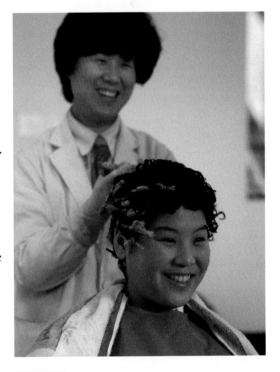

Figure 2

Permanent waves are the result of an acid–base reaction.

be poured onto spills, or the powder may simply be shaken onto the spill. One problem with such reactions is that they can be exothermic; dilution with large amounts of water is sometimes recommended as an additional step for acid spills.

Acid–Base Reactions in the Home

Since so many foods contain acids and bases, many of the reactions that occur in the kitchen are neutralization reactions. Fish oils contain bases called amines which have a distinctive odour. Lemon juice contains an acid that can react with the amines and eliminate the odour.

Oven cleaner is a very strong basic solution of caustic soda (sodium hydroxide) in a jelly or foam. After the cleaner has been allowed to react with the oven grease overnight, the unreacted base can be cleaned up with a solution of vinegar (acetic acid) in water. The acetic acid neutralizes the sodium hydroxide and prevents further reaction.

Acid–base reactions are also used by plumbers. Household hot water pipes or humidifier trays can become blocked by deposits of solid calcium carbonate (**Figure 3**). A simple way to remove the scale is to add a small amount of hydrochloric acid, which reacts with and dissolves the scale:

$$CaCO_{3(s)} + 2HCl_{(aq)} \rightarrow CaCl_{2(aq)} + H_2O_{(l)} + CO_{2(g)}$$

Did You Know?

When making acid solutions, always add the acid to a large volume of water, but never add water to acid. The heat of dissolving can cause the acid to spatter.

Acid–Base Reactions in Baking

Sodium bicarbonate ($NaHCO_3$) is also called baking soda. Baking soda is a base that can react with acids to produce carbon dioxide bubbles in baked goods (**Figure 4**). Recipes that involve baking soda usually include acids, such as vinegar (acetic acid), lemon juice (citric acid), yogurt, sour cream, or cream of tartar (tartaric acid). The baking soda and the acid react to produce gas bubbles that are trapped in the batter and cause it to rise as it bakes. For example, one common reaction is

baking soda + tartaric acid → sodium tartrate + carbon dioxide + water

Figure 3
Calcium carbonate scale can block water pipes.

Figure 4
Baking soda reacts with acids to make carbon dioxide bubbles that cause muffins to rise.

Some recipes require baking powder. Baking powder is a mixture of baking soda and a dry acid, such as cream of tartar. When the baking powder is added to water, the reaction begins. Double-acting baking powder contains cream of tartar and another acid. The second acid acts only at higher temperatures, such as when the batter is baking. This two-stage process produces more bubbles, and the result is a cake with a finer texture.

Antacids

Have you ever taken an antacid to calm your upset stomach (**Figure 5**)? As you know, the stomach contains a solution of hydrochloric acid called gastric juice, which has a normal pH of about 1.5. Gastric juice is important for digestion, but it may irritate the lining of the stomach and cause pain if the acid is too concentrated. An antacid tablet contains a very mild base that neutralizes the acid. In Investigation 8.11, you will use an indicator to test the ability of various antacid tablets to neutralize "stomach" acid.

Figure 5

Canadians spend more than $30 million on antacids every year.

 Challenge

3 You looked at some neutralization reactions in this lesson. What neutralization reactions can be used to prevent acid precipitation or deal with the problems that result from acid precipitation?

Understanding Concepts

1. Make a chart to summarize as many examples as possible of common or familiar acid–base reactions. If possible, specify the example, the area of the home or the workplace where the reaction occurs, and the specific acids and bases involved.

2. **(a)** What do we mean when we describe a solution as neutral?

   (b) Describe the pH changes that you would expect if a base was added to neutralize an acidic solution with a pH of 3.

3. Write word equations to represent the reaction between the following pairs of substances:

   (a) hydrochloric acid and sodium hydroxide

   (b) hydrochloric acid and potassium hydroxide

   (c) nitric acid and sodium hydroxide (Hint: Think of nitric acid as hydrogen nitrate.)

   (d) sulfuric acid and potassium hydrogen carbonate

4. Write balanced chemical equations for the neutralization reactions in question 3.

5. Explain the difference between baking soda and baking powder.

6. Explain why seafood restaurants often provide a bowl of water with a lemon slice in it after the meal.

7. Opening the oven door before a cake is fully baked can cause the cake to "fall." Why can this happen?

8. Why do people often leave a container of baking soda open in their refrigerators?

9. How are baking powder and Alka-Seltzer tablets similar?

Exploring

10. What kinds of recipes use baking soda or baking powder? Are there any patterns in the types of baked goods that use these products? What kinds of baked goods use yeast instead? Why? Investigate recipes in cookbooks, and write a brief report on your findings.

INQUIRY SKILLS MENU
- ○ Questioning
- ○ Hypothesizing
- ● Predicting
- ○ Planning
- ● Conducting
- ● Recording
- ● Analyzing
- ● Evaluating
- ● Communicating

Testing Antacids

Did you know that your stomach produces between 1 L and 2 L of gastric juice daily? The main constituent in this juice is hydrochloric acid, and the pH of a normal stomach is about 1.5 — acidic enough to dissolve magnesium metal! The purpose of this very acidic medium is to digest food. But the stomach itself is made of muscle, so why does it not digest itself? The stomach copes with normal levels of acidity because it completely replaces its lining every few days.

However, if the concentrations of acid in the stomach are too high, problems can occur. Pain, swelling, inflammation, and bleeding in the stomach's lining can cause a condition commonly called acid indigestion. One solution to the problem is to take a medication that contains an **antacid** — a mild base that can neutralize acid. The typical bases found in common antacids are listed in **Table 1**.

Table 1 Antacids and Their Ingredients

Product	Active ingredient
Alka-Seltzer	sodium hydrogen carbonate
Tums	calcium carbonate
Rolaids	calcium carbonate
Maalox	magnesium hydroxide, aluminum hydroxide
milk of magnesia	magnesium hydroxide

A typical pharmacy may offer 30 different antacids to choose from. Which one do you choose? *Consumer Report* has hired you to answer that question.

Question

How do antacid tablets compare in their acid-neutralizing ability to baking soda? Are all antacid tablets equally effective?

Prediction

(a) Make predictions to answer the Questions.

Design

You will react a measured mass of baking soda with hydrochloric acid of roughly the same pH as stomach acid. You will then react a measured mass of an antacid with hydrochloric acid and compare the acid-neutralizing effectiveness of the baking soda and the antacid.

(b) Design a table to record all your observations.

Materials

- apron
- safety goggles
- sodium bicarbonate (baking soda)
- balance
- 100-mL beakers
- water
- 10-mL graduated cylinder
- universal indicator, with colour chart
- stirring rod
- hydrochloric acid solution (2.5% or 0.3 mol/L, pH roughly 0.5)
- microdropper
- various antacid tablets
- mortar and pestle

 Hydrochloric acid is corrosive. Any spills on the skin, in the eyes, or on clothing should be washed immediately with plenty of cold water. Report any spills to your teacher.

Procedure

1 Put on your apron and safety goggles.

2 ⓛ₂ Measure 2 g of baking soda into a 100-mL beaker.

3 Add 5 mL of water and a few drops of universal indicator.

4 While stirring the baking soda with the stirring rod, add hydrochloric acid slowly using a microdropper. Count the number of drops you add. Continue adding and counting drops of hydrochloric acid until you reach a pH of 2 as indicated on the universal indicator chart.

(c) In your data table, record the mass of baking soda and the number of drops of acid required.

5 Determine the mass of an antacid tablet. Crush the tablet to a fine powder with a mortar and pestle (**Figure 1**). Transfer a measured mass (between 1 and 2 g) into a 100-mL beaker. Repeat steps 3 and 4 for the antacid tablet.

(d) In your data table, record the antacid tablet's name, total tablet mass, mass of tablet reacted, and number of drops of acid required.

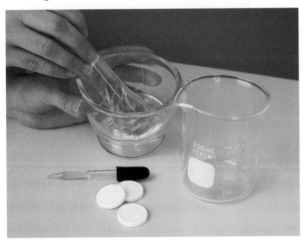

Figure 1

6 Repeat step 5 for the other antacid tablets provided by your teacher.

7 Dispose of the mixtures in the beakers, and clean and put away your materials as instructed by your teacher. Clean up your work station. Wash your hands.

Analysis and Evaluation

(e) Why is it necessary to stir the mixture as the acid is added?

(f) Why did the colour of the indicator change when the acid was added?

(g) To compare the neutralizing ability per gram of each antacid, calculate the number of drops of acid that would be neutralized by 1 g of each antacid. Use the following equation:

$$\text{drops/gram} = \frac{\text{drops of acid}}{\text{mass of antacid reacted (g)}}$$

(h) To compare the neutralizing ability by tablet, calculate the number of drops that would be neutralized by one tablet using the following equation:

$$\text{drops/tablet} = \text{drops/gram} \times \text{mass of tablet (g)}$$

(i) Prepare your summary for *Consumer Report*. Include your results in the form of a bar graph. Ⓞ Ⓥ

Understanding Concepts

1. Given your results, which antacid tablet would you consider taking if you had an acid stomach problem? Explain.

2. Why did you stop the neutralization at pH 2 rather than at pH 7?

Making Connections

3. **(a)** Would you want an antacid to dissolve in your stomach instantly or over a period of time? Explain.

   (b) What is one possible advantage of liquid medicines over solid medicines?

   (c) What is one possible advantage of solid medicines over liquid medicines?

   (d) What other variables would you consider, when choosing an antacid?

Exploring

4. Another issue in deciding whether or not to purchase a product is price. Find out the price of the antacids per tablet, per gram, or per recommended dosage. Analyze and report on the cost value of various brands of antacids.

Putting It All Together: Acids and Bases in Industry

Chemistry is the science that answers questions about matter. What makes sodium sulfide different from sodium sulfate? What happens when a piece of zinc falls into sulfuric acid? Why does coal dust explode when ignited, while a lump of the same material burns slowly? How do acids and bases differ? In this unit, you have learned about chemicals and their names, the types of reactions they undergo, and some ways to control the speed of these reactions.

You have also learned that chemistry is the science of making practical materials that people use every day. These materials are produced by the chemical industry — one of the driving forces in our economy (**Figure 1**).

Figure 1

The chemical industry provides jobs and useful products.

(a) Give as many reasons as you can why the chemical industry is important.

The top eight industrial chemicals produced in North America are listed in **Table 1**. Each of these chemicals is produced in the tens of billions of kilograms each year! As you can see, five of the top eight industrial chemicals (the ones shown in bold type) are acids or bases. What are the uses of these chemicals?

(b) What acids are among the top eight industrial chemicals in North America?
(c) What bases are among the top eight industrial chemicals in North America?

Table 1	Top Eight Industrial Chemicals in North America (1995)			
Rank	Name	Chemical formula	Acid or base?	Applications
1	**sulfuric acid**	**H_2SO_4**	**acid**	**industrial processes (as a catalyst or as a reactant)**
2	nitrogen	N_2	–	fertilizer and industrial processes
3	oxygen	O_2	–	industrial processes
4	ethylene	C_2H_4	–	polymers and plastics
5	**lime**	**CaO**	**base**	**agriculture**
6	**ammonia**	**NH_3**	**base**	**fertilizer, cleaning agents, and manufacturing polymers and nitric acid**
7	**phosphoric acid**	**H_3PO_4**	**acid**	**detergents, fertilizers, and soft drinks**
8	**sodium hydroxide**	**NaOH**	**base**	**drain and oven cleaners, soap manufacture**

Lime

The most important industrial base is lime, or calcium oxide (CaO). Some crops do not grow well in soil that is too acidic. Lime neutralizes the acid and makes the soil more alkaline, or basic, so that the crops can flourish. Lime is also used to neutralize acidity in lakes in a process called liming (**Figure 2**).

(d) What would be the benefit of adding lime to lakes?

Figure 2

Specially equipped boats are used to "lime" lakes that have been affected by acid precipitation.

Sulfuric Acid

Sulfuric acid (H_2SO_4) is the most important industrial chemical in the world. Over 4.0×10^{10} kg (40 billion kilograms) are produced every year in North America alone. Sulfuric acid can act either as a reactant or as a catalyst in industrial processes. Most sulfuric acid is used in the production of fertilizers and other chemicals. It is also used in refining petroleum, in steel production, in producing organic compounds, and in refining metals such as nickel and manganese.

(e) What do we mean when we say that sulfuric acid can act either as a reactant or as a catalyst?

Sulfuric acid is produced in a series of steps. The first step is to burn sulfur to produce sulfur dioxide:

sulfur + oxygen → sulfur dioxide

The second step is called the contact process because the reactants are in contact with a catalyst, vanadium pentoxide. Sulfur dioxide and oxygen gases pass through a heated tube that contains pellets of the catalyst:

vanadium pentoxide

sulfur dioxide + oxygen → sulfur trioxide

(f) Which factors that affect the rate of reaction could be used to increase the rate of production of sulfur trioxide in the second step?

The third step involves the reaction of sulfur trioxide with water to produce sulfuric acid:

sulfur trioxide + water → sulfuric acid

(g) What type of reaction is each step? Why?
(h) Write a balanced chemical equation to represent each reaction.

Understanding Concepts

1. Nitric acid (HNO_3) could also be named hydrogen nitrate. What would be an alternative name for sulfuric acid?

2. If the formula of vanadium pentoxide is V_2O_5 and the ionic charge of oxygen is 2-, what must the ionic charge of vanadium be?

Making Connections

3. Some economists use the amount of sulfuric acid produced by a country as a measure of the strength of its economy. Why do you think this would be an accurate representation?

4. The jobs and products that the chemical industry produces are far more important than any concerns about industrial pollution. Do you agree or disagree with this statement? Write a paragraph expressing your opinion; be sure to provide supporting arguments.

Exploring

5. Choose one of the compounds listed in **Table 1.** Build a three-dimensional model of the molecule, and make the model part of a mobile that also includes a series of cards describing its manufacture and uses.

6. Investigate the uses of sulfuric acid in industry. Make a chart summarizing its uses as a catalyst and a reactant.

🖑 Work the Web

Visit the Science 10 web site at www.science.nelson.com. Follow the Science 10, 8.12 links to find a listing of the top 50 industrial chemicals. Classify each of these chemicals as an acid, a base, a salt, or another type of substance. Write the chemical formulas for as many of the substances as you can.

◕ Challenge

3 In this Case Study you looked at some industrial reactions. Which industrial reactions cause acid precipitation. How can you use this information to prepare your action plan?

Bruce Kosugi

Environmental Specialist

Bruce Kosugi is a team leader of the environmental group at Westcoast Energy's Pipeline and Field Services. Westcoast Energy gathers, processes, and transports gas for gas-producing companies such as Petro-Canada and Shell Canada. Bruce is based out of Fort St. John, British Columbia, and his team is responsible for managing environmental issues associated with the company's business. Much of the team's work involves ensuring the proper use of chemicals.

Several chemicals are involved in processing raw gas into the natural gas used to heat many Canadian homes. A key step is called "sweetening" gas. Raw gas that enters a processing plant from the gas fields contains mostly methane, but also impurities such as carbon dioxide and hydrogen sulfide gas, known as acid gases. When gas is sweetened, these acid gases are removed with various chemical solutions, leaving the methane or natural gas.

Among the people on Bruce's environmental team are specialists in air quality, water quality, and soil and ground-water quality. The team also includes four environmental health and safety advisers who work in various field locations.

On a typical work day, Bruce and his team might assess plans for using new chemicals to ensure that these don't create any environmental problems. On a day-to-day basis, they help the operations side of the company ensure that air emissions and any effluents (water used in processing) meet permitted quality standards. The team regularly reports to federal and provincial agencies to prove that they have met government-set environmental requirements.

Bruce grew up in Toronto and always had an interest in nature and environmental issues. During high school, his academic interests and talents were focused on science. He credits an inspiring chemistry teacher with influencing him to take chemistry at university. He earned an honours degree in chemistry from the University of Waterloo.

Bruce especially enjoys his work when it takes him into the outdoors to inspect the company's pipelines and facilities. The remote wilderness is so vast that many inspections must be conducted from a helicopter.

When Bruce Kosugi isn't working to protect the environment, he spends much of his recreational time enjoying it: canoeing, hiking, and fishing for walleye.

Making Connections

1. Choose a university and a college that you would like to attend. List environment-related programs offered at the schools. Identify the program that most interests you. Note the programs in which a strong background in chemistry would be useful or is required.

🖑 Work the Web

(a) Visit www.science.nelson.com and follow the links to Science 10, 8.13 to find at least three environmentally related careers in the petroleum industry.

(b) Find out about environmental regulations governing the gas industry. How does the industry regulate itself? What careers might be associated with environmental regulation processes?

Key Expectations

Throughout the chapter, you have had opportunities to do the following things:

- Explain the interrelationships between metals and nonmetals, acidic and basic oxides, and acids, bases, salts. (8.1, 8.2, 8.4, 8.5, 8.6, 8.7, 8.8, 8.9, 8.10)

- Use appropriate apparatus and apply WHMIS safety procedures for handling, storage, disposal, and recycling of materials in the lab. (8.1, 8.4, 8.5, 8.8, 8.9, 8.11)

- Describe experimental procedures in the form of a lab report. (8.1, 8.4, 8.5, 8.8, 8.9, 8.11)

- Use appropriate vocabulary, SI units, tables, and descriptions of procedures using the scientific method. (8.1, 8.4, 8.8, 8.9, 8.11)

- Conduct an experiment to determine the acidity and basicity of common household substances. (8.1, 8.4, 8.5)

- Recognize the relationships between chemical formulas, composition, and names. (8.2, 8.6, 8.7, 8.10, 8.12)

- Describe how the pH scale is used to determine the acidity of solutions. (8.3, 8.4)

- Analyze data and information, evaluate evidence and sources of information, and identify errors and bias. (8.3, 8.4, 8.5, 8.7, 8.8, 8.11)

- Plan and conduct an inquiry into chemical processes using a range of tools, controlling variables, and adapting or extending procedures where required. (8.4, 8.8, 8.9, 8.11)

- Formulate questions about practical problems and issues involving chemical processes. (8.5, 8.7, 8.8, 8.9, 8.11)

- Represent chemical reactions using models, word equations, and balanced chemical equations. (8.2, 8.5, 8.6, 8.8, 8.9, 8.11)

- Explain how environmental challenges can be addressed through an understanding of chemical substances. (8.6, 8.7, 8.8, 8,12)

- Select and integrate information from many sources including electronic, print, and community resources, and personally collected data. (8.7, 8.12)

- Describe how an understanding of chemical reactions has led to new consumer products and technological processes. (8.7, 8.11, 8.12)

- Conduct an experiment on the combustion of metals and nonmetals, and react the oxides formed with water to produce an acid or a base. (8.5)

- Design an experiment to determine qualitatively the factors that influence the rate of a reaction. (8.8)

- Describe acid-base neutralization by observing acid-base reactions. (8.9, 8.10, 8.11)

- Explore careers based on technologies that use chemical reactions. (8.13)

Key Terms

acid	metal oxide
acid precipitation	neutralization
acidic oxide	nonmetal oxide
alkaline	pH scale
antacid	pollutant
base	salt
basic oxide	titration
indicator	universal indicator

Make a Summary

Make a concept map to summarize what you have learned about acids and bases.

Reflect on your Learning

Revisit your answers to the Reflect on your Learning questions, p. 289, in the Getting Started.

- How has your thinking changed?
- What new questions do you have?

Understanding Concepts

1. Make a chart to compare acids and bases. Possible headings could include *Physical properties, Reaction with metals, Reaction with carbonates, Effect on indicators, Type of element in formula,* and *Examples.*

2. For each of the following, replace the description with one or two words:
    (a) reacting an acid and a base;
    (b) rain or snow with a low pH;
    (c) number that represents the degree of acidity;
    (d) reacts with water to form a base;
    (e) adding calcium oxide to lakes;
    (f) changes colour in an acid or a base;
    (g) a product of neutralization.

3. The sentences below contain errors or are incomplete. Write complete, correct versions.
    (a) Phenolphthalein indicator turns pink in acids.
    (b) Another name for a metal oxide is an acidic oxide.
    (c) Litmus is an example of a universal indicator.
    (d) Metals are found on the right side of the periodic table.
    (e) Neutralization produces water and a base.
    (f) Titration may also be called qualitative neutralization.
    (g) Stomach acid contains sulfuric acid.
    (h) Neutralization involves the reaction of hydrogen and oxide ions.
    (i) Metal oxides react with oxygen to produce bases.
    (j) Baking soda is an example of a common acid.

4. (a) Explain what is meant by the term "natural indicator."
    (b) What are some examples of natural indicators?

5. Complete the following equations for reactions that involve acids and bases:
    (a) zinc and hydrobromic acid $\rightarrow$ zinc bromide + ?
    (b) sulfuric acid + calcium carbonate $\rightarrow$ calcium sulfate + water + ?
    (c) hydrobromic acid + sodium hydroxide $\rightarrow$ sodium bromide + ?
    (d) phosphoric acid + potassium hydroxide $\rightarrow$ potassium phosphate + ?

6. Write balanced chemical equations for the reactions in question 5.

7. What are three safety precautions that should be followed when working with acids and bases?

8. Identify each of the following substances as an acid or a base:
    (a) H_2SO_3
    (b) calcium hydroxide
    (c) potassium hydrogen carbonate
    (d) a solution with a pH of 3

9. Freshwater swimming pools are kept at a pH between 7.2 and 7.6 to maintain the correct level of chlorine in the water (**Figure 1**).
    (a) Is the pool water acidic, basic, or neutral? Explain.
    (b) If a pool technician finds that the pH is 7.9, should the technician add an acid or a base to the pool to readjust its pH? Explain.

Figure 1

10. (a) How much more acidic is a solution with a pH of 3 than a solution with a pH of 5?
    (b) How much more basic is a solution with a pH of 10.8 than a solution with a pH of 9.8?

11. Write word equations for the following synthesis reactions:
    (a) potassium and oxygen
    (b) lithium oxide and water
    (c) carbon and oxygen
    (d) carbon dioxide and water

12. Write balanced chemical equations for each of the word equations in question 11.

13. If each of the following oxides were added to water, what type of solution would you expect to form? (Use the periodic table at the back of this book to help you answer this question.)
    (a) strontium oxide
    (b) arsenic oxide
    (c) iodine monoxide
    (d) rubidium oxide

14. "Litmus paper is a chemical indicator, and a lake trout is a biological indicator. Both can be used to indicate the level of acidity in a lake."
    Explain this statement.

15. (a) What pollutants are major contributors to acid precipitation?
(b) What are some methods that can be used to decrease production of these pollutants?

Applying Inquiry Skills

16. A student obtains a sample of blue nelsonberry juice. He adds a few crystals of baking soda to the juice, and the juice turns yellow. He adds a few millilitres of vinegar to the baking soda–juice solution, and the solution turns blue again. Explain the colour that you would expect if he were to add each of the following:
(a) a few millilitres of ammonia window cleaner;
(b) some battery acid;
(c) some carbonated soda water;
(d) a few crystals of drain cleaner.

17. You can use homemade indicators to test foods for acidity. Using the natural indicator of your choice, test the cooking water from boiled vegetables (such as peas, beans, onions, carrots, turnips, celery, asparagus, and broccoli) and the liquids from canned vegetables and fruits. Make a chart to summarize your findings.

18. Design and perform an experiment (using all necessary safety precautions) to test the neutralization reactions in baking of various combinations of baking soda, baking powders, and acids (such as cream of tartar, tartaric acid, buttermilk, or lemon juice). A muffin recipe, using very small amounts, is a possibility. Write a report on your results.

19. A student performs an experiment to test the effectiveness of two antacid tablets, Ianox and Sallusil. Each tablet is dissolved in the same volume of water in a separate beaker; a sample of each solution is then transferred to its own test tube. An indicator is added to each test tube, and then drops of acid are added until the antacid is neutralized. The student obtains the data shown in **Table 1**.

Table 1 **Results of Antacid Experiment**

Antacid	Size of antacid sample	Drops of acid needed to neutralize
Ianox	10 mL	15
Sallusil	10 mL	30

(a) Which antacid is likely to be more effective? Explain.
(b) If the solution of Ianox had a pH of 7.5, was the pH of the Sallusil solution likely higher, lower, or the same? Explain.

Making Connections

20. You hear your younger brother crying in the kitchen, and you rush in to investigate. He thought the can he was playing with contained whipped cream, and pressed its bright red button. Now he has oven cleaner all over his hands and the lower part of his face. The recommended first aid is to flush the cleaner with large amounts of water, not to try to neutralize the strong base with an acid. Why? How can accidents like this be prevented?

21. Some people like to put a few drops of lemon juice in their tea (**Figure 2**). When they add the juice, the tea changes colour. Explain this observation, based on what you have learned in this chapter.

Figure 2

22. Think about the area in which you live. What do you think are the main sources of air pollution in your area? What are some strategies that would work in your local area to deal with the issue? For example, is traffic a major problem? Do you live in an area where coal is burned for power? Is limestone for acid scrubbing readily available? Make a poster suggesting ways by which pollution could be reduced in your area.

Chemical Processes and Society

Chemical reactions create various products that have an enormous impact on society. The demand for these products has created a huge chemical industry that employs millions of people around the world. But the same chemical reactions that are used to create products have also created environmental challenges. Each of the challenges presented below provides an opportunity to explore how chemical processes affect society.

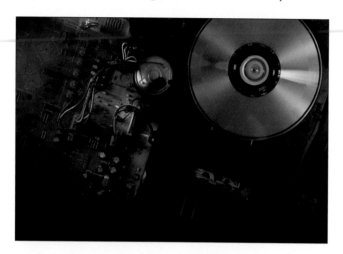

1 Making a Consumer Product

You will build a display to explain to local people how a new factory, that will be built in their town, will affect them. The factory will produce a new consumer product. Identify the raw materials that it is made of, find out where the raw materials come from, how they are transformed in the chemical industry, and what effects these processes have on local people.

Design and build a display that includes

- a flow chart that shows the progression from raw materials to the final product;
- the names and formulas of the substances involved;
- a diagram of a key component in the production of the product or one of its raw materials;
- information about the product's economic impact (jobs created or consumer spending); and
- information about the environmental impact of the product or the industrial processes used.

2 Marketing Alternative Fuels

You will prepare a marketing proposal to promote an alternative energy source as the fuel of the future. Most conventional vehicles burn gasoline, but there is increasing interest in developing and using alternative fuels, such as hydrogen, methane, and alcohol. First, research the substances and chemical processes that are used to power vehicles today. Then research alternative sources of chemical energy. Choose one of these sources as your focus.

Prepare and present a proposal that includes

- the names, chemical structures, and chemical formulas of conventional and alternative fuels;
- the chemical reactions that are used to power vehicles today;
- examples of alternative energy sources;
- a chart that critically compares conventional and alternative sources of energy from economic and environmental perspectives; and
- an argument in which you promote your choice of alternative fuel.

3   Acid Rain Action Plan

You know that air pollution is an environmental problem. The demand for electricity to power our technological devices and our consumption of fossil fuels create huge amounts of air pollutants. Perhaps you have decided that people are accepting environmental pollution — specifically acid rain — as a consequence of their lifestyle choices. You want to change people's attitudes and encourage them to think about how their actions affect the environment. Create a local or community action plan to encourage people to "Think Globally, Act Locally."

Prepare a community action plan that includes

- an environmental awareness poster that describes how acid rain is produced as a consequence of human actions;
- the names and chemical formulas of the reactants, and the chemical reactions that are involved in the production of acid rain;
- a survey of people's knowledge and attitudes toward the acid rain problem; and
- an action plan for your school or community that will encourage people to adopt more "environment-friendly" habits.

 Assessment

Your completed Challenge will be assessed according to the following:

Process
- understand the specific challenge
- develop a plan
- choose and safely use appropriate tools, equipment, materials, and computer software
- analyze the results

Communication
- prepare an appropriate presentation of the task
- use correct terms, symbols, and SI units
- incorporate information technology

Product
- meet established criteria
- show understanding of the concepts, principles, laws, and theories
- show effective use of materials
- address the identified situation/problem

 When preparing to use a chemical test, carry out an experiment, or to build or test a device, be sure to have your plan approved by your teacher before you begin.

Unit 2 Review

Understanding Concepts

1. Copy each of the following statements in your notebook. Fill in the blanks with the word or phrase that correctly completes the sentence.
   (a) A ___?___ property is one that involves the production of a new substance.
   (b) The starting materials in chemical reactions are called ___?___ .
   (c) The electron is a subatomic particle that has a ___?___ charge.
   (d) An ion that contains more than one atom is called a ___?___ ion.
   (e) The number written in front of a chemical compound is called a ___?___ .
   (f) The burning of a substance is called ___?___ .
   (g) A solid compound that contains water molecules is called a ___?___ .
   (h) A reaction between elements is a ___?___ reaction.
   (i) The speed at which a reaction occurs is the ___?___ of reaction.
   (j) A solution that contains a large amount of solute compared to solvent is called ___?___ .
   (k) A reaction that absorbs heat is called ___?___ .
   (l) A substance that speeds up chemical reactions is called a ___?___ .
   (m) A substance that changes colour in acids and bases is an ___?___ .
   (n) The ___?___ scale describes the acidity of a solution as a number.
   (o) An acidic ___?___ forms an acid when dissolved in water.
   (p) ___?___ a lake involves adding a base to neutralize acid.

2. Indicate whether each of the following statements is TRUE or FALSE. If you think the statement is FALSE, rewrite it to make it true.
   (a) Compounds that contain carbon and hydrogen are called ionic compounds.
   (b) An artificially made substance may also be called synthetic.
   (c) Another term for combining capacity is valence.
   (d) An alkaline earth metal element forms an ion with a 1– ionic charge.
   (e) A skeleton equation describes only the names of the reactants and products.
   (f) The Law of Conservation of Mass states that the numbers of atoms of reactants and products must be the same.
   (g) The combustion of hydrocarbons produces hydrogen and carbon dioxide.
   (h) The heating of calcium carbonate is a synthesis reaction.
   (i) The reaction of barium nitrate and sodium sulfide would be a double displacement reaction.
   (j) Grinding a solid into a dust increases its surface area.
   (k) A biological catalyst is also called an inhibitor.
   (l) A catalytic converter in automobiles reduces pollution.
   (m) A metallic oxide reacts with water to form a base.
   (n) The mixing of an acid and a base is called precipitation.
   (o) An antacid is a base taken to neutralize stomach acid.
   (p) Neutralization produces carbon dioxide and a salt.

3. Describe the similarities and/or differences between each pair of terms listed below:
   (a) physical property, chemical property
   (b) proton, neutron
   (c) atom, ion
   (d) ionic compound, molecular compound
   (e) skeleton equation, chemical equation
   (f) synthesis, decomposition
   (g) single displacement, double displacement
   (h) combustion, incomplete combustion
   (i) concentrated, dilute
   (j) catalyst, enzyme
   (k) catalyst, inhibitor
   (l) endothermic, exothermic
   (m) acid, base
   (n) metallic oxide, nonmetallic oxide
   (o) acidic, alkaline
   (p) neutralization, titration

For questions 4 to 11, choose the best answer and write the full statement in your notebook.

4. What is the formula for the compound sodium sulfate?
   (a) SSO_4
   (b) Na_2S
   (c) NaS_2
   (d) Na_2SO_4
   (e) $NaSO_4$

5. What is the name of the compound PCl_3?
   (a) phosphorus chloride
   (b) potassium carbide
   (c) phosphate chloride
   (d) phosphorus carbide
   (e) potassium carbide

6. What type of reaction occurs between magnesium and hydrochloric acid?
   (a) synthesis
   (b) decomposition
   (c) single displacement
   (d) double displacement
   (e) combustion

7. What type of reaction occurs between sodium and chlorine?
   (a) synthesis
   (b) decomposition
   (c) single displacement
   (d) double displacement
   (e) combustion

8. When chalk is ground into a powder, it reacts more quickly in acid. This is an example of the effect of
   (a) concentration
   (b) surface area
   (c) temperature
   (d) a catalyst
   (e) an inhibitor

9. Cake batter rises when the cake is baked. This is an example of the effect of
   (a) concentration
   (b) surface area
   (c) temperature
   (d) a catalyst
   (e) an inhibitor

10. Element X reacts with oxygen to form Compound Y. Compound Y reacts with water to form a solution that turns litmus red. What is Element X?
    (a) metal
    (b) nonmetal
    (c) basic oxide
    (d) acidic oxide
    (e) acid

11. Element X reacts with oxygen to form Compound Y. Compound Y reacts with water to form a solution that turns litmus blue. What is Compound Y?
    (a) metal
    (b) nonmetal
    (c) basic oxide
    (d) acidic oxide
    (e) base

12. Name the following compounds:
    (a) NaBr
    (b) MgI_2
    (c) $Ca(NO_3)_2$
    (d) $FeCl_3$
    (e) K_2SO_4

13. Write formulas for the following ionic compounds:
    (a) lithium phosphate
    (b) calcium carbonate
    (c) silver iodide
    (d) aluminum bromide
    (e) lead(II) oxide

14. Write the corresponding name or formula for the following molecular compounds:
    (a) phosphorus trichloride
    (b) sulfur trioxide
    (c) CBr_4
    (d) NO_2

15. Balance each of the following equations:
    (a) $Br_2 + KI \rightarrow KBr + I_2$
    (b) $K + O_2 \rightarrow K_2O$
    (c) $Na + O_2 \rightarrow Na_2O$
    (d) $Sr + N_2 \rightarrow Sr_3N_2$
    (e) $Na + N_2 \rightarrow Na_3N$
    (f) $Ca + H_2O \rightarrow Ca(OH)_2 + H_2$

16. Identify each of the following equations as a synthesis, decomposition, single displacement, double displacement, or combustion reaction:
    (a) zinc + iron(III) nitrate→ iron + zinc nitrate
    (b) magnesium carbonate → magnesium oxide + carbon dioxide
    (c) silver nitrate + calcium iodide → silver iodide + calcium nitrate
    (d) methane + oxygen → carbon dioxide + water
    (e) potassium + oxygen → potassium oxide

17. (a) Write skeleton equations for each of the equations in question 16.
    (b) Balance each of the equations.

18. The grey around the yolk of a hard-boiled egg (**Figure 1**) is iron(II) sulfide. It is formed when hydrogen sulfide in the white of the egg reacts with iron in the yolk. The iron is released from protein molecules when the egg is cooked enough to release the iron.
    (a) What is the chemical formula of iron(II) sulfide?
    (b) What kind of reaction happens when iron and hydrogen sulfide combine?
    (c) Why do you think there is no iron(II) sulfide produced when the egg is "soft-boiled" or cooked for less time?

Figure 1

19. (a) What are four factors that affect the rate of reaction?
    (b) Use the collision theory to explain why each factor affects rate of reaction.

20. (a) What is meant by the pH of a solution?
    (b) Consider a solution with a pH of 3 and a solution with a pH of 5. Which is more acidic? How much more acidic is it?

Applying Inquiry Skills

21. Consider an experiment in which solid zinc metal reacts with hydrochloric acid solution in the following equation:

$$Zn + HCl \rightarrow ZnCl_2 + H_2$$

    (a) What would you expect to observe as this reaction occurred?
    (b) What type of reaction is this?
    (c) Balance the equation.
    (d) Suggest four different ways in the rate of this reaction could be increased.
    (e) How could you tell when the reaction was complete?
    (f) How could you determine whether the acid had completely reacted?

22. A shiny, malleable substance (X), which is an excellent conductor of electricity, is burned in air to produce a white solid (Y). When this solid is placed in water, it slowly dissolves to form a colourless solution (Z).
    (a) What kind of substance is X? Explain.
    (b) What kind of substance is Y? Explain.
    (c) What kind of solution is Z? Explain.
    (d) What effect would you expect Z to have on litmus or phenolphthalein indicator?

23. A series of experiments are performed by Chris Student, who is investigating the time required for a chemical reaction between solutions A and B. Chris tries different combinations of variables as shown in Table 1. Chris records times for each of the trials, but unfortunately, does not record which time matches which trial. The times recorded are: 20 s, 40 s, 100 s, and 200 s.
    (a) Use your knowledge of rates of reaction to predict which time matches which experiment.

    (b) Do you think Chris should claim and report these times? Explain.

24. Preservatives are not the only additives in foods. Some cereals that advertise themselves as containing dietary iron actually contain the element itself as iron filings! Design and conduct an experiment to identify cereals that contain elemental iron. Make sure to have your procedure approved by your teacher before beginning. Make a poster to summarize the results of your experiment.

25. Design and carry out an experiment to test the effectiveness of liquid antacids. Make sure to include all necessary safety precautions, and check your procedure with your teacher before starting.

26. Amylase is an enzyme found in saliva that speeds up the breakdown of carbohydrates into sugars. Try chewing crackers for a long time without swallowing. Explain your observations.

Making Connections

27. Many toxic chemicals are byproducts of agriculture, industrial processes, and household use. Many of these chemicals are seen as necessary by their users. How is hazardous chemical waste disposed of in your area? Write a report to describe local methods and suggest improvements.

28. Should we be burning hydrocarbons when they can be made into useful synthetic products? Make a "P-M-I" graphic organizer to classify the arguments and questions around this issue.

29. Imagine that you are living in a rural county where there has been debate over the use of synthetic chemicals as pesticides. Many farmers use chemical sprays to help them grow vegetables, grains, and fruit. Write a letter to your local member of parliament to express your opinion on whether these synthetic chemicals should or should not be used in growing crops. Back up your opinion with research.

30. Automobiles have many plastic parts that are formed in polymerization reactions. Most of these reactions are very slow under normal conditions; industrial catalysts make the production of these plastics possible by increasing the rate of reaction. The

Table 1

Experiment	Concentration of solution A (mol/L)	Concentration of solution B (mol/L)	Temperature (°C)
A	1.0	1.0	20
B	2.0	1.0	20
C	1.0	1.0	30
D	2.0	1.0	30

antifreeze used in automobile cooling systems also contains inhibitors that slow down the natural corrosion reactions that attack the radiator and other metal parts in the cooling system. Research and report on the use of catalysts in the automobile industry.

31. Choose an example of an important acid or base. Design a website to promote the importance of this molecule.

32. "Acids are both helpful and harmful." Write a short essay to explain this statement.

33. You are a member of a commission that must decide whether to allow a cooperative oil company/government consortium to build a huge oil-drilling field in the ocean waters off Nova Scotia. The comments of 10 people who spoke before the commission are listed below:

A. "Oil rigs are dangerous places to work. The companies have to agree to better regulations to protect the workers before they are allowed to start."

B. "The industry cannot guarantee that there would never be a major spill from this field. Such a spill would be an ecological disaster — killing fish and permanently fouling the shoreline nearby."

C. "This is a bad investment for the Canadian economy. The government should be trying to stimulate the high technology industry rather than financing another resource project."

D. "The oil field will have a dramatic effect on local business and employment. With the influx of dollars into our provincial economy, transfer payments from central Canada will decrease. Ultimately, the rest of the country will benefit as well."

E. "I will be able to get off unemployment insurance. I'll have to spend time away from my family, but at least I will be able to keep a roof over their heads."

F. "Oil rigs in the North Sea near Great Britain have been shown to act as artificial reef ecosystems. Fish populations actually increase around the rigs."

G. "Oil companies must not be allowed to hire workers off the street. They should use experienced oil industry workers who have been laid off in other provinces, and pay for the costs of their relocation."

H. "Oil rigs are going to be a terrible hazard for navigation. Either we will lose boats in storms or we will not be able to use some prime areas to earn our living."

I. "This project shows that government and industry can cooperate for the good of all. Resources can be developed without destroying the environment, and this project will prove it."

J. "This industry is the driving force of Canadian economy. To survive and stay competitive with foreign suppliers, we have to expand into new areas."

(a) The opinions expressed represent different points of view. Is it likely that all of the points of view are correct? Why?

(b) Which of the individuals in **Table 2** are likely to have expressed the opinions stated above? Study the information about each person, and match the statement with the person. Include an explanation for your choice.

(c) Which of the opinions are based on scientific evidence? Should any further evidence be obtained before a decision is made? Explain.

(d) Are there any other viewpoints that could be expressed? Explain.

(e) Write a commission report to summarize your decision on the oil field project, and the reasons for your decision.

Table 2 **List of Speakers**

Speaker	Residence	Employer
politician	Ottawa, Ont.	federal government
information officer	Toronto, Ont.	accident prevention organization
marine biologist	Vancouver, B.C.	university
union organizer	Calgary, Alta.	oil workers' union
writer	Halifax, N.S.	environmental magazine
finance minister	Halifax, N.S.	provincial government
economist	London, Ont.	university
mechanic	Sydney, N.S.	unemployed
fisher	Lunenburg, N.S.	self-employed
president	Edmonton, Alta.	oil company

Motion

Almost everyone moves from place to place on a daily basis. We go to work, school, stores, or places for entertainment, and we do this in a variety of ways — walking, bicycling, or riding in cars, trucks, buses, trains, or planes. Motion, the subject of this unit, is part of our daily lives.

Unit 3 Overview

Overall Expectations

In this unit, you will be able to

- understand different forms of straight-line motion including their algebraic descriptions;
- design and conduct investigations of uniform and accelerated motion;
- analyze motion and its effects in everyday phenomena and technologies.

Chapter 9
Distance and Speed

People have probably always been interested in how long it takes them to get from here to there. Now we travel even more and have better technologies to measure distances and time. The study of distance, time, and speed is even more relevant now than in the past.

In this chapter, you will be able to

- use a variety of technologies to measure the distance travelled in a given amount of time;
- design and conduct experiments to determine average speed;
- create, understand, test, and use an equation involving average speed, distance, and time;
- draw and interpret distance-time graphs for uniform motion;
- describe the difference between constant speed and average speed;
- evaluate technologies used for personal transportation;
- develop an understanding of how physics concepts are created, tested, and used.

Chapter 10
Distance, Speed, and Acceleration

You do not always travel at the same speed. To begin moving and get up to speed, you need to accelerate. This chapter investigates the rate of change of speed.

In this chapter, you will be able to

- use various designs to conduct experiments to measure distance and time to determine average acceleration;
- create, test, and use an equation for calculating acceleration from rate of change in speed;
- use and compare the definitions, equations, units, and distance–time and speed–time graphs for acceleration;
- formulate scientific questions related to motion;
- research information about motion using a variety of sources.

Chapter 11
Displacement and Velocity

You can travel various routes to reach a destination. Your journey might include changes in direction as you travel along a path with a particular speed. The addition of direction to descriptions of motion is the subject of this chapter.

In this chapter, you will be able to

- understand and give examples of the differences among distance, displacement, and position, and between speed and velocity;
- demonstrate motion with direction using simple graphs;
- add displacement vectors using vector diagrams and algebraic calculations;
- analyze the methods and outline the scientific benefits of technology used to track the motion of objects;
- create, test, and use the equations for average velocity, displacement, and time;
- distinguish between constant and average velocity.

Chapter 12
Displacement, Velocity, and Acceleration

Direction is important for all types of motion. In this chapter, you will extend your previous knowledge of motion and direction. Your improved understanding will include a more complete description of the equations, units, and graphs for both constant velocity and constant acceleration.

In this chapter, you will be able to

- distinguish among constant, instantaneous, and average velocity;
- create and interpret position–time and velocity–time graphs ;
- create, test and use an equation involving acceleration, change in velocity, and time;
- use and evaluate previous and new designs to conduct experiments to determine average acceleration, including acceleration due to gravity;
- identify, explain, and express sources of error and uncertainty in an experiment;
- develop and use the equations for average velocity and displacement from a velocity–time graph;
- describe performance-enhancing features of a piece of sports equipment;
- demonstrate an understanding of the history and nature of science.

Motion

Motion is part of the everyday physical world. We learn to walk, run, and drive without a formal understanding of the physics of motion. We do, however, have an intuitive idea of motion and its effects and causes. For example, do heavier objects fall faster than lighter ones? Which automobile goes from 0 to 100 km/h in the shortest time? Which athlete can run 100 m fastest? What distance does the athlete run in the first second compared to the fifth second? Is the acceleration constant over the total distance? We are curious, and demand greater and greater precision in our answers to these questions. Fortunately, new technologies are constantly being developed to give us the required precision. By the end of this unit of study, you will have used some of the technologies, and found answers to many of the questions.

Scientific Perspective on Motion

What is the physics of motion all about? In our study of motion we will be trying to describe, explain, and predict motion as simply and precisely as possible. For example, if an astronomer observes an asteroid approaching Earth, she would predict its closest approach to Earth based on a knowledge of the physics of motion. We, too, will start from what we know and build on that. Sometimes, when testing the current concept of motion, we might find that it is not accurate: the concept is not consistent with what we observe in the laboratory or in everyday life. When this occurs, we must decide whether it is our evidence or the concept that is faulty. If we decide that the evidence is valid, we have to discard our concept. We will try to replace it with one that describes, explains, and predicts the real world more accurately. In this unit, and in completing a challenge, will you have an opportunity to test both established concepts and your own personal concepts of motion.

Challenge

Motion from a Scientific Perspective

As you learn about the physics of motion, you will encounter and create concepts about motion, test those concepts, and then use them in analyzing motion in your everyday life.

1 Measuring Time

It seems that most technological advances result in further scientific breakthroughs. Throughout the ages, the lack of adequate tools to measure distance and time has hindered advances in the study of motion. Research and complete a report on an ancient method for measuring time. Construct at least one working model, discuss the reliability, accuracy, and precision of the device, and use it to analyze the motion of a runner.

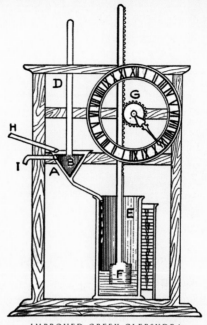

IMPROVED GREEK CLEPSYDRA

2 Testing Laws of Motion

People have developed new laws of motion over the years as our understanding of the physics of motion has evolved. Aristotle and Galileo were two prominent thinkers who developed laws of motion.

Search the literature for Aristotle's and Galileo's laws, and then design and conduct an experiment to test at least one of these laws for yourself. Present your findings and evaluate whether they support or refute the law.

3 Driver Training

It is easier to remember and use rules for safe driving if the driver understands why they exist. Use your understanding of motion to create a physics handbook to supplement the manual for a driver-training course. Include equations, calculations, and graphs to assist student drivers with passing the written and road tests and to drive safely.

To start your own Challenge see page 488.

Record your ideas for your Challenge as you progress through this unit and when you see

Challenge

Distance and Speed

Getting Started

WHAT KINDS OF DISTANCES CAN YOU picture in your mind?

The 100-m race and the 42-km marathon are two commonly known distances. **Distance**, the amount of space between two objects or points, is a quantity that we practise measuring from an early age. The most common unit of distance is the metre. We know approximately how long a metre is because we use it almost daily as a unit of measurement. But some distances are hard to imagine simply because they are so unfamiliar. The human mind just doesn't seem capable of imagining distances like 4.1×10^{16} m (**Figure 1**) or 3×10^{-10} m (**Figure 2**). What is amazing is that scientists are able to measure this full range of distances — even though we can't really imagine how large and small they might be. Scientists have developed an astonishing variety of tools, from telescopes to microscopes, to measure a wide range of distances. Some people have trained themselves to estimate distances to a high degree of accuracy without using any tools. People who work with measurements every day become more and more accurate with their estimates of distance. For example, surveyors work with distances and angles every day and become pretty good at estimating them.

Time is duration between two events and is usually measured in seconds, minutes, or hours. Fortunately we seem to understand time intuitively: we talk about a race lasting about 10 s, or a space shuttle orbiting Earth every 1.5 h. We have a feeling for the passage of time. We understand that we can study an event by investigating what is happening during several successive time periods, such as the distance travelled during each second.

The range of speeds that we encounter on Earth is fairly narrow until we start investigating outside of our normal observations. We might walk at 6 km/h, drive at 100 km/h, or take an airplane that travels at 450 km/h. We need to measure distance and time in order to determine the speed of an object. Scientists and technologists have developed many new devices to measure a wide range of distances and periods of time.

Figure 1
Alpha Centauri, the closest visible star system to our Sun, is 4.3 light years (4.1×10^{16} m) away.

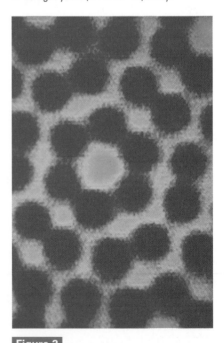

Figure 2
The distance across an atom is about 3×10^{-10} m.

Reflect on your Learning

1. What is your impression of when and where the concepts and measurement of distance, time, and speed got started? Why, do you think, did they start to develop at this point?

2. Suggest several technologies that might have been used to measure distance, time, and speed since these concepts began.

3. If you were to teach someone about the concept of speed, how would you describe speed in your own words?

4. Science and technology are closely related. Provide some examples of how science depends on technology.

5. Why do you think some non-metric units of measurement (such as miles and pounds) persist in Canada even though the system was changed to SI metric in the mid-1970s?

6. How do you and/or scientists express uncertainty about measurements and calculations?

Throughout this chapter, note any changes in your ideas as you learn new concepts and develop your skills.

Try This
Activity   Measuring by Hand

Most measurement systems originated when the human body was used to help determine distances. After all, everybody had one! This practice is still very useful when we do not have access to a ruler or tape measure.

- Use a metric ruler, metre stick, or tape measure to determine the answers to the following questions. Memorize the following answers for your own body.

(a) The width of which of your fingers or fingernails is closest to 1.0 cm?

(b) Which part of your hand (width or length) is approximately 10 cm?

(c) What is the maximum span of your spread hand (i.e., width from thumb tip to little-finger tip) in centimetres?

(d) A horizontal distance of 1.0 m is from the tip of your fingers on your outstretched arm to where on your body?

(e) How many of your foot or shoe lengths (plus a fraction, if necessary) equals 1.0 m (**Figure 3**)?

(f) What are the lengths of your natural and stretched strides in metres? Can you stride 1.0 m?

- Now use the answers to the above questions to determine the length, in centimetres or metres, of the following objects. Measure each object at least three times, using different parts of your body each time.

(g) What is the length of your pencil or pen?

(h) What is the length of a page of paper?

(i) What is the length of your desk or table?

(j) What is the length of your room?

Did you always get the same lengths for each object? Why, or why not?

(k) Repeat questions (g)–(j) using a metre stick. Compare the new measurements with those you obtained by using your body. Account for any differences. Which are likely to be more accurate?

- What are the likely maximum and minimum distances you could conveniently measure, using

(l) your finger/fingernail width?

(m) your hand span?

(n) your foot/shoe length?

(o) your stride?

Figure 3
How many of your foot lengths make up 1.0 m?

DECISION-MAKING SKILLS MENU

○ Define the Issue   ● Analyze the Issue
● Identify Alternatives   ● Defend a Decision
● Research   ○ Evaluate

Progress and Speed on our Highways

In earlier times, people moved about on foot or in handmade vehicles drawn by animals. Travelling was slow and arduous. Journeys of more than a few kilometres were major expeditions, so people generally lived and worked in the same place. Towns were relatively small and compact.

All this has changed in the last few decades, with the development of the internal combustion engine, and other vehicle technology. Many people in North America now live quite far away from their place of work. Our cities have grown quickly and residential suburbs have developed. A large proportion of the population now travels by private vehicle.

As the population of our urban areas continues to grow, more people want to travel daily between the city and the suburbs. This leads to more traffic on the roads and highways. Traffic congestion and noise pollution are nuisances, but chemical pollution is a serious health threat. Motor vehicles are the single largest source of air pollution in urban areas (**Figure 1**). On average, vehicles produce about 75% of the carbon monoxide, 48% of the nitrogen oxides, and 13% of the particulates (solid particles of pollution) in the atmosphere.

As our pace of life increases, and vehicle and highway technologies improve, many of us want to get where we are going in the shortest possible time. Maximum speed has several advantages:

- less time is lost in travelling;
- shorter journey times may mean less driver fatigue;
- vehicles are on the highways for shorter periods of time, reducing congestion; and
- high highway speeds, so long as all vehicles are travelling equally fast and road conditions are good, result in no more accidents than lower speeds.

People in favour of raising highway speed limits use all these reasons in their arguments.

Figure 1

Rush-hour traffic in a major metropolitan centre may not involve *rushing*.

Figure 2

It is often appropriate to travel slower than the posted speed limit.

SKILLS HANDBOOK: ⒹIdentifying Alternatives

Not everyone agrees that faster is better, though. Those in favour of lowering highway speed limits point out that

- accidents at high speeds tend to be more serious than those at lower speeds;
- travelling fast uses considerably more fuel (and therefore results in more pollution) per kilometre;
- high-speed vehicles need more space between them, so actually take up *more* space on the highways;
- conditions are frequently less than ideal on Canadian roads, so slower driving would result in fewer accidents (**Figure 2**); and
- lower speed limits might even persuade some people to take less polluting forms of public transportation, such as buses or trains.

Of course, even when the posted speed limit is quite high, there are always some people who want to go faster. The police are responsible for enforcing the speed limit. "Speeders" may receive a warning, have "demerit points" recorded on their driver's licence, be fined, or even be charged with a criminal offence such as dangerous driving. The severity of the consequence depends on the car's speed, compared to the speed limit, but is also largely at the discretion of the police officer. The police have a number of ways to identify speeders, including photo-radar, highway patrol cars, and speed traps. But however zealously speeders are identified, and whatever penalties are imposed, we haven't yet found a way of making everybody obey the posted speed limits. Some say that this is another good reason for raising speed limits: Raise the maximum speed and enforce it strictly, they say, and everyone will travel at the same speed, making the highways considerably safer.

Many organizations are looking into the issue of highway speed limits, such as provincial ministries or departments of transportation, municipal governments, various police forces, environmental groups, and many other nongovernmental organizations. They all have views on whether highway speed limits should be lower, higher, or maintained at their present level.

Understanding the Issue

1. What is the largest source of air pollutants in urban areas?

2. Compare the travelling times of a fast car and a slower truck, that have covered the same distance.

3. Under what conditions might high highway speeds be as safe as slower speeds?

🖑 Work the Web

To research the issue of speed limits, visit www.science.nelson.com and follow the links from Science 10, 9.1.

⬤ Challenge

3 Student drivers must understand both the laws of the road and the practical aspects of driving. Why have the laws of the road and particularly those relating to speed, been established?

Role Play Raising the Limit

A public meeting is being held to solicit feedback on a proposal to raise the speed limit on all the major highways in the province to 125 km/h. You have been invited to take part and to present your views on this issue.

- Select a role, such as police officer, commercial truck driver, antipollution activist, cottager, student driver, highway engineer, or car designer.
- (D) • Using the perspective of your chosen role, research to collect information and prepare your
- (G) position.
- (R) • Assemble your arguments into a short presentation.
- (S) • Deliver your presentation at the public meeting.

Measurement and Calculations

It is important to measure correctly. If we can't trust the measurements, we can put no faith in reports of scientific research. Imagine what would happen if the surveyors were wildly inaccurate in their measurements when the Chalk River particle accelerator was under construction (**Figure 1**). Imagine that the accelerator was made several metres too long, and nobody noticed the error. All the scientists who subsequently worked there would be including those inaccuracies in their calculations, and arriving at faulty conclusions.

Certainty and Significant Digits

When you are communicating in science you should express how certain you are about your measurements. This is called the degree of certainty or uncertainty. Every measurement has uncertainty, so scientists have come up with ways to express their degree of certainty when stating their results.

There is an international agreement about the correct way to record measurements: record all those digits that are certain plus one uncertain digit, and no more. These "certain-plus-one" digits are called **significant digits**. The **certainty** of a measurement is determined by how many certain digits (plus one) are obtained by the measuring instrument. Certainty is measured by the number of significant digits.

For example, in **Figure 2** the measurement "1 to 4" reads 9.05 cm. The last digit in the measurement, 5, is estimated (a trained guess) by looking between the lines on the scale of the measuring instrument. Two certain digits (the 9 and the 0) plus one uncertain digit (5) yields a certainty of three significant digits. The greater the number of significant digits, the greater the certainty of the measurement.

All digits included in a stated value (except leading zeros) are significant digits.

The position of the decimal point is not important when counting significant digits; ignore the decimal point. For example, the Start and Finish lines for a rubber duck race along a river are measured as being 30.75 m apart.

This measurement contains four significant digits. **Table 1** gives the certainty of several measurements. Study these examples to learn the rule for counting significant digits.

Figure 1

Surveyors check their measurements during construction of the Chalk River particle accelerator. The facility itself was built during the winter of 1944–45. The first particle accelerator was built in 1959 and given to the University of Montreal. The second was built in 1967 and is currently inoperative because of lack of funds.

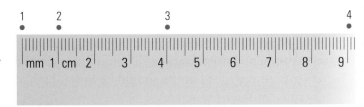

Figure 2

The measurement of the distance from the centre of point 1 to the centre of point 4 reads 9.05 cm, with a certainty of three significant digits.

Table 1	Certainty of Measurements
Measurement	**Certainty**
307.0 cm	4 significant digits
61 m/s	2 significant digits
0.03 m	1 significant digit
0.5060 km	4 significant digits
3.00 x 10^8 m/s	3 significant digits

Counted or Defined Values

When you directly count the number of students in your class, this is an exact value. We think of such exact values as containing an infinite number of significant digits. When you use a defined value, such as 100 cm/m or 60 s/min, this is also an exact value. Defined values also have an infinite number of significant digits. Some examples are provided in **Table 2** and **Figure 3**.

Table 2	Exact Values	
Counted values	**Defined values**
4 dogs	1000 m/km
10 CDs	10 mm/cm
3 Blue Jays	1 h/60 min

Certainty Rule for Multiplying and Dividing

While correctly taken measurements yield only significant digits, there is a decision to be made when we multiply or divide measurements. Try multiplying two four-digit numbers together on your calculator. The answer has seven or eight digits. Common sense tells us that the answer can be no more certain than the original numbers. In order to determine the certainty of the answer (as given in significant digits), follow this **certainty rule** or generalization: state those digits that are certain plus one uncertain digit. In other words:

When multiplying and/or dividing, the answer has the same number of significant digits as the measurement with the fewest number of significant digits.

This rule ensures that the certainty of the answer depends on the least certain original value.

In our multiplication example, therefore, the answer should have only four significant digits. As with most other rules or generalizations, there are exceptions, but this rule works well most of the time. You can see how it is used in the sample problems below.

Figure 3
There are exactly four dogs pulling the sled; not nearly four, or four-and-a-bit: exactly four.

Sample Problem 1

Calculate the answer for the following question and state the answer with the correct certainty and units.

Using the equation for the area of a triangle

$$\text{area} = \frac{1}{2} \times \text{base} \times \text{height}$$

or

$$A = \frac{1}{2} bh$$

and given values of b and h, find A.

$b = 3.2$ cm

$h = 10.1$ cm

$$A = \frac{1}{2} \times 3.2 \text{ cm} \times 10.1 \text{ cm}$$

$$= 16 \text{ cm}^2, \text{ which was rounded to two significant digits from } 16.16 \text{ cm}^2$$

Note that 3.2 cm with a certainty of two significant digits is multiplied by 10.1 cm with a certainty of three significant digits, so the answer has the certainty of the least certain original number: two significant digits.

Rounding

We need a rule (generalization) for rounding the answer from a calculation in order to obtain the correct certainty. First you must decide what the certainty (in significant digits) of the answer should be by using the appropriate calculation rule, such as the multiplication and division rule given above.

If the digit after the digit to be retained as significant is a 5 or greater, round up.

If the digit after the last significant digit is 4 or less, leave the last significant digit as it is. For example, rounding 9.147 cm to three significant digits would give 9.15 cm and rounding 7.23 g to two significant digits would give 7.2 g.

    Remember, for multiple-step calculations, leave all digits in your calculator until you have finished all your calculations, then round the final answer. Otherwise you could be introducing error into your calculations.

Sample Problem 2

Calculate the answer to the following question and state the answer with the correct certainty and units.

Using the equation $A = \dfrac{1}{2} bh$, and given b and h, find A.

$b = 6.21$ cm

$h = 8.0$ cm

$$A = \dfrac{1}{2} \times 6.21 \text{ cm} \times 8.0 \text{ cm}$$

$$= 25 \text{ cm}^2, \text{ which was rounded to two significant digits from } 24.84$$

Precision Rule for Adding and Subtracting

Precision is defined as the place value of the last digit obtained from a measurement or calculation. Precision is measured by the number of decimal places in a measured or calculated value. The following **precision rule** ensures that the precision of the answer depends on the least precise original value.

When adding and subtracting measured values of known precision, the answer has the same number of decimal places as the measured value with the fewest decimal places.

For example, when adding values of 1.2 mm, 3.05 mm, and 7.60 mm, the answer can be no more precise (as measured by decimal places) then the least precise value: 1.2 mm. Therefore, the answer (11.85 mm) is rounded off to 11.9 mm.

Sample Problem 3

What is the total distance travelled by a car when the following distances are recorded by different individuals using a variety of instruments? (Δd means "distance travelled.")

$\Delta d_1 = 104.2$ km

$\Delta d_2 = 11$ km

$\Delta d_3 = 0.67$ km

$\quad \Delta d_t = \Delta d_1 + \Delta d_2 + \Delta d_3 = 104.2$ km $+$ 11 km $+$ 0.67 km

$\quad\quad\quad = 116$ km

The total distance travelled is 116 km.
The sum displayed on the calculator screen is 115.87 km, which is rounded to 116 km. The least precise measurement is 11 km, since it has the fewest decimal places.

Sample Problem 4

A group of students recorded the following measurements using a variety of measuring devices: 5.5 m by strides; 0.597 m with a metre rule; and 0.1262 m with a ruler. What is the total distance measured?

$\quad d_t = 5.5$ m $+$ 0.597 m $+$ 0.1262 m $= 6.2$ m (rounded from 6.2332 m)

The total distance measured is 6.2 m (to 1 decimal place).

Note that in all the following Sample Problems in this unit, the answer that appears on the calculator is not given: only the rounded answer is provided.

Conventions of Communication

The rules provided above are generalizations. Fortunately, although the generalizations do not always provide the best individual answer, they work most of the time and are simple to use. Conventions of communication are important to any community. They allow members of the community to understand each other without confusion. In this case everyone in the community accepts and uses the same rules, and understands that there are limitations to the rules.

The international community of scientists has agreed on a system of measurement and communication called **SI** (the International System of Units from the French *Système international d'unités*). An international system is very useful for efficiently and accurately exchanging information among scientists. The SI convention includes both quantity and unit symbols. Note that these are symbols (e.g., 60 km/h) and are not abbreviations (e.g., 40 mi./hr.). You should learn and use these symbols in all your scientific communication.

An example of miscommunication is provided by the $125-million mistake made on a 1999 Earth-to-Mars space probe (**Figure 4**). The specifications for the probe were sent by the contractor in British units but were interpreted by NASA as being in metric units. The probe ended up crashing on Mars instead of orbiting.

Figure 4

In October 1999, a Mars probe was destroyed because its makers did not follow the scientific convention of communication.

Solving Equations

Have you ever tried to solve an equation but found that the unknown variable is mixed up with a group of other variables on the right, instead of being neatly on its own on the left? When doing calculations you often have to rearrange the defining equation to solve for a different variable. A **defining equation** is the definition of a quantity expressed in quantity symbols. In other words, it is the word definition translated into symbols. You will meet several defining equations in this unit. When rearranging an equation you must keep the equation equal by performing the same operation on both sides of the equation, such as multiplying or dividing both sides of the equation by the same value or variable.

Sample Problem 5

Rearrange the following defining equation to solve for the other variables (b and then h) in the equation.

Solve for b.

Defining equation: $A = \dfrac{1}{2}bh$

Multiply by 2: $2A = bh$

Divide by h: $\dfrac{2A}{h} = b$

Rewrite: $b = \dfrac{2A}{h}$

Solve for h.

Defining equation: $A = \dfrac{1}{2}bh$

Multiply by 2: $2A = bh$

Divide by b: $\dfrac{2A}{b} = h$

Rewrite: $h = \dfrac{2A}{b}$

Converting Units

Sometimes you might be able to convert units in your head by, for example, dividing or multiplying by 1000. However, some unit conversions need to be written down. The method most commonly used is multiplying by conversion factors (equalities), which are memorized or referenced. It is important to pay close attention to the units, which are also converted by multiplying by a conversion factor.

Sample Problem 6

An athlete completed a 5-km race in 19.5 min. Convert this time into hours.

$$t = 19.5 \; \cancel{\text{min}} \times \frac{1 \text{ h}}{60 \; \cancel{\text{min}}} = 0.325 \text{ h}$$

The athlete finished the race in 0.325 h.

Sample Problem 7

A train is travelling at 95 km/h. Convert 95 km/h into metres per second.

$$v = 95 \; \frac{\cancel{\text{km}}}{\cancel{\text{h}}} \times \frac{1 \cancel{\text{h}}}{60 \; \cancel{\text{min}}} \times \frac{1 \; \cancel{\text{min}}}{60 \text{ s}} \times \frac{1000 \text{ m}}{1 \; \cancel{\text{km}}} = 26 \text{ m/s}$$

Note that the certainty of two significant digits in 95 km/h results in the same certainty for the answer, 26 m/s. The conversion factors are all defined, or exact, values with infinite certainty.

For more information on measurements and calculations, see Ⓤ Using the Calculator and Ⓦ Calculating in the Skills Handbook.

Understanding Concepts

1. A system of units is necessary to state and use measurements. What is the SI base unit name and unit symbol for each of the following quantities?

   (a) distance

   (b) time

2. Record the length of the nail in **Figure 5** in centimetres. Indicate which digits are certain and which uncertain.

Figure 5

3. Copy each of the following measured or calculated values. Place a check mark (✓) above each certain digit and a question mark (?) above each estimated or uncertain digit. Finally, state the certainty as a number of significant digits.

   (a) 7.65 mm

   (b) 20.2 m/s

   (c) 50.0 cm

   (d) 0.084 km

4. Round the following values to a certainty of three significant digits.

   (a) 32.674 km

   (b) 0.003 922 g

   (c) 107.51 s

5. In your own words, state

   (a) the rule for the number of digits allowed in the final answer obtained from a multiplication or division.

   (b) the rule for the number of decimal places allowed in the final answer obtained from addition or subtraction.

6. Complete the following calculations by providing the correctly rounded answer with units.

   (a) $22.4 \text{ h} \times \dfrac{0.1 \text{ mm}}{\text{h}} =$

   (b) $\dfrac{465 \text{ km}}{5.21 \text{ h}} =$

   (c) $18 \text{ cm}^3 \times \dfrac{1.10 \text{ g}}{\text{cm}^3} =$

   (d) $72.5 \text{ min} \times \dfrac{1 \text{ h}}{60 \text{ min}} =$

   (e) 17.5 mL + 95 mL + 8.25 mL =

   (f) 32.1 m + 960 m + 20.02 m =

   (g) 0.2 cm + 23.91 cm + 0.62 cm =

   (h) 13.63 h − 0.5 h =

   (i) 35.1 mm + 67.04 mm =

   (j) 7.52 s + 8.678 s + 0.24 s =

7. Solve for the stated variable using the given definition.

   (a) $C = 2\pi r \qquad r = ?$

   (b) $D = \dfrac{m}{V} \qquad m = ? \qquad V = ?$

   (c) $y = mx + b \qquad x = ?$

   (d) $A = \dfrac{1}{2}bh \qquad b = ?$

   (e) $v = \dfrac{d}{t} \qquad d = ?$

   (f) $A = \pi r^2 \qquad r = ?$

8. Determine the area of the following shapes to the correct number of significant digits.

   (a) A rectangle with a base of 100.0 m and a height of 12 m

   (b) A triangle with a base of 8.23 cm and a height of 0.68 cm

9. Convert the following quantities into the units stated. Round your answer to the correct number of significant digits.

   (a) 34 min into hours

   (b) 0.510 km into metres

   (c) 0.021 h into seconds

   (d) 25 km/h into metres per second

Making Connections

10. A soft drink salesperson claims that the company puts exactly 355 mL of pop into each can. Is this possible? What do you think is a better description of the volume?

Reflecting

11. Comment on this statement: "No measurement can ever be perfect or exact."

12. How are communication systems such as SI like a language?

 Challenge

1 What does it mean for a timepiece to be more reliable, more precise, and more accurate?

Measuring Large and Small Distances

Measuring distances becomes a complicated problem when the thing to be measured is a size that we cannot directly perceive or imagine. We must find some indirect method to calculate the distance in question.

The Circumference of Earth

One well-documented instance of an indirect measuring technique occurred about 2200 years ago. The Greek astronomer Eratosthenes wanted to know the circumference of Earth. He noted that at noon on the summer solstice the Sun was directly overhead at Syene (modern Aswan in Egypt). However, when he performed the same measurement in Alexandria, on the northern coast (**Figure 1**), he discovered that the Sun's rays were 7° from the vertical. Assuming Earth's surface was evenly curved and knowing the distance between the two cities, he extrapolated the distance for 7° to a distance for 360°. His value for the circumference of Earth, about 4×10^7 m, is amazingly close to the modern value.

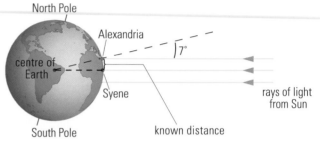

Figure 1

Eratosthenes' design for determining the circumference of Earth

It is interesting to note that Eratosthenes' value for the circumference of Earth made many people very uncomfortable. It meant that the known world of that time was a much smaller part of the planet than had previously been thought. In fact, the astronomer Ptolemy incorrectly calculated a much smaller value two hundred years later. Ptolemy's value was accepted until the beginning of modern times (probably because it was less controversial), and was the value that led Columbus to believe that Asia lay within reach by sailing west from Spain.

(a) Based on this information, how far apart were Syene and Alexandria?

(b) Why might people have accepted Ptolemy's value rather than that of Eratosthenes?

Pillars of Creation

On April 1, 1995, Jeff Hester and Paul Scowen of Arizona State University used NASA's Hubble Space Telescope (HST) to make a series of colour images of the Eagle Nebula. The composite picture shown in **Figure 2** is one of the HST's most famous photographs. Astronomers propose that the gas columns in the picture are the remains of a huge hydrogen gas cloud. We believe that

Figure 2

This picture of the Eagle Nebula is very popular as a poster.

new stars are being formed in globular regions within the pillars where the gas is relatively dense.

Recent devices such as the Hubble Telescope have greatly improved the information available and make this an exciting time for astronomers. The accepted value for the distance to the pillars is about 7000 light-years, and the tallest pillar is about 1 light-year long from base to top. Measuring distances in space presents a modern challenge similar to the one faced by Eratosthenes. It isn't possible to go there; therefore, we must use our minds to correctly interpret what we can see.

(c) A light-year is the distance travelled by light in a time of one year. Assume a year length of 365 days and the speed of light to be 3.00×10^8 m/s. Calculate the number of kilometres from Earth to the Eagle Nebula.

On Beyond Microscopic

The other side of the measurement coin involves the measuring of things too small to see directly. Before microscopes were invented in the late 1500s, knowledge of living and non-living things was limited to what could be seen directly. With microscopes, scientists discovered that we share our planet with a lot of living things we can't perceive. This was a terrifying idea at the time because this was an unknown microscopic world and many people fear the unknown. More recently, scientists have obtained fairly direct evidence for the existence of atoms.

Figure 3 shows a photomicrograph of gallium nitride—a typical semiconductor. This photograph represents the first time that people have been able to locate and distinguish atoms in a structure. This technological advance is just as important to semiconductor manufacturers as the ability to see bacteria in a tissue sample is to a medical laboratory technician. The columns of gallium atoms in the photograph are 113 pm or one hundred and thirteen trillionths of a metre apart. (One picometre, pm, is 10^{-12} m.)

(d) In a sample of solid nickel metal, such as a Canadian dime, the atoms of nickel are 175 pm apart. If a dime is 18 mm in diameter, how many nickel atoms are there across the diameter of the coin?

Figure 3

In the projection at the rear, the nitrogen atoms are thought to be the much smaller ones within the structure formed by the large gallium atoms.

Understanding Concepts

1. What are the columns that appear in the Eagle Nebula?

2. List some examples of living organisms discovered after the invention of microscopes.

3. Which are smaller, bacteria or atoms? Explain briefly.

Making Connections

4. For reasons other than scientific, why is it useful to know

   (a) the circumference of Earth?

   (b) the structure of a semiconductor?

5. The study of astronomy is a good example of the interaction between science and technology. Describe in your own words how science and technology interact in astronomy. Provide an example.

Exploring

6. Modern medicine is very concerned with viral diseases, which are a problem partly because viruses are extremely small. Research and report on some of the tools and techniques used to examine viruses and their effects.

7. "Black holes" were first predicted theoretically.
   Ⓘ However, obtaining evidence for black holes presented an interesting challenge. Why is it difficult to directly observe and measure black holes? Research how this problem was solved. Summarize your findings in a short article suitable for publication.

INQUIRY SKILLS MENU
- ○ Questioning
- ○ Hypothesizing
- ○ Predicting
- ● Planning
- ● Conducting
- ● Recording
- ● Analyzing
- ● Evaluating
- ● Communicating

Your Speed

We all depend on ways of transporting ourselves from one place to another. Devices that provide personal transportation, such as bicycles, wheelchairs, and cars, can be evaluated from a wide variety of perspectives. In this investigation you will gather one kind of evidence (the normal, safe speed) by which to judge a transportation device of your choice. You may also use other perspectives, such as safety, esthetics (beauty), economic cost, peer appeal, and environmental impact to evaluate your means of personal transportation.

Once you have completed this investigation you will compare your results with those of other students. Remember: this is not a race. Pay particular attention to how you take your measurements, perform your calculations, and write up your lab report.

Figure 1
You will be able to measure your speed over a larger distance if you can work outside.

Question

What is the speed of your personal transportation device?

Design

Measure the total distance and the total time in order to calculate the speed of your device for personal transportation. The controlled variables will be the transportation device, the force of propulsion, and the speed. Distance will be the independent variable, and time will be the dependent variable.

(a) Design a neat, labelled table in which to record your observations.

Materials

- personal transportation (e.g., shoes, bicycle, skateboard, wheelchair, or cross-country skis)
- distance measuring device (e.g., pace, tape measure, bicycle wheel, odometer)
- timing device (e.g., wristwatch, stopwatch, water clock, or pendulum)
- safety equipment as required (e.g., helmet, wrist guards, reflective clothing)

Use the recommended safety equipment for your chosen means of transport. Use a safe area, away from traffic, and on even, uncluttered ground.

Procedure

1 Find a safe environment within the school grounds and wear all appropriate safety equipment.

2 Select an appropriate distance over which to travel. Mark the Start and Finish points.

3 Measure and record the total time required to safely transport you or your partner over the total distance (**Figure 1**).

4 Measure and record the total distance travelled in that period of time.

SKILLS HANDBOOK: (K7) Preparing Tables of Evidence (N4) Answering the Question

5 Repeat steps 3 and 4 at least three times.

6 Choose a different distance and repeat steps 2 to 5 twice more, giving data for three different distances, in total.

7 Return all equipment to storage.

Analysis and Evaluation

(b) Calculate the speed for each trial, using the formula

$$\text{speed} = \frac{\text{distance}}{\text{time}}$$

(c) Answer the initial question based on your calculations from (b).

(d) Evaluate the evidence gathered by making judgments on the Design, Materials, Procedure, and your own skills.

(e) Compare your results with those of other groups. Explain any similarities and differences.

(f) Evaluate your personal transportation device based only on speed.

(g) How else could you evaluate your chosen means of transport? Would you value your transportation differently, using other perspectives?

(h) Could your answers be used to help you choose a personal transportation system? Why or why not?

(i) Write a formal lab report for this investigation.

Challenge

1 How does the timing device you used in this investigation differ from those available to Galileo?

Understanding Concepts

1. Scientists are always looking for relationships among variables. The following questions investigate such a relationship.

   (a) If the distance of travel increases and the time remains the same, what has happened to the average speed?

   (b) If the distance of travel remains the same and the time increases, what has happened to the average speed?

   (c) If the speed of travel increases and the time remains the same, what happens to the distance travelled?

   (d) If the speed of travel remains the same and the time increases, what happens to the distance travelled?

   (e) If the speed of travel increases and the distance remains the same, what happens to the time required for the trip?

   (f) If the speed of travel remains the same and the distance increases, what happens to the time required for the trip?

2. The relationship between two variables such as speed and distance may be, among others, a direct variation (such as x and y in the formula $y = kx$) or an inverse variation (such as x and y in $y = \frac{k}{x}$). Use these terms to describe the relationship between

   (a) speed and distance;

   (b) speed and time;

   (c) distance and time.

3. Combining the relationships described in the previous question, create an algebraic definition (equation) for the relationships among speed, distance, and time.

Exploring

4. List at least five different personal transportation devices. Consider when each first came into common use.

   (a) What trends can you detect developing over time? (Consider, for example, materials used, power source, and speed of each means of transportation.)

   (b) What might be the safety and environmental impacts of these trends?

5. Complete a risk-benefit analysis of at least five personal transportation devices.

6. Plan an investigation to find the speed of the traffic passing your school. Your equipment could include a stop watch, "Start" and "Finish" markers, a 30-m tape measure, and a clipboard. Draw conclusions about illegal speeding in your school's neighbourhood.

Relating Speed to Distance and Time

If you are in a car that travels 80 km along a road in one hour, we say that you are travelling at, on average, 80 km/h. You might not have been travelling at the same speed all the time: you might have speeded up to 100 km/h to pass other vehicles, or even stopped for gas. But overall, during the entire hour, your average speed was 80 km/h.

Average Speed

To find the speed of a car in units of kilometres per hour (km/h), we divide the distance (in kilometres) by the time (in hours). Therefore speed v is distance Δd divided by the time Δt. (Some examples of units for distance, time, and speed are given in **Table 1**.) **Average speed**, v_{av}, is the total distance divided by the total time for a trip. Transformed into quantity symbols, the defining equation looks like this.

$$v_{av} = \frac{\Delta d}{\Delta t}$$

v_{av} is read as "average speed."

Δ is read as "change in" (delta is the fourth capital letter in the Greek alphabet).

Δd is read as "change in distance," "elapsed distance," or "distance."

$\Delta d = d_2 - d_1$, where d_1 is one distance measurement and d_2 is a later distance measurement; d_1 is often zero.

Δt is read as "change in time," "elapsed time," "period of time," or "time."

$\Delta t = t_2 - t_1$, where t_1 is one time measurement and t_2 is a later time measurement.

t_1, the starting time, is often zero.

Table 1	Some SI Quantities and Units		
Quantity	**Quantity symbol**	**Sample unit**	**Unit symbol**
distance	d	millimetre	mm
		centimetre	cm
		metre	m
		kilometre	km
time	t	second	s
		minute	min
		hour	h
		year	a
speed	v	metres per second	m/s
		kilometres per hour	km/h

Quantity symbols (**Table 1**) are italic letters used to represent quantities (such as distance, time, and speed) in scientific equations. These quantity symbols have general international agreement, although alternatives are sometimes suggested. The quantity symbols are not unique because there are only 26 letters in our alphabet, while there are many more quantities. For example, d can represent distance, diameter, or density, t can communicate time or temperature, and v can refer to speed or volume. Quantity symbols are always typed in italics while unit symbols are not. For example, while m is the quantity symbol for mass, m is the unit symbol for metres. Quantity symbols are found in equations (e.g., $E = mc^2$) while unit symbols are found with values (e.g., 3.7 m).

Instantaneous Speed

The car in **Figure 1**, at the time the photo was taken, was stationary. Its speed at that moment was 0 km/h. When the car was passing a truck on the road, its speedometer might have shown a speed of 100 km/h. These are examples of instantaneous speeds. **Instantaneous speed** is the speed at which an object is travelling at a particular instant. It is not affected by its previous speed, or by how long it has been moving.

High instantaneous speeds contribute to the seriousness of road traffic accidents. The two most familiar instruments that measure instantaneous speed were designed to improve road safety: the speedometer and the "radar gun."

Figure 1

At this moment the instantaneous speed of the car is zero, but this will change when the traffic light becomes green.

Constant Speed

If the instantaneous speed of a car remains the same over a period of time, then we say that the car is travelling with **constant speed** (or **uniform motion**). Some vehicles have cruise control to keep them moving along at a fairly constant speed. Few objects maintain constant speed over a lengthy period of time, however, often because of friction. However, we often assume constant (uniform) speed for the purposes of simplifying our physics calculations.

The average speed of an object is the same as its instantaneous speed if that object is travelling at constant speed.

Did You Know?

The Greeks did not have a concept of speed until Autolycus of Pitane (about 300 B.C.), defined constant speed as a speed in which equal distances are traversed in equal times. We use the same definition today.

Sample Problem 1

Eiko skates to school, a total distance of 4.5 km (**Figure 2**). She has to slow down twice to cross busy streets, but overall the journey takes her 0.62 h. What is Eiko's average speed during the trip?

$\Delta d = 4.5$ km

$\Delta t = 0.62$ h

$v_{av} = ?$

$$v_{av} = \frac{\Delta d}{\Delta t}$$

$$= \frac{4.5 \text{ km}}{0.62 \text{ h}}$$

$$= 7.3 \text{ km/h}$$

Eiko's average skating speed is 7.3 km/h.

Figure 2

In-line skating is often a quick way to get to school.

Sample Problem 2

Imagine that you are riding on the Cariboo Dayliner, in the dome car of course (**Figure 3**), and you see a sign that reads 120 km. You decide, after seeing several such signs, that you are going to measure the elapsed time between the next two signs, which are 10 km apart. You read the elapsed time as 390.6 s. Determine the speed of the train in kilometres per hour during the elapsed time.

$\Delta d = 10 \text{ km}$

$\Delta t = 390.6 \text{ s} \times \dfrac{1 \text{ min}}{60 \text{ s}} \times \dfrac{1 \text{ h}}{60 \text{ min}} = 0.1085 \text{ h}$

$v_{av} = ?$

$$v_{av} = \dfrac{\Delta d}{\Delta t}$$

$$= \dfrac{10 \text{ km}}{0.1085 \text{ h}}$$

$$= 92 \text{ km/h}$$

The average speed of your train is 92 km/h.

Sample Problem 3

Kira is trying to predict the time required to ride her bike to the nearby beach. She knows that the distance is 45 km and, from other trips, that she can usually average about 20 km/h, including slowing down for climbing hills. Predict how long the trip will take.

$\Delta d = 45 \text{ km}$

$v_{av} = 20 \text{ km/h}$

$\Delta t = ?$

$$v_{av} = \dfrac{\Delta d}{\Delta t}$$

$$\Delta t = \dfrac{\Delta d}{v_{av}}$$

$$= \dfrac{45 \text{ km}}{20 \frac{\text{km}}{\text{h}}}$$

$$= 2.3 \text{ h}$$

There is an easy method of converting between km/h and m/s.

1 m/s = 3.6 km/h

exactly, because all of the conversion factors used were exact values, by definition.

Alternatively, you can substitute and then rearrange the equation.

$\Delta d = 45 \text{ km}$

$v_{av} = 20 \text{ km/h}$

$\Delta t = ?$

$$v_{av} = \dfrac{\Delta d}{\Delta t}$$

$$20 \ \dfrac{\text{km}}{\text{h}} = \dfrac{45 \text{ km}}{\Delta t}$$

$$\Delta t = \dfrac{45 \text{ km}}{20 \frac{\text{km}}{\text{h}}}$$

$$= 2.3 \text{ h}$$

Kira should be able to make the trip in about 2.3 h.

Did You Know?

On April 15, 1999, a Japanese magnetically levitated train broke its own world speed record by travelling at 552 km/h.

Note that the units in Sample Problem 3 simplify as follows:

$$\frac{km}{\frac{km}{h}} = \cancel{km} \times \frac{h}{\cancel{km}} = h$$

Sample Problem 4

Janna has a summer job helping with bison research (**Figure 4**). She notes that they graze (move and eat grass) at an average speed of about 110 m/h for about 7.0 h/d. What distance, in kilometres, will the herd travel in two weeks (14 d)?

$v_{av} = 110$ m/h

$\Delta t = 7.0 \dfrac{h}{\cancel{d}} \times 14 \cancel{d} = 98$ h

$\Delta d = ?$

$v_{av} = \dfrac{\Delta d}{\Delta t}$ 　　or　　 $v_{av} = \dfrac{\Delta d}{\Delta t}$

$\Delta d = v_{av}\Delta t$ 　　　　　　 $110 \dfrac{m}{h} = \dfrac{\Delta d}{98\ h}$

$= 110 \dfrac{m}{\cancel{h}} \times 98 \cancel{h}$ 　　　 $\Delta d = 110 \dfrac{m}{\cancel{h}} \times 98 \cancel{h}$

$= 11$ km 　　　　　　　　　　 $= 11$ km

According to Janna's observations, after two weeks the bison will have covered a distance of about 11 km.

Figure 4
A few buffalo still roam.

Understanding Concepts

1. **(a)** How is average speed different from instantaneous speed?

   (b) When are they the same?

2. A car and a truck travel along the same highway with the car moving faster than the truck.

   (a) How do their distances travelled compare after the same length of time?

   (b) How do their times compare after travelling the same distance?

3. Holidays might mean a multiday trip to be taken by foot, boat, train, or automobile. The Trans Canada Trail (**Figure 5**), for example, has become a popular hiking and cycling vacation route.

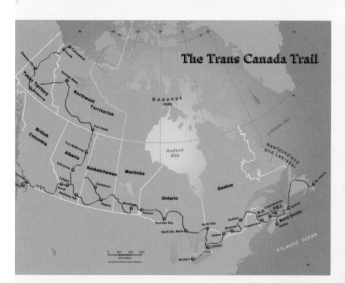

Figure 5

   (a) If two hikers walk the Trans Canada Trail for 6.0 h, and covered 31 km, what is their average speed for the day?

   (b) If three bike riders on the Trail cycle for 6.0 h one day, and cover 85 km, what is their average speed for the day?

   (c) Mary walked for 2.1 h along a portion of the Trans Canada Trail at a speed of 3.6 km/h. What distance did Mary travel?

   (d) What length of time would it take a hiker to travel a total distance of 25.0 km at an average speed of 5.2 km/h?

4. The cruise control of a car is set at 90.0 km/h. What distance is travelled by the car during 2.50 h?

5. Show that 1 m/s = 3.6 km/h.

6. Use the conversion factor in question 5 to convert

   (a) 92 km/h to m/s;

   (b) 21 m/s to km/h.

7. **(a)** The *Breitling Orbiter 3* balloon (**Figure 6**) set world records in 1999 by travelling 40 814 km in 19 d, 21 h, and 47 min. On March 1, 1999, the balloon lifted off from a village in the Swiss Alps. It eventually landed in Egypt on March 21. Calculate the average speed of the balloon.

   (b) Using the average speed you calculated in **(a)**, what length of time did it take the *Breitling Orbiter 3* to cross the Atlantic Ocean, a distance of 6670 km?

   (c) In the final leg of the round-the-world trip, the balloon flew for 18 h at an average speed of 210 km/h. How far did it travel?

Figure 6

8. In 1997, *Thrust SSC*, the world's fastest jet-engine car, travelled 604 m at an average speed of 341 m/s.

   (a) What length of time did this take?

   (b) Convert 341 m/s to kilometres per hour.

9. In a marathon race, one runner moving at 5.0 m/s passes a second runner moving at 4.5 m/s. What is the distance between the runners 10 min after the one runner passed the other?

10. The "hand" of the Canadarm (**Figure 7**) used on the space shuttle can move up to 60 cm/s without a load attached.

   (a) What is the minimum time for the Canadarm's hand to move 1.20 m?

   (b) When the Canadarm is moving an object, the speed is slightly less than 60 cm/s. To move the same distance of 1.20 m, will the time be more or less than your answer to **(a)**? Explain your answer.

   (c) The Canadarm takes 30 s to move some equipment from the cargo bay. During this time, the space shuttle moves 232 km through space. What is the speed of the space shuttle in kilometres per second? in kilometres per hour?

Figure 7

11. The following lab report describes how recordings were taken during a road trip. Complete the Analysis and Evaluation section using the observation, recorded in **Table 2**.

Question

What is the average speed for a multiple-stage car trip to my grandparents' home?

Evidence

Table 2 **A Trip to the Grandparents'**

Time period or stage of trip	Initial odometer reading (km)	Final odometer reading (km)	Initial time (h:min)	Final time (h:min)
1	36 252.1	36 260.7	8:04	8:14
2	36 260.7	36 260.7	8:14	8:32
3	36 260.7	36 542.3	8:32	11:30
4	36 542.3	36 542.3	11:30	11:52
5	36 542.3	36 709.6	11:52	13:27

Analysis and Evaluation

   (a) During which time periods was the car moving? Calculate the speed during each of these separate time periods.

   (b) Calculate the average speed for the trip as a whole, from the beginning of Stage 1 to the end of Stage 5.

   (c) Explain the differences in your answers for **(a)** and **(b)**.

   (8A) Evaluate the experimental design. What would have made the design more efficient? Would this modification have changed the answer?

Reflecting

12. Sample Problem 4 on page 357 shows the calculation of the distance moved by the bison herd after 14 d. Is Janna likely to find the bison 11 km away? What does the calculated distance not take into account? What information is missing in the distance the bison move?

 Challenge

2 Laws are created, tested, and then used. How would you test the average speed equation (a law)?

3 Relate what you have just learned to driving. How does a car's speed affect the distance it travels during the driver's "reaction time"?

INQUIRY SKILLS MENU
○ Questioning ● Planning ● Analyzing
○ Hypothesizing ● Conducting ● Evaluating
○ Predicting ● Recording ● Communicating

Balloon Car Contest

The balloon car contest (**Figure 1**) is an exercise in technological problem solving: the trial-and-error approach. As you go around the cycle (**Figure 2**), you either keep refining the same general design or reach a dead end and switch to a completely new approach. Each cycle has its own design, procedure, evidence, and analysis until you reach a product or, in some cases, a process with a satisfactory result. The technological process for producing the balloon car is also a product, and so, perhaps, are one or more technological skills for operating the balloon car.

You will start with a general design and procedure. As you gather evidence you will modify the product (the car) and process (skills for building and operating the car). By trying various designs and techniques, you will produce a car that travels along a 3-m track.

(a)

Question

What design, procedures, and skills yield your best balloon car?

Design

Attach a balloon to a toy car. Race the balloon-powered car over 3.00 m. The car must move on its wheels and the sole source of propulsion must be provided by the balloon. Two trials are allowed in the final race. Judge the best car using a variety of perspectives (including technological, economic, and aesthetics or beauty).

(a) Design a table in which to record the
(K7) quantitative and qualitative evidence gathered in this investigation. The column headings could include *Trial number*, *Distance travelled* (*m*), *Time taken* (*s*), and *Comments*.

Materials

- balloon
- toy car with wheels
- stopwatch or wristwatch
- metre stick
- other assorted materials as required

(b)

Figure 1
Balloon car races

SKILLS HANDBOOK: (K7) Creating Tables of Evidence

Procedure

1 Locate a safe place for the trials.

2 Mark out a distance of 3.00 m.

3 Attach the balloon to the car.

4 Release the car with the balloon in the direction of the finish line.

5 Measure and record the time to run 3.00 m or until stopped short of the line.

6 Measure and record any distance travelled under 3.00 m.

7 Modify your car or the process of starting your car to improve its performance.

8 Repeat steps 3–7 as many times as required, adjusting your design to get the most reliable (consistent) and satisfactory results.

9 Race your car against other designs. You will be allowed two trials.

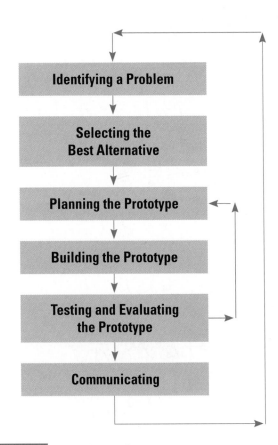

Figure 2

The problem-solving cycle

Analysis and Evaluation

(b) Answer the Question. Include information
Ⓚ₂ about the car from a variety of perspectives, including technological, economic, and aesthetics (beauty). Remember to consider procedures and skills, as well as the car itself.

(c) Evaluate your design, procedure, and skills. For
Ⓞ₂ example, did you experience any problems making your measurements? How would this affect your evidence? Include any general improvements you would make.

(d) Present your car and its performance and
Ⓢ features to the class.

Understanding Concepts

1. Describe the process of technological problem solving and list some of the things that you learned about this approach.

2. What criteria did you use to help you decide which was your "best" balloon car?

3. Calculate the average speed for the best trial of your balloon car.

4. Describe, in your own words, the motion of your balloon car.

Reflecting

5. As you worked on solving your technological problem, how well did your group work together? What personal attitudes are important in group work?

6. Did you use your knowledge of science to guide your design? If so, in what way?

7. How does technological problem-solving compare with scientific problem-solving?

 Challenge

1 Even if you are following an established design, there will be some trial-and-error as you construct your timepiece. Keep a record of your modifications and how they affect your model.

Distance–Time Graphs

Imagine that you are a wildlife biologist and have collected information on the distances travelled by a white-tailed deer running at top speed (**Table 1**), escaping from a wolf. Now you need to communicate this information to a colleague. You could use words in either a spoken or written report; you could make a drawing or diagram showing how far the deer travels during a certain time interval; you could present a table of your quantitative observations; or you could plot the information on a graph. Graphs are used to communicate quantitative information visually. Most people, scientists included, can understand a graph more quickly and easily than they can a table of evidence or a couple of paragraphs of text.

Whether graphs are your first choice or not, most people agree that graphs help us to understand the relationship between two variables. We can see whether the dependent variable increases or decreases with the independent variable. On a distance–time graph, time is usually the independent variable (plotted on the *x*-axis) and distance is the dependent variable (plotted on the *y*-axis). **Figure 1** shows a graph for a running deer. The line on this graph is straight and pointing upward to the right. This indicates that there is a direct relationship between distance and time and that the relationship follows the general equation for a straight line.

How can the slope of the best-fit line represent both $\Delta d = v\,\Delta t$ (the equation relating distance, speed, and time) and $y = mx + b$ (the general equation for a straight line)? The equations certainly don't look the same. Let's examine both equations more closely.

Recall that
$y = mx + b$ where y is the dependent variable (on the *y*-axis)
x is the independent variable (on the *x*-axis)
m is the slope of the line
b is the *y* intercept of the line.

In the case of a distance–time graph of an object with constant speed,

$$y = mx + b$$
becomes $\Delta d = v\,\Delta t + 0$
or simply $\Delta d = v\,\Delta t$ where Δd (distance travelled) is the dependent variable
Δt (time) is the independent variable
v (speed) is the slope of the line
0 (initial distance, d_1) is the *y* intercept.

Table 1	A Running White-Tailed Deer
Time (s)	**Distance (m)**
0	0
1.0	13
2.0	25
3.0	40
4.0	51
5.0	66
6.0	78

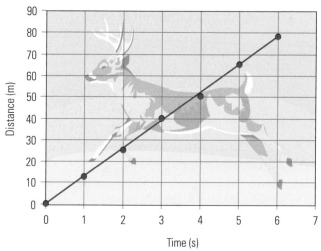

A Running White-Tailed Deer

Figure 1
The graph of the deer's motion shows that it was running at a fairly constant speed.

Now you can see how the general equation for a straight line on a graph, $y = mx + b$, also represents $\Delta d = v\,\Delta t$.

Logic and consistency are two ways of testing scientific knowledge, and your own knowledge too. The idea that distance and time are related directly and linearly passes the test of logic and consistency. We can conclude that the **slope of a line** on a distance–time graph represents speed.

Slope and Speed

The greater the speed, the greater the slope of the line of a distance–time graph. To put it another way, the greater the slope of a line on a distance–time graph, the greater the speed. **Figure 2** is a graph of three different ways of getting around. The fastest means of transportation (the bicycle) has the steepest slope. In-line skates are the next fastest, and walking is the slowest.

Canada's Joanne Malar swims the individual medley of butterfly, backstroke, breaststroke, and freestyle. In training, an overhead video camera records and analyzes the total distances covered during the first five 5.0-s intervals of each lap. We can use the information in **Table 2** to draw a graph comparing Malar's fastest and slowest strokes.

In the first 25.0 s, Malar had travelled the greatest distance during her freestyle lap, and the shortest distance during the breaststroke lap. It is these two strokes that should appear on the graph, which will look like **Figure 3**.

We can extract information on speed simply by looking at the slopes of lines on distance–time graphs. For example, in **Figure 3** we can see that Malar's freestyle lap is considerably faster than her breaststroke lap. But how do we find the actual speeds from a graph? Scientists and engineers want more than a comparison; they want the quantitative (number) value for the speeds depicted by distance–time graphs.

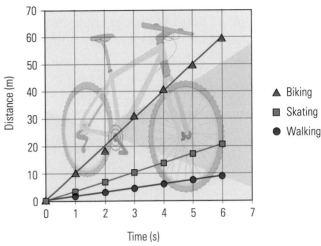

Walking, Skating, and Biking

- ▲ Biking
- ■ Skating
- ● Walking

Figure 2

Comparing walking, skating, and biking

Table 2	The 200-m Individual Medley			
Time (s)	Butterfly distance (m)	Backstroke distance (m)	Breaststroke distance (m)	Freestyle distance (m)
0.0	0.0	0.0	0.0	0.0
5.0	8.2	8.0	7.5	9.5
10.0	16.2	17.0	15.1	18.5
15.0	24.7	24.5	22.7	27.0
20.0	32.8	31.5	30.5	35.5
25.0	42.0	39.0	36.5	45.0

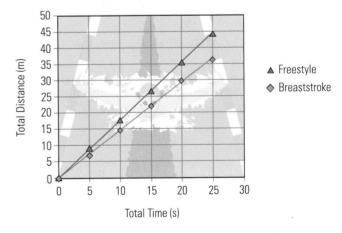

The Individual Medley Strokes

- ▲ Freestyle
- ◆ Breaststroke

Figure 3

Graph of Malar's fastest and slowest strokes

When you analyze the slopes of graphs you are really comparing the change in distance (Δd) during equal intervals of time (Δt). For example, how can you determine which stroke takes the swimmer farthest in 1.0 s? Mathematically, you are comparing the ratios of Δd to Δt. The ratio of $\Delta d : \Delta t$ is, of course, the speed, but it is also the slope of the line. (Note that Δd to Δt, $\Delta d : \Delta t$, and Δd over Δt all mean the same thing.)

$$slope = \frac{rise}{run}$$

$$v = \frac{\Delta d}{\Delta t}$$

The slope of a distance–time graph is determined from the rise over the run, which also happens to be the distance over the time, which in turn is the speed. **Speed is determined from the slope of the best-fit straight line of a distance–time graph.**

Table 3 gives observed data for the travels of a Hummer on a narrow country road.

The graph (**Figure 4**) shows the total distance travelled during 10 min. Notice that the shape of the line is straight. This means that the speed is fairly constant. We call this constant (or uniform) speed. We use a significant portion (2/3 to 3/4) of the graph to find the average speed of the Hummer. The advantage of the triangle displayed is that the triangle is separated from the x-axis and is easy to see on the graph. A smaller triangle produces more error. The triangle is attached to the line and not to observed data points on the line.

$$slope = \frac{rise}{run}$$

$$v = \frac{\Delta d}{\Delta t}$$

$$= \frac{(9.0 - 2.0)\ km}{(9.0 - 2.0)\ min}$$

$$= 1.0\ km/min$$

In summary, **the speed of an object in motion can be determined from the slope of a distance–time graph.**

Table 3	A Hummer Travelling on a Country Road

Time (min)	Distance (km)
0	0
1.0	1.0
2.0	1.8
3.0	2.9
4.0	4.2
5.0	5.0
6.0	5.9
7.0	6.9
8.0	8.2
9.0	9.2
10.0	10.0

The Travels of a Hummer

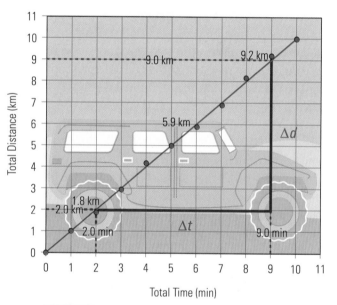

Figure 4

Fairly constant speed from a Hummer (2, 1.8)

Understanding Concepts

1. Explain, in your own words, why a graph is sometimes more useful than an equation.

2. What does the slope of a distance–time graph represent?

3. What interpretation can be made about a moving car if the line on a distance–time graph for the car has the following characteristics?

   (a) a high or steep slope

   (b) a low or less steep slope

   (c) a zero slope

   (d) a short line on the graph

   (e) a long line on the graph

4. Sketch a distance–time graph for a car cruising at 80 km/h.

5. A car leaves Borden-Carleton, PEI, on its way across the Confederation Bridge into New Brunswick. The distances and times from the toll booth in PEI are listed in **Table 4**. They include a short stretch of road beyond the end of the 12.9-km bridge.

Table 4	Car Crossing Confederation Bridge
Time (min)	**Distance (km)**
0.0	0.0
2.0	2.4
4.0	4.8
6.0	7.2
8.0	9.6
10.0	12.0
12.0	14.4

   (a) Plot a distance–time graph using the information in **Table 4**. Draw a best-fit straight line.

   (b) Using your graph, find the distance travelled after 5.0 min.

   (c) Using your graph, find the time required to cross the bridge.

   (d) Was the speed constant during the car's trip across the Confederation Bridge? How do you know?

   (e) Calculate the slope of the graph. What does this slope represent?

   (f) What is the speed of the car in kilometres per hour?

6. In **Figure 5**, the motion of two bicycle riders, Tom and Jerry, is described on a distance–time graph.

Motion of Two Bicycle Riders

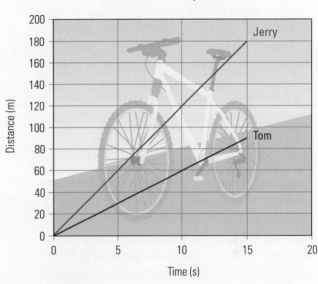

Figure 5
These two cyclists are travelling at different speeds.

   (a) From a qualitative observation of the lines on the graph, which rider has the greater speed?

   (b) Calculate the speed of each rider by determining the slope of each line. Does this quantitative result match your answer to (a)?

   (c) If one of the bicycle riders suddenly stopped, how would the graph of that rider change?

Reflecting

7. When studying motion in physics, it is customary to plot time on the horizontal axis and distance on the vertical axis even if distance is the independent variable in a particular experiment. Suggest a reason for this general rule.

👆 Work the Web

Visit www.nelson.science.com and follow the links from Science 10, 9.7 to research the times for the top five finishers in the most recent Toronto Indy race. Compare their average speeds. Other than the characteristics of each car, what are some factors that affect the average speed over the whole race?

🔺 Challenge

3 You will need to create graphs to illustrate how cars, travelling at different speeds, cover different distances in the same amount of time. What will be plotted on each axis? What units will you use?

Smart Highways

Canada is steadily becoming more urbanized and, as more people choose to live in major cities like Toronto, traffic problems are increasing dramatically. Journey times lengthen, wasting the travellers' time; accidents are more frequent, costing society dearly in injury and property damage (**Figure 1**); pollution levels increase, increasing health costs and decreasing quality of life; and human frustration and stress levels become more pronounced.

Figure 1

Major accidents such as the one pictured may be avoided by the use of high-tech highway systems.

Automated Highways

A suggested improvement to decrease many traffic problems involves the automation of highways in high traffic areas. The Japanese government and several states in the United States, along with many individual companies and agencies, have been investigating this concept. In 1997 a preliminary test of an automation system was conducted on a short stretch of highway north of San Diego, California.

A fully automated highway system might work by having computers control the entry of cars onto a highway, the speed and spacing of cars on the highway, and the cars' dashboard display screens. Drivers would have available a running display of information such as distance to the next exit, current position, and speed. In some proposals drivers have an emergency override, although that has been a problem with the system design to date. No system can work properly unless all vehicles "cooperate." Therefore, driver override would probably be limited to pulling out of the traffic flow and slowing to a stop on the shoulder of the road.

While on a fully automated highway, a car's steering, braking, and speed would all be computer controlled. An automobile could possibly be retrofitted with all the necessary equipment for $1500 or less, according to manufacturers' current estimates. In one highway model, the roadway has magnetic plugs in it for the car steering system to detect, and each car has sensors to measure the front and rear spacing between it and other vehicles (**Figure 2**). Cars can also detect their position by reflecting infrared light from lane markers. Fixed laser beams can be used to sense cars passing and feed this information to a controlling computer.

(a) Suggest reasons why San Diego was chosen for a trial project.
(b) Why is it important that all vehicles "cooperate" on an automated highway? What might be the result of non-cooperation?
(c) Do you think it would be possible to retrofit all vehicles to use the automated highway? What effect would this have? Would everyone want to retrofit their vehicle? What would be the consequences of some people choosing not to retrofit?

Probably the most important change will be the distances between cars. Improvements can be achieved just by controlling vehicles' spacing and speed because in congested traffic all vehicles must necessarily move at the speed of the slowest. Computer-controlled cars can be merged into traffic and exited smoothly at the same speed as the traffic flow, even when visibility is poor. The really significant factor with automated control is that it should be possible to space vehicles as little as 3 m apart while they travel! Currently, drivers are advised to leave enough space between their vehicle and the one ahead to allow at least two seconds for reaction time in case of accidents. Dramatically reducing this spacing allows many more cars to use the roadway without the necessity of altering traffic flow speed.

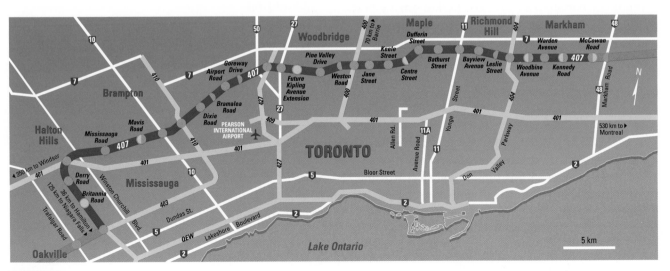

Heads-up display projected on windshield is like display of a modern jet fighter. It lets the driver monitor speed, spacing between cars without taking eyes off the road.

Magnetic nails in pavement are detected by car's automatic steering system.

Onboard computer in car's trunk stays in contact with driver, road, other cars, and central controller.

Ideal spacing: **3 metres**

Radar system helps prevent collisions.

The car's brakes, steering, and throttle are computer-controlled when system takes over (similar to current cruise control systems). Driver has a manual override.

Cars' infrared light detectors pick up light as it bounces off reflective lane markers.

A series of lasers monitors spacing between cars by notifying the network's computer when each car passes.

Figure 2
Multiple road and car sensors linked to a central computer control all aspects of traffic flow.

(d) At 90 km/h, what distance in metres is represented by a 2.0-s reaction time interval? What is the distance for 2.0 s at 120 km/h?

(e) Allowing 5.0 m for an average automobile length and 3.0 m spacing between cars, how many *extra* cars could be added by using an automated highway system compared with the reaction-time distance at 90 km/h from the previous question?

Ontario's "Smart Highway"

Hwy. 407 Express Toll Route (ETR) runs east-west across the north of Toronto and is the world's first all-electronic toll highway (**Figure 3**). Although not a complete automated highway, it is certainly a working illustration of the capability of modern electronic technology to monitor and reduce traffic congestion in a large metropolitan area. Within two years

Figure 3
Hwy. 407 is a privately owned electronic toll road.

of its opening in October 1997, more than 250 000 people used this highway on weekdays, and the number is increasing monthly. By August 2001, paying customers will be able to travel 108 km from Brant Street, Burlington, to Brock Road, Pickering, on 4- or 6-lane roads. Future plans include lane expansion to as many as 10 lanes if necessary to accommodate increasing traffic loads.

The electronic toll road, unlike other toll roads with toll booths, does not require any stopping or slowing down. Along Hwy. 407, each vehicle's entry and exit are detected and recorded electronically from an overhead gantry. For local residents who use the highway frequently, the electronic transaction is handled most conveniently by registering a transponder — a small radio transmitter that is attached to the inside of the windshield behind the rear-view mirror. The electronic equipment on the gantries records the location, time, and identity of the transponder and sends this information over a fibre-optic cable to a central computer. The same process occurs when the vehicle leaves the highway at an interchange. The registered owner of the transponder then receives a monthly bill for the use of the road. For vehicles without transponders, a high-quality video recorder sends a video image of the vehicle to a central processing computer which automatically scans and records the vehicle licence plate number. This is done on entry and exit and the bill is sent to the registered owner of the vehicle. The cost of travelling on this highway depends on the type of vehicle, distance travelled and time of day. For example, driving a car on Hwy. 407 will cost 4 ¢/km at night (11 p.m. to 6 a.m.) and 10 ¢/km during peak traffic in the morning and late afternoon. Large trucks can pay up to 30 ¢/km during peak hours.

(f) A car driver enters Hwy. 407 at the Hwy. 410 interchange at 7:35 a.m. and exits at Yonge Street at 7:56 a.m. From the transponder signal, the computer records a distance of 31.02 km. What is the cost to the driver?

(g) One of the controversies discussed in the early stages of this highway project was the potential for electronic speeding tickets. In your own words, describe how this might be done, with equipment now in place.

(h) The private owners of Hwy. 407 have assured the public that speeding will not be monitored and no information will be transmitted to the police. Do you think the OPP should have the right to charge motorists for speeding using evidence from the Hwy. 407 electronic system?

(i) The speed limit on Hwy. 407 is 100 km/h. Was the driver in (f) speeding? Show your work to justify your answer.

Understanding Concepts

1. State in your own words, what is meant by a smart highway.

2. What are the two most important factors controlled by an automated highway system?

3. What are the advantages of an electronic toll highway over a regular toll highway with toll booths?

4. Summarize the costs (disadvantages) and benefits (advantages) of smart highways in a table with two columns: "Costs" and "Benefits." Write as many points in each column as you can.

Making Connections

5. List several different technologies involved in the proposed automation of highways. Are these technologies current or proposed technologies?

6. It is estimated that an automated highway system would significantly cut pollution on highway routes that are now congested or "gridlocked" daily. Explain what factors would affect pollutant emissions.

Exploring

7. Research recent developments toward automated highways in Canada. Briefly describe how one system, either in proposal or already operating, might work.

✍ Work the Web

Visit www.science.nelson.com and follow the links from Science 10, 9.8. Search for current information about automated highway systems and report on the progress that has been made in this area.

Simulation: Average Speed on an Air Table

To study motion you need to be able to measure distances travelled and the time required for each distance. You can do this with a ruler and stopwatch but this is not very accurate, especially if the distances and times are relatively short. One of the more accurate technologies for studying motion in the laboratory is the air table (**Figure 1**). It works on the reverse principle of the air-hockey table: the air puck rides on a cushion of air that projects out of the bottom of the puck (**Figure 2**). This is similar to how a hovercraft works (**Figure 3**). The high voltage applied between the puck electrode and the carbon paper on the table causes a spark to jump through the paper (making a tiny hole), hit the carbon paper, and "splash" some carbon onto the underside of the paper. This sparking occurs at a constant time interval, which is determined by the setting on the air table controls. Each dot shows where the puck was at that instant.

The purpose of this simulated investigation is to gain some knowledge about the air table and to practise analyzing and evaluating the evidence gathered from this kind of technology. In this activity you are provided with the air table results. Later you will collect your own evidence.

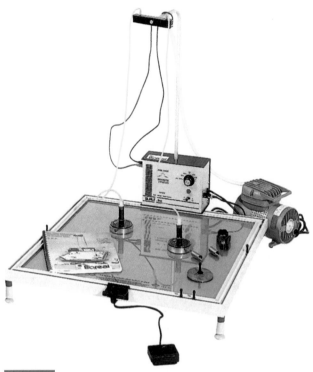

Figure 1

An air table is very convenient for studying motion on a surface because there is little friction.

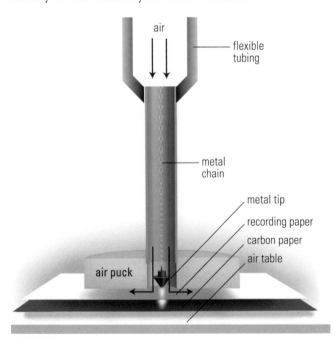

Figure 2

The spark "splashes" some carbon onto the bottom of the paper.

Figure 3

The air puck and the hovercraft both travel on a cushion of air.

Report: Average Speed on an Air Table

Question

What is the average speed of a puck crossing a horizontal air table?

Design

The air puck is given an initial push to send it across a horizontal air table. A graph of total distance versus total time is plotted, and analyzed to determine the average speed of the air puck.

controlled variable: slope of air table
independent variable: time elapsed
dependent variable: total distance travelled

Materials

- air table with timer
- 2 air pucks
- air pump
- legal-sized paper

Table 1 **The Travels of an Air Puck**

Dot	Total time (ms)	Total distance (mm)
1	0	0
2		
3		

Procedure

1 To avoid a shock, follow the instructions for holding the air puck and not touching the table. Students with known heart problems should stay away from the table.

2 Turn on the air pump and timer.

3 Set and record the time interval between sparks at 100 ms.

4 Secure one air puck along one edge of the table using a piece of tape. (This air puck has to remain above the carbon paper for the air table to operate properly.)

5 Place a piece of paper on the air table.

6 Set the other air puck in the centre of the table. Adjust the level of the table to stop the puck from drifting.

7 Set this air puck on the edge of the paper.

8 Press the foot pedal down and hold it to start the spark timer.

9 Give the air puck a brief initial push across the paper.

10 Release the spark pedal when the puck reaches the other side of the paper.

11 Remove the paper. If the spark trail is not satisfactory, repeat steps 5 to 10 with new paper.

Figure 5
Measure from the centre of the first acceptable dot to the centre of each dot.

Analysis and Evaluation

(a) **Figure 4** shows typical results of this (M2) investigation. Starting at the dot (labelled "start") where the dots begin to be about equal distances apart, measure the total distance travelled from the start dot (1) to each subsequent dot (as shown in **Figure 5**).

(b) Why were you instructed to ignore the first few dots?

(c) Record this distance, along with the total elapsed time from the "start" dot, in your table.

(d) Repeat Step (c) for about 10 dots in **Figure 4**.

(e) Draw a total distance versus total elapsed time (V) graph of the evidence gathered.

(f) Calculate the slope of the best-fit straight line to determine the average speed of the puck in metres per second.

(g) Based on your graph, describe the motion of the air puck.

(h) How can information about the size of (O2) experimental uncertainties or errors be obtained from your graph?

(i) Evaluate the design.

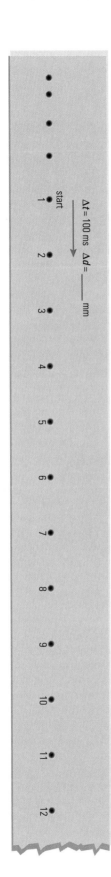

Figure 4
Analyze the results shown on this air table record. The timer is set to make a dot every 100 ms.

Understanding Concepts

1. What are two features of the air table that make it useful in studying motion over short distances?

2. If the air table is not completely horizontal, what complication arises? How would you notice this on the spark timer tracks?

Exploring

3. Sketch what **Figure 4** might look like if the timer on the air table were set to spark more slowly.

Determining an Average Speed

A ticker tape timer is the most commonly used technology for recording distances at regular time intervals for objects moving in a straight line (**Figure 1**). As the object attached to the end of the paper tape moves, it pulls the tape through the timer (**Figure 2**). As the tape moves through the timer, dots are recorded at constant time intervals. This method is not as accurate as the air table because the moving tape passing through the timer experiences greater friction than an air puck on the stationary paper of the air table. Another experimental uncertainty is the length of the time interval, which may vary slightly. However, the dot pattern (**Figure 4** on page 371) and the analysis of this pattern (**Figure 5** on page 371) are the same for both air table and ticker tape timer evidence.

The purpose of this investigation is to determine the average speed of an object by using a ticker tape timer, and to evaluate the experimental design, materials, and procedure.

Question

What is the average speed of the object in uniform motion?

Design

Attach a cart to the ticker tape and let it run down a smooth, slightly inclined ramp at a constant speed. Calculate the slope of a graph of distance versus time to determine the average speed of the cart.

controlled variables: cart, ramp
independent variable: time elapsed
dependent variable: total distance travelled

(a) Prepare a table, similar to **Table 1**, in which to record your evidence.

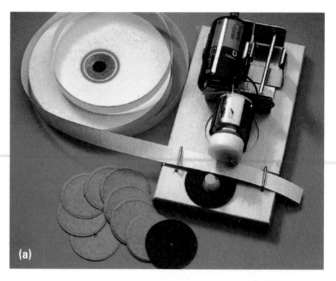

(a)

(b)

Figure 1
(a) The standard ticker tape timer has a small hammer or chain that strikes the paper tape with a carbon paper underneath.
(b) Newer timers produce a spark that leaves a mark on special paper tape.

Table 1	Motion of a Cart	
Dot	**Total time (ms)**	**Total distance (mm)**
1	0	0
2		
3		

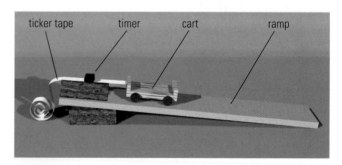

ticker tape   timer   cart   ramp

Figure 2
Studying motion with ticker tape timers is a common experiment in physics.

Materials

- ticker tape timer
- roll of tape
- cart
- about 1–2 m smooth board
- small wood blocks or books
- adhesive tape
- (optional) stand and clamps for timer and/or tape roll

Procedure

1 Place the cart at one end of the board and adjust the height of the board until the cart just starts to move.

2 Set up the ticker tape timer at the upper end of the ramp and either hold or clamp it in place.

3 Attach the end of the tape to the cart with a piece of adhesive tape.

4 Do a trial run to make sure that the tape runs smoothly through the timer when the cart is released, and that the cart's speed is about constant.

5 Return the cart to the top of the track, turn on the timer and then immediately release the cart.

6 Turn off the timer and stop the cart when it reaches the end of the ramp.

7 Cut the tape near the timer and remove the tape from the cart.

8 Record the timer setting in milliseconds.

(b) Starting at the dot where the dots begin to be
(M2) about equal distances apart, measure the total distance travelled (from the beginning) for each subsequent dot. It may be that only every second or sixth dot is used, as directed by your teacher. Measure the total distance to the nearest half millimetre.

(c) Enter the values of the time and distance measurements into your table. Use about 10 distance measurements.

9 Clean up the laboratory station and dispose of, or recycle, any waste.

Analysis and Evaluation

(V) (d) Draw a total distance versus total elapsed time graph of the evidence gathered.

(e) Calculate the slope of the best-fit straight line to determine the average speed of the cart in metres per second.

(02) (f) Evaluate the design, procedure, and materials.

(Q) (g) Write a formal lab report for this investigation.

Understanding Concepts

1. The design used in this investigation tried to compensate for the effect of friction. Briefly explain how this was done.

2. Did your cart travel at a constant speed in this investigation? How do you know?

3. Suppose your cart hit a small imperfection such as a knot or groove in the board and you did not notice this when you were doing this investigation. How might this appear on your ticker tape? Describe and explain the appearance of the dots on the tape.

4. Suggest an experimental design for this investigation that would answer the same question using different equipment.

Exploring

5. Repeat the investigation with the ramp at a different angle. Predict how your results will be affected. Carry out the investigation to test your prediction.

 Challenge

1 Compare the timing device used in this investigation with those available to Galileo. In what ways can timing devices be compared?

Marilyn Reynolds

Police Constable

Marilyn Reynolds has worked as a police constable for over 14 years with Toronto Police Services. She specializes in collision reconstruction, which involves using the laws of physics to determine the cause of serious accidents.

Even at about five, Marilyn remembers thinking about a police career, but it took time to reach her career destination. After finishing some university work, she completed her police training at the Ontario police training facility in Alymer, Ontario. Then it was on to police patrol duties, which meant responding to radio calls that could be domestic disputes, drug cases, or thefts.

During high school, Marilyn particularly enjoyed mathematics and sciences. She discovered, on the job, that police accident reconstruction allowed her to apply her interests and abilities. After hours, she took specialized courses in accident reconstruction offered at Charles O. Bick College, the Toronto police college.

On a typical work day, Marilyn will visit an accident scene once it is determined that the accident is serious. Initially, she looks for evidence such as skid marks and debris. She inspects each vehicle to match up the contact points with the other involved vehicle(s) to determine how they interacted in the collision. Marilyn relies on a total station, a sophisticated type of survey equipment, to help her evaluate an accident scene.

"My reconstruction team collects all the distance measurements with our total station. The information is collected in a data recorder and then downloaded into the computer. With all the significant distance information, we make a scale diagram of the crash site."

"By analyzing skid marks, we can determine a minimum speed that vehicles were travelling at before the accident. We can also get an approximate speed from the amount of crush that the vehicles have undergone."

The information Marilyn obtains is often used in court, to settle insurance claims, and in accident inquests.

Asked what she most enjoys about her work, Marilyn says, "Figuring out exactly what happened in the accident so that we can help the victim's family cope. The investigation also helps the person who caused the collision to learn from his or her mistake. Our findings might point out the need for a caution sign, a stoplight, or even changes in legislation."

After years of accident reconstruction work, Marilyn concludes that the best way to prevent collisions is to "drive defensively and be courteous to other users of the road."

Making Connections

1. Accident reconstruction is just one area of specialization in police work. Find out about other specialty areas. Which ones apply principles of physics? How?

2. Research local, provincial, and national police career opportunities. What are the educational requirements for entry? What high school courses would help you to meet them?

☞ Work the Web

The Toronto Police Service web site is http://www.torontopolice.on.ca. From the site information, list questions you have about a police career.

Key Expectations

Throughout the chapter, you have had opportunities to do the following things:

- Evaluate the costs and benefits, including safety and environmental factors, of transportation technologies. (9.1, 9.4, 9.8)

- Describe and analyze how technology is used to measure objects, obtain scientific knowledge, and to track the motion of traffic. (9.3, 9.4, 9.8, 9.9, 9.10)

- Describe quantitatively and graphically the relationship among average speed, distance and time, and solve simple problems using this relationship. (9.4, 9.5, 9.7)

- Demonstrate the skills required to plan an inquiry into motion, controlling variables, and adapting procedures. (9.4)

- Use a broad range of tools and techniques safely, accurately, and effectively to obtain, organize and analyze distance and motion. (9.4, 9.6, 9.9, 9.10)

- Analyze everyday phenomena and technologies in terms of the motions involved. (9.4, 9.8)

- Conduct and analyze experiments to determine average speed. (9.4, 9.9, 9.10)

- Analyze and evaluate evidence to identify some experimental uncertainties or errors. (9.4, 9.9, 9.10)

- Distinguish among constant, instantaneous, and average speed. (9.5)

- Select and use appropriate vocabulary, SI units, quantity symbols, and graphs to communicate scientific and technological concepts, measurements and analyses. (all)

Key Terms

average speed	precision rule
certainty	quantity symbols
certainty rule	rounding
constant speed	SI
defining equation	significant digits
distance	slope of a line
instantaneous speed	time
precision	uniform motion

Make a Summary

Speed can be described or obtained in a variety of ways. Use the categories listed below to describe or obtain the speed of, for example, a cross-country skier.

- empirical (descriptive) definition in words
- defining equation in symbols
- common units of measure
- graphical representation
- design of an experiment

Reflect on your Learning

Revisit your answers to the Reflect on your Learning questions, page 341, in the Getting Started.

- How has your thinking changed?

- What new questions do you have?

Chapter 9 Review

Understanding Concepts

1. State the number of significant digits in each of the following values.
   (a) 10.2 km
   (b) 0.02 m
   (c) 5.0 cm

2. State, in your own words, the rule for determining the number of digits allowed in an answer calculated by multiplying two measured values.

3. If metres per second, m/s, is the unit of measure of a value,
   (a) what is the defining equation for the value?
   (b) what evidence is collected to calculate the value?
   (c) what labels are on the axes of the graph used to present the evidence?
   (d) what does the slope of this graph yield?

4. Two runners, Tiiu and Laura, compete in a marathon race. In one particular part of the race, Tiiu has twice the average speed of Laura.
   (a) Compare their distances travelled during the same time interval.
   (b) Compare their times required to run the same distance.
   (c) How would their distance-time graphs compare? Sketch the graphs to illustrate your answer.

5. On some major highways, lines were drawn across the highway at regular intervals. Police in an aircraft flew high above the road and monitored the vehicles travelling on the road. If a speeding vehicle was found, police on the ground were notified. What information did the police in the aircraft have to know and measure to determine the speed of a particular car?

6. When designing experiments to measure the speed of an object in a classroom laboratory, what are three different technologies that could be used?

Applying Inquiry Skills

7. Percy Williams is the only Canadian athlete to have ever won gold Olympic medals in both the 100-m and the 200-m sprints. He accomplished this amazing feat in the 1928 Amsterdam Olympics. Calculate the missing quantities in **Table 1**. Show your work.

Table 1 Percy Williams' Gold Medal Performances

Average speed (m/s)	Distance (m)	Time (s)
(a)	100	10.8
9.17	200	(b)

8. In the 1999 World Solar Car Challenge, the Queen's University *Radiance* car came second, completing the 2998.7-km course across Australia in a time of 41.58 h. What was the average speed of the *Radiance* (**Figure 1**)?

Figure 1

9. A car is moving at a constant 88 km/h when a dog suddenly appears on the road ahead. The driver immediately brakes to avoid hitting the dog.
   (a) Convert 88 km/h into metres per second.
   (b) If the reaction time of the driver is 0.2 s, how far has the car moved by the time the driver just touches the brake pedal?

10. In 1979, Bryan Allen pedalled the *Gossamer Albatross* aircraft 35 km across the English Channel in a time of 169 min (**Figure 2**).
    (a) Calculate the average speed of the aircraft.
    (b) During his famous flight, Allen had to battle a headwind that slowed him down. With no wind, he is capable of pedalling at a constant rate to keep the plane flying at 19 km/h. How long would the crossing have taken flying at 19 km/h?

Figure 2

11. Bill starts jogging down the road and 10 s later his younger brother, Mark, runs after him. The distance–time graph for both Bill (B) and Mark (M) is shown in **Figure 3**. Use the graph to answer the following questions.

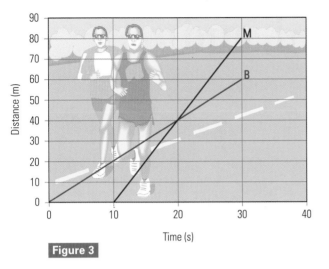

Bill's and Mark's Speeds

Figure 3

(a) What is Bill's average speed?
(b) What is Mark's average speed, from the time when he starts to run?
(c) At what distance does Mark catch up to Bill?
(d) How far is Mark ahead of Bill at the end of 30 s?

12. Complete the Analysis and Evaluation in the following lab report.

Question
What is Heather's average swimming speed over 50 m?

Design
Several of Heather's teammates are positioned every 10.0 m with stopwatches. All teammates start their stopwatches when Heather dives into the pool and each stops their watch when Heather reaches their assigned distance.

Evidence

Table 2   Heather's Swimming Record

Distance (m)	Time (s)
0.0	0.0
10.0	4.1
20.0	9.9
30.0	15.9
40.0	19.5
50.0	25.2

Analysis and Evaluation
(a) Plot a distance–time graph of Heather's swim.
(b) Calculate the slope of the best-fit straight line and answer the Question.
(c) Evaluate the design. What alternative design would be more efficient?

13. Suppose someone designed the following technology to sell to police forces for monitoring speeding vehicles. A cable, attached to a control box, is placed across a single lane of traffic. When the front wheels of a vehicle cross the cable (**Figure 4**), a timer starts and then stops when the rear wheels of the vehicle cross the cable. The control box calculates the average speed of the vehicle and transmits this information to a nearby police cruiser.

Figure 4

(a) What is the basic flaw in this design?
(b) Suggest a way to fix this design so that it will be accurate.

Making Connections

14. Cell phone technology has developed to the point that good quality units are readily available and affordable.
(a) What is a significant benefit of having a cell phone in a vehicle?
(b) What are some risks created when someone uses a cell phone while driving a vehicle?
(c) It takes about 5.0 s to dial a number on a cell phone. How far would a vehicle travel while the number is being dialed, if the vehicle is moving at a constant speed of 60 km/h?
(d) What can you do to reduce the risks when cell phones are used in vehicles?

15. Dmitri has three alternative means of getting to school: taking the bus, catching a ride in his friend's car, or riding his bike. Each mode of transportation follows a slightly different route from Dmitri's house to his school. The bus travels a distance of 7.5 km at an average speed of 18 km/h; the car travels 6.0 km at 24 km/h, and the bike travels 5.6 km at 16 km/h. Calculate the time each alternative takes. Evaluate each of the three modes of transportation from economic, environmental, health, and social perspectives.

10 Distance, Speed, and Acceleration

Getting Started

HOW DO YOU KNOW IF YOU ARE MOVING?

This seems like a simple question with an obvious answer. If you are napping on a comfortable sofa or standing at a bus stop, you would say that you are not moving. Perhaps, using physics language, you might say that you are "at rest." You know you are not moving because it does not look as though your fixed surroundings are moving, and you do not feel as though you are moving. In fact, you and everything else on Earth are moving around the Sun at an amazing thirty kilometres per second (30 km/s) (**Figure 1**). Why do we not notice this? There are three main reasons: we cannot see ourselves moving past anything else; we do not feel any movement because we are moving at a fairly constant speed; and the air is moving with us.

Imagine that you are in an elevator (**Figure 2**). If the elevator is travelling at a constant speed in the middle of its trip, you have little

Figure 1
We cannot sense Earth's rapid motion through space.

Figure 2
You can feel the acceleration when an elevator starts and stops.

sensation of movement. However, if the elevator is speeding up or slowing down, you can feel the effect of this change in speed in your body. If you were carrying a bag of groceries, the effect of a changing speed would be quite noticeable in your arms.

The feeling of rapidly changing speed is something that many people enjoy. Many amusement park rides, such as roller coasters (**Figure 3**), are specifically designed to produce rapid changes in speed and direction. The next time you are enjoying some kind of motion, take a moment to think about the physics behind the movement.

When you start to walk, run, or ride, you must increase your speed and, therefore, you must accelerate (**Figure 4**). The study of acceleration is, in part, the study of increasing and decreasing speed. Not only can you feel the acceleration but you can also measure it. Measuring the acceleration is important to sprinters as they train for their races. One of the most important performance indicators for natural and machine motion is acceleration.

Figure 3
Acceleration is very noticeable on a roller coaster.

Figure 4
Accelerating up to speed

Reflect on your Learning

1. Is it possible for you to be somewhere and not be moving? Where would this place be?

2. What is your impression of what happens to the speed of a rock when it is dropped?

3. Is it possible to move an object that is initially at rest from one place to another without accelerating it? Explain your answer.

4. As speed increases, what happens to the distance travelled in each second?

5. Try this "thought experiment": You are in a car that is gradually increasing its speed. You are measuring the time it takes to travel from one telephone pole to the next. Would the time between each pair of poles be the same? If not, how would it change?

Throughout this chapter, note any changes in your ideas as you learn new concepts and develop your skills.

Try This Activity Leaving a Trail

🖐 Wear all appropriate safety equipment, including a helmet and padding.

You will need a skateboard, in-line skates, or a bicycle, plus the appropriate helmet and pads. (Alternatively, you could just run!) You will also need a bottle that slowly drips water, which you can use to mark equal time intervals. Choose an

open, safe place such as a paved area in the school grounds. While speeding up, travelling at constant speed, and slowing down, use the dripping bottle to make marks on the ground at regular time intervals.

(a) Describe the pattern of marks left by the water.

Distance, Speed, and Acceleration **379**

DECISION-MAKING SKILLS MENU
- ● Defining the Issue
- ○ Identifying Alternatives
- ● Researching
- ● Analyzing the Issue
- ● Defending a Decision
- ○ Evaluating

Travelling Off-Road

Given the nature of our landscape, it is perhaps natural that many Canadians feel a need to drive vehicles that can travel over a wide variety of terrain (**Figures 1** and **2**). In 1922, Joseph Armand Bombardier, a mechanic from Valcourt, Québec, designed a propeller-driven sled, the first of many snow vehicles that he was to develop. Bombardier made the vehicle more practical by incorporating steering by skis in front of double looped tracks. In the mid-1950s, the introduction of the air-cooled, two-stroke engine made possible the small, powerful sports models common today, such as the Ski-Doo and the Lynx.

Snowmobiles provide transportation into areas previously impassable except on skis, snowshoes, or dogsled. In the north of Canada, snowmobiles are the main means of surface transportation for many months of the year. They deliver mail, aid in search-and-rescue missions, and provide emergency medical help. They also allow people to use cabins and cottages year-round. There are snowmobile trails in many parts of the country, and snowmobile racing is a popular sport. But the explosion in the use of snowmobiles brings serious concerns about noise, environmental damage, and rider safety. Each year, as more and more people take to the backcountry on their snowmobiles, there are more deaths from avalanches or falling through thin ice. While the snowmobile is an extremely useful vehicle, its misuse sometimes involves vandalism, habitat destruction, and poaching. For these reasons, plus the fact that snowmobiles are powerful machines capable of travelling up to 160 km/h, all provinces have passed regulations governing and restricting the use of snowmobiles. Many snowmobile clubs have also set safety rules.

Motorized travel in the backcountry is no longer limited to the winter months as the development of the all-terrain vehicle (ATV) makes off-road areas accessible year-round. Over 20 million ATVs have been sold in North America. While farmers, ranchers, trappers, forestry workers, and environmental scientists use ATVs for work, the tremendous increase in ATV sales is largely due to their recreational use. Like snowmobiles, ATVs can have a serious impact on the environment (**Figure 3**). New, unplanned trails form as riders compete to see who can climb the steepest hill. Soil loses its organic material and becomes compacted, increasing water runoff and leading to serious erosion. Sand dunes are particularly fragile and can be permanently destroyed if ATVs disturb the vegetation that stabilizes the dunes. Even fish can suffer, when their streams are used as trails.

Figure 1

Snowmobiling is a popular winter recreation and sport, as well as being an essential means for transportation.

Figure 2

ATVs have opened up many backcountry areas. As people travel faster on more powerful machines and seek more challenging routes, accidents increase.

As the numbers of ATVs and snowmobiles increase, so does the number of accidents, most frequently involving young, inexperienced, and untrained riders. Alcohol is often a contributing factor. Riders' associations have established safety courses that teach operators about the safe and proper use of their machines. The public is becoming increasingly concerned about the impact of personal recreational vehicles, leading provincial governments to enact regulations governing their use.

Figure 3
Continuous use of ATVs can create considerable environmental damage. Here, repeated use of a trail is causing erosion.

🖑 **Work the Web**

Visit www.science.nelson.com and follow the links through Science 10 to 10.1. Find some accident statistics on snowmobile and ATV use. Use these in your article to support your position.

Understanding the Issue

1. In your own words, describe the origin of the snowmobile.

2. List three nonrecreational uses of snowmobiles.

3. List at least three positive and three negative aspects of snowmobile use.

4. Describe the environmental impact of the backcountry use of ATVs.

5. Give four examples of unsafe uses of snowmobiles or ATVs.

Take a Stand   Should off-road vehicles be more closely regulated?

Point

Opinion of environmentalist
The environmental impact of ATVs is clearly shown by the damage to soil, vegetation, wildlife, and water. We need stricter laws to protect the environment and threatened species' habitat.

Opinion of police officer
Many riders involved in snowmobile and ATV accidents are under 16 years old. Mandatory training, testing, and licensing are required to reduce the number of ATV injuries and fatalities.

Counterpoint

Opinion of recreation group member
People who travel in the backcountry should be monitoring these vehicles' use. It would be better for recreation groups to educate the public on outdoor ethics than for governments to bring in laws.

Opinion of ATV owner
It is the parents' responsibility to train their children to use ATVs safely. My children only drive on private land and they should be free to enjoy the great outdoors without bureaucratic regulation.

What do you think?

1. Find out what regulations govern the use of snowmobiles and ATVs in your province. Research Ⓘ licensing requirements, operating regulations, access to public land, and education programs.
2. Produce an information pamphlet for teenagers about the dangers associated with ATVs, or Ⓡ prepare a multi-media presentation about the regulations and issues associated with off-road vehicles.

Speed Comparisons

Speed is one of many topics included in the study of motion. However, even within the topic of speed, there are many possible classifications or categories: constant or changing, increasing or decreasing, in a straight line, a circle, or on some other path. Classification is an important part of science. Scientists observe, classify, and organize information. This is all part of the process of trying to find patterns in the world around us. Eventually the aim of science is to explain these patterns. The purpose of this activity is to practise describing, interpreting, and classifying speed in different situations.

Question

What are some different categories of the speed of an object?

Design

In **Figures 1** to **4** you can see different examples or categories of speed represented. Study each one carefully so that you can clearly describe each situation, make distinctions among them, and eventually develop your own idea of what each situation represents.

Evidence

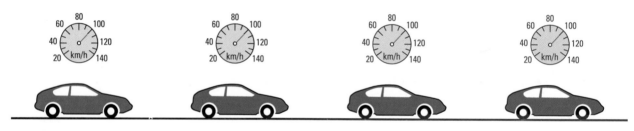

Figure 1

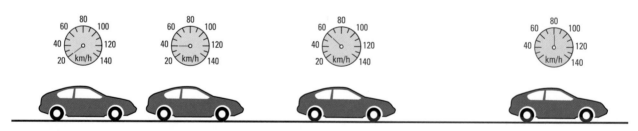

Figure 2

Analysis

(a) Observe and interpret what is happening in **Figures 1** to **4**. Using words, graphs, and any other method of communication, describe as much as you can about the distances travelled, speed, and changes in speed of the four vehicles.

(b) Classify the four situations into categories.

(c) Which categories (from question 2) are easiest to classify? Why?

 Challenge

3 How might you collect speed–time evidence to construct graphs?

Understanding Concepts

1. How would a student demonstrate, on a bicycle, the different categories of speed that you classified in the Analysis?

2. What are some limitations of trying to represent speed in drawings, such as **Figures 1** to **4**?

3. **(a)** Write a scientific question in terms of independent
   (K2) and dependent variables and related to one of the motions represented in **Figures 1** to **4**.

   (b) Briefly describe an experiment that might answer your question.

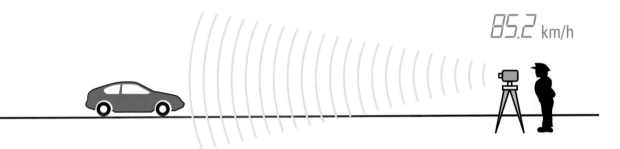

Figure 3

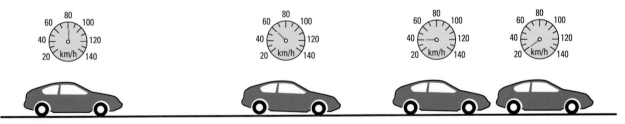

Figure 4

Defining Acceleration

Suppose you are riding in a bus moving at a constant speed of 100 km/h (**Figure 1**). This means that for every hour on the bus, you travel a distance of 100 km. Of course, this also means that the bus travels 200 km every two hours or 50 km every half-hour. All these ratios of distance to time are the same. However, when the bus starts from rest, its speed increases.

When the speed is not constant, it may be changing slowly or rapidly. It may be increasing or decreasing. One aim of science is to describe these events as precisely and simply as possible. The term acceleration describes all situations in which the speed is changing. **Acceleration** (a) is the rate of change in speed and is calculated by the ratio of the change in speed (Δv) to the time interval (Δt) during which this change occurred.

$$a = \frac{\Delta v}{\Delta t} \quad \text{or} \quad a_{av} = \frac{\Delta v}{\Delta t}$$

If this ratio remains constant throughout the acceleration, then the acceleration is called constant (or uniform) acceleration. During **constant acceleration**, the same change in speed (Δv) occurs in each equal interval of time (Δt).

When acceleration varies over a period of time, we generally describe the object's average acceleration. **Average acceleration** (a_{av}) is the average rate of change in speed of an object.

For all calculations in this unit of study, the acceleration is assumed to be constant so either of the equations above can be used correctly.

Suppose you speed up on a motorcycle from rest (0 m/s) to 9.0 m/s in a time of 2.0 s. Your change in speed is 9.0 m/s and your average acceleration is calculated as follows:

$\Delta v = 9.0 \text{ m/s}$

$\Delta t = 2.0 \text{ s}$

$a_{av} = ?$

$$a_{av} = \frac{\Delta v}{\Delta t}$$

$$= \frac{9.0 \frac{m}{s}}{2.0 \text{ s}}$$

$$= 4.5 \frac{m/s}{s}$$

The average acceleration is $4.5 \frac{m/s}{s}$. (This answer is read as "four point five metres per second per second.")

In other words, you will increase your speed by an average of 4.5 m/s during every second of travel. Starting from rest, your speed is 4.5 m/s at the end of the 1st second; 9.0 m/s at the end of the 2nd second; and 13.5 m/s at the end of the 3rd second.

Did You Know?

Astronauts are launched in a horizontal position because in that position the human body can briefly tolerate acclerations of as much as 120 m/s². In the vertical position, acclerations of only 30 m/s² usually result in unconsciousness.

The units for acceleration are the units of the speed divided by the units of time, exactly as specified in the definition of acceleration. For convenience and efficiency the final units are usually simplified from $\frac{m/s}{s}$ to m/s².

$$4.5 \frac{m/s}{s} = 4.5 \frac{m}{s^2} \quad \text{or} \quad 4.5 \text{ m/s}^2$$

This is read as "four point five metres per second squared." It means the same as "metres per second per second."

We can use other units for acceleration, as long as they include the ratio of speed units to time units. The most common example is the result of an acceleration road test for cars. It is convenient for the people testing the cars and for the consumers to know the change in speed in kilometres per hour and the time in seconds. A particularly powerful car may accelerate from 0 to 100 km/h in 6.0 s. The average acceleration of this car can be calculated:

$\Delta v = 100$ km/h

$\Delta t = 6.0$ s

$a_{av} = ?$

$$a_{av} = \frac{\Delta v}{\Delta t}$$

$$= \frac{100 \frac{km}{h}}{6.0 \text{ s}}$$

$$= 17 \frac{km/h}{s} \text{ or } 17 \text{ (km/h)/s}$$

The average acceleration is $17 \frac{km/h}{s}$. This is read as "seventeen kilometres per hour per second." What does this value mean? It means that, on average, at the end of each second, the car is moving 17 km/h faster than it was at the end of the previous second.

The following examples work through some acceleration questions.

Sample Problem 1

Myriam Bédard accelerates at an average 2.5 m/s² for 1.5 s (**Figure 2**). What is her change in speed at the end of 1.5 s?

$a_{av} = 2.5$ m/s²

$\Delta t = 1.5$ s

$\Delta v = ?$

$$a_{av} = \frac{\Delta v}{\Delta t} \qquad \text{or} \qquad a_{av} = \frac{\Delta v}{\Delta t}$$

$$\Delta v = a_{av} \Delta t \qquad\qquad 2.5 \frac{m}{s^2} = \frac{\Delta v}{1.5 \text{ s}}$$

$$= 2.5 \frac{m}{s^2} \times 1.5 \text{ s} \qquad \Delta v = 2.5 \frac{m}{s^2} \times 1.5 \text{ s}$$

$$= 3.8 \frac{m}{s} \qquad\qquad\qquad = 3.8 \frac{m}{s}$$

Bédard's change in speed is 3.8 m/s.

Figure 2
Canadian Myriam Bédard won two gold medals in biathlon in the 1994 Winter Olympics.

> The cancellation of units for $a_{av}\Delta t$ can be shown as
>
> $$\Delta v = 2.5 \frac{m}{s^2} \times 1.5 \text{ s} \quad \text{or}$$
>
> $$\Delta v = 2.5 \frac{m}{s^{21}} \times 1.5 \text{ s}$$

Sample Problem 2

A skateboarder rolls down a hill and changes his speed from rest to 1.9 m/s (**Figure 3**). If the average acceleration down the hill is 0.40 m/s², for how long was the skateboarder on the hill?

$\Delta v = 1.9$ m/s

$a_{av} = 0.40$ m/s²

$\Delta t = ?$

$$a_{av} = \frac{\Delta v}{\Delta t} \qquad \text{or} \qquad a_{av} = \frac{\Delta v}{\Delta t}$$

$$\Delta t = \frac{\Delta v}{a_{av}}$$

$$0.40 \frac{m}{s^2} = \frac{1.9 \frac{m}{s}}{\Delta t}$$

$$= \frac{1.9 \frac{\cancel{m}}{\cancel{s}}}{0.40 \frac{\cancel{m}}{\cancel{s^2}}}$$

$$0.40 \frac{m}{s^2} \times \Delta t = 1.9 \frac{m}{s}$$

$$= 4.8 \text{ s}$$

$$\Delta t = \frac{1.9 \frac{\cancel{m}}{\cancel{s}}}{0.40 \frac{\cancel{m}}{\cancel{s^2}}}$$

$$= 4.8 \text{ s}$$

A quick way to simplify the units in this calculation is to think of the units in the denominator as a fraction and multiply by the reciprocal.

$$\Delta t = \frac{1.9 \frac{m}{s}}{0.40 \frac{m}{s^2}} = 4.8 \frac{\cancel{m}}{\cancel{s}} \cdot \frac{s^{\cancel{2}}}{\cancel{m}} = 4.8 \text{ s}$$

The skateboarder had spent 4.8 s on the hill.

In Sample Problems 1 and 2, the information given in the questions has a certainty of two significant digits. Therefore, the final answer should also have a certainty of two significant digits.

Refining the Acceleration Equation

In the real world, when you accelerate in a car, you usually know your initial speed. Typically, you would accelerate to some final speed such as the speed limit. Both the initial speed (v_1) and the final speed (v_2) affect your change in speed.

$$\Delta v = v_2 - v_1$$

The acceleration definition, $a_{av} = \frac{\Delta v}{\Delta t}$, can now be written more specifically as $a_{av} = \frac{v_2 - v_1}{\Delta t}$.

Note that other symbols are sometimes used in place of v_1 and v_2, such as v_i and v_f or u and v, respectively. You may see these in other books or web sites.

Sample Problem 3

Kerrin Lee-Gartner is moving at 1.8 m/s near the top of a hill (**Figure 4**). 4.2 s later she is travelling at 8.3 m/s. What is her average acceleration?

$v_1 = 1.8$ m/s

$\Delta t = 4.2$ s

$v_2 = 8.3$ m/s

$a_{av} = ?$

$$a_{av} = \frac{v_2 - v_1}{\Delta t}$$

$$= \frac{(8.3 - 1.8) \frac{m}{s}}{4.2 \text{ s}}$$

$$= 1.5 \frac{m}{s^2}$$

Lee-Gartner's average acceleration is 1.5 m/s².

Another way of thinking about acceleration is to realize that your final speed is determined by your initial speed plus your change in speed. If you are initially moving at 5.0 m/s and gain 2.0 m/s while accelerating, then your final speed is 7.0 m/s.

$$v_2 = v_1 + \Delta v$$
$$= 5.0\,\frac{m}{s} + 2.0\,\frac{m}{s}$$
$$= 7.0 \text{ m/s}$$

The change in speed, Δv, is the result of the acceleration and equals $a_{av}\Delta t$. Substituting $a_{av}\Delta t$ into the above equation gives a convenient equation for acceleration but in a different format from the above equation.

$$v_2 = v_1 + a_{av}\Delta t$$

This equation is particularly convenient when you are predicting a final speed (Sample Problem 4) and some people also find it useful for predicting initial speeds (Sample Problem 5).

Sample Problem 4

A bus with an initial speed of 12 m/s accelerates at 0.62 m/s^2 for 15 s (**Figure 5**). What is the final speed of the bus?

$v_1 = 12$ m/s
$a_{av} = 0.62$ m/s^2
$\Delta t = 15$ s
$v_2 = ?$

$$v_2 = v_1 + a_{av}\Delta t$$
$$= 12\,\frac{m}{s} + 0.62\,\frac{m}{s^2} \times 15\,\cancel{s}$$
$$= 21\,\frac{m}{s}$$

The final speed of the bus is 21 m/s.

Sample Problem 5

A snowmobile reaches a final speed of 22.5 m/s after accelerating at 1.2 m/s^2 for 17 s (**Figure 6**). What was the initial speed of the snowmobile?

$v_2 = 22.5$ m/s
$a_{av} = 1.2$ m/s^2
$\Delta t = 17$ s
$v_1 = ?$

$$v_2 = v_1 + a_{av}\Delta t$$
$$v_1 = v_2 - a_{av}\Delta t$$
$$v_1 = 22.5\,\frac{m}{s} - 1.2\,\frac{m}{s^2} \times 17\,\cancel{s}$$
$$= 2.1\,\frac{m}{s}$$

or

$$v_2 = v_1 + a_{av}\Delta t$$
$$22.5\,\frac{m}{s} = v_1 + 1.2\,\frac{m}{s^2} \times 17\text{ s}$$
$$v_1 = 22.5\,\frac{m}{s} - 1.2\,\frac{m}{s^2} \times 17\,\cancel{s}$$
$$= 2.1\,\frac{m}{s}$$

The initial speed of the snowmobile was 2.1 m/s.

Acceleration While Slowing Down

All vehicles that speed up eventually have to slow down. How quickly this occurs is an important safety consideration. The definition of acceleration includes a change in speed that can be either an increase or a decrease. There is no difference in the procedure for solving problems if the speed decreases, but the acceleration you obtain or use will have a negative sign.

Sample Problem 6

In a race, a car travelling at 100 km/h comes to a stop in 5.0 s. What is the average acceleration?

$v_1 = 100$ km/h

$v_2 = 0$

$\Delta t = 5.0$ s

$a_{av} = ?$

$$a_{av} = \frac{v_2 - v_1}{\Delta t}$$

$$= \frac{0 - 100 \frac{km}{h}}{5.0 \text{ s}}$$

$$= -20 \frac{km/h}{s}$$

The average acceleration of the car is −20 (km/h)/s.

Understanding Concepts

1. In uniform or constant speed, the speed is the same during each time interval. In constant acceleration, what is the same in each time interval?

2. You and your friend are on your bicycles and accelerate from rest. If your average acceleration is double that of your friend, how will your change in speed compare with your friend's after the same time interval?

3. In a road test, car A accelerates from rest (0 km/h) to 100.0 km/h in 16.0 s and car B takes 8.0 s in the same test. Which car has the greater average acceleration? By how many times?

4. A cyclist increases her speed by 5.0 m/s in a time of 4.5 s. What is her acceleration?

5. A roller coaster car accelerates at 8.0 m/s² for 4.0 s. What is the change in the speed of the roller coaster car?

6. The human heart pumps about 60 mL of blood into the aorta during a single stroke, which lasts about 0.1 s. In a single stroke, a pulse of blood is accelerated from rest to about 50 cm/s. Calculate the average acceleration of the blood in metres per second squared.

7. A downhill skier moving at 2.5 m/s accelerates to 20.0 m/s in a time of 3.8 s.

   (a) Calculate the average acceleration of the skier.

   (b) What does this acceleration mean?

8. An electric car accelerates from rest to 50.0 km/h in 8.20 s.

   (a) What is the average acceleration of the electric car in kilometres per hour per second?

   (b) Assuming constant acceleration, what time would the car take to accelerate from 40 km/h to 60 km/h?

Figure 7

9. A baseball player running at 6.0 m/s slides into home plate and stops in 2.5 s (**Figure 7**). What is the average acceleration of the baseball player?

Questions 10–14 require you to rearrange the acceleration equation.

10. You are coasting on your skateboard at 1.4 m/s and you decide to speed up. If you accelerate at 0.50 m/s² for 7.0 s, what is your final speed?

11. A train is moving at 5.0 km/h and accelerates at 95 km/h² for 0.50 h. What is the final speed at the end of the 0.50 h?

12. A car travelling at a constant speed approaches the top of a hill. The car rolls down the hill at an acceleration of 2.0 m/s² for 8.0 s and reaches a final speed of 26 m/s. What was the initial speed of the car before accelerating down the hill?

13. An octopus can accelerate rapidly by squirting a stream of water for propulsion. An octopus moving at 0.10 m/s accelerates at 5.5 m/s² to a final speed of 3.5 m/s. What is the elapsed time during the acceleration?

14. The NASA space shuttle touches down on a runway at an initial speed of 95 m/s and accelerates at a rate of –4.40 m/s² (**Figure 8**). How much time does it take for the shuttle to stop?

Figure 8

Making Connections

15. Complete the analysis for the following investigation.

Question
Which minivan has the greatest average acceleration?

Design
Tests by *Consumer Report* provide evidence for the time for various minivans to reach 100 km/h from rest. These values are used to determine their average acceleration.

Table 1	Time for Minivans to Reach 100 km/h		
Minivan	**Initial speed (km/h)**	**Final speed (km/h)**	**Time (s)**
Plymouth Grand Voyager	0	100	11.2
Ford Windstar	0	100	9.5
Pontiac Trans Sport	0	100	10.3
Chevrolet Venture	0	100	10.0

Analysis
(a) Calculate the average acceleration for each minivan.

(b) Which minivan has the greatest average acceleration?

16. It is said that nobody is killed by falling, only by the sudden stop at the end of the fall. Interpret this statement in terms of acceleration. How do stunt performers survive their falls?

Exploring

17. Choose one of the following Guinness® World Record questions and provide the answers in metric units.

(a) What is the acceleration of the world-record, most-expensive production car?

(b) What is the world record for the acceleration of a land vehicle with a driver?

(c) Describe the world record for the longest free fall by a stunt person.

Challenge

3 Braking results in accelerating while slowing down. Use the formula $a = \dfrac{v_2 - v_1}{\Delta t}$, choose a fixed value for a, and find out how much time it takes for a car to stop from a variety of speeds (v_1).

👆Work the Web

A jet on an aircraft carrier has a limited distance and time to become airborne. Similarly, it has to land and stop very rapidly. What are some typical accelerations of a jet taking off from, and landing on, an aircraft carrier? How are these accelerations achieved? Visit science.nelson.com and link through Science 10 to 10.3 to help you with your research. Illustrate your discoveries with a series of labelled sketches.

Speed–Time Graphs for Acceleration

Scientists use many different ways of communicating what they observe: some methods are simple (such as a straightforward observation); some are more comprehensive (such as a graph); and others are more powerful (such as a scientific law). Knowing and using a variety of ways of communicating helps us to develop a better understanding of a topic such as acceleration.

Acceleration is a description of the relationship between speed and time. In the previous section we described acceleration using words, a number with units, and a mathematical definition. In this section we will use tables and graphs to communicate acceleration.

Acceleration is basically a change in speed over time. **Figures 1** and **2** show speed increasing or decreasing as a function of time. As you know, the slope of a line on a graph indicates the rate of change in one variable (Δy) compared to a second variable (Δx). If the variables are speed (on the *y*-axis) and time (on the *x*-axis), then the slope ($\Delta y/\Delta x$) corresponds to the mathematical definition of acceleration ($\Delta v/\Delta t$). The units of the slope of a speed–time graph are the units of speed divided by the units of time. For example, in **Figure 3**

$$\text{slope} = \frac{\text{rise}}{\text{run}} = \frac{\Delta y}{\Delta x}$$

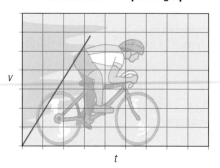

Acceleration — Speeding Up

Figure 1

A cyclist accelerates at the start of a race.

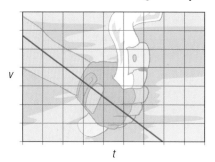

Acceleration — Slowing to a Stop

Figure 2

Braking results in negative acceleration.

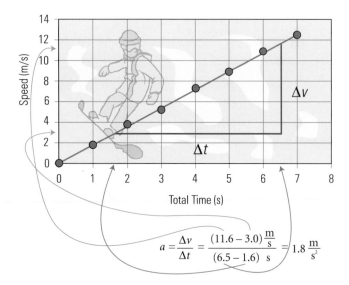

Acceleration of a Snowboarder

$$a = \frac{\Delta v}{\Delta t} = \frac{(11.6 - 3.0)\frac{m}{s}}{(6.5 - 1.6)\ s} = 1.8\ \frac{m}{s^2}$$

Figure 3

Acceleration of a snowboarder

The type of slope of a speed–time graph tells us a lot about the type of acceleration (**Table 1**): a positive slope represents positive acceleration (an object speeding up); a negative slope represents negative acceleration (an object slowing down). In addition, the steepness of the slope represents the size of the acceleration.

In summary, the **slope of the line** on a speed-time graph provides the acceleration. A positive slope represents positive acceleration (object speeding up) and a negative slope represents negative acceleration (object slowing down). Now let's consider the area under the line on a speed-time graph. What does it give us?

Area Under the Line on a Speed–Time Graph

Suppose you are training for a bicycle race and your racing partner records your speed every 10 s over a total distance of 250 m (**Table 2**). Notice that the speed increases by 2.0 m/s every 10.0 s. This represents a constant acceleration because the increase in speed, Δv, is the same for every equal time interval, Δt. The speed–time graph (**Figure 4**) illustrates constant acceleration. You know that the slope of the line on a speed–time graph represents the acceleration. What feature, if any, of this graph would give us the distance travelled: 250 m? Notice that the distance units (m) can be obtained from multiplying speed (m/s) by time (s).

For example,

$$1\ \text{m} = 1\frac{\text{m}}{\text{s}} \times 1\ \text{s}$$

This also corresponds to the distance as calculated from the defining equation for speed:

$$v = \frac{\Delta d}{\Delta t} \qquad \Delta d = v\Delta t$$

Two variables multiplied together suggest the area of a geometric shape. Is there an area corresponding to 250 m in the speed–time graph in **Figure 4**? The area of the rectangle bounded by the axes and dotted lines would be 500 m.

$$\text{area} = 10\frac{\text{m}}{\text{s}} \times 50\ \text{s}$$
$$= 500\ \text{m}$$

The distance travelled is actually 250 m or one-half of this area. The area of the triangle underneath the line on the graph is one-half the area of the complete rectangle. Does the area of this triangle relate to the distance travelled?

We have no proof, but rather a mathematical theorem at this point. Testing this theorem in the laboratory clearly shows that **the area under the line in a speed–time graph equals the distance travelled during the time interval.**

Table 1   **Relationship Between Slope and Acceleration**

Slope	Sample Speed–Time Graph	Interpretation
high positive value		high positive acceleration (rapidly increasing speed)
low positive value		low positive acceleration (slowly increasing speed)
zero		zero acceleration (constant speed)
negative value		moderate negative acceleration (decreasing speed)

Table 2   **Acceleration on a Bicycle**

Time (s)	Speed (m/s)
0.0	0.0
10.0	2.0
20.0	4.0
30.0	6.0
40.0	8.0
50.0	10.0

Acceleration on a Bicycle

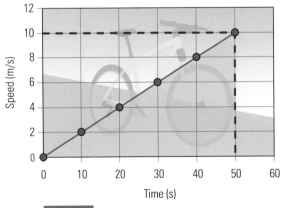

Figure 4

How is the speed changing with time?

For constant acceleration, starting from rest, the area under the line will always be the area of a triangle. From your experience in mathematics, you know that the area of the triangle is one-half of the base times the height of the triangle. From **Figure 4** the distance travelled is calculated as follows:

$$A = \frac{1}{2}hb \quad \text{or} \quad (area = \frac{1}{2} \times height \times base)$$

$$\Delta d = v_{av}\Delta t$$

$$= \frac{1}{2} \times \frac{10.0 \text{ m}}{\cancel{s}} \times 50.0 \cancel{s}$$

$$= 250 \text{ m}$$

As indicated by the area under the line, the distance travelled during the 50.0 s time interval is 250 m. You will study areas and distances travelled in more detail in Chapter 12. At this point we will restrict ourselves to the area of a rectangle or a triangle.

Sample Problem 1

A boat on the St. Lawrence River travels at full throttle for 1.5 h. From the area under the line of the speed–time graph (**Figure 5**), determine the distance travelled.

$$v = 30 \text{ km/h}$$

$$t = 1.5 \text{ h}$$

$$\Delta d = ?$$

$$A = wl$$

$$\Delta d = 30 \frac{\text{km}}{\cancel{h}} \times 1.5 \cancel{h}$$

$$= 45 \text{ km}$$

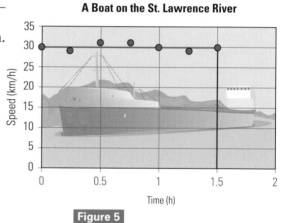

A Boat on the St. Lawrence River

Speed (km/h) vs Time (h)

Figure 5
Speed–time graph for a boat

Based upon the area under the line of the graph, the distance travelled by the boat is 45 km.

Note that, in Sample Problem 1, the speed is a fairly constant 30 km/h. This is also the average speed.

Let's now look at an example of a uniformly accelerating object.

Sample Problem 2

Galileo rolls a ball down a long grooved inclined plane. According to a speed–time graph (**Figure 6**), what is the distance travelled in 6.0 s?

$$A = \frac{1}{2}hb$$

$$\Delta d = v_{av}t$$

$$\Delta d = \frac{1}{2} \times 7.2 \frac{\text{m}}{\cancel{s}} \times 6.0 \cancel{s}$$

$$= 22 \text{ m}$$

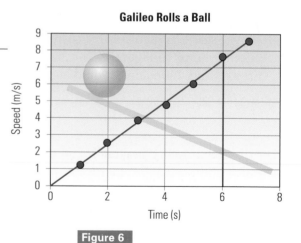

Galileo Rolls a Ball

Speed (m/s) vs Time (s)

Figure 6
Speed–time graph for a ball

Based upon the area under the line of the graph, the distance travelled by the ball in 6.0 s is 22 m.

Understanding Concepts

1. How can you tell from a speed–time table whether an object is accelerating?

2. How can you tell from a speed–time graph whether an object is accelerating?

3. Sketch a speed–time graph with two separate labelled lines for

   (a) high positive acceleration;

   (b) low negative acceleration.

4. What feature of a speed–time graph communicates

   (a) the acceleration?

   (b) the distance travelled?

5. Two runners, Cathryn and Keir, take part in a fundraising marathon. The graph in **Figure 7** shows how their speeds change for the first 100 s from the start of the marathon.

Cathryn and Keir's Acceleration

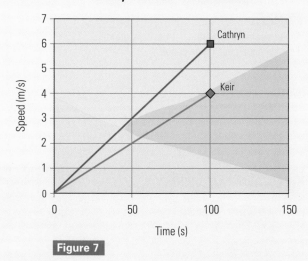

Figure 7

   (a) Which runner has the greater acceleration? Show this by calculating the acceleration of each.

   (b) Which runner is ahead after 100 s? Calculate and compare the distance travelled by each.

6. The cheetah is the fastest land animal and can accelerate rapidly in an attack. **Table 3** shows some typical speeds and times for a cheetah.

   (a) Draw a speed–time graph using the information in **Table 3**.

   (b) Using your graph, calculate the average acceleration of the cheetah. (V)

   (c) Using your graph, calculate the total distance travelled by the cheetah by the end of 2.0 s.

Table 3	Acceleration of Cheetah
Time (s)	**Speed (m/s)**
0.0	0.0
0.5	5.0
1.0	10.0
1.5	15.0
2.0	20.0

7. Create a scientific question about the acceleration (K2) characteristics of different vehicles. State the variables clearly.

8. Sketch and label distance–time and speed–time graphs for constant speed and a speed–time graph for constant acceleration (three graphs in total).

9. Why does $\Delta d = v_{av}\Delta t$ but $A = \frac{1}{2}hb$? Where does the half (1/2) come from? If $\Delta d = A$ and $\Delta t = b$, then why does $v_{av} = \frac{1}{2}h$?

10. Draw a speed–time graph for your movements as you go from your desk in the classroom to the pencil sharpener.

11. Clayton sets out on his motorcycle. His speed at different times is shown on the graph in **Figure 8**.

Clayton's Speed on his Motorcycle

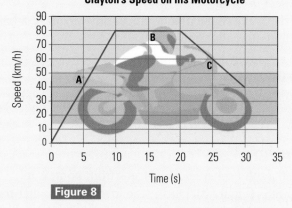

Figure 8

   (a) Calculate the accelerations during each of the time intervals, A, B, and C.

   (b) Without calculating, list the time intervals during which the distances travelled are, in order, from largest to smallest.

Reflecting

12. What assumption have you been making about acceleration in this chapter?

INQUIRY SKILLS MENU
- ○ Questioning
- ● Planning
- ● Analyzing
- ○ Hypothesizing
- ● Conducting
- ● Evaluating
- ● Predicting
- ● Recording
- ● Communicating

Graphing Distances During Acceleration

In all sciences, especially physics, technology is crucial to scientific investigations. Technology is particularly valuable for collecting and analyzing evidence from an experiment of motion (**Figure 1**). Many technological instruments initially depended on scientific research for their invention, and then science was advanced by the use of these instruments. Laser photogates (**Figure 2**) and spark timers are two examples of this interplay between science and technology. In this experiment you will use very simple technologies—a stopwatch and a ruler—to discover the relationship between distance travelled and time when an object is accelerating. The results obtained will not be as precise or as certain as they would be if we used other, more modern, technologies. This is an important point to realize when evaluating an experiment.

The purpose of this investigation is to determine the shape of a distance–time graph for acceleration and to practise evaluating experiments.

Figure 1

As the airplane accelerates, it travels a greater distance during each time period.

Question

What is the shape of a distance–time graph of a ball rolling down a ramp?

Prediction

(a) Sketch a distance–time graph, predicting what
Ⓥ② the slope will look like.

Design

Roll a solid sphere down a track from point A to point B (**Figure 3**). During the investigation, alter the distance between A and B (the independent variable) from about 25 cm to 150 cm. For each distance, measure time (the dependent variable) using a stopwatch. Use the same ball, track, and slope of track (controlled variables) for all measurements.

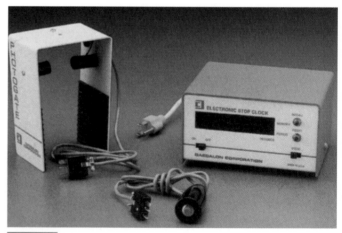

Figure 2

A laser photogate detects the time when an object crosses the beam between the bottom ends of the U-bracket.

(b) Prepare a labelled table in which to record your
Ⓚ⑦ evidence. You will need to record both the independent and the dependent variables.

(c) Using the information presented above, write
Ⓚ⑥ out the numbered steps that you will follow to carry out this experiment. Include all necessary safety precautions.

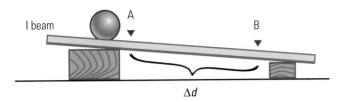

I beam   A   B

Figure 3
A ball rolls down the I-beam from point A to point B.

Materials

- I-beam track and supports (about 2 m long)
- large wood or steel ball
- metre stick or metric tape
- stopwatch

Procedure

(d) When your teacher has approved your procedure, carry it out and record your observations.

Analysis and Evaluation

(e) Construct a graph of distance versus time and
ⓥ2 answer the question. Use the *y*-axis for distance and the *x*-axis for time.

(f) Compare your graph from (e) with your prediction in (a). Account for any differences by explaining what you have learned in this investigation.

(g) Evaluate the experimental design, materials,
ⓞ procedure, and your skills. Note any flaws, and suggest improvements for this experiment. Identify and describe sources of experimental uncertainty.

(h) Share your procedure by meeting with other groups or as part of a class discussion. Note what others have done that your group did not. After this discussion you should be able to improve your evaluation of this experiment.

Understanding Concepts

1. Suggest another experiment related to this one. Using
ⓚ2 clearly stated variables, write the question that would be answered by the related experiment.

2. Repeating experiments is an important part of the scientific process. Why is it important?

Exploring

3. **(a)** Predict how your results would change if the ramp were more steeply sloped.

   (b) What difficulties would this steep ramp introduce into the experimental procedure?

Reflecting

4. Generally, when creating graphs, we place the independent variable on the *x*-axis. What, do you suppose, is the reason for breaking this rule when we draw speed–time and distance–time graphs?

 # Challenge

2 Galileo used an experimental set-up similar to that shown in **Figure 3**. Why?

Buying a Car?

When people in Western countries travel, they use mostly cars. Advertising about cars may focus on beauty, lifestyle, image, aerodynamics, fuel economy, safety, or acceleration (**Figure 1**). Many magazines are dedicated to discussions of automobiles and their characteristics (**Figures 2** and **3**). The buying, selling, and advertising of cars occupies significant space in daily newspapers, and time on radio and TV stations. In short, our society seems to be preoccupied with the automobile.

(a) In general, how much of all car advertising would you consider to be practical (related to useful performance and safety) and how much is devoted to all other aspects of the car?

(b) If you were going out to buy a car tomorrow, what would be your top three expectations for your ideal car?

Many potential buyers read road-test information. The purpose of road tests is to compare different vehicles and to give an idea of how each car will perform. To understanding the results of these tests, you need to understand the basic concepts of the physics of motion.

Figure 1

The performance of a car is important for enjoyment as well as for safety reasons.

Figure 2

Professional drivers test cars under carefully controlled conditions.

Figure 3

Testing the performance of a car involves taking many measurements with high-tech equipment.

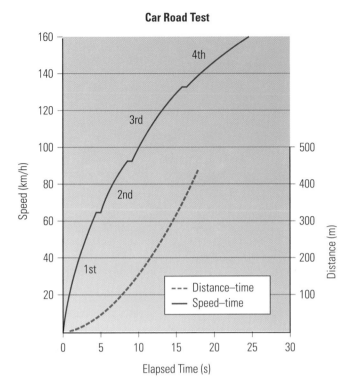

Car Road Test

Figure 4

A standard road test provides speed–time and distance–time graphs. In this case the graphs are plotted on the same time axis.

Figure 4 displays some of the typical road test information in graphical form. The speed–time graph provides the speed during a 25-s time interval and the distance travelled during an 18-s time interval. Car magazines typically plot the speed and distance graphs on a common time (*x*-) axis. The curved shapes of both lines demonstrate acceleration. In this figure the speed is plotted as the car accelerates from the first gear on through the fourth gear. You can see on the graph where the driver shifted gears.

(c) According to the speed–time graph in the road test (**Figure 4**), in what gear is the average acceleration of the car the greatest? In what gear is it the least?

(d) What happens in the car at the small level sections that divide the speed–time curve into four parts?

(e) Calculate the average acceleration of the vehicle in (km/h)/s during the first 15 s.

(f) According to **Figure 4**, what is the approximate distance travelled in the first 10.0 s?

Table 1 presents the braking distances for the same car to come to rest from the specified speed.

Braking distance is a performance standard that relates to safety. There are, of course, other safety standards that can be compared from car to car.

Table 1	Braking Distances
Speed (km/h)	**Distance (m)**
100	51
130	91

(g) How does the braking distance at 100 km/h compare with the braking distance at 130 km/h (**Table 1**)? What does this suggest about the safe distance between cars travelling in the same direction along a road?

(h) Braking distance includes only the distance travelled once the brakes are applied. What other factor is important once you realize that you have to stop quickly?

If you are trying to decide among different models and brands, road tests provide quantitative information in a standard way. We can use the information to compare the performance of various vehicles.

(i) If you were comparing cars for possible purchase, what information in a standard road test would interest you the most? Why?

(j) What important consumer information is not given in the standard road test?

Understanding Concepts

1. Picture two vehicles with the same change in speed, Δv. If the elapsed time for one (A) is half the value for the other (B), how do their average accelerations compare?

Exploring

2. Outline a procedure for doing a road test similar to
(K4) **Figure 4** for a bicycle with gears. Plan to obtain the same kind of information as car road tests but using a scale suitable for bicycles. Decide on your independent, dependent, and controlled variables. Assume that you have access to a stopwatch and other required materials.

 Challenge

3 From a distance–speed graph, how would you determine the braking distance for a variety of speeds?

Instantaneous Speed

When you glance at the speedometer while travelling in a car, what you see is the speed at that particular instant. Whether this was the speed earlier in the trip, or not, does not affect the current reading. **Instantaneous speed** is the speed at a particular moment in time.

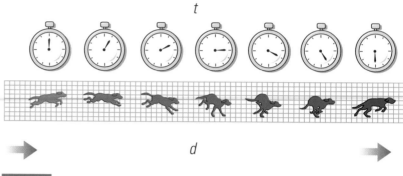

Figure 1

A dog running at a constant speed covers the same distance in each equal time interval.

The dog in **Figure 1** is covering the same distance in each time interval. If you take the pictures in rapid succession, with a shorter time interval, the dog will still travel equal distances for each time interval. The dog is moving at a uniform or constant speed. **Figure 2** shows the same information in the form of a distance–time graph. The ratio of the distance travelled to the time interval over which this occurs is the slope. Because the speed is constant, the slope is constant. On a speed–time graph (**Figure 3**), a constant speed is shown as a horizontal line. The speed at any instant of time, such as 1 s, 2 s, or 3 s, is always the same.

For any object moving at a constant speed, the instantaneous speed is the same at any time, and equals the constant speed.

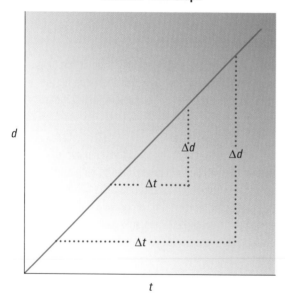

Distance–Time Graph

Figure 2
The slope of a distance–time graph represents the speed. The slopes at different times are always the same if the speed is constant.

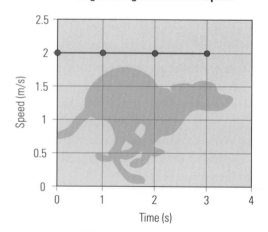

Dog Running at a Constant Speed

Figure 3
The instantaneous speed at 1 s, 2 s, and 3 s is the same value as at any other time.

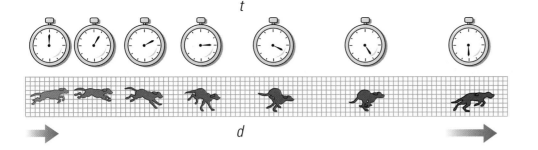

t

d

Figure 4

A dog is accelerating and covering greater distances in each successive time interval. The distance–time ratio increases.

Now suppose that the dog sees something interesting and accelerates to investigate. Notice that the distance travelled in each successive time interval increases (**Figure 4**). This means that the ratio of Δd to Δt, or the speed, increases (**Figure 5(a)**). However, if you want an accurate instantaneous speed from the distance–time graph, you need to make the time interval very small. Mathematically, this is accomplished by drawing a tangent to the curve at a particular instant of time. A **tangent** is a straight line that just touches a curve at one point, and represents the instantaneous slope of the line at that point. Notice in **Figure 5(b)** how the slopes of the tangents increase along the curve. Every tangent that you could possibly draw has a different slope and each value of the slope produces a point on the speed–time graph (**Figure 5(c)**).

- On a distance–time graph, the instantaneous speed is the slope of a tangent to the curve at that moment.
- On a speed–time graph, the instantaneous speed is read directly from the line on the graph for that moment.

<section><p>**Did You Know?**

A series of definitions of speed, instantaneous speed, non-uniform speed, and constant acceleration was created by a group of mathematicians from Merton College, England, from 1325 to 1350. They are known in history as the Merton Group.</p></section>

(a)   **Distance–Time Graph**

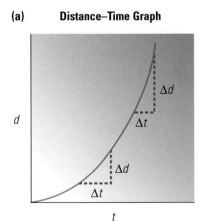

(b)   **Distance–Time Graph**

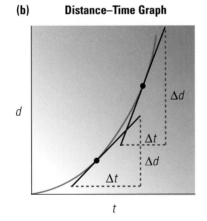

(c)   **Speed–Time Graph**

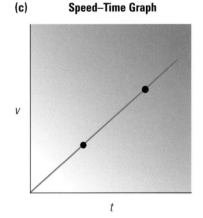

Figure 5

(a) A slope calculation on a curved line can only be approximate because the graph's line is not straight.

(b) A tangent estimated at a point along a curve represents the slope of the line at that point in time. The slope of the line is, of course, the speed at that moment—the instantaneous speed.

(c) It is much easier to read the instantaneous speed at different times on a speed–time graph than on a distance–time graph.

<section><p>*Distance, Speed, and Acceleration*   **399**</p></section>

Average Speed

For the dog running at a constant speed, the average speed is the same as the constant speed (**Figure 3**). When the dog is accelerating, the speed is continually changing (**Figure 5**). What is the average speed for the accelerating dog? You can calculate this as you did before by dividing the total distance travelled by the total time.

$$v_{av} = \frac{\Delta d}{\Delta t}$$

Alternatively, you can find average speed from a speed-time graph (**Figure 6**).

Classifying speed as constant, non-constant (changing), instantaneous, or average is useful for organizing and presenting our knowledge about the motion of an object.

An Accelerating Object

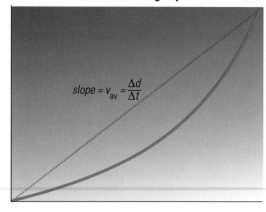

d

$$slope = v_{av} = \frac{\Delta d}{\Delta t}$$

t

Figure 6

Whatever the curve we find the average speed from the slope of the straight line joining two points on the curve.

Understanding Concepts

1. State, in your own words, the meaning of constant speed, average speed, and instantaneous speed.

2. **(a)** Describe the situation (for example, for the dog in **Figures 1** and **4**) when the instantaneous speed and the average speed are always the same.

   (b) Describe the situation when the instantaneous speed is equal to the average speed at only one moment in time.

3. **(a)** If a cat is running at a constant speed of 10 km/h for 5 s, what is its average speed and what is its instantaneous speed at 4 s?

   (b) If the cat is walking at 2 km/h and then accelerates constantly to a final speed of 14 km/h, what is its average speed?

4. How is the instantaneous speed obtained from a speed–time graph?

5. Instantaneous speed is the slope of a tangent to the curve on a distance–time graph.

   (a) Show how it would be possible to use two or more tangents, at different points along the curve, to calculate acceleration.

   (b) What error might there be in this situation?

6. The performance of a new Mercury Cougar is determined on a test track (**Figure 7**). The car covered a total distance of 402 m during the 16-s time interval.

   (a) During which time interval(s) is the acceleration approximately constant?

   (b) What is the instantaneous speed at 2 s, 8 s, and 14 s?

   (c) What is the average speed for the whole road test? (Note that the acceleration is not constant throughout the test.)

Mercury Cougar Road Test

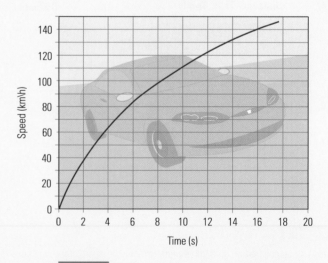

Figure 7

7. Figure 8 shows three different bicycle trips labelled A, B, and C.

Three Bicycle Trips

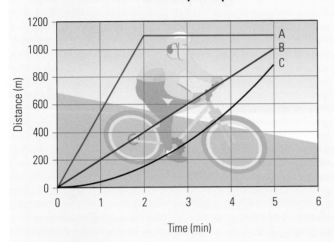

Figure 8

(a) Which graph illustrates a constant speed for the whole trip?

(b) Which graph shows a constantly changing speed?

(c) Which graph(s) has (have) an instantaneous speed of zero at some point?

(d) What is the instantaneous speed at 1.0 min for each graph?

(e) Calculate the average speed for 0 to 5.0 min for each cyclist.

8. When a police officer uses a radar gun to measure a vehicle's speed, what type of speed is measured?

9. Sketch three graphs on one set of axes to illustrate what happens to a distance–graph at medium, low, and and high accelerations.

Making Connections

10. A photograph of a hummingbird may show the bird's body very clearly but the wings are often blurred (**Figure 9**). What does this suggest about the instantaneous speed of the bird's wings and why the photograph is blurred? Using your knowledge of motion and specifically distance, speed, and time, state what is required to get a clear photograph of the bird's wings.

Figure 9

Exploring

11. Describe a common situation in which the same instantaneous speed occurs at least twice but the object is not travelling at a constant speed.

 Challenge

3 Which kind of speed (instantaneous or average) is a more important consideration for safe driving? Why? What are some sources of information about this speed, for a driver?

Analyzing Distance–Time Evidence

There are many experimental designs that will provide distance and time evidence for an object that is accelerating. You used a simple design with a ruler and stopwatch in Investigation 9.6 (page 360), and a more sophisticated design with a ticker-tape timer in Investigation 9.10 (page 372). How do you get a value for acceleration from a record of distances travelled at different times?

The following example illustrates how to answer the question, "What is the acceleration of an air puck sliding down an inclined air table?" An air puck slides down a tilted air table and leaves a series of dots (**Figure 1**). In this example the timer is set at 100 ms. This means that the space between any adjacent two dots represents a 100-ms time interval. (Remember to count spaces, not dots.) After identifying the first clear and distinct dot, place the "0" of your ruler at the centre of this first dot and align your ruler along all of the dots. You then read, to the nearest 0.5 mm, the distances shown on your ruler to the centre of each of the dots (**Table 1**, column C). Sometimes you may be asked to measure distances at a multiple of the set time interval, such as every 4 spaces or 10 spaces. This may occur if there are more dots than you need or they are very closely spaced.

To begin analyzing the evidence, find the difference between each consecutive pair of distances. This gives the distance travelled, Δd, (**Table 1**, column E) in each successive 100-ms time interval, Δt, (**Table 1**, column D). You can now calculate the average speed during that interval (**Table 1**, column F). For example, for the time interval from 200 ms to 300 ms:

$$v_{av} = \frac{\Delta d}{\Delta t}$$

$$= \frac{15.0 \text{ mm}}{100 \text{ ms}}$$

$$= 0.150 \text{ m/s}$$

The answer you have is an average speed during the time interval from 200 ms to 300 ms. Assuming that the change in speed is constant (constant acceleration), this average speed will be the instantaneous speed in the middle of the time interval. In other words, this speed of 0.150 m/s occurs at 250 ms (0.250 s), midway between 200 ms and 300 ms (**Table 1**, column G). Finally, convert the mid-interval times from milliseconds into seconds (**Table 1**, column H).

The purpose of an analysis is to answer the question asked at the start of the investigation. In this example the question is "What is the acceleration of an air puck sliding down an inclined air table?" You can obtain the acceleration of the air puck by drawing a graph of speed versus time using the calculations recorded in the shaded columns of **Table 1**, and by finding the slope of the best-fit line (**Figure 2**).

Figure 1

A spark is fired at regular time intervals and leaves a series of dots indicating the position of the air puck after each time interval.

Table 1 **Analysis of Air-Table Evidence**

A Dot #	B Time from start (ms)	C Distance from start (mm)	D Interval time* (ms)	E Interval distance (mm)	F Average speed (m/s)	G Mid-Interval time (ms)	H (s)
1	0	0					
			100	4.0	0.040	50	0.050
2	100	4.0					
			100	8.5	0.085	150	0.150
3	200	12.5					
			100	15.0	0.150	250	0.250
4	300	27.5					
			100	20.5	0.205	350	0.350
5	400	48.0					
			100	29.0	0.290	450	0.450
6	500	77.0					
			100	33.5	0.335	550	0.550
7	600	110.5					
			100	40.5	0.405	650	0.650
8	700	151.0					
			100	46.5	0.465	750	0.750
9	800	197.5					
			100	52.5	0.525	850	0.850
10	900	250.0					

*Note that this measurement has three significant digits due to the precision of the timing device.

For the graph shown in **Figure 2**,

$$\text{slope} = \frac{\text{rise}}{\text{run}}$$

$$a = \frac{\Delta v}{\Delta t}$$

$$= \frac{(0.50 - 0.00)\ \text{m/s}}{(0.80 - 0.00)\ \text{s}}$$

$$= 0.63\ \frac{\text{m}}{\text{s}^2}$$

According to the evidence collected in this experiment, the acceleration of the air puck on an inclined air table is 0.63 m/s².

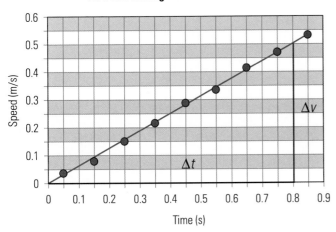

Air Puck Sliding Down Inclined Air Table

Figure 2
Determining slope of a speed–time graph

Understanding Concepts

1. State three different designs that can be used to obtain distance and time evidence in an experiment.

2. Does it matter which two points on a best-fit line are used to calculate the slope? To test your answer, calculate the slope between these two points: 0.80 s, 0.50 m/s and 0.40 s, 0.25 m/s. Compare your answer to 0.63 m/s², as calculated at left.

3. (a) In almost every experiment, there are uncertainties in the measurements that are made. In the example discussed in this section, what measurements were made?

   (b) It is not possible for you to estimate the uncertainty for the timer unless you consulted the manufacturer's specifications. However, you also made measurements with your ruler. What would you guess is the maximum error that you might have in a distance measurement, assuming you didn't misread the ruler?

   (c) Other than the time and the distance measurements, (02) what are some other sources of uncertainty in an experiment like the one described in this section?

◆ Challenge

1 How does the timing device used here compare to the device you are creating for your Challenge?

INQUIRY SKILLS MENU
- ○ Questioning
- ○ Hypothesizing
- ○ Predicting
- ○ Planning
- ● Conducting
- ● Recording
- ● Analyzing
- ● Evaluating
- ● Communicating

Constant Acceleration

Accelerated motion is common in both natural and technological systems (**Figures 1** and **2**). An understanding of all kinds of motion, including accelerated motion, is necessary before we can begin to ask questions about why objects move or change their motion.

The starting point for studying motion is to determine how far an object travels in measured periods of time. From this basic information the acceleration can be obtained. The purpose of this laboratory investigation is to determine the acceleration of an object sliding or rolling down a ramp.

Figure 1
The apple is stationary when in the tree, but moving just before it hits the ground, so it must be accelerating during its fall.

Question

What is the acceleration of a cart rolling down a ramp?

Design

You will be using a ticker-tape timer with a known frequency to record the distance travelled by a cart on a ramp (**Figure 3**). Time is the independent variable and distance is the dependent variable. Controlled variables include the cart and the slope of the ramp. (It is possible to use other technologies, for example photogates and a computer, to determine acceleration. If you use other technologies, adjust the procedure accordingly.)

(a) Create a table in which to record your
K7 observations and analysis. Refer to Section 10.8, Table 1, for a sample table.

Materials

- smooth board (0.5 to 1.0 m long)
- books or blocks
- low-friction cart
- ticker-tape timer
- clamp and stand
- about 50 cm of ticker tape
- small piece of masking tape
- metre stick

Figure 2
This Canadian boat competed at the Super Boat World Championship in 1999. The boats must accelerate after they round each marker in the race.

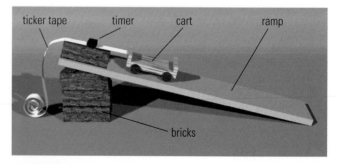

ticker tape   timer   cart   ramp

bricks

Figure 3
The cart with a timer tape attached is ready to be released down the ramp.

SKILLS HANDBOOK: K7 Creating Tables of Evidence

Procedure

1 Raise one end of the board with the books or blocks.

2 Clamp the timer near the top end of the board or to a stand placed near the board (**Figure 3**).

3 Set and hold the cart near the ticker-tape timer.

4 Insert the ticker tape through the timer and attach the end of the tape to the cart with a piece of masking tape.

5 Start the timer. Then immediately release the cart, being careful not to push the cart. (Note that the timer should start just before the cart is released.)

6 Turn off the timer when the cart nears the bottom of the ramp or the tape has passed completely through the timer.

7 Catch the cart at the bottom of the ramp.

8 Check the tape to make sure that the dots are clear and that there are no missing dots.

9 Identify the first clear and distinct dot and label it "dot 1." This is the starting point for your time and distance measurements.

10 Number some or all of the other dots as instructed by your teacher. (The number of dots used depends on the particular timer used.)

11 Using the time interval provided by your teacher, record the time from the start beside each labelled dot.

12 Using the first dot as a reference, measure the distance from the start to each labelled dot. Record these distances on your tape.

Analysis and Evaluation

(b) Calculate the distance travelled and the speed for each time interval.

(c) Construct a speed–time graph and determine the slope to answer the initial Question. Ⓤ²

(d) Evaluate the design, materials, and procedure, Ⓞ including possible flaws, suggested improvements, and sources of experimental uncertainty.

(e) Prepare a formal lab report for this experiment. Ⓠ

Understanding Concepts

1. What is the difference between constant speed and changing speed (accelerated motion) when looking at the evidence on a ticker tape?

Making Connections

2. How does the equipment that is available for measuring distance and time affect values obtained for speed and acceleration?

Exploring

3. (a) Enter your evidence from this investigation into a Ⓥ⁴ spreadsheet.

(b) Generate the speed in each interval, and enter the mid-interval times.

(c) Graph the speed–time information using the graphing function of the spreadsheet.

(d) Generate a best-fit (linear regression) line and have the program determine the slope. Compare this slope with the one you obtained in the Analysis and Evaluation section above.

☝Work the Web

An accelerometer is an instrument used to measure acceleration. There are simple, commercial, and research accelerometers. Find out how each type works by visiting www.science.nelson.com and following the links through Science 10 and 10.9. Using diagrams, report on how one accelerometer works.

 Challenge

2 This is a classic investigation. How is it similar to the investigation you have chosen to test a law? How is it different?

INQUIRY SKILLS MENU
- Questioning
- Hypothesizing
- Predicting
- Planning
- Conducting
- Recording
- Analyzing
- Evaluating
- Communicating

Acceleration of Different Vehicles

When purchasing a vehicle, several perspectives are used to help make a final decision. Cost is important to most people, as well as aesthetic and technical considerations (**Figure 1**). Designers and engineers for all major automobile manufacturers try to produce a series of vehicles of different types to attract as many potential buyers as possible. One factor important to some people is the acceleration characteristic of the vehicle. Some characteristics of a variety of vehicles are shown in **Table 1**.

Table 1 Characteristics of Various Automatic-Transmission Compact 2-Door Coupe-Style Automobiles

| Car | Cost ($) | Mass (kg) | Type of engine | | | Est. fuel use (L/100 km) city/highway | Acceleration time 0 to 100 km/h (s) |
			No. of cylinders	Volume (L)	Power (hp; kW) @ rpm		
A	28 500	1340	4	1.80	150; 112 @ 5800	9.4/7.6	7.1
B	26 200	1160	4	1.80	160; 120 @ 7600	9.1/7.6	7.4
C	29 500	1250	4	2.50	165; 123 @ 6500	10.7/8.4	8.0
D	33 900	1190	4	1.80	170; 127 @ 7600	9.4/7.6	7.2
E	34 800	1420	6	2.97	200; 149 @ 5500	11.8/8.4	7.0
F	37 500	1160	4	1.80	180; 134 @ 7600	9.1/5.9	6.8

Key: hp = horsepower
rpm = revolutions per minute

Figure 1
Small, two-door cars are available from many automobile manufacturers.

Question

(a) Write a scientific question about the acceleration characteristics of different vehicles. Be specific about the variables from **Table 1** that you will investigate.

(K2)

Prediction/Hypothesis

(b) Write a prediction, including your reasoning.

(K3)

Design

(c) Outline a plan to use information from **Table 1** about the characteristics that you have chosen that may be related to acceleration. Identify independent, dependent, and controlled variables in this study.

(K4)

Analysis and Evaluation

(d) Prepare a graph, placing the chosen variables on the appropriate axes.

(V)

(e) What interpretation(s) can be made about the relationship, if any, between your independent and dependent variables?

(f) Write a statement to answer your Question.

(g) Evaluate this experiment, including any flaws in the design, any assumptions that may not be correct, and any biases that may be present.

(0)

Understanding Concepts

1. List the cars in **Table 1** in order of increasing acceleration ability.

2. List four different factors that people may consider when purchasing a vehicle.

3. Give some reasons why it is difficult to compare different vehicles.

Making Connections

4. All major automobile manufacturers are designing and building electric cars. What are the most important advantages and disadvantages of electric cars?

5. (a) If you could design a car of your own, what acceleration characteristics would you want it to have?

   (b) Give reasons for your decision.

   (c) From whose perspective are you considering your decision?

   (d) Design an advertisement for your vehicle and present it to your class. You can use any medium, such as radio, print, or TV.

Exploring

6. Research hybrid electric vehicles and compare them with both gasoline and electric cars.

 Work the Web

Visit www.science.nelson.com and follow the links from Science 10, 10.10 to access **Table 1**. Import the data into a spreadsheet program. Create graphs using several pairs of variables. Briefly explain, as best you can, the relationships that appear.

Challenge

3 The performance of a vehicle is assessed, in part, by how quickly it accelerates. How might high positive acceleration result in breaking the law? How could this be shown on a graph?

Volker Nolte

Coaching Educator

Volker Nolte has found a career that allows him to promote his interests in world-class rowing and in coaching education.

Since 1992, Volker has been a rowing coach with the Canadian National team. He is responsible for talent identification, training, counselling, and preparation of boats for world championships and the Olympic Games.

Every fourth year, Volker moves to training facilities in Victoria, British Columbia, to work with Olympic rowers. Says Volker, "You learn technique only when you row. So we go to one of the few place in Canada where you can row all year round—Victoria, B.C."

For the remainder of the time, he teaches coaching and biomechanics at the University of Western Ontario in London, Ontario.

Volker knows his rowing well, having successfully competed at the junior and senior world-championship levels in his native Germany. It was from his experiences as a high-level rowing competitor that he began considering ways to improve coaching. "When I was an athlete, I found that my coaches were often lacking in education themselves. I thought if they had received better training, perhaps they could have given me better advice, counselling, and feedback. When I finished my rowing career, I thought I'd try to put something back into the sport and educate coaches and athletes."

Although he holds a Ph.D. in biomechanics, to be a good coach requires taking "a little from every kind of education I've had," Volker says.

As a scientist, Volker is highly interested in the technological side of the sport, which can involve using cameras, electronics, and computers to collect and analyze information about a boat's speed and acceleration. But, "Good coaching is part science and part art. On the science side, the coach has to learn how the body functions, body mechanics, how to apply forces to achieve the fastest and strongest movement. Then, there's the art side, where a coach has to understand how to motivate and lead people."

As a coach, his goals—like those of his athletes—are high and, especially leading up to Olympic years, clearly focused. "On the national rowing team we obviously want to be the best in the world."

Making Connections

1. Make a concept map that summarizes the personal qualities needed to be a good coach. Tick off your own personal qualities. Write a few sentences explaining if and how you could develop qualities you don't already possess.
2. Make a two-column chart in which you identify the scientific and human dimensions of good sports coaching. First list information from the profile, then record ideas from your own sports experiences.

☜ Work the Web

Visit www.science.nelson.com and follow the links from Science 10, 10.11. List at least five ways in which rowing is related to physics. Share and discuss your lists with a small group of classmates.

Chapter 10 Summary

Expectations

Throughout this chapter, you have had opportunities to do the following:

- Analyze everyday phenomena and technologies in terms of the motions involved. (10.3, 10.6, 10.10)

- Evaluate the costs and benefits, including safety and environmental factors, of transportation technologies which have enabled us to travel at ever-greater speeds and the impact of this on behaviour and injuries. (10.1)

- Distinguish among constant, instantaneous and average speed, and give examples involving uniform and non-uniform motion. (10.2, 10.7)

- Describe quantitatively the relationship among average acceleration a_{av}, change in speed Δv, and elapsed time Δt, and solve simple problems involving these physical quantities;

$$a_{av} = \frac{\Delta v}{\Delta t} \quad (10.3)$$

- Draw distance–time and speed–time graphs for constant acceleration, and calculate the constant acceleration and distance from velocity-time graphs. (10.4, 10.5, 10.9, 10.10)

- Use a broad range of tools and techniques safely, accurately and effectively to obtain, organize and analyze distance and motion. (10.5, 10.8, 10.9)

- Analyze and evaluate evidence to identify some experimental uncertainties or errors. (10.5, 10.8, 10.9, 10.10)

- Draw distance–time graphs and calculate the average speed and instantaneous speed from such graphs. (10.7, 10.8)

- Design, conduct and/or analyze experiments to determine acceleration. (10.8, 10.9)

- Formulate scientific questions about observed relationships, ideas, problems, and issues related to motion. (10.10)

- Demonstrate the skills required to plan an inquiry into motion, controlling variables and adapting procedures. (10.10)

- Select and integrate information from various sources, including electronic and print resources, to answer the questions chosen. (10.10)

- Select and use appropriate vocabulary, SI units, quantity symbols and graphs to communicate scientific and technological concepts, measurements and analyses. (all)

Key Terms

acceleration

area under the line

average acceleration

constant acceleration

instantaneous speed

slope of the line

tangent

Make a Summary

Sketch distance–time and speed–time graphs for constant speed and for constant acceleration. Indicate beside each of these four graphs what the slope and area represents, if anything.

Reflect on your Learning

Revisit your answers to the Reflect on your Learning questions, page 379, in the Getting Started.

- How has your thinking changed?

- What new questions do you have?

Chapter 10 Review

Understanding Concepts

1. In constant acceleration, What is "constant" ?

2. Match the type of speed in the first column of **Table 1** with its definition in the second column.

Table 1   Definitions of Speed

Type	Definition
A. constant speed	1. a speed calculated over the entire trip
B. average speed	2. a speed at a particular moment in time
C. instantaneous speed	3. a speed that does not change over time

3. For each of the following graphs or descriptions of a graph, write a description of the motion represented.

(a)

(b)

(c)

(d)

(e) speed–time graph with a positively sloped line
(f) acceleration–time graph with a horizontal line
(g) acceleration–time graph with a curved line

4. Properties of a graph, such as slope and area, usually have some significance. Copy **Table 2**, and state what the slope or area represents, if anything, for the property indicated. If there is no significance, write "none."

Table 2   Features of Graphs

Type of Graph	Slope	Area under Line
distance-time		
speed-time		

5. What sources of experimental error or uncertainty have you encountered in your experiments with acceleration?

6. You are a passenger in a car, driving slowly along a road beside a row of hydro towers, each 82.5 m apart. You decide to use your digital watch to measure the time at which you pass each of the towers. The results are shown in **Table 3**.

Table 3   Passing Hydro Towers

Tower	Time on watch (h:min:s)
1	2:27:10
2	2:27:21
3	2:27:31
4	2:27:42
5	2:27:54
6	2:28:05
7	2:28:15
8	2:28:26

(a) Calculate the speed for each "tower interval" and create a speed–time graph for the car.
(b) From your graph, calculate the distance travelled.
(c) Compare your answer in (b) to the sum of the distances between the eight poles. Account for any differences.

7. A motorboat accelerates from rest to a final speed of 6.0 m/s in a time of 3.0 s. What is the average acceleration of the motorboat?

8. A car is struck from behind by a large truck. The impact lasts 0.10 s and causes an acceleration of 45 m/s^2 of the car. What is the car's change in speed?

9. A mallard duck, resting on the water, takes off and reaches a speed of 35 km/h in 4.0 min. Calculate the average acceleration of the duck.

10. While pulling a barge, a tugboat accelerates at 0.10 m/s^2 to produce a 5.0 m/s change in speed of the barge. How long did this take?

11. A flea may have the world record for high jumping if relative size is taken into account. A flea can jump an amazing 130 times its own height. This feat is achieved by a phenomenal acceleration of about 1.5 km/s^2, but over a very short time of 1.0 ms. What is the final speed of the flea at the end of 1.0 ms?

Applying Inquiry Skills

12. A bottle-nosed dolphin is cruising along and then accelerates at 0.50 m/s² to reach a final speed of 9.7 m/s after 15 s. What was the initial speed of the dolphin?

13. In Donovan Bailey's 1996 Olympic gold medal run (**Figure 1**), his winning time for 100 m was 9.84 s. In the first part of the race his average acceleration was about 1.86 m/s² until he reached his maximum speed at 6.5 s, which he maintained until the end of the race.

Figure 1

(a) Calculate Bailey's maximum speed at 6.5 s.
(b) What was his average speed for the whole race?
(c) Sketch a graph to clearly illustrate Bailey's motion.

14. The speed and time record for a high-speed dragster is shown in **Table 4**.

Table 4 **Speeds of a Dragster**

Time from Start (s)	Instantaneous Speed (m/s)
0.0	0.0
1.0	9.8
2.0	19.8
3.0	29.6
4.0	39.6
5.0	49.5

(a) Plot and label a speed–time graph of this information.
(b) Using your graph, determine the average acceleration of the dragster.
(c) How far did the dragster travel from 0 to 5.0 s?

15. The distance–time graphs shown in **Figure 2** show the motion of two different cars. Using your knowledge about the properties of distance–time graphs, write a qualitative description of the motion of each car indicating how you arrived at your interpretations.

Graph for Car A

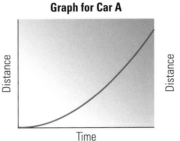

Graph for Car B

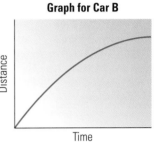

Figure 2

16. What is the acceleration of a world-class ski jumper down the main hill of the ski jump? (**Table 5**)

Experimental Design
The skier is photographed with a rapid-fire flash at dusk. The multiple-exposure picture is analyzed to obtain distances at the fixed time intervals of the flash.

Evidence

Table 5 **Acceleration of a Ski Jumper**

Time from Start (s)	Distance from Start (m/s)
0.00	0.0
0.50	1.0
1.00	3.9
1.50	8.8
2.00	15.6
2.50	24.4
3.00	35.1
3.50	47.8

Analysis
Construct a speed–time graph, determine the slope, and answer the Question. Record the results of your calculations in a neat, labelled table.

Making Connections

16. How do driving habits affect the fuel economy of a car?

17. Investigate the benefits and risks to the individual and the community of high-speed commuter trains.

"ARE WE THERE YET?"

When we are on a long journey, perhaps heading from Ontario to a Newfoundland harbour, we tend to focus on how far we have travelled toward our destination (**Figure 1**). The distance and the direction are important. Detours usually increase the total distance and the time — just the opposite of shortcuts. If we want to get there quickly, we would probably choose to travel, if possible, in a straight line (as an airplane flies) between home and our destination. Unfortunately, this is not possible when travelling by car. If we wanted to do some sightseeing we might actually increase the distance travelled in order to see, for example, a waterfall that is not on the main road.

On a short trip we might increase the time by taking a slower form of transportation, such as horseback or a bicycle, so we can enjoy the countryside more closely. Distance and time can be manipulated in a variety of ways. However, by the end of the journey the straight-line distance between home and the destination is the same.

Figure 1

Canada has many adventure routes for you to explore.

Let's imagine a different journey: we are going to a friend's home on another street several city blocks away. Measured on a map, the friend's house is 395 m (straight) from our starting point. Following the instructions to "Go one block north, one west, one north, one west, one more north, and back one block east" we travel a total distance of 750 m (**Figure 2**). Does distance tell us everything we need to know about a trip? Consider the instructions to the friend's home: We needed both the distances and the directions to get there.

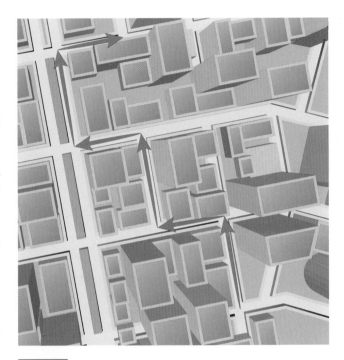

Figure 2

Walking to a friend's home

Giving directions isn't always easy — it forces us to think about things we do automatically.

(a) Working in a group, write clear instructions for getting from where you are to some other target location in your school or schoolyard.

(b) Produce a map, drawn to scale, showing the route to the target location.

(c) Exchange instructions and/or maps with another group and try to reach their target location by following their directions.

(d) Evaluate the other group's map and instructions. Can you propose a better form of communication? Suggest some improvements to the instructions. What are some sources of uncertainty? How confident are you in their set of instructions?

Reflect on your Learning

1. If you leave home on a trip, and then end up back at home at the end of the trip, the total distance travelled is not zero, but something is zero. What is zero, and, how does this depend on direction?

2. How can we show direction on a graph?

3. When providing directions for a visitor, what are some of the different ways of indicating direction?

4. Why is it important to agree on ways of communicating where your are, where you are going, and how long it takes to get there?

Throughout this chapter, note any changes in your ideas as you learn new concepts and develop your skills.

Vectors: Position and Displacement

If a new student told you that she travelled 2 km to get to school today, you would only know the distance she travelled and her destination. You would not know her starting point or the directions she took to get to school. To give directions we need a reference point. All distances and directions are generally stated relative to the **reference point**, which is usually the origin or starting point. For example, if you start a trip from home, then you would choose your home as the reference point.

Specifying where you are or where you are going requires you to indicate the direction. Unless you are going up or down, the clearest way of communicating your direction in writing is as north [N], east [E], south [S], and west [W] or by using a compass symbol (**Figure 1**).

Figure 1
The compass symbol is one way to indicate direction.

Position

Your **position** is the separation and direction from a reference point. For example, you may be at a position of 152 m [W] — one hundred and fifty-two metres west of the reference point (**Figure 2**). The direction is given in square brackets, and is usually either a compass direction or a right/left or forward/backward direction. Notice that you must state both the straight-line distance and the direction in order to state your position clearly.

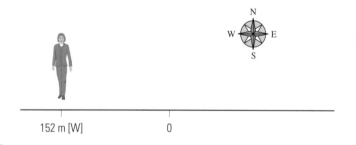

152 m [W]   0

Figure 2
One hundred and fifty-two metres west (152 m [W]) of the reference point

A quantity that involves a direction, such as position, is called a **vector quantity**. A vector quantity has both size (with units) and direction; e.g., 73 m [N]. The direction is specified in square brackets after the units. A quantity that involves only size, but not direction, is called a **scalar quantity**. Mass is a scalar quantity because a mass such as 10 kg has no direction associated with it. Vector quantities are represented by symbols that include a small arrow over the quantity symbol; scalar quantity symbols never have this arrow over the symbol (**Table 1**).

Table 1	Some Scalar and Vector Quantities	
Quantity Symbol	**Example**	
scalar quantity		
distance	Δd	292 km
time	Δt	3.0 h
vector quantity		
position	$\vec{d}$	2 km [E] (from city hall)
displacement	$\vec{\Delta d}$	292 km [S]

On a straight line, such as a track or street, position, $\vec{d}$, is sometimes stated as a positive or negative value relative to a zero point. This is just like a number line in your math class or an x-axis on a graph. Imagine that you got off a bus at a downtown bus stop, which we will define as the zero point and your initial position, $\vec{d}_1$. The music store that you want to visit is at +72 m, but the shoe store is at −16 m relative to the bus stop. These positions can be shown on a straight-line diagram (**Figure 3**).

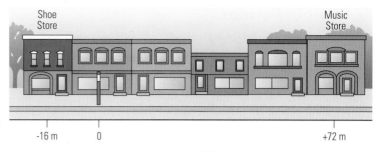

Figure 3

The music store is at 72 m [forward] and the shoe store is at 16 m [backward], relative to the bus stop.

Displacement

In Chapter 9 we looked at distance. Distance is a scalar quantity and is communicated as the size of the quantity and the units (33 m, for example). It could be the distance travelled in a circle, in a straight line, or along a winding path. **Displacement** is defined as the change in position. The symbol for displacement, $\Delta\vec{d}$, includes the symbols Δ ("delta," meaning a change in) and $\vec{d}$ (the symbol for position). A change in position from to $\vec{d}_1$ to $\vec{d}_2$ is calculated as the final minus the initial positions.

$$\Delta\vec{d} = \vec{d}_2 - \vec{d}_1$$

Displacement is a vector quantity and is communicated as the size of the quantity (including the units), and the direction (such as 33 m [W]). It represents the straight-line distance (e.g., 33 m) from some initial position in a given direction (e.g., [W]) to a final position.

On a straight line with positive and negative numbers, the numbers are positive in one direction. We will call this the positive or forward direction. In the opposite direction, the numbers are negative, and we will call this the negative or backward direction. Returning to our example shown in **Figure 3**, you are at the bus stop ($\vec{d}_1 = 0$) and decide to go to the shoe store first, as it is closer. To get there you will be moving in the backward (−) direction. When you reach the shoe store, your position, $\vec{d}_2$, is −16m and your displacement is also −16 m or 16 m [backward].

$$\begin{aligned}\Delta\vec{d} &= \vec{d}_2 - \vec{d}_1 \\ &= (-16\text{ m}) - 0 \\ &= -16\text{ m or }16\text{ m [backward]}\end{aligned}$$

After buying your shoes you start walking again, this time in a forward (+) direction, to the music store. You will move from the shoe store ($\vec{d}_1 = -16$ m) to your new position at the music store ($\vec{d}_2 = +72$ m). Your displacement will now be +88 m or 88 m [forward].

$$\begin{aligned}\Delta\vec{d} &= \vec{d}_2 - \vec{d}_1 \\ &= (+72\text{ m}) - (-16\text{ m}) \\ &= +88\text{ m or }88\text{ m [forward]}\end{aligned}$$

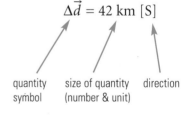

$$\Delta\vec{d} = 42\text{ km [S]}$$

quantity symbol   size of quantity (number & unit)   direction

Figure 4

The symbol format is a recognized format for writing vector quantities, such as displacement.

Symbol Format

When communicating a value for a vector quantity, the value is accompanied by a direction (for example, 52 m [N]). There is an international convention for writing vectors, using number symbols, SI unit symbols, and direction symbols (**Figure 4**). Using words, such as forward and backward, could be misinterpreted. Compass points (e.g., N, E, S, and W or a compass symbol as in **Figure 1**) are more internationally recognized than English words and so are more acceptable for scientific communication.

Drawing Vectors

An alternative way of communicating vector quantities is to use vectors. A **vector** is a line segment that represents the size and direction of a vector quantity. For example, displacements of 75 km [E], 38 km [W], 57 m [N], and 19 m [S] are communicated in symbol format and in vector format in **Figure 5**. Note that vectors are drawn to a scale that should be stated. The vectors should visually communicate both the size and the direction of the quantity, and should always be labelled.

Follow these rules when drawing a single vector:
- State the direction—usually using N, E, S, or W as reference.
- Draw the line to the stated scale or write the size of the vector next to the line.
- The direction of the line represents the direction of the vector, and the length of the line represents the size of the vector.

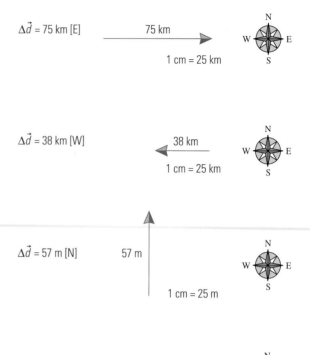

Figure 5
Vector quantities expressed as both symbols and vectors

🖑 Work the Web

Use the Internet to find some information on orienteering or car rallies. Are there any clubs nearby? How might participants in these activities use the knowledge presented above?

Understanding Concepts

1. Classify the following quantities as scalar or vector quantities:
   (a) distance;
   (b) mass;
   (c) position;
   (d) displacement;
   (e) time;
   (f) change in position.

2. Distinguish, in your own words, between position and displacement.

3. Why is it convenient to choose your starting point as the reference point when stating your position during your travels?

4. Create a mnemonic (memory aid) to help you remember the order [N], [E], [S], and [W] on a compass.

5. Communicate the final position, $\vec{d_2}$, including a reference point, after each of the following moves. Use symbol format.
   (a) A Toronto Blue Jays baseball player is on the first base, 24.4 m east of home plate.
   (b) The runner was on second base, but has managed to steal third base, 24.4 m to the west.
   (c) A batter hits a home run and ends up safely at home plate.

6. Communicate the displacement, $\Delta\vec{d}$, after each of the following moves. Use symbol format.

(a) A puck is shot 25 m from the centre-ice (red) line south into the Ottawa Senators' zone.

(b) Karen Kain, a retired Canadian prima ballerina, completed a pirouette by leaping 1.5 m toward stage right (west).

(c) Kim, a high school volleyball player, leaps toward the net (north) by 1.9 m while delivering a spike.

(d) Kurt Browning (Canadian and world figure-skating champion from 1989–91) completed the first quad jump in competition. He jumped 3.2 m in an easterly direction.

7. The Hamilton Tiger-Cats football team moves on a straight downfield pass from the Toronto 45-yard line to the Toronto 20-yard line, and then loses 5 yards on the next running play (**Figure 6**).

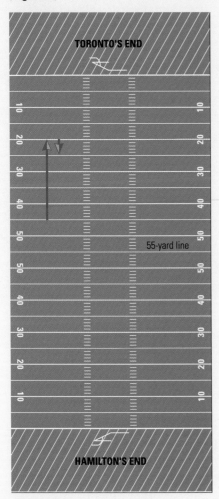

Figure 6

(a) Using Toronto's 45-yard line as the reference point, what is the ball's

   (i) position after the pass?

   (ii) final position?

   (iii) final displacement?

   (iv) total distance travelled?

(b) Using mid-field as the reference point, what is the ball's

   (i) position after the pass?

   (ii) final position?

   (iii) final displacement?

   (iv) total distance travelled?

(c) Which of the quantities listed above depend on the choice of reference point? Which do not?

8. Radar can be used to indicate the position of outgoing aircraft. Use a scale (such as 1 cm = 10 km) to communicate the following aircraft displacements as vectors:

(a) seventy-five kilometres east;

(b) 30 km [N];

(c) 45 km [W];

(d) fifty-two kilometres south.

9. As a shopper in conversation with a friend, when would you talk about distance and when would you talk about displacement and position — even though you might not use these words?

10. Relate a personal experience during the last week where your distance travelled and your displacement were not equal.

11. Suppose you have a list of instructions to find a buried treasure chest. How does this relate to the concepts discussed in this section?

Exploring

12. In real life your actual position is often too complicated to communicate by the systems presented here. Provide a personal example. Suggest a way to clearly communicate this position.

13. Communicate your answers to (a) to (c) in symbol format. No work need be shown.

(a) What is your displacement if you walk from home 0.45 km [N] to school and then return home at the end of the day?

(b) What is your displacement if you ride a bike 2.0 km [S] and then a further 1.5 km [S]?

(c) What is your displacement if you walk 30 m [E] and then back 40 m [W]?

(d) What kind of restriction is being placed on the questions asked above in order to keep the situations simpler than they might otherwise be?

Walk the Graph

Imagine that you're monitoring someone's movements electronically. You may have seen this kind of thing on a detective show on television. You have attached a tracer to a person or car and a flashing dot is shown on a city map. Another common application is the monitoring of an aircraft's position by the use of radar. A radar beam is sent out and bounces back to the detector. A more recent development is the global positioning system (GPS) which can be used to monitor your position by satellite (**Figure 1**). In the laboratory a beam of ultrasound (sound beyond the frequency of human hearing) can be emitted, strike you, and be reflected back to a detector. The total time for the reflection to return to the detector determines your distance from the detector.

In this activity you will use either a low-technology method of monitoring your position over time or a more high-technology method. The low-technology method uses one-metre markers and a stopwatch. The high-technology method makes use of an ultrasonic motion sensor connected to a computer interface. On the screen you will be able to see both the ideal graph you are trying to demonstrate and a line representing your own motion. Depending on the technology available in your school, you will complete either Option 1 or Option 2.

The purpose of this activity is to experience the motion represented by a graph. The more ways you experience the graph, the better will be your understanding of what the graph means. In the previous two chapters you came to understand the distance–time relationship through a defining equation, through units of measurement, and through distance–time graphs, simulated lab work, and actual lab work. We learn better by experiencing many ways of knowing. Likewise a scientific concept is better established in the scientific community by logically and consistently working in a variety of situations. Test your understanding of position and motion by walking a graph.

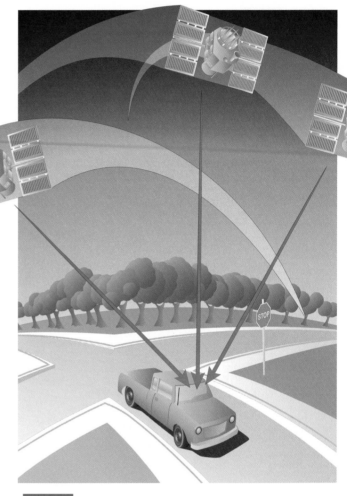

Figure 1

Signals from GPS satellites can be used to pinpoint the location of the receiver.

Option 1: Stopwatch Design

Materials
- predrawn position–time graphs
- masking tape or equivalent
- metre stick or metric tape measure
- two stopwatches or other timepieces

Procedure

1. Clear a safe path for walking in the classroom, hallway, gym, or laboratory.

2. Work in pairs, with one person walking and one coaching.

3 Use the masking tape to mark one-metre intervals for 5 to 10 m.

4 Take turns walking your graph while simultaneously watching your stopwatch and the position markings. Your partner acts as a coach.

5 Repeat the walk until you are satisfied that you are close to representing the motion communicated by the graph.

6 Switch with your partner and repeat Steps 4 and 5. The second person could walk the same or a different graph.

7 Remove the tape and clean up and/or restore the area.

Option 2: Motion-Sensor Design

Materials
- computer with sensor interface
- computer projector or TV (optional)
- motion sensor
- prepared graph on a screen

Procedure

1 Clear a safe path for walking in the classroom, hallway, gym, or laboratory.

2 Connect the computer interface to the computer and the sensor to the interface.

3 Load the graph onto the computer and display it on a TV or other screen.

4 Align the motion sensor in a straight line along the path for walking.

5 Stand in front of the sensor and move backward, stop and/or move forward to walk the graph. Watch the screen to match the line representing your movement to the line of the predrawn graph.

Analysis and Evaluation

(a) Compare your walk to that of another student. Which of you was able to "walk the graph" most accurately?

Understanding Concepts

1. What necessary restriction was placed on the motion and positions that you were allowed to take in this activity? In how many directions were you allowed to move?

2. Since position is a vector quantity, how is direction indicated on your position–time graph?

3. If the total time required for an ultrasonic sound beam ($v = 340$ m/s) to travel to you and back to the detector is 18 ms (0.018 s), how far away are you from the detector?

Exploring

4. Describe a situation in your everyday life that involves changes in position in a straight line. Predict the shape of the position–time graph for this situation.

5. What other ways could you have used to monitor your position over time during this activity? Suggest an alternative experimental or technological design. If you have the technology available, plan and carry out (with your teacher's approval) some alternative activities to analyze a person's movement.

Reflecting

6. How and why was the graph of your own motion different from the provided graph?

7. From your previous experience, what do you think the slope of the position–time graph represents?

8. Can you imagine a position–time graph representing continuous and repetitive back-and-forth motions about a reference point? What might it look like? Sketch the graph.

 Challenge

1 If a motion sensor uses sound waves travelling at 340 m/s, what precision is needed in the built-in timing device to differentiate between an object 3 m away, and one 4 m away?

Adding Vectors Along a Straight Line

In the hallway of your school, or on a shopping trip, you can make many starts and stops resulting in many changes in position (**Figure 1**). The result will be that you end up either at a new position or back where you started. Walking back and forth to the fridge, school, or mall involves more than one displacement vector. We can investigate the result of these different segments of your trip by doing some math or by drawing some diagrams. In section 11.1 you drew individual vectors to represent displacement. Now we want to consider two or more vectors in a straight line — in one dimension. In other words, we will restrict ourselves to vectors that are either in the same direction or in opposite directions. There are three methods for solving vector problems. Each of these methods has advantages and disadvantages. Once you have learned the methods and language for adding vectors in a straight line, you will work with vectors at an angle (section 11.5).

Figure 1

Shopping quite often involves many different displacement segments.

Vector Diagrams

When you add vector quantities such as displacements, you need to consider both the size and the direction of each quantity being added. This can be accomplished by combining vectors in a diagram according to the following "head-to-tail" rule:

Join each vector by connecting the "head" end of one vector to the "tail" end of the next vector [Figure 2(a)].

Recall from section 11.1 that a vector is a line segment representing the size and direction of a vector quantity. Therefore, the head-to-tail rule includes the sizes and directions for all vectors that are joined together. Now that we have a method of combining vectors, what is the total or sum? For vectors, the final sum is called the resultant.

Find the resultant by drawing an arrow from the tail of the first vector to the head of the last vector [Figure 2(b)].

The **resultant displacement**, $\Delta \vec{d}_R$, is a single displacement that has the same effect as all of the individual displacements combined. When you combine vectors head to tail and draw the resultant vector, you have a **vector diagram** [Figures 2(a) and 2(b)].

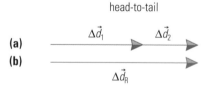

Figure 2

A displacement vector diagram

Adding Vectors Using Scale Diagrams

We can add straight-line (one-dimensional) vectors by drawing a vector diagram and then measuring the distance and direction of the resultant vector (**Figure 2**). The first vector ($\Delta \vec{d}_1$) is drawn to scale with an appropriate length. The second vector ($\Delta \vec{d}_2$) is then drawn, to the same scale, with its tail to the head of $\Delta \vec{d}_1$. Any other vectors are added to the diagram in the same way: drawn head to tail. The resultant vector, $\Delta \vec{d}_R$, is drawn from the tail of the first vector to the head of the last vector ($\Delta \vec{d}_2$, if there are only two vectors). Scale diagrams are not as efficient as other methods and require that you draw and measure carefully.

Sample Problem 1

Anne takes her dog, Zak, for a walk. They walk 250 m [W] and then back 215 m [E] before stopping to talk to a neighbour. Draw a vector diagram to find their resultant displacement at this point.

$\Delta \vec{d}_1 = 250$ m [W]
$\Delta \vec{d}_2 = 215$ m [E]
$\Delta \vec{d}_R = ?$

Scale: 1 cm = 50 m

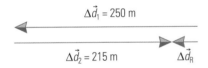

$$\Delta \vec{d}_R = 0.70 \text{ cm} \times \frac{50 \text{ m}}{1 \text{ cm}} = 35 \text{ m [W]}$$

The resultant displacement for Anne and Zak is 35 m [W].

Summary of Scale Diagram Method

1. State the directions (e.g., with a compass symbol).
2. List the givens and indicate what variable is being solved.
3. State the scale to be used (e.g., 1 cm = 5 km).
4. Draw one of the initial vectors to scale.
5. Join the second and additional vectors head to tail and to scale.
6. Draw and label the resultant vector.
7. Measure the resultant vector and convert the length using your scale.
8. Write a statement including both the size and direction of the resultant vector.

This method may seem tedious and inefficient here, but it will be much more useful later in the unit, when you are dealing with vectors that are not on a straight line.

Adding Vectors Algebraically

When we add vectors algebraically, we assign a positive or negative direction to the value of the quantity, just as we learned in Section 11.1. To decide which direction is positive and which is negative, there are several conventions (systems). Some choose the initial direction as positive, while others choose north and east as being positive. Use the system indicated by your teacher, but always state the convention used in each problem that you solve. At the end of the calculations, the positive or negative sign needs to be translated back into a direction. Algebraic addition is the most efficient method of adding vectors along a straight line.

Sample Problem 2

This time, Anne's daughter, Cathryn, takes Zak for a walk. They leave home and walk 250 m [W] and then back 175 m [E] before stopping to talk to a friend. What is the resultant displacement at this position?

Let [E] be positive and [W] be negative.

$\Delta \vec{d}_1 = 250 \text{ m [W]} = -250 \text{ m}$

$\Delta \vec{d}_2 = 175 \text{ m [E]} = +175 \text{ m}$

$\Delta \vec{d}_R = ?$

$$\Delta \vec{d}_R = \Delta \vec{d}_1 + \Delta \vec{d}_2$$

$$= (-250 \text{ m}) + (+175 \text{ m})$$

$$= -75 \text{ m}$$

The resultant displacement for Cathryn and Zak is 75 m [W].

Summary of Algebraic Method

1. Indicate which direction is positive and which is negative.
2. List the givens and indicate what variable is being solved.
3. Write the equation for adding the vectors.
4. Substitute numbers (with correct signs) into the equation, and solve.
5. Write a statement with your answer (including size and direction).

A Combined Method

Vector addition can be done by combining vector diagrams and algebraic addition. When these are combined, the inefficiency of drawing scale diagrams is removed but the visual advantage of vector diagrams is retained. The vector diagram is sketched, representing the relative sizes of the vectors (without stating a scale), and labelled appropriately. It is important that you draw the vectors approximately accurately, relative to each other. For example, if one displacement is 10 m [N] and a second displacement is 20 m [S], the south vector should be approximately twice the length of the north vector. With the aid of a sketch, the vector addition is done algebraically. The combined method is particularly useful when vectors at an angle are solved mathematically, which you will see in future physics courses. Your teacher may indicate which of the three methods will be the convention to use in your classroom.

Sample Problem 3

Zak decides to take himself for a walk. He heads 30 m [W], stops, then goes a farther 50 m [W] before returning 60 m [E]. What is Zak's resultant displacement?

East is the positive direction; west is negative.

$$\Delta \vec{d}_R = \Delta \vec{d}_1 + \Delta \vec{d}_2 + \Delta \vec{d}_3$$

$$= (-30 \text{ m}) + (-50 \text{ m}) + (+60 \text{ m})$$

$$= -20 \text{ m}$$

The resultant displacement for Zak is 20 m [W].

Did You Know?

The study of motion in physics involves

- kinematics: the "how" (describing motion — the effect), and
- dynamics: the "why" (explaining motion — the cause).

In this book you are learning the basics of the "how" (kinematics) part of motion.

Summary of Combined Method

1. State which direction is positive and which is negative.
2. Sketch a labelled vector diagram—not to scale, but using relative sizes.
3. Write the equation for adding the vectors.
4. Substitute numbers (with correct signs) into the equation, and solve.
5. Write a statement with your answer (including size and direction).

Understanding Concepts

1. What is the rule for adding vectors in a vector diagram?

2. What is the rule for drawing the resultant vector in a vector diagram?

3. A soccer player leaves the bench and runs 25 m [N] and then 40 m [S]. Use a scale vector diagram to find the resultant displacement. Show the full problem-solving approach.

4. What is the rule for adding vectors algebraically?

5. An actor walks 5 m stage right (east in this case) and then 15 m stage left.

   (a) Find the resultant displacement algebraically.

   (b) Draw a scale vector diagram to find the resultant displacement.

   (c) Compare your answers and account for any differences.

6. A shopper walks 35 m west, another 17 m west, and then 67 m east. Show the full problem-solving approach for finding the resultant displacement by the combined method.

7. On a paper delivery route, Julia walks from home three blocks north to collect her newspapers, walks back eight blocks south while delivering the papers, and then returns home. State Julia's resultant displacement and position (including the reference point).

8. Prepare a table to list the three problem-solving methods used in this section and the advantages and disadvantages of each method.

Making Connections

9. Draw a scale vector diagram of a segment of a one-dimensional journey in your daily life. Use paces for your distances. Determine the resultant displacement from the diagram and then test your answer by pacing it out. How close is the "paced" value to your calculated resultant value?

Exploring

10. If you start in a corner and walk around the perimeter of a football field (assume 100 m by 40 m), what is your displacement when you are halfway around?

    (a) Draw a scale vector diagram to determine your resultant displacement.

    (b) Suggest another new method, not mentioned in this section, that might be used for solving this problem.

Reflecting

11. Why do you think the scale diagram method was introduced here, even though it is more time consuming?

Adding Displacement Vectors

Any vector motion we have considered in this chapter has been restricted to forward or backward along a straight line. However, in the real world, motion and direction are seldom this simple. Nearly everywhere you go on any day involves turning and changing direction.

The purpose of this activity is to help you visualize individual displacements and resultant displacements that are not along one straight line. You will use toothpicks or straws to represent displacement vectors with values of 1, 2, and 3 units of length. Each toothpick represents a displacement: $\Delta \vec{d}_1$ = single length [N], $\Delta \vec{d}_2$ = double length [E], and $\Delta \vec{d}_3$ = triple length [S].

Question

What is the resultant displacement of three displacement vectors?

Materials

- 6 toothpicks or 2 straws
- scissors
- tape
- marker or pencil
- lined or graph paper
- ruler
- protractor

 Use the toothpicks and scissors with care.

Procedure

1 Tape two toothpicks and then three toothpicks end to end. (Alternatively, cut two straws to obtain lengths of approximately 4 cm, 8 cm, and 12 cm.)

2 Using a marker, colour one end of each of the "vectors" to represent the arrowhead. For the straws, you may want to colour a small piece of tape placed on the end of each straw.

3 Draw a compass symbol near the top of your paper and place an "X" near the left margin, about 10 cm from the top of the paper.

4 Place the component vectors in the order $\Delta \vec{d}_1 + \Delta \vec{d}_2 + \Delta \vec{d}_3$, using a head-to-tail procedure starting from position X. Their directions are N, E and S, respectively.

5 Place a dot at the head end of the last vector ($\Delta \vec{d}_3$ in this case). Label this point Y.

6 Using a ruler, draw an arrow and write a label for each of the three vectors.

7 Repeat steps 3 to 6 three separate times, using separate pieces of paper, and placing the vectors in different orders. Remember that $\Delta \vec{d}_1$ always points north, $\Delta \vec{d}_2$ points east, and $\Delta \vec{d}_3$ points south.

Analysis

(a) For each arrangement of vectors, draw the resultant displacement. Remember to include an arrowhead to indicate the direction, from X to Y.

(M2) (b) For each combination of displacement vectors:
- Measure and record the size (length) of the resultant displacement.
- Using the protractor and compass directions, devise a method to report the direction of the resultant displacement.
- Record each resultant displacement in a table.

(c) What do you notice about the final position of all the displacement vector additions?

(d) What do you notice about the length of each of the resultant displacements?

(e) Using your answers to these Analysis questions, answer the initial question.

(f) Compare your answers with those of other people. How did others communicate the direction of their resultant displacement?

Understanding Concepts

1. In your own words, state the rule for the addition of vectors including the direction of the resultant vector.

2. How are the size and direction of a vector represented in a vector diagram?

3. Does the order of addition of individual vectors affect the final resultant vector? Check your answer by using your values from the activity to draw vector diagrams to represent the addition of

$\Delta \vec{d}_1 + \Delta \vec{d}_2$ and $\Delta \vec{d}_2 + \Delta \vec{d}_1$,

$\Delta \vec{d}_1 + \Delta \vec{d}_3$ and $\Delta \vec{d}_3 + \Delta \vec{d}_1$, and

$\Delta \vec{d}_2 + \Delta \vec{d}_3$ and $\Delta \vec{d}_3 + \Delta \vec{d}_2$.

4. (a) If you are at a street corner (X) and you want to go to a store located at Y (**Figure 1**), what is one possible set of displacements to go from X to Y? (Use 1 block as a unit of length.)

(b) List two other sets of displacements that would produce the same resultant displacement from X to Y.

(c) Using what you have learned in this activity, how would you describe the resultant displacement vector from X to Y?

Making Connections

5. Describe a couple of situations in your life where different routes lead to the same resultant displacement. What factors or perspectives might you consider when choosing which route to take?

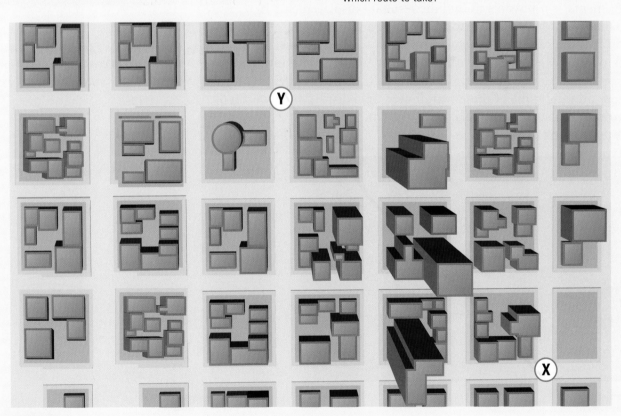

Figure 1

Adding Vectors at an Angle

Baseballs curve; hockey players deke; race cars corner; pole-vaulters flip. All of these examples, like almost all movements in the world, involve changing directions. As you know, some athletes cover large distances during competition, but their final displacement is near zero (**Figure 1**).

When a car's odometer measures the distance travelled, it ignores direction. An odometer, therefore, does not provide displacement. On the other hand, a GPS (global positioning system) device will only provide the resultant displacement (**Figure 2**). If, for example, you were on a wilderness canoe trip on a meandering river, the distance you travel could easily be twice your displacement.

If we know the size and direction of motion, that movement can be expressed as a vector. A series of movements often involves changes in direction. Each movement then becomes a separate vector in a vector diagram. Vectors that are not on the same straight line create two-dimensional vector diagrams. This means that there is some kind of change of direction between/among initial vectors (**Figure 3**).

If we know the distances and directions of a series of movements, is it possible to find the resultant displacement? It certainly is. By following a few simple rules and measuring accurately, we can draw a vector diagram to scale to represent the path of a moving object. We can then compare the final position to the reference point, and determine the resultant displacement. Before drawing some of these two-dimensional displacement vector diagrams, we need to establish some conventions for communicating direction.

Figure 1

Racing tracks are oval; in distance races the finish line is at most a few hundred metres from the start.

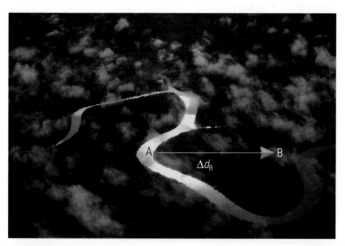

Figure 2

Using a meandering river for transportation involves much larger distances than displacements. Some GPS units provide the displacement between positions A and B.

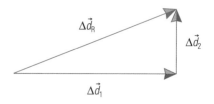

Figure 3

Two initial displacement vectors can be added to obtain a resultant displacement, $\Delta \vec{d}_R$.

Communicating Direction

Directions are very important when we are investigating vectors. There are several systems of communicating direction. We will choose one that is simple, logical, and consistent. It uses points of the compass, such as north [N] or west [W]. If the direction does not exactly match one of the compass points, we write it as an angle from the closest compass point. Measure the angle from one of the four compass directions, and specify which side of that direction your line is on. For example, in **Figure 4**, the vector's direction is written as [30° E of S].

For example, if a plane is flying 10° east of north, we write this direction as [10° E of N] and draw it as in **Figure 5**.

Figure 6 shows how other directions are written.

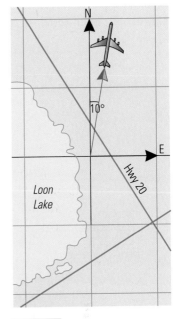

Figure 5

The airplane is flying in the direction [10° E of N].

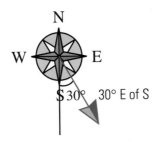

Figure 4

Angles are measured relative to a compass direction.

Adding Two-dimensional Vectors Using Scale Diagrams

If we know the size and direction of each separate displacement, we can draw a vector diagram to determine the resultant displacement.

1. You will need a sharp pencil, a ruler, and a protractor.
2. Choose and state a scale that fits your page or space available. Remember that a bigger scale gives a more precise result.
3. Calculate the length, to scale, of each of the vectors.
4. Draw the compass symbol on your page, with north toward the top.
5. Draw the first vector using your ruler and protractor. Be sure to draw it precisely, the correct length, and pointing in the appropriate direction.
6. Draw the second vector with its tail at the head of the first. Again, draw it precisely, the correct length, and pointing in the right direction.
7. Continue adding as many vectors as necessary, always placing the tail of the next vector at the head of the previous arrow.
8. Draw the resultant displacement as an arrow from the tail of the first vector (the initial position) to the head of the last vector (the final position). Label the resultant displacement, $\Delta \vec{d}_R$.
9. Use your protractor to find its angle from a compass direction, and your ruler to measure its length.
10. Using your scale, convert the measured length to the actual resultant displacement.
11. State the resultant displacement, including size (with units) and direction.

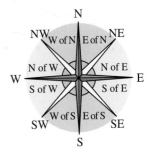

Figure 6

Indicating directions on either side of compass points

Did You Know?

About a century ago, a British mathematician, Oliver Heaviside (1850–1925), invented the vector diagram to simplify, communicate, and solve complex systems of motion.

Sample Problem 1

Denise walks to Jean's home by going one block east and then one block north (**Figure 7**). Each block is 160 m long. What is Denise's final displacement?

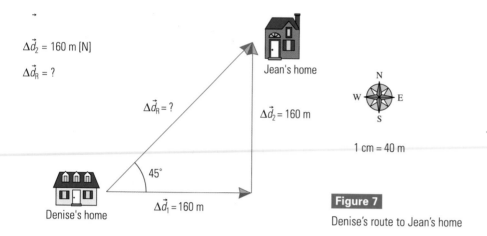

Figure 7
Denise's route to Jean's home

$$\Delta \vec{d}_R = 5.65 \ \text{cm} \times \frac{40 \ \text{m}}{1 \ \text{cm}} = 226 \ \text{m}$$

Based upon the scale diagram, Denise's displacement when walking to Jean's home is 226 m [45° N of E]. Because 45° N of E is northeast (NE), this answer can also be written as 226 m [NE].

Understanding Concepts

1. Measure the angle and indicate the direction of the following vectors from the black reference line.

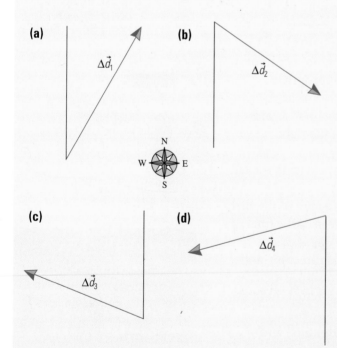

2. Draw a vector to represent 20 km in each of the following directions.

   (a) 27° W of N

   (b) 32° E of S

   (c) 40° W of S

   (d) 19° N of E

3. Measure and record the length and angle of each vector and each resultant displacement (shown in red in **Figure 8**) to determine their magnitudes and directions. (Do not write in your textbook.)

4. Draw scale diagrams to represent the vector addition in parts (a) and (b) below. Communicate the size and direction of the resultant displacement vectors.

   (a) Lorraine steered her boat out of the harbour, heading east. She travelled 500 m to one buoy and then turned north and headed 300 m to another buoy.

   (b) Jeff also left the harbour, pointed his boat 300 m [N] to a buoy, and then went 500 m [E].

   (c) State Jeff's position, relative to Lorraine's, after the two boats have finished moving as described in (a) and (b).

   (d) If Lorraine and Jeff race straight back, in what direction are they headed?

(a)   Scale: 1 cm = 1 km

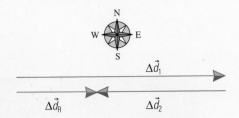

(b)

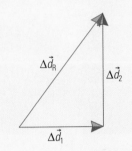

(c)

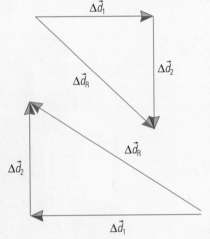

(d)

(e)

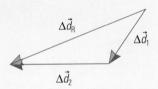

Figure 8

5. For each of the following situations, calculate the distance travelled and draw vector diagrams and determine the resultant displacement.

(a) Gary and Elaine are competing as a team in an orienteering event. They follow instructions telling them to go 50 m [N], 75 m [NE], and 100 m [30° E of S].

(b) Raj and Bernie enter into a car-rally competition. Determine their resultant displacement after completing four segments of the competition — 4.0 km [SE], 3.5 km [E], 5.0 km [N], and 4.5 km [NW].

Making Connections

6. Even though you may not use physics words like "resultant displacement" in your everyday life, you do use the concepts regularly.

(a) Describe a couple of contexts in your life where different distances travelled lead to the same displacement.

(b) What other things should you consider, besides the shortest distance, used when choosing a route to school or other places?

7. Imagine a forest fire in which teams of firefighters can communicate only by radio. How might they use a knowledge of position and displacement to work together?

8. When someone is lost in a forest or at sea, the searchers use a grid pattern to search. What does this mean?

9. How can the GPS technology help scientists learn more about animals? Provide an example.

10. From a scale map of your province, determine the position of three locations using the provincial capital as the reference point.

Exploring

11. The property line of a property runs directly across a lake. A surveyor measured around the lake 300 m [E] and then 400 m [N] to get from one corner to another corner of this property. Use a method other than a scale diagram to solve for the displacement from corner to corner.

12. Harjit shoots a ball from one corner of a pool table to the middle of the cushion on the far end to rebound the ball back to the corner pocket on his right (**Figure 9**). If the pool table measures 1.20 m by 2.40 m, what are the displacement of and the distance travelled by the ball?

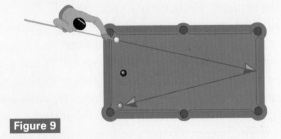

Figure 9

Reflecting

13. Mim rode her horse while checking the fence line on her farm. She travelled along the fence, up and down hills west 1.7 km and then north 1.1 km. At this position, what assumption(s) must you make in order to determine her resultant displacement? (No calculations are expected from you.)

11.6 Explore an Issue

DECISION-MAKING SKILLS
○ Define the Issue ● Analyze the Issue
● Identify Alternatives ● Defend a Decision
● Research ○ Evaluate

Athletes on the Edge

Every year new world records are set in sporting events such as track and field, speed skating, rowing, and swimming. Intense competition in modern sports prompts competitors to experiment with new products and processes, attempting to gain even a slight edge in acceleration, speed, and endurance. Every competitive athlete wants to enhance his or her performance. Performance enhancement can be separated into three general categories: technological; biological or "natural"; and chemical.

Technological approaches to performance enhancement in sports include new designs and materials for equipment, clothing, and footwear. Technology plays a major part in the continual improvement of sports equipment, thereby contributing to setting new athletic records. For example, a new skate design gave the Canadian speed-skating team a competitive edge in the Nagano Winter Olympics. The clap skate has the blade hinged in the front so that the entire blade stays in contact with the ice for the full stride of the skater, giving a longer push (**Figure 1**). Similarly, the development of lighter, more manoeuverable wheelchairs has enabled athletes to play faster and more exciting wheelchair basketball (**Figure 2**). Pole-vaulting provides another example of how improved equipment technology can make a dramatic difference in a sporting event (**Figure 3**). The pole used in this event has successively been made of wood, bamboo, tubular steel, and finally, in the 1950s, fiberglass. The great advantage of the fiberglass pole is its flexibility: the bend and whip that it gives is directly related to the vaulter's weight and take-off position. Whenever a new technology is developed, the sports organizers have to decide whether or not it will be permitted, resulting in very strict regulations concerning all aspects of athletes' equipment and clothing.

Biological approaches include improving athletes' training and diet. Professional trainers teach athletes the correct techniques to attain more power and speed. Training equipment has been developed to help athletes develop their speed, agility, endurance, and overall strength. Rigorous training and a proper diet together produce a healthy, powerful athlete.

The desire to move faster and soar higher is accompanied by the increasing use of performance-enhancing drugs. This could be described as chemical performance enhancement, and is generally forbidden. The strict regulations set by the International Olympic Committee (IOC) are intended to give all competitors an equal chance to do their best without endangering their health. During the last 30 years the use of performance-enhancing drugs has become a major issue in sports. The deliberate or inadvertent use of a banned substance is called doping.

Figure 1
A Canadian invention — the clap skate

Figure 2
The Canadian wheelchair basketball team

Figure 3
Pole-vaulters enhance performance through both technological and biological approaches.

The prohibition protects athletes from the harmful side effects of drugs and discourages any athlete from trying to gain an unfair advantage. There are five categories of substances banned by the IOC: stimulants, narcotics, anabolic steroids, diuretics, and hormones. The doping control process involves testing athletes' urine samples for traces of banned substances, but it seems that the development of new performance-enhancing chemicals is constantly running ahead of our ability to detect them.

Avoiding banned substances is more complicated than it might seem, because many common remedies (such as cough syrups, hayfever pills, and herbal products) and prescription medications contain banned substances. Another complication is that more substances are banned from amateur competition than from professional competition, so that when professional athletes compete in the Olympics they can be disqualified for having used substances that are allowed in professional sports. In Canada an athlete is banned from competition for four years for a first infraction, and banned for life after a second infraction.

Sometimes developments in performance enhancement are based upon scientific predictions. More often, however, they result from the systematic trial-and-error approach of technological research. The role of science is more often to explain the created technology. Technology is a separate but parallel activity to science. Science can take neither the blame nor the praise for performance enhancement in sport.

Understanding the Issue

1. Give one example of how technology can enhance performance in sports.

2. List two "natural" biological approaches to improving athletic performance.

3. Why are performance-enhancing drugs banned by the IOC?

4. How are science and the technology of performance enhancement inter-related?

Work the Web

Visit www.science.nelson.com and follow the links for Science 10, 11.6 to find out more about how athletes improve their performances.

Take a Stand   Performance Enhancement

The whole point of athletic competition is to discover who is the best athlete. What can be done to ensure that all athletes have an equal chance to do their best without endangering their health? Use the following questions to initiate a class discussion of the issue. The aim is to develop recommendations that you will present to a provincial sport organization.

- Who (if anyone) should approve the use of new designs and materials for sports equipment, clothing, and footwear?
- Should the same performance-enhancing drugs be banned in professional sport as in amateur sport?
- Should the doping control process be changed?
- Can the system be changed to allow athletes to take normal medications when required (e.g., cough and cold medications, hay-fever medication)?
- Should the same rules apply to all athletes, including those who are physically or mentally challenged?
- Should the penalties for doping be changed?

Forming an Opinion

1. Working in small groups, select a sport on which to focus.

2. Conduct further research on performance enhancement in your chosen sport.

3. Summarize your thoughts in a concise and well-reasoned letter to the appropriate provincial amateur sport association.

Velocity

When you are outside and notice a brisk wind blowing, or you are riding in a car at 60 km/h, you are simply considering the speed of motion — a scalar quantity. Sometimes, however, direction is also important or even crucial. A wind blowing from the north or from the west (**Figure 1**) is significant for information about approaching weather systems. It could also affect planes as they take off, fly, and land. Airlines could not operate without wind direction as part of their flight plans. A speed along with a direction is called **velocity**. Velocity is a vector quantity and is communicated in a variety of formats, for example,

- a quantity symbol, $\vec{v}$
- an actual quantity, 60 km/h [E]
- a labelled vector arrow, $\vec{v}_1 \longrightarrow$ or $60 \text{ km/h} \longrightarrow$

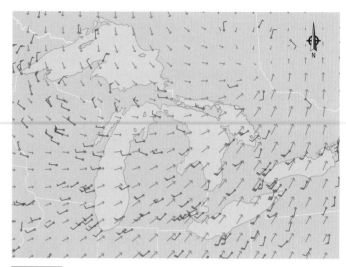

Figure 1

Wind velocities are part of the description of weather systems.

All of these formats represent a **constant velocity**, which means that both the size (speed) and the direction stay the same.

Just as a constant speed is represented by a straight line on a distance–time graph, a constant velocity appears as a straight line on a position–time graph (**Figure 2**).

As you know, displacement is a vector quantity. It includes a size and a direction. Velocity is also a vector quantity because it is a change in displacement in a given time. Just as a change in distance in a given time is used to calculate speed, a change in position (displacement) in a given time is used to calculate velocity. The direction of the velocity is always the same as the direction of the displacement.

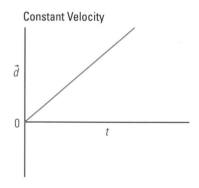

Figure 2

The line representing velocity passes through the origin. What does this indicate?

Sample Problem 1

A train travels at a constant speed through the countryside and has a displacement 150 km [E] in a time of 1.7 h. What is the velocity of the train?

$\Delta \vec{d} = 150 \text{ km [E]}$

$\Delta t = 1.7 \text{ h}$

$\vec{v} = ?$

$$\vec{v} = \frac{\Delta \vec{d}}{\Delta t}$$

$$= \frac{150 \text{ km [E]}}{1.7 \text{ h}}$$

$$= 88 \text{ km/h [E]}$$

The velocity of the train is 88 km/h [E].

On a plane trip from Toronto to Vancouver, the pilot will usually announce an air speed such as 425 km/h. However, both the pilot and the passengers know that the direction is west, so the velocity is 425 km/h [W].

Average Velocity

Average velocity is defined as the overall rate of change of position from start to finish. It is calculated by dividing the resultant displacement (which is the change of position) by the total time (**Figure 3**). The average velocity is expressed mathematically as

$$\vec{v}_{av} = \frac{\Delta \vec{d}_R}{\Delta t}$$

The displacement, $\Delta \vec{d}_R$, is a vector quantity and the direction of the average velocity, $\vec{v}_{av}$, will always be the direction of the displacement.

We refer to average velocity, and use it for calculations, in two situations:

1. if we know the resultant displacement and time but have no information on the velocities at any time during the trip; or
2. if the velocity varies (either in direction or size) during the journey, but we are only interested in the average velocity overall.

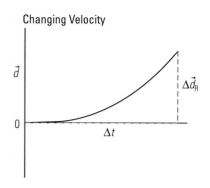

Changing Velocity

Figure 3

A curved line on a position–time graph represents a changing velocity because the slope of the line is changing.

Sample Problem 2

Monarch butterflies migrate from Eastern Canada to central Mexico (**Figure 4**), a resultant displacement of about 3500 km [SW] in a time of about 91 d. What is the average velocity of the monarch butterflies in kilometres per hour?

$\Delta \vec{d}_R$ = 3500 km [SW]

$\Delta t = 91 \, d \times \dfrac{24 \, h}{d} = 2.2 \times 10^3$ h (or 2184 h)

$\vec{v}_{av}$ = ?

$$\vec{v}_{av} = \frac{\Delta \vec{d}_R}{\Delta t}$$

$$= \frac{3500 \text{ km [SW]}}{2.2 \times 10^3}$$

$$= 1.6 \text{ km/h [SW]}$$

The average velocity of the monarch butterflies, as they fly to Mexico, is about 1.6 km/h [SW]. (Because the measurements of displacement and time are estimates—"about"—it is best to assume a certainty of only two significant digits in the answer.)

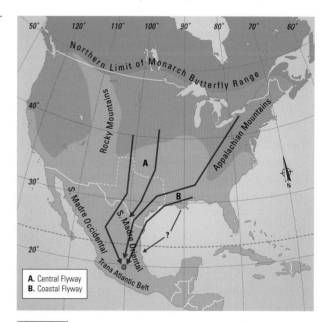

Figure 4

Monarch butterflies east of the Rocky Mountains all migrate to one valley in the central Chincua mountains of Mexico.

The velocity equation can be rearranged to solve for either time or distance. Notice that both average velocity and displacement are vector quantities but time is a scalar quantity. Therefore, if the time interval is the unknown variable, the answer will not include a direction.

Sample Problem 3

A monarch butterfly usually flies during the day and rests at night on its migration. If a particular butterfly is travelling at an average velocity of 19 km/h [S] for 230 km [S] on one part of its journey to Mexico, how long does this take?

$\Delta \vec{d} = 230$ km [S]

$\vec{v}_{av} = 19$ km/h [S]

$\Delta t = ?$

$$\vec{v}_{av} = \frac{\Delta \vec{d}}{\Delta t} \qquad \text{or} \qquad \vec{v}_{av} = \frac{\Delta \vec{d}}{\Delta t}$$

$$\Delta t = \frac{\Delta \vec{d}}{\vec{v}_{av}} \qquad\qquad 19\,\frac{\text{km [S]}}{\text{h}} = \frac{230\text{ km [S]}}{\Delta t}$$

$$= \frac{230 \text{ k\!\!\!/m [\!\!\!/S]}}{19\,\frac{\text{k\!\!\!/m}}{\text{h}}[\!\!\!/S]} \qquad\qquad \Delta t = \frac{230 \text{ k\!\!\!/m [\!\!\!/S]}}{19\,\frac{\text{k\!\!\!/m}}{\text{h}}[\!\!\!/S]}$$

The butterfly would take 12 h to travel 230 km [S] at an average velocity of 19 km/h [S].

Notice that the direction divides out just like units. (This ensures that the time answer is a scalar quantity.)

Sometimes we may need to find the resultant displacement before we can calculate the average velocity. For example, a jogger runs 52 m [E] in 10.0 s and then 41 m [W] for 8.0 s. What is the jogger's average velocity?

$$\vec{v}_{av} = \frac{\Delta \vec{d}_R}{\Delta t}$$

To calculate the average velocity you need to know the resultant displacement from start to finish. This displacement can be found by adding the two displacement vectors for the two parts of the run. From the vector diagram (**Figure 5**), the resultant displacement must be 11 m [E]. However, a vector diagram is not necessary if you assign [E] as positive (+) and [W] as negative (−). Then you can add algebraically:

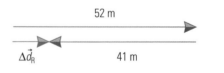

52 m

$\Delta \vec{d}_R$ 41 m

Figure 5

$\Delta \vec{d}_R = (+52 \text{ m}) + (-41 \text{ m})$

$\qquad = +11 \text{ m} \text{ or } 11 \text{ m [E]}$

The total time taken for this displacement is 18.0 s. The average velocity is calculated from the resultant displacement and the total time.

$$\vec{v}_{av} = \frac{\Delta \vec{d}_R}{\Delta t}$$

$$= \frac{11 \text{ m [E]}}{18.0 \text{ s}}$$

$$= 0.61 \text{ m/s [E]}$$

The average velocity of the jogger is 0.61 m/s [E].

The average velocity of the jogger is based only on the resultant displacement and the total time. This average velocity is not directly related to the velocities during each displacement. For example, when the jogger runs 52 m [E] in 10.0 s, the jogger's velocity is 5.2 m/s [E]. For the second part, 41 m [W] in 8.0 s corresponds to a velocity of 5.1 m/s [W].

1st displacement	2nd displacement
$\vec{v}_1 = \dfrac{\Delta \vec{d}}{\Delta t}$	$\vec{v}_2 = \dfrac{\Delta \vec{d}}{\Delta t}$
$= \dfrac{52 \text{ m [E]}}{10.0 \text{ s}}$	$= \dfrac{41 \text{ m [W]}}{8.0 \text{ s}}$
$= 5.2 \text{ m/s [E]}$	$= 5.1 \text{ m/s [W]}$

As you can see, these velocities are not obviously related to the average velocity of 0.61 m/s [E].

Comparing Average Speed and Average Velocity

As you recall from Chapter 9, average speed is calculated as the total distance travelled during a certain length of time. Because speed is a scalar quantity, this calculation ignores the direction taken. The jogger in the previous example travels 52 m in 10.0 s and then 41 m in 8.0 s for a total distance of 93 m in a total time of 18.0 s. The average speed of the jogger is calculated as follows:

average speed	average velocity
$v_{av} = \dfrac{\Delta d}{\Delta t}$	$\vec{v}_{av} = \dfrac{\Delta \vec{d}_R}{\Delta t}$
$= \dfrac{93 \text{ m}}{18.0 \text{ s}}$	$= \dfrac{11 \text{ m [E]}}{18.0 \text{ s}}$
$= 5.2 \text{ m/s}$	$= 0.61 \text{ m/s[E]}$

Compare the average speed, 5.2 m/s, to the average velocity, 0.61 m/s [E], for the same jogger. Note that the size of the average velocity is unrelated to the average speed. Average velocity is the resultant displacement from start to finish, divided by the total time taken. Average velocity does not depend on the path taken or the speeds throughout this path.

Understanding Concepts

1. Explain in your own words how velocity differs from speed.

2. What is constant in "constant speed" and in "constant velocity"? Give an example of each.

3. Translate each of the following vectors into a complete written vector quantity.

(a)

40 km/h

(b)

10 m/s

(c)

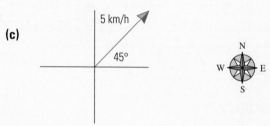

5 km/h

45°

4. Grey whales migrate from the Chukchi Sea to the Aleutian Islands in an average time of 25 d before heading east to travel along the coast. What is the grey whales' average velocity, in kilometres per day, between points A and B on the map shown in **Figure 6**? (Note that the distance between latitude lines 10° apart is equal to 1100 km.)

5. While delivering fliers, Brad walks 1.00 km [N], 0.50 km [E], 1.00 km [S], and finally 0.50 km [W] in a total time of 1.5 h.

   (a) What is the total distance travelled?

   (b) What is Brad's average speed?

   (c) What is the resultant displacement?

   (d) What is Brad's average velocity?

   (e) Why are you able to calculate the average velocity without knowing the times for each part of the trip?

6. A student travels 6.0 m [E] in 3.0 s and then 10.0 m [N] in 4.0 s.

   (a) What is her speed while travelling east?

   (b) What is her speed while travelling north?

   (c) Calculate the student's average speed.

   (d) What is her velocity while travelling east?

   (e) What is her velocity while travelling north?

   (f) Draw a vector diagram to determine the resultant displacement.

   (g) Calculate the student's average velocity.

7. A fisher sets out to check his fishing nets and heads 15 km/h [N] for 0.20 h. After stopping for 0.50 h, he travels at 12 km/h [E] for 0.10 h to get to the next set of fishing nets.

   (a) What is the fisher's displacement to get to the first set of nets?

   (b) What is the displacement when going from the first to the next set of nets?

   (c) What is the fisher's resultant displacement from the dock to the second set of nets?

   (d) What is average velocity from the dock to the second set of nets?

   (e) What is the average speed from the dock to the second set of nets?

   (f) The fisher returns to the dock. Now what are his resultant displacement and average velocity?

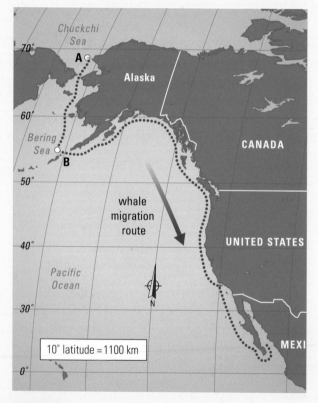

Figure 6

Ricardo Browne

Pilot and Flight Instructor

Ricardo Browne first dreamed of becoming a pilot back in his childhood home, the island of St. Vincent in the Caribbean. The chief export of St. Vincent is bananas, and Ricardo was fascinated watching the pilot who flew the local plane spraying banana crops.

"The pilot was good, and he used to fly very low. He was an acrobatic pilot and sometimes flew inverted, performing stunts and manoeuvres. I must have been about ten and thought that someday I'd like to do that."

Ricardo realized his dream of becoming a certified pilot in 1992, and now he's a flight instructor for Island Air Flight School located at Toronto City Centre Airport. He completed pilot training in Canada, one of the first students enrolled in the school.

In his training, Ricardo had to master practical flight skills, aviation theory, and regulations. To obtain a private pilot's licence, Transport Canada, the government agency that licenses pilots, requires a minimum of 45 hours of flight time. However, the average person completes 60 or 70 hours in the air. Then, the candidate must pass a Transport Canada written exam and a physical exam.

Ricardo obtains a great deal of satisfaction from his work as a pilot and flight instructor. "It's a rush to get up there in the air. I thrive on the sense of speed and power. Also, I really enjoy teaching my flight-school pupils. The greatest feeling is when one of my students successfully completes his or her pilot's exam."

Ricardo advises that it takes hard work and dedication to become a pilot, but it is a very realizable goal. "We always say that pilots are not born — they're made." Some of the personal qualities Ricardo possesses, and that he stresses are requisite to being a good pilot, are maturity, responsibility, and confidence.

Increasingly, flying is becoming more computerized — Ricardo says when pilots fly using computer systems it's called "flying by wire" — so a comfort level with technology is important.

"And you have to learn how to manage risk and assess the dangers involved in executing any flight manoeuvre."

High school courses necessary for flight school are geography, mathematics, and sciences, including physics. Basic physics knowledge required for flying includes an understanding of lift and of vectors, which are used in navigation planning.

Whatever pilot training route you might take, it will likely require a lot of money — because learning to fly is expensive. On the plus side, earning a pilot's licence can lead to exciting career opportunities such as flying water bombers to fight forest fires, piloting sightseeing tours — as Ricardo did — in the Caribbean, or being a flight examiner who tests candidates after they have completed their training at flight schools.

Ricardo's love of flying has continued to grow since he first saw that acrobatic, crop-dusting plane on St. Vincent.

Making Connections

1. Ricardo Browne says that pilot training programs can be expensive. Find out the cost of at least two programs offered in your province. Which program best suits your career goals?

🖑 Work the Web

Check out the pilot training programs at Humber College (www.humberc.on.ca) and Seneca College (www.senecac.on.ca). What training do these colleges offer to provide students with a good grounding for aviation careers?

Tracking and Position

Wildlife conservation depends on collecting and interpreting information, much of it to do with the movements of animals. Biologists need to answer many distance/speed/time questions, such as: where precisely do wild animals live; what routes do they use for migration and how rapidly do they travel; how much territory do they require for food supply; and how far are they normally chased by predators?

(a) Suggest some methods that could be used to collect this information.
(b) Why do you think that wildlife biologists need this information?

Anyone in unfamiliar territory, whether a wildlife bioligist or a city dweller who has accidentally taken the wrong bus, wants to find out where he/she is, and how to return to more familiar ground. Current technology may change the way we think about being "lost": the satellite Global Positioning System (GPS) now makes it possible for anyone to use small and relatively inexpensive receivers to display his/her precise location anywhere on Earth.

Figure 1

A deer wearing a tracking device

Tracking Animals

The more elusive a wild animal is, the more important tracking becomes to biologists (**Figure 1**). It may often be the only way to collect information on the animal's movements. A classic example of acquiring tracking data involved placing radio transmitters on endangered whooping cranes during their migration north from wintering grounds in Texas. Knowing precisely where the birds go allows better protection along their migration route.

Another recent study in Canada involves tracking peregrine falcons (a species almost made extinct in the 20th century by pesticide use). The Canadian Peregrine Foundation's "Project Track-'em" has followed the travels of four juvenile peregrines from Ontario. Each of the four birds, Eco, Rouge, Lincoln, and Nate, was outfitted with a satellite transmitter and released in the summer of 1999. The transmitters send out signals every four days. These signals are picked up by the *Argos* satellite, relayed to Earth, and converted into positions. Nate (**Figure 2**) remained in the area of Richmond Hill until October 2 and then began his journey south. **Table 1** gives Nate's position (latitude and longitude) and the distance flown from the start of his migration.

Figure 2

Nate was introduced to Richmond Hill in the summer of 1999 through the Canadian Peregrine Foundation's Project Release.

(c) Using the information from **Figure 3** and **Table 1**, draw a scale vector diagram showing each of Nate's displacements from October 2 to November 9. Use a full sheet of paper with a grid marked on the page. Plan your scale so that the starting position is near the top and the final position near the bottom.

(d) Find Nate's resultant displacement, including both size (in kilometres) and direction.

(e) How does the size of your resultant displacement compare with the distance of 3684 km calculated along the surface of Earth from the starting to final positions? Give some reasons for any differences between these two values.

(f) What velocity calculations can you make from the data in **Table 1**? What assumptions must you make? Comment on the validity of the results you would obtain.

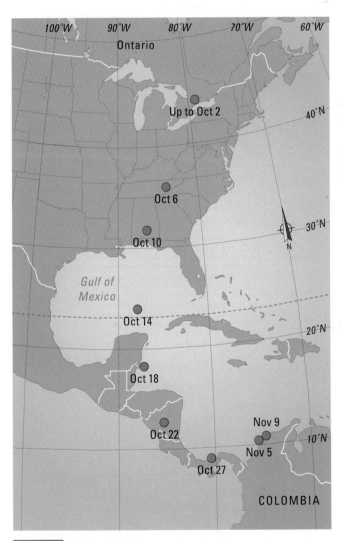

Figure 3

Nate's journey south ended along the Colombian coast where he remained for several months.

Table 1	Nate's Migration	
Date	**Position on Earth (°N, °W)**	**Distance flown from start (km)**
Oct 2	43.8, 79.4	0
Oct 6	35.7, 84.3	994
Oct 10	31.6, 86.4	1490
Oct 14	25.1, 87.3	2219
Oct 18	18.6, 87.3	2942
Oct 22	12.7, 85.0	3643
Oct 27	9.2, 80.8	4245
Nov 5	10.6, 75.4	4857
Nov 9	10.9, 75.2	4897

Tracking Ourselves

In 1973 the United States Department of Defense commissioned a system of 24 orbital radio satellites in staggered 12-h circular orbits at altitudes of 20 200 km, which it called the Globe Positioning System (GPS). There are now about 30 of these satellites in orbit. A receiver on Earth now has line-of-sight access to between five and nine of these satellites at any given time. The receiver detects signals from these satellites and, since the positions of these satellites are always very precisely known, is able to calculate its location on Earth's surface. Most hand-held receivers (**Figures 4** and **5**) give a location that is precise to ±2 m, but military and scientific receivers give values within millimetres in three dimensions (including altitude).

Commercially, these systems are mostly used by fishers; they are also used by boaters, hunters, and hikers. The devices can locate any particular place by latitude and longitude, so that it can easily be found again later. A GPS receiver can also mark a reference point (such as a campsite or dock) and then, when moved to another location, calculate the displacement of the new location from the initial reference point.

(g) Draw a sketch to show how a hiker's GPS receiver could indicate that the displacement back to camp is 150 m [NE], when the hiker has travelled 1200 m since leaving camp.

Figure 4
A GPS receiver can be useful on a hike through unfamiliar territory

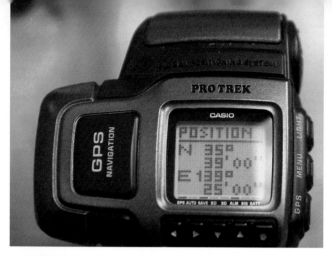

Figure 5
Using a GPS (global positioning system) receiver

Understanding Concepts

1. List some examples of how the use of modern tracking devices can increase scientific knowledge.

2. How precise are the positions obtained from the GPS?

3. A biologist obtains and records the position of a migrating bird when it has stopped to rest for the night. She repeats this procedure every night from the start to the end of the migration. What information is required to determine

   (a) the bird's displacement for any given day?

   (b) the bird's displacement for the whole migration?

Making Connections

4. How can GPS technology help you if you are travelling by car in a large, unfamiliar city? What might be the disadvantages of such a system?

Exploring

5. Find out what is meant by the term, "biotelemetry." Who uses this information and for what purposes?

☝ Work the Web

Search for peregrine falcons at www.science.nelson.com and follow the links for Science 10, 11.9.

(a) What is the longest daily flight by a peregrine falcon that any biologist has listed?

(b) Peregrine falcons often dive at very high speed to catch prey — such as pigeons or ducks — in midair. In a full dive they may be the fastest-moving living things. Find the maximum diving speed of these birds.

Chapter 11 Summary

Key Expectations

Throughout the chapter, you have had opportunities to do the following things:

- Analyze everyday phenomena and technologies in terms of the motions involved. (11.1, 11.2, 11.7, 11.9)
- Distinguish among and provide examples of scalar and vector quantities as they relate to the description of linear motion. (11.1, 11.7)
- Use simple graphs and vector diagrams to describe predicted and observed motion in one dimension. (11.2, 11.3, 11.4)
- Analyze how technology is used for tracking the motion of objects and outline the kinds of scientific knowledge gained through the use of such technologies. (11.2, 11.8, 11.9)
- Use a broad range of tools and techniques safely, accurately, and effectively to compile, record and analyze data and information, and apply mathematical and conceptual models to develop and assess possible explanations. (11.2, 11.3, 11.4, 11.5, 11.9)
- Add one-dimensional displacement vectors algebraically and graphically, and two-dimensional displacement vectors graphically. (11.3, 11.4, 11.5)
- Select and integrate information from various sources, including electronic and print resources, to answer questions. (11.6, 11.8, 11.9)
- Demonstrate an understanding of different kinds of motion and of the quantitative relationships between displacement and velocity, and solve simple problems involving displacement and velocity. (11.7, 11.9)
- Distinguish between constant and average velocity. (11.7)
- Describe quantitatively the relationship among one-dimensional average velocity $\vec{v}_{av}$, displacement $\Delta\vec{d}$, and elapsed time Δt, and solve simple problems involving these physical quantities; $\vec{v}_{av} = \dfrac{\Delta\vec{d}}{\Delta t}$. (11.7)
- Select and use appropriate vocabulary, SI units and symbols, and vector representations. (all)

Key Terms

average velocity

constant velocity

displacement

position

reference point

resultant displacement

scalar quantity

vector

vector diagram

vector quantity

velocity

Make a Summary

Using the Key Terms and Key Expectations, make a concept map to summarize what you have learned in this chapter.

Figure 1

How would you connect the concepts and terms in this chapter to this airline route map?

Reflect on your Learning

Revisit your answers to the Reflect on your Learning questions, page 413, in the Getting Started.

- How has your thinking changed?
- What new questions do you have?

Chapter 11 Review

Understanding Concepts

1. Explain what is meant by a vector quantity, and give two examples.

2. Explain what is meant by a scalar quantity, and give two examples.

3. Give two examples of scalar quantities that can be changed to vector quantities, and two that cannot.

4. Identify the following quantities as distance, position, displacement, speed, or velocity:
   (a) Nicole lives 1.60 km southwest of her school.
   (b) Su-Lin averages 18 km/h when she rides her bike to school.
   (c) Brad ran 15 km in the Terry Fox Run.
   (d) Kim jogged 1.0 km [S] and then 2.5 km [W].
   (e) Jean encountered a 45-km/h north wind on his bike trip.

5. Describe two ways of communicating vector quantities, other than with words.

6. Can the displacement of a moving object in any time interval exceed the distance travelled? Sketch vector diagrams to explain.

7. For scale vector diagrams describe the conventions for each of the following:
   (a) the orientation of a compass on the page;
   (b) how vector 2 is added to vector 1;
   (c) how the resultant vector is drawn;
   (d) how the size and direction of the resultant vector are determined.

8. A student, Lynn, walks a graph presented in **Figure 1**. Assuming that she walks it perfectly, answer the following questions.

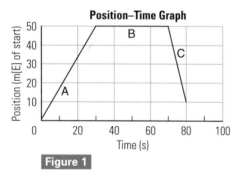

Figure 1

   (a) Describe Lynn's motion during each section: A, B, and C.
   (b) Draw a scale vector diagram of displacements to represent the motion graphed in **Figure 1**.
   (c) What information can you get from a position–time graph that you cannot get from a vector diagram? Can you draw a position–time graph from a vector diagram?

9. If Doug leaves home on a trip to the lake that takes him to a position 80 km [W] of home, what is his displacement? Do you know the distance that he travelled? Explain.

10. A volunteer, delivering fliers from home, walks down the street 200 m [W], back up the other side 350 m [E], and then returns home.
    (a) What is the volunteer's resultant displacement?
    (b) Use the full algebraic method to prove your answer in (a).
    (c) Use a scale vector diagram to prove your answer in (a).

11. An air-traffic controller is monitoring aircraft on radar. Draw vectors to scale from one reference point representing each of the following displacements:
    (a) 5.0 km [52° E of N];
    (b) 12.0 km [13° W of S];
    (c) 20.0 km [W];
    (d) 32.5 km [NW].

12. If you were at the geographic North Pole and travelled 5 km [S], 5 km [E], and 5 km [N], what would be your final position and displacement?

Applying Inquiry Skills

13. Plan an investigation (write a design) to determine which of the routes you can take home from school results in the greatest average velocity.

14. (a) Measure and record in your notebook the length and direction of each displacement and the resultant displacement in each of the vector diagrams in **Figure 2**. The scale is 1 cm = 10 km.

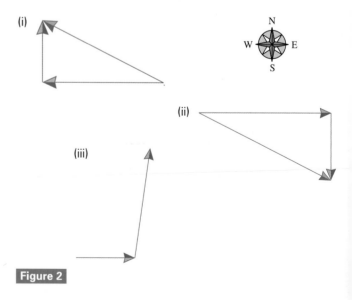

Figure 2

(b) If the total time in each case was 2.0 h, calculate the average speed and average velocity for each diagram.

15. One weekend Kevin and Leroy drove out to Rabbit Hill to ski. Starting from Kevin's home, they drove 6.4 km [S], 3.2 km [E], 16.0 km [S], and 12.8 km [W] to get to the ski hill in 45 min.
    (a) Draw a scale diagram to represent all the initial displacement vectors and the resultant displacement vector for the trip to the ski hill.
    (b) What distance did Kevin and Leroy drive in getting to the ski hill?
    (c) What was their average speed?
    (d) When they were at the ski hill, what was their position relative to Kevin's home?
    (e) What was their average velocity?
    (f) Can average velocity for any trip be greater than the average speed for the trip? Explain your answer.

16. In order to get from her classroom to the lab without going through the crowded rotunda, Jodie walks 14 m [E], 42 m [S], 32 m [W], 13 m [S], and 9 m [E].
    (a) Draw a scale diagram to represent all the initial displacement vectors and the resultant displacement vector in Jodie's walk to the lab.
    (b) What distance did Jodie walk in getting to the lab?
    (c) What is the position of the lab with respect to the classroom?

17. When Jasmine goes to school, she rides her bike 1.00 km [E], 0.70 km [S], 0.80 km [E], and 0.50 km [S]. When Jack goes to school, he rides his skateboard 0.30 km [W] and 1.70 km [S].
    (a) Draw a scale diagram to represent all the initial displacement vectors and the resultant displacement vector in their trips to school. (Hint: Start at the school and work back to their homes.)
    (b) What distances do Jasmine and Jack travel in getting to school?
    (c) When Jack is at school, what is his position with respect to his home?
    (d) If Jack takes 30 min to get to school, what is his average speed?
    (e) What is Jack's average velocity for his trip to school?
    (f) When Jack is at Jasmine's house, what is his position with respect to his home?

18. A hockey player "skating lines" at a hockey practice skates 10 m [S], 30 m [N], and 10 m [S].

(a) Sketch a vector diagram and show an algebraic problem-solving solution to determine her resultant displacement.
(b) Sketch a position–time graph to represent the motion.

19. Sandy is racing her sister home, but they each take a different route. Who will win: the one with the greatest average speed or the one with the greatest average velocity? Explain, using some sample numbers.

20. Assume that Environment Canada is tracking a violent storm travelling 30 km/h [E]. The storm is 50 km [W] of your school. It is 2:00 p.m. and school dismisses at 3:30 p.m.
    (a) Will it be possible for you to leave the school before the storm arrives?
    (b) What assumptions have you made to reach your conclusion?

Making Connections

21. **(a)** Why is it more important for an aircraft pilot to know the wind velocity than the wind speed?
    (b) Why is it important for all pilots to use the same conventions when describing velocity?

22. Some new luxury vehicles are being produced with on-board GPS units and software to determine position and displacement. Some units also have road and street maps that can be displayed, showing current position and the destination.
    (a) What are some advantages and disadvantages of this technology?
    (b) If you were buying a car, would you be willing to pay extra for this feature? Explain.

23. A new east-west road is planned to link two existing roads. The two roads are 7.2 km apart at their closest point. If the new road were to be constructed in a straight line, it would pass through a sensitive wetland area. A revised plan, making the road curve north around the wetland, would add 2.4 km to the length of the road, and push up construction costs.
    (a) Sketch the original and revised routes.
    (b) Compare the distance and the displacement of cars travelling both proposed routes.
    (c) Brainstorm some benefits and drawbacks of the revised plan.
    (d) Perform a risk-benefit analysis to develop recommendation for action.

12 Displacement, Velocity, and Acceleration

WHAT IS SO AMUSING ABOUT AMUSEMENT PARKS?
Most of us would agree that it's the rides, of course. The most popular ride
has always been the roller coaster with its thrilling high speeds, turns, and
drops. We pay good money for an experience that would be a nightmare in
an airplane. There are many famous roller
coasters in North America and
Europe, and still more are
being built.

The Millennium Force in the United States has a vertical drop of almost 100 m, a length of 2 km, and a maximum speed of about 150 km/h.

Some roller coasters emphasize high speeds or heights; others, a dizzying array of twists and turns. Many terrify us with free falls: offering as much as 5 to 10 s of weightlessness in a single trip. The popularity of roller coasters goes beyond the amusement parks. There are roller coaster organizations, magazines, software, Internet web sites, and even an Internet game in which you design your own equipment and on-line visitors take a virtual ride.

Common to all roller coasters are speed and acceleration in a variety of directions. In other words, displacement, velocity, and acceleration all play key roles in the excitement of a roller coaster ride. Roller coaster designers need a strong training in physics, and a knowledge of the strength of building materials. They must be able to interpret graphs like those in **Figure 1** as a first step in understanding the motion. Newer roller coasters are right at the edge of extreme motion and safe performance.

Figure 1

Changes in motion produce the thrill of a roller coaster ride.

Reflect on your Learning

1. How are graphs, like the ones shown in **Figure 1**, useful in describing motion with direction?

2. What other everyday examples of motion simulate, to a lesser extent, the motion of a roller coaster?

3. If any of $\Delta \vec{d}$, $\vec{v}$, or $\vec{a}$ is zero, does that mean the other quantities are also zero?

Throughout this chapter, note any changes in your ideas as you learn new concepts and develop your skills.

Try This
Activity   Extreme Wheels

Assemble a race car set to simulate the same kinds of motion as a roller coaster (**Figure 1**). Your set-up could be an actual toy race car set (**Figure 2**), or a computer game version of a race car set.

(a) Describe the motion in different sections of the track in as many different ways as you can: use words, vector quantities, equations, and graphs. In what ways are the motions of the toy race car similar to the motions of a roller coaster car? In what ways are they different?

(b) How might this toy race car set serve as a model for the design of a roller coaster ride? What would be some limitations?

Figure 2

Getting the car to stay on the track can be a major challenge.

Position–Time Graphs

We know that position and displacement are vectors, and include direction. Is it possible to represent vector motion on a graph? Absolutely. Position is represented on a **position–time graph**, which looks very much like a distance–time graph. Look at **Figures 1** and **2**. One has a scalar quantity on the *y*-axis, while the other has a vector quantity. What differences can you detect?

If a bird is flying at constant speed in a straight line (**Figure 3**), it is covering equal distances in equal intervals of time. This is illustrated by the straight line on a distance–time (*d-t*) graph (**Figure 1**). A position–time ($\vec{d}$-*t*) graph for this motion (**Figure 2**) looks identical to the distance–time graph: the shape and units are the same, but the position–time graph includes the direction of motion in the label for the *y*-axis.

Figures 4 and **5** represent the same trip to the video store. They show that not all distance–time and corresponding position–time graphs are the same (as in **Figures 1** and **2**). How many ways are **Figure 4** and **Figure 5** different? Firstly, the *y*-axis is labelled differently. Secondly, the last segment of the trip is different only in that the line is sloped upward (**Figure 4**) rather than downward (**Figure 5**). All line segments in both graphs are the same length and slope (except for the negative versus positive slope for the last segment). This illustrates how position (a vector quantity) is different from distance (a scalar quantitiy). More information is included in a position–time graph. We know, for example, that the video store is north of the reference point (assume home). We also know from the position–time graph that the shopper has returned home.

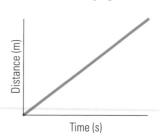

A Crane Flying

Distance (m) / Time (s)

Figure 1

Distance–time graph showing motion with constant speed

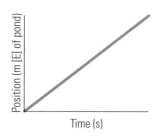

A Crane Flying

Position (m [E] of pond) / Time (s)

Figure 2

Position–time graph showing motion eastward with constant velocity

Figure 3

Motion with fairly constant speed

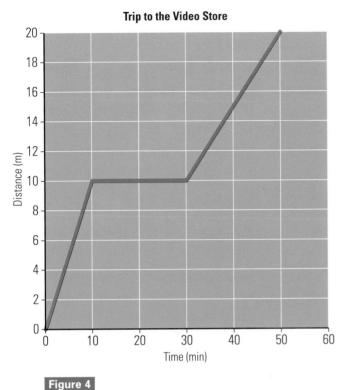

Figure 4

Distance–time graph, showing a return trip to the video store

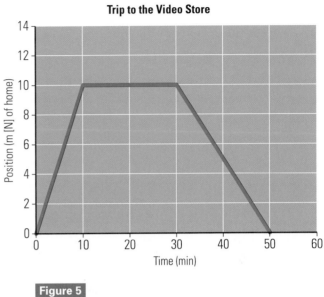

Figure 5

Position–time graph, showing the same return trip to the video store as **Figure 4**

Let us now look at a graph that is a little different (**Figure 6**). How would you "walk-the-graph"? You would

1. start from the reference point (home, 0) and move east at a constant velocity;
2. stop (for whatever reason) for about an equal period of time;
3. start walking back home at about the same speed (approximately the same size of slope) but in the opposite direction (velocity is negative);
4. walk right past your home and continue west for a while (a negative displacement);
5. slow down gradually before stopping and turning east, toward home, again; then
6. return to your original position, home.

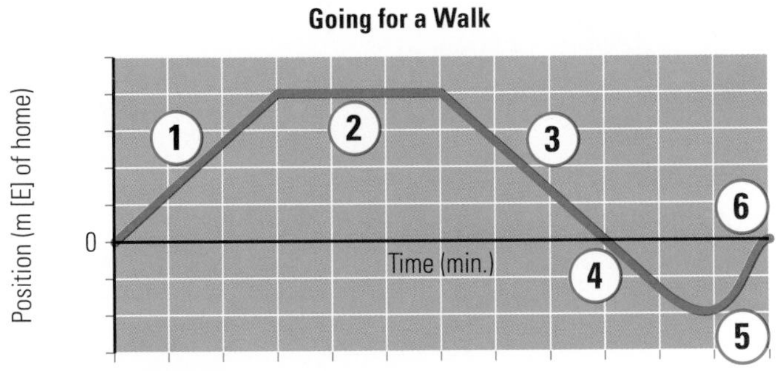

Going for a Walk

Figure 6

A position–time graph of a short walk from home

As you can see, position–time graphs can have a negative slope (a decreasing value of $\Delta\vec{d}$), whereas distance–time graphs cannot. This is because position can decrease while distance always increases. Recall that the slope of a distance–time graph is rise over run, which is the same as the speed of the motion.

The slope of a position–time graph is, likewise, the rise/run or the velocity of the motion.

Distance–Time Graph

$$\text{slope} = \frac{\text{rise}}{\text{run}}$$

$$\text{slope} = \frac{\text{distance}}{\text{time}}$$

$$v = \frac{\Delta d}{\Delta t}$$

Position–Time Graph

$$\text{slope} = \frac{\text{rise}}{\text{run}}$$

$$\text{slope} = \frac{\text{displacement}}{\text{time}}$$

$$\vec{v} = \frac{\Delta\vec{d}}{\Delta t}$$

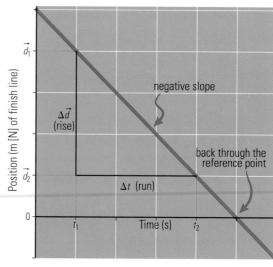

Finishing a Race at the Start/Finish Line

Figure 7

In which direction is the runner moving? What is happening to the runner as the line crosses the x-axis?

Note that in **Figure 7** the displacement $\Delta\vec{d}\ (\vec{d}_2 - \vec{d}_1)$, is negative, therefore the slope is negative, and so the velocity is negative. What does this mean? We can see that positive on the graph is defined as north, so negative is therefore south. The runner is heading south. A negative slope on a position–time graph indicates motion in the opposite direction. A negative slope above the x-axis indicates motion toward the reference point, but the same slope below the x-axis indicates motion away from the reference point. Position and displacement are vector quantities: they have both size and direction. This means that they can be either positive or negative. Notice that **Figure 7** shows the runner going a short distance beyond the reference point (the finish line).

Sample Problem 1

Canadians Donovan Bailey, Bruny Surin, Glenroy Gilbert, and Robert Esmie won the 1996 Olympic gold medal in the 4×100 m relay race. When Bailey finished the 4×100 m relay race the team's time was 37.69 s, as described graphically in **Figure 8**. From the graph, determine Bailey's velocity in the final stretch of his 100-m leg of the race.

Assume that north is positive and south, negative.

$\vec{d}_1 = +20.0$ m

$\vec{d}_2 = +5.0$ m

$t_1 = 35.2$ s

$t_2 = 37.1$ s

$$\text{slope} = \frac{\text{rise}}{\text{run}}$$

$$\vec{v} = \frac{\Delta\vec{d}}{\Delta t}$$

$$= \frac{(5.0 - 20.0)\text{ m}}{(37.2 - 35.8)\text{s}}$$

$$= -11 \text{ m/s}$$

From the slope of the line on the position–time graph, Bailey's velocity while finishing the race was 11 m/s [S].

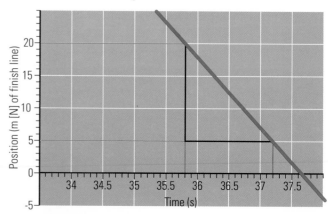

Bailey Finishes the Race

Figure 8

The last few seconds of the 4×100 m relay of the winning Canadian team

The constant slope in **Figure 8** shows that the velocity of the runner is constant. This means that the instantaneous velocity has the same value throughout.

Recall what a distance–time graph for constant acceleration looks like. Consider now the case of the constant acceleration of a boat from rest (**Figure 9**). You can see from the graph that the slope of the line is steadily increasing. What does this mean? Since the slope of the line on the position–time graph is increasing, the velocity must be increasing. It is no longer constant. Now we can do something new: we can determine the instantaneous velocity at, say, 4.7 s. We do this by drawing a tangent to the curve at that point.

The slope of the tangent at a point on a position-time graph yields the instantaneous velocity.

Instantaneous velocity is the change in position over an extremely short period of time. Instantaneous velocity is like instantaneous speed plus a direction. Both quantities are calculated from a slope, but instantaneous velocity must include a direction because it is a vector quantity.

Sample Problem 2

A boat accelerates uniformly for seven seconds (**Figure 9**). What is the instantaneous velocity at 4.9 s?
    Assume that east is positive.

$\vec{d}_1$ = +44 m

$\vec{d}_2$ = +5 m

t_1 = 3.0 s

t_2 = 7.0 s

$$\text{slope} = \frac{\text{rise}}{\text{run}}$$

$$\vec{v} = \frac{\Delta \vec{d}}{\Delta t}$$

$$= \frac{(44 - 5)\ \text{m}}{(7.0 - 3.0)\text{s}}$$

$$= 9.8\ \text{m/s}$$

The instantaneous velocity of the boat at 4.9 s is 9.8 m/s [E].

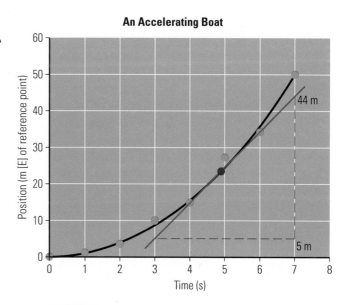

An Accelerating Boat

Figure 9

A tangent to the curve at any point yields the instantaneous velocity at that point.

Understanding Concepts

1. How can the velocity of an object be determined from a position–time graph?

2. Using the labels on the graphs in **Figure 10**, write brief descriptions about the motion that the graphs might describe. Include the direction and relative size of the different velocities.

(a)

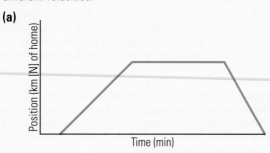

(b)

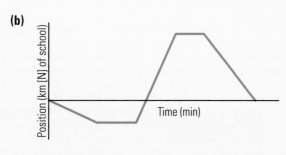

Figure 10

3. **Figure 11** presents a position–time graph for a ball rolling down a slight incline.

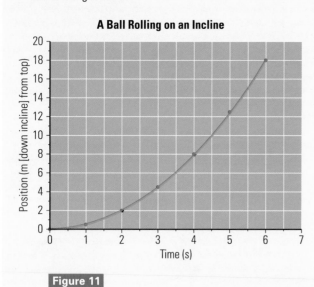

Figure 11

(a) What is happening to the velocity as the ball rolls down the incline? How does the graph show this information?

(b) What kind of motion does the position–time graph represent?

(c) What is the displacement after 2.0 s, 4.0 s and 6.0 s?

Use **Figure 12** to answer questions 4 and 5.

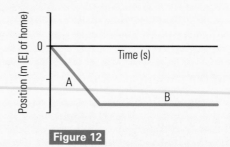

Figure 12

4. Describe the velocity for graph segment A by indicating

(a) whether the motion represents constant velocity;

(b) how the average velocity is found;

(c) whether the instantaneous velocity changes;

(d) how the size and direction of the average and instantaneous velocities compare.

5. What are the similarities and differences between segments A and B?

6. **(a)** Draw a position–time graph for the motion of the air puck ⓥ2 (**Table 1**).

Table 1	The Travels of an Air Puck	
Dot number	**Total time (ms)**	**Position (mm [N])**
1	0	0
2	20.0	30.0
3	40.0	58.5
4	60.0	121.5
5	80.0	153.0
6	100.0	181.0
7	120.0	209.5

(b) Determine the instantaneous velocity at 30.0 ms, 50.0 ms, ⓥ3 and 90.0 ms.

(c) Describe the velocity of the air puck from start to finish.

(d) Calculate the average velocity for the total time period.

(e) How do the instantaneous velocities, calculated in (b), compare with the average velocity from (d)?

SKILLS HANDBOOK: ⓥ2 Constructing a Line Graph ⓥ3 Slopes and Intercepts

7. A wind-up toy is attached to a ticker tape and released. **Table 2** shows the positions immediately after release.

Table 2   **A Ticker Tape Experiment**

Dot number	Total time (ms)	Position (mm [E] of start)
1	0	0
2	10.0	9.0
3	20.0	39.5
4	30.0	90.0
5	40.0	158.0
6	50.0	252.5
7	60.0	357.0

(a) Draw a position–time graph for the toy.

(b) What is the displacement between

    (i) 20.0 ms and 30.0 ms?

    (ii) 30.0 ms and 40.0 ms?

(c) What do your answers to (b) tell you about the motion of the toy?

(d) How would you reach the same conclusion as you did in (c), just by looking at the graph?

(e) Determine the instantaneous velocity at 25.0 ms and 35.0 ms.

(f) Calculate the average velocity for the total time period.

Exploring

8. Look again at the graph in **Figure 6** (page 447). Show the same motion as

(a) a displacement vector diagram (without a scale)

(b) a distance–time graph

(c) a velocity–time graph

9. Which method of communication in question 8 provides the best information? Explain your answer.

10. Consider Canadian mountain-bike champion, Alison Sydor's false start in a race. The dots in **Figure 13** represent Sydor's position every 0.5 s from the start (position = 0).

(a) Sketch a position–time graph for Sydor's false start.

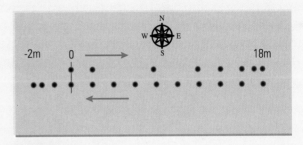

Figure 13

(b) Draw a scale vector diagram to represent Sydor's displacement.

Reflecting

11. When new concepts are being created, scientists go through a stage of confusion before everything seems to fit into place again. In this regard, how do you feel right now about the introduction of position–time graphs? Do you have confidence in your understanding of this new concept?

 # Challenge

1,2 Aristotle and Galileo had trouble visualizing and measuring acceleration due to gravity. Why?

Velocity–Time Graphs

How are velocities represented on a graph? You can translate the situation shown in **Figure 1** into a velocity–time graph by first assigning one direction, for example east, as the positive direction, and therefore west as the negative direction. You know that a graph can have positive and negative axes. Therefore, you can show the velocities of both the car and truck on a velocity–time graph by using the negative *y*-axis (below the *x*-axis) for velocities in the negative direction (**Figure 2**).

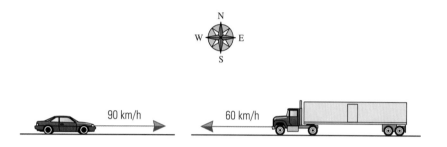

Figure 1

A car is travelling at a constant velocity of 90 km/h [E] while a truck is travelling at a constant velocity of 60 km/h [W]. The size of each instantaneous velocity is measured on each vehicle's speedometer. The direction of each is determined from a map or perhaps an onboard compass.

Just as the slope of a speed–time graph represents acceleration, the slope of a velocity–time graph also represents acceleration. **Acceleration** can be calculated as the change in velocity over time. Now, however, the acceleration has a direction associated with it, and so is a vector quantity. The symbol for vector acceleration is written as $\vec{a}$.

In **Figure 2**, the car and the truck are each travelling at a constant velocity. This is shown by the horizontal lines (zero slope) on the velocity–time graph.

Now let's consider some changes in velocity shown on velocity–time graphs.

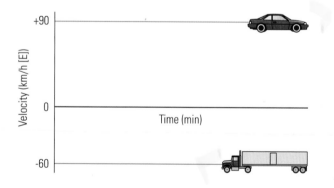

Figure 2

A car is travelling at 90 km/h [E] while a truck is travelling at 60 km/h [W].

Sample Problem 1

A jogger is out for a run. The velocity–time graph is shown in **Figure 3**. For each lettered section of the graph, describe the motion of the jogger. Be sure to specify the direction of the motion.

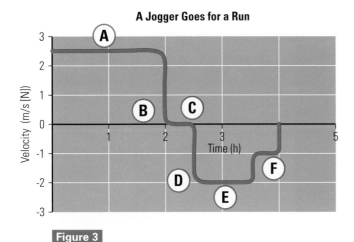

A Jogger Goes for a Run

Figure 3

A jogger goes for a long run.

According to the velocity-time graph, the jogger
A. runs north at a constant velocity of 2.5 m/s for about the first two hours;
B. slows and then stops at the end of 2.0 h;
C. remains stationary for about 0.5 h;
D. accelerates rapidly toward the south after about 2.5 h;
E. runs at 2.0 m/s [S] from about 2.5 h to about 3.5 h;
F. abruptly changes her velocity to 1.0 m/s [S] (a walk) for about 0.5 h before stopping.

Constant Acceleration

Now let's consider an example of uniformly-changing velocity (constant acceleration). For example, suppose a bird, such as a kingfisher, dives from rest and drops under the influence of gravity. If we assume there is no friction, the downward velocity will increase uniformly.

$$\text{slope} = \frac{\text{rise}}{\text{run}} \text{ (from a velocity–time graph)}$$

$$\vec{a} = \frac{\Delta \vec{v}}{\Delta t}$$

Remember that we are now considering acceleration to be a vector quantity. In Chapter 10 we calculated the size of the acceleration without considering the direction. Now we will communicate both the size and the direction of the acceleration. If the object's velocity is increasing, the direction of the acceleration is always the same as the direction of the velocity. If the velocity is established as north and the velocity increases to the north, then the acceleration is north. If the velocity is north but decreasing, then the acceleration is south. Fortunately, using these conventions, we can easily find the direction of the acceleration from the calculation. Even if the motion is in the up/down dimension, one of these directions can be assigned a positive sign.

Sample Problem 2

What is the acceleration of the diving kingfisher in **Figure 4**?
Up is the positive direction and down is negative.

$\vec{v}_1 = -2.0$ m/s

$\vec{v}_2 = -8.0$ m/s

$t_1 = 0.20$ s

$t_2 = 0.80$ s

$$\text{slope} = \frac{\text{rise}}{\text{run}}$$

$$\vec{a} = \frac{\Delta \vec{v}}{\Delta t}$$

$$= \frac{\vec{v}_2 - \vec{v}_1}{\Delta t}$$

$$= \frac{(-8.0 - (-2.0))\ \text{m/s}}{(0.80 - 0.20)\ \text{s}}$$

$$= -10\ \text{m/s}^2$$

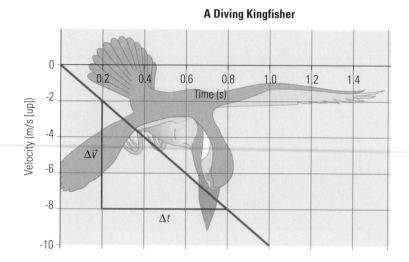

A Diving Kingfisher

Figure 4

The slope of a velocity-time graph represents the kingfisher's acceleration.

According to the slope of the velocity-time graph,
the average acceleration of the kingfisher is 10 m/s² [down].

Average Velocity

As you may recall from Chapter 10, the average speed of an object in motion can be determined from the ratio of total distance divided by total elapsed time. Similarly, the average velocity of an object in motion can be determined from the ratio of total (resultant) displacement divided by total time.

$$\vec{v}_{av} = \frac{\Delta \vec{d}_R}{\Delta t}$$

Sample Problem 3

In January of 2000 Canadian Jeremy Wotherspoon (**Figure 5**) broke his own speed skating world record in the 500-m event with a time of 34.63 s.
(a) What was his average speed during the skate?
(b) What was the average velocity of his skate? Assume that north is positive and that the start and finish line were in the same place.

(a) $v_{av} = \dfrac{\Delta d}{\Delta t}$
$\quad = \dfrac{500\ \text{m}}{34.63\ \text{s}}$
$\quad = 14.3\ \text{m/s}$

(b) $\vec{v}_{av} = \dfrac{\Delta \vec{d}_R}{\Delta t}$
$\quad = \dfrac{0\ \text{m [N]}}{34.63\ \text{s}}$
$\quad = 0\ \text{m/s [N]}$

Figure 5

Jeremy Wotherspoon may have been disappointed by his average velocity.

Jeremy Wotherspoon skated at an average speed of 14.3 m/s during his world-record-breaking skate. However, his average velocity is zero since his resultant displacement was zero. He started and finished the race at the same position.

The average velocity of a uniformly accelerating object can also be determined in the same way as the average of most things: adding the largest value and the smallest value and then dividing by two:

$$\vec{v}_{av} = \frac{\vec{v}_1 + \vec{v}_2}{2}$$

The average velocity has the same value as the instantaneous velocity at the mid-time point for constant acceleration (**Figure 6**). It is important to note that the formula given above and the velocity at the mid-time point only work when the velocity-time graph is straight (indicating uniform acceleration).

Finding Average Velocity from a Graph

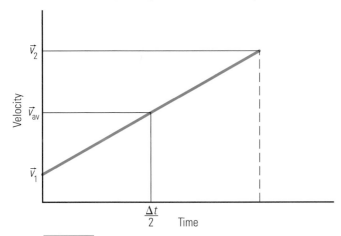

Figure 6
To find the average velocity, locate the mid-time point, and read the velocity at that time.

Sample Problem 4

What is the average velocity during the interval of a car crash if the initial velocity is 12 m/s [NE] and the car comes to rest 0.11 s later? (Assume that the car crash involves constant acceleration.)

Let the north-east direction be positive.

$\vec{v}_1 = +12$ m/s

$\vec{v}_2 = 0$ m/s

$$\vec{v}_{av} = \frac{\vec{v}_1 + \vec{v}_2}{2}$$

$$= \frac{(+12 \text{ m/s}) + (0 \text{ m/s})}{2}$$

$$= +6.0 \text{ m/s}$$

The average velocity during the interval of the car crash is 6.0 m/s [NE].

Understanding Concepts

1. What information does the slope of a velocity–time graph give us?

2. A tennis player practises by hitting a tennis ball toward a brick wall. Interpret the velocity–time graph in **Figure 7** to describe what is happening to the ball in each segment of its trip.

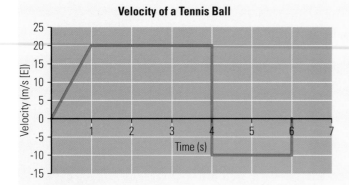

Figure 7

3. The Queen's Plate is a horse race for Canadian-bred three-year-old horses. The race is run at Woodbine Racetrack in Toronto, Ontario (**Figure 8**). The record for the 2012-m race is 2:02 (two minutes and two seconds). The horses start running westward, go past the finish, complete a circuit of the track, and finish in front of the stands, 700 m [W] of where they began.

   (a) What is the average speed for the record run?

   (b) What is the average velocity for the record run?

Figure 8

4. What is the average velocity in the following situations?

   (a) You walk to school and back home.

   (b) A car accelerates uniformly from rest to 60 km/h [W].

   (c) The instantaneous velocity at the midpoint of constant positive acceleration is 45 km/h [S].

   (d) A diver enters the water at 17 m/s [down] and is stopped by the water within 2.5 m. What assumption is made in this calculation?

5. In a 200-m race, an athlete accelerates rapidly out of the blocks for 3 s before the false start pistol is fired. The athlete stops within 2 s, and then takes 10 s to walk slowly back to the starting blocks. Sketch a velocity–time graph for this athlete. Compare this graph to the position–time graph that you drew in question 10 in 12.1

6. Video analysis of a space shuttle launch (**Figure 9**) provides a table of evidence (**Table 1**).

Figure 9

Table 1 **Launching a Space Shuttle**

Interval	Total time (s)	Velocity (m/s [up])
1	0.8	4.6
2	1.6	7.2
3	2.4	10.4
4	3.2	12.1
5	3.6	14.2
6	4.0	15.0
7	4.4	16.1
8	4.8	17.3
9	5.2	19.0

   (a) Draw a velocity–time graph from this evidence and
   Ⓥ determine the acceleration of the shuttle during this segment of the launch. (The best-fit line need not pass through the origin.)

(b) Does the acceleration of the space shuttle appear constant? Explain.

(c) If the acceleration is constant, use your graph to determine the average velocity of the space shuttle over the entire 5.2 s.

7. A car, leaving a city speed zone of 45 km/h [E], accelerates uniformly to the new speed limit of 105 km/h [E] in 7.0 s. What is the average velocity of the car during this constant acceleration?

8. Refer to **Figure 4** on page 454.

(a) If downward is defined as the positive direction, how would the graph change?

(b) Recalculate Sample Problem 2 (page 454) using down as positive.

(c) Which method do you prefer? Why?

9. Draw a velocity–time graph and a speed–time graph for a shopping trip in a car from home that involves

(a) accelerating quickly to 40 km/h [S];

(b) driving at a constant 40 km/h [S] for 10 min;

(c) stopping to shop for 10 min;

(d) accelerating rapidly to 40 km/h [N];

(e) driving at 40 km/h [N] for 10 min;

(f) stopping at home.

10. How can you determine the instantaneous velocity from

(a) a straight line on a position–time graph?

(b) a curved line on a position–time graph?

(c) a straight line on a velocity-time graph?

(d) a curved line on a velocity-time graph?

Making Connections

11. Driving habits in city traffic have a variety of environmental and economic consequences. Sketch a velocity-time graph for a poor or undesirable driving habit in stop-and-go traffic, and another graph illustrating a better or more desirable driving habit for the same trip. Be prepared to discuss the differences in the two graphs from at least two perspectives.

12. When the police investigate accident scenes, they collect a variety of evidence. What are some examples of information that might be recorded? What kinds of results might the police hope to obtain from the analysis of the evidence?

Exploring

13. What information can we find from

(a) the area under the curve of a velocity–time graph?

(b) the area under the curve of a position–time graph?

14. Look again at **Figure 2** (page 452).

(a) List at least four pieces of information that you can obtain from the graph.

(b) What information can you not obtain from the graph?

15. Draw a velocity vector diagram to represent the shopping trip in question 9.

16. Which, of the two graphs in question 9 and the vector diagram in question 15, provides the best information? Explain.

Reflecting

17. In the two sections of this chapter that you have just completed, you have learned about position–time and velocity–time graphs. How did understanding distance–time and speed–time graphs help you to understand these new graphs? What is the main difference between these new graphs and the old ones?

Technology and Skiing

Winter sports and recreations are popular in cold-climate countries such as ours. Participation in both alpine and cross-country skiing is steadily growing in Canada as people apply technology to turn snow, normally a challenge to winter mobility, into a form of exercise and entertainment. The form and structure of skis has been constantly modified ever since the first styles were developed in Scandinavia to allow people to move freely across otherwise impassable winter landscapes.

Alpine ski technology, unlike that for cross-country skiing, is focused on sliding down slopes—fast enough to be exhilarating, and slow enough to allow the skier enough directional control to keep on course (**Figure 1**). The basic technology involves making the ski base of very smooth waxed plastic composite, and the bottom edges of very sharp metal strips. Such a ski is designed to slide forward very easily, but to dig in to prevent any side slip when a skier "carves" a turn—even on very hard-packed smooth snow or on ice. To this end, alpine bindings lock the boot firmly to the ski, and the boot is very tight and stiff, so that any foot movement is transmitted instantly and directly to the ski.

A problem arises whenever a skier falls, of course. A binding must allow the ski to come loose when a skier loses control, or the ski may twist the leg and break it. Modern bindings are technological marvels and are being constantly researched and improved (**Figure 2**). Making a device that clamps very firmly so that it will also release easily under only certain specific movements is very complicated, especially when you add in requirements that it must work perfectly wet or dry, warm or cold, and when full of snow and/or ice. Knowledgeable alpine skiers worry much more about the quality of their bindings than about the quality of their other equipment.

Since a loose ski hurtling down a steep slope is very dangerous, all skis also have ski brakes: prongs that project down into the snow whenever there is no boot in the binding.

(a) How does a ski brake differ from a bicycle brake?

Turning control involves another technology. Because the entire edge must grip the snow during a turn, the ski must flex easily.

Figure 1

Whether you are a recreational skier or a Canadian champion, such as Edi Podivinsky, science and technology make skiing more fun.

Figure 2

The combination of technologies on a downhill ski is incredible: boot, binding, ski shape, edges, and brakes.

At the same time the ski must not be too elastic and flexible or the base will bounce or chatter over uneven surfaces, reducing the skier's control. These contradictory requirements are met by making skis of many composite layers, each with different characteristics.

(b) Some skiers have different skis for different conditions. Under what conditions would you expect a skier to choose a very flexible ski?

The latest design advance in recreational alpine skis is the carving ski, which is significantly narrower and thicker in the centre than the standard design. Such a ski curves more easily in a turn, reducing effort and improving control at the same time. These skis, although expensive, have become very popular very quickly, because they allow skiers to ski steeper slopes under control, at the same technique level.

On January 15, 2000, Canadian World Cup competitor Edi Podivinski (**Figure 1**) won a bronze medal for his finish time in a downhill race on the Lauberhorn run at Wengen, in Switzerland. His time for the run was 2 min 30.56 s. World Cup events include the slalom, giant slalom, and supergiant slalom, where competitors must ski a precise route around markers, and the downhill, where the shortest time (fastest average speed) is all that counts. Downhill skiers use long skis with special low-friction waxes for maximum speed. In a sport where hundredths of a second count, any tiny decrease in friction will be of value to the skier. Recent technology includes the development of fluorocarbon compound waxes that are super-slippery on snow. Even the fabrics used for racers' ski suits are controlled by rules, and competitors usually don't wear warm underclothing, because the extra bulk would increase their wind resistance (air friction). The Lauberhorn run is the longest World Cup downhill race at 4408 m, and has a total vertical drop of 810 m.

On December 19, 1999, Podivinski won a bronze medal for his finish in the downhill race on the Saslöng run at Val Gardena, Italy. This run has a vertical drop of 839 m, and is 3446 m long.

The maximum positive acceleration a skier could possibly have would be 9.81 m/s^2 (straight down, of course). We may safely assume no competitor would want to maintain this acceleration for very long. Consider that downhill racers' speeds *average* better than 100 km/h, and you get a real appreciation for their training, ability, and courage. Next time you are in a car travelling at highway speed, look out the window and imagine what it would be like to be moving at that speed over ice and hard snow, wearing only a thin suit and a helmet for protection. Perhaps then you can imagine what it feels like to be a downhill ski racer.

(c) What sources of friction do downhill skiers experience? What is probably the greatest source of friction? Considering your answer, what technique should a skier use to slow down, while staying on course?

Understanding Concepts

1. When the length of the course is divided by a skier's race time, what would you call the resulting value?

2. At an acceleration exactly half that of the acceleration due to gravity (9.81 m/s^2), how long would it take a skier starting from rest to get to a speed of 100 km/h?

Making Connections

3. Skis are designed to glide forward over snow and ice. Vehicle tires are designed to do the opposite. What features should a tire have, for safe winter driving?

Exploring

4. The steeper the ski slope, the greater the skier's positive acceleration down the slope. This is because acceleration is a vector quantity, and the smaller the angle between the resultant (the ski slope) and straight down, the greater the acceleration. Sketch vector diagrams to illustrate this concept.

5. The steepest part of the Saslöng course has a 57% (of vertical) slope. Calculate this slope in degrees.

🖑 Work the Web

Follow the links from Science 10, 12.3 at www.science.nelson.com.

1. Find times for a Canadian skier at the Lauberhorn race. Calculate his average speed. Express this speed as a percentage of the terminal speed for a human falling through air: about 55 m/s for a spread-eagle position.

2. Research a new development in ski boots, bindings, clothing, or helmets, and report on the development to your class in an oral presentation.

INQUIRY SKILLS MENU
- ○ Questioning
- ● Hypothesizing
- ● Predicting
- ○ Planning
- ● Conducting
- ● Recording
- ● Analyzing
- ● Evaluating
- ● Communicating

Speeding Up and Slowing Down

In this investigation you will look at a common situation: an object such as a car accelerates from rest and then brakes to slow down to a stop. As a model for this common situation, you will use a sloped ramp to speed up a cart and a spring to provide the braking force to bring it to a stop. The purpose of this exercise is to study the motion of an accelerating object through use of position–time and velocity–time graphs.

Question

What are the shapes of the position–time graph and velocity–time graph for a cart accelerating positively and negatively on a sloped ramp?

Hypothesis/Prediction

(a) Using your previous knowledge, predict and
 explain the shapes of the position–time graph and velocity-time graph.

Design

A string tied to a spring is attached to a cart sitting on the upper part of an inclined plane (**Figure 1**). The cart rolls freely until the string is taut and the spring begins to stretch, bringing the cart to a stop. The motion of the cart is recorded using a ticker-tape timer.

The mass of the cart, the type of spring, and the slope of the ramp are all controlled variables.

(b) Prepare a table (similar to **Table 1** in section 10.8) in which to record your measurements.

Materials

- safety glasses or goggles
- track or board, 1–2 m long
- wood blocks
- ticker-tape timer and clamp (or timer clamped to laboratory stand)
- ticker tape
- 50 cm of string
- short piece of adhesive tape
- light spring
- cart

✋ Keep your face away from the apparatus, as the cart may bounce as the spring returns to its normal length.

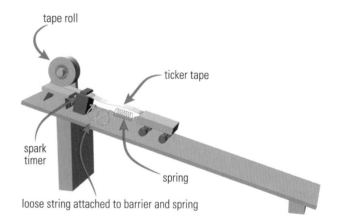

Figure 1

The cart accelerates freely down the ramp until it reaches the end of the string. At this point the spring attached to the string starts to extend and the cart slows to a stop.

Procedure

1 Put on your safety glasses.

2 Set up the apparatus as shown in **Figure 1**.

3 Attach the one end of the string to the spring.

4 Attach the spring to the cart and the free end of the string to a support on the upper part of the ramp. Check that the string will be able to move freely.

5 Place the cart near the top of the ramp, about 30 to 40 cm before the point at which the string is completely extended. Hold the cart in place with a pen or pencil in front of the cart.

6 Attach the end of the ticker tape to the cart with a piece of tape. Be sure the tape is aligned with the roll and will move smoothly.

7 (L1) Plug in the timer and make sure that it is set as instructed by your teacher.

8 Switch on the timer and immediately release the cart.

9 Switch off the timer as soon as the cart first comes to a stop.

10 Label "beginning" and "end" of ticker tape before you tear the piece from the roll.

11 Record the time interval of the timer on the tape.

12 (M) Using the first isolated dot ("dot 1") as the start, measure the position from the start to each subsequent dot.

Analysis and Evaluation

(c) Calculate the displacement during each time interval and the average velocity for the midpoint in each time interval. Summarize all results in your table.

(d) Plot position–time and velocity–time graphs.

(e) Answer the Question by describing the shape of each graph in words.

(f) (O) Evaluate the design of this investigation. Suggest any improvements in the plan, materials, and procedure.

(g) Identify some sources of experimental error or uncertainty and explain ways to reduce these.

(h) Evaluate your predictions of the shapes of the graphs. Were they generally verified, inconclusive, or falsified? Include a brief discussion to justify your judgment.

(i) Evaluate your reasoning or hypothesis. Based on your judgment of the prediction, does your reasoning appear acceptable?

(j) (Q) Prepare a complete written report of this investigation.

Understanding Concepts

1. What information about an object's motion can be obtained from its position–time graph and its velocity–time graph?

2. Calculate the slope of the straightest portions of the velocity–time graph before the spring starts to stretch and while the spring is stretching. What do these two slopes represent?

3. (K4) Suggest an alternative experimental design for this investigation.

Making Connections

4. Compare the experimental set-up you are using in this investigation to the common situation of a car accelerating from rest and later slowing down to a stop. Discuss how this investigation helps you to understand the motion of the car. In what ways does the cart on the ramp fail to accurately represent the motion of the car?

Exploring

5. If you have a simulation program such as Interactive Physics® available, run the prepared experiment or create your own simulation similar to the design of this investigation. How do the position–time and velocity–time graphs of the computer simulation compare to your graphs? Account for any differences.

 Challenge

2 In what ways is this investigation different from Galileo's investigation of acceleration on a ramp?

Acceleration and Velocity

Calculations of acceleration and velocity (vector quantities) are very similar to the calculations of scalar quantities that you did in Section 10.3. You know that acceleration can be calculated as change in speed in a given time:

$$a = \frac{v_2 - v_1}{\Delta t}.$$

Similarly, vector acceleration is change in velocity in a given time:

$$\vec{a} = \frac{\vec{v}_2 - \vec{v}_1}{\Delta t}.$$

The only difference from scalar to vector acceleration is the addition of a direction indicated by either a positive or negative sign.
We will continue to use the same convention of north as positive in situations involving north and south, and east as positive in situations involving east and west.

All of the equations used in previous chapters can be used for vector quantities as long as the direction is the same for all variables.

Sample Problem 1

An airplane waits to receive clearance from the air-traffic controller before it is allowed to start accelerating down the assigned runway (**Figure 1**). Suppose the plane starts from rest and accelerates to a final velocity of 270 km/h [E] in a time of 32 s. Calculate the acceleration of the airplane. Assume that vectors to the east are positive.

$\vec{v}_1 = 0$ km/h

$\vec{v}_2 = +270$ km/h

$\Delta t = 32$ s

$\vec{a} = ?$

$$\vec{a} = \frac{\vec{v}_2 - \vec{v}_1}{\Delta t}$$

$$= \frac{\left(+270 \ \frac{km}{h} \right) - 0}{32 s}$$

$$= +8.4 \ \frac{km/h}{s}$$

The acceleration of the airplane is 8.4 (km/h)/s [E].

In Sample Problem 1, because the signs of the velocity and the acceleration are the same, the size (or magnitude) of the velocity is increasing.

Figure 1

Airplanes must accelerate rapidly to reach takeoff speed.

Sample Problem 2

Suppose the same plane as in Sample Problem 1 reaches its destination and touches down on the runway travelling at 305 km/h [E]. If the plane takes 25 s to come to a complete stop, what is its acceleration, with direction? Assign east as the positive direction.

$\vec{v}_1 = +305$ km/h

$\vec{v}_2 = 0$ km/h

$\Delta t = 25$ s

$\vec{a} = ?$

$$\vec{a} = \frac{\vec{v}_2 - \vec{v}_1}{\Delta t}$$

$$= \frac{0 - \left(+305 \dfrac{km}{h}\right)}{25 \text{ s}}$$

$$= -12 \frac{km/h}{s}$$

The acceleration of the airplane when landing is 12 (km/h)/s [W].

> As an alternative to using positive and negative, you may substitute the actual direction into the equation. However, be aware that an answer that has a –[E] direction is opposite to east, or west.

Note that the initial velocity and acceleration in Sample Problem 2 are in opposite directions: east and west. Therefore, the plane is slowing down.

Whenever the initial velocity and acceleration are in opposite directions, the object starts slowing. What if the acceleration continues, even after the object has slowed to a stop? This can happen when something like a spring, or even Earth, continues to pull on the object. The object may reverse its original direction of motion and then start speeding up. Sample Problems 3 and 4 look at this situation.

Sample Problem 3

An air puck on an air table is attached to a spring. The puck is fired across the table at an initial velocity of 0.45 m/s [right] and the spring accelerates the air puck at an average acceleration of 1.0 m/s² [left]. What is the velocity of the air puck after 0.60 s?

Assume that right is positive and left is negative.

$\vec{v}_1 = + 0.45$ m/s

$\vec{a}_{av} = -1.0$ m/s²

$\Delta t = 0.60$ s

$\vec{v}_2 = ?$

$$\vec{a}_{av} = \frac{\vec{v}_2 - \vec{v}_1}{\Delta t}$$

$$\vec{v}_2 = \vec{v}_1 + \vec{a}_{av}\Delta t$$

$$= +0.45 \frac{m}{s} + \left(-1.0 \frac{m}{s^2}\right) \times 0.60 \text{ s}$$

$$= -0.15 \frac{m}{s}$$

or

$$\vec{a}_{av} = \frac{\vec{v}_2 - \vec{v}_1}{\Delta t}$$

$$-1.0 \frac{m}{s^2} = \frac{\vec{v}_2 - \left(+0.45 \dfrac{m}{s}\right)}{0.60 \text{ s}}$$

$$-1.0 \frac{m}{s^2} \times 0.60 \text{ s} = \vec{v}_2 - \left(+0.45 \frac{m}{s}\right)$$

$$\vec{v}_2 = +0.45 \frac{m}{s} + \left(-1.0 \frac{m}{s^2}\right) \times 0.60 \text{ s}$$

$$= -0.15 \frac{m}{s}$$

The velocity of the air puck after 0.60 s is 0.15 m/s [left].

Figure 2 illustrates Sample Problem 3. Notice that the average acceleration is in the opposite direction to the initial velocity. This means that the puck will start slowing down. However, the spring keeps pulling on the air puck, causing it to reverse direction.

The air puck is initially pushed across the table, thus stretching the spring.

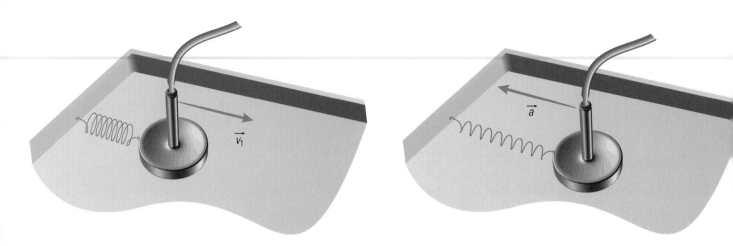

Now think about a ball thrown up in the air. You know that it will slow down initially, then eventually it will fall back to the ground. Sample Problem 4 shows the calculations for this common situation.

Sample Problem 4

A person throws a ball straight up from the ground. The ball leaves the person's hand with an initial velocity of 10.0 m/s [up]. The acceleration of the ball is 9.81 m/s² [down].

Assume that up is positive and down negative.

(a) What is the velocity of the ball after 0.50 s?

$\vec{v}_1 = +10.0$ m/s

$\Delta t = 0.50$ s

$\vec{a} = -9.81$ m/s²

$\vec{v}_2 = ?$

$$\vec{a}_{av} = \frac{\vec{v}_2 - \vec{v}_1}{\Delta t}$$

$$\vec{v}_2 = \vec{v}_1 + \vec{a}\Delta t$$

$$= \left(+10.0 \frac{m}{s}\right) + \left(-9.81 \frac{m}{s^2}\right) \times 0.50 \text{ s}$$

$$= +5.1 \frac{m}{s}$$

or

$$\vec{a}_{av} = \frac{\vec{v}_2 - \vec{v}_1}{\Delta t}$$

$$-9.81 \frac{m}{s^2} = \frac{\vec{v}_2 - \left(+10.0 \frac{m}{s}\right)}{0.50 \text{ s}}$$

$$-9.81 \frac{m}{s^2} \times 0.50 \text{ s} = \vec{v}_2 - \left(+10.0 \frac{m}{s}\right)$$

$$\vec{v}_2 = +10.0 \frac{m}{s} + \left(-9.81 \frac{m}{s^2}\right) \times 0.50 \text{ s}$$

$$= +5.1 \frac{m}{s}$$

The velocity of the ball after 0.50 s is 5.1 m/s [up].

(b) What is the velocity of the ball after 1.50 s?

$\vec{v}_1 = +10.0$ m/s

$\Delta t = 1.50$ s

$\vec{a} = -9.81$ m/s^2

$\vec{v}_2 = ?$

$$\vec{a} = \frac{\vec{v}_2 - \vec{v}_1}{\Delta t}$$

$$\vec{v}_2 = \vec{v}_1 + \vec{a}\Delta t$$

$$= (+10.0\ \tfrac{m}{s}) + (-9.81\ \tfrac{m}{s^2}) \times 1.50\ s$$

$$= -4.7\ \tfrac{m}{s}$$

or

$$\vec{a} = \frac{\vec{v}_2 - \vec{v}_1}{\Delta t}$$

$$-9.81\ \tfrac{m}{s^2} = \frac{\vec{v}_2 - (+10.0\ \tfrac{m}{s})}{1.50\ s}$$

$$-9.81\ \tfrac{m}{s^2} \times 1.50\ s = \vec{v}_2 - (+10.0)\ \tfrac{m}{s}$$

$$\vec{v}_2 = +10.0\ \tfrac{m}{s} + (-9.81\ \tfrac{m}{s^2}) \times 1.50\ s$$

$$= -4.7\ \tfrac{m}{s}$$

The final velocity of the ball after 1.5 s is 4.7 m/s [down].

Notice in Sample Problem 4 that the formula predicts both the size and direction of the velocity, no matter whether the instantaneous velocity is up or down at a given time.

As you have seen in Sample Problems 1 to 4, there are several combinations of directions of velocity and acceleration that result in different motions. **Table 1** provides a summary of how the motion of an object changes, depending on the directions of the instantaneous velocity and acceleration.

Table 1   **Comparing Instantaneous Velocity and Acceleration Signs**

Velocity direction	Acceleration direction	Size of velocity (speed)
+	+	increases
−	−	increases
+	−	decreases
−	+	decreases

Understanding Concepts

1. Compare the calculations of the scalar quantities, speed and acceleration, with the calculations of the corresponding vector quantities. What is the same and what is different?

2. You are riding your bicycle at a constant velocity west. If you decide to increase your velocity, in what direction is your acceleration?

3. While riding in a car at 90 km/h [N], the brakes are suddenly applied. In what direction is the acceleration?

4. A rabbit, eating in a field, scents a fox nearby and races off. It takes only 1.8 s to reach a top velocity of 7.5 m/s [N]. What is the rabbit's acceleration during this time?

5. A bungee jumper is falling at a velocity of 25 m/s [down] when the bungee cord just starts to stretch. After the cord stretches for 2.5 s, the velocity is 11 m/s [down]. Assume that the acceleration is constant.

   (a) What is the acceleration of the jumper?

   (b) What is the total time for the jumper to slow down from 25 m/s [down] to zero?

6. A spacecraft needs to alter its course. The retrorockets fire for 213 s to produce an acceleration of −3.25 m/s^2 [forward].

   (a) What is the change in velocity of the spacecraft?

   (b) What is the significance of the negative sign of the change in velocity?

   (c) If the velocity of the spacecraft before the rockets fired was 2635 m/s [forward], what is the velocity after the rockets have fired for 213 s?

7. A supertanker coming west into port started accelerating 2.0 h before arriving. If the ship slowed at 25 km/h^2 [E] before coming to a stop, what was the initial velocity?

8. A car travelling at 26 m/s brakes and accelerates at −10m/s^2 for 2.5 s. Does the car come to a stop? Support your answer with an appropriate calculation.

Making Connections

9. When you are inside a car you are moving at the same velocity as the car. If the car stops suddenly, for a while you will continue moving. Describe the motion of a driver with and without deployment of an airbag.

Displacement from Velocity–Time Graphs

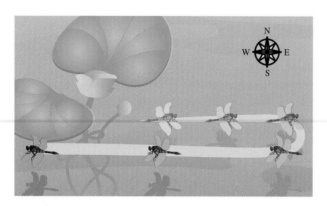

Figure 1

(a) A dragonfly flies at a constant velocity east and then at a different constant velocity west.

A dragonfly is flying east, spots an insect behind, and immediately turns around and flies west at twice the speed. We can see the displacements of the dragonfly directly [**Figure 1(a)**], and can describe them by drawing displacement vectors [**Figure 1(b)**] and a position–time graph [**Figure 1(c)**]. The velocity–time graph [**Figure 1(d)**] shows the velocity of the dragonfly when flying east for 5.0 s and then flying west for another 5.0 s.

As you know from your study of speed–time graphs, the total distance travelled is represented by the area under the line on a speed–time graph. Similarly, we can find the resultant **displacement** from the area under the line (that is, between the line and the time axis) on a velocity–time graph [**Figure 1(d)**].

To calculate the resultant displacement from the velocity–time graph [**Figure 1(d)**], first we must calculate the total area under the line.

$$\vec{\Delta d_R} = \vec{\Delta d_1} + \vec{\Delta d_2}$$
$$= (+0.40 \text{ m/s} \times 5.0 \text{ s}) + (-0.80 \text{ m/s} \times 5.0 \text{ s})$$
$$= (+2.0 \text{ m}) + (-4.0 \text{ m})$$
$$= -2.0 \text{ m} \quad \text{or} \quad 2.0 \text{ m [W]}$$

For all velocity–time graphs, no matter what the shape of the graph, the area between the line and the time axis represents the displacement during the time interval covered by the line.

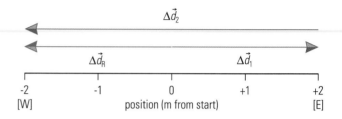

(b) The resultant displacement of the dragonfly is 2.0 m [W].

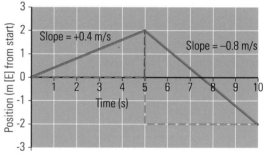

(c) The straight line segments of the position–time graph indicate constant velocities; the slope of each line represents the velocity.

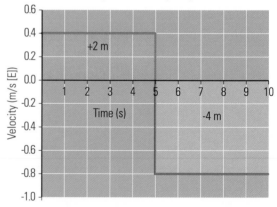

(d) A velocity–time graph of the motion of the dragonfly includes both velocity and displacement information.

Try This Activity Cut-and-Paste Graph

- On a piece of blank paper, carefully draw a 10-cm by 15-cm rectangle.
- Draw a diagonal line from the bottom left corner to the top right corner. If the left vertical side represents the velocity axis and the bottom of the rectangle represents the time axis, this diagonal line represents a constant positive acceleration.
- With a pencil or crayon, shade the area under the diagonal line.
- Using dashed lines, divide the rectangle in half both horizontally and vertically. If you have done this carefully, the two dashed lines and the diagonal line should all cross at the same point.
- Using scissors, carefully cut out the shaded small triangle at the top right corner of the rectangle (**Figure 2**). Move this triangle into the bottom left corner.

(a) What is the shape of the shaded area?

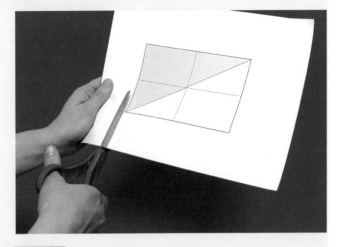

Figure 2

(b) What do you notice about the height of this shape (along the *y*-axis)?

(c) Using symbols, $\vec{v}_{av}$ and Δt, write the formula for the area of the shaded shape that you have formed.

Displacement During Constant Acceleration

Both horses in **Figure 3** start and finish at the same time, but their motion during the run is not identical. Horse A accelerates from an initial velocity, $\vec{v}_1$, to a final velocity, $\vec{v}_2$. Horse B is travelling at a constant velocity, which is the average of $\vec{v}_1$ and $\vec{v}_2$.

Figure 3

The first horse has a constant positive acceleration and the second horse has a constant velocity.

Horse A (accelerated motion)

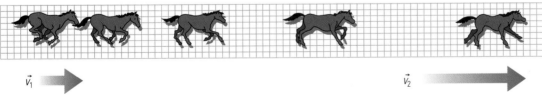

$\vec{v}_1$ $\vec{v}_2$

Horse B (constant motion)

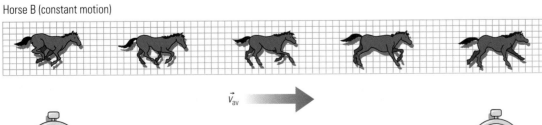

$\vec{v}_{av}$

Displacement, Velocity, and Acceleration **467**

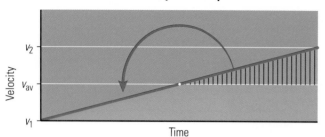

General Velocity–Time Graph

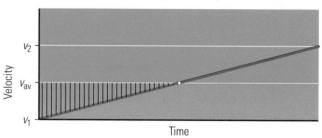

General Velocity-Time Graph

Figure 4

If the shaded triangle in the top right corner is moved into the space in the bottom left corner, it will fit exactly.

In other words, horse B's velocity is equal to the midpoint between $\vec{v}_1$ and $\vec{v}_2$ of horse A. The graphical proof of this relationship was first shown in 1360 by Nicolas Oresme. He compared velocity–time graphs of constant acceleration and constant velocity. He found that, if the triangle representing the part of the displacement between $\vec{v}_{av}$ and $\vec{v}_2$ is moved as shown in **Figure 4**, a rectangle is formed whose height is $\vec{v}_{av}$. The area of this rectangle, which represents the total or resultant displacement, is simply $\vec{v}_{av}\Delta t$.

This graphical proof shows that we can calculate displacement during a constant acceleration by combining the equations of displacement and average velocity.

$$\Delta\vec{d} = \vec{v}_{av}\Delta t \quad \text{and} \quad \vec{v}_{av} = \frac{\vec{v}_1 + \vec{v}_2}{2}$$

combine to give

$$\Delta\vec{d} = \left(\frac{\vec{v}_1 + \vec{v}_2}{2}\right)\Delta t$$

Sample Problem 1

Suppose horse A in **Figure 3** accelerates constantly from 6.0 m/s [E] to 16.0 m/s [E] in a time of 7.4 s. Using the equations above, find the displacement of the horse during that time.

Assume that [E] is positive.

$\vec{v}_1 = +6.0$ m/s
$\vec{v}_2 = +16.0$ m/s
$\Delta t = 7.4$ s
$\Delta\vec{d} = ?$

$$\Delta\vec{d} = \left(\frac{\vec{v}_1 + \vec{v}_2}{2}\right)\Delta t$$

$$= \left(\frac{\left(+6.0\,\frac{m}{s}\right) + \left(16.0\,\frac{m}{s}\right)}{2}\right) \times 7.4\,s$$

$$= +81 \text{ m}$$

The displacement of the horse is 81 m [E].

Sample Problem 2

A grasshopper is displaced 0.040 m [up] while extending its legs at the beginning of a jump. It accelerates positively from 0 to 3.4 m/s [up]. Assuming constant acceleration, calculate how long this takes.

Assume that up is positive.

$\Delta \vec{d} = +0.040$ m

$\vec{v}_1 = 0$ m/s

$\vec{v}_2 = +3.4$ m/s

$\Delta t = ?$

$$\Delta \vec{d} = \left(\frac{\vec{v}_1 + \vec{v}_2}{2} \right) \Delta t \qquad \text{or} \qquad \Delta \vec{d} = \left(\frac{\vec{v}_1 + \vec{v}_2}{2} \right) \Delta t$$

$$\Delta t = \frac{2\Delta \vec{d}}{\vec{v}_1 + \vec{v}_2} \qquad\qquad\qquad +0.040 \text{ m} = \left(\frac{0\,\frac{m}{s} + \left(+3.40\,\frac{m}{s} \right)}{2} \right) \Delta t$$

$$= \frac{2 \times (+0.040\ \cancel{m})}{0\,\frac{\cancel{m}}{s} + \left(+3.4\,\frac{\cancel{m}}{s} \right)} \qquad 2 \times (+0.04 \text{ m}) = \left(3.4\,\frac{m}{s} \right) \Delta t$$

$$= 0.024 \text{ s} \qquad\qquad\qquad\qquad \Delta t = \frac{2 \times (+0.040\ \cancel{m})}{3.4\,\frac{\cancel{m}}{s}}$$

$$= 0.024 \text{ s}$$

The grasshopper takes 0.024 s to move 0.040 m [up].

As the previous sample problems demonstrate, there is a relationship among displacement, average velocity, and time for an accelerating object. Displacement also depends on acceleration. Sometimes we may not know the final velocity of an object accelerating from a standing start. It would be useful to have an expression for displacement that does not include the final velocity. Because mathematicians were developing graphs of motion and studying areas on these graphs in the 1300s, it seems likely that they discovered other relationships for displacements based on areas on graphs. For example, Nicolas Oresme developed Oresme's Rule: The distance covered in the second half of a period of constant acceleration (starting from rest) is three times the distance covered in the first half of the same period of motion. You can check this yourself in **Figure 5** or use your graph from the Try This Activity on page 467.

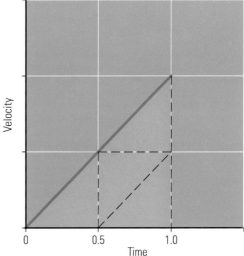

Velocity–Time Graph

Figure 5

If we use a shaded triangle as a unit of displacement, there is one triangle in the first half of the time and three identical triangles in the second half of the time.

Suppose we were to continue with the same acceleration shown in **Figure 5** for an additional time interval of 0.5t. What additional displacement occurs? Counting the number of equal-area triangles describes the displacement in a simple way that does not require any algebra (**Figure 6**). Using this technique, we notice a pattern (**Table 1**): if the time interval is doubled, the total displacement is multiplied by 4 or 2^2, and if the time interval is tripled, the displacement is multiplied by 9 or 3^2. This strongly suggests that the displacement varies directly with the square of the time interval.

$$\Delta \vec{d} \propto \Delta t^2$$

We can develop this direct squared relationship further by combining the displacement equation for average velocity with an equation for constant acceleration.

$$\Delta \vec{d} = \left(\frac{\vec{v}_1 + \vec{v}_2}{2}\right)\Delta t \quad \text{and} \quad \vec{v}_2 = \vec{v}_1 + \vec{a}\,\Delta t$$

Now, substituting $\vec{v}_2 = \vec{v}_1 + \vec{a}\Delta t$ in the displacement equation and rearranging terms, we have

$$\Delta \vec{d} = \left(\frac{\vec{v}_1 + \vec{v}_1 + \vec{a}\,\Delta t}{2}\right)\Delta t$$

$$= \frac{1}{2}(2\vec{v}_1 + \vec{a}\Delta t)\Delta t$$

$$= \vec{v}_1 \Delta t + \frac{1}{2}\vec{a}(\Delta t)^2$$

If $\vec{v}_1$ is zero, as is often the case, then $\Delta \vec{d} = \frac{1}{2}\vec{a}(\Delta t)^2$.

For constant acceleration, this equation shows that the displacement varies directly with the square of the time interval.

If the initial velocity is not zero, we can develop the same equation for displacement by considering the area under the graph to be the area of a rectangle plus the area of a triangle (**Figure 7**). The total displacement is then the sum of these two areas.

$$\Delta \vec{d} = (\text{area of rectangle}) + (\text{area of triangle})$$

$$= \vec{v}_1 \Delta t + \frac{1}{2}(\vec{v}_2 - \vec{v}_1)\Delta t$$

since $\vec{a} = \dfrac{\vec{v}_2 - \vec{v}_1}{\Delta t}$, therefore $\vec{v}_2 - \vec{v}_1 = \vec{a}\Delta t$

$$\Delta \vec{d} = \vec{v}_1 \Delta t + \frac{1}{2}(\vec{a}\Delta t)\Delta t$$

$$\Delta \vec{d} = \vec{v}_1 \Delta t + \frac{1}{2}\vec{a}(\Delta t)^2$$

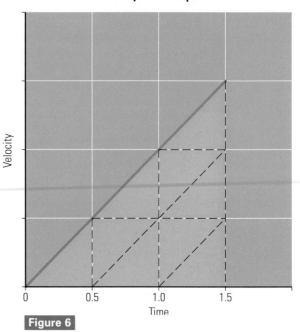

Velocity–Time Graph

Figure 6

If the constant acceleration continues for another 0.5 t, an additional displacement of five triangles occurs.

Table 1	Displacements During Constant Acceleration	

Time interval	Displacement during interval (# of equal triangles)
0 to 0.5t	$1 = 1^2$
0 to 1.0t	$1 + 3 = 4 = 2^2$
0 to 1.5t	$1 + 3 + 5 = 9 = 3^2$

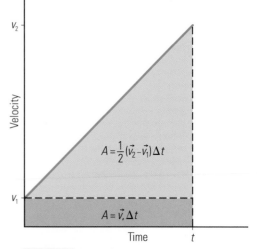

General Velocity–Time Graph

$$A = \frac{1}{2}(\vec{v}_2 - \vec{v}_1)\Delta t$$

$$A = \vec{v}_1 \Delta t$$

Figure 7

One simple way to find the area under this line is to divide the area into two parts: a triangle on top of a rectangle.

Sample Problem 3

A kangaroo leaves the ground with an initial velocity of 7.0 m/s [up] and an acceleration of 9.81 m/s² [down]. The kangaroo reaches its maximum height in 0.71 s. What is the displacement (height) at the top of the jump? Assign up as positive.

$\vec{v}_1 = +7.0$ m/s

$\Delta t = 0.71$ s

$\vec{a} = -9.81$ m/s²

$\Delta \vec{d} = ?$

$$\Delta \vec{d} = \vec{v}_1 \Delta t + \frac{1}{2}\vec{a}(\Delta t)^2$$

$$= \left(+7.0 \frac{m}{s}\right) \times 0.71 s + \frac{1}{2}\left(-9.81 \frac{m}{s^2}\right)(0.71 s)^2$$

$$= +5.0 \text{ m} + (-2.5 \text{ m})$$

$$= +2.5 \text{ m}$$

The displacement at the top of the kangaroo's jump is 2.5 m [up].

Sample Problem 4

A speedboat accelerates constantly from rest at 2.1 m/s² [S] for a displacement of 70.0 m [S]. For how long did this acceleration last?
Assign south as positive.

$\vec{v}_1 = 0$

$\vec{a} = +2.1$ m/s²

$\Delta \vec{d} = +70.0$ m

$\Delta t = ?$

$$\Delta \vec{d} = \vec{v}_1 \Delta t + \frac{1}{2}\vec{a}(\Delta t)^2 \qquad \text{or} \qquad \Delta \vec{d} = \vec{v}_1 \Delta t + \frac{1}{2}\vec{a}(\Delta t)^2$$

$$\Delta \vec{d} = \frac{1}{2}\vec{a}(\Delta t)^2 \text{ because } \vec{v}_1 = 0 \qquad\qquad +70.0 \text{ m} = 0 + \frac{1}{2}\times\left(+2.1 \frac{m}{s^2}\right)(\Delta t)^2$$

$$(\Delta t)^2 = \frac{2\Delta \vec{d}}{\vec{a}} \qquad\qquad 2\times(+70.0 \text{ m}) = \left(+2.1 \frac{m}{s^2}\right)(\Delta t)^2$$

$$\Delta t^2 = \frac{2\times(+70.0 \text{ m})}{+2.1 \frac{m}{s^2}} \qquad\qquad (\Delta t)^2 = \frac{2\times(+70.0 \text{ m})}{+2.1 \frac{m}{s^2}}$$

$$\Delta t = \sqrt{\frac{2\times(+70.0 \text{ m})}{+2.1 \frac{m}{s^2}}} \qquad\qquad \Delta t = \sqrt{\frac{2\times(+70.0 \text{ m})}{+2.1 \frac{m}{s^2}}}$$

$$= 8.2 \text{ s} \qquad\qquad = 8.2 \text{ s}$$

The acceleration of the speedboat lasted for 8.2 s.

Displacement for Constant and Changing Velocity

You have seen how we can calculate displacement from a velocity–time graph if the velocity is constant in **Figure 1(d)** and if the velocity changes during a constant acceleration (**Figures 4 and 7**).

For all velocity–time graphs, no matter what the shape of the graph, the area between the line and the time-axis represents the displacement during the time interval covered by the line.

Suppose a car travels along a highway at a constant velocity of 80 km/h [E] for 1.0 h and then uniformly accelerates to 100 km/h [E] in 0.50 h (**Figure 8**). To find the total displacement we need to find the total area using the same technique of areas of rectangles and triangles as we used in previous examples. Note that, in examples where the velocity is sometimes constant and sometimes changing, no one mathematical formula will work. In these cases, we need to draw a graph, consider each unique area separately, and add all the areas to calculate the total area.

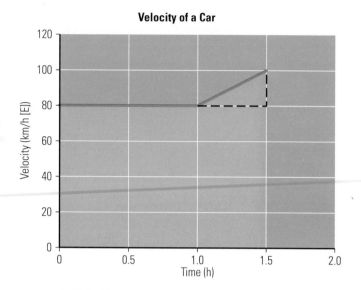

Figure 8

When a velocity–time graph has more than one straight line, we can calculate the displacement from the total area of any combination of rectangles and triangles between the line and the time axis, such as the rectangle of 80 km/h by 1.5 h plus the triangle between 80 and 100 km/h.

Understanding Concepts

1. State the rule for determining the displacement of an object using its velocity–time graph.

2. Explain, in your own words, why the two horses (**Figure 3**) have the same displacement after the same interval of time.

3. **(a)** Redraw and extend **Figure 6** to show the displacement triangles for $2.0t$ and $2.5t$.

   (b) Copy and extend **Table 1** to show how many $\vec{\Delta d}$ triangles make up the total displacements for $2.0t$ and $2.5t$.

4. For each of the velocity–time graphs in **Figure 9**, calculate the displacement of the object represented by the graph.

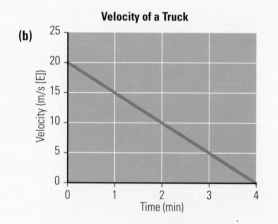

(b)

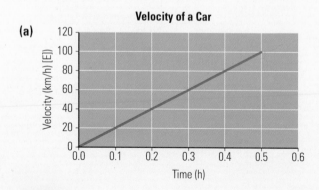

(a)

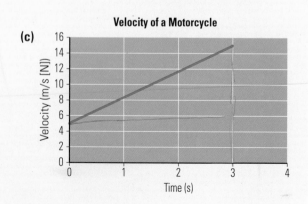

(c)

Figure 9

For questions 5 to 9, assume constant acceleration and calculate your answers from defining equations.

5. A dragster slows down from 28 m/s [N] to 13 m/s [N] in a time of 12 s using a parachute and brakes. Calculate the displacement during this acceleration.

6. A baseball pitcher throws the ball at 28 m/s [S] toward a batter. The ball is in contact with the bat for 2.0 ms and leaves the bat travelling at 46 m/s [N]. What is the displacement of the ball while in contact with the bat?

7. A golfer hits a golf ball sitting at rest on a tee. The ball leaves the club at 64 m/s after a displacement of 35 mm. For how long was the club in contact with the ball?

8. While driving along a highway at 25 m/s [N], a driver spots an animal crossing the road. She brakes sharply for 2.0 s. If the car's acceleration is 10 m/s² [S], what is the displacement of the car while braking?

9. A speedboat travels at 6.0 m/s [E] for 90 s and then accelerates uniformly at 2.0 m/s² [E] for 5.0 s. Calculate the displacement of the speedboat.

10. Calculate the displacement of the car described in **Figure 8.**

11. A train accelerates from the railway station and then maintains a constant velocity (**Figure 10**). Using the graph, determine the displacement of the train after 1.5 h.

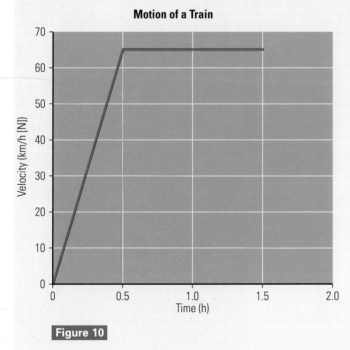

Motion of a Train

Figure 10

Making Connections

12. Air bags in cars are designed to slow down a moving person safely. **Figure 11** shows a simplified velocity–time graph of a person protected by an air bag in an automobile collision. Use the graph to find the resultant displacement of the person initially sitting upright in a car seat ($t = 0$ s is the time of the collision).

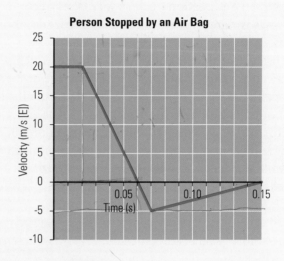

Person Stopped by an Air Bag

Figure 11

13. There have been many advances in the technology of running shoes. Some modifications in the sole of the shoe are designed to reduce injuries caused by the foot accelerating as it strikes the ground. Do we want an extremely sudden stop or a more gradual acceleration? How does the design of a running shoe relate to displacement, velocity, and acceleration of the foot as it strikes the ground?

🖱 Work the Web

If you are having difficulties solving motion problems in one dimension, you are not alone. Even physicists find it challenging. There are still some unsolved problems for one-dimensional acceleration. Find out, in general, what types of problems remain unsolved by following the Science 10, 12.6 link at www.science.nelson.com. Try to offer some solutions!

 **Challenge**

3 Where can the equation for displacement developed in this section be used for calculating values needed in a driver's manual?

Acceleration Due to Gravity

In daily life we use many kinds of information or knowledge. We also "know" in different ways. Some things we know by experience, such as tying our shoelaces. Others we know because we understand an explanation, such as why lakes freeze in the winter. Some things we simply memorize, such as friends' phone numbers.

Science uses different kinds of knowledge, which scientists classify as either **empirical** (that we can observe or measure) or **theoretical** (that we cannot observe, but that explains the world around us). Your study of physics at this stage is entirely empirical. The theoretical knowledge will come later in your studies. Most scientific understanding follows this progression from empirical to theoretical knowledge. For example, acceleration was empirically described and related to distance and time by Galileo (c.1604). Then Isaac Newton (c.1687) empirically explained acceleration as being due to an unbalanced force such as the force of gravity, which causes objects to fall. Next in the progression was a theoretical explanation of how an unbalanced force is created at the atomic level in an object producing the force (1900s).

Look at **Figures 1** and **2**. What do they all have in common? Of course, the people in all of these situations are falling. Why? The simple answer is to say "gravity." One consequence of gravity is that objects released near the surface of Earth (or other planets) naturally fall toward the centre. Around 1604 Galileo announced the results of his experiments with accelerating objects. First he had to overcome the problem of the lack of a precise and accurate clock to time falling objects. His solution was to invent a pendulum clock and to use an inclined plane to slow the acceleration

Figure 1

Many amusement park rides include dramatic drops.

(**Figure 3**). From his work he discovered that the acceleration due to gravity (sometimes called free fall) is constant. **Acceleration due to gravity** describes the motion of an object falling toward a large body, such as a planet. It is probably the most important example of constant acceleration.

Figure 2

Sylvie Bernier joins other divers, Beverley Boys and Irene MacDonald, in Canada's Sports Hall of Fame.

What is the acceleration of falling objects? For almost two thousand years it was accepted teaching that heavier objects fell at a greater speed than lighter objects. Even today, this is a fairly good description of what happens to a falling hammer compared to a falling feather (**Figure 4**). However, in the 1600s, Galileo demonstrated experimentally that if air resistance (friction) is reduced and controlled, all objects fall with the same acceleration. The feather and the hammer will hit the ground at the same time, with the same velocity: if there is no air resistance, falling feathers and falling hammers have the same acceleration. Modern experiments have shown that this even applies to individual atoms dropped in a vacuum: their acceleration is the same as that of any other object dropped near the surface of Earth. As Galileo realized, we need a carefully controlled experiment to eliminate or control the effects of air resistance.

However, for the short displacements and relatively small velocities that we are investigating, ignoring air resistance does not lead to significant error.

The value of the acceleration due to gravity, $\vec{a}_g$, varies slightly at different locations on Earth. According to the Geodetic Survey Division of the Department of Natural Resources Canada, the Canadian average for this acceleration is 9.81 m/s² [down].

To solve equations involving acceleration due to gravity, we can use the equation $\Delta\vec{d} = \vec{v}\Delta t + \frac{1}{2}\vec{a}(\Delta t)^2$. By convention, we consider [down] to be positive.

Figure 3

Galileo ingeniously developed the technologies necessary to advance scientific knowledge.

Did You Know?

Aristotle's physics dominated the Western world for about eighteen centuries. One of his concepts was that objects fall with a constant speed that is proportional to their mass. Heavy objects, he observed, fall at a greater constant speed than lighter objects.

Figure 4

Astronaut David Scott, on the *Apollo 15* mission to the Moon, dropped a feather and a hammer. Both landed at the same time on the lunar surface. Why? Because the Moon has no atmosphere to slow the fall of either object.

Sample Problem 1

A baseball is dropped from a height of 1.238 m at the North Pole. Repeated trials showed that the average time for the baseball to fall from rest was 0.502 s. Calculate the acceleration due to gravity at the North Pole. Assume that down is positive.

$\Delta \vec{d} = +1.238$ m

$\vec{v}_1 = 0$

$\Delta t = 0.502$ s

$\vec{a}_g = ?$

$\Delta \vec{d} = \vec{v}_1 \Delta t + \frac{1}{2} \vec{a}(\Delta t)^2$ or

since $\vec{v}_1$ is zero, then $\Delta \vec{d} = \frac{1}{2} \vec{a}(\Delta t)^2$

$\vec{a}_g = \dfrac{2\Delta \vec{d}}{(\Delta t)^2}$

$= \dfrac{2 \times (+1.238 \text{ m})}{(0.502 \text{ s})^2}$

$= +9.83 \dfrac{\text{m}}{\text{s}^2}$

$\Delta \vec{d} = \vec{v}_1 \Delta t + \frac{1}{2} \vec{a}(\Delta t)^2$

$1.238 \text{ m} = 0 \text{ m/s} \times 0.502 \text{ s} + \frac{1}{2} \vec{a}_g (0.502 \text{ s})^2$

$2 \times (+1.238 \text{ m}) = \vec{a}_g (0.502 \text{ s})^2$

$\vec{a}_g = \dfrac{2 \times (+1.238 \text{ m})}{(0.502 \text{ s})^2}$

$= +9.83 \dfrac{\text{m}}{\text{s}^2}$

The acceleration due to gravity at the North Pole is 9.83 m/s² [down].

Try This Activity Catch a Falling Bill

Hold a flat, five-dollar bill so that the midpoint hangs between the thumb and forefinger of a friend's hand. Challenge your friend to catch the bill as you drop it. Can you find anyone who can catch the bill? Now replace the bill with a ruler.

Drop the ruler with the 0-cm mark between the thumb and forefinger. Determine the average distance the ruler falls before being caught. What is the person's reaction time?

Understanding Concepts

1. Why is Galileo credited with the most important empirical (experimental) work on falling objects?

2. What is the most common example of constant acceleration?

3. What techniques did Galileo use to determine that acceleration due to gravity is constant (**Figure 3**)?

4. Some sea birds, such as the royal tern, dive from considerable heights into the water to catch fish.

   (a) By how much does the velocity of a royal tern increase each second, ignoring air resistance?

(b) How long, in seconds, does it take a falling royal tern to increase its velocity by 15 m/s?

(c) What is the final velocity of a royal tern just before it hits the water after falling from rest for 1.75 s?

5. A ballast bag of sand is dropped from a hot air balloon. Assuming an acceleration of 9.81 m/s² [down], calculate the velocity of the falling sandbag after 2.0 s.

6. Calculate the velocity of a baseball 3.5 s after it is thrown vertically down with an initial velocity of 5.0 m/s. Assume there is no air resistance.

7. An experiment is conducted to determine the acceleration due to gravity on the Moon. Complete the questions in the Analysis section.

Question
What is the acceleration due to gravity on the Moon?

Design
A video is made of a ball falling toward the surface of the Moon. The video is computer-analyzed to obtain velocities at different times (**Table 1**).

Evidence

Table 1   **Acceleration on the Moon**

Time (s)	Velocity (m/s) [down]
0.0	0.0
1.0	1.6
2.0	3.1
3.0	4.9
4.0	6.3
5.0	8.1

Analysis

(a) Use the information in **Table 1** to draw a velocity-time graph.

(b) Use your graph to determine the acceleration due to gravity on the Moon.

8. The reaction time of a person's hand to grab an object depends on the speed of an electrical impulse to travel from the eye to the brain and then to the hand. This typically takes about 0.14 s. In the Try This Activity above, a five-dollar bill was dropped.

(a) What is the speed of the five-dollar bill after falling from rest for 0.14 s?

(b) How far does the bill fall in 0.14 s? Could *anyone* catch this falling bill?

Making Connections

9. List as many examples as you can of different technologies (manufactured devices) in which gravity is used as part of their operation.

☝Work the Web

NASA has conducted and continues to conduct many experiments in conditions known as "free fall". Visit www.science.nelson.com and follow the Science 10, 12.7 link. What does free fall mean for a spacecraft in orbit around Earth? What are some of the purposes of these experiments? How are they done? What information has been obtained? What are some other questions left to be answered?

Exploring

10. A sky-diver with arms and legs spread-eagled reaches a terminal velocity (final velocity) of 200 km/h [down] in about 620 m [down] (**Figure 5**).

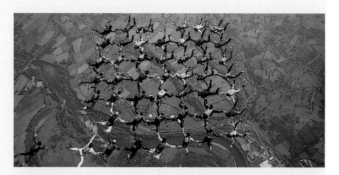

Figure 5

(a) Why does the sky-diver reach a terminal velocity?

(b) How could the sky-diver reach a higher terminal velocity?

(c) What is the average velocity during the time to reach terminal velocity?

(d) What assumptions did you make, when calculating the average velocity?

(e) How much time does the sky-diver take to reach the terminal velocity?

(f) Sketch a velocity-time graph to represent this motion.

(g) If there were no air resistance, how much time would a sky-diver take to reach 200 km/h?

(h) What time is required to drop a further 1000 m at a terminal velocity of 200 km/h?

(i) If the sky-diver opens a parachute and quickly reaches a terminal velocity of 30 km/h [down] at a height of 500 m [up] from the ground, how much time does she take to reach the ground?

11. Design an experiment to test the prediction that balls of
Ⓚ different masses fall with the same acceleration.

Reflection

12. In your experience do heavy objects fall faster than light objects? Explain your answer.

13. Devise a hypothesis to answer the question: Why do
Ⓚ3 objects accelerate in free fall?

◕ Challenge

1 How does a pendulum, as used by Galileo, serve as a clock?

Gravitational Acceleration Near Earth

We know the value of the acceleration due to gravity near the surface of Earth from precise experiments that have been done. You could use any of several different designs (**Figures 1, 2,** and **3**) to determine this value in an experiment. In this investigation you will find the acceleration due to gravity and then use the accuracy of your result to evaluate the design and apparatus that you used. **Accuracy** is a comparison of an experimental value with an accepted value and is usually expressed as a percentage error. There are two important uses of accuracy in science: to test a prediction based on some authority or to test an experimental design. The purpose of this investigation is to evaluate an experimental design.

Question

What is the acceleration due to gravity at your location?

Prediction

Acceleration due to gravity at this location will be equal to the Canadian average as determined by the Geodetic Survey of Canada: 9.81 m/s² [down].

Design

In the ticker-tape timer, electronic timer, and strobe photograph (**Figures 1, 2,** and **3**), release a ball from a height of about 1 m and record the total distance and total time from the start. In the other design, release a ball or other suitable object from a height of at least 5 m. In all designs, the particular ball or object used is a controlled variable.

(a) Using the information presented above, write
(K6) out the numbered steps that you
will follow to carry out this experiment.
(B) Be sure to start with all necessary safety precautions.
(b) Create a table in which to record your results.

Materials

(c) List the materials to be used in this investigation.

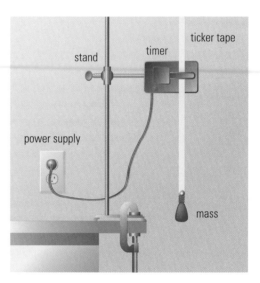

Figure 1

The ticker tape provides a record of distance and time as the ball falls.

Figure 2

In this electronic timer design, an electromagnet releases a metal ball. This starts the timer, which then stops the moment the ball hits the switch plate at the bottom.

SKILLS HANDBOOK: (K6) Writing the Procedure (B) Safety in the Laboratory (K5) Selecting Materials

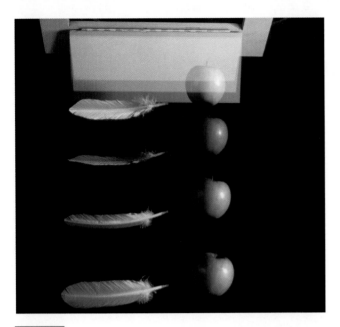

Distance and time evidence can be obtained from the photograph by using the distance scale of the photograph and the time interval of the flashing strobe light.

Procedure

(d) When your teacher has approved your procedure, carry it out. Record all observations (total distance and total time) for each trial conducted.

(K5)

Analysis and Evaluation

(e) Using the average values of the total distance and time, calculate the acceleration due to gravity.

(M2)

(f) Calculate the percentage error to assess the accuracy of your result. The formula for percentage error is

$$\% \text{ error} = \left| \frac{\text{experimental} - \text{accepted}}{\text{accepted}} \right| \times 100 \%$$

(g) Use the accuracy you obtained to evaluate the design of this experiment. What were the sources of error and uncertainty? Comment on what might be done to improve the accuracy of the design.

(O)

(h) If you used more than one design, which design was the most accurate? Considering several factors, such as experimental error, cost, ease of use, and reproducibility, which do you think is the best design for finding the acceleration due to gravity?

(i) Prepare a report on your findings and present it to the class.

(S)

🖱 Work the Web

The Geodetic Survey Division of the Department of Natural Resources Canada has measured the acceleration due to gravity at thousands of locations across the country. Why have they done this? Who uses this information? How precise are their measurements? (In other words, to how many decimal places?) Visit www.science.nelson.com and follow the links for Science 10, 12.8.

Understanding Concepts

1. Define "accuracy" in your own words.

2. What, in this investigation, are we evaluating by calculating accuracy?

3. In repeated trials for dropping a ball 15.0 m, the average time taken for the ball to hit the ground was 1.8 s.

   (a) Based upon this evidence, calculate the acceleration due to gravity.

   (b) What is the percentage error of your calculated value?

4. The speed of light is one of the most important constants in physics and the accepted value is $2.997\ 924\ 58 \times 10^8$ m/s. In an experiment to test a new design, the speed of light is measured as 3.105×10^8 m/s. What is the accuracy of this experimental value?

5. Why is it very important to do multiple trials whenever possible in an experiment?

Making Connections

6. Is accuracy always important? Comment on the importance of accuracy for each of the following:

   (a) the mass of a chocolate bar printed on the package

   (b) the mass of the active ingredient in a prescription drug, printed on the container

   (c) the speedometer in a vehicle

Exploring

7. Research the controversy that arose when science historians looked at the original lab books of the famous American physicist, Robert A. Millikan, long after he passed away. What did they discover about the trials conducted and reported? Was he dishonest or very clever?

Acceleration of Different Masses

In the previous investigation you determined the acceleration due to gravity for a ball whose mass, size, and other properties were controlled. What if the mass were manipulated (**Figure 1**)? In the process of science, scientists speculate about a possible variable, predict its effect based on some reasoning or hypothesis, and then test their prediction in an experiment. The purpose of this investigation is to test your prediction about the effect of mass on the measured value of the acceleration due to gravity.

Question

What effect does the mass of a free-falling ball have on the value of its acceleration?

Prediction/Hypothesis

(a) Using your own concepts and reasons write a
(K3) prediction and a hypothesis.

Design

(b) Write a brief plan for this experiment, including
(K4) the identification of independent, dependent, and controlled variables.
(c) Using the information presented above, write
(K6) out the numbered steps that you will follow to carry out this experiment. Begin with all necessary safety precautions.
(K7) (d) Prepare a labelled table to record your evidence.

Materials

- safety goggles
- several balls of the same size but different materials (with different masses)
- balance
- metre stick or tape measure
- ticker-tape timer, stroboscope and camera, stopwatch, or free-fall apparatus

Figure 1
These two skydivers have different masses. Will this affect their velocity and acceleration during free fall?

SKILLS HANDBOOK: (K3) Developing the Prediction and Hypothesis (K4) Creating the Design (K6) Writing a Procedure

Procedure

(e) When your teacher has approved your procedure, carry it out. Record all observations.

Analysis and Evaluation

(f) Using the average distances and times for each ball, calculate the value of the acceleration due to gravity.

(g) Calculate the percentage error between the experimental value for the acceleration due to gravity for each ball and the accepted value. Compare the results for all of the balls and answer the question.

(h) Evaluate the experiment noting flaws, if any, and suggesting improvements in the design, materials, procedure, and your technological skills.

(i) Identify and describe sources of experimental error or uncertainty.

(j) Was your prediction verified, falsified, or inconclusive? State your reasons.

(k) Evaluate the hypothesis you used to make your prediction.

(l) Form a discussion group consisting of your lab group and several other groups. Each lab group should report their results to the others. Which experimental design has the greatest accuracy (smallest percentage error)? Try to reach a consensus on the answer to the Question investigated in this experiment. Appoint one member of the discussion group to present the group's conclusions to the rest of the class.

Understanding Concepts

1. What are four different designs that can be used to experimentally determine the acceleration due to gravity?

2. Why is it important in science to have different groups do the same experiment and then share their results?

Making Connections

3. Suppose we lived in a different universe, where the acceleration due to gravity were directly related to the mass of the object. How might that affect the way we lived or travelled?

Exploring

4. How are the results of experiments usually shared within the international scientific community? How has this changed in the last 10 to 15 years?

5. Imagine that a hammer and an anvil are dropped off a cliff. Which would fall faster? If the hammer and anvil were tied together, what would happen?

6. (a) Design an experiment to investigate the acceleration of a falling ball, while manipulating height as a variable. Include safety precautions in your procedure.

   (b) Make a prediction.

   (c) After your teacher has approved your procedure and materials, carry out your investigation.

   (d) Present your findings in a lab report.

7. List some technological applications in which the combination of acceleration due to gravity and mass plays an important role.

Challenge

2 What were Aristotle's laws of motion in relation to the speed and acceleration of falling bodies?

"Nothing by Authority"

Authority is often something to be rejected and yet we all use authorities to justify our knowledge — even when it is "Because I said so!" What kinds of authorities do you accept for knowledge gained through, for example, television, radio, the Internet, or person-to-person conversation? Do you accept the opinions of famous persons? Do you believe in astrological or psychic predictions? Do you believe in aliens? Do you evaluate the evidence presented?

There are many authorities from which to choose. Authorities for knowledge may include peers, relatives, famous people, teachers, books, magazines, religion, reasoning, and evidence. At one time the words of the Greek philosopher, Aristotle (**Figure 1**), were alone considered to be the greatest authority in science. Aristotle's own authorities were qualitative observations and logical reasoning. He developed generalizations of motion, stating that falling bodies

- fall at constant speed;
- fall faster, if heavier; and
- fall slower, if meeting resistance.

Through the Dark Ages (A.D. ~500–1000) in Europe, many manuscripts of Greek work were lost or destroyed, although some were hidden and saved. During the 13th century some of Aristotle's manuscripts were rediscovered, translated into Latin by monks and clerics, and reconciled with the views of the Christian Church. With the backing of the Church, Aristotle remained the authority on many things until about A.D. 1600.

Aristotle's authority in science began to decline when mathematicians and scientists began to emphasize quantitative observations and mathematical calculations. Galileo (**Figure 2**) devised and constructed clocks and inclined planes to make quantitative measurements, and used mathematical equations to calculate speed and acceleration. By doing this, Galileo experimentally tested Aristotle's statements, and found them false. People began to doubt Aristotle's laws. Galileo believed in new authorities, including controlled experiments, quantitative measurements, and mathematical calculations, in addition to Aristotle's qualitative observations and logical reasoning. Since many of us still observe the world qualitatively and use our logical reasoning to interpret those observations, many of Aristotle's notions of motion are still believed today.

Over a period of many years, Galileo developed the following generalizations of motion from his experiments:

- A body moving on a horizontal plane will continue at the same speed unless a force (such as friction) opposes it.
- In a vacuum, all bodies fall at the same acceleration regardless of their mass or composition.
- A body falling freely or rolling down an inclined plane undergoes constant acceleration.

Figure 1

Aristotle (384–322 B.C.): the authority for 2000 y●

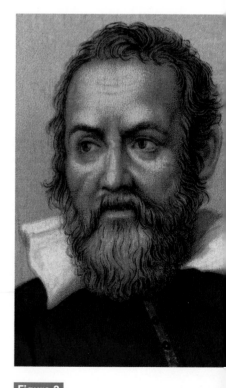

Figure 2

Galileo (1564–1642): the questioner of authority

Galileo, himself, made mistakes, including his idea in 1604 that the velocity of a falling body was proportional to the distance of falling. He corrected this mistake himself in 1609. Of course, his most trusted authorities were not his own writings but quantitative experiments and mathematical calculations. Galileo believed that science was self-correcting and that all scientific knowledge should be tested experimentally. This, among other reasons, is why Galileo is credited as being the founder of modern science.

Robert Boyle (1627–1691) was a scientist who continued Galileo's example of quantitative work. He was responsible for creating the motto for the British Royal Society (of science) — "Nothing by Authority." The motto was aimed at Aristotle's authority. Boyle wanted scientists to challenge Aristotle's concepts rigorously. Boyle's philosophy was supported by other scientists such as Lord Kelvin (1824–1907) who is quoted as saying:

"If you can measure that of which you speak, and can express it by a number, you know something of your subject; but if you cannot measure it your knowledge is meagre and unsatisfactory."

Perhaps Lord Kelvin's position is an extreme, but you can see that the nature of science changed dramatically during the Scientific Revolution begun in the early 17th century by Galileo.

Understanding the Issue

1. What kinds of authorities are now used to judge scientific and other knowledge as acceptable?

2. Which of Aristotle's generalization(s) of motion did Galileo overturn/refute?

3. Who is considered to be the founder of modern science?

4. How did Galileo's approach to knowledge differ from Aristotle's?

5. Would you classify your experimental process in this unit as more similar to that of Aristotle or Galileo?

🖑 Work the Web

Explore the Web to find pictures and stories related to Galileo: his appearance; his clocks and inclined planes; and his experiments. Report on one of your findings in an illustrated poster.

Role Play Perpectives on Authority

Pair up with someone in class and write some dialogue for an imaginary meeting between Galileo and Aristotle. Each character should describe and debate free-falling bodies, and defend his own position. Research and include
(E) ideas such as
- authorities for accepting knowledge
- qualitative versus quantitative observations
- mathematical calculations
- clocks and inclined planes

Conclude your dialogue with the addition of a
(H) "modern student" into the discussion. Include
- what you have learned about motion in this physics unit
- then-current technologies versus modern technologies
- the authorities upon which a modern perspective of motion is based

Forming an Opinion

1. Before writing your dialogue, consider the perspectives of your characters. Was Aristotle's emphasis on qualitative observation and logical reasoning wrong? Is Galileo's emphasis on quantitative observation (measurement) right? What makes some scientific knowledge more certain than other scientific knowledge? Which authorities are best?

(S) 2. Perform your dialogue for the class.

Kristi Watson

Air Traffic Controller

Kirsti Watson has spent her 25-year career as an air traffic controller working in the Toronto Area Control Centre at Pearson International Airport. Her employer is NAV CANADA, the private, not-for-profit corporation that operates the civil air traffic control system across the country.

You might think that all air traffic controllers work in airport control towers. Says Kirsti, "I've never worked in a control tower. There are two types of air traffic control work. One is called Visual Flight Rule Air Traffic Control. The other type, the type I do, is called Instrument Flight Rule. This kind of air traffic control is done in radar environments. Here, controllers can't see the planes but are in constant radar and voice contact with them. We don't even have to be at an airport."

Kirsti didn't become an air traffic controller until her mid-twenties, after finishing a university degree in arts and mathematics, and working at what she calls a "dead-end job." By luck, a friend was a flight instructor and informed Kirsti that there was a need for air traffic controllers. Until then, she admits, "I didn't even know that air traffic control existed."

The air traffic controller application and training processes were long and demanding. As part of the application process, Kirsti had to complete an aptitude test with several questions about aircraft speed and distance travelled. Questions were also posed around a simulated radar display to determine if she could spot potential flight route conflicts between planes. Next came a series of tough interviews.

On a typical work day, Kirsti alternates between two positions in the area control centre. Her first job is a radar position, in which she communicates directly with pilots, giving them instructions via radio. In the other job, called a Data position, she communicates with air traffic controllers in neigbouring areas to give them advanced warning of the flights coming from her air space into theirs. Besides speed, distance, and direction there are other factors affecting Kirsti's decisions. For instance, bigger airplanes can set up vortexes off their wing tips. She explains, "The vortexes are like whirlpools coming off the wings. As a result, I cannot put a small airplane too close to a bigger airplane and slightly below it, because the larger plane could flip the smaller aircraft."

"I am preventing airplanes from getting too close to each other. So, I have to consider all the means at my disposal for preventing this. I might have to decide: Can I use altitude to separate the planes, so they are one above the other? If the planes are flying in the same direction, can I use speed control to separate them, so they are one behind the other? Or, do I use vectors, a change in the direction of flight, to prevent the planes from getting too close?"

Kirsti says the qualities needed to be a good air traffic controller include initiative, cooperativeness, alertness, and, perhaps most important, "the ability to think quickly on your feet."

Making Connections

1. Brainstorm a list of aviation-related careers. In small groups, compare and discuss your lists. Make a group list. Which of the careers on your list are most suited to your interests and abilities?

✋ Work the Web

Check out the NAV CANADA site at www.navcanda.ca. Visit the "Careers" section of the site. Which positions is NAV CANADA currently trying to fill?

Key Expectations

Throughout this chapter, you have had opportunities to do the following:

- Draw position–time graphs and calculate the average and instantaneous velocity from such graphs. (12.1)

- Draw position–time and velocity–time graphs for constant velocity and for constant acceleration, and calculate the constant acceleration from velocity–time graphs. (12.1, 12.2, 12.4, 12.6)

- Analyze everyday phenomena and technologies in terms of the motions involved. (12.1, 12.2, 12.3, 12.4, 12.5, 12.6, 12.7)

- Use simple graphs and vector diagrams to describe predicted and observed motion. (12.2)

- Describe the features of a piece of sports equipment that relate to optimum performance. (12.3)

- Select and integrate information from various sources, including electronic and print resources, to answer questions. (12.3, 12.10)

- Conduct and evaluate experiments to measure the displacement, velocity, and constant acceleration of a moving object. (12.4, 12.8, 12.9)

- Use a broad range of tools and techniques safely, accurately, and effectively to compile, record, and analyze data and information, and apply mathematical and conceptual models to develop and assess possible explanations. (12.4, 12.8, 12.9)

- Analyze data and information and evaluate evidence and sources of information, identifying flaws such as errors and bias. (12.4, 12.8, 12.9)

- Identify, explain, and express sources of error and uncertainty in experimental measurements. (12.4, 12.8, 12.9)

- Design and conduct investigations on the displacement, velocity, and acceleration of an object. (12.4, 12.8, 12.9)

- Demonstrate an understanding of different kinds of motion and of the quantitative relationships among displacement, velocity, and acceleration. (12.5, 12.6, 12.7, 12.10)

- Describe quantitatively the relationship among average acceleration $\vec{a}$, change in velocity $\Delta \vec{v}$, and elapsed time Δt, and solve simple problems involving these physical quantities; $\vec{a}_{av} = \dfrac{\Delta \vec{v}}{\Delta t}$. (12.5)

- Use a velocity–time graph for constant acceleration to derive and use the equation for average velocity, $\vec{v}_{av} = \dfrac{\vec{v}_1 + \vec{v}_2}{2}$, and the equations for displacement $\Delta \vec{d} = \left(\dfrac{\vec{v}_1 + \vec{v}_2}{2} \right)$ and $\Delta \vec{d} = \vec{v}_1 t + \dfrac{1}{2}\vec{a}(\Delta t)^2$. (12.6)

- Demonstrate the skills required to plan and conduct an inquiry into motion, controlling major variables and adapting procedures where required. (12.8, 12.9)

- Design, conduct, and evaluate an experiment to measure acceleration due to gravity. (12.8, 12.9)

- Select and use appropriate vocabulary, SI units, numbers, symbols and graphs to communicate scientific ideas, plans, results, and conclusions. (all)

Key Terms

acceleration

acceleration due to gravity

displacement

empirical knowledge

instantaneous velocity

position–time graph

theoretical knowledge

velocity–time graph

Make a Summary

Using the Key Terms and Key Expectations, make a concept map to summarize what you have learned in this chapter. Start with the key words in the title of this chapter and include word descriptions, units, defining equations, and graph relationships.

Reflect on your Learning

Revisit your answers to the Reflect on your Learning questions, page 445, in the Getting Started.

- How has your thinking changed?

- What new questions do you have?

Understanding Concepts

1. Describe, using words and sketches, how the following information is obtained from a position–time graph:
   (a) the displacement of a moving object in a particular time interval;
   (b) the velocity of a moving object at a given time;
   (c) the total distance travelled by a moving object.

2. Explain the following aspects of position–time graphs:
   (a) how the slope of a straight line segment is calculated;
   (b) how the slope of a tangent to a point on a curved line is calculated;
   (c) the meaning of a positive slope;
   (d) the meaning of a negative slope;
   (e) the meaning of a zero slope (horizontal line).

3. Sketch and label a graph to show that the formula for calculating the slope of the line in a velocity–time graph is the same as the algebraic formula for determining acceleration.

4. Describe at least two differences between distance–time and position–time graphs.

5. List three facts about a moving object that can be obtained from a velocity–time graph.

6. Kristin rode east along the bike path on her way to the mall. She stopped at the top of a slope before coasting down, accelerating constantly at 0.75 m/s² for 24 s. She then applied her brakes and slowed to 10 m/s in 5.0 s. *Velocity*
   (a) What was Kristin's velocity after 24 s?
   (b) Sketch a velocity–time graph of Kristin's bike ride.
   (c) What was her acceleration while she braked?
   (d) What was her displacement after 29 s?

7. Raja is travelling south on his motorcycle at 60 km/h when he merges onto the freeway. He accelerates to 100 km/h[S] in 15 s.
   (a) Convert Raja's initial and final velocities to m/s.
   (b) Calculate Raja's acceleration.
   (d) What was his displacement while accelerating?

8. Brett starts from rest on his skateboard and accelerates at 0.50 m/s² [N] for 12 s, and then maintains his velocity for 15 s before falling off his board. He slides along on his back until he comes to rest, accelerating at –2.4 m/s².
   (a) Calculate the highest instantaneous velocity that Brett reaches.

   (b) How long did it take Brett to come to rest after falling?
   (c) Draw a velocity-time graph for the total time.
   (d) What is his displacement in the first 12 s?
   (e) What is his displacement while maintaining a constant velocity?
   (f) What is his displacement after he fell?
   (g) What is Brett's average velocity over the total time?

9. Sartaj helps Brett look for the calculator that flew out of his backpack when he fell off his skateboard. **Figure 1** is a position–time graph for their movements as they search for the missing calculator. The positions are all with respect to the place where Brett came to rest.
   (a) What is their position at $t = 9$ s?
   (b) What is their instantaneous velocity at $t = 5$ s, 7 s, and 9 s?
   (c) Draw a velocity-time graph for 0 s to 12 s.

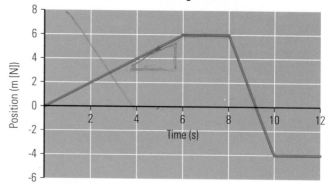

Search for the Missing Calculator

Figure 1

10. Dini is riding her bike eastward at a constant 9.5 m/s when a car pulls out of a side street a short distance in front of her. Dini applies her brakes and manages to stop in 2.5 s, just in time to avoid running into the car.
    (a) Calculate Dini's average acceleration.
    (b) How far does she travel while stopping?

11. An antique trolley car travels along an old railroad track that runs between a trendy new neighbourhood and the city centre. **Table 1** lists the positions at different times for a typical round trip on the trolley. The city centre station is the starting point.
    (a) Plot a position–time graph using the information in **Table 1**.

Table 1	Round Trip of a Trolley Car
Time (min)	Position (km) [N] of city centre
0	0.0
2	1.0
4	2.0
6	3.0
10	4.0
14	5.0
16	5.0
18	4.4
22	3.2
26	2.0
28	1.4
33	0.0

(b) What total distance is travelled in a round trip on the trolley?
(c) Calculate the average speed of the trolley.
(d) What is the instantaneous velocity at $t = 4$ min, $t = 10$ min, and $t = 15$ min?
(e) What is the average velocity for the round trip?
(f) During what time interval does the trolley maintain the greater velocity?
(g) How long does the trolley stop during the round trip?

12. Trevor is driving north along a street with a posted speed limit of 60 km/h. He notices an unmarked van parked along the curb and assumes that it is a photo-radar unit. **Figure 2** shows the changes in Trevor's velocity after he notices the van.

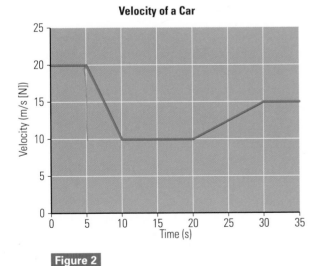

Velocity of a Car

Figure 2

(a) Convert Trevor's initial velocity into km/h. Is he travelling above the speed limit?

(b) Calculate his acceleration from 5 s to 10 s and from 20 s to 30 s.
(c) Determine the displacement from 0 to 35 s.
(e) Determine Trevor's average velocity during the time shown in the graph.

Applying Inquiry Skills

13. Describe an experimental design used to measure the acceleration due to gravity. Specify how you would make your measurements.

14. A student dropped a mass, attached to a ticker tape and timer, to determine the acceleration due to gravity. Analysis of the dot pattern produced a value of 9.45 m/s² [down]. Calculate the percentage error of this experimental result compared to the Canadian average.

15. You are assigned to design an experiment to measure the acceleration due to gravity as part of a future NASA mission to Mars.
    (a) List some experimental designs that could be used.
    (b) Which design would you expect to be the most accurate? Give your reasons.
    (c) What other factors should you consider before choosing the final design?

16. Using only a ruler, design an experiment to measure a person's reaction time. Include your question, experimental design, safety precautions, materials, and procedure. Once you have planned this experiment and obtained your teacher's approval, try it with a variety of people. Answer your initial question.

Making Connections

17. Air-traffic controllers monitor all flights in the area surrounding an airport. How are vector quantities involved in this job?

18. The value of the acceleration due to gravity varies slightly at different locations on Earth's surface. The value is the lowest at the equator (9.780 m/s²) and the highest at the poles (9.832 m/s²). Propose a hypothesis, with reasons, to explain this trend.

Scientific Perspectives on Motion

How do scientists know whether to trust their knowledge? To increase their confidence in concepts, scientists *test* the concepts. Does the concept help to *describe* motion? For example, does the object fall at constant velocity or with constant acceleration? Does the concept *predict* motion? What is the velocity of an object after it has fallen for 2.0 s? Two reasons that scientific concepts of motion are widely trusted are that they are created from evidence that has been evaluated carefully, and that they have been tested rigorously by their ability to describe and explain observed motion and to predict motion not yet observed.

Once scientific concepts have been created and tested, they can be *used* with confidence. For example, we can use concepts of motion to describe and predict the motion of a car. Create, test, use: the Challenges reflect this sequence in the stages of scientific work.

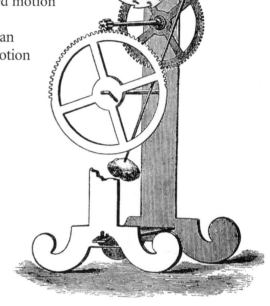

1 Measuring Time

At each step in the advancement of the study of motion, scientists had to wait until more precise and accurate timepieces were invented. Without a modern stopwatch or ticker-tape apparatus, it is very difficult to measure whether one velocity is larger than another, or whether velocity is constant or changing. Your challenge is to produce a timepiece and use it to measure motion.

In creating your timepiece you should

- research ancient timepieces and create a report that includes plans for several devices;
- build a working model of an ancient timepiece or design and build a device of your own;
- use your timepiece to analyze the motion of a runner in a 100 m race;
- evaluate your timepiece in terms of its reliability, precision, and accuracy.

2 Testing Laws of Motion

Aristotle created laws of motion more than 2000 years ago. After Galileo had considered and tested Aristotle's laws, he created new laws of his own, which were accepted by scientists until Newton revised the laws again. How were Aristotle's and Galileo's laws tested? Your challenge is to test a law of either Aristotle or Galileo using investigation.

You should include

- an illustrated report on Aristotle's and Galileo's laws and how they were tested, based on research using a variety of sources;
- a design for one or more investigations that you will use to test one of the laws;
- a written report on your test of the law that would allow others to repeat your investigations.

3 Driver Training

The *use* of scientific knowledge allows a greater understanding. This is especially true, for example, during driver training. How far does the car travel at 80 km/h while you are moving your foot from the gas pedal to the brake pedal? What is the safe distance to be from the car in front at 100 km/h? A driver who can use scientific knowledge to calculate these distances and understand the answers is far more likely to understand how to safely drive a vehicle. Your challenge is to create a supplement to a standard driver training manual that will help student drivers to pass the written and driven parts of the driver's test and to become safe drivers.

Your manual supplement should

- help student drivers understand the ideas presented in a driver training manual by explaining the science behind these ideas;
- show the calculations of the distances, times, and speeds that are presented in the training manual;
- include some graphs to represent the ideas presented;
- suggest some experiments that a driver could do to determine safe limits for driving his or her vehicle.

 ## Assessment

Your completed challenge will be assessed according to the following:

Process

- understand the specific challenge
- develop a plan
- choose and safely use appropriate tools, equipment, materials, and computer software
- analyze the results

Communication

- prepare an appropriate presentation of the task
- use correct terms, symbols, and SI units
- incorporate information technology

Product

- meet established criteria
- show understanding of the concepts, principles, laws, and theories
- show effective use of materials
- address the identified situation/problem

 When preparing to use a chemical test, to carry out an experiment, or to build or test a device, be sure to have your plan approved by your teacher before you begin.

Understanding Concepts

1. What quantities must be measured to determine
   (a) the average speed of an object?
   (b) the average velocity of an object?

2. For each of the following types of motion, state what remains the same during each time interval:
   (a) constant speed;
   (b) constant velocity;
   (c) constant acceleration.

3. Match the terms *position, displacement, distance, speed, velocity,* and *acceleration* with the following descriptions:
   (a) length along a path;
   (b) displacement in a given time;
   (c) location relative to a reference point;
   (d) change in velocity in a given time;
   (e) change in position;
   (f) distance in a given time.

4. Distinguish between each of the following pairs of terms and provide an example:
   (a) constant speed; average speed;
   (b) scalar quantity; vector quantity;
   (c) average velocity; instantaneous velocity;
   (d) speed; velocity;
   (e) distance; displacement.

5. Classify the following quantities as distance, displacement, speed, or velocity.
   (a) Natalie lives 16 km from her school.
   (b) Carla averages 15 km/h when she skates around the pond.
   (c) Bob ran 2.5 km north.
   (d) Kim jogged due south at 150 m/min.
   (e) Jim encountered a 35 km/h east wind as he rode home.

6. All measurements have some uncertainty or error. Using a time interval measured by a stopwatch as an example (**Figure 1**),
   (a) Identify at least two sources of error.
   (b) Name another technology that could be used in place of a stopwatch.

Figure 1

7. State the number of significant digits in each of the following measurements.
   (a) 183 cm/s
   (b) 30.05 mm
   (c) 0.042 km

8. Calculate the average speed of the person in each of the following situations.
   (a) Kevin walks 2.5 km in 0.6 h.
   (b) Trevor drives 315 km in 3.2 h

9. Jolan competes in cycling races and likes to compute her average speed after each race.
   (a) If the length of the race increases and her time remains the same, what happens to her average speed?
   (b) If the length of the race remains the same and her time decreases, what happens to her average speed?
   (c) If the length of the race decreases and her time increases, what happens to her average speed?

10. When vector quantities are represented by arrows, what is the rule used to add two or more vectors? How is the resultant vector obtained?

11. Describe how scale vector diagrams are used to determine the magnitude and direction of the resultant displacement.

12. Find the resultant displacement for each of the following vector additions.
   Scale: 1 cm = 10 km
   (a)

   (b)

   (c)

13. Cindy has three different means of getting to school. Calculate the time that each alternative would take.
   (a) Catching a ride with her Dad involves travelling 3.4 km at a speed of 45 km/h.

(b) Taking the bus requires travelling 4.5 km at a speed of 35 km/h.

(c) Riding her bike, she maintains a speed of 22 km/h along the 2.5-km bike path.

14. State officials in Hawaii are informed about a large earthquake detected near the Gulf of Alaska. Because earthquakes may produce a devastating tidal wave, known as a tsunami (**Figure 2**), Hawaiians must be prepared to evacuate coastal areas. In one particular event, the displacement from the centre of the earthquake to Hawaii was 2235 km [S] and a relatively small wave arrived in Hawaii 3.75 h after the earthquake occurred.

Figure 2

(a) Calculate the velocity of the wave.

(b) Comment on the size of the velocity. What method of transportation has velocities of this size?

(c) Using your answer to (a), calculate the displacement of the wave in a time interval of 30.0 min.

15. While sitting near the front of a bus, Andrew notices that it takes 21 s for the bus to accelerate from rest to 55 km/h [N], and 12 s to slow down from 55 km/h [N] to a complete stop at a traffic light.

(a) Convert 55 km/h [N] into a velocity in metres per second.

(b) Calculate the acceleration during the first 21 s.

(c) What is the displacement of the bus at the end of the first 21 s?

(d) Calculate the acceleration during the last 12 s. How does this acceleration compare with the initial acceleration calculated in (b)?

16. Erin goes to the mall to buy a new music CD. Starting at the main entrance of the mall, she walks 25 m east, 42 m north, and 15 m west before finding the music store 3.0 min after entering the mall.

(a) What distance did Erin walk from the main entrance to the music store?

(b) What was her average speed?

(c) Explain how it is probable that Erin walked part of the journey at a speed faster than her average speed.

(d) Add each of Erin's displacements using a scale vector diagram. Draw her resultant displacement and determine its value and direction.

(e) What was Erin's average velocity?

17. A tourist is driving through a National Park at 19 m/s [W] when a bison calf wanders onto the highway and stops to stare at the oncoming traffic. The reaction time of the driver is 0.45 s and it takes an additional 7.50 s to slow down uniformly to a complete stop.

(a) What is the vehicle's displacement during the tourist's reaction time?

(b) What is the vehicle's displacement while braking to a stop?

(c) Draw a velocity–time graph for this situation including appropriate numbers on the axes.

(d) What is the acceleration of the car before braking? while braking?

18. In a final burst of energy near the end of a bike race, Julia accelerates at 0.32 m/s² for 15 s, attaining a final speed of 18.6 m/s.

(a) What was Julia's initial speed?

(b) How far did she travel while accelerating?

19. Mike is travelling north in his wheelchair at 2.0 m/s, accelerates uniformly to 9.0 m/s [N] in 15 s, travels at a constant velocity for the next 25 s, and then comes to a stop in 12 s.

(a) Draw a velocity–time graph for this motion.

(b) Calculate Mike's acceleration during each segment of the motion.

(c) Find the resultant displacement after 52 s.

(d) Which parts of the motion represent constant velocity and constant acceleration?

(e) Calculate Mike's average velocity.

20. Starting from rest, a subway train accelerates at 1.5 m/s². Copy and complete **Table 1** for the first 5.0 s of the train's motion.

Table 1   **Acceleration of a Subway Train**

Time (s)	Speed (m/s)	Distance travelled
0.0		
1.0		
2.0		
3.0		
4.0		
5.0		

Applying Inquiry Skills

21. A hiker and a cyclist start at the same time from the same location on the Trans-Canada Trail.

Table 2   **Travelling the Trans-Canada Trail**

Time (min)	Position of hiker (km [W])	Position of cyclist (km [W])
0	0.00	0.00
10	0.95	2.85
20	1.90	5.70
30	2.85	8.55
40	3.80	11.40
50	4.75	14.25
60	5.70	17.10

(a) Use the values in the **Table 2** to plot a position–time graph, including two lines: one for the hiker and one for the cyclist.
(b) Using your graph, how long did it take each person to travel 5.0 km?
(c) Using your graph, calculate the velocity of each person.
(d) Are the velocities you calculated in (c) constant velocities? How do you know?

22. Large ships generally have low accelerations. **Figure 3** shows the position of a cruise ship relative to a buoy outside a harbour.
(a) By inspecting the way the line curves, what can you conclude about the change in velocity of the ship?
(b) Determine the instantaneous velocity at 20 s, 80 s, and 120 s.
(c) What is the average velocity during the time period from 0 to 130 s?

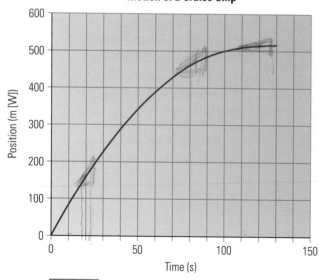

Motion of a Cruise Ship

Position (m [W]) vs *Time (s)*

Figure 3

23. In a bungee jump, a person's ankles are firmly attached to one end of an elastic cord, which is secured to the top of a high tower or bridge. The person falls freely from a high platform (**Figure 4**) until the cord begins to stretch, slowing the person to a momentary stop. After several oscillations up and down, the activity finishes when the person is pulled back up to the starting point.
(a) What is the shape of the velocity-time graph of the jumper from the top of the platform until the momentary stop at the lowest point? Predict the shape of the graph in a sketch. Write a hypothesis to explain your prediction.
(b) How would you test your prediction and hypothesis? Write an experimental design including a brief plan and a description of variables.
(c) Is the motion during a bungee jump best described as uniform or non-uniform motion? Explain your answer.
(d) What is the person's average velocity for the complete activity from start to finish? Explain briefly.
(e) What are some risks associated with this activity?

Figure 4

24. Suppose you walk along a path beside a river and then stop on a bridge looking down on the slow-moving river. You notice that there are often bits of debris such as leaves and twigs floating down the river. You decide to determine how fast the river is moving.
(a) Write an experimental design to determine the speed of the river.
(b) Make a list of materials for this investigation.
(c) Write a specific procedure based on your design and materials.

25. Most people have cans containing various foodstuffs and other substances in their cupboards. The contents of these cans may vary from a liquid that flows easily to different types of solids. Create and conduct an investigation about the motion of cans rolling down a ramp. Start by devising a scientific question and conclude with an evaluation of your evidence and prediction/hypothesis.

Making Connections

26. Provide the information to complete **Table 3**.

Table 3 **Ways of Communicating Empirical Knowledge**

Type of communication	Definition	Example
empirical description	observation(s)	The speed of a cyclist, freewheeling downhill, increases with time.
table of evidence	an organized group of observations (often in terms of variables)	(a)
(b)	a visual presentation of many observations or calculations	A position–time graph can be drawn from ticker-timer evidence.
empirical definition (also called operational definition)	a statement that defines an object or process in terms of its properties (including mathematical properties	(c)
generalization	(d)	If an object is accelerating, the slope of the speed–time graph is positive.
(e)	a statement of a major concept (based on a large body of empirical knowledge) widely accepted in the scientific community	In a vacuum, all experience the same acceleration, regardless of their mass or composition.

27. Project into the future when a colony of people lives in a large domed city on Mars. In a science experiment at the local Mars High School, students drop a steel ball from a height of 1.85 m to the floor. After repeated trials, using an electronic timer, they determined an average time of 1.028 s for the ball to reach the ground.
  (a) Why is it important to do several trials instead of only one?
  (b) Using the students' evidence, calculate the local value of the acceleration due to gravity on Mars.
  (c) The accepted value for gravitational acceleration on Mars is 3.74 m/s². What is the percent error of the students' results?
  (d) Suggest some sources of error in this experiment.
  (e) How would motion in daily life on Mars be different from Earth?
  (f) Choose a sport that might be significantly affected compared to the same sport on Earth. Describe briefly any differences.

28. You plan to measure the distance from Earth to the Moon every night for 27 nights. The materials available are a radio transmitter, a receiver and an electronic clock.
  (a) Suggest a problem (scientific question) that could be investigated.
  (b) Write a design for this investigation using the materials available. Clearly identify independent, dependent and controlled variables.
  (c) List some possible sources of error or uncertainty in this experiment.
  (d) Briefly state the scientific knowledge that could be obtained.
  (e) Search the library or Internet to find the distance from Earth to the Moon. Does this distance depend on the position of the Moon as it circles Earth?

29. Choose a piece of sports equipment that either rolls (in-line skates, skateboard, bicycle) or slides (snowboard, skis). Describe some features that have been modified in the last few years to improve the motion of the equipment.

30. Motorized personal watercraft, such as the SeaDoo®, have become very popular for summer recreation (**Figure 5**).
  (a) List some benefits of this technology.
  (b) List some problems or harmful effects of this technology.
  (c) Compare your two lists and evaluate whether the benefits outweigh the costs, in your opinion.

Figure 5

Weather Dynamics

Weather affects everybody on Earth. Knowing about weather and weather patterns helps us decide what to wear, what plans to make for vacations and outdoor activities, and when to perform a variety of tasks, from planting gardens to adding salt to highways to evacuating an area about to be hit by a major storm.

Forecasting the weather is difficult because so many factors affect it. We have to consider global factors, such as prevailing winds and ocean currents, as well as local factors, such as proximity to a lake. However, advances in weather theory, computer modelling, and modern technology are helping to improve forecasting, and we can be proud of Canada's contributions to these technologies.

Overall Expectations

In this unit, you will be able to

- understand the factors that determine and affect the processes of weather systems;
- investigate and analyze trends in local and global weather conditions to help you forecast local and global weather patterns;
- evaluate how technology is helping us to understand the physical factors that affect weather.

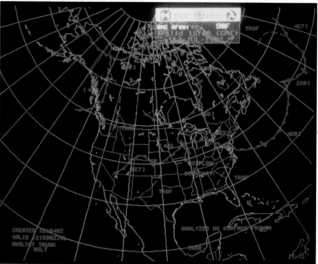

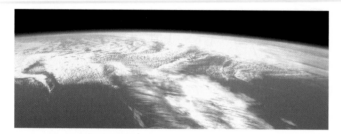

Chapter 13
Global Weather Dynamics

To understand why our weather continually changes, we must start by exploring how energy from the Sun interacts with the atmosphere, land, and hydrosphere (which includes all the forms of water).

In this chapter, you will be able to

- identify and describe the main characteristics of the atmosphere and hydrosphere;
- describe and explain heat transfer within the water cycle and how the atmosphere and hydrosphere store heat;
- describe and explain heat transfer in the atmosphere and hydrosphere and its effect on air and water currents;
- describe and explain the development of winds, clouds, and pressure gradients in the atmosphere;
- investigate factors that affect weather-related phenomena, such as the angle at which the Sun's rays strike Earth and the rate at which water evaporates;
- formulate and investigate questions about weather-related issues, including rescue operations during bad weather;
- explain how people have utilized their understanding of weather patterns to participate in activities such as hot-air ballooning.

Chapter 14
Forecasting the Weather

Forecasters apply their understanding of global weather dynamics to predict the weather for the days ahead. However, local factors must also be considered to improve the accuracy of weather forecasts.

In this chapter, you will be able to

- describe and explain how moving air masses affect the weather;
- explain different types of transformations of water vapour in the atmosphere and their effects;
- describe the factors contributing to Earth's temperature gradients and to wind speed and direction;
- describe cyclones in terms of the meeting of air masses and the jet stream;
- formulate questions about and investigate weather-related concepts and issues, such as the relationship between wind speed and air pressure, relative humidity, and weather forecasting for profit;
- interpret weather maps;
- forecast weather;
- compare various cultural and historical views on the origins and interpretations of weather;
- describe examples of Canadian technologies that contribute to meteorology.

Chapter 15
Extreme Weather Events

Hurricanes, tornadoes, blizzards, and other major storms may be interesting to watch on TV, but they are extremely dangerous and costly. Early forecasting of such extreme events helps to save lives and reduce property damage.

In this chapter, you will be able to

- describe and explain the development of extreme weather events such as thunderstorms, tornadoes, floods, droughts, hurricanes, blizzards, and ice storms;
- plan and conduct an investigation into plant growth under extreme conditions;
- investigate how El Niño affects global and local weather systems.

Chapter 16
Forecasting the Future

A major concern facing humans is what will happen to the average weather conditions on Earth in the future. There are many reasons why we should all address the possible changes.

In this chapter, you will be able to

- explain how weather affects environmental phenomena and how future changes in weather may affect us;
- explain how a scientific understanding of weather patterns can be used to modify environmental conditions;
- describe examples of Canadian technologies that contribute to meteorology;
- investigate how such factors as greenhouse gases and ozone affect the development, severity, and movement of global and local weather systems;
- select and integrate information from various sources, including electronic and print resources, to answer weather-related questions;
- use historical and current weather data to support a position on future weather patterns.

Why Study Weather Dynamics?

We all want to know what the weather will be like to help us plan an enjoyable, care-free day. But learning about weather is much more than that. Think of people whose lives are influenced by weather: people who design winter clothing, umbrellas that don't break in the wind, or better home insulation; those involved in tourism, recreation, or sports; people who truck goods across the continent, commute in the city, or operate any other type of transportation; people with weather-related careers, such as a forecaster; and people whose lives are saved thanks to the severe storm warnings issued by those forecasters.

Not only does weather influence people, but people also influence weather. Now more than 6 billion, the world's population is greater than it has ever been, and it continues to grow. Human activities — for example, burning fossil fuels — can alter the weather, so studying how an increasing population may affect weather patterns is important to the future of the planet. The more we learn about the human impact on weather, the more likely we will act in positive, responsible ways.

As you study this unit, you will discover numerous examples of modern technology applied to studying weather. Technologically sophisticated instruments, including satellites, gather data that are analyzed by powerful computers. Information is distributed around the world by computer-controlled communications systems. Many modern technological innovations are designed, built, and used in Canada.

But scientists are not satisfied with the current technology. They would like more data collection, better ways of storing the data, and faster rates of computer analysis. These improvements will help them predict with greater accuracy what might happen to Earth's weather in the future.

Working on your challenge will give you hands-on experience in applying what you have learned about weather-related technology and weather dynamics. You will have a better understanding of how difficult it can be to make an accurate weather forecast and how important weather is to all of us.

Challenge

Applying Ideas and Skills of Weather-Related Technology

As you learn about weather and the technology used to study weather, think about how you would accomplish these Challenges. For more information on the Challenges, see page 650.

1 Beat the Weather Forecaster

A weather station has several instruments that constantly gather weather data. Your task is to design a weather station and use it to forecast weather in your own area.

2 Create a Weather-Wise Community

A large city tends to have a different climate than the surrounding areas. This is caused by pollution, the lack of vegetation, and other factors that have an impact on the weather. Your task is to design a community that reduces the negative effects and is a better place for humans to live.

3 Join a Weather Network

Computers are used for storing and sharing weather-related data as well as for communicating with other people. You will create or join a weather network and create a database of weather information by combining your own ideas with ideas you find on the Internet and elsewhere.

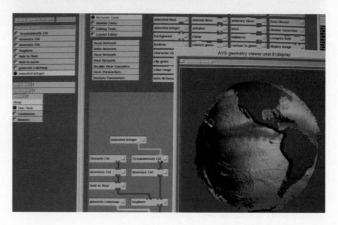

Record your ideas for your Challenge as you progress through this unit and when you see

 # Challenge

13 Global Weather Dynamics

HOW IS EARTH DIFFERENT FROM THE MOON?
In this photograph of Earth taken from the Moon (**Figure 1**) perhaps
the most obvious difference is the colour. Water, ice, air, and clouds
contribute to the colour combination of blue and white and are
responsible for the changing weather patterns on Earth.

Figure 1
Planet Earth is a unique place. This photograph of Earth
was taken by astronauts from the Moon.

If you could watch Earth for several days from space, you would notice that the clouds continuously move. This dynamic motion provides one clue about the causes of weather changes on Earth: things are in motion.

With the continuous bombardment of solar energy hitting Earth every day, why isn't Earth much hotter than it is? Something happens to all that energy to allow the total amount of energy on Earth to remain fairly constant, in other words, "in balance."

To understand why the clouds and other components of Earth's features are in motion and why the energy is in balance, we need to consider what happens to the Sun's energy that strikes Earth. In simple terms, this energy sets water and air in motion. But of course, **weather dynamics**, the study of how the motion of water and air causes weather patterns, is not quite as simple as that. This chapter explores what happens to the energy that hits the features on Earth's surface, namely, the atmosphere, land, water, and ice.

Try This
Activity Effects of Evaporation

As something cools, it loses energy; as it warms, it gains energy. But when liquids evaporate, do they cause their surroundings to become warmer or cooler? Think about how this question relates to weather before you follow the steps below.

Materials: apron, safety goggles, room-temperature water, rubbing alcohol in a dropper bottle, eye dropper

🛑 Rubbing alcohol is poisonous. Do not allow it to come in contact with your eyes or mouth. Do not inhale the fumes.

🔥 Rubbing alcohol is flammable. Do not put near an open flame.

• Put a drop of water on one index finger, and a drop of rubbing alcohol on the other index finger. Then hold both index fingers in the air and move them back and forth at the same rate.

(a) Describe what happens as you observe the liquids evaporate from your fingers. Compare how each finger feels. Explain your observations.

(b) Why do you think alcohol and water have different effects?

(c) Evaporation occurs on oceans and other bodies of water. Where does the energy come from for this evaporation?

(d) Clouds can form from condensation. Describe what you think happens to the temperature of the air when clouds form above an ocean.

• Using soap, wash any areas that came into contact with the rubbing alcohol.

A Closer Look at Earth

To begin our study of weather and changing weather patterns, we look at a worldwide, or global, view of Earth. A useful model to provide this view is a globe (**Figure 1**). The globe is tilted to represent Earth's tilt at an angle to an imaginary line between Earth and the Sun. Like Earth, the globe rotates on its axis, which is a line from the South Pole to the North Pole. A globe shows the oceans, continents, and countries of the world; some show major ocean and wind currents.

The main components of Earth that influence weather are the atmosphere, the land forms, and water in its various forms (solid, liquid, and vapour). If you look at a globe or a world map (**Figure 2**), you can see that a large portion of Earth's surface, about 70%, is covered by oceans. The remainder forms the continents. The atmosphere above the oceans and continents contains air, water vapour, and particles of dust and chemicals, all of which influence weather, especially when the atmosphere is in motion.

Figure 1

A globe is a three-dimensional model of Earth that is useful to refer to as you study weather dynamics. Globes are often tilted because the Earth itself is at an angle of 23.5° to the plane of its orbit around the Sun.

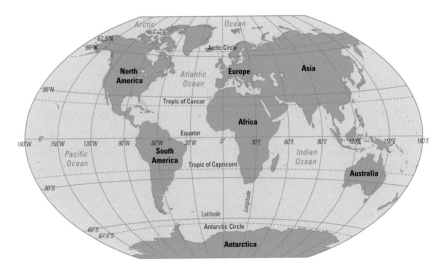

Figure 2

About 30% of Earth's surface is land; the rest consists of oceans and other bodies of water. The atmosphere extends above the surface to several hundred kilometres.

Comparing Weather and Climate

Before starting this unit, we should understand that weather and climate are different. **Weather** is the set of environmental conditions encountered from day to day. **Climate** is the set of environmental conditions averaged over many years. Consider a city located in southern Manitoba: its January *climate* is cold and fairly snowy and windy, with an average daytime high temperature of −12°C. This information is the average of years of data. However, for a week in January, its *weather* could be mild, with daytime high temperatures of 6°C, low winds, and sunny skies.

Work the Web

Visit www.science.nelson.com and follow the links for Science 10, 13.1. Find a site that has climate data for Canadian cities. Choose a city and graph the average monthly temperature and precipitation.

Global Geography

Longitude is the angle measured east or west from the 0° line, which passes through Greenwich, England. For example, the eastern tip of Cape Breton Island, Nova Scotia, is at 60° west longitude. Latitude is the angle measured north or south of the equator. For example, the border between the western Canadian provinces and the United States lies along the 49° north latitude line.

Notice the specially labelled latitudes on the map in **Figure 2**. The Tropic of Cancer, at 23.5° north latitude, is the most northerly location reached by the Sun's vertical rays on the first day of summer, around June 21, each year. The Arctic Circle, at 66.5° north latitude, is the most northerly location reached by any of the Sun's rays on the first day of winter, around December 21. The corresponding lines in the Southern Hemisphere are the Tropic of Capricorn and the Antarctic Circle.

Between the Tropic of Cancer and the Tropic of Capricorn lies the large equatorial region often called the tropics. The polar regions are found north of the Arctic Circle and south of the Antarctic Circle. Between the tropics and the polar regions are the mid-latitude regions. Most of the populated areas of Canada lie in the mid-latitude region.

◓ Challenge

1 Start collecting the five-day weather forecasts from a daily newspaper or another source (e.g., a web site). Store the forecasts so that you can analyze them as you learn more about weather forecasting.

2 Set up a portfolio of ideas and information so you can develop an understanding of what your weather-wise community will require. For example, which is more important to consider, the weather or the climate? Why?

3 Refer to the Nelson Science web site (www.science.nelson.com) to learn how to link your school to other schools where students are studying weather. Keep a record of how you accessed the network site.

Understanding Concepts

1. Describe today's weather conditions for your area.

2. Describe the climate for your area at this time of year.

3. Use two or three adjectives to describe the following climates:

   (a) winter in Canada's Arctic;

   (b) winter in Nova Scotia;

   (c) each of the seasons in your region.

4. List four or five decisions you have made in the past year that have depended on the weather.

5. Consult your atlas and state the latitude of

   (a) the equator;

   (b) the South Pole;

   (c) the southernmost land point in Canada;

   (d) your own area.

6. As you move from the equator to the poles (on a globe or Earth), what happens to the distance between the longitudinal lines?

7. Compare the following angles: the tilt of Earth's axis, the maximum latitude reached by the Sun's vertical rays on the first day of summer, and the latitudinal angle separating the Arctic Circle from the North Pole. What do you notice?

8. Classify the following locations as being in the tropics, mid-latitude regions, or polar regions:

   (a) Greenland;

   (b) Thailand;

   (c) your own location.

9. Explain why climate should be considered when planning each of the following events:

   (a) a fireworks display;

   (b) the Winter Olympics at a mountain resort;

   (c) a charity run.

Exploring

10. Research what Canada's astronauts have said about our
ⓘ planet as they viewed it from space. Are there any
ⓙ themes that emerge from their comments?

Earth's Energy Balance

Almost all the energy used on Earth to sustain life and cause our changing weather systems comes from the Sun. Different types of electromagnetic energy are emitted from the Sun, and they have different effects when they reach Earth. Without all this energy, plants would not grow, and the land, water, and air wouldn't stay warm enough for us to survive. But just enough energy is returned from Earth to space to keep the average surface temperature about 15°C.

Transfer of Energy

Energy can be transferred from one place to another by four methods: radiation, conduction, convection, and advection. These methods of transferring energy, called heat transfer, all contribute to Earth's weather.

Radiation is the transfer of energy by means of waves. Unlike water waves and sound waves, radiation waves do not require a medium. This is why they can travel from the Sun, through space, and reach Earth. The energy that comes to us from the Sun reaches us by radiation. Visible light is one example of the many forms of energy that can travel through space. Other forms are infrared radiation, ultraviolet waves, and X rays. The set of waves that can travel through empty space at the speed of light is called the **electromagnetic spectrum. Figure 1** shows these waves as well as some of their properties.

> **Did You Know?**
>
> A small portion of energy available on Earth comes from nuclear reactions in Earth's core.

Figure 1

The electromagnetic spectrum consists of several types of waves, all of which travel at the speed of 300 000 km/s in a vacuum.

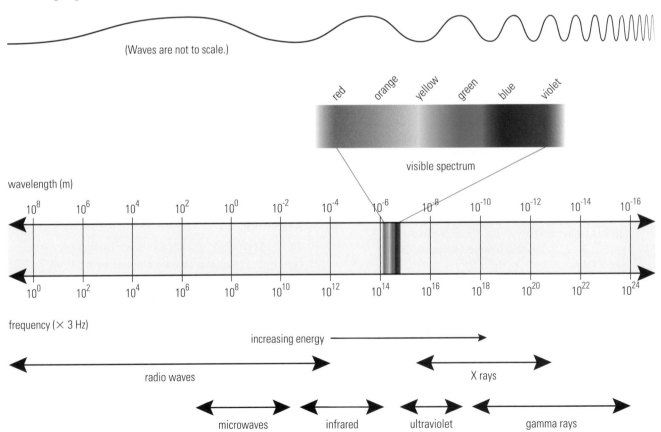

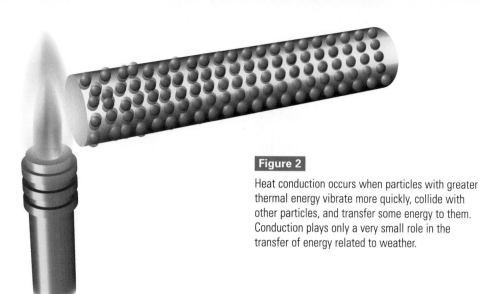

Figure 2

Heat conduction occurs when particles with greater thermal energy vibrate more quickly, collide with other particles, and transfer some energy to them. Conduction plays only a very small role in the transfer of energy related to weather.

The other methods of energy transfer, require particles of matter. **Conduction** is the transfer of energy through the collision of particles (**Figure 2**). Although conduction occurs most easily in metals such as steel, it also occurs to a small extent in substances on Earth's surface, including rock, sand, soil, and water.

Convection and **advection** are the transfer of energy by the movement of particles in a fluid (**Figure 3**). A fluid is either a liquid (such as water) or a gas (such as the components of the atmosphere). Convection transfers energy vertically and advection transfers energy horizontally. Since weather systems depend on the movement of particles in the atmosphere and in the oceans, you will often apply the concepts of convection and advection as you understand weather systems.

These four methods of energy transfer help to maintain Earth's energy balance as well as distribute energy around the world.

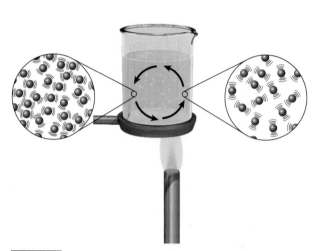

Figure 3

A convection current is set up when particles of a fluid gain energy. As their movement increases, they spread apart and that part of the fluid become less dense than the surroundings, and so it rises. The warm fluid is replaced by cooler fluid as the flow of the convection current begins.

Try This
Activity   Observing Convection in Water

To illustrate convection in water, use cold water with some dark food colouring added and clear hot water.

Materials: apron, safety goggles, two beakers, hot water, cold water, dark food colouring

✋ Hot water can scald you. Handle with care.

• Half fill a clear glass or plastic beaker with hot water and let the water settle. Very slowly and carefully, pour dyed cold water down the side of the beaker into the hot water.

(a) Observe what happens, then draw a sketch to explain what you observe.

• Reverse the process: add hot, clear water to cold, dyed water.

(b) Draw a sketch of your observations, and explain any differences between this step and the first one.

(c) Relate what happened in this activity to what you think happens to layers of water in oceans or layers of air in the atmosphere.

Reflection and Absorption of Energy

When the electromagnetic waves from the Sun reach Earth, some are reflected off the atmosphere and clouds back into space; some pass through the atmosphere and bounce off Earth's surface back into the atmosphere; and some get absorbed by the atmosphere, the ground, or the water at the surface. **Figure 4** shows what percentages of solar radiation are reflected and absorbed. For the radiation that reflects off the atmosphere and the surface features of Earth, the portion of energy reflected depends on the albedo of the material. Clean snow has a high albedo; it reflects a large portion of incoming energy. Black soil has a low albedo; it absorbs more energy than it reflects.

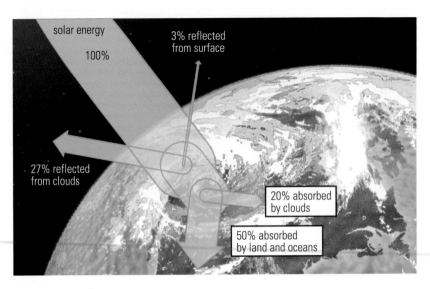

solar energy
100%

3% reflected
from surface

27% reflected
from clouds

20% absorbed
by clouds

50% absorbed
by land and oceans

Figure 4

Figure 4

Some radiation that hits Earth's atmosphere reflects off particles in the atmosphere and clouds back into space. The rest passes through the atmosphere, hitting water, land, and ice.

Any object or material that absorbs energy and becomes warmer is called a **heat sink**. A heat sink holds energy in a similar way to how a kitchen sink holds water. Even though water has a higher albedo than land and soil (water reflects more solar energy than it absorbs), the oceans are good heat sinks. When solar energy hits water, the water begins to move — this is convection activity — and to transfer energy hundreds of metres deep into the oceans. Soil and rock are poor heat sinks. Heat is conducted very slowly into these materials.

An important property of all substances is their **heat capacity**, which is the measure of how much heat a substance requires to increase its temperature or how much heat it releases as its temperature decreases. Soil and rock are poor heat sinks; their heat capacity is low. As **Figure 5** shows, water has a very high heat capacity, which means it can hold a lot of heat.

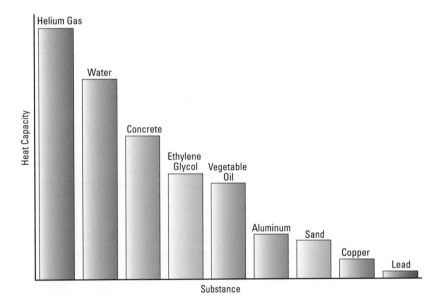

Figure 5

Heat capacities of common substances. To calculate the heat capacities of different substances, scientists use the same mass of each substance, yielding what is called the specific heat capacities measured in J/(kg·C°). Metals tend to have low specific heat capacities.

Try This
Activity Comparing Heat Capacities

Which of the following can heat up a 500 g sample of room-temperature water the most: 200 g of rock at 100°C, 200 g of steel at 100°C, or 200 g of water at 100°C?

(a) Design and carry out an investigation to
Ⓚ answer this question. (The masses should be equal, but they don't have to be 200 g.)

• Before carrying out the activity, get your teacher's approval, and ensure that you have included all necessary safety precautions. Be sure to observe all precautions when doing the activity.

(b) Use your findings to explain what you know about the heat capacity of substances.

Understanding Concepts

1. Explain why conduction, convection, and advection cannot occur in space.

2. Which part of the electromagnetic spectrum

    (a) allows us to see?

    (b) is used in ovens?

    (c) is used to take images of your teeth?

3. Does warm water rise or fall in cold water? Explain why this happens.

4. Explain why convection does not occur in solids.

5. Explain why rocks and soil are poor heat sinks.

6. List the following in order of highest to lowest albedo: dirty snow; clean snow; ocean water; an evergreen forest.

7. Two clouds are about the same size. One appears light in colour, and the other appears dark because it blocks more sunlight. Which would be a better heat sink? Why?

8. Describe what would happen to the temperature on Earth if the amount of energy reflected back to space

    (a) increased to 80%;

    (b) decreased to 5%.

Making Connections

9. "Night-vision" goggles, cameras, and displays in cars detect infrared radiation emitted by objects that have higher temperatures than their surroundings. What types of things can be seen by night-vision devices?

10. If the polar ice caps melted, how would this affect the overall albedo of Earth? What effect would you expect this to have on the global climate?

Exploring

11. Find out how Earth's albedo compares with the albedos of the other planets in the solar system. What patterns, if any, do you observe?

Challenge

2 How much heat a city absorbs from solar radiation depends on its albedo. What factors might change the albedo of a city?

3 When it is 9:00 a.m. in Sudbury, it is 10:00 a.m. in Sydney and 7:00 a.m. in Medicine Hat. When you want to communicate with students in other parts of Canada, how will you work with time differences?

13.3 Investigation

INQUIRY SKILLS MENU
- Questioning
- Hypothesizing
- Predicting
- Planning
- Conducting
- Recording
- Analyzing
- Evaluating
- Communicating

Seasons and the Angle of Sunlight

Much of Earth's weather, especially our changing seasons, is caused by Earth's revolution around the Sun combined with the tilt of Earth's axis. **Figure 1** shows that the axis, around which Earth rotates once each day, is tilted at an angle of 23.5° to an imaginary line joining the centre of Earth and the centre of the Sun. Around June 21 (the summer solstice, the longest day of the year), the Northern Hemisphere is at its maximum tilt toward the Sun. The Sun's rays are hitting the Northern Hemisphere's surface most directly at this time. Around December 21 (the winter solstice, the shortest day of the year), the Northern Hemisphere is at its maximum tilt away from the Sun. The Sun's rays are hitting the Northern Hemisphere's surface at a steep angle, and we experience the effects of winter. Of course, the opposite happens in the Southern Hemisphere.

On the equinoxes (the vernal equinox around March 21 and the autumnal equinox around September 23), the Sun's rays strike Earth's surface at the equator straight on. At these times, day and night are of equal length everywhere on Earth.

In this investigation, you will explore how the amount of energy received at a surface depends on the angle of the light rays striking the surface. To determine the intensity of light striking a surface, you can use a small photocell array connected to a voltmeter. As the light intensity striking the photocell increases, the voltmeter reading also increases.

Question

(a) Compose a question for this investigation. K2

Hypothesis/Prediction

(b) Read the procedure then predict what you will discover in this investigation. K3

(c) Write a hypothesis explaining your prediction.

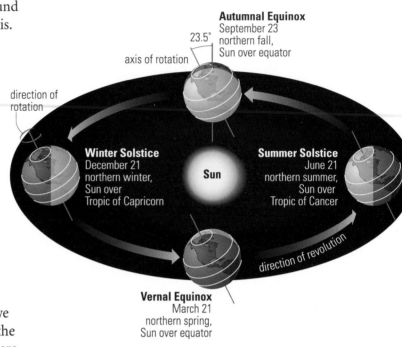

Figure 1

Can you see why the seasons in the Northern Hemisphere are the opposite of those in the Southern Hemisphere on the dates indicated?

Materials

- bright light source
- protractor
- photocell array
- voltmeter
- connecting wires

Design

This is a controlled experiment in which data collected can be analyzed by plotting a graph.

(d) Design a table to record voltmeter readings as the angle of incidence is varied. K7

(e) Identify and list the independent, dependent, and controlled variables in this investigation.

(f) Consider the best way to control the variables that must be kept constant: the light source; the photocell; the distance between the object and the photocell; the scale on the voltmeter.

SKILLS HANDBOOK: K2 Asking the Questions   K3 Developing the Prediction and Hypothesis

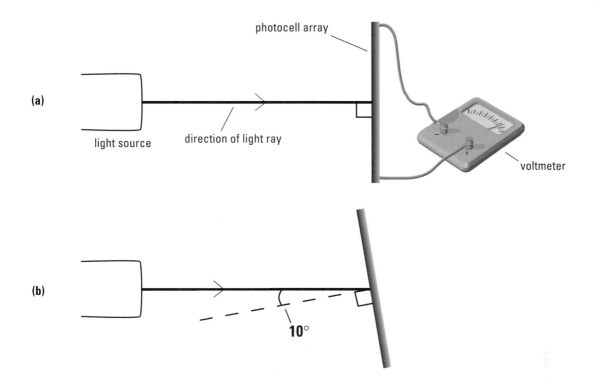

(a) photocell array

direction of light ray

light source

voltmeter

(b)

10°

Procedure

1 Connect a photocell to a voltmeter. Place a bright light source a fixed distance from the photocell, as shown in **Figure 2(a)**. (Choose a distance that produces a fairly high reading on the voltmeter.)

2 Aim the light so that it falls directly onto the photocell. Record the reading on the voltmeter.

3 Repeat Step 2 with the photocell at an angle of 10° to the light beam, as seen in **Figure 2(b)**. Record the new value. Repeat for angles of 20°, 30°, and so on, up to 80°. Record your data in your table.

Analysis and Evaluation

(V) (g) Plot a graph of the data obtained.
(h) Relate what you observed to what you know
(O3) about the seasons.
(i) If you were performing this investigation outdoors using the Sun as a source of energy, what variables besides the angle of incidence of light could you investigate?
(j) How could you improve the accuracy of the measurements you made in this investigation?
(k) Evaluate your prediction and hypothesis and summarize your findings in a paragraph.

Figure 2

The *angle of incidence* is the angle between the incident, or incoming, ray and the line perpendicular to the surface where the light strikes.
(a) The incident ray lies along the line perpendicular to the photocell, so the angle of incidence is 0°.
(b) The angle of incidence is 10°.

Understanding Concepts

1. Explain the difference between the terms "revolution" and "rotation."

2. In the Northern Hemisphere, on which date do we have the most hours of daylight? the least hours of daylight?

3. Refer to **Figure 1**. What position is Earth in when (a) Canadians and (b) Australians are most likely to be sunburned?

4. On the equinoxes, compare the amount of solar energy striking a surface at the equator with the amount striking a surface of the same area at 50° north latitude.

Making Connections

5. Emergency phones along some highways use solar-powered photocell arrays to provide needed electrical energy. List some of the advantages and disadvantages of this technology.

The Atmosphere

Earth's atmosphere may not be as easy to see as all the water and ice in the world, but it is very important for life as well as weather systems. Every time you see clouds in the sky, feel wind in your face, or even take a breath, you experience an effect of the atmosphere.

The **atmosphere** is the blanket of air and moisture that surrounds Earth. Most dense at sea level, where the molecules are pressed together by the weight of the air above, the atmosphere becomes less dense as the height above sea level increases. About 500 km up, there are hardly any molecules, and the vacuum of space begins.

Near Earth's surface, the atmosphere consists mainly of nitrogen (78%), oxygen (21%), and small amounts of other gases, such as argon, carbon dioxide, and water vapour (**Figure 1**).

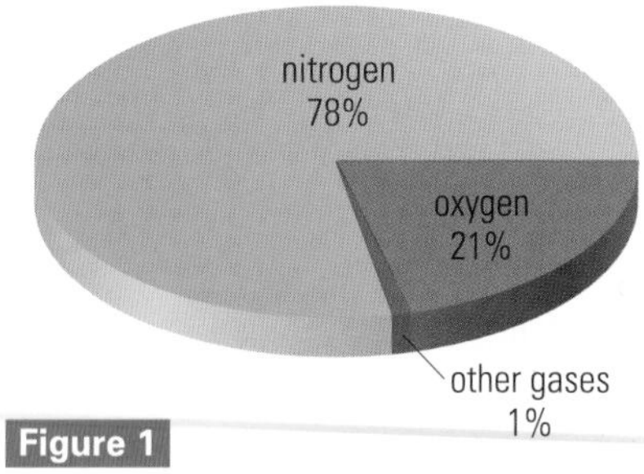

Figure 1

Besides nitrogen and oxygen, the atmosphere contains small amounts of water vapour, argon, carbon dioxide, neon, helium, krypton, hydrogen, and ozone.

Atmospheric Layers

The atmosphere consists of several layers, each with distinct properties. **Figure 2** shows these layers as well as their typical temperatures and altitude and the locations of clouds, aircraft, and spacecraft. **Altitude** is the height above sea level, usually measured in metres (m) or kilometres (km). (Altitude can also be called elevation.) All the layers are thicker above the equator than above the poles. The air at the equator is warmer, so it expands and takes up more space than the cold air at the poles.

The **troposphere** is the atmospheric layer closest to Earth's surface, up to an altitude of about 16 km at the equator and as low as 8 km at the poles. It contains most of the atmosphere's moisture and is responsible for most of our weather systems. As the altitude above Earth's surface increases, the temperature in the troposphere decreases.

Try This
Activity Modelling the Density of the Atmosphere

To get an idea of how the force of gravity acting on the atmosphere causes the air to be most closely packed (densest) at the ground, use a simple model of donut-shaped disc magnets.

Materials: five or six disc magnets, a pencil

- Place five or six disc magnets onto a vertical pencil so that they repel each other (**Figure 2**). Observe the spacing of the magnets. Sketch what you see.

(a) Explain your observations of the distances between the magnets.

(b) Explain how this model relates to the relationship between the density of the atmosphere and the distance above Earth's surface.

Figure 2

Gravity exerts a downward force, or pull, on the top magnet, but magnetic repulsion also exerts an upward force, or push, on it.

Where the troposphere ends is a thin boundary called the **tropopause**. At this level, the temperature no longer decreases with increasing altitude. In fact, the temperature rises because the tropopause contains a little more ozone, which absorbs ultraviolet radiation from the Sun, causing a temperature increase. The higher temperature of the tropopause helps to keep the molecules of the next higher layer separate from the troposphere.

Above the tropopause is the stratosphere, a dry atmospheric layer from about 12 km to 50 km that contains higher concentrations of ozone than any other layer. The ozone here helps protect Earth from much of the harmful ultraviolet radiation from the Sun, and its presence explains why the temperature of the stratosphere increases as the altitude increases. (Although ozone in the stratosphere is helpful, ozone near the ground is harmful.)

The middle layer in the atmosphere is called the mesosphere (*meso* means middle). With the exception of ozone and water vapour concentrations, the composition of the atmosphere up to and including the mesosphere is very similar. Here, the temperature and density of the gases are extremely low. This layer extends from about 50 km to 80 km.

Above the mesosphere is the thermosphere, where the density remains low but molecules have higher energy, producing higher temperatures than in the mesosphere. In the thermosphere, the highest-energy electromagnetic waves from the Sun (e.g., X rays) are absorbed, which increases the temperature. The thermosphere extends from about 80 km to about 500 km. The thermosphere is also called the "ionosphere" because in this layer, high-energy radiation from the Sun causes particles to become electrically charged ions. The ions produce the beautiful light displays called auroras, the Northern Lights and the Southern Lights.

Above the thermosphere is the exosphere, the thin outermost layer of the atmosphere. From the point of view of space travel, the exosphere can be called space because there are so few particles there, and what particles there are (mainly hydrogen) are spread out.

Notice in **Figure 3** that the temperature of the atmosphere is different at different altitudes. The change of temperature over a distance is called a **temperature gradient**. The temperature gradient of the troposphere is about –6°C per 1000 m. Beyond the troposphere, the temperature gradient in each layer becomes less uniform.

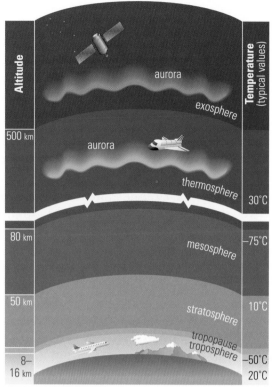

Figure 3

The atmosphere consists of six main layers, starting with the troposphere near the ground.

Supporting Life

Life as we know it would not be possible without the atmosphere. Oxygen and nitrogen in the atmosphere are needed to support life, and carbon dioxide is needed for green plants to thrive. Ozone in the upper atmosphere absorbs ultraviolet radiation, protecting us from this harmful radiation from the Sun. The atmosphere plays a role in the water cycle, which supplies Earth's surface with water. And it offers us protection from most of the meteors coming our way, since most of them vaporize due to the frictional effects when they speed through the atmosphere.

The atmosphere also helps to keep the average temperature within a life-supporting range. Gases such as water vapour and carbon dioxide trap energy in the form of heat radiated from the ground. And the atmosphere circulates air to help maintain a fairly constant balance of energy around the world.

Atmospheric Pressure

Atmospheric pressure is the pressure the air exerts as gravity pulls it toward the centre of Earth. It is greatest at sea level, where the molecules are closest together. At higher altitudes, atmospheric pressure decreases. Atmospheric pressure at a particular altitude also depends on other factors, such as whether the air is rising or falling. Thus, there are two variations to consider: vertical and horizontal.

Pressure gradient is a measure of the amount the atmospheric pressure changes across a set distance. Pressure gradients can be vertical or horizontal. **Figure 4(a)** shows that the atmospheric pressure decreases rapidly as the altitude above sea level increases. Mountain climbers and aircraft designers are among the many people who need to know the effects of low atmospheric pressure at high altitudes. **Figure 4(b)** shows a way of representing horizontal pressure gradients using lines of constant pressure. The gradient is greatest where the lines are closest together. These types of lines are used on weather maps to designate high- and low-pressure areas and to predict strengths and directions of winds.

Notice in **Figure 4** that atmospheric pressure is stated in kilopascals (kPa). Since kilo means 1000, 1 kPa = 1000 Pa. Thus, a pressure of 100 kPa is the same as 100 000 Pa. To get an idea of how much pressure this is, imagine an average-size student wearing flat shoes and standing on one foot. The pressure of the shoe on the floor would be about 100 kPa. Now imagine the same student holding a 1 kg bag of sugar; the pressure of the shoe on the floor would increase to about 102 kPa.

The most common instrument used to measure atmospheric pressure is the aneroid barometer. (The word "aneroid" means "without liquid.") As shown in **Figure 5**, this instrument consists of an enclosed container with thin metal walls that are sensitive to pressure changes. A needle attached to the container indicates the pressure.

Figure 4

At ground level, the average atmospheric pressure is approximately 100 kPa. The pressure decreases at higher altitudes. Pressure varies from the average of each altitude.

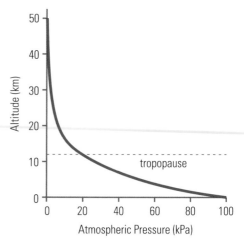

(a) Vertical pressure gradients

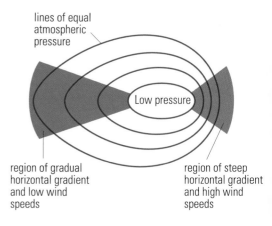

(b) Horizontal pressure gradients

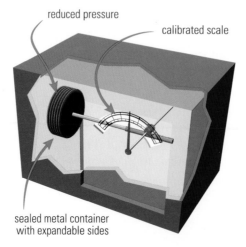

reduced pressure

calibrated scale

sealed metal container with expandable sides

Figure 5

The design of an aneroid barometer: as air pressure drops, the container expands, moving the bar attached to the needle. Some barometers indicate the atmospheric pressure on a scale; others simply indicate the type of weather to expect as the atmospheric pressure changes.

Exploring the Atmosphere

Scientists use various methods to study the atmosphere. To observe features high in the atmosphere, say up to 30 km, they launch balloons that carry a radiosonde, an instrument with electronic sensors that measure temperature, atmospheric pressure, and water vapour (**Figure 6**). Data are sent back to ground stations using radio signals. The balloons are also tracked by ground-based radar systems to measure wind speed and direction. Other methods are described in Chapter 14.

Figure 6

Weather balloons are launched regularly from many locations to keep track fo the changing conditions in the atmosphere. This one is being launched from a Canadian weather station.

Challenge

3 Atmospheric pressure is not stated in kilopascals in some countries, such as the United States. What other units are used? How can you convert them to kilopascals?

Understanding Concepts

1. Using dots to represent molecules of nitrogen, oxygen, and other components of the atmosphere, draw a diagram to show how the spacing between the molecules changes as altitude in the troposphere increases.

2. Explain why the altitude of the tropopause is lower above the poles than above the equator.

3. Which atmospheric layer do you expect you must learn more about before you understand weather systems. Why?

4. Using the temperature gradient of the troposphere, estimate the temperature of the air outside an airplane flying at an altitude of 10 km when the air temperature at ground level is

   (a) 20°C;

   (b) 0°C.

5. Explain why the temperature of the stratosphere is higher than the temperature of the tropopause.

6. Explain why atmospheric pressure is lower at the top of a mountain than in the valley below.

7. Suppose that today's weather map shows lines indicating equal pressure 5 mm apart in eastern Manitoba and 8 mm apart in western Manitoba. Explain which area has the higher pressure gradient.

8. Convert:

   (a) 101.3 kPa to pascals;

   (b) 99 900 Pa to kilopascals;

   (c) a change of atmospheric pressure of 0.3 kPa to pascals.

9. Which type of pressure gradient influences

   (a) convection of atmospheric gases?

   (b) advection of atmospheric gases?

Exploring

10. Research the use of an altimeter. Orally describe what you ⓘ discover to the class.

11. Research the causes and effects of altitude sickness, and then answer the following: if you were climbing a high mountain, such as Mount Everest, what could you do to reduce the effects of altitude sickness?

12. Some early balloonists risked their lives to find out more about the atmosphere. Pick two (e.g., James Glaisher and Robert Coxwell from England; Marie Elizabeth Thible and Teisserenc de Bort from France), and research their exploits. Create a poster with their pictures, if possible, and brief biographies.

Pressure of the Atmosphere

Why do your ears "pop" when you are riding in an elevator of a high-rise building or in an airplane that ascends or descends rapidly? They "pop" because of unequal pressure on the inside and outside of your eardrums. You can adjust the pressure by moving your jaw to open a passage that runs from your throat to inside your eardrum. Besides popping ears, many examples show that the atmosphere exerts a pressure. You will discover several such examples in this activity.

Question

What evidence do we have that the atmosphere exerts pressure?

Design

This is an exploratory investigation of air pressure.

(a) Create a table to record observations for the
(K7) procedure steps your class will do.

Materials

- apron
- safety goggles

(b) Refer to the procedure to identify and list the other materials and apparatus required to perform the steps.

Procedure

1 Determine how to get the maximum amount of water in an eyedropper or turkey baster (**Figure 1**).

Figure 1
Using an eyedropper

2 Determine how to obtain a strong suction when placing a suction cup on a vertical surface (**Figure 2**). Try a variety of surfaces, and determine whether the suction is stronger or weaker when the cup is moistened.

Figure 2
Using a suction cup

3 Find out which drinking straw works better: one with a hole in the side or one without (**Figure 3**).

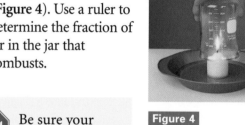

Figure 3
Drinking from a straw

Teacher Demonstration

4 Have your teacher place a short, wide candle on the bottom of a flat pan and add water to a depth of about 5 mm to the pan. The teacher will light the candle and place a glass jar over the candle (**Figure 4**). Use a ruler to determine the fraction of air in the jar that combusts.

Figure 4
Consuming part of the atmosphere

 Be sure your hand does not come into contact with the flame. Have a fire blanket and fire extinguisher nearby.

Teacher Demonstration

5 Have your teacher blow up a balloon a small amount, tie it, then place it in a vacuum jar and reduce the pressure in the jar (**Figure 5**).

Figure 5
Balloon in a partial vacuum

SKILLS HANDBOOK (K7) Preparing Talks of Evidence

Teacher Demonstration

6 Have your teacher add water to a depth of about 1 cm to an aluminum container and bring the water to boil (**Figure 6**). Using insulating mitts, your teacher will remove the can from the source of heat and screw the cap tightly onto the can. Observe what happens.

Figure 6
Steam in a sealed can

Teacher Demonstration

7 Have your teacher place a small amount of room-temperature water in an evaporating dish, then place the dish into a vacuum jar. Observe what happens as the air is removed from the jar (**Figure 7**).

 If boiling occurs, stop the demonstration.

Figure 7
Low-pressure boiling: to prevent moisture from getting into the vacuum pump, place a water-absorbing desiccant cartridge in the jar.

8 Fill a flask with water, then invert it and submerge it in a container of water. Cover the mouth of the flask with a piece of cardboard, and, while holding the cardboard tightly in place, remove the flask and hold it inverted above the tank (**Figure 8**).

Figure 8
Cardboard lid

9 Completely fill two flasks with water. Determine how the rate of emptying each flask depends on the size of the opening and the way in which the water drains out.

Analysis

(c) In steps 1 to 7, you observed effects that occur when atmospheric pressure is reduced. Using diagrams, explain what happened in each case by referring to the pressure exerted by the atmosphere.

(d) Explain what you observed in steps 8 and 9 in terms of atmospheric pressure.

(e) What is the answer to the Question?

(f) Communicate the main conclusions of this

ⓠ activity in a report.

Understanding Concepts

1. As you are ascending quickly in an elevator or in an airplane, would your eardrums tend to pop outward or inward? Why?

2. Vegetables take longer to cook at the top of a mountain than at sea level. Explain why by referring to boiling point.

3. Apply what you have learned in this activity to explain how a vacuum cleaner works.

4. Astronauts on the *International Space Station* float in space along with their drinks. They are above the atmosphere, and yet they can still use a straw. Explain how.

Exploring

5. Draw a diagram to show how the operation of a water pump relates to atmospheric pressure.

6. Describe how you could reduce the extra discomfort of a head cold experenced when travelling by air.

7. Describe what you think would happen in an airplane at a high altitude if a window broke.

Did You Know?

The drinking straw was patented in 1888. Some people might have thought this invention too simple to bother obtaining a patent.

Prevailing Wind Patterns

Of the many features we call weather, winds are one of the most important. A wind is a movement of air in the atmosphere. Some winds are local or regional, which means they occur in fairly small areas. But major wind patterns cover much larger areas. Winds that affect large areas are called **prevailing winds**. Since they affect weather around the world, we study them first. Later in the unit, we will explore some local and regional winds.

The Coriolis Effect

Earth's rotation causes anything that moves long distances, such as prevailing winds, to appear to change direction. The apparent change of direction of a moving object in a rotating system is called the **Coriolis effect**, after Gaspard de Coriolis, the French mathematician who first analyzed it.

To understand why the Coriolis effect causes a moving object to appear to change direction, imagine trying to slide a puck on a frictionless, rotating platform (**Figure 1**). In diagram (**a**), you are at position A, and the platform is not rotating. You slide the puck toward your friend at B. The puck slides in a straight line and your friend stops it. In diagram (**b**), the platform is rotating counterclockwise, and the point of view is from above the platform. Again you slide the puck toward your friend at B. This time, however, your friend misses the puck because the platform has rotated. Diagram (**c**) shows the same situation as in (**b**), this time from the point of view of A. Now the puck appears to curve toward the right, and of course your friend misses the puck. The puck actually travelled in a straight line; it just appeared to veer, or twist, to the right.

The situation in **Figure 1**(c) resembles what happens in the Northern Hemisphere. When viewed from a point above the North Pole, Earth rotates eastward, or counterclockwise. Thus, objects or particles in motion in the Northern Hemisphere appear to move toward the right. In the Southern Hemisphere, moving objects appear to move toward the left. Although Earth is still rotating eastward, viewed from a point above the South Pole the rotation is clockwise. The Coriolis effect is noticed least at the equator and most near the poles.

Observed Wind Patterns

When Christopher Columbus sailed from Europe across the Atlantic Ocean to North America in 1492, he took advantage of two important prevailing winds: the northeast trade winds to go westward and the mid-latitude westerlies to sail back to Europe. These prevailing winds, and several others, are shown in **Figure 2**.

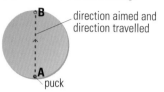

(a) The platform is not rotating.

direction aimed and direction travelled

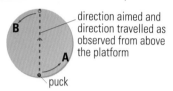

(b) View from above as the platform rotates

direction aimed and direction travelled as observed from above the platform

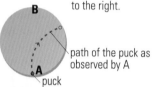

(c) From A's point of view, B is still on the opposite side, but the puck twists to the right.

path of the puck as observed by A

Figure 1

Sliding a puck on a platform illustrates the Coriolis effect.

→ Between 60° latitude and the poles, surface winds tend to flow from east to west. These are called the polar easterlies.

→ Between 30° and 60° latitude, surface winds tend to flow from west to east. These are called the mid-latitude westerlies.

→ Suface winds near the equator (0° latitude) tend to flow from east to west. North of the equator, these winds are called the northeast trade winds, and south of the equator, they are called the southeast trade winds.

→ **Jet streams** are high-speed winds in the upper regions of the troposphere, often around the mid-latitudes. They tend to move from west to east and steer most of the major weather systems, such as low-pressure and high-pressure systems.

Figure 2

This map shows the major large-scale prevailing winds. Study the map carefully to discover several important patterns that will help you understand properties of these winds.

Try This
Activity Twisting Winds

This activity will help you visualize why winds twist to the right in the Northern Hemisphere and to the left in the Southern Hemisphere.

Materials: Bristol board, a compass, scissors, a metre stick, a pencil, a pointer, a small stack of large-size paper

✋ Handle the compass and scissors with care.

- Use the compass to draw a circle (with a diameter of 30 cm to 40 cm) on the Bristol board. Cut out the circle and label the centre "North Pole" and the outside edge the "equator." Also draw a counterclockwise arrow near the equator and label it "direction of Earth's rotation."
- Place Earth flat on the small stack of extra paper, and poke the pointer through the Bristol board at the North Pole. Position the metre stick next to the pointer so that the metre stick divides Earth in two.

- While a student slowly but steadily rotates Earth counterclockwise, have another student draw a line along the metre stick at a constant speed from the equator toward the North Pole, then from the North Pole to the equator (**Figure 3**). Use an arrow to label the direction of the line.

(a) Does the line twist to the left or right?

- Repeat the process for the Southern Hemisphere using the reverse side of the Bristol board, but this time rotate Earth clockwise.

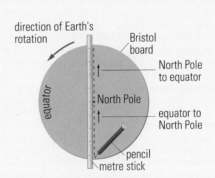

Figure 3
In this model, the moving pencil represents the wind moving first northward from the equator to the North Pole, then southward from the North Pole to the equator.

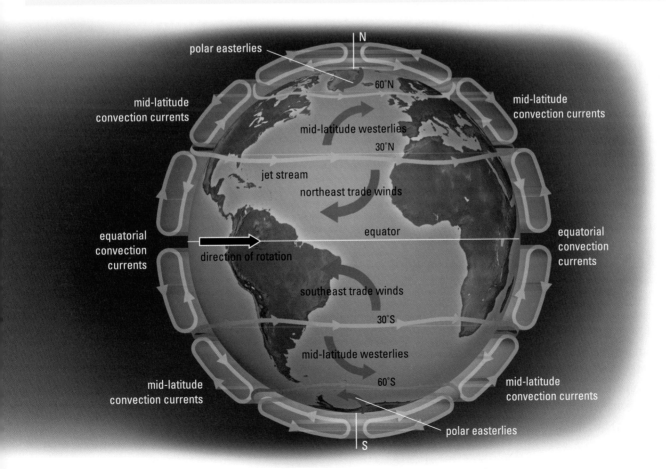

Causes of Prevailing Winds

Prevailing winds are caused by a combination of convection currents and Earth's eastward rotation. The explanations given here focus on the Northern Hemisphere.

Solar energy strikes most directly near the equator, heating the air, the land, and the water. The warmed air begins to form a convection current, called the *equatorial convection current* (**Figure 2**). The warm air rises and expands, leaving behind an area of lower pressure. When the rising air reaches the tropopause, it moves northward. Around 30° latitude, it has become colder and more dense, so it sinks down toward Earth's surface, creating an area of high pressure there. Air at the surface moves away from this area of high pressure toward the low-pressure area at the equator. This moving surface air twists to the right as it moves south, causing the northeast trade winds.

At 30° latitude, some of the descending air from the equatorial convection current is deflected northward, away from the high-pressure area toward an area of low pressure around 60° latitude. This low-pressure area is formed by another convection current, the *mid-latitude convection current*, as it begins rising where its warm air meets cold polar air. The surface air moving north toward the area of low pressure becomes part of this convection current. The air twists to the right as it flows northward, causing the mid-latitude westerlies.

Near the North Pole, the air is cold and dense, so it sinks, creating a high-pressure area at the surface. The surface air moves southward, away from this high-pressure area. At the same time, it twists to the right, causing the polar easterlies.

When the polar air reaches a latitude of about 60° it meets the rising warmer air from the mid-latitude convection currents. As the rising air nears the tropopause, its motion completes the convection currents shown in **Figure 2**, with some air moving toward the equator and the rest toward the North Pole.

To understand how the jet streams form, consider the atmospheric pressure at an altitude of 7000 m. At this altitude above the equator, there is still 7000 m of troposphere on top because warm air rises high. At an altitude of 7000 m above the 30° north latitude, there may be only 5000 m of troposphere above, which means that the pressure here is lower than at the same altitude above the equator. Since air moves from higher pressure to lower pressure, air at the 7000 m altitude at the equator moves northward while twisting to the right. This results in a high-altitude, eastward-flowing wind, the jet stream, around 30° latitude. A second jet stream may occur near 60° north latitude where, at 7000 m, the pressure is even lower than at 30° north latitude. (Farther north the temperature is lower, so the air at 30° latitude, while cool, is warmer than the air at 60° latitude.) The same thing can happen: the air moves from higher pressure to lower pressure, sometimes forming another jet stream. **Figure 4** shows formation of the jet streams.

Figure 4

In the Northern Hemisphere, jet streams form in the upper troposphere when air moves from high-pressure areas toward low-pressure areas while at the same time twisting to the right.

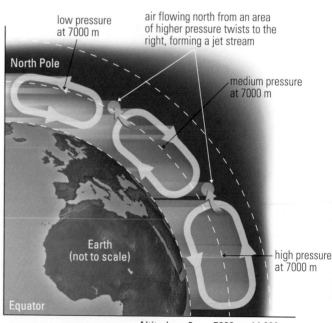

low pressure at 7000 m

air flowing north from an area of higher pressure twists to the right, forming a jet stream

North Pole

medium pressure at 7000 m

Earth (not to scale)

high pressure at 7000 m

Equator

Altitude   0   7000 m   14 000 m

Prevailing winds, including the jet streams, are affected by the changing seasons. For one thing, they change latitudes. A simple way to remember this is the saying, "winds follow the Sun." For example, in the Northern Hemisphere, the northeast trade winds move southward, closer to the equator, as the Sun's direct rays hit south of the equator during winter.

Effects of Prevailing Winds

Prevailing winds help to distribute large amounts of solar energy from the equator to the colder parts of the world. Because convection currents are involved in many of these winds, there is also a return flow of colder air southward. The prevailing winds also carry moisture, helping to cause a variety of precipitation such as snow and rain. To understand the effects of winds, you must remember that rising air tends to be warm and moist, while falling air tends to be cool and dry. Let us look at several effects of winds in the Northern Hemisphere.

Near the equator, wherever the two sets of equatorial convection currents (one in the Northern Hemisphere and one in the Southern) meet and rise, weather tends to be cloudy and rainy. At about 30° north latitude, the cool, falling air is dry, creating desert-like conditions. If you look at a globe or map of the world, you will find large deserts near this latitude, for example, the Gobi Desert in Asia, the Sahara Desert in Africa, and the Mojave, Great Basin, and Sonoran Deserts in North America.

At about 60° north latitude, two air systems meet and rise, creating unsettled conditions of cloud and precipitation. Winds and storms are stronger in winter because the Arctic region receives no sunlight, so it gets cold rapidly. This produces a larger temperature difference between the polar regions and the equator, which causes greater pressure differences and stronger winds.

Jet stream winds have an important influence on weather systems, as you will learn in the next chapter.

🖐 Work the Web

The katabatic wind in Antarctica is the most powerful wind in the world. Visit www.science.nelson.com and follow the Science 10, 13.6 links to find out more about katabatic and anabatic winds. Sketch the flow of air in katabatic and anabatic winds.

Understanding Concepts

1. In the Northern Hemisphere
   (a) in what general direction does energy flow?
   (b) in what general direction does warm air flow?
   (c) toward which side do winds tend to twist?

2. Using **Figure 4** as a reference, explain the cause of each of the following in the Southern Hemisphere:
   (a) the southeast trade winds;
   (b) the mid-latitude westerlies;
   (c) the polar easterlies;
   (d) the jet stream(s).

3. (a) Along which latitude in the Southern Hemisphere are deserts likely to be found? Explain why this happens.
   (b) Refer to a globe or world map to find the names of three or four Southern Hemisphere deserts.

Making Connections

4. If you were a pilot flying from Tokyo, Japan, to Vancouver, B.C., what would you do to minimize the time required to complete the flight? Why?

Exploring

5. Find a reference that shows the routes across the Atlantic Ocean taken by Columbus in 1492. Explain how the routes he took relate to the prevailing winds. Ⓘ

6. Research more about jet streams to find out when and how they were discovered. Report briefly on what you discover to the class. Ⓙ

7. Have you ever felt you were "in the doldrums"? Look up doldrums in the dictionary, then explain how the psychological meaning relates to the geographical meaning.

 Challenge

1 How could you measure wind speed and direction?
2 How will you design your community to counteract potential wind hazards? How could you reduce turbulence around buildings and the effects of blowing snow?
3 Which prevailing wind or winds do you think would be worthwhile to include in your network data?

The First Round-the-World Balloon Flight

Humans have often tested the limits of their endurance. From the first person to travel to the North Pole, to the first person to climb the world's highest mountain, Mount Everest, to the first person to step onto the Moon's surface, explorers have wanted to accomplish what had previously seemed impossible.

For thousands of years, humans have also learned how to take advantage of winds. Sailors used prevailing and local winds to sail to many places around the world. People in countries such as the Netherlands used windmills to grind grain and pump water. In many countries, including Canada, wind power is used to generate electricity, especially in remote, windy areas.

In March 1999, the spirit of exploration joined with knowledge of prevailing winds to allow two balloonists, Bertrand Piccard from Switzerland and Brian Jones from the United Kingdom, to become the first people to pilot a balloon nonstop around the world (**Figure 1**). This amazing feat, covering over 45 000 km in only 20 days, would not have been possible without the jet streams.

(a) List several "firsts" that human explorers have accomplished besides the examples described here.

(b) People have been travelling by balloon for centuries, but a nonstop trip around the world was impossible until recently. Suggest some reasons why.

The Flight of Orbiter 3

Pilots Piccard and Jones admit that the only way they could circle the world in a balloon was to harmonize with nature. They had to manoeuvre their balloon into the jet stream, which, as you have learned, is stronger and closer to the equator in winter. They chose March 1, 1999, to begin their flight from a village in the Swiss Alps.

Figure 1

The *Breitling Orbiter 3* is the technologically sophisticated balloon used by Piccard and Jones. Onboard the 55-m-tall balloon were 32 propane fuel tanks, a pressurized cabin, oxygen tanks, a kitchen with food supplies for 4 weeks, a computer linked by satellite to ground control, and solar panels.

Figure 2

The path of Orbiter 3's historic voyage

The balloon drifted southwest from Switzerland for three days, then finally, at an altitude of about 7000 m, it caught the jet stream above Africa. As shown in **Figure 2**, the balloon moved quickly and steadily across Africa and Asia, but ran into difficulties over the huge Pacific Ocean. The ground crew advised the pilots to give up the northern jet stream and drift southward to pick up one that was forming near the equator. After several days of slow travelling, the pilots took the balloon to 10 000 m and caught a powerful jet stream that sped them to Mexico at about 185 km/h.

More problems occurred when the balloon disengaged from the jet stream and floated toward South America. Finally, after climbing to over 10 000 m, the balloon caught a jet stream that took it swiftly across the Atlantic Ocean.

(c) Explain the importance of jet streams to the flight of Orbiter 3.

(d) If you were planning a round-the-world balloon trip leaving from Australia, what starting date would you choose? Why?

The Technology of Ballooning

Without modern technology, achieving the round-the-world flight would not have been possible. The skin of the *Breitling Orbiter 3* was made of an ultra-light synthetic material called Mylar. Special materials were used to make shields to protect the pilots from the extreme heat of the burners. Flotation devices were designed for the flight cabin (called the capsule) in case the balloon fell into water. The pilots communicated with ground control using a computer that received and sent messages through satellite communication systems. The ground control team analyzed weather data from around the world to predict the location and speed of the jet stream nearest the chosen path.

Other high-tech features of the balloon included the air-recycling system aboard the enclosed capsule. This system used special filters to remove excess carbon dioxide and add much-needed oxygen to the air in the cabin. Also, solar panels hanging from the balloon were used to operate electrical equipment including the food warmer.

Understanding Concepts

1. What is the purpose of the fuel carried aboard a balloon such as the Orbiter 3?

2. Explain how a pilot can control the altitude of a balloon.

Making Connections

3. Research and report on the extent and importance of the generation of electricity using wind power in:
   (a) Canada
   (b) other parts of the world

Exploring

4. Read the story of the *Breitling Orbiter 3* flight in the September 1999 issue of *National Geographic* magazine. Choose the most exciting part of the trip and describe in a paragraph why you find it interesting.

5. Research some of the major sailing competitions in the world. Choose one competition, and explain why its location and calendar dates are important.

Despite the sophisticated technology aboard, simple manual dexterity proved to be invaluable when ice that had formed on the fuel valves had to be carefully chipped away by hand.

(e) State three important examples of modern technology that helped make this balloon flight successful.

(f) The pilots allowed the balloon to drop below the 4000 m altitude to melt unwanted ice, change direction, or depressurize the cabin to perform outside chores. Why was a lower elevation chosen for these tasks?

(g) A technical problem on the flight occurred when the balloon itself prevented satellite signals from reaching the communications receiver on the capsule. What design change would prevent this problem?

The Hydrosphere

As the glacier in **Figure 1** slowly melts each summer, the released water joins water from melting snow to form freshwater streams, rivers, and lakes. But snow, ice, water in rivers and lakes, and water vapour in the atmosphere make up only a small portion of all the water on Earth. Most of the water is found in oceans where the water is salty so we can't drink it. All of Earth's water, both fresh and salt, forms what is called the **hydrosphere**. The map in **Figure 2** shows that the vast majority of Earth's surface is covered with water and ice.

Figure 1
This glacier in the Rocky Mountains was formed by layers of snow pressing down on previous layers.

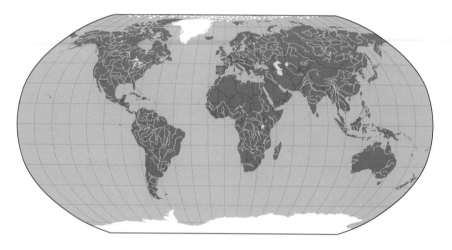

Figure 2
Approximately 70% of Earth's surface is covered with water; this includes salt and fresh water as well as ice.

Did You Know?

The Pacific Ocean is the largest ocean, comprising 46% of the total area of all oceans. The Arctic Ocean is the smallest, covering 2.6% of the total. The Pacific Ocean is also the world's deepest: one location has a depth of about 11 km, greater than Mount Everest.

Water Distribution in the Hydrosphere

The pie graphs in **Figure 3** show that only a very small portion of the hydrosphere consists of fresh water. Furthermore, most of this fresh water is frozen in glaciers and in the ice caps around the North and South Poles. In fact, if we represented all the water in the world by one litre of water, then all the fresh, unfrozen water in the atmosphere, lakes, and rivers would be less than one drop!

With its vast freshwater supplies, Canada is one of the luckiest countries in the world. Our population is just 0.5% of the world total, yet we have almost 10% of the world's supply of fresh water.

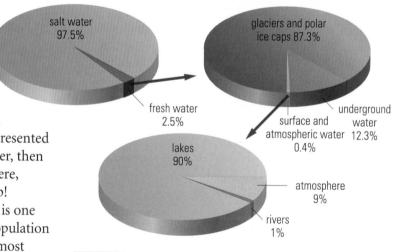

Figure 3
Earth's water resources

The Water Cycle

Because so much of Earth's surface is covered by water, our weather systems depend greatly on water in its three states: solid, liquid, and gas or vapour. **Figure 4** shows the water cycle. Energy, mostly from the Sun, causes water to evaporate (change from liquid to vapour) or ice to sublimate (change directly from solid to vapour). The invisible water vapour rises, and eventually, as the pressure and temperature decrease, this vapour condenses (changes from vapour to liquid) into fog, mist, and clouds. In some cases, the water vapour may form ice crystals in the reverse process of sublimation (also called deposition). The resulting precipitation falls to the ground, and the cycle starts again.

As you study the causes of weather patterns in this unit, think about how much evaporation or sublimation occurs in the various parts of the world.

The Hydrosphere and Human Habitat

Fresh water is vital for human survival. In the past, people lived near sources of fresh water, especially rivers and lakes. Today, a large portion of the world's population still lives near water, both fresh water and the oceans (**Figure 5**). Thus, weather systems on and near large bodies of water greatly affect large numbers of people. And in the future, these effects will be even more far reaching as the population increases.

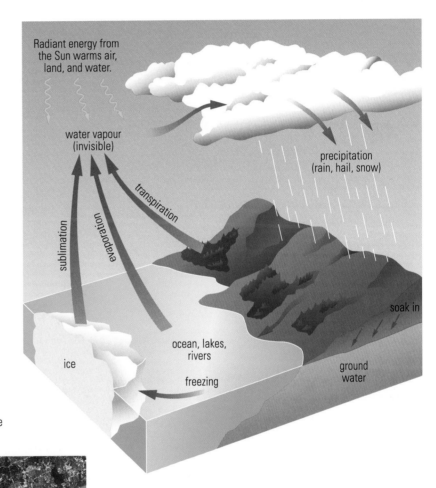

Figure 4

The water cycle

Figure 5

We need water to drink; we also use it as a source of food and for transportation. Shorelines all around the world are becoming crowded with people.

Try This Activity — Evaporating Salt Water

When salt water evaporates, does the vapour carry the salt with it?

Materials: apron, an evaporating dish or saucer, table salt, distilled water, a balance, a stirring rod

- Add a small amount of table salt to a dry evaporating dish or saucer, and use a balance to measure the combined mass of the dish and salt.

- Add water to the dish and stir the mixture until the salt is completely dissolved.
- Place the dish in a safe place and allow the water to evaporate completely. (This may take several days.) Record the time.
- Measure the mass of the dish.
- Wash your hands.

(a) How much salt was carried off in water vapour?

Understanding Concepts

1. In your own words, write a definition of the term "hydrosphere."

2. Explain why fresh water is more important to human life than salt water.

3. In a paragraph, explain why it is important to learn about salt water in order to understand weather.

4. A glacier may be thousands of years old, yet it is considered to be "fresh" water. Explain why.

5. Use the information in **Figure 3** to determine the percentage of Earth's hydrosphere that is found in

(a) underground water;

(b) freshwater lakes;

(c) the atmosphere.

Making Connections

6. The following famous lines are from the poem *The Rime of the Ancient Mariner*, by Samuel Taylor Coleridge:
Water, water, every where,
And all the boards did shrink;
Water, water, every where,
Nor any drop to drink.

In two or three sentences explain what these words mean.

7. As the world's freshwater supply becomes increasingly limited, people in some countries suggest more schemes to obtain water. One suggestion is to tow icebergs from the North Atlantic Ocean, near Greenland, through the Mediterranean Sea, to the Middle East. Speculate about some advantages and disadvantages of such a scheme.

8. The amount of fresh water available in the world through the water cycle is about 2×10^{16} L per year.

(a) Calculate approximately how much water this is for each person on the planet. (The world's population is estimated to be 6 billion.)

(b) If Canada has about 10% of the total amount of fresh water, repeat (a) for our population.

(c) What do you conclude about the availability of water to Canadians?

9. Bottled mineral water is becoming increasingly popular in Canada. Research and report on the supply and demand of this type of water, both in Canada and countries such as France, which have longer traditions of using bottled water.

Exploring

10. An aquifer is an underground body of water. The Ogallala Aquifer is the largest aquifer in the world. Research this aquifer and describe in a poster how it is used, how long it may last, and other pertinent facts.

11. The Gisborne Lake project proposed the bulk export of fresh water from a lake in southern Newfoundland. However, legislation was introduced to stop it. Research this project and write a brief report that describes what happened. Include your position on the issue.

 Challenge

1 How would you ensure that your weather forecasts are appropriate for people with a variety of interests or careers, such as people who fish, farm, grow fruit trees, play soccer, wash high-rise office windows, etc.?

2 What factors related to water are important for you to consider in your community design?

3 Find out where members of your network live. For example, do they live near a large body of water, on the top of a hill, in the centre of a large city?

SKILLS HANDBOOK: Ⓘ Ⓙ Research Skills

Major Ocean Currents

As you have seen, oceans are particularly important in weather dynamics. One reason is that they occupy so much of Earth's surface. To find another reason, look at a world map: there is little land mass at the equator, but if you circle the globe at, say, 45° north, there is considerable land mass. So there is a vast volume of water at the equator, where the radiation from the Sun is direct. One way in which all this direct energy absorbed by the oceans is spread around the world is by ocean currents.

You might expect countries such as Norway and Iceland, which are as far north as Canada's Arctic region, to have very cold winters. However, their Atlantic harbours remain ice-free all winter because of the Gulf Stream, an Atlantic Ocean current that transports warm water all the way from the Gulf of Mexico, near the equator, to the North Atlantic region. **Figure 1** shows the Gulf Stream and several other major ocean currents in the world. The warm ocean currents act like "conveyer belts," transporting energy (stored in the water) from warmer parts of the world to colder parts. The cold ocean currents from the North Atlantic and Pacific Oceans and the Antarctic circumpolar current flow toward the equator. These cold waters become warmer as they circulate through the equatorial regions of the world's oceans.

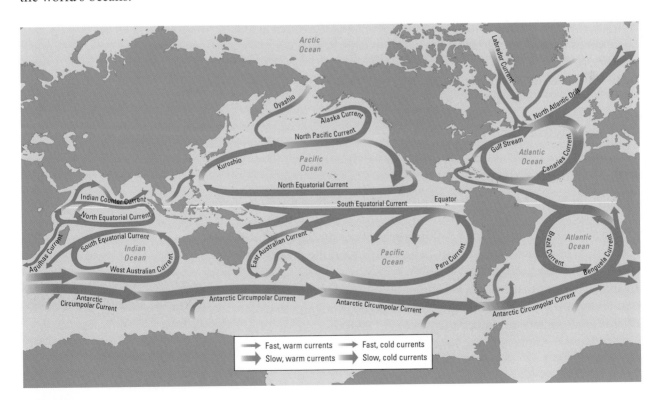

Figure 1

The major warm and cold ocean currents in the world. Compare the directions of the ocean currents with the directions of the major winds in Figure 2 in Section 13.6.

Causes of Ocean Currents

As you study the map of ocean currents in **Figure 1**, you will begin to notice certain patterns. Each of these patterns can be explained by considering convection currents, winds across the oceans, the influence of Earth's rotation, the shapes of the continents, the heat capacity of water, and the amount of salt in the oceans.

Warm water tends to travel from the equator toward the North or South Pole, and cold water tends to travel in the opposite direction. Solar energy strikes the oceans at the equator directly and therefore more intensely, heating the water and starting convection currents. As the warm, less dense water moves away from the equator, it is replaced by cooler, denser water, as shown in **Figure 2**. The convection currents are also influenced by the prevailing winds blowing at the surface and the twisting caused by the Coriolis effect.

Close to a continent, ocean currents are forced to travel along its edge, just like water in a river changes direction if it hits a rock or steep shoreline. Because of Earth's eastward rotation, ocean currents on the west sides of the oceans tend to be narrow and fast moving, travelling at about 6.5 km/h. Currents on the east sides tend to be wider and slower, travelling at about 1.1 km/h. Only one ocean current, the Antarctic Circumpolar Current, travels all the way around the world, with no continents in the way.

The oceans act as huge heat sinks because water has a high capacity to store heat. As water absorbs solar energy, it takes a long time to heat up. However, once it is warm, the water takes a long time to cool down again. These properties have an important effect on both world climate and local weather.

The salt in the water also affects ocean currents. For example, as the warm Gulf Stream flows northward, water evaporates, leaving increasingly saltier water. The saltier water is more dense, so it sinks, creating deepwater currents, and is replaced by warm, less dense water.

Effects of Ocean Currents

The Gulf Stream warming the coasts of Norway and Iceland is just one example of the effect of ocean currents. You will understand all the ocean current effects if you recognize the relationship between air temperature and its ability to hold moisture: the warmer a body of air, the greater its ability to hold moisture.

The ocean current that reaches Peru in western South America is cold, so the air above it is dry. Therefore, the coast of Peru is cool and dry, which helps to create a desert called the Atacama Desert beside the Pacific Ocean. (You have already seen how winds help create the dry conditions.) According to **Figure 1**, in what other coastal regions in the world could cold ocean currents help produce similar dry effects?

Along the western side of the huge Pacific Ocean, the warm waters evaporate, form clouds, and produce large quantities of precipitation. Which current causes a similar effect in Brazil, which has a large portion of Earth's rain forests?

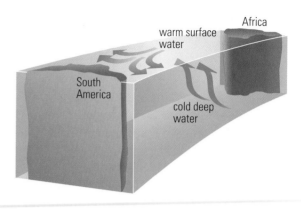

Figure 2

Ocean water near the equator absorbs the direct, intense solar energy. Since warm water is less dense than cold water, the warm water moves northward or southward at the surface, and is replaced by cold water from below, starting a convection current.

Did You Know?

Currents that go through narrow channels travel much faster than other currents. The strongest currents in the world are the Nakwakto Rapids, Slingsby Channel, British Columbia, where the current can flow as fast as 30 km/h.

Ocean currents are responsible for coastal regions being cooler in summer and warmer in winter than regions several kilometres inland. Large bodies of water and their currents moderate the climate. For example, the average early-morning January temperature in Ottawa, Ontario, is 30°C lower than the average early-morning July temperature. But in St. John's, on the east coast of Newfoundland, that difference is only 18°C. And Ottawa is farther south than St. John's! Newfoundland is warmer in winter because of the warm, moist air brought northward by the Gulf Stream.

The high heat capacity of water is one factor that causes seasonal changes to lag behind the daylight hour changes; that is, in the Northern Hemisphere the most daylight hours occur on June 21, yet the hottest months are June, July, and August rather than May, June, and July. This occurs partly because water takes a long time to warm up after the winter. Another factor that contributes to this lag is the flow of energy: in July the energy input in the Northern Hemisphere is greater than the energy output.

A similar lag occurs in winter when the fewest daylight hours occur on December 21, yet the coldest months are December, January, and February, rather than November, December, and January.

Ocean currents also affect the pressure of the air above them. For example, air above warm ocean currents becomes warmer and less dense, forming low-pressure systems. You will learn later how these systems influence weather.

 Challenge

1 How could you use record low and high temperatures and other statistics for your region to make your forecasts more interesting?

2 Where will your imaginary community be located? For what conditions will it be designed?

Understanding Concepts

1. Use **Figure 1** as a reference to answer these questions:

   (a) In what way are the ocean currents in the Southern Hemisphere "mirror images" of those in the Northern Hemisphere?

   (b) Name three fast-moving surface currents and three slow-moving currents.

   (c) On which side of Australia (east or west) would you expect to find deserts? rain forests? Explain why. Use a map of Australia to check your answer.

   (d) In what other regions of the world would you expect to find deserts? Why?

2. The text states that ocean currents act as "conveyer belts" of energy. Explain what this means.

3. Explain why the name "Antarctic Circumpolar Current" is appropriate.

4. A student who lives on the south coast of New Zealand places a message in a bottle, seals the bottle, and throws it into the coastal waters. About four years later, another student finds the same bottle floating in the ocean on the coast of Iceland. Describe how this is possible. Include the names of the ocean currents as well as the continents that the bottle passed on its route to Iceland.

5. Why is it impossible to have an Arctic Circumpolar Current?

6. The Namib Desert is on the west coast of southern Africa. Explain how this region can be dry, even though it is on the Atlantic Ocean.

7. Explain why the coldest months of the year in the Northern Hemisphere are December, January, and February, even though the fewest daylight hours occur in December.

Making Connections

8. When big ships enter a harbour or channel that is unfamiliar to the captain, a local navigator comes onboard to help. What are some possible hazards the visiting captain may not know about?

Exploring

9. Research how "eddies" form when warm and cold ocean currents meet. Why do fishing fleets like to track these slow-moving locations?

10. In the 1947 *Kon-Tiki* Expedition, six adventurers sailed a raft across the Pacific Ocean. Report on how currents and winds helped the sailors on their journey. Do you think the expedition accomplished its objectives?

13.10 Explore an Issue

DECISION MAKING SKILLS
○ Define the Issue   ● Analyze the Issue
○ Identify Alternatives   ● Defend a Decision
● Research   ○ Evaluate

The Costs of Rescue Operations

On Saturday, December 26, 1998, 115 yachts sailed out of the calm harbour in Sydney, Australia, in the annual race to Hobart, Tasmania, a distance of about 1200 km. Although the sky was clear, weather forecasters warned that a severe storm was coming; 58 yachts quit the race before the storm hit. The remaining yachts sailed onward, and within a day the leading racers were trying to navigate the treacherous Bass Straight in a major storm with 150-km/h winds and 12-m waves. The wind and waves tossed the yachts around like toys.

By the time the race ended a few days later, six yachts were sunk or abandoned, six men had died, and 55 sailors, many with injuries, had been rescued by helicopters. The rescuers, facing gales and high waves, put their own lives at risk during the storm (**Figure 1**).

Figure 1
Using a helicopter to resue people from a tossing boat is risky, especially in high winds and waves. Such rescues are also expensive.

This is just one example of people trying to outrun the weather or tackle adventures that may be unsafe. If and when these people meet with disaster, who should pay the cost of the rescue operation? And who is responsible if the brave rescuers are injured or die while trying to save the lives of others?

Currently, government agencies usually conduct rescue operations at no cost to the people rescued. Some people would like to continue this practice, while others would like to require people involved in risky adventures to post a bond (put money in a special account) that could be drawn on in case of an emergency.

Understanding the Issue

1. In general, who pays for emergency rescue operations?
2. Name three other weather-related adventures, besides those described here, in which people put their lives at risk.

🖑 Work the Web

Follow the links for Science 10, 13.10 from www.science.nelson.com to research the rescue attempts made during the storm in this section. Try to find some newspaper articles that offer an opinion on the rescue attempts.

Take a Stand   Who Should Pay for Risky Rescues?

Proposition

People who try to outrun the weather or tackle adventures that are unsafe should be required to prepay the costs of potential rescue operations.

There are arguments for collecting a bond before a risky adventure begins:

- Emergency rescue crews are meant to help accident victims, not people who deliberately risk disaster.
- Rescue equipment and operations are expensive, and taxpayers shouldn't have to pay the entire bill.
- The bond would be refunded if a rescue was not needed.
- It's better to collect before an event; it would not be easy to ask a person lying in a hospital bed with numerous broken bones for some money.

There are also arguments against bond-posting:

- The average taxpayer enjoys watching the exploits of daring adventurers and doesn't mind paying for rescue operations when they are needed.
- Advertisers or sponsors who benefit from the mass media reporting of major events could pay for rescue operations in an emergency.
- People will always explore and test the limits of their skills, and we all benefit, even if indirectly, by their adventures.

Forming an Opinion

- Read the arguments described above and add your own ideas to those listed.
- (E) Find more information to help you understand the issue more clearly.
- (F) In a group, discuss the issue.
- (R)(S)(T) Create a "position paper" in which you state your opinion and present arguments based on those opinions. It can be in the form of a video, an audio presentation, a web page, a letter, an essay, or some other creative way of communicating. The position paper can be for a corporate sponsor of a major risky sporting event or a government agency responsible for rescue operations. Make it as persuasive as you can.

Clouds and Fog

Artists, photographers, and poets often share their love of clouds in their creative works. The clouds they see have a beauty that we have always appreciated (**Figure 1**).

But clouds are more than objects to appreciate and write about; they are obvious indicators of weather and weather systems. Learning about the characteristics of the various types of clouds will help you predict what kind of weather is approaching.

Energy in the Water Cycle

Water in lakes, rivers, oceans, and plants gains energy either from the Sun directly or from the surroundings. This energy causes the water molecules to move more rapidly and the water to change from a liquid to a vapour. The water vapour rises in the heated, less dense air. When it reaches higher elevations where the pressure is lower and the temperature is cooler, it changes into liquid water again, that is, it condenses. This is one way in which the droplets of a cloud begin to form. (At colder temperatures, ice crystals form. Details of this process will be presented later.)

Why doesn't rain or snow fall from all clouds? The reason is that most condensed droplets of water in a cloud are very small and are easily carried by air molecules. Only when thousands of these tiny droplets join together to form a raindrop is the force of gravity strong enough to pull the drop toward the ground. (See **Figure 2**.)

How Do Clouds Form?

Cloud formation can be classified into three main categories. As you read about these methods of cloud formation, think about which way is most common in the region where you live.

Convective clouds are produced when air near the ground absorbs energy from heated surfaces (oceans, lakes, asphalt, concrete, dirt), becomes warmer and less dense, and rises in the atmosphere. As the warm air rises, it carries water vapour with it. As the air parcel reaches a higher level where the pressure is lower, it expands and cools because the particles lose energy as they get farther apart. (Temperature is a measure of the average energy of the particles.) The water vapour in the parcel cools along with it, until the point that it condenses, forming clouds. This process occurs wherever solar energy is absorbed by water and other surfaces.

Figure 1
This sunset scene would not be as beautiful without the changing cloud formations.

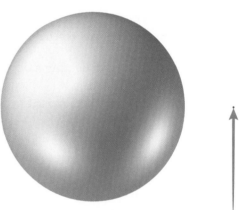

average raindrop
(magnified 25 times)

average cloud droplet
(magnified 25 times)

Figure 2
The average diameter of a cloud droplet is only about 0.02 mm. The average diameter of a raindrop is about 100 times larger, about 2 mm.

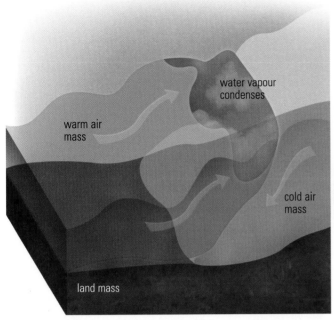

(a) A warm air mass and a cold air mass meet.

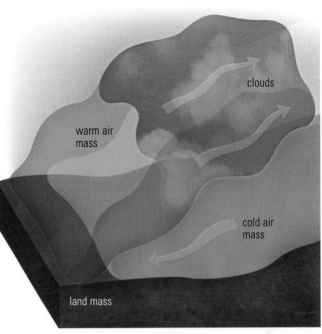

(b) The water vapour in the warm air mass condenses.

Frontal clouds form where the leading edge, or front, of a large moving mass of air meets another mass of air at a different temperature. (Fronts and air masses are discussed in more detail in Chapter 14.) Warm air masses are less dense than cold air masses and usually contain more water vapour. Thus, if a warm air mass moves over a cold one (**Figure 3**), or a cold air mass pushes under a warm air mass, the warm air rises, expands, and cools so that the moisture in it condenses to form clouds.

Orographic clouds form when air moves up a mountain, expands at the lower pressure, and cools. ("Oro" comes from the Greek word *oros*, which means mountain.) Moisture in this rising air condenses in the colder air as it goes up the mountain, producing clouds (**Figure 4**). Sometimes clouds form partway up the mountain, producing a shallow layer of cloud and leaving the peak in sunshine.

Figure 3
Clouds can form when the front of a warm air mass moves over a cool air mass.

Did You Know?

The number of water molecules in 1 L of liquid water is about 2 million times more than the number in 1 L of cloud.

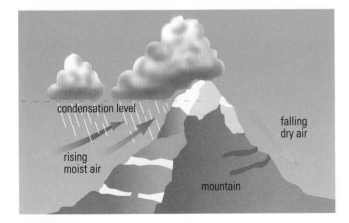

Figure 4
Air that is forced over mountains contains moisture that condenses into clouds at the higher altitudes. If rain or snow falls from the clouds over the mountains, the air falling down the far side of the mountain tends to be dry.

Try This
Activity Cloud in a Jar

Try this activity to see clouds forming in a jar.

Materials: apron, a jar with a metal lid (such as a pickle jar), hot water, ice cubes

- Pour hot water into the jar to a depth of about 1 cm.
- Put the metal lid on the jar and place the ice cubes on the top of the lid.

(a) Describe what you observe and explain why it happens.

Handle hot water with care.

Fog

Fog is actually a cloud that forms near the ground. The most common form of fog is produced on clear nights when energy from the surface radiates upward but is not reflected back to Earth by any clouds. Thus, the air near the ground cools, allowing water vapour to condense into fog.

Fog can form at other times too. When warm air passes over snow-covered ground, fog can form, and when moist sea air drifts over a cold current or a seashore, fog forms. This occurs frequently in coastal regions (**Figure 5**). Fog also forms when moist air rises up the sides of mountains during orographic lifting.

Fog has caused numerous deadly mishaps on highways and airport runways. Airline flights are usually cancelled during extremely dense fog.

Classifying Clouds

Classification systems usually begin with general terms. For example, memory systems for personal computers can be classified as hard drives or floppy disks. Similarly, cloud classification begins with two general shapes of clouds, illustrated in **Figure 6**. **Cumulus clouds** have a billowing, rounded shape. (Cumulus comes from a word meaning "heap.") These clouds, which tend to grow vertically, usually indicate unstable weather. They usually form as a result of convection currents, orographic lifting, or when a cold air front pushes into a warm air mass. **Stratus clouds** have a flattened, layered shape. (Stratus comes from a word meaning "spread out.") Stratus clouds, which tend to grow horizontally, indicate stable conditions. They usually form where the front of a warm air mass overruns a cold air mass.

To further classify clouds, they are given names according to their altitude in the atmosphere. Low-level clouds have the simple names, cumulus and stratus. Medium-level clouds start with the prefix *alto*, which means higher. High-level clouds are called *cirrus*, a word that means curly lock of hair.

One more cloud subclassification, the word *nimbus*, indicates a rain-holding cloud. **Figure 7** shows the specific names and locations of 10 types of clouds. Which types have you seen?

Figure 5

The depth of fog can be from 1 m to 300 m. The Avalon Peninsula in Newfoundland is Canada's foggiest location, with fog nearly 30% of the time.

Figure 6

(a) A typical cumulus cloud

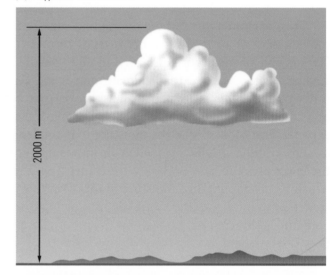

2000 m

(b) A typical stratus cloud

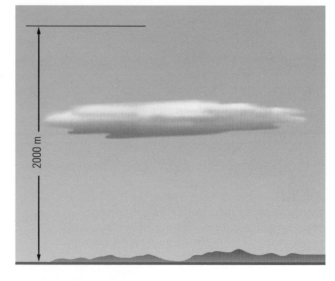

2000 m

Figure 7

The names and approximate altitudes of the 10 main classifications of clouds

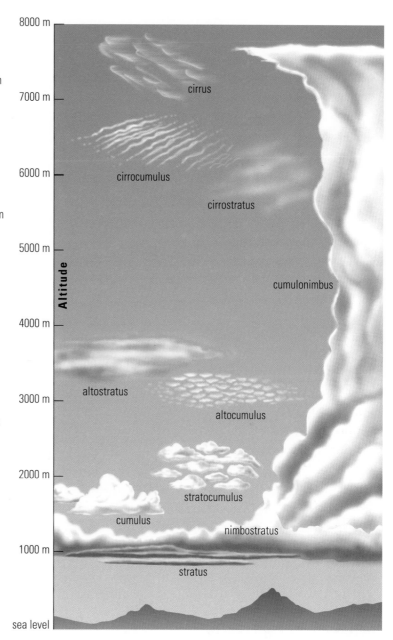

Cirrus (thin, wispy clouds made of ice crystals) below 8000 m

Cirrocumulus (thin, patchy clouds that form wavy patterns) 6000 to 8000 m

Cirrostratus (thin, veiled clouds that produce the halos we occasionally see around the Sun and Moon) 6000 to 8000 m

Cumulonimbus (large, darker clouds) low to 8000 m, sometimes reaching as high as 15 000 m

Altostratus (sheets of grey or blue; the Sun and Moon may appear as if behind frosted glass) 3000 to 7000 m

Altocumulus (grey or white puffy clouds, usually not continuous but alternating cloud and clear) 3000 to 7000 m

Stratocumulus (irregular rolling or puffy clouds, usually following a passing cold front) below 2000 m

Cumulus (low, rounded clouds) below 2000 m

Nimbostratus (true rain clouds; dark and wet looking) below 2000 m

Stratus (low, uniform sheet clouds, often with drizzle) below 2000 m

Try This
Activity Observing Clouds

Design and carry out a cloud-watching activity in which you observe clouds at least twice a day for about two weeks. Try to use your observations to predict the weather over the next 12 hours. You could tabulate your observations using these titles: Date, Time, Formation Classification, Drawing or Photograph, Physical Details. (Under "Physical Details" you could record the approximate altitude, speed, direction, and colour of the clouds as well as any other observations you make.) On the basis of your observations, add a weather prediction under Weather Indicated, and the weather as it occurred under Actual Weather.

Understanding Concepts

1. Starting with water at ground level, describe in your own words how a cloud forms. Include the energy flow that occurs at each stage.

2. Which type of cloud formation (convective, frontal, or orographic lifting) is likely to occur in each of the following. Provide reasons for your answers.

   (a) in eastern British Columbia

   (b) along the equator

   (c) along 60° north latitude in summer

   (d) near Lake Ontario

   (e) off the east coast of Nova Scotia

3. At approximately what altitude in the atmosphere would you find these clouds?

   (a) altostratus

   (b) cirrocumulus

   (c) cumulus

   (d) cumulonimbus

4. In your own words describe the shape, altitude, and other features for each of the following clouds:

   (a) altocumulus

   (b) cirrostratus

   (c) nimbostratus

   (d) stratus

5. **(a)** When a jet aircraft flies high overhead on a clear day, you can see a trail of water vapour, called a contrail, in its path. Which type of cloud does this contrail resemble?

(b) In a paragraph, speculate about the likely source of the contrail.

6. Use a globe or a world map to locate one or two places where you would expect to find

   (a) orographic clouds

   (b) convective clouds

   (c) frontal clouds

7. If you look up "alto" in a dictionary, you will find it means high. But types of clouds with the prefix alto are medium-level clouds. Explain this apparent discrepancy.

Making Connections

8. Do you think highways should be shut down during extremely dense fog? Justify your response.

Exploring

9. Various kits, CDs, and other resources are available to practise observing and naming clouds. Use one such resource, then share its advantages with others in your class in an oral presentation.

10. Find out in which type of clouds "mares'-tails" occur. Describe their appearance and the conditions in which they occur.

11. The technical terms for three types of fog are radiative fog, advection fog, and updraft fog. What do you think these terms mean? Find a resource to check your answer.

12. Which categories of clouds are most common in your area? Photograph and catalogue as many cloud types as you can. Present your photos and descriptions on a web page or in a poster.

Work the Web

To do research on cloud formation, visit www.science.nelson.com and follow the links for Science 10, 13.11. Sketch some of the less common cloud types not presented in this section.

Challenge

1 Use electronic or printed resources to find out more characteristics of the 10 main types of clouds described in this section. Provide more detail about the types of precipitation associated with certain clouds.

3 Practise identifying cloud types daily so that later, when you send weather data to other locations, you can be confident that your descriptions are accurate.

INQUIRY SKILLS MENU

○ Questioning   ● Planning   ● Analyzing
● Hypothesizing   ● Conducting   ● Evaluating
● Predicting   ● Recording   ● Communicating

What Affects the Evaporation of Water?

In order for clouds to form, water must evaporate from lakes, oceans, and plants. Of course, you wouldn't expect the same amount of evaporation above a desert as above an ocean. There are several other factors that affect the evaporation rate of water. In this investigation, you will design ways to test how evaporation depends on those other factors.

Question

What factors affect the evaporation rate of water?

Hypothesis/Prediction

In your group or as a class, discuss the factors that you think might affect the rate of evaporation of water.

(a) For each factor you can think of, write a
(K) prediction of how you believe it will affect the rate of evaporation of water.

(b) For each of your predictions, write a hypothesis explaining your prediction.

Design

For each prediction that you decide to investigate, design a controlled experiment to test your prediction and hypothesis. (If your factors are not assigned, you may want to reduce duplication of effort by discussing your decisions with classmates.)

(c) Describe the independent, dependent, and controlled variables for your experiment.

(d) Write a description of your procedure, step by step.

(e) Describe the safety precautions you will take.

(K7) (f) Design a table to record your observations.

Materials

(g) Make a list of the materials you require for your procedure.

Procedure

(h) Submit your procedure, safety precautions, observation table, and materials list to your teacher for approval.

(i) Carry out your procedure.

Analysis and Evaluation

(j) For each factor tested by your group and others in your class, state how changing the factor affected the evaporation rate of water.

(k) Describe any factors you were unable to test
(0) because of restraints, such as lack of materials.

(l) For the factors you investigated, explain whether your hypotheses and predictions were supported.

(m) If you were to perform your experiment again, describe and explain how it could be improved.

(n) Communicate the main conclusions of this
(Q) activity in a report.

Understanding Concepts

1. One litre of water is placed in a large jar, and an equal volume of water at the same temperature is placed in a pie plate. Predict which will evaporate faster. Explain your prediction.

2. Equal volumes of milk at the same temperature are placed in two identical saucers to feed cats. But the cats are wandering outdoors, and some milk evaporates before they have a drink. One saucer is in a corner of a room with closed windows. The other is near an open doorway where a breeze is blowing. Predict which milk will evaporate faster. Explain why.

3. One lake is located at a latitude of 23° north, and a lake of the same size is located at a latitude of 46° north. Assuming that the water temperature, surface area, and amount of wind blowing across each lake are the same, would the rate of evaporation of water also be the same? Explain.

4. Would you expect ocean water and fresh water to evaporate at the same rate? Assuming that conditions are identical except for salt content, explain how you would test your hypothesis.

5. Some people say that they feel more comfortable in Phoenix, Arizona, when the temperature is 33°C than in Toronto, at the same temperature. Why?

A Global Weather Model

You have learned about the atmosphere and prevailing winds, the hydrosphere and ocean currents, as well as cloud formation and types of clouds. You have seen that these weather factors are all driven by energy from the Sun. But the atmosphere, hydrosphere, and clouds are all related to each other. Although details of these relationships are presented in the next three chapters, a brief overview is given here.

Figure 1 summarizes the weather observed around the world during a typical, Northern Hemisphere winter day. Local effects are not shown although they are important on a day-to-day basis, as you will learn in Chapter 14.

(a) Solar Energy: During winter in the Northern Hemisphere, the far north receives no solar energy for months, so it is extremely cold there. In the rest of the world, the amount of solar energy received depends on the cloud cover and the angle at which the Sun's rays strike Earth. The rays hit most directly south of the equator, reaching 23.5° south latitude around December 21 each year.

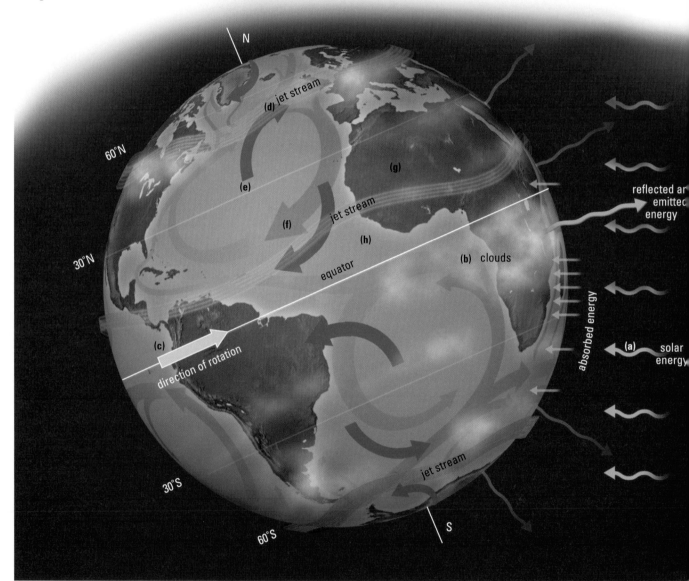

Figure 1

This global weather model summarizes the main factors that cause worldwide weather patterns.

(b) Cloud Cover: Clouds help maintain the energy balance on Earth. Clear skies allow solar energy to pass through the atmosphere and strike the surface, increasing the evaporation rate of water. This causes a build-up of clouds, which reflect much of the solar energy back into space, thus reducing the amount reaching the surface. Clouds also absorb infrared radiation both from the Sun and emitted from Earth's surface.

(c) Earth's Rotation: Earth spins eastward around its axis once every 24 h, causing our day-and-night cycle. This rotation also causes winds to tend to twist, toward the right in the Northern Hemisphere and toward the left in the Southern Hemisphere.

(d) Jet Streams: These high-speed winds in the upper troposphere are caused by pressure differences between the warm and cold regions of the world. They tend to travel in a wavy pattern from west to east. In winter, the temperature difference, and hence the pressure difference, is greater than in summer, so the jet streams are stronger. The jet streams play an important role in weather patterns.

(e) Prevailing Winds: Large-scale winds help maintain Earth's energy balance by moving energy from the hot equatorial regions toward the poles while at the same time moving cool air from the poles toward the equator. The directions of these winds are complex because of the Coriolis effect.

(f) Ocean Currents: Ocean currents also help distribute energy from the equatorial regions toward the poles and move cold water from the polar regions toward the equator. Surface currents are influenced by the winds above the surface, but when these currents hit land, their direction changes.

(g) Land Masses: Since land has a low heat capacity, it heats up and cools down much more quickly than water. This influences cloud formation and local weather effects.

(h) The Hydrosphere: The majority of Earth's surface is covered with water and ice. Water takes a long time to heat up (as summer approaches) and cool down (as winter approaches).

Understanding Concepts

1. Explain what you can conclude when you compare these pairs of features:

   (a) the north equatorial current and the northeast trade winds;

   (b) the south equatorial current and the southeast trade winds;

   (c) the north Pacific current and the mid-latitude westerlies;

   (d) the southern part of the Brazil Current and the mid-latitude westerlies;

   (e) the Oyashio Current and the polar easterlies.

2. **(a)** In which general direction do winds tend to twist in the Northern Hemisphere? in the Southern Hemisphere?

   (b) Explain why.

3. Assume that **Figure 1** was drawn on the day when the Sun's rays strike Earth as far south as possible.

   (a) On approximately what date does this occur?

   (b) At what latitude are the Sun's rays striking Earth vertically?

   (c) In the Southern Hemisphere, the hottest days won't occur for another month or so, even though by then the Sun's rays will have moved farther north. Explain why this lag occurs.

4. Clouds can be said to act as a feedback system. Explain this comparison, using diagrams.

5. If you drew a diagram similar to **Figure 1** to show a global weather model during summer in the Northern Hemisphere, what changes would you make to

   (a) the Sun's rays;

   (b) the jet streams.

6. State the general location where you would expect to find each of the following features, and state a reason for each answer:

   (a) tropical rain forests;

   (b) large desert areas;

   (c) temperate rain forests;

   (d) permanent ice caps.

7. The jet streams were not discovered until near the end of the Second World War. Why do you think they were not discovered earlier?

8. Along which latitudes would you expect convective clouds to form most readily? Why?

Sangeeta Sharma

Atmospheric Chemist

When most people think of a scientist, they don't imagine someone racing across the Georgia Basin in a hovercraft or braving −50°C temperatures at Alert in the Arctic. But this is all part of the job for Sangeeta Sharma. Sangeeta is an atmospheric chemist at Environment Canada.

Atmospheric chemists study the chemical composition of the atmosphere, observing the way liquids, solids, and gases interact with each other. They also examine how human activities affect the chemical and physical characteristics of the atmosphere.

Growing up in New Delhi, India, Sangeeta was always interested in the environment and what could be done to improve it. This interest led her to York University in Toronto where she completed a Bachelor of Science degree and then a Master's degree, specializing in atmospheric chemistry. During her years at school, she worked part time and during the summers in the Atmospheric Chemistry department. After spending a year working full time there, she got a job at Environment Canada.

Currently, Sangeeta is helping to lead a field study that measures the amount of aerosol black carbon concentrations in the atmosphere. Black carbon is produced as a result of incomplete combustion of fossil fuel, such as car exhaust or forest fires. It is a problem because it warms up the atmosphere by absorbing radiation from the Sun, which in turn can affect the climate. Sangeeta collects air samples from Canada's urban, rural, and remote regions. The samples are collected using a special instrument called an aethalometer. Once the samples have been gathered, she analyzes them in the laboratory and publishes results in various scientific journals.

When Sangeeta is not on one field study, she is planning another. Different projects are conducted every year, usually in collaboration with scientists from universities and other organizations. "This itself is a big challenge," says Sangeeta. "It involves organizing when and how things are going to take place and ordering and shipping the necessary equipment." She also spends time every month reading up on the latest advances in atmospheric sciences and attending national and international conferences to learn about new trends, skills, and technologies.

Making Connections

1. How would the warming of the atmosphere affect Earth's climate?
2. What can be done to lower the amount of aerosol black carbon?

🖑 Work the Web

Environment Canada considers climate change a significant environmental problem. Visit www.science.nelson.com and follow the links from Science 10, 13.14 to discover examples of research projects in this field. Pick one project for study. What kinds of scientists are involved? How large is the team? What qualifications do its members have?

Chapter 13 Summary

Key Expectations

Throughout the chapter, you have had the opportunity to do the following:

- Identify and describe the principal characteristics of the four regions of the atmosphere and the hydrosphere. (13.1, 13.4, 13.5, 13.8)

- Demonstrate the skills required to plan and conduct a weather-related inquiry, using a broad range of tools and techniques safely and accurately, and adapting or extending procedures where required. (13.2, 13.3, 13.12)

- Describe and explain heat transfer within the water cycle and how the hydrosphere and atmosphere act as heat sinks. (13.2, 13.8, 13.11, 13.13)

- Describe the factors contributing to Earth temperature gradients and to wind speed and direction. (13.1, 13.4, 13.6, 13.11)

- Describe and explain heat transfer in the hydrosphere and atmosphere and its effects on air and water currents. (13.6, 13.9)

- Explain how people have utilized their understanding of weather patterns for various purposes. (13.7)

- Formulate scientific questions about weather-related issues. (13.10)

- Explain different types of transformations of water vapour in the atmosphere and their effects. (13.11)

Key Terms

advection	heat sink
altitude	hydrosphere
atmosphere	jet stream
atmospheric pressure	orographic clouds
climate	pressure gradient
conduction	prevailing winds
convection	radiation
convective clouds	stratus clouds
Coriolis effect	temperature gradient
cumulus clouds	tropopause
electromagnetic spectrum	troposphere
frontal clouds	weather
heat capacity	weather dynamics

Make a Summary

In this chapter, you have studied how the atmosphere, land masses, and hydrosphere affect the energy from the Sun and give us weather patterns.

- To summarize your learning, create three separate lists titled "I can explain these in words," "I can explain these in diagrams," and "I must look these up to explain them." Then enter the concepts and words presented in this chapter in the list appropriate for you. When you have completed your chapter review, try to reduce the entries in the final list to none.

Reflect on your Learning

Revisit your answers to the Reflect on your Learning questions, page 501, in the Getting Started.

- How have your answers changed?

- What new questions do you have?

Chapter 13 Review

Understanding Concepts

1. By referring to the conditions in your own area, demonstrate your understanding of the difference between weather and climate.

2. Does conduction, convection, or advection occur in the transfer of energy from the Sun to Earth? Explain your answer.

3. Explain why oceans are considered to be major heat sinks.

4. Using a sketch, compare the intensity of light rays from the Sun striking the equator and the Arctic Circle at one of the equinoxes.

5. (a) In which atmospheric layer does most of Earth's weather occur?
   (b) What happens to the temperature in this layer as the altitude above Earth's surface increases?
   (c) Is your answer for 5(b) valid for other layers of the atmosphere? Explain.

6. A pressure cooker has a tight lid that presses down on the steam from boiling water, allowing food to cook faster than it does at atmospheric pressure. Explain why.

7. If you hold a $20 bill flat on the palm of your hand, the pressure exerted on your palm is about 1 Pa. Calculate the amount of money (in such bills) you would need to model the average atmospheric pressure.

8. Why do aircraft compartments have to be pressurized during flight?

9. Explain the process by which a liquid is able to rise up the tube of an eyedropper.

10. Use sketches to explain how each of the following Southern Hemisphere winds is set up:
    (a) the southeast trade winds;
    (b) the mid-latitude jet stream.

11. In northern Canada, winds and storms tend to be more powerful in winter than in summer. Why?

12. Why is knowledge of the jet stream important to aircraft?

13. Explain the statement, "Although the fraction of the hydrosphere found in the atmosphere is extremely small, it is very important to weather."

14. What physical factors that affect the directions of prevailing winds also affect the directions of major ocean currents?

15. Using your own words, write definitions for each of the following terms:
    (a) nimbus;
    (b) cirrus;
    (c) stratus.

16. Convection is one of the most important concepts presented in this chapter.
    (a) In which states of matter can convection occur? Explain.
    (b) Explain how convection influences the balance of energy on Earth.
    (c) Explain how convection influences cloud formation.

17. Describe how the evaporation rate of water is affected by
    (a) the temperature of the water;
    (b) wind striking the surface of the water;
    (c) the surface area of the water ;
    (d) the amount of water vapour in the air.

18. A crowd of people were watching a total solar eclipse. The weather was clear at the start, but as the eclipse progressed, clouds started to form. Why do you think this happened?

Applying Inquiry Skills

19. Describe and explain how to use longitude and latitude to find any location on Earth. Use a specific example to illustrate your answer.

20. Describe how you would test a substance to determine if it has a high or low heat capacity.

21. Create and perform a one-act mime titled "Explaining Earth's Seasons." Students can act as the Sun and Earth.

22. Explain how you would persuade a student in Grade 6 that the atmosphere exerts a pressure.

23. Imagine you and a friend are water molecules on the surface of the Atlantic Ocean at about 10° north latitude. Create a story that outlines where you and your friend will go after you have "evaporated" from the ocean. (Your friend can travel with you for a while, but eventually your paths will separate.)

24. Describe and explain how you would use common household materials to design a model that illustrates how a hot-air balloon rises (and falls). Include safety precautions in your design. (Do not make the model without your teacher's approval and supervision.)

25. (a) Design an experiment to demonstrate the effect that evaporation has on salt water. Predict what results you will observe.
    (b) Design an investigation to determine the evaporation rate of oil. Predict the effects a large oil spill in the ocean would have on the water cycle.

26. Design a set of two flow charts to show the flow of energy in the Northern Hemisphere mid-latitudes on June 21 and one month later. Be sure the flow charts show why there is a seasonal lag in temperature.

27. Identify the types of clouds shown in **Figure 1**. Which represents the most unstable weather?

Making Connections

28. In each of the following cases, which is more important: climate or weather? Explain your choice.
    (a) A tour operator is creating a web site to advertise vacation destinations.
    (b) A tourist has just arrived at one of the vacation destinations.

29. You are designing a solar-heated home. What heat capacity characteristic would you prefer for the substance you choose to store energy?

30. On December 3, 1999, Tori Murden arrived on the shore of the Caribbean Island of Guadeloupe after having spent 82 days rowing alone across the Atlantic Ocean from the Canary Islands.
    (a) Use a map and your knowledge of ocean currents and prevailing winds to describe how she accomplished this amazing feat.
    (b) People often sail across the Atlantic Ocean, but usually in the opposite direction. Where would they do this?
    (c) If Murden's boat had capsized and she was rescued by Navy helicopters, do you think she should have to pay the costs of her rescue? Justify your opinion.

31. Describe how satellite technology could help scientists keep track of changes in the hydrosphere.

32. If a large oil tanker in the Gulf of Mexico leaks oil, producing a huge oil slick, the precipitation in southeastern Canada may be affected. Explain why.

WHY ARE WEATHER FORECASTS SO OFTEN WRONG?

Actually, accuracy in weather forecasting has come a long way, although it is still more difficult to make an accurate five-day forecast than an accurate one-day forecast. However, as you are learning, there are many components to weather dynamics to take into account, so forecasting is not as accurate as we would like.

Figure 1

Modern technology, such as this Jimsonsphere, a form of weather balloon, improves data collection, which allows scientists to better understand and forecast the weather. Canada plays an important role in weather research, not only because of our technology, but also because our country is very large.

We have been forecasting weather for thousands of years, each culture in its own way. Daily observation of the sky and recognition of patterns in repeated events played important roles in most of these forecasts. More recently, weather forecasts have relied on technology to gather data from around the world (**Figure 1**). The data are analyzed to predict patterns for hours, days, and even weeks and seasons. The study of the atmosphere and weather forecasting is called **meteorology**, and the people who work in this field are called **meteorologists**. (The word "meteor" comes from a Greek word meaning "high in the air.")

Weather forecasts can be prepared for the short term or long term and for local or global purposes. On a day-to-day basis the forecasts we tend to care most about are the short-term, local ones. These forecasts help us plan our outdoor activities, our travel times, what to wear, and what precautions to take in case of an emergency. This chapter focuses on weather forecasting for relatively short times in areas that affect you and other Canadians.

Reflect on your Learning

1. Suggest why Buffalo, New York, gets so much more snow than Toronto, Ontario, even though they are fairly close to each other.

2. Why do you think many people feel sluggish on a hot, humid day?

3. Explain why you think dew occurs on some mornings and not others.

4. Suggest why five-day weather forecasts often seem to be inaccurate.

5. Why do you think temperatures drop so dramatically on clear, calm nights when the humidity is low?

Throughout this chapter, note any changes in your ideas as you learn new concepts and develop your skills.

Try This Activity Interpreting Weather Maps

As you study this chapter, you will increase your skill at interpreting weather maps. For this activity, try to identify the meanings of the symbols and patterns on these maps. If you already know what they mean, share your knowledge with the other students.

Materials: weather maps from as many sources as possible (local and national newspapers, the Internet) for three consecutive days, ending with yesterday

- Group the weather maps according to the newspaper or web site each came from. In a table record the names and dates of the newspapers or sites and the data source of the weather map (e.g., Environment Canada or The Weather Network).

- Choose a set of maps from one source, and look at the map for the first of the three days. List all the symbols on the map. Beside each

symbol, record its meaning according to the legend. If the meaning is not found in the legend, indicate that it is missing and use another reference source to determine the meaning.

- Arrange your set of maps in chronological order. Study the changes from Day 1 to Day 3. Record patterns that you observe, including motion of fronts, pressure systems, and precipitation. Indicate whether the motion is straight or rotating.

(a) According to yesterday's weather map, what is the forecast for your region for today? How accurate is that forecast?

(b) Compare and contrast the details and forecasts presented in the maps from the various sources. Rank the sources in order from your favourite to your least favourite. Give reasons for your ranking.

Air Speed and Air Pressure

There is a relationship between the pressure of a fluid and its speed. For example, as the speed of a wind increases, the pressure of the air decreases.

Consider what happens when you use a spray bottle of perfume or liquid glass cleaner: you push down on the stem and a fine spray flies out of the nozzle. A spray bottle works on the same principle that accounts for the low-pressure systems caused by high-speed winds. That principle is called **Bernoulli's principle**, after Daniel Bernoulli (1700–1782), a Swiss scientist. It states:

Where the speed of a fluid is high, the pressure is low, and where the speed of a fluid is low, the pressure is high.

Bernoulli's principle is used to understand effects observed in nature. For example, some of the highest winds on Earth occur on Mount Washington in New Hampshire, where fast-moving air at the top of the mountain reduces the pressure, causing an even greater pull on the uplifting air. This produces even greater winds in a sort of feedback system. The motion of a tornado can also be better predicted by knowing its speed of rotation.

In this activity you will observe Bernoulli's principle in action.

Hypothesis/Prediction

(a) Read each step and write a prediction of what you think will happen in each case. Use a diagram to explain each prediction.

Materials

- paper
- two empty pop cans
- several straws
- small beaker
- water
- beaker
- high-speed air supply
- cardboard
- thread spool
- pin
- air-flow toy (see **Figure 3**)

Procedure

1 Cut a piece of paper approximately 10 cm by 20 cm. Hold the short edge of the paper between your mouth and your nose and blow air under the paper to try to lift it. Now place the paper just below your mouth and blow again. Draw a cross-sectional diagram of each attempt to show what happens to the paper.

2 Arrange two pop cans on straws as shown in **Figure 1**. Blow air between the cans. Draw a top view to show what happens.

Figure 1

3 Set up the materials shown in **Figure 2**. Hold the vertical straw in place until you begin to blow. Blow air through the horizontal straw, which should be as close as possible to the top of the vertical straw. Draw a cross-sectional diagram of what you observe.

Figure 2

4 Place several small pieces of paper into a beaker. Use the high-speed air supply to try to cause the pieces of paper to fly out of the beaker. Determine what conditions provide the maximum lift. Draw a cross-sectional diagram of what happens.

5 Cut a thin piece of cardboard to the same size as the top of a thread spool. Hold it in place on top of the spool with a pin. Blow air through the middle of the spool from the bottom. Draw a cross-sectional diagram to show what happens.

6 Blow air through the toy shown in **Figure 3**. Does the air have to flow straight upward to make this toy work? Does the ball have to spin? In a cross-sectional diagram, describe in detail what you observe.

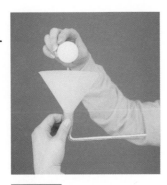

Figure 3
Can you make the ball levitate?

Analysis and Evaluation

(b) In the diagrams you drew for steps 1 to 5, add labels to show where the air speed was high and the air pressure was low. Then briefly explain in each case how the evidence supports Bernoulli's principle.

(c) To explain what you observed in step 6, draw a cross-sectional diagram in which the ball is shifted slightly to one side of the flow of air. Show how the ball's spinning affects its sideways motion.

(d) Which step or demonstration was most convincing at verifying Bernoulli's principle? Why?

(03) (e) Were your predictions accurate? Explain.

(Q) (f) Write a lab report to summarize what you learned in this activity.

Understanding Concepts

1. **(a)** Which step in the activity most closely resembles the operation of a spray bottle?

   (b) Explain how mist is produced when using a spray bottle.

2. Does a fire in a fireplace burn better when the outdoor air is calm or windy? Explain why.

3. Draw a cross-sectional diagram of a surface wave near the shore of an ocean that has a high wind blowing toward the shore. Use your diagram and Bernoulli's principle to help explain why water droplets from the wave's surface get lifted upward and blown toward the shore.

4. When engineers design subway and railway systems, they must take Bernoulli's principle into consideration.

   (a) If two trains are going in opposite directions on adjacent tracks, the tops of the cars tend to lean toward each other. Why does this happen? What design is needed to ensure that the cars don't touch?

   (b) In the station, lines are drawn on the platform so passengers won't get too close to the cars, especially when the cars first enter the station. Use the concept of changing pressure to explain the danger of getting too close to a fast-moving train.

5. Applying technology helps to reduce injuries and damage to buildings in areas that experience high winds. One method is to strengthen the joints between the walls and the roof of a house to prevent the roof from being lifted off the house. Explain how this is an application of Bernoulli's principle.

Exploring

6. Throwing curved balls in baseball applies Bernoulli's
(I) principle. Locate a resource that describes the curve ball, then try to maximize the curve while throwing a soft ball such as a nerf ball. Draw a diagram to explain the curved motion.

7. Bernoulli's principle is applied in aircraft flight. Research
(J) how airplane wings are designed to create upward forces of air on the wings (called "lift"). Draw a cross-sectional diagram to help explain what you discover.

Challenge

2 Winds that blow among the high-rise buildings in modern cities create a suction effect, sometimes making walking and cycling difficult. How can you reduce such effects in your community?

North American Weather Systems

Near the equator, the weather is fairly easy to forecast: it is usually hot and humid with a mix of sunshine and cloudiness. Near the North Pole, the weather is usually cold and dry, so it too is predictable. However, in the mid-latitude regions of North America, the weather is much more difficult to forecast because it changes so often.

A **weather system** is a set of temperature, wind, pressure, and moisture conditions for a certain region that moves as a unit for a period of days. In the middle parts of North America, weather systems — the bases of which are air masses (see below) — move from west to east. Recall the mid-latitude westerly winds.

As you study the causes of weather systems, remember that the winds and temperatures near the ground are not the only influences on the weather we experience; winds and other conditions higher in the atmosphere also greatly affect the weather. For example, low- and high-pressure areas are influenced by the high-altitude jet stream. Complete weather maps show weather conditions at ground level as well as at the jet stream level.

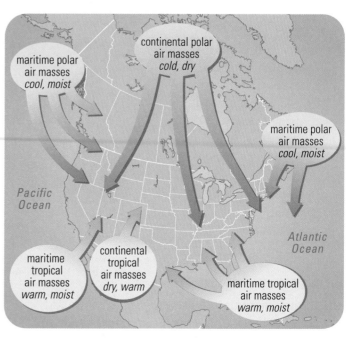

Figure 1

The air masses that affect weather in North America form in the cold north and warm south.

Air Masses

An **air mass** is a large body of air in which the temperature and moisture content at a specific altitude are fairly uniform. Air masses may be as small as 100 km across, but many are over 1000 km across. Most air masses form where the air above the ground or ocean is relatively still for days or weeks, allowing the air to take on the moisture and temperature properties of the surface.

The map in **Figure 1** shows a classification of North America air masses. Cold polar air over the North Pacific Ocean often brings wet, stormy weather to Canada's west coast because of evaporation over the ocean combined with orographic lifting over the mountains. Cold polar air over the continental part of North America is dry because little evaporation takes place in the high latitudes where the Sun's rays are at a very low angle or, in the winter, don't even reach the area. Warm air over the water around Mexico and the southern coasts of the United States can contain large amounts of moisture that can bring precipitation. Dry, warm air may be found in the desert areas of the southern United States and northern Mexico. Such air masses tend to be smaller than the other types because of the narrow shape of the continent toward the south.

It is evident from **Figure 1** that air masses help maintain the balance of Earth's energy: convection and prevailing winds move warm tropical air northward and cold polar air southward. When these warm and cold air masses move toward the mid-latitudes and interact, weather systems become more interesting and affect the majority of Canada's population.

Low-Pressure Systems

Low-pressure weather systems tend to bring cloudy skies and stormy weather. To see the development of low-pressure systems and, therefore, stormy weather, follow the four main stages of a typical storm shown in **Figure 2**.

In **Figure 2(a)**, a cold air mass and a warm air mass meet. Because of the different properties of the two air masses, they don't mix well, so a boundary, or **front,** forms between them. At this time the front is not moving. Fast-flowing air in the jet stream pulls air up out of both air masses, creating a low-pressure area near the ground. This low-pressure area pulls air near the surface in; the rising air begins to swirl in a counterclockwise direction, due to the Coriolis effect. As the amount of air pulled away by the jet stream increases, so does the amount of air pulled into the low-pressure area. The **warm front** (the leading edge of the warm air mass) gradually rises over the cold air mass and carries moisture with it. At the same time, the **cold front** (the leading edge of the cold air mass) pushes under the warm air mass, causing the warm, moist air to rise fairly steeply.

In **Figure 2(b)** a large region of precipitation develops ahead of the warm front as the jet stream continues to pull air away. Where the cold front pushes the warm air upward, billowing cumulonimbus clouds bring heavy rain or other precipitation.

In **Figure 2(c)**, an **occluded front** is forming as the warm front is caught by the cold front, cutting it off from the low. ("Occlude" means to cut off or close.) When this happens, the upper air flow no longer pulls air away from the low-pressure area, so the storm begins to weaken.

In **Figure 2(d)** the precipitation has ended and the area of low pressure now experiences increasing air pressure.

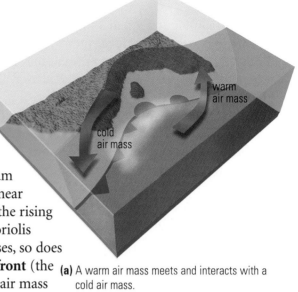

(a) A warm air mass meets and interacts with a cold air mass.

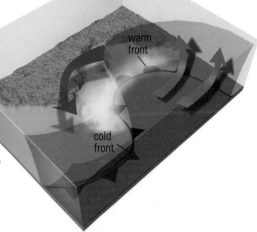

(b) Main stage: Some precipitation begins as the warm front rises above the cold air.

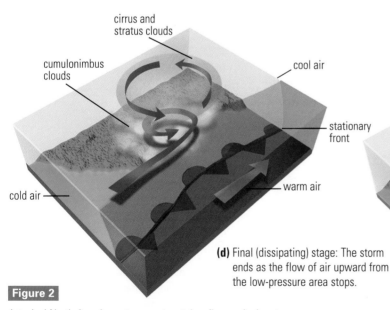

(d) Final (dissipating) stage: The storm ends as the flow of air upward from the low-pressure area stops.

Figure 2

A typical North American storm system takes five or six days to progress through the main stages. Notice the symbols: blue triangles for a cold front, red semicircles for a warm front, and triangles and semicircles together for an occluded front.

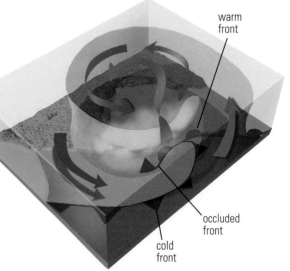

(c) Occluding stage: When the cold front catches up to the warm front, a single, occluded front begins to form. The storm weakens.

Notice in **Figures 2** and **3** that the direction of rotation of the storm is counterclockwise. Both also show a low-pressure area at the surface where the warm air rises and is carried away by the jet stream. The low-pressure, counterclockwise-swirling air forms what is called a **cyclone**. The process of creating a cyclone is called **cyclogenesis**. (The word "cyclogenesis" comes from the Greek words meaning "circle" and "beginning.") Cyclogenesis also occurs in the Southern Hemisphere, but the direction of rotation of the cyclones there is clockwise.

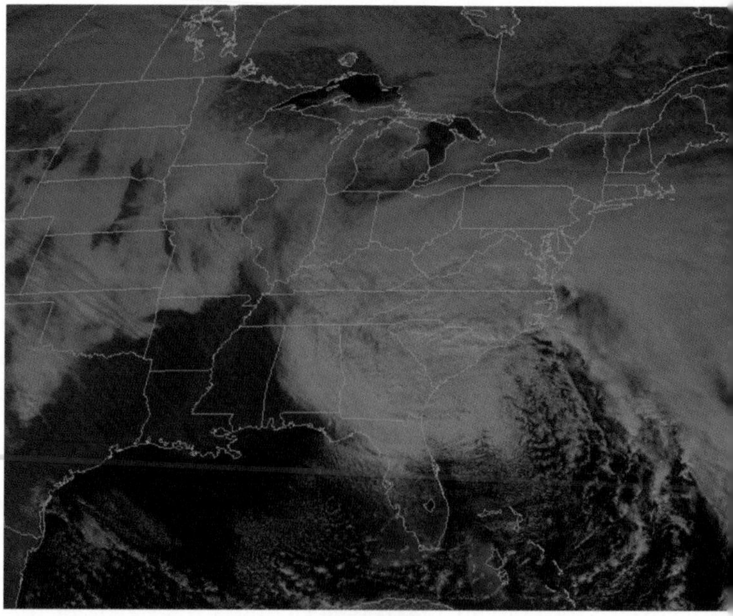

Stationary Fronts

Not all fronts experience the rotating motion shown in **Figures 2** and **3**. A **stationary front** occurs when the boundary between a warm air mass and a cold air mass remains fairly still for some time. This situation results in fairly stable weather until the air masses, influenced by upper-level winds, begin to move. Then a low-pressure cyclone may start to form. On a weather map, a stationary front is shown as blue triangles and red semicircles on opposite sides of the same line.

Figure 3

The pattern of clouds in a storm system reveals the counterclockwise rotation of a low-pressure system. This satellite image was obtained using visible light.

High-Pressure Systems

A cyclone is a low-pressure system that rotates counterclockwise and usually brings cloudy, stormy weather. Therefore, an **anticyclone** is a high-pressure system that rotates clockwise (in the Northern Hemisphere) and usually brings clear skies. Recall from Section 13.6 that by the time the air in the equatorial convection currents reaches about 30° latitude, it has become colder and more dense and is moving downward, toward Earth. So, this latitude is a common area of high-pressure systems. At this location, the anticyclone is a warm high-pressure system. More important to Canada is the cold high-pressure system that occurs in central Canada and the Arctic regions, especially in winter. The high atmospheric pressure near the ground results from the cold, descending Arctic air, which tends to be dry. This is one reason that the skies become clear as high pressure builds into an area.

ᐟᕒWork the Web

Visit www.science.nelson.com and follow the links for Science 10, 14.2 to a site that updates a current view of the jet stream. Study the flow of the jet stream for three or four days, and in your notebook describe how it appears to influence weather across Canada.

Challenge

1 What new ideas have you learned about weather forecasting in this section? How would you use a computer to store and manage data?

3 As you search for weather information on the Internet, by what criteria do you judge whether the site you are using is providing data that are scientifically valid?

Try This
Activity Pressure System Rotation

The rotation of high- and low-pressure systems can be modelled by thinking of how you screw in a light bulb. Imagine that a camera aboard a satellite high above you is videotaping the situations described below.

- Suppose you are holding a light bulb with the base facing downward, ready to be screwed into a table lamp. To screw the bulb into the lamp, you lower the bulb while turning it to the right. The satellite video shows the bulb turning clockwise as it moves lower into the socket. This situation represents air moving downward in a high-pressure system in the Northern Hemisphere.
- Now suppose you are holding the bulb with the base facing upward, toward a ceiling

fixture. To screw the bulb into the fixture, you press the bulb up into the socket, still turning it to the right — the same direction as in the first step.

- From your point of view, is the rotation clockwise or counterclockwise as you turn the bulb? Does the satellite video show clockwise or counterclockwise rotation? What situation does this represent?

(a) From one point of view, air rising in a low-pressure system spins clockwise, but from the other point of view it spins counterclockwise. What are these points of view?

(b) Which point of view is used when drawing weather maps?

Understanding Concepts

1. In your own words, explain why the weather is more difficult to forecast in the mid-latitude regions.

2. State which type of air masses would likely affect the following locations:
   (a) Saskatchewan
   (b) Labrador
   (c) Florida
   (d) coastal British Columbia

3. How do air masses help maintain Earth's energy balance?

4. If a weather map is shown in black and white, how can you distinguish a stationary front from an occluded front?

5. One way to forecast changing weather is to observe approaching clouds. Describe the progression of cloud types and appearance you would expect during the formation of a low-pressure system.

6. Another way to forecast weather is to analyze the changes in atmospheric pressure. Two sets of atmospheric pressure data, each taken over a 48-h period, are listed below. In each case, describe the type of weather that is approaching and give a reason for your answer.
   (a) 101.8 kPa; 101.2 kPa; 100.1 kPa
   (b) 100.4 kPa; 100.7 kPa; 101.1 kPa

7. Draw and label a series of diagrams (resembling those in **Figure 2**) to illustrate cyclogenesis in the Southern Hemisphere.

Making Connections

8. Is it important for Canadian meteorologists to exchange data and research studies with meteorologists from other countries? Justify your answer.

Exploring

9. Observe the cloud formations and atmospheric pressure in
(N3) your area over the next several days. Each day, use the changing patterns to predict the next day's weather. Keep track of your predictions and the actual weather.

Three Days of Canadian Weather

Weather maps are provided in daily newspapers and on web sites, and most forecasts on the TV news and weather stations show weather maps. However, interpreting weather maps takes much practice. You can improve your skill at understanding weather maps by studying the progress of weather patterns over a three-day period. Don't be fooled into thinking that the patterns you see are always regular; weather systems are complex. Canada's weather is particularly complex because it is influenced by air masses coming from several locations: the west coast, the Arctic, the southwestern United States, the Gulf of Mexico, and along the east coast of the continent. The weather is also affected by ocean currents and local conditions.

The information shown on the weather maps in **Figures 1** to **3** applies what you have learned about fronts, high- and low-pressure systems, and cyclogenesis. Many weather maps show even more detail. However, most TV and newspaper weather maps focus on the conditions near the ground. Meteorologists rely on the conditions higher in the troposphere to make more accurate forecasts. Thus, when you forecast weather using the newspaper maps in this case study, you can do so only on the basis of the current surface conditions. Such conditions may not persist if the jet stream causes changes that can't be observed at ground level.

(Note: the worldwide meteorological agencies use Greenwich mean time (GMT), and all data are based on GMT. However, for this activity we will use EST.)

DAY 1: Friday, 19:00 h EST

(a) Which pressure system in the map in **Figure 1** has the greatest amount of precipitation? the least? Explain how you made your decision.

(b) In cyclogenesis, cold fronts tend to rotate faster than warm fronts, thus catching up to the warm fronts and causing even more precipitation. Which weather system illustrates this principle?

(c) Create a 24-h weather forecast for your area based only on this map.

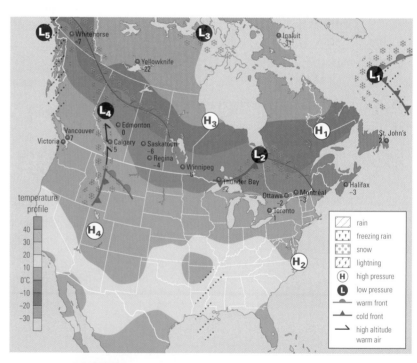

Figure 1

This map of current conditions on Friday shows the location of the various fronts and high- and low-pressure systems near the ground. To make tracking earier, each system has been numbered.

DAY 2: Saturday, 19:00 h EST

(d) In what general direction are the pressure systems in southern Canada moving?

(e) Do the pressure systems in the Arctic appear to be moving at the same speed as the systems in southern Canada? Explain your answer.

(f) Calculate the average speed of a mid-latitude pressure system over the past 24 h. (To help determine the distance travelled, assume that the distance from Victoria to St. John's is 4700 km.)

(g) Create a 24-h weather forecast for your area based on the maps in **Figures** 1 and 2.

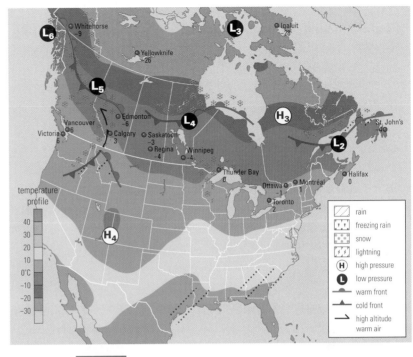

Figure 2

Saturday

DAY 3: Sunday, 19:00 h EST

(h) In the past 24 h, which region of Canada has had the greatest amount of precipitation? the most stable, pleasant weather? Explain your answers.

(i) In which area(s) of this map can you see cyclogenesis?

(j) Can you find any examples of precipitation being caused by moving air masses without cyclogenesis? If so, where?

(k) Create a 24-h weather forecast for Monday for your area based on **Figures** 1, 2, and 3.

(l) On a map of Canada (your teacher will provide one), draw what you think will be the weather map for all of Canada on Monday at 19:00 h, Day 4 of the sequence.

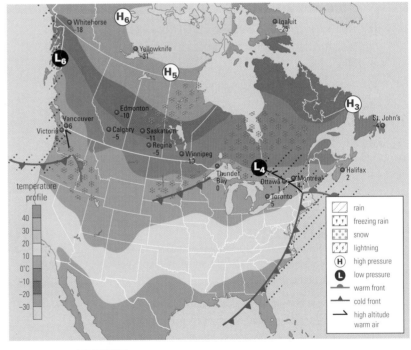

Figure 3

Sunday

Understanding Concepts

1. Compare the general direction of the pressure systems in southern Canada with the general direction of the mid-latitude global winds. What do you observe?

2. Explain the disadvantages of using a surface weather map to forecast weather.

3. During which season(s) could the weather maps in this Case Study have been produced? Explain your answer.

4. Refer to the weather map in the Skills Handbook, **Figure 10**, on page 683.

   (a) What extra features shown on that map are not included in the maps used for this Case Study?

   (b) Describe the advantages of the features you listed in **(a)**.

   (c) Why do you think some features are not included in certain weather maps?

Making Connections

5. A variety of media convey weather forecasts: newspapers, web sites, radio, and TV.

   (a) Describe at least one advantage and one disadvantage of each medium listed.

   (b) Which medium would best suit you on a day when you need a detailed weather forecast for the whole day? Why?

   (c) Suggest ways to distribute weather information to the public more conveniently. (Use your imagination. You don't have budget restrictions when answering open-ended questions!)

Exploring

6. Can the maps used to communicate weather forecasts be (K1) improved? Design and carry out a survey to determine what proportion of adults (or other people you want to test)

   (a) understand weather maps;

   (b) would be interested in knowing more about weather and weather maps.

   Communicate your findings in a way you think is unique.

7. On the weather map in the Skills Handbook, one word in the (N3) legend is "TROWAL," a term coined by Canadian meteorologists. According to the legend, what is this feature? Where do you think it is located in the atmosphere? Research to find out more about it and report to the class on your discovery.

Reflecting

8. Describe ways in which you can improve your skills in forecasting weather. (You can include your ability to gather data from various sophisticated sources.)

9. Farmers and sailors require different weather information. Explain how a marine forecast would differ from a local forecast.

Challenge

1 What is the advantage of indicating a standard time, such as EST, on a weather map?

2 Weather towers in some cities use coloured, flashing lights near the top to indicate basic weather forecasts. How could your modern city improve upon that older technique?

3 Assume that in your network you can connect to other students who live east, west, north, and south of where you live. From which students would you like to receive information to help you forecast the next day's weather? To which students would you send information to help them forecast weather? Explain why.

Work the Web

Find at least two weather web sites. Compare the sites by listing features of each site that you like and dislike.

Regional Weather

Weather patterns are influenced on a global scale by prevailing winds and ocean currents. A single weather system can cover a large part of our continent. But in many regions, certain conditions influence the weather in a much smaller area, such as along the shore of a large lake or on the sides of a mountain range. This section focuses on some of these regional weather effects. (Some smaller effects, such as winds blowing around the corner of a building, are not described here, although they may directly affect parts of your area.)

Thermals

If you reserved a ride on a hot-air balloon, you would certainly expect the pilot to understand that day's local wind patterns before lift-off (**Figure 1**). Some days and some locations may be ideal for ballooning, but often the pilot must rely on weather watchers in the nearest airport to determine whether the winds will carry the balloon in a safe direction.

In most areas, the winds are safe for balloon flights for two or three hours after sunrise or before sunset. To understand why, you can apply what you have learned about convection, one way that winds are generated. On a clear day, solar energy heats the land, which absorbs the energy; the energy is converted into heat and warms the air that comes into contact with it. The warm air expands and becomes less dense (or more buoyant). The less dense air rises and is replaced by cooler, denser air, setting up a convection current. A local convection current set up during the day is called a **thermal** or a thermal updraft.

Early in a sunny day, thermal updrafts are just beginning to form, causing weak local winds. By mid-morning, thermals can result in local updraft winds that are strong enough to allow birds of prey to soar lazily from one updraft to another (**Figure 2**). Toward sunset, the convection currents weaken, and the local winds subside. Because the local winds are weaker in the early morning and toward sunset, it is generally safer to take a hot-air balloon flight at these times.

Under more extreme conditions, daytime heating can lead to strong convective-air-mass thunderstorms in the summer.

Figure 1
The pilot of a hot-air balloon can control the balloon's altitude but relies on the local winds for direction.

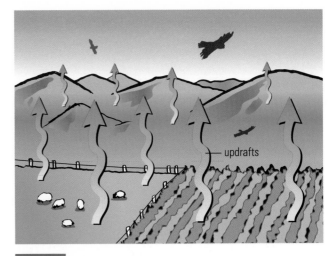

Figure 2
The updraft winds called thermals allow birds of prey, such as hawks, eagles, and turkey vultures, to soar in circles for hours. The birds often rise easily on one thermal, then glide down to another to start the cycle again.

Sea Breezes

When a thermal forms near a sea, an ocean, or a lake, it is called a **sea breeze**. As the day begins, solar energy warms the land faster than the water. (Recall that water has a high capacity to hold heat, so it heats up and cools down more slowly than land.) The convection current that results moves air from the water toward the land (**Figure 3**). This can affect the local weather near a large body of water. Often we hear in a summer forecast "but cooler near the lake," or in winter, "snow inland, but rain along the lake." If sea breezes did not exist, these types of forecasts would be very rare.

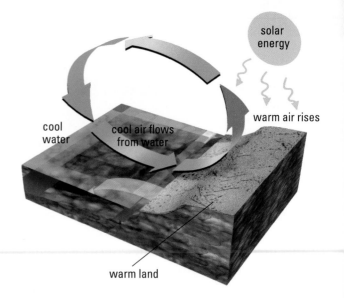

solar energy

warm air rises

cool water

cool air flows from water

warm land

Figure 3

A sea breeze results when heated air above the land rises and is replaced by cooler air from above the water.

Land Breezes

As the Sun sets on a warm day near the same large body of water, the land cools down more quickly than the water. Now, the air above the water rises and is replaced by cooler air from above the land. This causes a **land breeze**, a convection thermal that flows from the land toward the water. Although this breeze is usually weak, it often causes the water near the shore to become quite calm. In the winter, a similar weak breeze can form during the day near a body of water that is warmer than the land.

Lake-Effect Snow

When an air mass moves across a large body of water, such as one of the Great Lakes, it picks up moisture from the water. In winter, the water tends to be warmer than the surrounding land and air (again, because of heat capacity differences). When the moisture-laden air mass — which warms and rises as it travels across the water — reaches the far side of the body of water, where the temperature is lower, the moisture becomes snow (**Figure 4**).

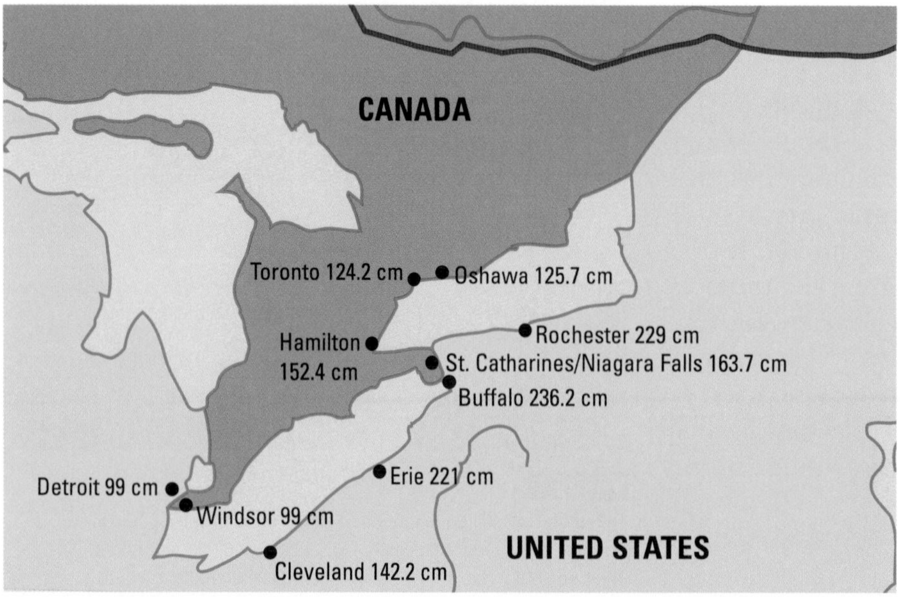

Did You Know?

On January 6, 1966, chinook winds raised the temperature in parts of Alberta by 21 Celsius degrees in only 4 minutes.

CANADA

Toronto 124.2 cm • • Oshawa 125.7 cm

Hamilton • 152.4 cm

• Rochester 229 cm

St. Catharines/Niagara Falls 163.7 cm

• Buffalo 236.2 cm

Detroit 99 cm •

• Erie 221 cm

• Windsor 99 cm

UNITED STATES

Cleveland 142.2 cm

Figure 4

The mean annual snowfall is greater on the downwind, or leeward, side of a large lake where the prevailing winds tend to produce local precipitation.

Chinook Winds

In winter, people who live just east of the Rocky Mountains can predict the arrival of a warm, dry wind simply by looking at the sky at the tops of the mountains. On the windward (in this case, west) side of the mountains, orographic lifting causes water vapour in the air to condense, forming clouds and snow or rain. Condensation of water vapour also releases energy, warming the air. The air that sinks on the leeward (in this case, east) side of the mountains has lost its moisture but has gained some heat. The resulting warm, dry wind is called a "chinook" in the Rocky Mountains. (This name comes from a First Nations tribe originally from Oregon.) This same type of wind has other names in other parts of the world.

Often a chinook wind is gentle. However, its speed increases if the prevailing westerly winds are higher. And the chinook winds can be extremely high if a rotating pressure system on the leeward side creates local winds in the same direction as the prevailing wind.

Figure 5
The arrival of a chinook is sometimes signalled in the sky. Here a warm, dry chinook is moving in from the west (right).

 Challenge

1 How do you intend to take local conditions into account in your weather forecasts?

2 How will the location of your community affect your design?

Understanding Concepts

1. Use the particle theory of matter to explain why air becomes less dense as it is warmed.

2. Under what weather conditions (cloudy, sunny, etc.) and during which season(s) would you expect the strongest thermals? Explain why.

3. Hang gliders (**Figure 6**) share a common interest with birds of prey. What is it?

Figure 6
Hang gliding is a popular sport where the atmospheric conditions are appropriate.

4. A hot-air balloon flight is offered near the St. Lawrence River. The pilot checks the weather forecast, but finds it is not specific enough to judge whether the balloon will drift across the river toward the United States. Explain how a small test balloon can help solve this problem.

5. Draw a cross-sectional diagram to show how a land breeze is set up.

6. Explain why Buffalo, New York, has a higher average annual snowfall than Toronto, Ontario.

Exploring

7. Research the migration habits of birds of prey and describe what atmospheric conditions they prefer when migrating. Do any of these birds use thermals as they migrate?

8. Research at least one of the following winds and describe how it compares to chinook winds: the foehn (also föhn) in Switzerland, the Santa Ana in the United States, and the zonda in Argentina.

Precipitation

What does the word "precipitation" mean to you? Of course, rain and snow are common, but there are many other types, some of which may occur in the area in which you live (**Figure 1**).

Precipitation is water that reaches the ground in either liquid or solid form. Thus, it is the stage in the water cycle that follows condensation, freezing, or sublimation. The type of precipitation depends greatly on the temperatures on the ground and in the atmosphere, as you can see in the descriptions in **Figure 2**.

cumulonimbus clouds

Water droplets and a few ice crystals form.

Ice crystals grow and combine to form snowflakes.

warm air

Water droplets form.

warm air

cold air

Water droplets collide and form drops.

Water drops collide and form larger drops.

Ice Pellets (Sleet)

Ice pellets, also known as sleet, are a solid form of water. They form when snow falls through a warm layer of air, partially melting, and then falls through a layer of air below 0°C. The resulting beads of ice are hard enough to bounce off the cold ground when they strike it.

cold surface

Wet Snow

Dry Snow

Drizzle

Drizzle is fine water droplets between about 40 μm and 0.5 mm in diameter. Depending on the intensity of precipitation, both rain and drizzle can be classified as light, moderate, and heavy.

Rain

Rain consists of falling water droplets between about 0.5 mm and 5 mm in diameter. If a larger drop forms, it breaks into pieces as it falls through the air.

Freezing Rain

When raindrops are close to freezing and strike a cold object on or near the ground, the drops freeze almost instantly.

Snow

Snow is formed when water vapour crystallizes on tiny particles of dust and other solid substances, such as smoke. Snow forms only when the air temperature, and therefore the water vapour, has cooled below 0°C.

Figure 2

Formation of the main types of precipitation

Understanding Concepts

1. Which is more important in classifying precipitation, the form of water in the atmosphere or the form that reaches the ground? Choose an example to illustrate your answer.

2. Name the forms of precipitation that are

   (a) solid

   (b) liquid.

3. Starting with evaporation at or near Earth's surface, list the changes of state of water that occur in order to form (a) dew, (b) frost, (c) drizzle, (d) snow, and (e) ice pellets.

4. Explain with examples how air temperature affects the formation of precipitation.

5. Town A is 100 km south of town B. For each situation named below, identify which town is town A and which is town B. Explain each choice.

   (a) Dew forms in one town, frost in the other.

   (b) Rain falls in one town, wet snow in the other.

   (c) Ice pellets fall in one town, freezing rain in the other.

6. Compare and contrast:

   (a) drizzle and rain;

   (b) wet snow and dry snow.

Making Connections

7. Of the types of precipitation described in this section, which type do you think would create the most dangerous situation at an airport? Justify your answer.

8. In several regions in Canada, salt is spread on roads when they are snowy or icy.

   (a) What is the normal melting temperature of ice (at sea level and atmospheric pressure)?

   (b) How does salt affect the melting points of snow and ice? Explain, using the particle theory of matter.

   (c) Describe a controlled experiment to determine how the melting point of ice depends on the amount of salt added.

   (d) Explain the advantages and disadvantages of adding salt to roads.

Exploring

9. Research "virga," a type of rain, and explain why it was (I) omitted from this section. Also explain why cloud bases are higher and virga more common in the prairies.

10. Research world and Canadian records for various forms (J) of precipitation, such as the greatest recorded amount of annual snowfall or rainfall, the greatest mean annual snowfall or rainfall, the largest recorded hailstones, and the largest single-day snowfall or rainfall. Create a display poster or other visual to illustrate what you discover.

Hail is a solid form of water that is created in cumulonimbus clouds high in the troposphere. Frozen raindrops move up and down in highly active thunderclouds, growing larger each time an updraft raises them through cold water droplets at high altitude. If you cut open a hailstone, you can find evidence of its growth: up to 20 layers of ice.

Dew forms when the air cools and the water vapour it contains condenses on a cool surface near the ground (**Figure 3**). If the surface is very cold, the water vapour sublimates, resulting in frost. On cold winter mornings, frost patterns can be seen on some windows (**Figure 4**).

Dew

When the air temperature is above freezing but cool enough to cause condensation, dew forms.

Figure 3

Frost

When the air temperature is below freezing and water molecules sublimate, frost forms.

Figure 4

 Challenge

1 How do you intend to measure the amount of precipitation?

2 How have you designed your community for various types of precipitation? For example, how easy will it be to remove unwanted snow? Where will the snow be taken?

3 Make a list of symbols used for the various types of precipitation.

Humidity

Imagine living with 40°C temperatures for the whole summer! Many people throughout the world cope with these temperatures quite comfortably because they live in places where the air is dry. However, if such temperatures are combined with high humidity, we call the weather oppressive, humid, and steamy. What is this thing we describe as humidity?

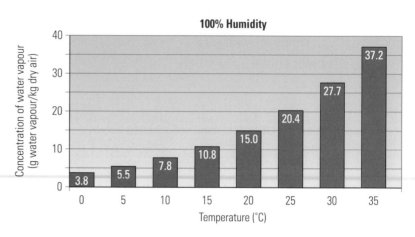

100% Humidity

Concentration of water vapour (g water vapour/kg dry air) vs *Temperature (°C)*

Temperature (°C)	0	5	10	15	20	25	30	35
Concentration	3.8	5.5	7.8	10.8	15.0	20.4	27.7	37.2

Figure 1
This bar graph shows the concentration of water vapour in grams per kilogram of dry air that gives a relative humidity of 100% in air at various temperatures.

Humidity is a measure of the amount of water vapour in the atmosphere. (Humidity is also called absolute humidity.) It affects the weather as well as how comfortable we feel. Low humidity means that evaporation can occur from bodies of water and other sources. High humidity means that clouds or fog may form, and those that have formed will persist rather than evaporate.

Relative Humidity

To predict human comfort, a slightly different humidity measurement is used. **Relative humidity** is the measure of the amount of water vapour actually in the air as a percentage of the maximum amount of water vapour the air could hold at that temperature. Thus, at 20°C a relative humidity of 50% means that there is half as much water vapour in the air as 20°C air could hold. From the graph in **Figure 1**, it is evident that warm air can hold much more moisture than cold air.

Sample Problem 1
Determine the concentration of water vapour in air at 20°C when the relative humidity is 50%.

From **Figure 1**, the concentration of water vapour at 20°C is 15 g/kg of dry air for 100% humidity. Therefore, at 50% relative humidity, the concentration is 50% of 15 g/kg, or 7.5 g/kg.

Sample Problem 2
If the concentration of water vapour at 0°C is 1.9 g/kg of dry air, what is the relative humidity?

$$\text{Relative humidity} = \frac{\text{concentration}}{\text{maximum concentration}} \times 100\%$$

$$= \frac{1.9\,\frac{g}{kg}}{3.8\,\frac{g}{kg}} \times 100\%$$

$$= 50\%$$

The relative humidity is 50%.

Saturated Air

If you dip a sponge into water and lift it out, some water runs out of it but the sponge retains a large quantity. The sponge is said to have reached the point of saturation. Similarly, **saturation** of air occurs when the air, at a particular temperature, is holding the maximum mass of water vapour that it can — its relative humidity is 100%. The concentrations shown in **Figure 1** are of saturated air.

Consider ways in which clouds and fog can form. One way is when more moisture is added to air already saturated with water vapour. The extra water vapour condenses, forming some type of cloud or precipitation in the atmosphere or fog at the surface. Another way involves rising air that has a relative humidity lower than 100% near the ground. As this air rises, it cools, eventually reaching the saturation temperature. That is when condensation begins and a cloud forms.

Dew and the Dew Point

We have all seen dew in the morning: water vapour that has condensed on plants, grass, or other objects near the ground. Dew forms when the air reaches the saturation temperature, in other words, when the relative humidity is 100%. The temperature at which dew forms is called the **dew point**.

Dew often forms on clear nights. During the day, when the temperature is higher, more evaporation takes place, and the air can contain a large amount of water vapour. At night, the ground radiates energy into the atmosphere and objects at ground level cool down quickly. When the temperature of these objects is at or below the dew point, water vapour condenses and gathers as dew drops. On a cloudy night, the energy radiated from the ground warms the clouds, which then radiate some energy back to the ground. This keeps the surface temperature higher. In desert areas, plants obtain much of their moisture from dew that forms each night under the clear sky (**Figure 2**).

No doubt you have noticed condensation on the outer surface of a cold drinking glass on a hot, humid day or on the bathroom mirror after your shower. In these cases the water vapour from the air has come into contact with a surface whose temperature is at or below the dew point, so dew forms.

Figure 2
This early-morning photograph of a cactus plant shows dewdrops that have collected overnight.

Try This Activity Finding the Dew Point

Can you estimate the dew point in your classroom right now?

Materials: apron, safety goggles, a shiny aluminum can, warm water, an alcohol thermometer, a stirring rod, some ice cubes

- Add warm water to half-fill the aluminum can, then add several ice cubes to the water. As you stir the water-ice mixture with the stirring rod,

watch the outside surface of the can carefully. As soon as you notice condensation, measure the temperature of the water-ice mixture. Record this "dew point temperature."

- Repeat this step twice more and take an average of the three readings.

(a) What factors do you have to consider when estimating the dew point?

Determining Relative Humidity

You know that if you hang up a wet towel in dry air it will dry much more quickly than if the air is filled with moisture. In scientific terms, if the air is saturated, it can't hold any more water vapour; but if the air is not saturated, water can evaporate into it.

This principle is applied in the use of a psychrometer. (Psychro comes from a Greek word meaning cold. Don't confuse it with psycho.) A **psychrometer** is an instrument used to indirectly determine the relative humidity in the atmosphere (indirectly because its readings must be compared with precalculated values). A common psychrometer uses two thermometers. The bulb of one thermometer is surrounded by a piece of moist gauze; this is called the wet-bulb thermometer. The other thermometer is called the dry-bulb thermometer (**Figure 3**).

As the water molecules in the gauze evaporate, they take heat from their surroundings, including the thermometer bulb. This causes the temperature of the bulb to drop. The drier the air, the more quickly the moisture evaporates and the cooler the thermometer becomes. The lower wet-bulb temperature is then compared with the air temperature on the dry-bulb thermometer, and the relative humidity can be determined from **Table 1**. (The wet-bulb temperature is higher than the dew point, except when the relative humidity is 100%: at that point, the dew point, wet-bulb temperature, and dry-bulb temperature are all equal.)

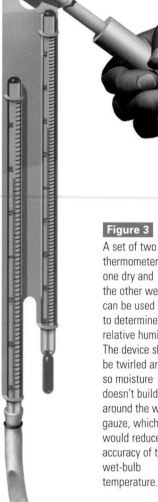

Figure 3

A set of two thermometers, one dry and the other wet, can be used to determine the relative humidity. The device should be twirled around so moisture doesn't build up around the wet gauze, which would reduce the accuracy of the wet-bulb temperature.

Sample Problem 3

The air temperature in a classroom is 22°C and the wet-bulb temperature is 17°C. Determine the relative humidity in the room.

The temperature difference is

22°C − 17°C = 5°C

Going down the 5°C column in **Table 1** to the 22°C dry-bulb temperature, we find that the relative humidity is 61%.

Table 1 **Determining Relative Humidity**

Dry-bulb temperature (°C)	Difference between wet-bulb and dry-bulb temperatures (°C)									
	1	2	3	4	5	6	7	8	9	10
	Relative humidity (%)									
10	88	77	66	55	44	34	24	15	6	
12	89	78	68	58	48	39	29	21	12	
14	90	79	70	60	51	42	34	26	18	10
16	90	81	71	63	54	46	38	30	23	15
18	91	82	73	65	57	49	41	34	27	20
20	91	83	74	67	59	53	46	39	32	26
22	92	83	76	68	61	54	47	40	34	28
24	92	84	77	69	62	56	49	43	37	31
26	92	85	78	71	64	58	51	46	40	34
28	93	85	78	72	65	59	53	48	42	37
30	93	86	79	73	67	61	55	50	44	39

Subtract the wet-bulb temperature from the dry-bulb temperature, and find the column that corresponds to the temperature difference. Go down that column to the row for the dry-bulb temperature to find the relative humidity.

Effects of Humidity

You have learned that dew forms when the temperature of the air and the water vapour it contains drop to the dew point. Other effects of humidity or water vapour are common.

When you perspire, your body is acting like a wet-bulb thermometer: as the perspiration evaporates from your body, it takes heat from your body, making you feel cooler. So it's not the perspiration that cools you; it's the evaporation. If the relative humidity is high, evaporation is not as fast, so you feel uncomfortable.

Cold winter air contains very little water vapour, and the air in a home or school contains approximately the same concentration of water vapour. Thus, the relative humidity in the warm indoors is very low. That is why the air inside a building feels so dry in the winter and evaporation occurs quickly. Skin may become uncomfortably dry under these conditions. People often use humidifiers to add moisture to their homes or offices.

 **Challenge**

1 Under what conditions would knowing the dew point improve your forecast?

2 How will an understanding of humidity affect your consideration of indoor air quality in your "weather-wise" community?

3 When sending or receiving weather information, how can relative humidity and absolute humidity be distinguished?

Understanding Concepts

1. Refer to the graph in **Figure 1** to answer these questions.

   (a) What is the mass of water vapour per kilogram of saturated air at 25°C?

   (b) Determine the mass of water vapour in 2 kg of saturated air at 5°C.

   (c) Air at 30°C is 50% saturated. Calculate the concentration of water vapour in this air.

2. Describe how you could use a sponge to illustrate a relative humidity of 0%, 100%, and 50%.

3. (a) Describe the conditions that allow dew to form.

   (b) During which months is dew most likely in your area? Based on your understanding of how dew forms, explain your answer.

4. Determine the relative humidity in each of the locations in **Table 2**, then state a possible outdoor location and time where the conditions might be found.

Table 2

Location	Dry-bulb temperature (°C)	Wet-bulb temperature (°C)
A	30	20
B	28	25
C	10	2

5. Why does 0°C with a 0°C dew point feel more uncomfortable than 0°C with a −10°C dew point? (The latter condition seems worse in wind.)

6. During which season(s) are dehumidifiers most commonly used? What advantages do they offer?

7. The air temperature in your bathroom is 22°C and the dew point is 12°C. After a warm shower adds moisture to the room, what is the new dew point? How does it compare with the original value? Describe why. (Assume the air temperature remains at 22°C.)

Making Connections

8. Some people say that the media oversimplify concepts by not being as precise as they could be. One example from a typical weather forecast is the statement that "the humidity is 70%."

   (a) What should the forecaster say to be more precise?

   (b) Explain the advantages and disadvantages of using precise scientific and technical terminology in the media.

9. One advantage of keeping the indoor air temperature at 21°C rather than 25°C in winter is that less heating fuel is needed. Another advantage is that the relative humidity is at a more comfortable level at the lower temperature. Explain the second advantage.

10. In the desert, dew on plants is a common event, yet fog is almost nonexistent. Why?

Exploring

11. At a temperature of 30°C, the concentration of water vapour is 10.81 g/kg of dry air. The saturated amount of this air would be 27.69 g/kg of dry air. Calculate the relative humidity.

Reflecting

12. How well do you think you could estimate the dew point on a given day? How could you improve this skill?

14.7 Investigation

INQUIRY SKILLS MENU
○ Questioning   ● Planning   ● Analyzing
○ Hypothesizing   ● Conducting   ● Evaluating
● Predicting   ● Recording   ● Communicating

Measuring Relative Humidity

Several instruments can be used to determine relative humidity. Some are sophisticated and relatively expensive; others are much simpler. In this investigation, you will design and build your own psychrometer and use it to determine the relative humidity at various locations and times.

To make this investigation more interesting and relevant, you can choose situations that resemble different outdoor conditions. For example, you could go into the school shower room 5 minutes after several people have showered, then determine the relative humidity. Also, if a humidifier and dehumidifier are available, you could test the effects each has on the relative humidity. Think of other ways of simulating actual environmental conditions that you think have a range of humidity.

Figure 1
Many types of psychrometers operate using two thermometers. Separate thermometers are the most accurate, since the cool air near a wet bulb can influence the temperature nearby.

You could have a major source of error in this investigation if your two thermometers do not read the same values. Always test the thermometers to be sure they read the same dry temperature before you use them.

Question

What factors affect the relative humidity in the air?

Prediction

Relative humidity depends on several factors. (Examples are air temperature, control devices, such as humidifiers, and location, such as indoors, outdoors, or in a shower room.)

(a) Choose which factor(s) you will investigate.
(b) For each factor, write a prediction describing
(K3) how you think it will affect relative humidity.

Design

(c) Design a controlled experiment, or several experiments, to investigate the factors you choose. You may want to choose a common location, such as the science classroom, for all groups to begin testing.
(d) Describe the independent, dependent, and controlled variables in your procedure.
(e) Create a procedure listing the steps you will take to test each prediction.
(f) Create a table in which you can record the data you gather. In the table, include space for recording qualitative observations (how the air "feels" to you).
(g) Design a psychrometer that you can use to investigate the factors you have chosen. (**Figure 1** shows various types of psychrometers.)
(h) Create a test you can use to determine the accuracy of your psychrometer.

SKILLS HANDBOOK: (K3) Developing the Prediction and Hypothesis

Part 1: Building a Psychrometer

Materials

(i) Make a list of the materials you will need to

(K5) build your own psychrometer.

Procedure

1 Have your teacher approve the design of your psychrometer and the test you will use to determine its accuracy.

2 Create a set of rules for the safe use of your psychrometer.

3 Build and test your psychrometer.

Part 2: Measuring Relative Humidity

4 Ask your teacher to approve your experimental design, your procedure, any safety precautions required, and your data table.

5 Carry out your investigation. Record the data

(K7) you collect in your table.

Analysis and Evaluation

(j) Evaluate your psychrometer. Based on your experiences while using it, how could it be improved?

(k) Compare your group's results for the relative humidity in your classroom (or other common area) with the results of other groups. Explain any discrepancies.

(l) Analyze your results. How does each factor you investigated affect relative humidity?

(m)Evaluate your predictions. Were they supported by the evidence you have collected?

(n) If you were to perform this investigation again, what changes could you make to improve the reliability of your results?

(Q) (o) Write a lab report for this investigation.

Understanding Concepts

1. Describe at least two ways to reduce the time needed for a wet-bulb thermometer to reach its lowest reading.

2. Is the relative humidity high or low when:

   (a) the wet- and dry-bulb temperatures are very close?

   (b) the wet- and dry-bulb temperatures are very different?

3. Is it possible for the dry-bulb temperature to be lower than that of the wet-bulb temperature? Explain your answer.

4. For the highest level of human comfort, how should the relative humidity indoors compare with that outdoors during (a) winter and (b) summer? Explain your answers.

5. How is relative humidity important to local weather events?

6. Sometimes condensation or frost forms on the inside of windows in buildings. Describe conditions that would cause these effects.

Making Connections

7. Would the psychrometer you designed in this investigation be convenient to use at a weather forecasting station? Describe any technical changes that would improve the design.

8. Design a feedback system that would keep the relative humidity at a comfortable level in your home during the winter. Use a diagram to help you describe your design.

Exploring

9. Is there any type of relative humidity meter or feedback system in your home? If there is, describe the device and its function.

 ## Challenge

1 How do the relative humidity readings you obtained compare with those given by local weather forecasters? Explain any differences.

2 Can you influence relative humidity in you community? What design factors might affect relatve humidity?

Weather Heritage

How many different types of snow and ice can you name? Some First Nations languages recognize up to 50 different forms of snow and ice, a system that allows detailed communication about weather conditions. The First Nations knowledge of weather is an example of our weather heritage, which consists of a great variety of words, sayings, and ideas that people have used over the years. Other examples of weather heritage involve legends and sayings that help people forecast weather by remembering what conditions cause changes and observing the variables associated with weather: atmospheric and cloud conditions, temperature, winds, and the reactions of animals and plants.

Figure 1
Thunderbird was a great champion of humanity who fought the water monster with lightning bolts.

Legend and Lore

Some of the cultural heritage related to weather is based on legends or myths. Cultures all over the world attribute the control of the Sun, Moon, winds, rain, snow, and other weather features to the actions of spirits and gods (**Figure 1**). When various North American tribes hold events such as a Sun Dance or a Rain Dance, they are celebrating rituals their ancestors performed in times of poor weather conditions. A legend to explain "Indian summer," a time of higher-than-average temperatures in the fall after first frost, tells of a god having one last smoke on his pipe before falling asleep for the winter.

Several of the sayings in the Try This Activity below are true in particular areas of the country or world. The most reliable sayings are those based on observations that have been made regularly for many years. Forecasts of the arrival of spring using a groundhog's shadow are less reliable (**Figure 2**).

Figure 2
This groundhog gains a lot of media attention each year on Groundhog Day, February 2. If it does not see its shadow, then the prediction is that spring will be early. But the groundhog's predictions come true only randomly.

Try This
Activity Forecast Sayings

Numerous expressions and rhymes that forecast the weather have been passed from generation to generation. Some may be local expressions, and others may have originated in other parts of the world. In a small group, discuss the following sayings, describe what you think each means, and think of a location where each might apply.

- Red sky at night, sailors delight; red sky in morning, sailors take warning.
- An east wind is a storm wind.

- Halo 'round the Sun or Moon, rain or snow coming soon.
- Clear Moon, frost soon.
- When the stars begin to huddle, Earth will soon become a puddle.
- A year of snow, a year of plenty.
- In like a lion, out like a lamb; in like a lamb, out like a lion (usually said of the month of March).
- When the sunset is grey, tomorrow may be a rainy day.

Naming Snow and Ice

What type of snow is best for building an igloo in Canada's Arctic? Rather than wet snow, snowflakes, or feathery snow, you would likely choose packed snow. These four examples are only a small sample of the many types of snow that Canadians experience. In English, most of these names use the word "snow" combined with a modifier. In some First Nations languages, however, the words are actually different. A similar set of words is used for ice (**Figure 3**).

Some of the English names for the numerous types of snow and ice observed by First Nations peoples are listed in **Table 1**. As you read them, try to identify which come from inland regions, which come from coastal regions, and which may come from both.

Sometimes pack ice gathers in a harbour even in July, preventing boats from leaving. People who live with such conditions have specific names for them.

Table 1   **First Nations Words for Snow and Ice**

West Greenlandic		Labradoran	
Inuit	**English**	**Inuit**	**English**
qaniit	snow falling in air	aput	snow
qanik	snowflake	massak	soft snow
nittaalaq	air thick with snow	mauja	soft, deep snow
nittaalaaqqat	hard grains of snow	tipvigut	snowdrift
pukak	snow crust	sikko	ice
putsinniq	wet snow on top of ice	tingenek	bare ice
qinuq	rotten snow, or slush on sea		
nilak	piece of freshwater ice		
nutarniq	new ice formed in crack in old ice		
uukkarnit	calved ice (broken off, as from an iceberg)		
kassuq	drifting lump of ice		

Nature's Forecasters

Some people say that pets or birds and wild animals can act as weather forecasters. There may be some truth to such claims. A thunderstorm produces static electricity in the air, which would affect a cat's fur and may explain why a cat would sneeze or scratch its face. On the Caribbean islands, twitching cats' tails are associated with approaching hurricanes. Some think it is caused by the sensitivity of cats to the high-pitched sounds of winds coming through door or window cracks.

Nature provides other examples of sensitivity associated with changing weather. The dropping air pressure that foretells unsettled weather causes swallows to fly lower than normal, deer and elk to come down from the mountains and seek shelter, and some animals to feed more than usual. The higher humidity before a storm causes some insects to leave trees and gather near the ground and some flowers to close up so rain doesn't get inside. In winter, the leaves of rhododendron plants curl up in self-preservation as the temperature drops (**Figure 4**).

Of course it's true that seeing a robin near the end of winter is a reliable sign of spring. But whether a long, cold winter can be predicted by squirrels being fatter or cats' fur becoming longer than usual in the fall is extremely difficult to test scientifically.

These photographs show the same rhododendron shrub.

(a) At 2°C the leaves are flat.

(b) At −10°C the leaves are curled.

Verifying Forecast Sayings

Consider a small selection of the forecast sayings in the Try This Activity on page 564. The ones that are short-term forecasts tend to be supported by scientific observation in some areas of the country.

Red sky at night, sailors delight. Reddish skies at sunset and sunrise are caused when sunlight scatters off dust and water vapour particles. Since condensation of water vapour begins on tiny dust particles, a reddish sky is associated with the possibility of rain. Since our weather systems move from west to east, the moisture content at night may be gone by the next day (a delight), whereas the moisture in the morning may turn into rain later in the day (a warning).

Halo 'round the Sun or Moon, rain or snow coming soon. The first clouds that appear when a warm front meets a cold air mass are high cirrus clouds. The ice crystals in these clouds bend the light from the Sun or Moon, forming a circular halo, thus warning that unsettled weather is approaching.

Clear Moon, frost soon. The Moon can't be seen well unless the sky is clear. At night, soil and other objects on the ground radiate energy upward, and clouds absorb some of that energy and radiate it back down. If the sky is clear, there is little or no reradiated energy, and the surface temperature drops more than it would on a cloudy night. Under favourable conditions, the low surface temperature will allow frost to form in the colder seasons.

Challenge

2 Have you considered using some interesting weather-related names for the avenues, parks, and recreational trails in your community?

3 How might heritage ideas of the weather add interest to your weather network?

Did You Know?

Some people with arthritis or other joint problems can foretell unsettled weather: the drop in atmospheric pressure causes more inflammation and pain than usual.

🖑 Work the Web

From www.science.nelson.com follow the links for Science 10, 14.8 to sites that focus on weather folklore. Choose one site and find at least one interesting story you can share with others.

Understanding Concepts

1. Explain why some First Nations languages have many names for ice and snow.

2. Is the behaviour of plants and animals more likely to be accurate in short- or long-term weather forecasting? Why?

Making Connections

3. Describe how you would design an investigation to determine the reliability of some of nature's short-term forecasters. Predict the results from your investigation.

4. Some people can estimate relative humidity by checking the (K) outdoor visibility range (the distance one can see with the naked eye). Describe how you would perform an experiment to determine the relationship between relative humidity and visibility range.

Exploring

5. *Phenology* is the study of plant growth throughout the (I) seasons. Find out more about this branch of science, and in (J) your notebook describe its major findings.

6. Research more of nature's forecasters such as the reactions of cows, bees, frogs, spiders, pine cones, and seaweed to changing weather. Create a visual presentation of what you discover.

Reflecting

7. Revisit your answers to the Try This Activity, page 564. (I) What ideas did you have then that you still believe to be (J) true now?

SKILLS HANDBOOK: (K) Planning an Investigation (I) (J) Research Skills

Weather Forecasting Technology

We live in a dynamic society. People are constantly on the move: we use buses, subways, or cars to commute to school or to work; we use trucks on complex highway systems to deliver food and manufactured products over much of the continent; some of us use air transportation to fly to vacation destinations or business meetings. Some people operate farms, ranches, orchards, vineyards, tree farms, ecotours, fishing fleets, fish farms, and nurseries (**Figure 1**).

We also lead active recreational lives: we cycle, jog, skateboard, snowboard, ski, and golf; play tennis, field hockey, soccer, football, baseball, and many other outdoor sports; and attend professional sporting events, often preferring to be outside during pleasant weather. We all need to know about the weather; we are the reason why our society devotes so many resources to weather forecasting.

Weather forecasting relies on the collection of weather-related data. Canada is a leading nation in collecting and analyzing such data, with many people involved in collecting that data, researching factors that affect weather, writing forecasts, and communicating weather information to the public.

Figure 1
Accurate forecasts are particularly important to those who work outdoors.

Changing Technologies

Up to about 1980, weather forecasts were accurate for the short term, only about one day unless the weather was stable. Currently, they are accurate for longer, often about three days. In the future, forecasts may be accurate for longer periods.

Weather forecasting has improved for several reasons. Many of the factors used to forecast weather have remained the same: temperature, atmospheric pressure, humidity and relative humidity, wind speed and direction, precipitation, and cloud formations. However, the technologies applied to observe, analyze, and communicate these factors are now greatly advanced. More importantly, however, the theories explaining how these factors are interrelated have advanced as computers became more powerful, more people became involved in research, more satellites were launched to observe weather patterns, and the number of observation stations increased.

Weather Satellites and Aircraft

A **weather satellite** is an orbiting spacecraft that regularly gathers weather-related data and obtains images, and relays them to stations on the ground (**Figure 2**). High-orbit satellites travel in a geosynchronous orbit, that is, they stay above a fixed point on Earth as Earth rotates on its axis. Their orbits are about 36 000 km above Earth's equator. Many lower-orbit satellites travel in polar orbits about 1000 km above Earth; they orbit Earth around the poles approximately once every 2 h.

> ### Did You Know?
>
> On March 1, 1977, Environment Canada issued its first five-day forecast. Until that date, the longest forecasts issued were for 48 h only.

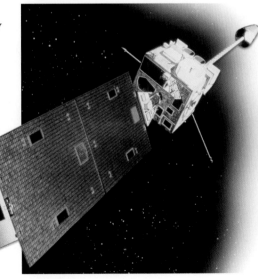

Figure 2
A weather satellite like this one took the image on page 568.

High-orbit satellites detect eletromagnetic radiation from various levels of the atmosphere. They provide images using visible light, which is especially useful to observe cloud cover, as well as infrared heat images, which show the amount of infrared radiation from the atmosphere and Earth's surface features.

Lower-orbit satellites gather data using infrared and microwave energies. Such data help detect changes in air temperature and water vapour at various levels in the atmosphere as well as global wind patterns such as the jet streams.

Special aircraft that travel at altitudes up to 20 km are also used in weather forecasting. For example, onboard instruments measure and collect samples of ice crystals in the atmosphere and report on the upper-level winds, the temperature, cloud heights, and turbulence.

Weather Balloons

A **weather balloon** is a helium-filled balloon used to gather weather-related data as it rises in the atmosphere (**Figure 3**). Weather balloons are launched two or more times each day from stations all across North America, and sometimes they are released from airplanes above the ocean. The balloon may rise to an altitude of 30 km, sending data to ground-based receivers as it rises and floats along with the winds.

Instruments carried by a weather balloon collect temperature, pressure, humidity, and ice-crystal data. The instruments send these data to receivers on the ground for analysis. Weather balloons can also be tracked by radio waves (radar systems), which allow observers to determine the speed and direction of upper-level winds.

Figure 3
Weather balloons are filled with a low-density gas, which allows them to rise high in the troposphere.

Try This
Activity Interpreting Satellite Images

Satellites use different wavelengths of the electromagnetic spectrum to produce the images used in weather forecasts. A visible light image looks just like a regular photograph. The image in **Figure 4** was obtained using visible light. Study it and answer these questions.

(a) Estimate the size of the area viewed in the image. (Use a map as reference.)

(b) Describe the characteristics of any weather systems you can see in the image, including pressure systems, fronts, and cyclones.

(c) What other weather-related factors would you need to know about in order to forecast the next day's weather?

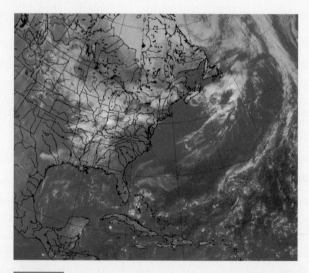

Figure 4

Ground-Based Technology

Across Canada and around the world, numerous weather stations and portable devices keep track of changing weather conditions. **Figure 5** shows some of the instruments used at these stations.

Computer Technology

If you have accessed some of the weather web sites, you already know that a huge amount of weather information is available online. Without computers, much of this information would be unavailable, even to the weather forecasters.

Computers are important to meteorologists for several reasons. Data from weather satellites, aircraft, weather balloons, and ground-based instruments are gathered, stored, and analyzed by computers. Computer models are used by researchers to study what could happen if certain factors are varied. And computers linked to satellite communication systems allow people to send and receive information quickly anywhere in the world.

Computers also offer a convenient and interesting way of learning about the weather. Games and weather simulators available for personal computers allow you to plot graphs of data you collect and forecast weather for situations presented in the program.

Figure 5

Weather stations measure the same factors you can measure at school. **(a)** Thermometer measures current minimum and maximum temperatures; **(b)** anemometer measures wind speed and direction; **(c)** rain gauge measures rainfall; **(d)** hydrometer measures relative humidity; **(e)** aneroid barometer measures atmospheric pressure.

Stations at School and at Home

If you were setting up a weather station at your school or home (**Figure 6**), you would need certain minimum requirements. In order to measure weather variables, you would need a regular thermometer, a wet-bulb thermometer, an anemometer (wind sensor), and a gauge to measure rainfall or snowfall. You could design some of these instruments or buy them commercially.

Portable weather stations are available commercially. These small, electronic stations can keep track of 4 to 20 or more variables, including those you have learned about in this unit. They also provide weather forecasts for the next 12 to 24 h.

Figure 6

The instruments in a weather station must be placed in a small, shuttered housing unit so that sunlight can't affect the data by raising the temperature.

Understanding Concepts

1. Record as many reasons as you can why weather forecasts are important to you and members of your family. Consider transportation, recreation, and work-related situations.

2. Critically evaluate the following statement: "Without electricity, weather forecasting would be much different."

3. According to the ideas in this section, list the parts of the electromagnetic spectrum that are used in weather forecasting technology. Describe an example of how each part is used.

4. Suggest a reason why helium is used in weather balloons.

5. Name the aspects of weather that can be measured by ground-based instruments or that cannot be measured by satellites and weather balloons.

Making Connections

6. Suggest and describe some ways in which environmental scientists could take advantage of the data-gathering technology introduced in this section.

Exploring

7. A radiosonde is an instrument carried aloft by a weather balloon to record a variety of data. Other types of "sondes" are the dropsonde and rawinsonde. Use a dictionary and other resources to find out about the sondes mentioned. Share what you discover with others in your class.

8. Research weather balloons and find out whether they are retrieved after they have sent the data they collected.

Challenge

1 What information could you gain by launching a small meteorological balloon?

2 How can people in your community receive and send weather and other data worldwide?

3 What source of information is best to access information about weather data collected daily?

Work the Web

Visit www.science.nelson.com, follow the links for Science 10, 14.9 to visit weather technology sites such as the Canadian Space Agency. Research the technologies presented in this section. Focus on one example and describe its advantages in a paragraph.

SKILLS HANDBOOK: Ⓙ Internet Research

14.10 Investigation

INQUIRY SKILLS MENU
- ○ Questioning
- ● Hypothesizing
- ○ Predicting
- ● Planning
- ● Conducting
- ● Recording
- ● Analyzing
- ● Evaluating
- ● Communicating

Forecasting the Weather

Traditional and technological approaches to weather forecasting share an important feature: both involve observations gathered over a period of time, from hours to days and longer. Thus, however simple or complex a weather investigation becomes, you can't expect to finish it in one day.

This investigation can be done individually or in small groups. It involves collecting North American data daily from various sources. After collecting and analyzing data for at least three days, you will forecast the weather for the next two days and compare your forecasts with the actual weather.

Question

What aspects of weather-related data, gathered from electronic or printed resources, are most important for constructing reliable short-term forecasts?

Hypothesis

(a) Reflect on the aspects of weather you will need (K3) and write a hypothesis that answers the question.

Design

(b) Design your investigation using the following questions to guide your planning:
- What aspects of weather data will you collect?
- How frequently, and at what times of the day, will you collect data?
- Will you need to collect some data more frequently than others?
- How will you record your data?
- How will you record your forecasts and the actual weather so that you can easily make accurate comparisons?
- How will you judge the accuracy of your predictions?
- How will you ensure the safety of the investigators and others in the community?

Materials

(c) Make a list of the materials you will need to accomplish the task.

Procedure

1. Submit your design to your teacher for approval.

2. Perform the investigation. Record your data, forecasts, and actual weather.

Analysis and Evaluation

(d) List all the factors or variables that you tracked in this investigation. Which of these factors were the most useful in forecasting the weather for the next day or two? Explain and justify your selection.

(e) Evaluate your forecasts by comparing them to actual weather.

(f) List your conclusions about which data are most important to forming reliable forecasts.

(Q) (g) Write a lab report of your investigation.

Making Connections

1. Explain which is more important in weather forecasting: the actual atmospheric pressure at a particular time or the trend in how the atmospheric pressure is changing.

2. Which do you think is more informative: the daily newspaper forecasts or the forecasts found on the Internet? Why?

3. Under what conditions are five-day forecasts likely to be
   (a) reliable?
   (b) quite unreliable?

Exploring

4. Analyze the local weather forecasts from two or three different sources. Do the forecasts agree? Describe what you discover.

 ## Challenge

1 How much more detail will you present in your Challenge than what was required in this investigation?

15 Extreme Weather Events

HOW STRONG DOES WIND HAVE TO BE TO TOPPLE A GARBAGE CAN?
Now imagine winds powerful enough to pick up a truck and toss it the
length of a football field. Winds of this magnitude sometimes happen
in a tornado (**Figure 1**).

A tornado is just one example of an extreme weather event.
In the previous two chapters you studied the main types of weather events.
Now you will learn about the causes and effects of extreme weather events.
It is during extreme events that records of the greatest winds, most rainfall,
and deepest snowfall are challenged and sometimes broken.

Figure 1

An approaching tornado is a terrifying sight. Notice the funnel shape of the storm cloud.

14.10 Investigation

INQUIRY SKILLS MENU
○ Questioning   ● Planning   ● Analyzing
● Hypothesizing   ● Conducting   ● Evaluating
○ Predicting   ● Recording   ● Communicating

Forecasting the Weather

Traditional and technological approaches to weather forecasting share an important feature: both involve observations gathered over a period of time, from hours to days and longer. Thus, however simple or complex a weather investigation becomes, you can't expect to finish it in one day.

This investigation can be done individually or in small groups. It involves collecting North American data daily from various sources. After collecting and analyzing data for at least three days, you will forecast the weather for the next two days and compare your forecasts with the actual weather.

Question

What aspects of weather-related data, gathered from electronic or printed resources, are most important for constructing reliable short-term forecasts?

Hypothesis

(a) Reflect on the aspects of weather you will need
(K3) and write a hypothesis that answers the question.

Design

(b) Design your investigation using the following questions to guide your planning:
- What aspects of weather data will you collect?
- How frequently, and at what times of the day, will you collect data?
- Will you need to collect some data more frequently than others?
- How will you record your data?
- How will you record your forecasts and the actual weather so that you can easily make accurate comparisons?
- How will you judge the accuracy of your predictions?
- How will you ensure the safety of the investigators and others in the community?

Materials

(c) Make a list of the materials you will need to accomplish the task.

Procedure

1 Submit your design to your teacher for approval.

2 Perform the investigation. Record your data, forecasts, and actual weather.

Analysis and Evaluation

(d) List all the factors or variables that you tracked in this investigation. Which of these factors were the most useful in forecasting the weather for the next day or two? Explain and justify your selection.
(e) Evaluate your forecasts by comparing them to actual weather.
(f) List your conclusions about which data are most important to forming reliable forecasts.
(Q) (g) Write a lab report of your investigation.

Making Connections

1. Explain which is more important in weather forecasting: the actual atmospheric pressure at a particular time or the trend in how the atmospheric pressure is changing.

2. Which do you think is more informative: the daily newspaper forecasts or the forecasts found on the Internet? Why?

3. Under what conditions are five-day forecasts likely to be
(a) reliable?
(b) quite unreliable?

Exploring

4. Analyze the local weather forecasts from two or three different sources. Do the forecasts agree? Describe what you discover.

◉ Challenge

1 How much more detail will you present in your Challenge than what was required in this investigation?

14.11 Explore an Issue

DECISION MAKING SKILLS
- Define the Issue
- Identify Alternatives
- Research
- Analyze the Issue
- Defend a Decision
- Evaluate

The Weather Forecasting Business

"Never cry wolf!" Weather forecasters sometimes hear this plea from people who face evacuation orders when a severe storm is forecast (**Figure 1**). It is extremely costly to evacuate up to hundreds of thousands of people, leaving behind homes, schools, and businesses. And if the forecast turns out to be wrong, the evacuated people return home blaming the forecasters for inaccurate predictions. How often would you go through this process before deciding to ignore warnings?

In contrast, if a weather forecaster fails to predict a severe storm that causes death and property destruction, he or she is blamed for the disaster. The modern forecaster faces a dilemma when lives and property are in danger.

Figure 1

Although the compulsory evacuation of an island off the Atlantic Coast of the United States may save many lives if a hurricane strikes, it can create frustrating traffic problems.

The Forecasting Business

Weather forecasting is a major economic business. Accurate forecasts can save harvests or affect the sales of soft drinks and other beverages, the use of heating fuels, the efficiency of electrical generation, and so on. Of course, saving lives and property is also important, and the insurance industry relies heavily on weather forecasts to ensure that it remains profitable.

Traditionally, national governments have been responsible for weather forecasts. In Canada, for example, Environment Canada is the branch of the federal government that gathers and distributes weather information. The World Meteorological Organization, which is part of the United Nations, organizes sharing of weather data among nearly 200 nations. However, private companies are becoming more involved in weather forecasting, mainly because they can make profits from it.

Using the Internet

Satellites cost hundreds of millions of dollars to design, construct, launch, and operate. Furthermore, the powerful computers needed to analyze the data collected are costly. So how do smaller, private companies make profits? They access the data available from the government-funded satellites to create their own forecasts for specific purposes. Then they sell the information to various markets, such as the media, shipping companies, businesspeople, and sports enthusiasts.

Although the United Nations has a regulation stating that a private company can sell weather information only in its own country, the Internet has made that regulation obsolete. The media do not mind paying for weather forecasts from private companies because weather forecasts generate money in another major way: advertising. Whether or not the forecasting business remains profitable, it is an issue worth exploring.

Role Play Weather Forecasting for Profit

Proposition

Only government-run and public enterprises, such as universities and meteorological services, should be allowed to profit from weather forecasting.

Point

- Taxes collected by the government pay for a lot of the research, technology development, and data collecting and analyzing, so profits should be returned to the government.

- If profits were made by government agencies, taxes could be reduced or redirected to other causes.

- Private companies may ignore small countries where profits may be small, whereas government agencies could share information with all countries.

- There is a moral obligation to share weather information freely because it can affect the safety of people and property. It is not right that such information be made available only to those who can afford to pay for it.

Counterpoint

- Profits should go to private companies only. If profits go to government agencies, then government policy might be influenced by money rather than by ideas.

- If a company invests money in gathering and analyzing weather information, it should be allowed to get its money back as well as profit for its investors.

- Small countries can access information from the Internet just as easily as large countries can.

- Government-run services must compete with private enterprises in order to perform to their potential.

Forming an Opinion

- You have been appointed to a panel to make a decision on the above proposition. You might be a
- Ⓓ meteorologist, a TV weather reporter, a relief-agency volunteer, a newspaper owner, an Internet provider, an advertising specialist, an insurance company president, an engineer at an electrical generating station, a taxpayer, the owner of a private weather information company, or someone else you think would have an opinion on the subject.
- Prepare a position you think someone in your role would adopt and defend that position in the
- Ⓖ panel discussion.
- Ⓢ

Understanding the Issue

1. Explain in your own words what the expression "never cry wolf" means in relation to weather forecasting.

2. The United Nations regulation regarding selling weather information is difficult to enforce. Explain why this is so.

🖑 Work the Web

To research private companies involved in weather forecasting and how government agencies operate, visit www.science.nelson.com and follow the links for Science 10, 14.11. Describe profitable services provided by both private companies and government agencies.

Understanding Concepts

1. Compare and contrast each pair of items listed below:
   (a) a maritime tropical air mass and a continental polar air mass;
   (b) a warm front and a cold front;
   (c) a cyclone and an anticyclone.

2. **Figure 1** shows a typical weather forecasting instrument found in many homes.
   (a) What is this instrument?
   (b) What does it measure?
   (c) How do the labels relate to atmospheric change?

3. Use Bernoulli's principle to explain the operation of a paint sprayer (**Figure 2**).

Figure 1

Figure 2

4. (a) In what part of a cyclone — the middle or the outside edge — is wind speed the greatest?
   (b) In what part of a cyclone is atmospheric pressure the least?
   (c) Use a scientific principle you studied to relate your answers in (a) and (b).

5. Name two locations in Canada where each of the following may occur (and explain your answers):
   (a) a sea breeze;
   (b) a thermal updraft.

6. It is possible to have dew without fog, but not fog without dew. Explain why.

7. If a car is left outdoors overnight, would you expect any dew or frost to form in each case described in **Table 1**? Explain why.

Table 1

	Daytime high (°C)	Dew point (°C)	Nighttime low (°C)
A	19	9	7
B	13	6	8
C	4	−3	−4

8. Draw a diagram to show the stages in the formation of (a) snow and (b) freezing rain.

9. A satellite records data from an instrument that measures infrared radiation from Earth's surface. State whether you think the radiation readings for the following situations would be high, medium, or low:
   (a) The nighttime sky is clear over farmland;
   (b) The nighttime sky is clear over ocean water;
   (c) The nighttime sky is cloudy over farmland;
   (d) The nighttime sky is cloudy over ocean water.

10. A student goes from indoors where the dry- and wet-bulb temperatures are 20°C and 14°C, respectively, to outdoors where the corresponding temperatures are 20°C and 18°C, respectively.
    (a) What happens to the comfort level?
    (b) A glass containing a cold drink has condensation on the outside when indoors. If the student takes the drink outdoors, what is likely to happen to the condensation? Explain.

11. Do meteorologists have to retrieve the instruments carried by a weather balloon in order to collect the measured data? Explain your answer.

12. Describe ways in which Canadians contribute to global meteorology.

13. One way to estimate outside temperature is to measure the rate of chirping of a cricket, one of nature's forecasters. At 10°C, crickets chirp about 9 times per minute, at 20°C about 15 times per minute, and at 30°C about 21 times per minute.
    (a) Plot the given data on a graph, with "temperature" on the horizontal axis.
    (b) What temperature corresponds to 18 chirps per minute? to 3 chirps per minute?

14. Several observations that can be used to forecast short-term weather follow. Enter each observation in a table with four columns: Continuing Fair Weather; Unsettled Weather Soon; Precipitation Soon; Clearing Weather Soon. Be prepared to explain your choices.

(a) The barometer is falling steadily or rapidly.
(b) A clear blue morning sky is seen to the west.
(c) The barometer reading is rising quickly.
(d) The barometer reading is steady or rising slightly.
(e) Rain is stopping and clouds are breaking up at sunset.
(f) Clouds are moving from east or northeast toward the south.
(g) Early morning fog is clearing.
(h) A halo is seen around the Sun or Moon.
(i) A cold front has passed over farmland (with no bodies of water) in the past 4 to 7 hours.
(j) A gentle wind is blowing from the west or northwest.
(k) The sky is dark and threatening to the west.
(l) There is morning fog or dew.
(m) There is a red sky in the morning.
(n) The wind shifts to the east and increases.

Applying Inquiry Skills

15. (a) Describe how you would determine the relative humidity in your classroom and outdoors.
    (b) How would you expect these two values to compare today? Give actual estimates of the relative humidity in each case.
    (c) Does your school have a system that controls relative humidity? How can you tell?

16. Describe how you would demonstrate and explain to Grade 8 students each of the following concepts:
    (a) the direction of rotation in a cyclone in the Northern Hemisphere;
    (b) the difference between a sea breeze and a land breeze;
    (c) the dew point in a classroom;
    (d) the formation of freezing rain.

17. Describe how you would use weather maps to determine the speed of a particular pressure system across Canada. Use estimated values to give a sample calculation.

18. Design an experiment you could perform to determine the relationship between the depth of snowfall and the equivalent depth of rain.

19. Starting with introductory comments and a scientific question, design an investigation to determine the validity of the long-term forecasts associated with Groundhog Day. Describe the results you would expect from your investigation.

20. Think of a way you could link the technical design of a barometer to Bernoulli's principle. Then describe a way to test your idea, including safety precautions. If your teacher approves, try it.

Making Connections

21. Imagine you are a TV weather reporter. Describe what you would do to try to get the highest ratings in your region for a weather forecasting show.

22. Humidifiers can pose a health hazard if not used properly. Suggest why.

23. Loosely packed snow provides excellent insulation but loses this property when packed down. How might snowmobiles affect the survival of animals hibernating directly underneath their trails?

24. Deicing airplanes is an important safety procedure (**Figure 3**).

Figure 3

(a) What weather conditions are likely to cause icing on airplanes?
(b) Research to find out more about the problem of icing and the procedure of deicing. Report on what you discover.

25. Snow fences are designed to reduce unwanted drifting (**Figure 4**).

Figure 4

(a) Speculate about where these fences would have the greatest benefit. Explain your reasoning.
(b) Research to find out how accurate your answers in (a) are.

26. Explain how climatological data can be used to choose locations for weather-sensitive entities such as airports and stadiums.

Getting Started

HOW STRONG DOES WIND HAVE TO BE TO TOPPLE A GARBAGE CAN? Now imagine winds powerful enough to pick up a truck and toss it the length of a football field. Winds of this magnitude sometimes happen in a tornado (**Figure 1**).

A tornado is just one example of an extreme weather event. In the previous two chapters you studied the main types of weather events. Now you will learn about the causes and effects of extreme weather events. It is during extreme events that records of the greatest winds, most rainfall, and deepest snowfall are challenged and sometimes broken.

Figure 1

An approaching tornado is a terrifying sight. Notice the funnel shape of the storm cloud.

Some of the extreme weather you will learn about occur elsewhere in the world, but many happen in Canada. Perhaps such an event has occurred in your area. How would you protect yourself during such an event?

Scientists use modern technology to research extreme weather, and sometimes in surprising places. For example, satellites and remote sensors gather temperature data and determine sea level heights from the Pacific Ocean; this information can help scientists understand and predict weather as far away as Central Canada.

Extreme weather events are major news items for the media, especially television, which can combine the sounds of horrendous winds or rushing water with the visual images of buildings blown out to sea or people on rooftops of flooded homes waiting to be rescued. Sometimes the media go beyond the dramatic visual highlights and try to explain the causes and newest theories of the extreme weather by interviewing experts. Another important media role is to warn the public of severe weather events. Many lives and properties have been saved because of warnings of dangerous storms.

Reflect on your Learning

1. List as many examples of dangerous, extreme weather events as you can. Suggest which is the easiest and which is the most difficult to forecast. Explain your selections.

2. For each of the following regions of Canada, state the extreme weather events you think are most likely to occur. (More than one event may be named for each region.)
   (a) British Columbia and western Alberta
   (b) the Prairies
   (c) the Arctic region
   (d) Ontario and Quebec
   (e) the Atlantic provinces

3. Which extreme weather events do you think could hit your town or city?

4. Human activities and natural phenomena can combine to create a different form of extreme weather event. Why do you think some locations get "air quality warnings" on certain hot summer days?

Throughout this chapter, note any changes in your ideas as you learn new concepts and develop your skills.

Try This
Activity   Dangerous Situations

In a group, discuss what actions you would take to survive in each situation described below. For each situation, provide a brief summary of your decisions.

- You are staying at a two-storey hotel on the beach of an ocean, and a hurricane is approaching.
- You are at home when you hear a tornado warning on the radio.
- You are canoeing on a lake, and you hear a thunderstorm approaching.

- You live on a cattle ranch near the banks of a river whose flooding waters will threaten the cattle in a few days.
- You live in a large city where freezing rain is forecast to last for 48 h.
- You are staying at an isolated, rural cottage as a blizzard is approaching. You know that last winter a similar storm blacked out electricity for a week.

Weather Records and Events

Imagine that you are responsible for choosing which weather-related events to report in the news or to classify as world records. What factors would be important in selecting the events? Would you consider the events with the highest winds, the greatest amount of precipitation, the greatest amount of flooding, or the highest and lowest temperatures? How important is property damage? How important are factors that can't be judged on the day of the disaster, such as long-term loss of income, the cost of repairs, and the stress on victims? And isn't the most important factor the number of lives lost and people injured?

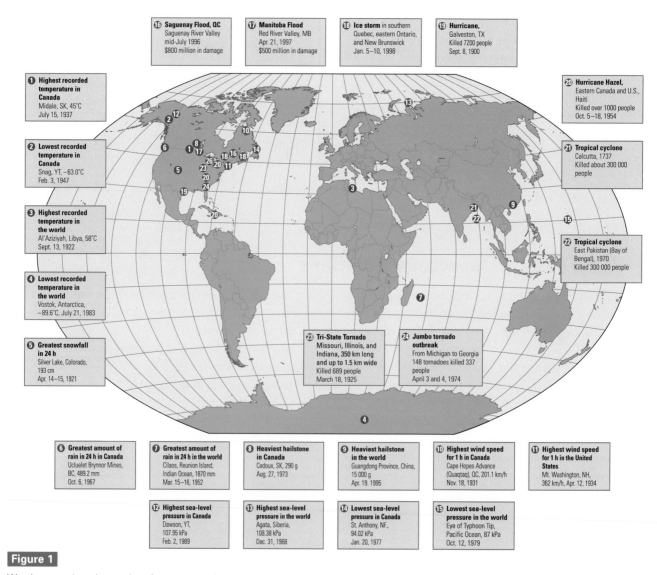

16 **Saguenay Flood, QC**
Saguenay River Valley
mid-July 1996
$800 million in damage

17 **Manitoba Flood**
Red River Valley, MB
Apr. 21, 1997
$500 million in damage

18 **Ice storm** in southern
Quebec, eastern Ontario,
and New Brunswick
Jan. 5–10, 1998

19 **Hurricane,**
Galveston, TX
Killed 7200 people
Sept. 8, 1900

1 **Highest recorded temperature in Canada**
Midale, SK, 45°C
July 15, 1937

2 **Lowest recorded temperature in Canada**
Snag, YT, –63.0°C
Feb. 3, 1947

3 **Highest recorded temperature in the world**
Al'Aziziyah, Libya, 58°C
Sept. 13, 1922

4 **Lowest recorded temperature in the world**
Vostok, Antarctica,
–89.6°C, July 21, 1983

5 **Greatest snowfall in 24 h**
Silver Lake, Colorado,
193 cm
Apr. 14–15, 1921

20 **Hurricane Hazel,**
Eastern Canada and U.S.,
Haiti
Killed over 1000 people
Oct. 5–18, 1954

21 **Tropical cyclone**
Calcutta, 1737
Killed about 300 000
people

22 **Tropical cyclone**
East Pakistan (Bay of
Bengal), 1970
Killed 300 000 people

23 **Tri-State Tornado**
Missouri, Illinois, and
Indiana, 350 km long
and up to 1.5 km wide
Killed 689 people
March 18, 1925

24 **Jumbo tornado outbreak**
From Michigan to Georgia
148 tornadoes killed 337
people
April 3 and 4, 1974

6 **Greatest amount of rain in 24 h in Canada**
Ucluelet Brynnor Mines,
BC, 489.2 mm
Oct. 6, 1967

7 **Greatest amount of rain in 24 h in the world**
Cilaos, Reunion Island,
Indian Ocean, 1870 mm
Mar. 15–16, 1952

8 **Heaviest hailstone in Canada**
Cedoux, SK, 290 g
Aug. 27, 1973

9 **Heaviest hailstone in the world**
Guangdong Province, China,
15 000 g
Apr. 19. 1995

10 **Highest wind speed for 1 h in Canada**
Cape Hopes Advance
(Quaqtaq), QC, 201.1 km/h
Nov. 18, 1931

11 **Highest wind speed for 1 h in the United States**
Mt. Washington, NH,
362 km/h, Apr. 12, 1934

12 **Highest sea-level pressure in Canada**
Dawson, YT,
107.95 kPa
Feb. 2, 1989

13 **Highest sea-level pressure in the world**
Agata, Siberia,
108.38 kPa
Dec. 31, 1968

14 **Lowest sea-level pressure in Canada**
St. Anthony, NF.,
94.02 kPa
Jan. 20, 1977

15 **Lowest sea-level pressure in the world**
Eye of Typhoon Tip,
Pacific Ocean, 87 kPa
Oct. 12, 1979

Figure 1

Weather records and examples of extreme weather events

When these events are reported in the media, usually all of these factors are considered. But the final decision of which events to report depends on whether the report will engage the viewing, listening, or reading audience. Therefore, the media focus on the immediate damage of a storm and put much less emphasis on the long-term effects.

When choosing weather events as world records, the main reason for acceptance is that the reported measurement was made at a weather station that has been in operation for several years. A record-breaking wind speed may be recorded at a new weather station, but it won't be accepted as a record.

The map in **Figure 1** shows many world and Canadian weather records. It also shows the types and locations of the extreme weather events you will learn about in this chapter.

Understanding Concepts

1. To find patterns of events and records on the map in **Figure 1**, you may have to refer to a globe or a more detailed map. Describe what you notice about the location of

   (a) record high temperatures;

   (b) record low temperatures;

   (c) record high rainfall;

   (d) record high snowfall.

2. Based on the map in **Figure 1**, describe some key ways in which Canada's weather is different from weather elsewhere in the world.

3. In terms of Canadian records and extreme weather events, how does your town or city compare with other areas in Canada? in the world?

4. Almost all the events featured in **Figure 1** occurred within the past 100 years. Why do you think that is?

Making Connections

5. If you were choosing weather-related events for today's news, which factor would you consider to be most important in helping you make your choice? Which would you consider least important? Justify your choices.

6. Suggest some technical difficulties scientists might face in trying to measure extreme values of precipitation, winds, and temperatures.

7. Several hurricanes stronger than the one in Galveston in 1900 have struck U.S. coastlines recently, but in most cases the number of people killed was much less than in that storm. Suggest some reasons why.

Exploring

8. Find at least one resource that provides up-to-date
   (J) information on world weather records. Are all the records shown in **Figure 1** still valid?

Reflecting

9. What are your memories of the worst storm(s) you have ever experienced? In a few paragraphs, describe your experiences in the storm and the emotions you felt.

Work the Web

Find at least one site that provides up-to-date information on extreme weather events around the world. Bookmark the site and describe the type of information it provides.

Challenge

2 How well will your community fare during an extreme weather event?

3 Which types of extreme weather events are possible in locations where students in your network live?

Weather in the News

Television and radio stations communicate three types of extreme weather alerts as public service announcements. The alerts are called "watches," "advisories," and "warnings." It is important to understand what these terms mean so that when you hear them on the news, you know how and when to react.

A **watch** means that conditions are present for extreme weather to occur in your area, so you should pay attention to further news updates. An **advisory** means that severe weather, likely to cause local problems and inconveniences, is predicted for your area. And a **warning** means that extreme weather is highly likely to arrive somewhere in your area or may already be happening, so you should take appropriate precautions. Weather alerts should be taken seriously; they are broadcast by the media only after they have been issued by the Meteorological Service of Canada.

Such forecasts are only one of the many services offered by the news media. In this activity you will find out as much as you can about the types of news and services available through the media, and compare the coverage of weather-related information by different media (**Figure 1**).

Materials

- resources such as a local daily newspaper, a weather radio station, a TV weather channel, the Internet, and a periodical magazine

Procedure

1 Discuss with other members of your group how (X) you will collect and record weather-related news for a predetermined amount of time, such as three weeks. Distribute the research responsibilities among the group members.

2 Collect and record news items presented in the media. Focus on daily news items and forecasts, weekly features, explanations of weather events, and items related to special events such as severe storms and disaster relief.

3 Compare and contrast the weather-related services for each medium your group researched.

Figure 1

These titles show a variety of weather-related topics presented in the media.

SKILLS HANDBOOK: (X) Working Together

Analysis and Evaluation

(a) In your opinion, which medium available to the public
   (i)   has the most information available on a daily basis?
   (ii)   has the least information available on a daily basis?
   (iii) is the most convenient for you to access?
   (iv)   is the least convenient for you to access?
   (v)   has the most detailed analysis of the causes of weather events?
   (vi)   is the most interesting to follow?
   (vii) is the most reliable?

(b) Did the various media agree or disagree with each other when they reported on the same events? Give examples to support your answer.

(c) Make at least one recommendation that you think would improve the reporting of weather news by
   (i)   newspapers;
   (ii)   radio stations;
   (iii) TV stations;
   (iv)   Internet sources;
   (v)   periodical magazines.

(d) Design a visual presentation of your findings.

Understanding Concepts

1. List the advantages and disadvantages of using a system of watches, advisories, and warnings for storms.

2. **(a)** List all the weather-related services provided by the media.
   (b) Which single medium provides the greatest number of the services you listed in **(a)**?

3. Suppose the Meteorological Service of Canada issues two alerts: a severe thunderstorm watch for southern and eastern Ontario and a severe thunderstorm warning for northern Ontario. Explain which alert is more serious.

Making Connections

4. An emergency worker needs to know when a severe storm warning is issued, but can't watch TV or listen to the radio constantly. Suggest how technology might solve the problem.

Exploring

5. Many newspapers have a weekly feature that describes natural events around the world. Which natural disasters are not related to weather?

6. Find out how many of your friends and family members understand the difference between storm watches, advisories, and warnings.

Reflecting

7. Of the weather warnings that might be given in your area, which are you most likely to heed? Why?

Work the Web

A web site that provides information about watches, advisories, and warnings is the Meteorological Service of Canada, a federal government agency. Why is this resource valuable to the media?

Challenge

2 How will you communicate storm watches or warnings in your community?
3 What difficulties would your network experience if a storm caused an electricity failure for several hours?

Thunderstorms and Tornadoes

Tornadoes can do more damage in a short time than any other storms on Earth because of their extremely high winds (**Figure 1**). Furthermore, tornadoes follow paths that are difficult to predict. A tornado watch may be issued a few hours ahead, but a warning for the precise area the tornado will strike may come with 20 minutes or less to prepare. So what would you do if you suddenly heard that a tornado was to strike your area in 20 minutes? Your decision could save your life.

To understand tornadoes we must first understand thunderstorms. A **thunderstorm** is a storm with lightning, thunder, heavy rain, and sometimes hail. A **tornado** is a severe component of a thunderstorm in which a rotating funnel of air extends from the base of the thunderstorm clouds to the ground.

Thunderstorms

Two conditions must be met for a thunderstorm to form:
1. moisture is needed to form clouds and precipitation; and
2. the lifting of the air, or uplift, must be very strong in order to produce clouds that reach high in the atmosphere (recall the shape of the huge cumulonimbus cloud in section 13.11 on page 533).

Because of the low temperatures at the high altitude, warm air from lower down rises rapidly (heat transfer is faster when there is a big temperature difference), producing a circulation system that is unstable, or "active." The system gains strength if upper-level high-speed winds (mainly the jet stream) carry the rising air away quickly.

Uplift is caused in various ways. For example, convection currents of the air just above the ground, heated by solar energy, carry warm air upward. If this air contains enough moisture, a thunderstorm may develop. This type of updraft happens frequently in areas such as Kansas and Oklahoma in the Midwest United States, in southern Ontario, and where the land meets the ocean, such as along the coast of Florida. Thunderstorms caused by this type of uplift are usually most severe on hot afternoons.

Uplift is also caused by a cold front pushing warm air upward. This is more common in mid-latitude regions, including Canada, in the spring, when there is a sharp contrast in air mass temperatures. Storms developed in this way can happen anytime during the day or night, but they are strongest when convection currents contribute to the updraft during hot afternoons.

Figure 2 shows the main stages in the development of a thunderstorm. In the developing stage, updrafts of warm air carry moisture upward. As the water vapour rises, it condenses, releasing energy to warm the air further. (Remember that energy is absorbed during evaporation and released during condensation.) This allows the warm air to rise even higher. If the temperature at the upper levels is low, the warm air may rise as high as the tropopause.

Figure 1

Powerful tornadoes can uproot large trees and cause severe property damage. A tornado struck this drive-in cinema, which was showing *Twister* at the time.

Did You Know?

Canada's thunderstorm capital is Windsor, Ontario, where the average summertime relative humidity is about 60%.

Figure 2

Thunderstorms have three main stages.

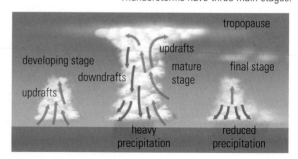

developing stage

updrafts

downdrafts

updrafts

mature stage

tropopause

final stage

heavy precipitation

reduced precipitation

In the mature stage of the thunderstorm, the cumulonimbus cloud spreads out at the top, reaching the stratosphere in the most severe cases. Cold air containing ice, rain, and sometimes hail falls downward in large downdrafts. This is the destructive part of the storm, when repeated updrafts and downdrafts produce hailstones. You can identify such a powerful storm by the anvil-shaped cloudtop that is high enough to be in the jet stream. These storms can be up to 20 km across; if a line of thunderstorms forms, it can be 300 km across. Thunderstorms can build higher than commercial airplanes travel, so pilots must detour around.

It is during the mature stage that we get lightning and thunder. One theory about how lightning happens is that it is a result of friction as ice crystals carried in the updrafts collide with drops and ice pellets in the downdrafts. In the collisions, a water shell is stripped from the ice pellets, leaving the ice negatively charged and the small droplets that form in the collision positively charged. As the ice pellets continue to fall and the water droplets rise, the result is that the cloud becomes positively charged at the top and negatively charged at the bottom. The charge builds up until it is strong enough to cause a discharge between the two areas. This discharge is lightning.

Most lightning discharges (called sheet lightning) take place within the storm clouds. But discharges can also occur between the cloud and the ground when the negative charges at the base of the cloud attract positive charges on the ground. These discharges appear as a streaked flash between the ground and the cloud. Thunder is created when the discharge heats the air, causing it to expand rapidly. Since light travels extremely quickly in air while sound travels much more slowly, we always see a lightning flash before we hear its thunder.

In the final stage of the thunderstorm, the downdrafts reduce the upward flow of air, and the storm weakens. Smaller clouds are seen above the lower cumulus clouds.

Tornadoes

Tornadoes form in the most severe thunderstorms. Fast-rising air in a thunderstorm sometimes begins spinning, forming a funnel of air and moisture. As more rising air is replaced by cooler air at the surface, the rotation becomes faster and faster. The rising air causes a pressure difference that increases with speed. (You should be able to use Bernoulli's principle from Chapter 14 to explain why.) The difference in pressure can lift roofs, cars, animals, trailer homes, and people, sending them flying through the air.

Figure 3(a) shows a typical tornado, which extends from the base of a cumulonimbus cloud to the ground. **Figure 3(b)** illustrates why the speed of the tornado's rotation increases toward the centre. Because of its shape, the rotating tornado cloud is called a funnel cloud. At the centre, or vortex, wind speeds can be as high as 500 km/h. Such winds can do unimaginable damage. (Research is being done to find out more about the cause of rotation in a tornado. Scientists don't understand all the details of why some rotate clockwise, while most in North America rotate counterclockwise.)

Figure 3

(a) A tornado has a distinctive funnel shape.

With arms extended, the skater's rotation is slow.

With arms in, the rotation rate increases.

(b) A skater spins faster when he or she folds in the arms. With the arms in, less area is covered—a smaller radius of rotation—so the speed increases.

Table 1 Tornado Intensity Scale

Scale	Winds (km/h)	Length of path (km)	Width	Damage
0 (very weak)	under 116	under 1.5	under 15 m	minor roof, tree, chimney, antenna, and sign damage
1 (weak)	117–180	1.6–5	50 m	barns torn apart, trees snapped
2 (strong)	181–252	5.1–15.9	160 m	roofs torn off buildings, trees uprooted
3 (severe)	253–332	16–50	161–500 m	weaker homes completely disappear
4 (devastating)	333–419	51–159	0.5–1.4 km	walls of homes blown apart, cars thrown into the air
5 (incredible)	420–512	160–507	1.5–16 km	strongly built homes completely blown away

Source: Environment Canada

The diameter of the funnel cloud can range from a few metres to 500 m, and tornados can last from only a few seconds to hours. They travel at speeds up to 100 km/h, usually from southwest to northeast, along narrow paths. To understand the damage that powerful winds can inflict, read the Tornado Intensity Scale in **Table 1** and the Beaufort Wind Scale in **Table 2**.

On average in Canada, Alberta has 21 tornadoes a year, Saskatchewan has 23, Manitoba has 13, and Ontario has 28. These numbers are small compared with 65, the average number of tornadoes a year in the region called "Tornado Alley" in the United States, which stretches from Texas to Nebraska.

Table 2 The Beaufort Wind Scale

Beaufort wind force	Wind speed (km/h)	Wind type	Descriptive effects
0	0–1	calm	smoke rises vertically
1	2–5	light air	smoke drifts slowly
2	6–11	light breeze	leaves rustle, wind vanes move
3	12–19	gentle breeze	leaves and twigs in constant motion
4	20–29	moderate breeze	small branches move
5	30–38	fresh breeze	small trees sway
6	39–50	strong breeze	large branches in continuous motion
7	51–61	near gale	wind affects walking
8	62–74	gale	small branches break off trees
9	75–87	strong gale	large branches break
10	88–101	storm	trees uproot, damage to buildings
11	102–117	violent storm	property damage widespread
12	119+	hurricane	severe and extensive damage

Source: Environment Canada

Try This
Activity Estimating the Distance to Lightning

In a typical thunderstorm, the sound from thunder travels at about 335 m/s. (Light from the lightning travels at about 3×10^8 m/s.) You can use the uniform motion equation for speed from Unit 3 to calculate the distance between you and the lightning bolt if you measure the time between seeing the lightning and hearing the thunder it caused.

(a) Determine the distance if the time measured is (i) 5.0 s and (ii) 2.0 s.
(b) Repeat the calculation using 3.0 s, and convert your answer to kilometres. Make up a "three-second rule" that can be applied to estimate the distance to a lightning bolt.
(c) During a thunderstorm, estimate how far away the lightning is from you.

Storm Tracking

An important technology used by meteorologists when following the development of thunderstorms and tornadoes is Doppler radar. Radio waves sent out from antennas on the radar instrument bounce off the water drops and ice particles in the storm. Some bounce back to the instrument. These reflected waves reveal the location of the drops and particles as well as their speeds. **Figure 4** shows a typical Doppler radar image used by meteorologists to track storms.

To relate the images on a radar screen to the actual events, "storm chasers" get as close as possible to thunderstorms and tornadoes. They gather data using video and still cameras, portable Doppler radar instruments, and weather balloons launched within the storm. (Storm chasers were featured in the movie *Twister.*) This information is added to the data collected from the larger Doppler radar systems and fed into computers. The computers analyze the data, which contribute to our understanding of these fierce storms and now enable meteorologists to issue tornado warnings giving people enough time to take cover.

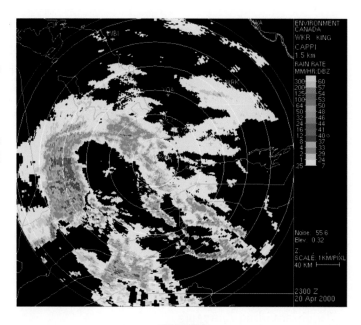

Figure 4

A Doppler radar image reveals rainfall within a radius of about 120 km of the radar instrument. In this image Lake Huron is at top left, and Lake Ontario at centre right. Predict the weather for Belleville over the next few hours.

Storm Alert (Thunderstorms)

Each year in North America, lightning kills about 100 people and injures several hundred more. Here are some precautions to take when lightning approaches (remember the three-second rule):

- A car is a safe place to be during lightning because it is made mostly of metal and acts as a conductor. The charge from the lightning is conducted over the body of the car and into the ground.
- Since lightning tends to strike high objects, never stand beneath a lone tree or utility pole during a thunderstorm.
- Avoid open areas such as the tops of hills, open water, and sports fields. If you are in an exposed area and you feel a strong tingling sensation, put your feet together and squat down with your arms around your body. Do not lie flat or touch the ground with your hands.
- It is fairly safe to be indoors during lightning, but avoid touching electrical appliances and water pipes.
- If someone near you is struck by lightning and is unconscious, apply artificial resuscitation immediately.

Did You Know?

In May 1986, 13 school children in China were hoisted into the air by a tornado and carried 19 km before falling gently to the ground.

Storm Alert (Tornadoes)

Similar suggestions apply during tornadoes because lightning also accompanies these systems. However, the high winds require extra precautions:

- Try to get inside a house or other building so you can avoid flying debris.
- Stay in a small, interior room, such as a washroom or a room in the basement; these are stronger than large rooms. Stay away from windows.

Challenge

1 Can your measuring devices withstand high winds? If not, suggest how they could be improved.
2 How will your community design take into account the potential effects of thunderstorms and tornadoes?

Understanding Concepts

1. If you were looking at the sky, what evidence would indicate an approaching thunderstorm? Give details, such as the direction you would look, the shape of the clouds, and the changes you would expect.

2. A convection current is stronger when the temperature difference between the bottom and top of the current is greater. Use this fact to explain why thunderstorms are much more common in spring and summer than in winter.

3. Use Bernoulli's principle to explain why the suction exerted by a tornado changes as the speed of the tornado's winds increases.

4. If you take cover from a tornado in a basement, the southwest corner is likely the safest place to choose (assuming there are no windows there). Explain why by using a diagram that shows the rotation of the tornado and the general direction of the storm.

5. Use the Tornado Intensity and Beaufort Wind scales from **Tables 1** and **2** to determine the range of wind speeds of
   (a) a thunderstorm with gale-force winds;
   (b) a severe tornado.

6. Look at the data in the Tornado Intensity Scale, **Table 1**. Describe the relationship between the width of a tornado and its wind speed.

Making Connections

7. Assume you attend a school in a location where tornadoes are possible. What procedure would you suggest for a safety drill for the entire school in the event of a tornado warning? If your school already runs such drills, how would you improve them?

8. Tornadoes are particularly devastating when their paths cut through mobile home communities because, unlike homes with concrete foundations, mobile homes are easier to move and contain fewer secure rooms. Suggest procedures and/or technologies that could reduce this problem.

Exploring

9. Find out the locations and some interesting facts about a thunderstorm or tornado that occurred in the past year. Share what you discover with others.

10. **(a)** Research and report on how Sir Francis Beaufort developed the wind scale.
    (b) The Tornado Intensity Scale was developed by Dr. T. Theodore Fujita. Research Fujita and his contributions to meteorology. Briefly summarize what you discover.

11. Research waterspouts and dust devils and describe how they differ from a tornado.

Reflecting

12. Critically evaluate the movie *Twister*. Identify the scientific accuracies, exaggerations, and fallacies in the movie.

SKILLS HANDBOOK: (J) (I) Research Skills

Floods and Droughts

Suppose a flood in your area is expected to raise water levels one metre above ground level. How many sandbags (**Figure 1**) would you need to protect your school? The number would probably be in the thousands. Imagine the work: shovelling the sand into the bags, tying the bags closed, loading the bags onto a truck, unloading the bags, stacking them in place, and removing the sandbags after the floodwaters have subsided. It's worth it, though, if the floodwaters don't rise above the sandbags and if flooding doesn't happen too often.

A **flood** is an excess of water from rain, rivers, or oceans over land that cannot soak up any more water. Floods can happen anywhere in the world except Antarctica. They account for about 40% of all deaths from natural disasters in the world. The two main types of floods — flash and broadside — are described below.

A **drought** is a long period with much less rainfall than average. Droughts are discussed along with floods because both events relate to water, and sometimes they happen in the same region.

In Canada, floods and droughts are the weather-related disasters with the greatest economic impact. Many people are concerned that these events may become even more extreme in the future, a concept discussed in Chapter 16.

Figure 1

With enough warning, people can stack sandbags to reduce the chances of damage in some locations during floods. But this practice can worsen the effects of flooding downstream. Can you think of other ways to control water levels?

Floods

A flash flood — as the name suggests — is flooding that occurs with little or no warning. While flash floods are becoming more common in cities when water from heavy rain can't be drained away quickly enough by storm sewers, this type of flooding usually occurs in mountain valleys and gorges when a spring rain adds to the runoff from melting snow and produces more water than normal. Mud slides often accompany these floods. Water can even fill normally empty gorges in deserts.

Flash floods can also happen when a dam bursts or overflows, allowing water and debris to sweep away trees, animals, houses, and topsoil.

Flash floods have been a problem in many areas of Canada. The most devastating flood in Canadian history struck the Saguenay area of Quebec in the summer of 1996 (**Figure 2**). Beginning on July 19, heavy rains fell on an area where the soil was already saturated. Within 36 h, up to 280 mm of rain had fallen. Then, on July 20, water flowed over the walls of a dam rather than through the gates. Soon an old soil dike broke, and flash flooding began. The affected area included several rivers, and the flooding lasted for two months, causing 10 related deaths and about $800 million in damages.

Figure 2

Dams, buildings, roads, bridges, and vehicles were all victims in the fast-flowing waters of the Saguenay flood.

Broadside floods cover large areas of land and can last for months. Often this type of flood can be predicted days or even weeks before it happens. As you read about the various causes of broadside floods, try to identify why some floods are easier to predict than others.

- The delta areas of some rivers flood every year in spring, due to melting in the mountains where the rivers originate. Famous examples are the Nile River in Africa and the Yangtze River in China.
- Some rivers flood after a winter of heavy snowfall followed by heavy rains in the spring. The Red River flood in 1997 in Manitoba, which took weeks to peak, was a devastating example (**Figure 3**).
- Rainfall that is much higher than normal saturates the ground, and any further rainfall causes flooding.
- Tropical storms, such as hurricanes, bring large amounts of rainfall to areas along coastlines, stretching far inland. These regions quickly become saturated, and serious flooding results.

Flood Controls

Dams on rivers and lakes help to control flooding. Before expected heavy rains and winter runoff, conservation authorities lower the water levels in dammed lakes, allowing the water to flow away gradually in the drainage river. This creates space for storing large amounts of water.

Another way to control flooding is to build spillways, or floodways. Spillways are canals that divert the excess water from the regular flow of a river during a flood. The Red River floodway near Winnipeg helped save that city from major damage in the 1997 flood (**Figure 4**).

A less obvious form of flood control takes advantage of nature. Soils with plants can absorb water more readily than hard, dry clay or concrete. Thus, the "greening" of cities and flood-prone areas with tree planting and soil improvement programs helps to reduce the chances of soil saturation.

Flood Alert

Since floods can cause major damage and even deaths in Canada, we should be aware of the following precautions and considerations.

- Avoid fast-moving floodwaters. Cars and trucks driven into flowing water can easily be swept away.
- Children should be kept away from swollen creeks, streams, and even drainage ditches during flood periods.
- In areas prone to flash floods, watch for signs of a thunderstorm.

Figure 3

Ste. Agathe was just one of the towns covered by water in the 1997 Red River flood in Manitoba.

Figure 4

This floodway east of Winnipeg is like a giant eavestrough: it carries excess water away from the part of the Red River that flows through the city.

🌐 Challenge

1 What factors would you observe in order to forecast (a) a flash flood, (b) a broadside flood, and (c) a drought?
2 How could you design your community to reduce the chances of flash floods or the effects of a drought?
3 The Red River flooded areas in the United States before it flowed northward into Manitoba in the 1997 flood. How might networking have helped people in Manitoba prepare for the flood?

Droughts

Droughts are natural events that occur whenever precipitation is scarce over a long time.

As you learned in Chapter 13, the areas at latitudes 30° north and south of the equator are regions of high pressure where the average yearly rainfall is fairly low. In these areas droughts are more likely. Wildfires in California are one example of the damage serious droughts can cause.

In the mid-latitudes, around 45° north and south of the equator, droughts may last several months or even years. In some areas, the average annual precipitation may seem to be adequate, but the total yearly amount of precipitation may fall in a short time, leaving the rest of the year very dry. This explains why some regions can be victims of both floods and droughts.

The most devastating drought in Canada was in the mid-1930s when precipitation on the Prairies was much lower than average. During this time, topsoil blew off the farmland, prompting the name "Dust Bowl." The soil dried out and cracked, crops withered, livestock died, and farmers went broke (**Figure 5**).

Long-term planning helps to reduce the impact of droughts. For example, in times of above average rainfall, people should be careful not to become overconfident. They should not overgraze pastures or move too close to normally dry areas and should use water efficiently to prevent major shortages in the future. Reservoirs can be built to store water in case of drought.

Figure 5

Drought can create more problems than just a shortage of water. High winds blowing over open, dry soil can creat a dust storm like this one in Saskatchewan. The loss of topsoil can be devastating to farmers.

Understanding Concepts

1. Which floods are easiest to forecast? Which are the most difficult to forecast? Explain why.

2. One of the reasons the Saguenay flood of 1996 was so devastating was that orographic lifting occurred over the Laurentian Mountains in Quebec. How would orographic lifting intensify the precipitation?

3. List ways, other than using sandbags, that people have used to try to control water levels.

4. A desert area can have a flash flood even during a drought. Explain how this is possible.

5. List advantages and disadvantages of damming large rivers. Consider the environmental, economic, and social impacts.

6. Explain why some areas experience both droughts and floods. Give an example in your answer.

7. Suggest why floods do not occur in Antarctica.

8. You are in charge of a sandbag operation: You have to order enough sandbags to boost the height of a dike. The dike is 30 km long, and you must increase the height by 1.2 m. Assume each sandbag is 0.5 m long, 0.3 m wide, and 0.2 m deep. Determine how many sandbags to order.

Making Connections

9. Broadside flooding brings silt eroded from the mountains to the plains. Explain how this type of flood could be beneficial.

Exploring

10. Research one or more of the items listed below, and create a visual presentation that summarizes what you (I) discover. Consider the environmental, economic, and (J) social impacts of

   (a) the Saguenay flood in Quebec in 1996 or the Red River flood in Manitoba in 1997;

   (b) the construction either of the Nasser Dam on the Nile River in Egypt or the Yangtze River Dam in China;

   (c) the drought on the Canadian Prairies in the 1930s;

   (d) current ideas on how to reduce the effects of floods or droughts.

INQUIRY SKILLS MENU
○ Questioning   ● Planning   ● Analyzing
● Hypothesizing   ● Conducting   ● Evaluating
● Predicting   ● Recording   ● Communicating

Water-Wise Plant Growth

Many people like to grow outdoor plants to add colour and beauty to their surroundings (**Figure 1**). As you have discovered, there are other reasons for encouraging the growth of plants, particularly in areas where flash floods are likely. However, such places are often dry, and most plants require a lot of water. What can be done to grow plants successfully using the least amount of water? Perhaps your answer to this question will help thousands of Canadians learn to use our precious resource of water wisely.

Many variables affect the ability of plants to grow in a region of low rainfall. Consider each of the following factors. Which do you think could affect a plant's survival in low-rainfall conditions?

- leaf shape (broad, narrow, spiny)
- type of soil (sand, clay, silt)
- type of fertilizer (root, leaf, flower)
- type of watering (from above, at root level, drip watering from above, drip watering at root level)
- temperature
- amount of shade (total shade, partial shade, full sunlight)
- wind speed (calm, breezy, windy)

Question

How do the variables above affect the ability of plants to survive and flourish in drought-like conditions?

Hypothesis/Prediction

(a) As a class, develop hypotheses and predictions
Ⓚ for each of the listed variables you think may be important.

Design

(b) Design a controlled experiment to test one of the hypotheses developed by your class. Describe the dependent, independent, and controlled variables for your experiment. Note that one of the variables you should control is the amount of water given to the plants. The

Figure 1
The plants in this nursery have leaves in a variety of shapes and colours. Does leaf shape affect the plant's need for water?

size of the plants and the volume of the pots or area of soil they fill will affect the plants' needs, but you may want to try 5 mL of water per day per plant.

(c) Develop a procedure for your investigation, including safety precautions.

(d) Create a data table to record your observations.

Materials

(e) List the materials you will need to carry out your investigation. Your living materials will have the greatest effect on the results of your investigation. When putting together a group of plants, you will want to keep differences in the size and shapes of the plants to a minimum.

Procedure

1 Have your teacher approve your hypotheses/predictions, materials list, and procedure steps.

2 Carry out your investigation and record all your
Ⓜ observations and results.

Analysis and Evaluation

(f) Analyse your observations and describe how the
Ⓝ④ independent variable you tested affected the ability of plants to survive.

(g) Does the investigation support the hypothesis developed by the class? Explain your conclusion.

(h) Evaluate your design, focusing on your controls.
Ⓞ How confident are you that the controls you used were adequate? How would you modify the design if you were to repeat the experiment?

(i) Discuss any difficulties you had measuring the dependent variable for your investigation.

(j) Write a lab report for your investigation and
Ⓠ share it with your classmates.

(k) On the basis of your shared results, make recommendations for planting and cultivating plants in low-rainfall or drought-prone areas.

(l) Suggest some follow-up investigations you or
Ⓞ④ other investigators could carry out that would increase your confidence in your recommendations.

Understanding Concepts

1. Describe two ways in which desert plants are adapted to their surroundings.

2. **(a)** During what time(s) of the year do deciduous trees require the most water for survival?

   (b) Explain how your answer relates to transpiration.

3. It is better to water a lawn and garden for three hours once every six days than for a half-hour every day. Explain why.

4. List advantages and disadvantages of an underground drip-watering system for outdoor plants.

5. What are the advantages and disadvantages of using mulch in an area prone to drought?

6. List suggestions for minimizing water use in an outdoor ornamental garden.

Making Connections

7. During drought or semi-drought conditions, local governments put restrictions on water use for gardens and lawns.

   (a) Brainstorm and list methods used to control water usage in cities.

   (b) Suggest a fair way to control water usage in your area.

8. What is your responsibility to a young tree you plant? How long does that responsibility last?

Exploring

9. Research how genetic engineering of a crop plant can
Ⓙ alter its ability to survive higher- or lower-than-normal
Ⓘ rainfall. Explain why researchers are interested in the potential of this type of engineering and what concerns some people have about growing and consuming genetically engineered crops.

◢ Challenge

2 How does the design of your weather-wise community combine beauty with the wise use of water?

Hurricanes, Typhoons, and Tropical Cyclones

In 1954, Hurricane Hazel caused great damage to many parts of Canada. Although the winds weakened as Hazel travelled over land, tremendous volumes of rain fell, causing flooding (**Figure 1**). However, most Atlantic hurricanes that affect Canada move northward along the southeastern U.S. coast toward the Atlantic provinces, sometimes causing severe damage and releasing enormous volumes of rain across much of eastern Canada.

You learned that cyclones are low-pressure systems that develop in the mid-latitudes when cold and warm fronts interact. Near the equator cyclones develop in a different way, although they are also low-pressure systems.

When cyclones near the equator become large enough, they are further classified as a hurricane, a typhoon, or a tropical cyclone, depending on where they are located. A **hurricane** is a severe cyclone that occurs in the western Atlantic Ocean, the Caribbean Sea, the Gulf of Mexico, or the eastern Pacific Ocean. (The word "hurricane" may come from the name Hunraken, the Mayan god of winds.) A **typhoon** is a severe cyclone that develops in the northwestern Pacific Ocean or the China Sea. (The word "typhoon" comes from the Mandarin words for great wind, *tái feng*.) A **tropical cyclone** is a severe cyclone that develops in the Indian Ocean and the area around Australia.

Figure 1

Hurricane Hazel reached southern Ontario in 1954, causing rivers to flood.

Cyclogenesis Near the Equator

Since typhoons, tropical cyclones, and hurricanes are simply different names for the same type of storm, the cyclogenesis for each is the same. So to understand how all three form, we only need to look at one, the one closest to home: an Atlantic hurricane.

A typical Atlantic hurricane season, in which up to 20 hurricanes may develop, may start as early as June and end as late as November. Meteorologists have learned that most Atlantic hurricanes form north of the equator off the west coast of Africa, where the highest surface water temperatures of the Atlantic Ocean are found. This happens when the Sun's rays strike most directly during the summer. **Figure 2** shows the typical stages and a possible path of a hurricane.

Like other storms, hurricanes are fed by convection currents. Near the equator the air above the ocean is warm, so it rises. Scientists have discovered that if the surface water temperature is at least 27°C, evaporation occurs rapidly, and the warm, rising air carries a lot of moisture with it. As the warm, moist air reaches higher altitudes, the water vapour condenses, releasing heat that increases the rate at which the air rises. Warm ocean water acts as fuel, continuously feeding the convection currents.

> **Did You Know?**
>
> Powerful cyclones are also given local names. *Baquiros* is the term used in the Philippines.

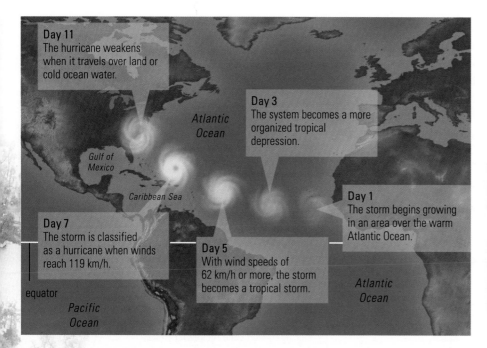

Day 11
The hurricane weakens when it travels over land or cold ocean water.

Atlantic Ocean

Gulf of Mexico

Caribbean Sea

Day 3
The system becomes a more organized tropical depression.

Day 1
The storm begins growing in an area over the warm Atlantic Ocean.

Day 7
The storm is classified as a hurricane when winds reach 119 km/h.

Day 5
With wind speeds of 62 km/h or more, the storm becomes a tropical storm.

equator

Pacific Ocean

Atlantic Ocean

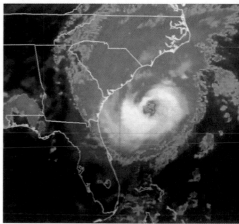

Figure 2

Atlantic hurricanes develop north of the equator where the surface waters are warmest. The stages of a typical hurricane are shown.

Figure 3

This satellite image shows Hurricane Dennis approaching the Atlantic coast of the southeastern United States in August 1999. The swirling white area is the most severe part of the hurricane. Dennis peaked at wind speeds near 175 km/h.

Because rising air leaves behind a low-pressure area, the first stage of the type of storm that becomes a hurricane is called a "low." Within the storm, the rising air turns to the right (in the Northern Hemisphere), resulting in a storm system that begins to rotate counterclockwise. When viewed from a satellite, a hurricane looks like a spiral (**Figure 3**). High above the surface low a high-pressure area forms as air pushes up into the less dense upper levels of the troposphere. This air flows out over the storm, descending and turning to the right (clockwise) as it goes. The faster this upper air is pushed away, the easier the surface air can rise. The faster the air is rising, the lower the pressure becomes in the centre of the storm, and the faster the surrounding air moves into the low-pressure area. As the storm develops, surface winds become increasingly strong. When wind speeds reach 62 km/h the storm is classified as a tropical storm. At 119 km/h the system is officially a hurricane.

The central core of a hurricane is called the **eye**. Here the air is calm, air pressure is very low, and the sky is clear. The eye is created as air from the edge of the storm swirls in toward the centre. The stronger the low at the centre of the storm, the faster the winds move toward it (curving as they go), and the greater the rate of rotation becomes. When the rate of rotation becomes extreme, the air tries to fly outward. The air can't get any closer to the centre, so it must rise around the eye. (You can simulate the creation of an eye in a fluid system by swirling water in a round container.) The eye can be up to 50 km across. At the border of the eye is the **eye wall**, where the swirling winds are moving fastest and the volume of rainfall is greatest (**Figure 4**).

The entire storm system is carried westward by the trade winds, but at a much lower average speed, around 25 km/h. Its huge cumulonimbus clouds are accompanied by heavy rainfall.

Figure 4

If you were to stand in the eye of a hurricane, you would experience fairly calm, clear skies overhead but powerful winds and heavy rainfall at the eye wall.

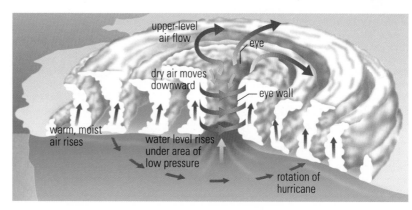

upper-level air flow

eye

dry air moves downward

eye wall

warm, moist air rises

water level rises under area of low pressure

rotation of hurricane

Typhoons and tropical cyclones can be even more devastating than Atlantic hurricanes. These storms become powerful because of their vast supply of energy from the warm waters of the Pacific and Indian Oceans. In the western Pacific Ocean, the typhoon season is from April to December and affects coastal areas of several countries, including China, Vietnam, and Japan. Tropical cyclones strike areas north of the equator in the Indian Ocean from May to December, causing devastation in India, Pakistan, and Bangladesh. Tropical cyclones strike areas south of the equator from December to April.

Hurricanes and other major cyclones are classified according to their strengths. The hurricane intensity scale in **Table 1** summarizes the five categories of hurricanes.

Effects of Hurricanes

Although hurricane winds are extremely strong, up to 300 km/h or more, they are lower than the maximum wind speeds of tornadoes. However, hurricanes are much larger than tornadoes and can last several days — even two weeks — as long as they are above their source of energy, warm water. Hence their damage is much more widespread than that of a tornado.

Certainly the high winds are a major source of devastation (**Figure 5**). When a hurricane reaches land, boats, trees, cars, shingles, and other objects fly through the air, crashing into buildings and killing or injuring people.

Another disastrous effect of a hurricane is a **storm surge:** a huge amount of sea water piled up by the intense winds and pushed onto the shore. The water level in the surge, which may be more than 6 m higher than normal, can cause tremendous damage as it flows inland and then back out to sea (**Figure 6**). Cities at sea level and located in potential hurricane territory are particularly vulnerable to storm surges. New Orleans,

Figure 5

Few buildings are left untouched when a powerful hurricane strikes. The devastation shown here was caused by Hurricane Andrew in 1992.

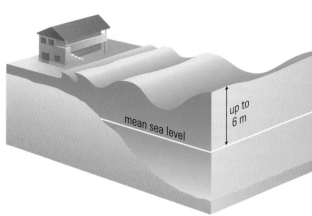

Figure 6

A storm surge can force large amounts of water inland along low-lying coastal areas.

Table 1 **Hurricane Intensity Scale**

Category	Maximum sustained wind speed (km/h)	Minimum surface pressure (kPa)	Storm surge (m)	Remarks
1 (minimal)	119–153	98.0 or more	1.0–1.7	damage to trees and signs, flooding in low-lying areas
2 (moderate)	154–177	97.9–96.5	1.8–2.6	trees blown down, evacuation of shore areas
3 (extensive)	178–209	96.4–94.5	2.7–3.8	serious coastal flooding, mobile homes destroyed
4 (extreme)	210–249	94.4–92.0	3.9–5.6	extensive damage to buildings, evacuation from shore required
5 (catastrophic)	above 250	under 92.0	above 5.6	buildings destroyed, evacuation up to 20 km inland required

Source: *1999 Canadian Global Almanac*

Louisiana, is actually below sea level, protected by dikes and levees. It could face severe flooding in a Gulf of Mexico hurricane.

Farther inland, the most serious devastation is often caused by the huge amounts of rainfall in a hurricane, often up to 50 or 60 cm in a day. The ground becomes saturated and cannot hold all this water, so, with nowhere else to go, the water floods the area, sometimes for several weeks. Along the east coast of Canada and the United States, the flooding is mainly of the broadside type, but the mountainous regions of Central America experience flash floods and mud slides.

Storm Alert

Meteorologists use satellite images to track tropical depressions. Each year, the ability to forecast where and when a hurricane, typhoon, or tropical storm will strike land improves slightly. Listed below are some actions that can reduce the potential damage of hurricanes.

- Board up windows for protection from winds and flying debris.
- Reinforce buildings to withstand greater winds.
- Evacuate people inland to higher ground to miss storm surges and flooding.
- Store emergency rations of water, food, medical supplies, and equipment, such as a camp stove to boil water.

 **Challenge**

3 How could network communication help people in developing countries before, during, and after a major tropical storm?

Understanding Concepts

1. Create a table to compare the features of hurricanes, typhoons, and tropical cyclones. Include location, countries hit, months in the storm season, hemisphere, and direction of rotation.

2. Explain how measuring the surface temperatures of the Atlantic Ocean would help you forecast the strengths of hurricanes in a particular season.

3. Explain why huge tropical storms in the Northern Hemisphere form at a different time of the year than those in the Southern Hemisphere.

4. Describe briefly the disastrous short- and long-term effects of hurricanes. Consider the social, environmental, and economic effects.

5. Which types of hurricane damage would be possible in
   (a) parts of Ontario or Quebec?
   (b) the Atlantic provinces?

6. Sometimes a category 3 hurricane can do more long-term damage than a category 4 hurricane. Explain why this could happen.

7. Why do hurricanes quickly lose strength as they move over land or cold water?

Making Connections

8. Explain why the number of people killed or injured in North American hurricanes has decreased in recent decades, yet property damage has greatly increased.

9. During major tropical storms, developing countries experience a higher death rate than North America. Suggest reasons for this and ways to reduce the number of deaths.

10. Devise an evacuation plan that could quickly and smoothly get all residents of your community out of the path of a major storm. Illustrate your plan with maps and diagrams.

Exploring

11. Research hurricanes, typhoons, tropical cyclones, and other (I) extreme weather events that have occurred in the past (J) year. Create a database to record what you find. Include location, interesting facts, the maximum wind speeds, the total rainfall, the duration, the number of lives lost, and the cost of damage.

12. Research names chosen for Atlantic hurricanes.
   (a) Describe the use of male and female names.
   (b) Which letters of the alphabet are not used?
   (c) Create your own list of Atlantic hurricane names for the next season.

Blizzards

Some heavy snowfalls turn a dull grey landscape into a beautiful winter wonderland, with clean, moist snow bending tree branches and children laughing as they fall into the soft snow. But when biting winds blast the snow, beauty changes to danger. A **blizzard** is a severe snow storm with strong winds and low temperatures. A storm is classified as a blizzard if the winds exceed 55 km/h, the temperature is well below normal, and visibility is reduced to less than 0.2 km. Most Canadians have witnessed blizzards and are aware of the many dangers they can bring (**Figure 1**).

Causes of Blizzards

Some blizzards develop in much the same way as thunderstorms; however, cold temperatures bring snow rather than rain and there is seldom any lightning. Some of the worst blizzards in Canada and the northern United States develop when a warm air mass, filled with moisture from the Gulf of Mexico and the Atlantic Ocean, moves northward and meets a cold Arctic air mass under a strong jet stream. The resulting mid-latitude storm, rotating counterclockwise, may drop up to a metre of snow in 24 h.

Another cause of blizzards is the combination of strong winds and the lake effect (discussed in Chapter 14). In Ontario, for example, prevailing winds often bring large snowfalls to regions east of Lake Huron and Georgian Bay. Lake-effect blizzards can last for days.

Dangers of Blizzards

Blizzards usually have devastating effects on transportation. They cause whiteout conditions on the highways, roads, and even on water, making driving dangerous and navigation along coastal waters impossible without radar. Blizzards can close airports when air travel becomes too dangerous. Public transportation usually grinds to a halt (**Figure 2**); bridges become icy and extremely dangerous in the winds; emergency road crews have difficulty clearing the snow because more blows into the areas just cleared; and people get stranded when their vehicles get stuck in snowdrifts.

Blizzards (and other heavy snowfalls) can also cause avalanches in mountains. These snow slides occur when loose, new snow, piled on a hard snow base, breaks loose and slides down the mountainside.

Another danger that may result from a blizzard is the loss of electricity. If power lines break or utility poles are blown over, electricity could be cut off for several days or even a few weeks. Since our society relies heavily on electricity, this problem can be very serious.

Figure 1

Blizzard conditions, with slippery roads and poor visibility, require extra caution on highways.

Did You Know?

In a blizzard on January 26, 1978, snowdrifts estimated at 15 m deep were reported in the Midwestern United States. That's as high as a five-storey building! The same storm stalled over Eastern Canada, causing havoc and closing schools and businesses.

Figure 2
A storm in January 1999 caused so much havoc to Toronto's transportation systems that the Canadian Armed Forces were asked to help clear the snow.

Storm Alert

Today's forecasters can give us enough time to prepare for a blizzard. When you hear that a blizzard is approaching, take the warning seriously.

- If possible, stay off highways, especially in open rural areas where blowing snow can cause whiteouts. Avoid bridges as well.
- If you are in a vehicle that gets stuck, stay with the vehicle, but don't keep the engine running just to keep warm. Carbon monoxide from the exhaust could kill you. (If you need warmth, start the engine for a few minutes, but roll a window down a little bit.)
- Take blankets, extra warm clothing, food, candles, and matches routinely on winter car trips.
- At home, have enough supplies on hand to help you cope with an electrical failure that may last several days.

🔵 Challenge

1 What local conditions would help you distinguish a blizzard from a simple heavy snowfall?
2 How could your community cope with a blizzard without calling for military assistance?

Understanding Concepts

1. Why are blizzards often more hazardous than other snowfalls?

2. List precautions that should be taken by each of the following when a severe blizzard is forecast:

   (a) a ski resort operator in British Columbia;

   (b) an ostrich rancher in Alberta;

   (c) a cattle rancher in southern Saskatchewan;

   (d) an airplane pilot in Nunavut;

   (e) a worker at the Toronto Zoo;

   (f) a transport truck driver in New Brunswick;

   (g) a shipping director in the Halifax harbour;

   (h) a school bus driver in Newfoundland;

   (i) a senior citizen living alone in the country.

3. Do you think blizzards are more dangerous in cities or rural areas? Explain your answer.

Making Connections

4. Some roads and highways in mountains or other areas that receive high snowfall have markers or vertical sticks along their edges. Explain their purpose.

5. Portable, gasoline-run generators can be used during electrical failures. List the advantages and disadvantages of these generators.

Exploring

6. Find out the location and some interesting facts about ⓙ the most recent blizzards. Summarize your findings in a table.

7. What is the policy of your school or school board if a blizzard is forecast? Do you think the policy is adequate? Justify your answer. How would you recommend improving it?

8. Prepare a list of emergency supplies that should be carried in a vehicle. Share this with the entire student body through posters and radio broadcasts.

9. Find a place in Canada or the United States where blizzards are uncommon and which have little equipment to deal with the snow. Find out how people cope with unexpected storms. Share what you discover with your class.

Reflecting

10. Talk to people who come from a country where snow never falls. Describe their reactions to their first Canadian snowfall or blizzard.

Surviving the 1998 Ice Storm

The worst ice storm in Canada's history occurred January 5 to 10, 1998, in eastern Ontario, southern Quebec, and parts of New Brunswick (**Figure 1**). This storm lasted longest, affected more people, covered more land area, produced more accumulated ice, and caused worse economic losses than any other ice storm in history. Trees, roads, and buildings in Cornwall, Ontario, one of the hardest-hit communities, accumulated 108 mm of ice!

An **ice storm** consists of freezing rain that usually lasts for a few hours. During the 1998 storm, freezing rain fell for over 80 hours!

In the 1998 ice storm, a southern jet stream swept warm, moist air northward from the Gulf of Mexico into southern Ontario and Quebec. At the same time, a large Arctic high-pressure area, held stationary by the northern jet stream, hovered over Hudson Bay and Quebec. When the air masses met, the cold Arctic air stayed close to the ground, under the warm air. As the warm air was pushed upward, the moisture it was holding condensed to form clouds and ice crystals. The ice crystals fell through the warm air mass, melting to form rain. As the raindrops fell through the cold air mass, they cooled and then froze instantly when they hit a cold object.

(a) Draw a vertical profile (from the ground to the clouds) of the atmosphere during the ice storm. Label the temperatures at various heights.

The reason the storm lasted so long was due to the influence of a large, semi-permanent high-pressure system in the Atlantic near Bermuda—the Bermuda high. The Bermuda high diverted warm, moist air from its normal course toward Iceland, and more moisture-laden air flowed into Ontario and Quebec, where it met the cold Arctic air.

Figure 1

During the 1998 ice storm, some areas received more than 10 cm of accumulated ice, creating dangerous conditions and damaging trees, buildings, and power lines.

Freezing rain can fall from any rain cloud, as long as the air near the ground is cold enough. But ice storms are not easy to predict because a change in temperature of only one or two degrees can make the difference between rain, freezing rain, and snow.

Several families who lived through the 1998 ice storm were asked to share their observations about the storm. One family had experienced both the Manitoba flood and the ice storm. Here are their stories.

How much warning did you have that an ice storm was approaching?
"There was no serious warning about the ice storm, just the usual precaution for a storm."

How accurate were the storm forecasts?
"Freezing rain was forecast, but not for any extended period of time."

What plans did you have in place before the storm arrived?
"We had no plans in place. What a mistake!"

Fires were sometimes the result for people using unfamiliar portable generators (**Figure 2**). *What are your worst personal memories of the storm?*
"Highways were closed. We were unable to drive home, so we checked into a hotel that soon lost its electricity and had no safety lights."
"My daughter at university in Kingston had to look for emergency shelter when the residence was closed."
"Living without hot water and showers was most unpleasant."
"The house became colder and colder as the days without electricity went on."

What are the worst things that happened to other people in your area?
"The farmers suffered greatly; they lost a lot of animals and were working around the clock trying to keep their animals alive."
"The elderly had great difficulty, especially those whose power stayed off for more than three weeks. The weather became extremely cold, which added to their problems."
"People abandoned their houses and pets. Pipes broke when water froze, leaving a real mess."
"A few people injured their eyes badly trying to chip ice from their car windshields."
"Falling trees and branches caused great damage."

(b) Are all people equally at risk in a severe ice storm? Explain your answer.
(c) What strategies could you and your family follow if a large ice storm hit your area?

What are your favourite stories of human compassion and other interest during the storm?
"People who had a heat source, such as wood stoves or propane heaters, took others into their homes."

Figure 2
Four people were badly burned when fire broke out in this house. A gas-fire generator was the source of the fire.

"Many volunteers worked long days to help others — setting up shelters; delivering firewood, water, food, and medicine; and checking on victims."

"Radio announcers worked overtime, organizing help, keeping people informed, and cheering us up."

"People with gasoline-powered generators shared them with others."

"Volunteers came from other parts of Canada and the United States to help clean up the mess and restore electricity after so many power lines were downed (**Figure 3**)."

"We went to a hockey game at the university arena in Kingston that had electric power even though much of the city did not. The irony was that the heat could not be turned off, so the arena got too hot and the doors to the cold outside had to be left open to keep the ice frozen!"

"An emergency crew went to deliver a truckload of firewood to a lady who lives on a farm. She was surprised by their compassion — she had operated her farm by herself for 30 years with no need for electricity from the provincial power grid!"

"We heard of a family who kept the fan on their furnace going by hooking up a bicycle to the fan and taking turns peddling the bike." (One of the family members was an engineer who knew how to hook up a battery to operate the fuel flow safely.)

"Many people agree that they had more time for fun with family and friends than they had had for a long time. Young kids seemed to enjoy the disaster more than others."

"One of our friends who works for Ontario Hydro is an expert archer. He used his skills to shoot arrows with cords attached over hydro wires to help get rid of ice — a neat problem-solving technique."

What were some human reactions that you hope will never happen again?

"A few generators were stolen. Imagine if someone in the house was on a life-supporting respirator! The punishment should be severe for such a crime during emergencies."

"Some people charged exorbitant prices for emergency items."

(d) If you were writing a newspaper report or TV story on the ice storm for local people, would you focus on the positive stories of human compassion, or the negative stories of crime and greed? Would your focus change if you were writing for a national audience? Explain your reasoning.

What plans do you have in place if another ice storm happens?

"We would have more food and water on hand, as well as candles, flashlights, matches, medical supplies, and warm clothing."

"I would be sure the gasoline tank in the car was filled up."

"We installed a gas fireplace after the storm. We're ready for the next one!"

Figure 3

The weight of the ice was enough to bring down hydro poles in cities **(a)**, and also the towers that carry electricity to cities **(b)**.

What suggestions can you make to weather forecasters, businesses, insurance companies, emergency crews, government agencies, or others regarding potential ice storms in the future?

"Government agencies should not be so hasty to hand out money; some people who had power out for only three days got much more help than some who were without electricity for weeks."

"Install underground cables in cities; that would prevent problems in an earthquake as well."

"We should all be encouraged to rely less on the power grid for electricity; we should become more self-sufficient."

    (e) Evaluate the recommendations of the people who lived through the storm. Do you see any flaws in the suggestions? What additional recommendations would you make?

What advice can you give people who live in regions that may experience a prolonged ice storm?

"Don't sit around and do nothing — get up and find something useful to do if you're in an ice storm or any other kind of disaster."

"During a prolonged storm, reduce your living area and get a source of heat, such as a fireplace."

"Be aware of live fallen wires — they can be extremely dangerous."

In your opinion, how did the Manitoba flood compare to the ice storm?

"We had more warning about the flood — about two weeks."

"The ice storm damage was far more extensive."

"We had the impression that people in Manitoba were better prepared for disasters than people in the ice storm. But now many more people here are well prepared for the next ice storm, should it happen."

    (f) Why would people in Manitoba have been better prepared for the flood than people in eastern Canada were for the ice storm?

Challenge

1 Describe the conditions you would watch for to help you forecast an ice storm in your area.

2 Could your community survive without electricity for an extended period of time?

Understanding Concepts

1. Explain why an ice storm is difficult to forecast.

2. For each person listed below, suggest the greatest difficulties he or she would have to face during an ice storm:

   (a) a homeless person;

   (b) a shut-in senior citizen who lives alone;

   (c) a person who uses a wheelchair;

   (d) yourself.

3. Assume that a snowfall occurs after an ice storm ends but before the ice has thawed or has been removed. Evaluate the danger in this situation.

Making Connections

4. Write a "Storm Alert" for a severe, prolonged ice storm.

Exploring

5. Research "black ice." What is it? Why is it so dangerous?

6. Find out more about the ice storm of 1998. Describe your most interesting discoveries.

7. When was the most recent ice storm of note in your area or elsewhere? How severe was it, and what problems did it create?

8. (a) Estimate how long your family could survive without electricity. Explain how you reached your estimate.

   (b) What could you do to make this condition less devastating?

Reflecting

9. What could governments do to ensure that people affected by disasters are not victims of theft or price gouging? Explain your answer.

Extreme Heat and Cold

Imagine you see a young jogger collapse on a very hot, humid summer day. What may have caused the collapse, and what could you do to help the victim?

Now imagine the season has changed to winter and you are at a mountain ski-and-snowboarding resort. You want to try trails much higher than you've ever tried before. In the resort's parking lot the temperature is –6°C, the winds are light, and the Sun's rays feel warm, so you leave your tuque in the car. As you ride the chairlift up the mountain, you start to get cold. At the top of the mountain the temperature is –17°C, the winds are brisk and clouds have moved in, blocking the Sun's rays. And the wind feels even stronger as you ski or snowboard at high speed down the slope.

The healthy human body functions best with an internal temperature of 37°C. Any extreme conditions that make it difficult for the body to maintain its normal temperature are dangerous and may even cause death (**Figure 1**).

Figure 1

Intense physical exercise on a hot day can cause dehydration. Without adequate water, this could lead to serious health problems.

Heat Waves and the Humidex Scale

The young, healthy jogger is much more likely to collapse during a **heat wave,** which is a period of more than three days at or above 32°C. The jogger may have suffered from heat exhaustion, a condition in which loss of body water and salts causes dizziness and weakness.

Extreme heat is complex to define. What is too hot for one person may be quite comfortable for another. However, people with health problems, such as respiratory ailments, tend to be more susceptible than others to extreme heat.

Heat waves in North America become more intense when the Bermuda high, a subtropical high-pressure area in the Atlantic, extends its reach over North America. The high pressure brings clear skies, which allows more direct and intense solar heating of an already hot area.

Heat waves can feel hotter with high humidity. A humid air mass becomes even more humid as the direct sunlight and high temperatures increase the rate of evaporation from bodies of surface water.

The most extreme heat waves happen when the temperature gradient in the atmosphere turns upside down. Normally, the temperature in the troposphere decreases with increasing altitude. But sometimes a **temperature inversion** forms, in which a warm layer of air in a high-pressure system moves over and pushes down on cooler air. When this occurs at a low altitude, the air at ground level (that normally rises as it is heated) gets trapped near the ground (**Figure 2**). This stable air doesn't move much; it just hangs around for days, keeping the air near the ground humid and often polluted. Because this air is not mixing, any air pollution generated in the inversion "pocket" can't be diluted, so pollution levels rise. When this type of temperature inversion occurs over populated areas, breathing becomes difficult, even hazardous, for some people. That is when an air quality advisory or warning is issued.

Although everyone reacts differently to high temperatures and humidity, meteorologists have devised a scale to compare comfort levels in extreme heat. The humidex scale (**Table 1**) measures how hot, humid weather feels to humans. ("Humidex" was coined from "humidity" and "index.") This scale combines the temperature and relative humidity. From the humidex scale, you can see that if the air (or dry-bulb) temperature is 30°C and the relative humidity is 65%, then the humidex reading is 40°C. People start to feel uncomfortable at a humidex reading of 30°C, and at 40°C almost everybody feels uncomfortable.

The humidex scale is not meant to be precise. However, it is a useful guide to help people decide what to wear, how much outdoor activity to participate in, and how careful to be if they have health problems.

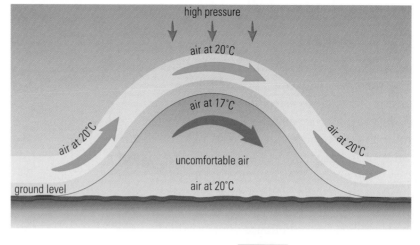

Figure 2

A low-level temperature inversion occurs when warm air from a high-pressure system blows over cooler air at ground level. Since the air near the ground is cooler than the air above, it tends to hang around.

Heat Alert

A heat wave becomes more dangerous as the days pass. Here are some of those dangers and ways to cope with them, from least to most serious.

- Dehydration: drink plenty of water to replenish losses.
- Heat cramps (especially in legs): these result from reduced salts in the body as your body perspires. Stop exercising and drink plenty of water with some salty food, such as popcorn.
- Fainting: this can happen if the body's blood pressure drops. Again, stop exercising and drink plenty of water.
- Heat exhaustion: this is caused by extreme loss of water and salts. The body temperature rises to about 39°C. If a person is normally healthy, treatment is similar to that for fainting. An elderly person or a person in poor health should be hospitalized.
- Heatstroke: this results when the body's regulating system fails. The body temperature rises to 41°C or more. Confusion, unconsciousness, and even death can follow. Immediate medical aid is required.

Table 1 **Partial Humidex Scale**

Dry-bulb temperature (°C)	Relative humidity (%)															
	100	95	90	85	80	75	70	65	60	55	50	45	40	35	30	25
36			58	57	56	54	53	51	50	48	47	46	43	42	40	38
35		58	57	56	54	52	51	49	48	47	45	43	42	41	38	37
34	58	57	55	53	52	51	49	48	47	45	43	42	41	38	37	36
33	55	54	52	51	50	48	47	46	44	43	42	40	38	37	36	34
32	52	51	50	49	47	46	45	43	42	41	39	38	37	36	34	33
31	50	49	48	46	45	44	43	41	40	39	38	36	35	34	33	31
30	48	47	45	44	43	42	41	40	38	37	36	35	34	33	31	31
29	46	45	44	43	42	41	39	38	37	36	34	33	32	31	30	
28	43	42	41	41	38	38	37	36	35	34	33	32	31	29	28	

humidex (equivalent °C)	degree of comfort
20–29	comfortable
30–39	varying degrees of discomfort
40–45	almost everyone uncomfortable
46 and over	many types of labour must be restricted

Extreme Cold and Wind Chill

Extreme cold can be a major problem in Canada, especially if people are not prepared for it. The human body can't cope with extreme cold in the same way that many animals and birds can, so we must protect ourselves from it.

Just as high temperatures have an added factor (humidity) that affects how we feel, cold temperatures also have an added factor: wind. When a spoonful of soup is too hot, we blow on it to cool it down. Similarly, when wind blows against a person, it removes body heat and the body cools down more quickly. When brisk winds accompany cold temperatures, people try to cope by covering up and facing away from the wind (**Figure 3**). To take the cooling effect of wind into account, meteorologists calculate the rate of heat loss and report it as the **wind chill factor.**

The wind chill factor is shown in **Table 2** and in a graph in **Figure 4**. The wind chill temperature is more correctly called the "wind chill equivalent temperature" because it indicates what the temperature would feel like with the wind. Wind chill values were developed in the 1940s using experimental results from Antarctica, one of the coldest and windiest places on Earth. These experiments were done using less sophisticated equipment than is available today, and water was used rather than people, so the scale is controversial. However, it provides a useful guide to help us decide what to wear and what activities are safe in the cold.

From **Table 2,** you can see that a temperature of –20°C with a wind speed of 36 km/h feels like about –40°C. At this value, exposed human flesh freezes.

Figure 3

Most Canadians are aware of how important it is to be protected from cold winds.

Table 2 Wind Chill Factor

	Actual temperature (0°C)						
	30	20	10	0	–10	–20	–30
Wind speed (km/h)	Wind chill temperature (0°C)						
8	30	20	10	0	–10	–20	–30
18	29	17	5	–7	–19	–31	–43
36	29	15	1	–13	–27	–40	–54
54	29	14	–1	–16	–30	–45	–60
72	28	13	–2	–17	–32	–48	–63

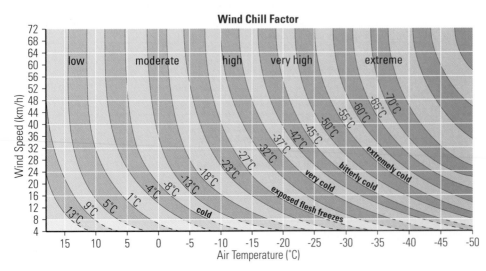

Figure 4

A graphic representation of the wind chill factor.

Cold Alert

Two major problems are caused by exposure to extreme cold: frostbite and hypothermia.

- Frostbite: frostbite is skin damage caused by freezing. The ears, nose, hands, and feet are the first to freeze. Severe frostbite causes pain and sensitivity to cold that lasts for years. Extreme frostbite may require amputation.
- Hypothermia: this happens when the core body temperature falls to 35°C or lower. The person becomes disoriented and may become unconscious and die. The very young and the elderly are most susceptible to hypothermia. Proper protective clothing and staying dry and out of the cold are the best defences against the effects of extreme cold.

> ### Did You Know?
> Mail carriers in Winnipeg, Manitoba, were excused from walking their routes when the wind chill factor dropped to −65°C.

Understanding Concepts

1. Explain what a person's body temperature indicates about the state of his or her health. (Give examples of temperatures during both good and poor health.)

2. Use the humidex and wind chill temperatures in **Tables 1** and **2** to determine what the temperature in each of the following situations feels like.

   (a) air temperature = 28°C; relative humidity = 95%

   (b) air temperature = 36°C; relative humidity = 30%

   (c) air temperature = −30°C; wind speed = 54 km/h

   (d) air temperature = −10°C; wind speed = 18 km/h

3. State at least one location and time in the world where you would find each of the situations in question **2**.

4. Explain why the term "temperature inversion" is appropriate.

5. Explain why a temperature inversion contributes to poor air quality.

6. Explain why the ears, nose, fingers, and feet freeze before other body parts when exposed to cold weather.

Making Connections

7. One of the reasons elderly people suffer during periods of extreme cold is that they may turn down the heat to try to save money. Describe ways that you think society could prevent this from happening.

Exploring

8. Some people take salt tablets during conditions of extreme
   (I) heat. Find out and explain the reason for this, as well as any potential risks in doing so.

9. Research the wind chill scale that uses watts per square
   (I) metre. (One resource is *The Canadian Global Almanac*, published annually.) Compare and contrast it to the scale that uses degrees Celsius.

(I) 10. Where in Canada are heat waves most common and why?

11. From the source of your choice, collect daily maximum and
    (I) minimum winter temperatures for your area, both the actual air temperatures and the wind chill temperatures.
    (J) Graph the data, and explain any patterns you observe.

12. Interview a long-distance runner from your school's track team. Find out how he or she copes with wind chill, frostbite, heat exhaustion, and cramps. Summarize the interview and present it orally to your class.

15.10 Explore an Issue

DECISION MAKING SKILLS
○ Define the Issue   ● Analyze the Issue
● Identify Alternatives ● Defend a Decision
● Research   ● Evaluate

Winter Shelters for the Homeless

In cities and towns across Canada, people can be found living outdoors (**Figure 1**). In Canada's largest city, Toronto, approximately 30 000 people use shelters and hostels each year. At no time of the year is the issue of shelters for the homeless more important than in winter, when temperatures drop and winds add to the hazards of living outdoors. The public became aware of how serious the problem was when three Toronto homeless people died during cold weather in 1995. After that, the Public Health Department set up a warning and response system to implement when a cold weather warning was issued by Environment Canada.

Figure 1
Within sight of downtown Toronto, this structure provides more protection from poor weather conditions than many homeless people get. But living here becomes dangerous during extremely cold weather.

Cold Weather Plan

Most of the permanent shelters set up for the homeless are run by the local municipal governments or subsidized by the government. (Some organizations and places of worship operate volunteer shelter facilities on a rotating basis, usually in the winter.) When an extreme weather warning is issued by Environment Canada and the Municipal Medical Officer of Health, these shelters go into emergency mode.

A cold weather warning is given if the temperature is forecast to be −15°C or lower. At that time, the following steps, funded by the taxpayer, are implemented:

- Extra beds are made available.
- Extra staff is brought in to assist the regular workers.
  - Street patrols of a non-profit organization warn the homeless people personally about the impending weather. (The homeless are unlikely to have radios or televisions and therefore will likely be unaware of severe weather warnings.)
  - The shelter workers distribute tickets for public transportation to shelters.
  - A telephone hotline is made available to those who wish to ask for help or find out which shelters have beds available.
- Curfew rules are relaxed.

Understanding the Issue

1. **(a)** List two objective factors presented in the issue.

   (b) List two subjective factors presented in the issue.

   (c) Did one type of factor appear more prevalent in this issue? Explain your answer.

2. If the policy makers choose a cut-off temperature for initiating an emergency response to severe winter weather, what do you think the cut-off temperature should be? Justify your answer based on your understanding of the issue and the wind chill factor as well as on your own experience.

Homeless Shelter Openings

Problem

When should shelters for the homeless be open? Should they always be in "cold weather" mode during the winter? Under what conditions should street patrols be sent out to warn homeless people that bad weather is approaching? A meeting of city council will be held to discuss the homeless issue.

There are arguments for the shelters accommodating extra users throughout the entire winter:
- Forecast temperatures and even wind chills are not necessarily accurate because buildings affect winds at street level.
- In the long term, it would cost less to have facilities available for all winter conditions than to treat people in hospitals for health problems that may come with exposure to severe conditions.

There are arguments against changing the current situation:
- Our taxes are stretched to the limit. We can let volunteer organizations look after the serious problems when they occur.
- Some people don't want to spend a night in a shelter; they would prefer to stay in their makeshift shelter, even in extreme cold.

The Roles

- A homeless person speaks for those most directly affected by the final decision.
- A meteorologist explains what is meant by wind chill and why it should be considered in the issue.
- A physician explains the effects of hypothermia and frostbite.
- An outside worker for the city describes the benefits and dangers of the locations where some homeless people and their families sleep.
- A volunteer relates stories of several homeless people who do not want to go to shelters.
- A representative of private industry urges the governments to give tax breaks to companies and communities that build low-cost housing projects.
- An economist argues that better job creation would mean fewer homeless people and less need for shelters.
- The operator of the local food bank argues that any available extra funding should go to the food bank.
- Councillors can question presenters and must make the final decision.

Forming an Opinion

1. Choose a role and find out more information to help you design a successful presentation. You can
(D) start by considering the arguments above.
2. Set up a city council hearing in which each person or group concerned with the situation has three minutes to explain his or her position.
3. After the arguments are complete, the city councillors discuss the merits of the presentations, then propose and vote on a final decision.

ᕦ Work the Web

Visit www.science.nelson.com and follow the links from Science 10, 15.10. Research how large cities in Canada handle homelessness.

Reporting an Extreme Weather Event

Have you ever timed the length of a TV weather forecast or a news report about an extreme weather event? Timing is vital in TV broadcasting. A lot of information has to be communicated quickly, efficiently, and in a highly visual manner that will grab and hold the attention of the viewers (**Figure 1**).

Weather broadcasting on TV provides a good example of group cooperation. Meteorologists gather and analyze weather data and then decide which information is most appropriate to communicate to the TV audience. Researchers find background information to explain weather-related phenomena. A design team works with the producer and director to decide how to present the information in a clear, interesting fashion. A technical team is responsible for the lighting, sound mixing, and other technical jobs, all of which are computer-linked. Specialists in art and computer-assisted design ensure the set and weather maps are correct and attractive. Finally, there is the one person who appears before the TV camera: the weather reporter.

Figure 1

A TV weather reporter is only one of many people involved in producing a weather broadcast.

In this activity, your group will choose one type of extreme weather event described in this chapter and design a TV weather report or broadcast to communicate your ideas about the event to the public. Your TV broadcast will have two main timed components: one to explain the event and the other to present the design of "emergency kits" to help people prepare for the event. You can simulate a real broadcast by recording the presentation with a video camera.

Materials

(a) Create the materials list after your group has agreed on the format of the broadcast.

Procedure

1 As a class, decide which group will cover which of the following extreme weather events: thunderstorm, tornado, flood, drought, hurricane, blizzard, ice storm, heat wave, or extreme cold. Also, decide on the time allowed for each broadcast. (An example is three minutes for the information component and one minute to present the emergency kit.)

2 In your group, discuss which features of the event you think the public should know about. Some examples are: location; season(s); duration of the event; hazards; precautions before, during, and after the event; amount of time of advance warning; potential accuracy of forecasts; a weather map; interesting facts about the type of event chosen. (You can choose an actual event, or you can make up an event based on what you learned in this chapter.) Ⓧ

3 Brainstorm the design of the emergency kits people would need to prepare for the event or the emergency steps to take in case there is no time. For the kits, think of what people would need at school, at home, and in a car. Decide how you will present your kit suggestions and emergency steps in a short period of time.

4 Discuss the format you intend to use to communicate your group's ideas. Distribute the responsibilities in a fair way.

5 Do the necessary planning and research, and then create a storyboard for the TV broadcast.

6 Practise the broadcast to be sure it fills, but does not exceed, the required time interval.

7 Present the broadcast to your class and, if possible, record it live on video.

8 Be prepared to make evaluation notes as other groups present their broadcasts.

Analysis and Evaluation

(b) List the features of a good TV broadcast of an extreme weather event.

(c) Suggest some ways that the broadcasts in this activity (including your own) could be improved.

(d) If you were to produce another TV weather broadcast, explain how you would improve your planning.

(e) Explain the ways in which teamwork was important in this activity.

(f) If you were to visit a TV production studio or a meteorological service location where weather reports are produced, what are four questions that you would like to have answered?

Understanding Concepts

1. **(a)** Which components of an emergency kit will be common for all extreme weather events?

   (b) Explain why they are so important.

2. **(a)** Which extreme weather emergency kits will include components that are likely not needed in any other events?

   (b) Explain why these components are important.

Making Connections

3. A TV weather reporter stands in front of a wall that looks like a weather map to the viewer, but is in fact totally blank. The colour of this blank wall must be different from any of the colours of the reporter's clothing, hair, and face because a filter on the TV camera removes the colour of the wall.

   (a) If you were the reporter, what colour of wall would you choose? Explain your choice.

   (b) Have you ever noticed a connecting cord or even a reporter's sleeve disappearing from the set as you were watching a weather report on TV? How could this happen?

   (c) Suggest how a weather reporter and TV crew could play tricks on the audience during a weather forecast on Hallowe'en or April Fool's day.

Exploring

4. Time the length of weather report segments on various TV channels. What patterns do you observe?

Reflecting

5. Who is your favourite TV weather reporter? What qualities does this person possess that make him or her a good reporter?

El Niño and La Niña

What do the following reports have in common?

- Toward the end of 1997, countries in the western Pacific Ocean, such as the Philippines, that normally get heavy rains experienced a severe drought. In Indonesia, the worst drought in 50 years set the stage for huge forest fires (**Figure 1**).
- At the same time in countries along the west coast of South America, such as Peru, the normally dry regions sprang to life with wildflowers after heavy rainfall.
- Also at the same time, torrential rains fell in the normally dry regions of Somalia and Kenya in east Africa.
- The winter of 1997/1998 on the west coast of North America was much wetter than average. Record snowfalls fell in the Rocky Mountains, and snow fell in Guadalajara, Mexico, for the first time since 1881.
- The winter of 1997/1998 for eastern North America was much milder than average. The most devastating ice storm in Canadian history (the storm of 1998) struck a region that would normally be too cold for that type of weather.
- The 1997 Atlantic hurricane season was much less active than average.

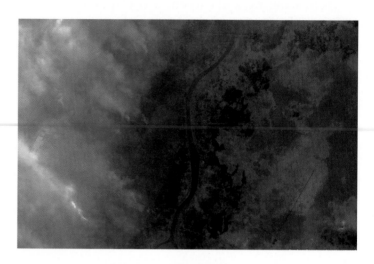

Figure 1

With much lower-than-average rainfall in 1997, forest fires became a major problem in regions of the western Pacific Ocean, as shown by this satellite image. These fires in Indonesia destroyed vast areas of forest and created severe pollution.

The answer is that the extreme weather events around the world were a result of El Niño. **El Niño** is a shift in the ocean currents, temperatures (water becomes warmer), and atmospheric conditions in the tropical Pacific Ocean. Only in recent years have scientists realized how much El Niño affects weather patterns in most areas of the world.

What Causes El Niño?

It may be difficult to visualize something as huge as the Pacific Ocean as water sloshing back and forth in a pan, but in some ways this image works. The atmospheric and surface water temperatures appear to go through cycles from low to normal to high, then back to low again. Therefore, the ocean currents, surface winds, and atmospheric pressures also go through cycles. Scientists use observations of temperatures, elevation of sea levels, and other factors to follow the cycles.

El Niño occurs during the part of the cycle when the surface temperatures of the tropical Pacific Ocean off the coast of South America are higher than average. The model in **Figure 2** shows the extreme changes in ocean temperatures during the 1997–98 El Niño event.

Figure 3 shows the currents and winds related to the cycles. During the normal period, the north and south equatorial currents flow westward, and the Pacific northeast and southeast trade winds also blow westward as they come together near the equator. This westward flow of water and air carries the warm surface waters westward. As a result, the water level on the west side of the Pacific Ocean is normally about 50 cm higher than on the east side. The warm water causes stronger convection currents of air, which carry moisture into the atmosphere, producing thunderstorms and heavy rainfall in Indonesia, the Philippines, and northern Australia. In the eastern Pacific, the westward moving warm water is replaced by cold water moving in a convection current. Because this water is cool, less upward convection of air occurs, so rainfall on the west coast of South America is minimal.

When the surface water temperature and the water level in the western Pacific become much higher than normal, El Niño begins. The extra water begins to push eastward, reversing the equatorial current flow and weakening the trade winds. This is much like carrying water in a flat pan: it sloshes back and forth. The warm waters and air cause the thunderstorms and rainfall to move eastward across the Pacific Ocean, eventually reaching the coast of South America.

One country that often receives the full extent of El Niño is Peru. Peruvians noticed that the reversal of the temperatures and other factors often seemed to happen at the end of December, so they named the event "El Niño," which means little boy or infant, after Jesus, whose birth is celebrated on December 25.

El Niño events vary in how often they occur and in how long they last. They may last for only a few months or, more often, continue for one or two years. They usually occur once every three to five years, but they may also wait for 10 years to return. Extreme El Niño events may occur once every 20 to 50 years.

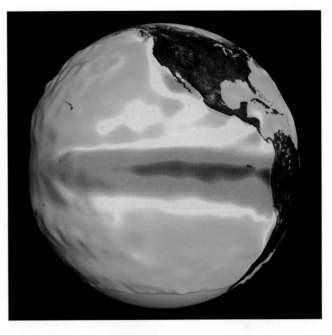

Figure 2

This model, generated from NASA satellite data, shows both unusual sea surface elevations and surface water temperatures during the El Niño event of 1997–98. Red indicates higher-than-normal temperatures, blue lower-than-normal.

Figure 3

Comparing a normal year with an El Niño year.
(a) During a normal year
(b) During an El Niño year

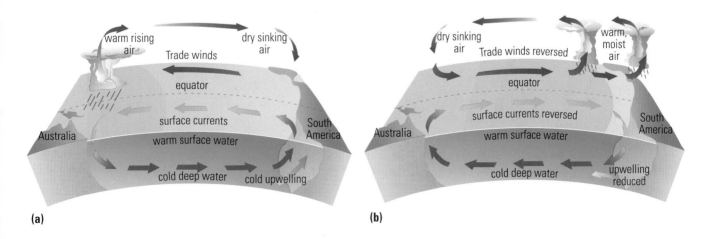

(a)

(b)

Other Effects of El Niño

Many of the effects of El Niño occur in and around the Pacific Ocean. For example, off the west coast of South America, normally the rising cold waters that flow in a convection current bring rich nutrients to the surface. These nutrients provide food for some of the largest fish populations in the world. But when the warm El Niño waters arrive, they prevent the cold water from rising. Thus, the fish have no food, and both the fish and animals that depend on the fish, such as birds and sea mammals, must move or die. The fishing industry also collapses.

But because the Pacific Ocean is so large, El Niño also affects ocean currents and prevailing winds around the world. For example, El Niño's influence on jet streams can be seen in North America. In the winter, El Niño pushes the polar jet stream farther north, preventing much cold Arctic air from reaching parts of eastern Canada and the United States, causing milder than average winters. El Niño also pushes the subtropical jet stream farther south than normal, resulting in higher than average precipitation in the southern parts of North America. This eastward flowing jet stream also pushes against the westward moving tropical storms in the Atlantic Ocean, reducing the chances that these storms can develop into hurricanes.

These observations lead to an important concept: evidence suggests that most (if not all) of the extreme events presented in this chapter become even more extreme during various parts of the El Niño cycle. More research will help us understand why.

Researching El Niño

Not many years ago, the public knew little or nothing about El Niño. (A 1980 university text on atmospheric science devoted only one short paragraph to the phenomenon.) Scientists now believe that El Niño is so important that it has become the subject of major concern and research. Satellites keep track of sea levels and changing water temperatures. Ocean-going ships carry instruments that record data, which are transmitted to research stations. Numerous platforms and buoys have been set up at regular intervals in the Pacific Ocean to check water temperatures both at and beneath the surface. Researchers have gathered samples of ice, soil, and coral from locations around the Pacific Ocean to look for cycles that may have occurred over the past hundreds and thousands of years. This research will lead to better understanding and forecasts.

La Niña

At the opposite end of the cycle to El Niño is **La Niña,** which is a shift to colder than average ocean temperatures in the eastern Pacific. (La Niña means "little girl.") During this shift, the surface water temperature off the coast of Peru can drop to as low as 24°C. The effects are opposite to those of El Niño. Indonesia and northern Australia receive higher than normal precipitation. The jet streams are also affected. For instance, the summer jet stream above North America shifts northward, so its effect on the build-up of Atlantic hurricanes north of the equator is reduced.

Hurricanes develop more easily. Thus, you can see that measuring the surface water temperature off the coast of Peru helps meteorologists predict the number of Atlantic hurricanes. This is just one example of why meteorologists want to share their exciting research and discoveries with the public in general and students in particular.

Understanding Concepts

1. A student once asked, "Could we say that the Pacific Ocean has a healthy body temperature of 28°C?" Why is that a good question?

2. **(a)** Under normal conditions, in what general direction do the Pacific equatorial currents flow?

   (b) Describe what happens to those currents during El Niño.

   (c) What happens to the Pacific Ocean trade winds during El Niño?

3. The Galápagos Islands archipelago, located on the equator 1000 km west of Ecuador, supports two types of iguanas: land iguanas **(Figure 4)** and sea iguanas.

   (a) Which type of iguana would survive better during El Niño? Explain why.

   (b) Which type would survive better during normal conditions? Why?

Figure 4

4. Describe how North American weather is influenced by El Niño and La Niña.

Making Connections

5. During an extreme El Niño, the fishing industry in Peru does poorly, but fishers off the west coast of North America report catching fish never before seen there. Explain why there is such a change.

6. Arrange the following statements in an order that demonstrates how a severe El Niño can affect the price of soybeans:

   (a) With an increased demand and lower supply, soybean prices rise.

   (b) The anchovies feed on the ocean plants, so with no plants, there are no anchovies.

   (c) The warm El Niño current moves southward along the coast of Peru.

   (d) With no anchovies on the world market, there is no fish meal for animal feed.

   (e) The plants in the ocean do not get enough nutrients from the water to flourish.

   (f) Farmers need animal feed, so they buy soybeans, a substitute for fish meal.

   (g) With no anchovies, there is no food for the birds and larger fish, which puts a major dent in Peru's fishing economy.

   (h) The warmer water prevents the cool, nutrient-rich bottom water from rising.

Exploring

7. The term "El Niño/Southern Oscillation," or ENSO, can be used in place of simply El Niño. Explain why this term is appropriate.

8. What is weather analoguing, and how can it be used to
   (I) predict the severity of an El Niño at its onset? How can
   (J) satellite photo loops be used to predict the onset of El Niño?

🖱 Work the Web

To do more research on El Niño and La Niña, follow the links for Science 10, 15.12 at www.science.nelson.com. Which cycle is the Pacific Ocean now in? What new research is there about the El Niño and La Niña oscillation?

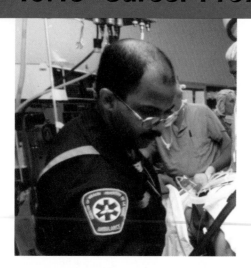

Patrick Auger

Paramedic

It is not unusual for Patrick Auger to travel over 200 km to help save someone's life. As a critical care flight paramedic, Pat travels onboard *Bandage 1*, the Helicopter Air Ambulance based out of Toronto. *Bandage 1* services most of southern Ontario, moving critically ill or injured patients from smaller hospitals, car accidents, or remote locations to larger regional hospitals that offer specialized care. He claims, "There is no such thing as a typical day for me. I never know what kind of situation I may find myself in. One day I may have to respond to a major car or boating accident, the next I'm racing to the scene of an explosion."

Patrick has been helping save lives since he was a teenager. Growing up in London, Ontario, he loved outdoor activities such as camping, hiking, sailing, and especially swimming, which led him to a job as a lifeguard. While training to qualify as a lifeguard, he took courses through St. John Ambulance, and these inspired him to become a paramedic. After completing an extensive two-year college course in basic life support at Fanshawe College in London, he did additional training in advanced life support at Sunnybrook Health Sciences Centre in Toronto, certifying as an Advanced Care Paramedic. He later took more specialized training at the Hospital for Sick Children and certified as a Critical Care Paramedic. He has to recertify every year. Medical technology is continually changing, so Patrick is required to spend about 100 h on continuing medical education each year as well as 40 h on safety training, which includes underwater escape and winter survival. He must also have sound knowledge of human anatomy, physiology, pathophysiology, pharmacology, and chemistry.

The first few minutes of care are extremely critical and in many instances will make the difference between life and death. "You need to be able to communicate effectively, assess situations, and make critical decisions in very short periods of time," Patrick says. "It is also very important to be physically fit so you can handle the demands of treating critically ill adults and children." Paramedics often perform procedures that are normally done in a hospital emergency department or intensive care unit, such as treating a collapsed lung or mixing a medication into a solution and administering it intravenously.

Paramedics also take verbal orders from a doctor at the base hospital using a cellular or satellite phone.

Patrick finds his work rewarding personally and professionally. "I like the idea of being able to work outdoors and provide a valuable service to the community," he says. His advice for anyone interested in being a paramedic: "Ensure that you enjoy working with people, are physically fit, and have the ability to communicate and work under very stressful conditions."

Making Connections

1. Does the use of air ambulance helicopters improve survival?
2. Paramedics must have sound knowledge of human anatomy, physiology, pathophysiology, pharmacology, and chemistry. Investigate why each of these is important.

🖑 Work the Web

Patrick was inspired by the courses he took through St. John Ambulance. Using the Internet, report on the history of this organization and the training it offers.

Chapter 15 Summary

Key Expectations

Throughout this chapter, you have had opportunities to do the following:

- Formulate scientific questions about weather-related phenomena, problems, and issues. (15.1, 15.2, 15.5, 15.8, 15.10, 15.11)
- Analyze data and information and evaluate evidence and sources of information, identifying flaws such as errors and bias. (15.2, 15.10, 15.11)
- Select and integrate information from various sources, including electronic and print resources, to answer the questions chosen. (15.2, 15.11)
- Describe and explain the effects of heat transfer within the hydrosphere and atmosphere on the development, severity, and movement of weather systems. (15.3, 15.6, 15.7, 15.8, 15.9, 15.12)
- Explain the effects of different types of transformations of water vapour in the atmosphere. (15.3, 15.4, 15.7, 15.8)
- Describe the factors that contribute to Earth temperature gradients and to wind speed and direction. (15.3, 15.6, 15.7, 15.12)
- Describe tornadoes, hurricanes, and cyclones in terms of the meeting of air masses, atmospheric humidity, and the jet stream. (15.3, 15.6)
- Demonstrate the skills required to plan and conduct a weather-related inquiry using a broad range of tools and techniques safely and accurately, and adapting or extending procedures where required. (15.5)
- Select and use appropriate vocabulary and numeric, symbolic, graphic, and linguistic modes of representation to communicate scientific ideas, plans, results, and conclusions. (15.5)
- Investigate factors that affect the development, severity, and movement of global and local weather systems. (15.6, 15.12)

Key Terms

advisory
blizzard
drought
El Niño
eye
eye wall
flood
heat wave
hurricane
ice storm
La Niña
storm surge
temperature inversion
thunderstorm
tornado
tropical cyclone
typhoon
warning
watch
wind chill factor

Make a Summary

In this chapter you studied extreme weather events. To summarize your learning, imagine you have unlimited funds to design a virtual "Extreme Weather Ride" at an amusement park. At various times on the ride, the riders would experience the sensations of all the extreme weather events presented in this chapter. Describe the features of your design using as many of the concepts and defined terms from this chapter as you can. (Be sure the ride is safe.)

Reflect on your Learning

Revisit your answers to the Reflect on your Learning questions, page 579, in the Getting Started.

- How has your thinking changed?
- What new questions do you have?

Understanding Concepts

1. Which extreme weather events affect Canadians directly? Are there any extreme weather events that do not affect Canada?

2. Explain which is more difficult to forecast: a tornado watch or a tornado warning.

3. Briefly describe the main stages in the development of each of the following extreme events:
   (a) a mid-latitude thunderstorm;
   (b) an Atlantic hurricane;
   (c) an ice storm;
   (d) a temperature inversion during a heat wave;
   (e) an El Niño event.

4. **Figure 1** shows a model used to demonstrate how a vortex forms. Relate the model to the shape of a tornado.

Figure 1

5. (a) Explain how lightning is created.
   (b) Explain how thunder is produced.
   (c) A clap of thunder is heard 6 s after the lightning that produces it is seen. Estimate the distance to the lightning.

6. For the area in which you live, state the important "storm alert" precautions for each of the extreme events possible.

7. Briefly describe ways of reducing the effects of broadside floods and flash floods.

8. Explain why warm water is called the "fuel" of a hurricane.

9. Explain how a high tide would affect the storm surge of a hurricane.

10. (a) What does the term "lake-effect blizzard" mean?
    (b) Give some examples of locations where this event occurs.

11. Explain why ice storms are difficult to forecast.

12. Refer to the scales for tornadoes, winds, and hurricanes.
    (a) Compare the winds of an extreme hurricane with those of a tornado.
    (b) Explain which is worse: a strong gale or a violent storm.

13. Describe in your own words the meaning of the following and how to determine each:
    (a) the humidex reading;
    (b) the wind chill factor.

14. Explain why El Niño is described in this chapter on extreme weather events.

15. A buoy in the mid-Pacific Ocean near the equator provides these surface water temperatures at the start of six consecutive months: 26°C, 27°C, 28°C, 29°C, 30°C, 31°C.
    (a) Name the event that is occurring.
    (b) Describe the causes of the temperature increases.
    (c) Predict whether the forthcoming Atlantic hurricane season will be mild or devastating. Justify your answer.

Applying Inquiry Skills

16. What advice would you give a student beginning to study weather on how to find good information about extreme weather events?

17. **Figure 2** shows part of a North American weather map.

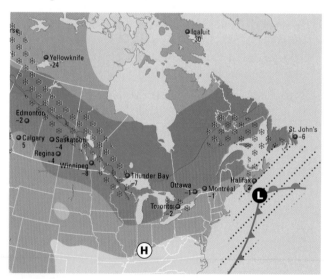

Figure 2

    (a) During which season was the map produced? How can you tell?
    (b) Describe the weather conditions to the east, north, west, and south of the low-pressure system.

18. **(a)** Describe an experiment to find out which plants best absorb moisture from the soil.
    (b) Explain how such information could be applied to reducing the effects of extreme weather events.

19. **Figure 3** shows a satellite image of part of North America and the Atlantic Ocean. What is happening? How can you tell?

Figure 3

20. **Figure 4** shows a Doppler radar image of a weather system over part of Canada. Interpret what you can from the image.

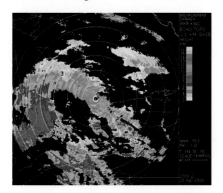

Figure 4

21. **Figure 5** shows the temperature profile of air above a city at two different times.

29.0°C   23.0°C

27.5°C   24.5°C

26.0°C Air temperature at ground level 26.0°C

Figure 5

   (a) Which situation is more stable? Explain why.
   (b) In which situation is a person more likely to be concerned about the humidex readings? Explain why.

22. On a summer day, Windsor, Ontario, has a dry-bulb temperature of 33°C and a relative humidity of 60%, while Kelowna, British Columbia, has the same dry-bulb temperature but a relative humidity of 30%. Explain which city is more likely to experience a thunderstorm.

23. Explain why learning about El Niño and La Niña would help to improve your long-term weather forecasting skills.

Making Connections

24. In a brainstorming session, list as many careers as possible in which people would benefit by knowing about weather watches, advisories, and warnings. In a column, classify the careers under one of two headings: Nice to know the weather; Must know the weather.

25. Since the 1940s, the federal government and the housing construction industry have worked together to research better building materials and housing designs, as well as stricter building codes. Since then, Canada has been a world leader in house construction, energy efficiency, and the use of modern technology. Propose ways in which developing countries could benefit from this leadership and why it is important they do so.

26. In spring, some rivers flood when backed-up water suddenly bursts through and over large chunks of ice. Residents along the Danube River in Europe are trying to prevent this type of flooding by keeping the river clear of ice all winter.
    (a) Propose some methods that could be used to try to keep ice from forming in a river.
    (b) Do you think this would be a wise procedure in Canada, for example, along the Red River? Explain your answer.

27. List some technological advances that have helped to improve the forecasting of hurricanes.

28. If all electrical, telephone, and cable wires were buried, the problem of fallen poles and wires would be eliminated. What are some disadvantages of this idea?

29. An extreme weather event has struck an area adjacent to your school during the winter. Hundreds of homes, apartments, and other buildings will be without electricity for several days. Your school has become an emergency shelter. What advice would you give to a volunteer who greets the people affected by the weather event as they arrive at the school?

30. Explain why international cooperation is important in studying El Niño and La Niña.

16 Forecasting the Future

HOW WOULD GLOBAL WARMING AFFECT OUR CLIMATE?
At a higher temperature, some glaciers and polar ice would melt, which would cause ocean levels to rise. This could be devastating for people who live along coastlines. The cold water from the melting glaciers and polar ice would also affect ocean currents, which would have a significant impact on the world climate.

A higher temperature would also cause stronger winds and more precipitation in many areas (**Figure 1**), which would affect agriculture and the severity of storms such as tornadoes and hurricanes. Dry areas might become even drier, and forests, crops, and other plant life would move farther north and higher up mountains. Frozen soils in the north would begin to thaw. Perhaps parts of Canada currently too harsh to live in would be able to support human communities.

Alternatively, what do you think would happen to Canada's climate if the average global temperature were to decrease? Winters would be longer and more severe. Precipitation in much of the country would change from rain to snow. Lakes, rivers, and streams would freeze, and some would not thaw in the summer. In extreme conditions, ice might cover large areas of the country, just as it did during the last ice age.

Figure 1

Would floods like this become more common, or more devastating, on a warmer Earth?

We don't know exactly when and by how much the average global temperature will increase or decrease, but we do know that change will happen. In fact, as you will learn in this chapter, if global warming becomes extreme, it could be followed by dramatic global cooling.

How can scientists predict climate change? One important step is to find out what events — both natural and caused by humans — happened in the past. Another is to study current weather events, both natural and those caused by human activities. Finally, using the most advanced computer modelling, scientists try to predict changes based on current trends.

In this chapter you will learn how scientists use modern technology to analyze patterns of past and current weather changes and to model what may happen in the future. You will read about how technology is used to try to control certain aspects of the weather. You will apply your skills of designing and carrying out investigations to observe air pollution in your area. You will also study the impact of human activities and how we as individuals can reduce their negative effects. After completing this chapter, you will appreciate the complexity of forecasting future weather and climate.

Reflect on your Learning

1. Describe what you know about the last great ice age. When was it? What caused it? How did it affect what is now Canada? Could an ice age happen again?

2. Describe what you know about the UV index. What do you think it has to do with the ozone layer?

3. Why do you think big cities are usually warmer than the surrounding areas?

4. Describe what you know about the greenhouse effect. What do you think greenhouse gases are, and what effects do you think they have on Earth's climate? Do you think that deforestation affects greenhouse gases?

5. Why do you think scientists predict that climate changes will lead to more severe weather?

6. What do you think an individual can do about air pollution, global warming, or ozone depletion?

Throughout this chapter, note any changes in your ideas as you learn new concepts and develop your skills.

Try This
Activity Estimating Temperature

In order to understand today's climate, climatologists estimate the temperatures over the past thousands of years. One way they do this is by measuring the amount of dissolved gases in ice samples. This is based on our understanding of how gases act at different temperatures. To demonstrate, your teacher will place three cans of pop at different temperatures at the front of the classroom, and you can estimate the temperature of each.

- As each can is opened, listen for the sound produced.
- As the pop is poured into three clear beakers, observe each sample carefully.

(a) Without touching the beakers, estimate the temperature of each liquid.

(b) Record your estimations, giving reasons for your answers.

(c) After measuring the three temperatures, compare your estimates to the actual values.

(d) Describe how you think scientists can apply what you discovered here to estimating global temperatures in the past.

Evidence of Change

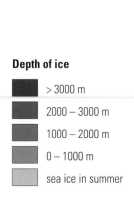

About 18 000 years ago, the last great ice age had the world in its grip. Would your home have been covered with ice at that time? To find out, look at the map of North America in **Figure 1**. It shows that most of Canada was covered with ice sheets, thick layers of ice. By about 10 000 years ago, much of the ice had melted, leaving behind thousands of new lakes and river beds and an ocean level that was up to 100 m higher than it had been during the peak of the ice age. Paleoclimatologists have used various techniques to study how the ice age occurred, why it ended, and what has happened since it fully retreated.

Depth of ice

■ > 3000 m

■ 2000 – 3000 m

■ 1000 – 2000 m

■ 0 – 1000 m

□ sea ice in summer

Gathering Weather Data of the Past

Detailed weather information has been recorded in many regions of the world for about 150 years, and only recently in some areas. Because of this limited amount of data, scientists must search for clues about past weather in nature. Three examples of such clues are described here.

First, the spacing of tree rings tells us approximately how warm and how wet the summers were in the regions where the trees grew (**Figure 2**). This spacing can provide temperature and rainfall information from the past hundreds or even thousands of years.

Second, evidence from layers of ice provides clues to climate up to 200 000 years ago. Using a process called core sampling, scientists drill into the ice in Greenland and Antarctica to extract samples. The thickness of each layer reveals the amount of snowfall in a season; dust particles in the ice are from natural events, such as volcanic eruptions and impacts of asteroids and meteorites; and gas bubbles trapped in each layer tell us about the composition of the atmosphere at the time the ice was formed. For example, the amount of trapped carbon dioxide can tell us about the temperature of water vapour: the lower the temperature, the more carbon dioxide can dissolve in water. (This is why carbonated pop fizzes more at higher temperatures.)

Third, to learn about climate conditions up to a million years ago, scientists study rocks and silt that were swept along by swift-flowing water when the ice melted toward the end of various ice ages. They also study coral beds in oceans and layers of sediment on the lake and ocean beds. For example, pollen found in the sediment in lake beds reveals which plants grew in that region. This, in turn, reveals the weather conditions that contributed to plant growth.

Figure 1

During the last great ice age, much of North America was covered with ice. Most of northern Asia and Europe were also covered with ice sheets.

Figure 2

The number of tree rings reveals the age of a tree. The wider spacing between the rings indicates greater growth during a warm, wet season.

Temperatures over 1 000 000 Years

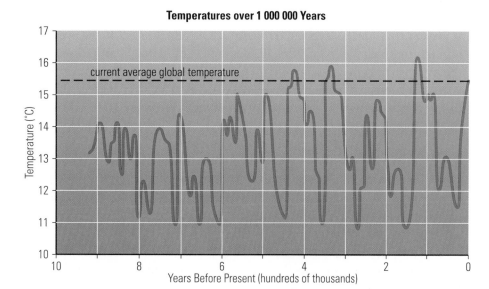

current average global temperature

Figure 3

The current average global temperature is higher than most of the averages throughout the past million years.

Using the weather data they gather, scientists can estimate the changes in the average global temperature of the atmosphere for the past millions of years. **Figure 3** shows that during much of the last one million years, the average global temperature has varied from about 11°C during the major ice ages to a little over 16°C during the warmest periods. Currently, the average temperature is 15°C, which is somewhat warmer than during most of the times shown. There have been 10 major ice ages in the past million years. The most recent one ended about 10 000 years ago.

Figure 4 shows a more detailed graph of temperatures since the last ice age. As temperatures rose and new lakes and rivers formed, conditions became more suitable for humans. About 6000 to 8000 years ago, agriculture began to flourish, and humans started to establish villages and towns.

The graph in **Figure 4** shows that a colder-than-average period occurred from about A.D. 1550 to 1850. During this "little ice age," glaciers in some parts of the world became larger, and winters in the middle latitudes were colder and longer than they are now.

Temperatures over 10 000 Years

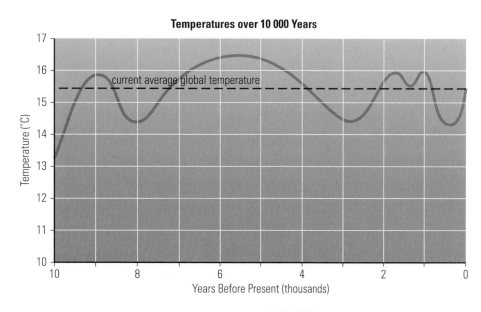

current average global temperature

Figure 4

The world's average temperature has not been constant since the end of the last ice age.

Theories of Temperature Change

It is clear that Earth's average temperature has fluctuated. If the average temperature decreases by 5 Celsius degrees, the average temperature near the equator may decrease by only 2 Celsius degrees, whereas near the poles the average temperature may decrease by 9 Celsius degrees. This difference explains why layers of ice cover areas far from the equator during a major ice age.

However, scientists do not know the reasons for the fluctuations and why there have been so many ice ages followed by periods of warmth. One theory is that Earth's orbit around the Sun goes through a cycle that takes about 100 000 years, causing temperature changes. Another theory proposes that the Sun's energy output is not constant, so we receive varying amounts of solar energy. If either, or both, of these theories is true, we can't do anything about them because they are beyond our control.

Another theory suggests that changes to atmospheric gases and to major ocean currents are responsible for the temperature fluctuations, while another suggests that the fluctuations change the currents. Since these factors may be affected by human activities, we will focus our attention on them throughout the chapter.

Understanding Concepts

1. During the peak of the last major ice age (**Figure 1**), how deep was the ice over (a) southern Ontario? (b) eastern Newfoundland?

2. Describe what happens to the average sea level of the oceans when Earth's average temperature drops. Explain why this happens.

3. How would the tree rings of a tree in Labrador compare with the rings of a similar type of tree growing in Florida? Explain your reasoning.

4. Assume that scientists discover that a huge volcano erupted about 25 000 years ago. How and where do you think scientists could gather the evidence for their discovery? (Try to give at least two examples.)

5. Describe how towns and cities along ocean coasts would be affected by:

   (a) an increase in the average global temperature of 2 Celsius degrees;

   (b) a decrease in the average global temperature of 2 Celsius degrees.

6. Using the concept of albedo, explain why the temperatures of the regions far from the equator decrease more during global cooling than those of regions near the equator.

Making Connections

7. Suggest how the Industrial Revolution of the 1800s might have affected the snow deposited on the ice fields of Greenland. Explain your answer.

8. If ice cores are taken from Greenland 500 years from now, what general properties will be observed for the time period around the year 2000? Give reasons for your answer.

Exploring

9. Closely examine the tree rings in **Figure 2**. Describe what conclusions can be drawn about the weather when this tree grew.

10. In North America, jack-pine forests started growing farther south during the last major ice age, then started growing farther north again as the ice retreated. In Europe, the same type of forest did not undergo this "ice-age migration." Look at a globe or a map of North America and Europe and suggest why there was a difference in jack-pine survival.

11. Using a dictionary and other resources, find out what a climatologist and a paleoclimatologist do.

Reflecting

12. How does the solubility of carbon dioxide in a liquid depend on the liquid's temperature? Relate your answer to your observations in the Try This Activity in the Getting Started.

The Greenhouse Effect and Ozone Depletion

Have you ever done anything that could harm the atmosphere? The answer is yes, you have, although you didn't intend any long-term destruction. As you will discover in this section, human activities do affect Earth's atmosphere, and scientists are trying to discover how changes in the atmosphere will affect weather in the future.

The Greenhouse Effect

Mercury, the planet closest to the Sun, has no atmosphere. Its surface temperature rises to about 430°C during its daytime and drops to −180°C during its nighttime. The next planet, Venus, has a very dense atmosphere consisting mainly of carbon dioxide (CO_2); this reduces the energy radiated to space, keeping the surface temperature at about 470°C both day and night.

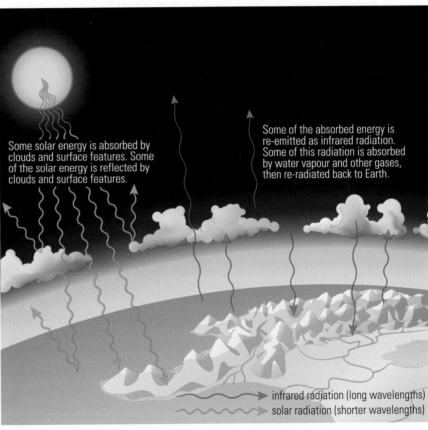

Some solar energy is absorbed by clouds and surface features. Some of the solar energy is reflected by clouds and surface features.

Some of the absorbed energy is re-emitted as infrared radiation. Some of this radiation is absorbed by water vapour and other gases, then re-radiated back to Earth.

infrared radiation (long wavelengths)
solar radiation (shorter wavelengths)

Figure 1

The greenhouse effect

Conditions on the third planet, Earth, lie between these two extremes: our atmosphere has large amounts of nitrogen and oxygen and lesser amounts of other gases such as CO_2, water vapour, and ozone.

You learned earlier that when electromagnetic energy from the Sun strikes Earth, some is absorbed by clouds, some is reflected by clouds back into space, and some passes through the atmosphere and strikes Earth's surface. Some of the energy that is absorbed by the surface and clouds is re-radiated as infrared energy, which has a longer wavelength and lower energy than visible light (**Figure 1**). This energy can pass through some of the gases in the atmosphere, such as nitrogen and oxygen, but it is absorbed by other gas molecules, increasing their temperature. These molecules re-emit infrared energy to the surface, helping to maintain the range of temperatures that support life on Earth. The process by which gases build up thermal energy in the atmosphere by absorbing infrared radiation from Earth's surface is called the **greenhouse effect**. In principle, the effect is similar to how a greenhouse works: the glass transmits the short-wavelength solar radiation, which is absorbed by the plants, soil, and other materials in the greenhouse. These heated materials then radiate infrared energy, which is blocked by the glass, trapping the energy inside the greenhouse.

Greenhouse Gases

The greenhouse effect is a natural phenomenon. The atmospheric gases that absorb and re-emit infrared radiation are called **greenhouse gases**. The most common ones are water vapour and carbon dioxide. Other greenhouse gases found in lesser amounts are methane, nitrous oxides, ozone, and CFCs. (CFCs, or chlorofluorocarbons, now banned in North America, are chemical compounds consisting of chlorine, fluorine, and carbon.) **Figure 2** shows examples of how these greenhouse gases are produced.

Effects of Human Activities on Greenhouse Gases

Look carefully at the information in **Figure 2**. A few of the important processes that produce greenhouse gases are natural, such as the evaporation of water, transpiration, and forest fires caused by lightning. However, many of the processes that produce greenhouse gases result from human activities, such as burning fossil fuels, cutting down forests, piling garbage in dumps, and using air conditioning. Some of these activities began after the Industrial Revolution in the 1800s. Scientists estimate that since that time, carbon dioxide levels in the atmosphere have increased by about 50%, and the amount of methane alone has doubled. With the production of more greenhouse gases, Earth may become even warmer.

Figure 2

Production of greenhouse gases

Water vapour **Carbon dioxide** **Ozone** **Methane** **Nitrous oxides** **CFCs**

(a) Water vapour is added to the atmosphere by evaporation of water, transpiration, and burning fuels.

(b) Carbon dioxide is released through forest fires, burning fossil fuels, the natural rotting of plants, and by respiration. When forests are cut down, less carbon dioxide is removed from the atmosphere.

(c) Ozone near Earth's surface, called ground-level ozone, is produced when solar energy interacts with some natural gases and emissions from industries and vehicles. At this level, ozone is a major component of urban pollution and is harmful to life.

(d) Methane is released by bacteria in cud-chewing animals such as cows; by decaying material in swamps, sewage, and landfill sites; and by leaks in gas pipes.

(e) Nitrous oxides are emitted by vehicles, industry, and part of the process of crop growing.

(f) CFCs were used as a coolant (such as Freon) in refrigerators and air conditioners, as an insulating gas in foam plastics, as a propellant in aerosol sprays, and as a solvent. CFC molecules are released to the atmosphere during the manufacture and careless use of these products.

The Ozone Layer

Ozone is one of the gases that absorbs infrared radiation. Chemically, **ozone** is a gas that consists of three oxygen atoms (O_3) (**Figure 3**). Thus, it has one more oxygen atom than the oxygen gas (O_2) that supports burning and that organisms need for cellular respiration. The ground-level ozone described in **Figure 2** is harmful to the environment and to humans. But the upper-level ozone, at altitudes between 10 km and 50 km, is extremely important because it absorbs harmful ultraviolet (UV) radiation from the Sun, preventing it from reaching Earth's surface.

Ultraviolet radiation, with its shorter wavelength and higher energy than visible light, can be dangerous: it can cause skin cancer, especially in fair-skinned people; it can cause cataracts in the eyes of people and animals; and it can damage plants, reducing agricultural productivity. It can also penetrate the upper layers of oceans and interfere with the production of plankton, which is the beginning of food webs involving krill, fish, seabirds, penguins, whales, and other organisms.

In nature, ozone is produced when UV radiation interacts with ordinary oxygen molecules. Thus, ozone can be depleted if the amount of UV radiation from the Sun decreases or if there is a large volcanic eruption that darkens the sky. These natural activities have caused the amount of upper-level ozone to vary somewhat for millions of years, while still remaining at a safe level. In recent decades, however, human activities have upset the balance.

Probably the biggest cause of the ozone depletion has been the use of CFCs. These chemicals are very stable so they persist in the environment for a long time. They drift into the stratosphere and break apart, producing chlorine, a chemical that destroys ozone very effectively.

Ozone depletion is most evident over the polar regions, especially over Antarctica. Since 1978, the *Nimbus 7* satellite has been travelling in a polar orbit obtaining daily measurements of upper-level ozone around the world. The ozone layer over Antarctica has been depleting since measurement began (**Figure 4**). The large opening in the ozone layer above Antarctica is called an **ozone hole**. It is worst after the cold winter, when swirling winds trap CFCs above the South Pole. Ozone holes also develop to a lesser extent over the Arctic and northern latitudes and, recently, have developed over Australia and New Zealand.

(a)

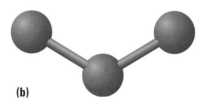
(b)

Figure 3

Comparing ordinary oxygen and ozone
(a) An oxygen gas molecule consists of two oxygen atoms.
(b) An ozone molecule consists of three oxygen atoms

Figure 4

This satellite image of the atmosphere over Antarctica, taken in October of 1999, shows a dark blue "hole" where the concentration of ozone is very low. (According to the colour scale, red indicates the highest concentration of ozone and dark blue the lowest.)

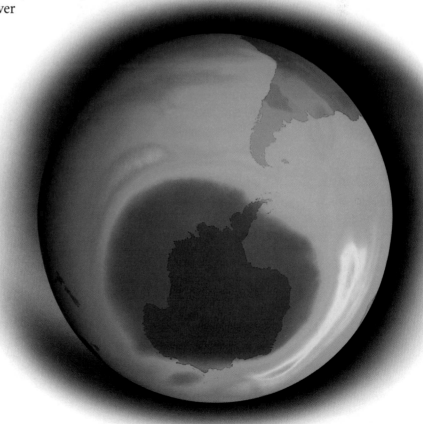

Global Reaction to Ozone Depletion

Canada is a world leader in reacting to the problem of ozone depletion. As this problem became more evident, scientists realized that Earth's natural protection against harmful UV radiation from the Sun was diminishing. Canada was the first country to introduce the **UV index,** a scale that tells us how much time in the Sun would cause sunburn on a specific day. The index, shown in **Table 1,** is announced only during the summer, when the Sun's rays are most direct. Many other countries have followed Canada's lead and are now issuing similar warnings.

Table 1 **The UV Index**

Index	0–3.9	4.0–6.9	7.0–8.9	9.0–up
Category	Low	Moderate	High	Extreme
Average time to sunburn[a]	Greater than 1 h	About 30 min	About 20 min	Less than 15 min

Source: Environment Canada

[a] Sunburn times are for light, untanned skin; times would be longer for darker skin.

In 1993, Canada set up an ozone observatory on Ellesmere Island in the Arctic. A Canadian company designed and now manufactures an accurate ozone-measuring device that is used in more than 30 countries. Many refrigeration companies have trained people in the recovery of ozone-depleting chemicals. For example, expert technicians now collect and recycle Freon used in refrigerators and air-conditioning systems rather than allowing the chemical to leak into the atmosphere.

🖑 Work the Web

Environment Canada provides a vast amount of information related to greenhouse gases and ozone depletion. Through www.science.nelson.com and links to Science 10, 16.2 find out Canada's current actions to reduce these problems. List several of these actions, and describe what more you think could be done.

◕ Challenge

1 What factors would you need to consider before you could issue the UV index for a particular day?

2 How will your community take greenhouse gas emissions and ozone-depleting chemicals into consideration?

Understanding Concepts

1. List several human activities that you have observed in the past week that had an influence on greenhouse gases and ozone depletion.

2. State, with a reason, whether the greenhouse effect would occur: (a) on the Moon; (b) on Venus; (c) in a car with the windows up in the summer.

3. Explain why deforestation contributes to the problem of the greenhouse effect.

4. Ozone can be both helpful and harmful. Explain why.

5. Give reasons why greenhouse gases produced by human activities were not a problem until about 200 years ago.

6. Increased UV radiation causes a type of "chain reaction" in oceans. Explain what this means.

7. In 1987, Canada hosted an international conference, which resulted in an agreement called the Montreal Protocol. This agreement called for a ban on the production of CFCs (which is now in effect) and other steps to reduce pollution (which are partially in effect). Even if CFCs were no longer used anywhere in the world, they would still pose a problem in the atmosphere. Explain why.

Making Connections

8. Phytoplankton, tiny ocean plants sensitive to UV radiation, are far more prevalent near the poles than near the equator.

   (a) Explain the likely reason for this.

   (b) Describe how ozone depletion will affect the growth of phytoplankton.

Exploring

9. Keep a journal for a week to record all the activities in your neighbourhood that create or release greenhouse gases. Describe ways in which these activities could be changed to reduce their effects.

10. Research sunscreen products that are advertised to provide protection against harmful UV radiation. Do these products perform as advertised? Display your findings in a poster.

11. Using a plastic UV Intensity Meter and Lens Tester, determine the UV index under various conditions outdoors. Also, test the ability of your sunglasses to absorb UV radiation. Summarize what you discover in a brief report.

Thien Nguyen

Fire Ranger

Fire! Fire! Quick, get some foam! This might sound strange to you, but it's not an unusual request for Thien Nguyen, a fire ranger. Fire rangers fight forest fires, usually in remote areas of the country.

Thien has always felt comfortable in the forest. Growing up in Sudbury, Ontario, he enjoyed outdoor activities, such as hiking and camping. As a Boy Scout, he attained the Chief Scout of Canada award. His interest in fighting fires was sparked when he saw an advertisement for a summer job as a fire ranger. He got the job, but before he could start work, he had to complete a course about fire fighting equipment, fire behaviour, and how to fight fires. Next he obtained a first-aid certificate. Finally he passed the regulation fitness test. "These three things are mandatory in order to apply. There are no height or weight requirements. As long as you're physically fit you can pass," Thien says.

Thien works at the Falcon Attack Base near Sudbury. Fire rangers are divided into three-person crews. They work eight-hour shifts, eight days in a row. When fighting a fire, working conditions can extend to 16 hours a day, for 19 days in a row. Thien says, "Crews are put on different types of alerts depending on the intensity of the fire. A Red Alert means you must be ready immediately, a Yellow Alert means you must be ready in half an hour, and a Blue Alert allows you four hours."

Fire rangers are transported by helicopter because most fires are not accessible by road. Upon reaching the fire, they pump water from the nearest source: lake, river or swamp. Once the pump is working, they attach a small container onto the nozzle that produces a fire retardant foam. Foam increases the cycle of water effectiveness. Water alone will evaporate quickly and seep into the ground. Foam stays above the ground and sticks to the sides of trees, large rocks, and hills.

There's a lot more to fire fighting than spraying foam. Fire rangers must know how different fuels react when burned and have some knowledge of meteorology and topography. Other methods of fighting fires include using planes to bomb the fire with water, bulldozers to clear a path that the fire cannot cross, and controlled burning of the area around the fire to use up potential fuel.

Thien is very proud to be a fire ranger. "We Canadians are so well known for our effectiveness and efficiency in handling forest fires that we've been invited to places such as China to lecture on our skills." His only regret is that the fire-ranger season is just four months long.

Making Connections

1. How does weather affect the intensity and spread of a forest fire?
2. What are some necessary on-the-job safety precautions?

👆 Work the Web

Rangers use a drought code, duff moisture code, and fine fuel moisture code. Visit www.science.nelson.com and follow the links for Science 10, 16.3 to research and report on the meaning of these terms.

INQUIRY SKILLS MENU
- Questioning
- Planning
- Analyzing
- Hypothesizing
- Conducting
- Evaluating
- Predicting
- Recording
- Communicating

Observing Pollution

Do you ever get sore eyes or have breathing problems when the air seems dirty? Air pollution consists of damaging gases and tiny particles of dust and smoke that come from both natural and human-made sources. People with asthma and other respiratory problems and many people who wear contact lenses may be very sensitive to air pollution.

In this investigation you will investigate factors that affect the air quality in your area to determine how clear or polluted the air is (**Figure 1**). In order to control the variables involved, you will need to know the direction of the prevailing winds in your area; the locations of highways, busy streets, and industries; and the weather conditions on the days you take observations. As you are gathering data, think about the relationship between air pollution and weather in the future.

Question

(K2) (a) Compose a question to guide your investigation.

Figure 1

How long does it take snow in your area to become this polluted?

Hypothesis/Prediction

(b) Predict what you will discover in your
(K3) investigation. Explain your prediction.

Design

The aim of this investigation is to gather air-borne particles to help you evaluate the extent of local air pollution. However, you need to control certain factors, such as locations, times, and weather conditions in order to make the investigation fair.

Read all the statements listed below, which will give you clues about how to design this investigation.

- A wide piece of masking tape, with the sticky side exposed, is useful for collecting air-borne particles.
- A fair test requires that each measurement be done using the same process. What process can you use to count the number of particles on each piece of masking tape so you can compare measurements from different locations?
- A fair test also requires the duration of exposing the tape to be constant for each trial. A good initial starting time is 48 h, but more time may be needed.
- Precipitation may ruin the samples. But immediately after precipitation, you could determine if the air has become cleaner.
- One factor that could be investigated is location. You could compare downwind with upwind from a major street, road, or industry.
- Another factor that could be investigated is weather condition. Do weather conditions affect the pollution?
- Air-borne particles can be analyzed both qualitatively (using a microscope or a magnifying lens) or quantitatively by determining the number of particles on a specific surface area.
- Observations would be more complete and more interesting if data from several groups were combined. A map of your area with details of roads, industries, tests performed, and observations recorded would help communicate the results.

(c) Decide how you will carry out the investigation,
(K4) what observations you will make, how you will
analyze the observations, and how you intend
to communicate your observations.

(d) Create a detailed set of procedure steps you
(K6) intend to take including safety precautions.
Have these approved by your teacher.

Materials

- masking tape
- support bases for the tape
- magnifying glass or microscope

Procedure

1 Carry out your procedure, and record your
observations.

Analysis and Evaluation

(O2) (e) Present and interpret your observations.

(f) Evaluate the quality of your investigation
in terms of its reliability and accuracy.

(g) What are the limitations of your investigation?
Did you address all forms of air pollution?

(h) If you were a government environmental
inspector, how would you extend this type
of investigation to make it more useful?

(Q) (i) Write a lab report for this investigation.

Challenge

2 How has your community design taken air pollution into
consideration?

Understanding Concepts

1. How would you expect samples of pollution particles to
compare in each of the following pairs of locations?
Justify each answer. (Assume that in each case other
variables are controlled at the locations named.)

   (a) A is downwind from an expressway; B is upwind
   from the same expressway.

   (b) C is near a coal-fired generating station; D is near a
   hydroelectric generating station.

   (c) E is on the top of an office tower; F is at street level
   beside the office tower.

   (d) G is in the middle of a large city park; H is at the
   outer edge of the same park.

   (e) I is on a hot, humid day; J is on a cold, dry day.

   (f) K is during a temperature inversion in a big city;
   L is before the inversion occurred.

2. Under what environmental conditions should people
with asthma or sensitive eyes exercise precaution?

Making Connections

3. Explain how the results of your investigation could help
you decide where and when outdoor activities would
be unhealthy.

4. Many recent model cars have air filter systems to reduce
(K4) pollution inside the car. Describe how you would design
a test to determine the effectiveness of these filters.

5. The owner of a large restaurant with an open, vented
grill would like to determine the air quality in the
smoking and non-smoking areas of the restaurant as
well as in the kitchen.

   (a) How would the owner perform a fair test of the air
   quality?

   (b) What results would you expect? Explain your answer.

Exploring

6. Report on a current method used to eliminate pollutants
in plumes of waste gases produced during industrial
processes.

7. Should companies be given tax incentives to install
equipment that reduces pollution emissions? Should the
tax breaks be large enough that all competition must
follow suit? In a brief essay, explore these questions
and suggest other ways to achieve this result.

Microclimates

Large cities are dominated by roads, sidewalks, parking lots, buildings, millions of people, and thousands of vehicles. All these help make the city climate different from that in rural areas (**Figure 1**). A **microclimate** is the set of atmospheric conditions at any particular location that differ noticeably from those of surrounding areas. An urban microclimate encompasses a city. A rural microclimate extends over a less populated area. Other microclimates can be in a backyard, on a mountaintop, or on a bay.

Urban Microclimates

As urban areas grow, soil and plant life are replaced by roads, houses, high-rise apartment buildings, office towers, and parking lots. These human-made structures act as heat sinks, absorbing solar energy during the day and becoming warmer than farmland or forests would become. The warm surfaces re-radiate infrared energy, which helps to cause the nighttime temperatures in and above a city to be as much as 5°C higher than they would be in a rural area.

Other factors also contribute to the urban microclimate. **Smog**, a word derived from smoke and fog, is produced by the emissions from all the cars, trucks, buses, and industries that burn fossil fuels interacting with solar energy. Some components of smog are greenhouse gases, such as carbon dioxide, nitrous oxide, and ozone. Other components include carbon monoxide, a poisonous gas that causes headaches and can kill in enclosed spaces; lead particles that cause brain damage; and benzene, a carcinogen. Heating and air-conditioning systems also contribute excess heat. Tall buildings influence the flow of air, sometimes causing very gusty winds. Finally, much less moisture is available for evaporation in a city because of the lack of green space and the efficient drainage of rainwater. Because less energy can be absorbed by evaporation, not as much cooling occurs, contributing even more to high temperatures in urban microclimates.

Smog Alerts

When the air quality in an urban area worsens, Environment Canada issues a smog alert. Like storm alerts, a smog alert has three stages, depending on the amount of smog in the air.

- A mild alert is a warning that people's health may be at risk. Pregnant women, children, the elderly, and people with heart or lung diseases should be indoors. Everyone should avoid vigorous outdoor activities.
- At a more severe smog level, industries and drivers are asked to voluntarily cut back on manufacturing processes and travel.
- When the smog becomes extreme, a compulsory cutback is ordered for industries and transportation systems that cause pollution. This is most likely when a temperature inversion occurs in an urban area.

Figure 1

In some cities, such as Bangkok in Thailand, air pollution has become so bad that police officers and other public officials have been issued with filtering masks.

Improving the Urban Microclimate

In order to reduce the negative effects of their city's future growth, urban planners try to create healthy microclimates by taking advantage of solar energy, by allowing air flow to take away pollutants, and by reducing the amount of greenhouse gases released to the atmosphere. The advantages of these steps are many: people enjoy better health and more natural beauty; less energy is wasted; and money is saved.

Cities can be designed so that streets are aligned parallel to the prevailing winds so the summer winds will take away stale air. Buildings can be designed with different shapes, sizes, and heights to help reduce updrafts and wind gusts. Building construction can use materials that reflect solar energy rather than absorb it. More efficient heating and air-conditioning systems can be used. Public transportation can be more efficient, more affordable, and faster. Bicycle lanes can be created.

Adding parks, trees, shrubs, and flower beds helps to absorb energy during transpiration. The plants absorb carbon dioxide and release oxygen to the air. **Figure 2** shows how the urban microclimate can be improved creatively.

Rural Microclimates

Different rural microclimates are found throughout the country. On summer days, the middle of a forest is cooler than the surrounding open areas because water transpiring from trees absorbs energy. At night, the same forest is warmer than the surrounding open areas; with fewer or no trees and buildings in the open areas, infrared radiation from the ground radiates upward to the atmosphere more easily, allowing the ground to cool more rapidly.

Consider the microclimate illustrated in **Figure 3**. In the Northern Hemisphere, the south side of a hill or mountain receives much more direct sunlight than the north side. This affects plant growth and snow melting in spring. Agricultural crops that require a lot of sunshine, such as grapes, are grown on the south sides of hills.

◓ Challenge

1. During what weather conditions would you keep watch for smog?
2. What features of your community would reduce the negative effects of an urban microclimate?

Figure 2

This urban rooftop garden partially replaces the vegetation that was removed when the building was constructed.

Figure 3

The south-facing slope of this hill receives more sunlight than a north-facing slope, providing a sunny microclimate for the growth of grapes.

Understanding Concepts

1. The term "heat island" describes one type of microclimate. Identify which type it is. Explain your choice.

2. Use the concept of albedo to explain some of the differences between a rural microclimate and an urban microclimate.

3. Some components of smog absorb infrared radiation then emit it efficiently. Would this increase or decrease the urban temperature? Explain.

4. Explain why vigorous exercise is not advisable during a smog alert.

Making Connections

5. Suggest transportation options in urban areas that would reduce the production of smog and excess heat.

Exploring

6. Mexico City is smog prone. List several reasons why and Ⓙ explain how each contributes to the smog problem.

16.6 Investigation

INQUIRY SKILLS MENU
- Questioning
- Hypothesizing
- Predicting
- Planning
- Conducting
- Recording
- Analyzing
- Evaluating
- Communicating

Temperature and Materials

Before architects, engineers, and urban planners decide on the construction materials to build roads and buildings, they must research features of each material. To create a healthy microclimate, they use materials that absorb radiation where solar energy would be beneficial or reflect radiation where solar energy would result in excess energy. Designers can often learn about the features of construction materials by observing what is used elsewhere.

You will design and carry out a controlled experiment in which you compare the temperatures at a constant height above the surfaces of various materials used in constructing sidewalks, driveways, patio decks, and other structures. Consider making observations in at least three different locations. Consider such concepts as convection currents, albedo, solar energy, time of day, time of year, materials, energy conservation, weather conditions, and the function of the materials. You might also compare sunny and shady locations.

In your final report, you can suggest the types of materials that would minimize the excess heat produced in an urban area.

Question

(K1) (a) Compose an appropriate question.

Hypothesis

(b) Write your own hypothesis.

Design

(c) Write your own design, including how you intend to record data. Write your procedure steps, including safety precautions, then get them approved by your teacher.

Materials

(d) Draw up your own materials list.

Procedure

1. Carry out your procedure and record your observations.

Analysis and Evaluation

(e) Present and analyze your observations.
(f) Evaluate the quality of your investigation in
(02) terms of its reliability, accuracy, and usefulness.
(g) Write a complete lab report for this
(Q) investigation.

Understanding Concepts

1. Describe how your suggestions for construction materials chosen would change after a period of
   (a) global warming.
   (b) global cooling.

Making Connections

2. You are an urban planner for a city council in charge of deciding what materials to use for the flat roof of the new city hall. Describe the arguments you would expect to receive from groups that want to
   (a) maximize the use of solar energy.
   (b) maximize light reflection.
   (c) achieve a balance of absorption, reflection, and natural beauty.

Reflecting

3. Are you satisfied with your skills of independently designing, performing, and reporting on investigations? Describe what you could do to improve these skills.

 ## Challenge

2 Describe how the results of this investigation will affect your choice of construction materials for various parts of your community.

SKILLS HANDBOOK: (K1) Planning an Investigation (02) Evaluating the Evidence (Q) Lab Reports

Our Disappearing Forests

"Save the forests" is a slogan that has appeared many times in the media and on fliers that ask for money to buy a small part of a forest. When most people see such a slogan, they think of the tropical rain forests of South America, Australia, and parts of Asia. However, other types of forests are also in danger of depletion, including forests in Canada.

Deforestation reduces the amount of carbon dioxide absorbed from the atmosphere and the amount of oxygen released into it. However, other effects of deforestation relate directly to weather and future extreme weather events.

Effects of Deforestation

Figure 1 shows a typical forested region. The trees and surrounding areas absorb between 90% and 95% of the incoming solar energy. Much of this energy is used to induce transpiration, heat the plants and ground, and promote plant growth. Air temperatures are moderated by forests. In other words, forested areas are cooler in the daytime and warmer at night than surrounding open areas. Trees and soft soil absorb rainfall, reducing the local area's susceptibility to flooding. Plant roots keep the soil stable. Plants, animals, insects, and birds have an established habitat.

Figure 2 shows the effects of deforestation. Roads make the hillside less stable. Water vapour decreases. Temperatures fluctuate more widely. Total rainfall may be reduced, but when rain does come, the water cannot be absorbed as easily and the rapid water runoff causes erosion of topsoil, mud slides, rock slides, and flooding. Plants and animals lose their habitat. Silt builds up in rivers and behind dams.

Global deforestation statistics are alarming. Deforestation accounts for nearly half as much carbon dioxide added to the world's atmosphere as the burning of fossil fuels does. In Madagascar, a large island in the Indian Ocean, thousands of landslides followed the destruction of unique forests. Tropical rain forests in Brazil, Colombia, Indonesia, Thailand, Laos, Central America, and Africa are being cut down for timber or burned to make room for mining, farming, ranching, or hydroelectric dams.

Each year in Brazil alone, an area of rain forest equal to the combined area of Nova Scotia and New Brunswick is destroyed. Some scientists believe this could have widespread effects: with fewer trees, the soil dries out faster, reducing the amount of water evaporated into the air. This could affect the local rainfall, which could lower the level of the Amazon River. This could reduce the flood season, which would affect the fishing industry and hydroelectric projects.

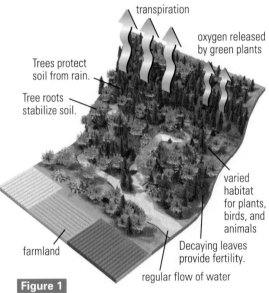

transpiration

oxygen released by green plants

Trees protect soil from rain.

Tree roots stabilize soil.

varied habitat for plants, birds, and animals

Decaying leaves provide fertility.

farmland

regular flow of water

Figure 1

An established forested region

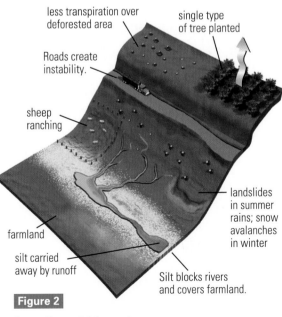

less transpiration over deforested area

single type of tree planted

Roads create instability.

sheep ranching

landslides in summer rains; snow avalanches in winter

farmland

silt carried away by runoff

Silt blocks rivers and covers farmland.

Figure 2

Some effects of deforestation

Deforestation does benefit some people, at least in the short term. It is difficult to blame loggers, farmers, and ranchers in tropical countries for wanting an income. Moreover, since the soil in a tropical forest is not very fertile, its nutrients are leached by rainfall after only a few years, which leaves the farmers and ranchers little choice but to cut and burn more of the forest.

Canadian Forests

Canada is home to approximately 10% of Earth's forests. The west coast of British Columbia has a temperate rain forest, with rare ancient trees and a unique habitat. Almost half of our land is covered with temperate and boreal, or northern, forests. These consist of deciduous forests (with trees that lose their leaves each winter) and, farther north, coniferous forests (with evergreen trees). What happens in Canada's forests and in boreal forests in other parts of the world, especially Siberia, could be of great importance to the future of global weather.

You can imagine the difficulty scientists have trying to forecast what will happen in the future due to human activities. A forest that took hundreds or perhaps thousands of years to develop can be cut down in a few weeks. Trees planted to replace those cut may mature in 40 to 80 years, but the characteristics of the new forest will not be the same as the old one. Direct experimentation on the impact of such changes is extremely difficult. Thus, deforestation is potentially a major risk to our Earth. In fact, deforestation of temperate and boreal forests could have an even greater effect on world weather and climates than deforestation of rain forests. To understand why, recall what you learned about albedo.

Before and after deforestation in the tropics, the albedo of the surface doesn't change much. However, after deforestation of a more northern forest, the albedo of the area rises sharply, especially when snow is on the ground. Thus, much less energy is absorbed, causing a drop in average temperature. It is difficult to know how much this cooling would balance the global warming caused by other human activities. Probably the most important thing for us to realize is that deforestation may have a huge impact on Earth's future and we should plan our actions accordingly.

Understanding Concepts

1. Explain how forests have a moderating effect on local temperatures.

2. People have been cutting down and burning trees for thousands of years. Suggest some reasons why these practices are becoming more widespread and more of a problem now than ever before.

3. Explain why the deforestation of tropical rain forests is only a short-term solution to the need for agricultural lands.

4. Explain why Canada's forests are important to the future of global weather patterns.

5. Assume the Brazilian rain forest covers an area of 6 000 000 km². At a deforestation rate of 120 000 km²/year, how long will the rain forest last? Show your calculation.

Exploring

6. Research the controversy of the Temagami Forest in Ontario. (I) Have the arguments been resolved? If not, describe the (J) arguments. (Consider economic, health, social, and environmental aspects of the arguments.)

7. A soil thermometer has a probe that can be inserted into the ground. Design and carry out a simple test to compare the soil temperature at various depths, such as 5 cm and 10 cm. Also compare the soil temperatures to the air temperature. Describe how your results would likely differ in the other seasons of the year.

Canada's Fragile North

Most of Canada's highways, cities, and towns are in the southern part of the country. North of these populated regions lie vast areas with features and climates that make life somewhat difficult. Farther north, the ground is often frozen throughout most of the year, thawing only at the surface in the summer. Winters are cold and long, with short or no daylight hours. Summers are short and usually cool, with the Sun low in the sky, giving a short growing season for the plants. (See **Figure 1**.)

This fragile area has already been affected by increasing average temperatures. Will the plants and animals be able to survive even more increases in temperature? There is no easy answer, but the question is important to consider.

The Northern Habitat

At the northern limits of Canada's forests (called the tree line), the trees become smaller and smaller. In the extreme far north, some islands in the Arctic Ocean have areas that are permanently covered with ice. Between these two areas lies the **tundra**, a vast treeless region where the ground beneath the surface is frozen. This region is characterized by little precipitation and windy conditions. The frozen ground, or permafrost, prevents water drainage, so shallow lakes and bogs are found in the summer. Average temperatures in July may be 10°C, but in the far north they may be only 2°C. Average temperatures in January range from –20°C to a bitter –37°C at the north end of Ellesmere Island.

Despite the harsh conditions, the tundra has about 200 species of flowering plants, well suited to growing in microclimates in cracks in rocks, in small valleys and dips in the landscape, and even in clumps surrounded by other plants. The most common plants are grasses and sedges. Mosses and lichens also survive well (**Figure 2**).

Birds and animals are well equipped to handle the harsh conditions. The musk ox, for example, has hair that is longer than that of any other animal, 60 cm to 90 cm long. And in the winter, the brown summer fur of hares and foxes is replaced with white fur, which acts as camouflage from predators or prey. The ptarmigan, which remains in the Arctic all year round, flies directly into a deep snow bank to sleep, leaving no tracks for predators. Other birds breed in the Arctic and migrate south for winter (**Figure 3**).

Figure 1

Although conditions in Canada's north are harsh, the wildlife and birds are fascinating, and the scenery can be spectacular.

Figure 2

Lichens and mosses can grow on rock; other plants must fit in where the thin soil of the tundra allows.

Figure 3

Few birds live on Canada's tundra all year. The snowy owl breeds there in summer. In winter, it flies south to the less harsh climate of the Prairies, fields, and marshes.

One of the most obvious effects of human activities has been the production of greenhouse gases. Computer programs can model what might happen when different amounts of carbon dioxide, water vapour, and other greenhouse gases are added to the atmosphere. **Figure 2** shows what might happen to the world's average temperature under two different sets of conditions. Remember that the increase in temperatures at far northern and southern latitudes is greater than the average global increase.

One of the problems in trying to determine whether global warming is natural, human-caused, or both is obtaining reliable experimental observations. Detailed data have been gathered for only a fairly short time, whereas changes occur over decades, centuries, and longer. Even so, waiting to see what happens in 25 years is probably not a good idea. Imagine how foolish it would be if you stopped cleaning your teeth regularly just because your teeth feel fine. It wouldn't take long before you had gum problems and tooth decay. We will all be better off in the long term if we find some kind of "insurance" against the potentially negative effects of global warming.

Could There Be Another Ice Age?

Some think that Canada will benefit greatly from global warming. However, consider this: global warming may help cause another ice age, which could affect Canada and northern Europe. The theory that suggests this phenomenon relates to the ocean currents in the Atlantic Ocean.

Figure 3 shows the Gulf Stream flowing toward the north Atlantic Ocean. As the warm water flows northward, the surface waters evaporate, leaving behind water that becomes increasingly salty. Since salty water is fairly dense, it sinks lower in the ocean. The sinking water is continually replaced by the Gulf Stream water, which brings warmth to northern Europe.

Now consider what happens to this current flow as global temperatures rise. As more snow falls in the northern latitudes and more Arctic ice melts, much more fresh water would flow from the areas around Greenland into the Atlantic Ocean. This cold, fresh water would dilute the salt content of the northward-flowing water. If this happened, the water may not sink, and the flow of the Gulf Stream could slow down or, in an extreme case, even stop. Some scientists think this theory explains how global warming may have contributed to some ice ages of the past. Note, however, that this theory doesn't suggest that changes *will* occur, only that they *could* occur.

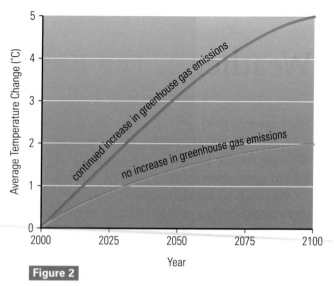

Figure 2

Possible changes in the average global temperature, depending on greenhouse gas emissions by human activities in the 21st century

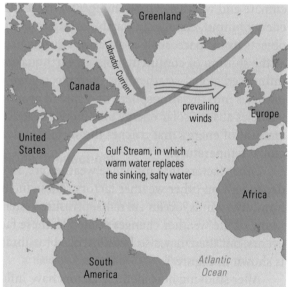

Figure 3

Prevailing winds that blow across the warm waters of the Gulf Stream bring warm temperatures to Iceland and northern Europe. The Gulf Stream flow depends partly on the salt concentration of the water.

Manipulating the Weather

A greater understanding of weather dynamics, combined with experimentation and modern technology, allows us to exert some control over some aspects of the weather.

One example of this is extracting fresh water from fog. Thousands of litres of fresh, potable water can be extracted from fog in dry, coastal windy areas, for example, in Peru, Ecuador, and Chile in South America and Oman in Saudi Arabia. The principle is simple and the design inexpensive: specially chosen plastic mesh is supported by wooden poles (**Figure 4**). As the wind blows the fog through the mesh, large drops form on the mesh, run down, and drop into a trough, which carries the fresh water to a reservoir. Production of this environmentally friendly source of water does not require electrical or fossil fuel energy, and the water is delivered to the reservoir by gravity.

Canada has played a very active role in the development of this technology. In addition, through the International Development Research Centre and the Canadian International Development Agency, Canada also funds fog collection projects around the world. When visibility is reduced by fog to less than a few hundred metres, a mesh of just 1 m × 1 m can extract 3 L to 15 L of fresh water per day. Large fog collectors, with a surface area of 50 m², can extract 250 L to 500 L of water per day. Arrays of 10 to 100 of these large collectors are providing enough fresh water to keep normally dry villages supplied with all of their water needs.

Another example of attempting to manipulate the weather is **cloud seeding**, the process of adding tiny particles of silver iodide or dry ice to clouds to control the formation of rain droplets and ice crystals. For years, the Canadian insurance industry has funded a cloud-seeding program in Alberta to help reduce the size of hailstones. Recall what you learned about cloud formation in section 13.11: water vapour forms into water droplets or ice crystals only if there are tiny particles on which to form. As a thunderstorm develops, the convection currents of rising air don't have enough tiny particles for all of the water vapour to condense or freeze on, so the ice crystals grow larger and larger, becoming hailstones. Adding "seeds" to the clouds provides more particles on which ice crystals can form, so the hailstones don't get a chance to build up in size (**Figure 5**). The cloud-seeding program in Alberta — in which over 100 storms have been seeded — has greatly reduced the insurance claims for hail damage.

Figure 4

An array of large fog collectors at El Tofo, Chile. The flat fibres (1 mm wide) in the mesh (inset) of the fog collectors are efficient at collecting tiny, wind-blown fog droplets.

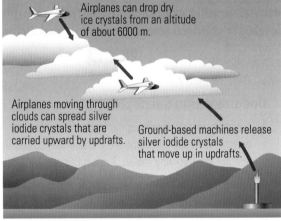

Airplanes can drop dry ice crystals from an altitude of about 6000 m.

Airplanes moving through clouds can spread silver iodide crystals that are carried upward by updrafts.

Ground-based machines release silver iodide crystals that move up in updrafts.

Figure 5

Scientists have experimented with the three ways of seeding clouds illustrated here: from the ground; from within the clouds; and from above the clouds.

Weather Wisdom

Understanding the weather is vital to our society. Farmers need to know the best times to plant and harvest; fishers need to be able to predict where they can find fish and when they should not set out to sea; city planners need to know the wildest weather they can expect and design their cities accordingly; and you, of course, need to plan your day. To help us understand how it all works, we use technology to gather information about the weather, to share it, and to use it.

1 Beat the Weather Forecaster

Instruments are used to measure weather conditions and to make detailed observations. As technology improves and becomes more sophisticated, so do these instruments. However, the weather predictions that you see on television or read in the newspaper are still sometimes wrong. It's no fun to plan a trip based on a sunny forecast and then wake up to pouring rain. Your task is to beat the weather forecaster by providing more accurate forecasts of the weather in your area. To do this, you will design, build, and maintain a weather station and use the observations you record to predict the weather.

In designing and making your station you should

- decide which instruments your station needs and design a station to hold them;
- choose a suitable location for your weather station;
- gather weather observations and use them to produce three-day forecasts that include predictions of daily temperature highs and lows and precipitation, such as rain and snow;
- produce a report that compares the accuracy of your predictions with the accuracy of those by a local forecaster.

2 Create a Weather-Wise Community

Most new North American cities are designed with wide streets, numerous parking lots, and few places where people can easily walk and enjoy nature; they are designed for automobile use. This design has led to cities with microclimates with excess heat and increased pollution. Urban planners, using scientific observation and computer simulation, are striving now to design more weather-wise cities. Your task is to design a community that has a more pleasant microclimate.

Your design for a weather-wise community should include

- outdoor trails and facilities for people to exercise and travel;
- an efficient public transportation system;
- efficient routes for emergency vehicles;
- ways of reducing buildup of excess heat;
- ways of minimizing pollution;
- ways of dealing with extreme weather;
- a model or set of plans for the community in a display explaining your design and communicating its advantages.

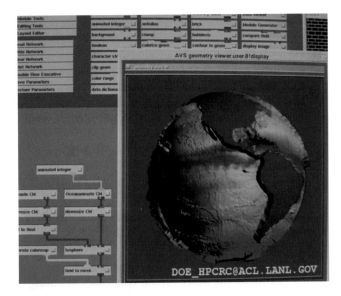

DOE_HPCRC@ACL.LANL.GOV

3   Join a Weather Network

Vast amounts of weather data are being gathered, shared, and stored for future research. Thanks to the rapid development of modern technology, we now use computers to record data, create simulations of events such as hurricanes, and exchange data with people around the world. The more data we collect and share, the better our simulations and predictions will be. Your task is to create a database of weather information and to share that data with others to make long-term forecasts over a wide area.

To take part in the network you should

- create a database of resources, such as web sites, software, and reference books, including a classification of the resources according to how useful they are;
- create a database of local weather, including temperatures, precipitation, and unusual weather events;
- create or join a network using the Internet and share your databases with other schools;
- use the shared information available on your network to make a week-long weather prediction for a large area.

 ## Assessment

Your completed challenge will be assessed according to the following:

Process

- understand the specific challenge
- develop a plan
- choose and safely use appropriate tools, equipment, materials, and computer software
- analyze the results

Communication

- prepare an appropriate presentation of the task
- use correct terms, symbols, and SI units
- incorporate information technology

Product

- meet established criteria
- show understanding of the concepts, principles, laws, and theories
- show effective use of materials
- address the identified situation/problem

 When preparing to use a chemical test, carry out an experiment, or build or test a device, be sure to have your plan approved by your teacher before you begin.

Applying Inquiry Skills

17. In part of an investigation to determine how various factors affect the evaporation rate of water, one group chooses to determine the time it takes the same mass of water to evaporate from rectangular containers of different surface areas. The data they collect are shown in **Table 1**.

Table 1   **Evaporation Rate from Containers**

Container	Length (cm)	Width (cm)	Evaporation time (h)
A	5	10	100
B	10	10	51
C	15	10	33
D	20	10	24

(a) Write an appropriate question for the investigation performed by this group.
(b) State the independent and dependent variables in this investigation.
(c) What factors must be kept constant in order to have a fair test?
(d) In order to answer the question, calculations must be performed. Calculate the necessary values, showing your calculations. Create a new data table using the two variables you wish to analyze.
(e) Use the data from your table to plot a line graph to show how evaporation time depends on the independent variable. Describe how the graph relates to the experiment.
(f) Use the graph to give an example of interpolation and extrapolation.
(g) Describe sources of error in this investigation.
(h) Explain why working well with others is important in completing an investigation of this nature.

Figure 2

18. **Figure 2** shows a "salt farm" on the coast of Gozo, Malta, in the Mediterranean Sea.
(a) Describe how the results of the investigation described in question 17 could be applied to design a process to extract salt from sea water.
(b) Name three locations in the world (besides the one shown in **Figure 2**) where the climate would be ideal for establishing this type of activity.

19. Find your own location on the weather map in **Figure 10** in the Skills Handbook, page 683. Use the map to describe what the weather is likely to be in your area at the time shown and in the following two days.

20. Refer to **Figure 1**, section 14.6, page 558.
(a) Determine the concentration of water vapour in air at 5°C when the relative humidity is 35%.
(b) If the concentration of water vapour at 30°C is 22.1 g/kg of dry air, what is the relative humidity?
(c) Describe the comfort levels in (a) and (b) above.

21. (a) Estimate the relative humidity and dew point in the room where you are currently located.
(b) Describe the process you would use to experimentally determine the accuracy of your estimates.

22. Refer to **Table 1**, section 14.6, page 560.
(a) Determine the relative humidity if the air temperature is 22°C and the wet-bulb temperature is 14°C.
(b) If the relative humidity is 65% in a room where the air temperature is 18°C, what is the wet-bulb temperature?

23. (a) Describe difficulties and sources of error in using satellite images and other modern ways to forecast the weather.
(b) Suggest some ways that might be used in the future to try to reduce those difficulties and sources of error. Make specific suggestions.

24. Having learned that green plants absorb carbon dioxide and release oxygen during photosynthesis, students in a science class decide to set up a controlled experiment to see if they could observe these effects in a small greenhouse. They know that a burning candle requires oxygen and releases carbon dioxide, so they predict that a candle will burn out more quickly in a greenhouse with no green plants than in a greenhouse with green plants.
(a) Compose a title, question, hypothesis, and design statement for this experiment.
(b) Create a list of materials you would need and procedure steps you would carry out to answer your question.
(c) Identify possible sources of error in your experiment.

(d) Assume that the candle burned out in 12 min without plants in the greenhouse, and in 15 min with plants in the greenhouse. Do these results support or refute your hypothesis? Explain your answer.

(e) Describe ways that the results of this experiment could be applied to benefit future weather and climate.

25. Describe how your skills of designing, conducting, and reporting on investigations have changed throughout this unit and this course.

26. As a class, set up a value line to share ideas about global warming based on what you have learned in this unit. Students who believe that Canada should be more active in reducing activities that may contribute to global warming should be at one end of the line. Students who think nothing should be done about global warming should be at the other end of the line. Students whose ideas fall between these two extremes should be in the middle. Each group can discuss the issue for a limited amount of time, then elect a spokesperson to present the best arguments supporting the group's position.

(a) In your notebook, record the most important point of view of each group.

(b) Explain the advantages and disadvantages of using a value line to discuss an issue.

(c) Describe the importance of developing communication skills when discussing points of view with others.

Making Connections

27. In the tundra, the water in shallow lakes and bogs will seep farther into the ground as a result of global warming.

(a) During which season(s) will this effect happen?

(b) Describe how this change will affect birds and other wildlife in the tundra.

28. Table 2 shows carbon dioxide emission and energy use statistics. The numbers are for 5 of the world's 10 worst per capita carbon dioxide emitting countries. All are oil-producing countries. (In oil production CO_2 is released directly and as a result of "flares," in which unwanted methane is burned.)

| Table 2 | Carbon Dioxide Emissions and Energy Consumption for Five Countries |

Country	CO_2 Emissions (tonnes per capita, 1995)[a]	World ranking	Energy Consumed (kg of oil equivalent per capita, 1999)[b]	World ranking	Population (millions)
Kuwait	31.5	1	8167	2	1.9
United Arab Emirates	27.8	2	13 155	1	2
United States	20.8	4	8015	3	277
Canada	14.7	7	7880	4	30
Trinidad/ Tobago	13.3	10	6081	7	1.3

[a] Source: *The Economist*
[b] Source: The World Bank

(a) Describe factors that contribute to the values in Table 2. (Use a map to locate countries you are unfamiliar with.)

(b) Knowing that "per capita" means per person, calculate the total carbon dioxide emissions from each of the five countries. What do these calculations reveal?

(c) Repeat (b) for energy consumption.

(d) Predict changes that the data in Table 2 may undergo in the next 50 years. Give possible reasons for your predictions.

29. One of the methods of manipulating weather described in this unit is extracting water from fog.

(a) Describe how this process might affect weather and climate if it is done on only a small scale.

(b) Repeat (a) if it is done on a large scale.

(c) Besides this process and cloud seeding, what are two other feasible ideas you think scientists may apply to manipulate weather? Explain how your ideas might be tried.

(d) Describe both positive and negative effects of your suggestions in (c) above.

30. Compose a letter to the Minister of Natural Resources in Ottawa expressing your point of view on whether sale of fossil fuels such as coal, gasoline, natural gas, and heating oil should be regulated. In your letter, show that you understand the effects of global warming on climate.

31. Critically analyze the following questions related to consumer products.

(a) Is an "all-weather coat" useful in all weather conditions?

(b) How can a manufacturer who claims that certain boots are "good to −100°C" prove that claim?

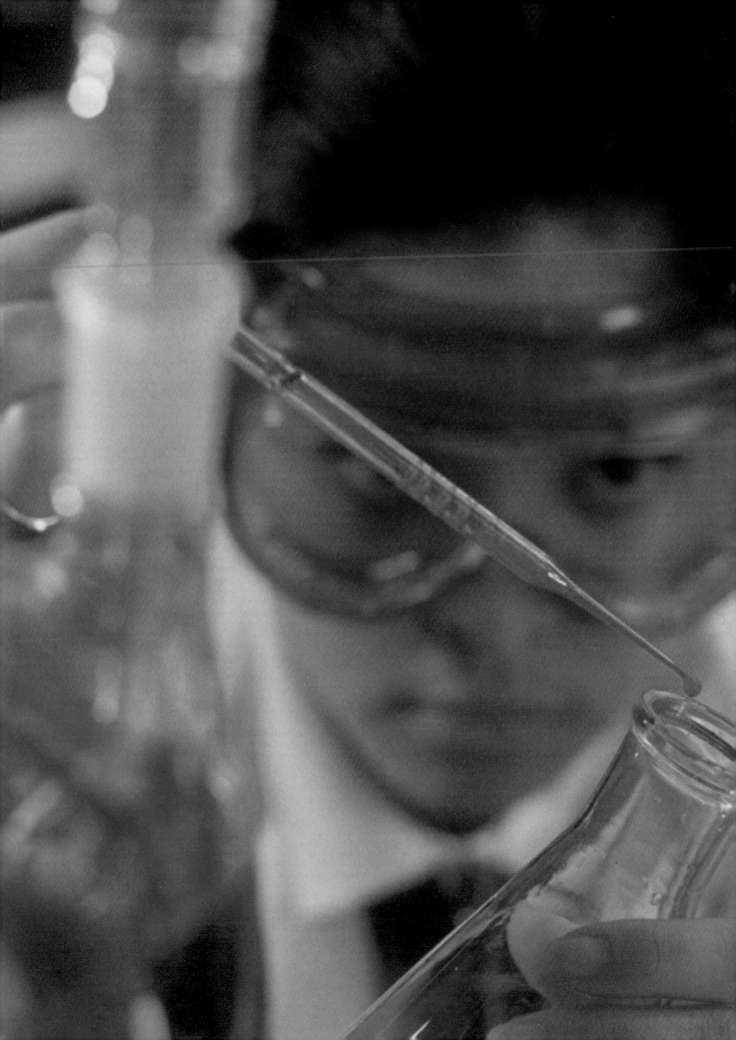

Skills Handbook

A Safety Conventions and Symbols

Safety Conventions in *Nelson Science 10*

When you perform the investigations in *Nelson Science 10*, you will find them challenging, interesting, and safe. However, you should be aware that accidents can happen. In this text, chemicals, equipment, and procedures that are hazardous are highlighted in red and are preceded either by the appropriate WHMIS symbol (**Figure 1**) or by .

You should always read cautions carefully and make sure you understand what they mean before you proceed. If you are in doubt about anything, be sure to ask someone who knows, such as your teacher, a classmate, or a parent.

Workplace Hazardous Materials Information System (WHMIS) Symbols

The Workplace Hazardous Materials Information System (WHMIS) symbols in **Figure 1** were developed to standardize the labelling of dangerous materials used in all workplaces, including schools. Become familiar with these warning symbols and pay attention to them when they appear in *Nelson Science 10* and on any products or materials that you handle.

Hazardous Household Product Symbols (HHPS)

You are probably familiar with the warning symbols in **Figure 2**. They appear on a number of products that are common in most households. These warning symbols were developed to indicate exactly why and to what degree a product is dangerous.

 compressed gas

 dangerously reactive material

 flammable and combustible material

 biohazardous infectious material

 oxidizing material

 poisonous and infectious material causing immediate and serious toxic effects

 corrosive material

 poisonous and infectious material causing other toxic effects

Figure 1

	Poisonous	Flammable	Explosive	Corrosive
Danger				
Warning				
Caution				

Figure 2

B Safety in the Laboratory

The Importance of Safety

Certain safety hazards exist in any laboratory. You should know about them and about the precautions you must take to reduce the risk of an accident.

Safety in the laboratory combines common sense with the foresight to consider the worst-case scenario. The activities in this textbook have been tested and are safe, as long as they are done with proper care. While your teacher will give you specific information about safety rules for your classroom and for conducting investigations, you should always consider setting your own safety rules.

Preventing Accidents

Most accidents that occur in the lab are caused by carelessness. Knowing the most common causes of accidents can help you prevent them. These include:

- applying too much pressure to glass equipment (including microscope slides and cover slips)
- handling hot equipment carelessly
- measuring and/or mixing chemicals incorrectly
- working in a messy or disorganized space
- paying too little attention to instructions and working distractedly
- failing to tie back long hair or loose clothing

Before You Start

1. Learn the location and proper use of the safety equipment available to you, such as safety goggles, protective aprons, heat-resistant gloves, eye wash station, broken glass container, first-aid kit, fire extinguishers, and fire blankets. Find out the location of the nearest fire alarm.

2. Inform your teacher of any allergies, medical conditions, or other physical impairments you may have. You should not wear contact lenses when conducting investigations—if a foreign substance became trapped beneath the lens, it would be difficult to remove it.

3. Read the procedure of an investigation carefully before you start. Clear the laboratory bench of all materials except those you will use in the investigation. If there is anything you do not understand, ask your teacher to explain. If you are designing your own experiment, obtain your teacher's approval before carrying out the experiment.

4. Wear safety goggles and protective clothing (a lab apron or a lab coat), and tie back long hair. Remove loose jewellery. Wear closed shoes in the laboratory, not open sandals.

5. Use stands, clamps, and holders to secure any potentially dangerous or fragile equipment that could be hazardous if tipped over.

6. Never work alone in the laboratory.

Working with Chemicals

7. Do not taste, touch, or smell any material unless you are asked to do so by your teacher. Do not chew gum, eat, or drink in the laboratory.

8. Be aware of where the MSDS (Material Safety Data Sheet) manual is kept. Know any relevant MSDS information for the chemicals you are using.

9. Label all containers. When taking something from a bottle or other container, double-check the label to be sure you are taking exactly what you need.

10. If any part of your body comes in contact with a chemical or specimen, wash the area immediately and thoroughly with water. If your eyes are affected, do not touch them but wash them immediately and continuously with cool water for at least 15 min and inform your teacher.

11. Handle all chemicals carefully. When you are instructed to smell a chemical in the laboratory, take a few deep breaths before waving the vapour toward your nose. This way, you can smell the material without inhaling too much into your lungs. Only this technique should be used to smell chemicals in the laboratory. Never put your nose close to a chemical.

12. Place test tubes in a rack before pouring liquids into them. If you must hold a test tube, tilt it away from you before pouring in a liquid.

13. Clean up any spilled materials immediately, following instructions given by your teacher.

14. Do not return unused chemicals to the original containers, and do not pour them down the drain. Dispose of chemicals as instructed by your teacher.

Heating

15. Whenever possible, use electric hot plates for heating materials. Use a flame only if instructed to do so. If a Bunsen burner is used in your science classroom, make sure you follow the procedures listed below.
    - Obtain instructions from your teacher on the proper method of lighting and adjusting the Bunsen burner (**Figure 3**).

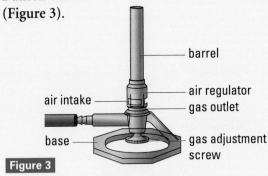

barrel

air regulator

air intake

gas outlet

base

gas adjustment screw

Figure 3
The Bunsen burner

    - Do not heat a flammable material (for example, alcohol) over a Bunsen burner. Make sure there are no flammable materials nearby.
    - Do not leave a lighted Bunsen burner unattended.
    - Always turn off the gas at the valve, not at the base, of the Bunsen burner.

16. When heating liquids in glass containers, make sure you use clean Pyrex or Kimax. Do not use broken or cracked glassware. If the liquid is to be heated to boiling, use boiling chips to prevent "bumping." Always keep the open end pointed away from yourself and others. Never allow a container to boil dry.

17. When heating a test tube over a flame, use a test-tube holder. Hold the test tube at an angle, with the opening facing away from yourself and others. Heat the upper half of the liquid first,

then move it gently in the flame to distribute the heat evenly.

18. Be careful when handling hot objects and objects that might be hot. Hot plates can take up to 60 min to cool completely. Test that they are cool enough to move by touching first with a damp paper towel. If you hear sizzling or see steam, wait a little longer! If you burn yourself, immediately apply cold water or ice, and inform your teacher.

Other Hazards

19. Keep water and wet hands away from electrical cords, plugs, and sockets. Always unplug electrical cords by pulling on the plug, not the cord. Report any frayed cords or damaged outlets to your teacher. Make sure electrical cords are not placed where someone could trip over them.

20. Place broken and waste glass in the specially marked containers. Wear heavy gloves while picking up the pieces.

21. Follow your teacher's instructions when disposing of waste materials.

22. Report to your teacher all accidents (no matter how minor), broken equipment, damaged or defective facilities, and suspicious-looking chemicals.

23. Wash your hands thoroughly, using soap and warm water, after working in the science laboratory. This practice is especially important when you handle chemicals, biological specimens, and microorganisms.

Decision-Making Skills

① Identify both the issue and the question to investigate.

② Brainstorm or hypothesize the various perspectives that different stakeholders would take. This could be based on prior knowledge and experience with the issue. If the issue is new to you, speculate about the possible perspectives.

③ Plan, identify potential sources of information, and gather, sort, select, and integrate relevant information.

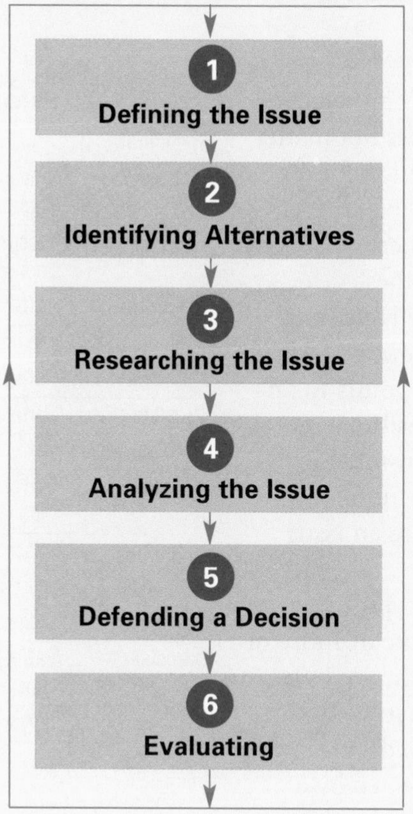

Figure 1
The decision-making process

1. Defining the Issue
2. Identifying Alternatives
3. Researching the Issue
4. Analyzing the Issue
5. Defending a Decision
6. Evaluating

④ Establish criteria for, and evaluate, the information you have researched; clarify perspectives; evaluate the sources of information; distinguish fact from opinion; identify, assess, and challenge assumptions; detect fallacies in reasoning; determine causal, sequential, or structural relationships; identify and evaluate alternatives; and complete risk-benefit analysis on each alternative.

⑤ Clarify values; make the decision or take a position; identify supporting information; evaluate and justify the supporting information; communicate the decision or position; and act on the decision.

⑥ Evaluate the decision itself and the process employed in arriving at it.

ⓒ Defining the Issue

Modern life is filled with environmental and social issues that have scientific and technological dimensions. For example, El Niño alters global weather patterns, resulting in severe droughts and floods in different regions of the world. These weather disturbances, in turn, disrupt established ecological cycles, affecting many organisms including humans. Specifically, the migration pattern of fish off the west coast of South America is changed, and fewer fish come close to shore. Local fishers suffer, and the effects are felt as far away as the barns of eastern Canada. Who, if anyone, should be helped when El Niño strikes? What form should this aid take? This is our issue. The first step in understanding such an issue is to explain why it is an issue and to identify the different groups who may be affected by it.

- Describe what problems arise out of the issue for individuals and groups, and why they are problems.
- Identify potential **stakeholders** — individuals or groups who may be positively or negatively affected by the issue.
- Brainstorm questions to research the issue. Begin with the six questions used in journalism: Who? What? Where? When? Why? How?
- Develop background information on the issue by clarifying facts and concepts, and identifying relevant attributes, features, or characteristics of the problems.

Ⓓ Identifying Alternatives/Positions

Examine the issue and think of as many alternative solutions as you can. At this point it does not matter if they seem unrealistic. A possible solution for our fishers affected by El Niño may be to triple the price of fish caught to make up for the number of fish lost.

To begin the process of analyzing these alternatives, we must also examine the issue from a variety of perspectives, or points of view. Stakeholders may bring different viewpoints to an issue and these may influence their positions on the issue. **Table 1** lists some perspectives from which STSE issues may be analyzed. You may develop others as you work through the Explore an Issue activities in *Nelson Science 10*.

To identify possible perspectives or positions on an issue, put yourself in the place of one or more of the stakeholders. Brainstorm or hypothesize how she or he would feel about your alternative. In our El Niño example, the local people who depend on fishing for their incomes would be affected by a change in fish prices. What would be their perspective? What would be the perspective of a local politician? A farmer? A marine biologist? An economist? A nutritionist?

Remember that one person could have more than one perspective, such as cultural and social, or technological, economic, and ecological. It is even possible that two people, looking at an issue from the same perspective, might disagree about the issue. For example, two economists might disagree about the impacts of the change in fish prices on the local economy.

Table 1	Perspectives on an Issue
cultural	customs and practices of a particular group
ecological	involving an interaction among organisms and their natural habitat
economic	focusing on the production, distribution, and consumption of wealth
educational	affecting learning
emotional	to do with feelings
environmental	affecting physical surroundings
esthetic	artistic, tasteful, beautiful
moral/ethical	affected by beliefs about what is good/bad, right/wrong
legal	involving laws describing rights and responsibilities of individuals and groups in society
spiritual	based on faith/personal belief systems
political	furthering the aims of some group or party
scientific	logical or research-based
social	affecting human relationships, the community, or society
technological	involving machines or industrial processes

As another example, consider the design of an urban park. Two landscape architects might come up with completely different designs, even though both were considering the esthetics of the park. A neighbourhood parent might look at the park design from a social perspective ("Will it be a good place for my children to play?"), an economic perspective ("Is it going to take a lot of tax money?"), and an environmental perspective ("Will it help to bring birds and butterflies back to the neighbourhood?").

Ⓔ Researching the Issue

Begin your research on the issue by formulating a research question that helps to limit, narrow, or define the issue. Then develop a plan to identify and find reliable and relevant sources of information. Use a flow chart, concept map, or other graphic organizer to outline the stages of your information search: gathering, sorting, evaluating, selecting, and integrating relevant information on the issue. Carry out the plan by gathering information from a number of different sources, including newspapers, news magazines, the Internet, and the neighbourhood or school library. For more information on how to conduct your research, see Ⓘ General Research (p. 666) and Ⓙ Internet Research (p. 667).

(F) Analyzing the Issue

This step in the decision-making process will help you organize your research and clarify where you stand on the issue. There are five steps that must be completed to effectively analyze the issue.

(1) Establishing Criteria for Evaluating Information

By evaluating the gathered information, you are determining the relevance and significance of the data. First, you must decide on a set of standards for assessing the information. Second, rank the criteria with reference to the perspectives they represent. For example, in this issue is an economic consideration more important than an aesthetic one? Using a graphic organizer may assist in both evaluating the information and clarifying the perspectives identified earlier.

(2) Evaluating the Sources of Information

It is important to separate fact from opinion when you are evaluating your information. Critically assess each source of information. Ask questions about each source: Is it credible? Are you able to confirm the facts given? If one piece is written by a politician, and another by an environmental activist, what perspectives and biases are the authors bringing to the reader? Frameworks such as PERCS (see (I) General Research, p. 666) are useful for evaluating the credibility of information gathered from different sources.

(3) Identifying and Challenging Assumptions

A piece of writing often includes assumptions, sometimes supported by factual information, sometimes not. When you are analyzing your sources of information, determine what assumptions have been made, and whether or not they are supported (or whether enough information was provided for you to make that decision). It is helpful to use a chart to organize this step. If there is not enough supporting evidence, then that assumption should be challenged.

(4) Determining Causal, Sequential, or Structural Relationships

Often an issue is not black or white. There may be secondary and tertiary consequences that arise from the original issue. If we look at the El Niño example, one of the problems is that people who fish to earn a living have reduced incomes. That may lead to families moving to nearby cities in search of work, which could put pressure on social services in that city.

(5) Evaluating Alternatives

After the issue has been analyzed, it is time to evaluate the alternative solutions.

You may decide to carry out a **risk-benefit analysis** — a decision-making tool that helps you look at each possible result of a proposed action to decide whether or not to proceed.

- Research as many different aspects of the proposal as possible. Look at it from different perspectives. Collect as much evidence as you possibly can, including reasonable projections. Classify every individual potential result as being either a benefit or a risk.
- Quantify the size of the potential benefit or risk (perhaps as a dollar figure, or a number of lives affected, or on a scale of 1 to 5).
- Estimate the probability of that event occurring.
- By multiplying the size of a benefit (or risk) by the probability of it happening, you can calculate a "probability value" of each potential result.
- Total the probability values of all the potential risks, and all the potential benefits.
- Compare the sums to help you decide whether to proceed with the proposed action.

Table 2 gives an example of how one alternative in our El Niño example could be analyzed.

| Table 2 | Risk-Benefit Analysis of Increasing Fish Prices |

Risk				Benefit			
Possible result	Cost of that result (scale of 1 to 5)	Probability of result occurring	Cost × probability	Possible result	Benefit of that result (scale of 1 to 5)	Probability of result occurring	Benefit × probability
People will stop buying fish.	serious = 4	quite likely = 60%	240	Fishers learn other trades.	slight = 2	quite likely = 60%	120
Fishers will catch too many fish and deplete stocks.	very serious = 5	unlikely (given low-tech fishing techniques) = 10%	50	Fishers' incomes increase.	great = 5	unlikely (given reduced numbers of fish) = 10%	50

A risk-benefit analysis would also be an appropriate tool to use if you had to decide whether the company you work for should build a new factory. Is this a good idea? The future of the company rests on this decision. You will need to research and weigh the risks of the expansion against the benefits. They may not be immediately obvious. For example, one of the benefits to consider might be the cost of not expanding and possibly losing your competitive position in the marketplace. After you have done the research and analysis you may find enough evidence to make a recommendation one way or the other. Careers may ride on your report.

Ⓖ Defending a Decision

Once you have completed your analysis of the information, you can answer your research question and take an informed position on the issue. Your position must be justified using supporting information that you have researched. You should be able to defend your solution to people with different perspectives. Ask yourself the following questions:

- Do I have supporting evidence from a variety of sources?
- Can I state my position clearly?
- Can I show why this issue is relevant and important to society?
- Do I have solid arguments (with solid evidence) supporting my position?

- Have I considered arguments against my position, and identified their faults?
- Have I analyzed the strong and weak points of each perspective?

When you are able to effectively defend your position, you can communicate your decision in an appropriate format. For example, you can make a presentation, participate in a debate, or write a supported opinion piece, a letter, or an editorial for a newspaper or magazine. For more information on how to communicate your decision, see Ⓡ Writing for Specific Audiences (p. 693), Ⓢ Oral Presentations (p. 695), or Ⓣ Electronic Communication (p. 696).

(H) Evaluating

The final phase of decision making includes reflecting on the decision itself and the process used to reach the decision. After you have made a decision, carefully examine the thinking that led to the decision. Conduct a step-by-step evaluation of the procedures and processes you used to reach the decision. Some questions to guide your reflection include:

- How did I determine what the issue was?
- What was my initial perspective on the issue?
- How did I gather information about the issue?
- What criteria did I use to evaluate the information I researched?
- What facts did I consider to be most important in making my decision?
- Before making my decision, whose perspectives did I consider?
- What options did I consider? How would each option affect the stakeholders involved?
- How did I make my decision? What process did I use? What steps did I follow?
- In what ways does my decision resolve the issue?
- What are the likely short- and long-term effects of the decision?
- How might the decision affect the various stakeholders?
- To what extent am I satisfied with my final decision?
- What reasons would I give to explain the decision taken?
- How has my perspective changed since I first began to explore this issue?
- If I had to make this decision again, what would I do differently?

Figure 2

General Research

There is an incredible amount of information available to us, from many different sources. We now have the ability to access more information than at any other time in history. Information is simply information, however. Before you can make effective use of it, you must know how to gather information efficiently and how to assess its credibility.

Collecting Information

- Before you begin your research, list the most important words associated with your research, so you can search for appropriate topics.
- Brainstorm a list of possible resources. Consider all the sources of information available to you. Rank the list, starting with the most useful resource.
- Search out and collect information from a variety of resources.
- Ask yourself: "Do I understand what this resource is telling me?"
- Check when the resource was published. Is it up to date?
- Consider the source of the information. From what perspective is it written? Is it likely to be biased?
- Keep organized notes or files while doing your research.
- Keep a complete list of the resources you used, so you can quickly find the source again if you need to, and so you can make a bibliography when writing your report.
- Review your notes. After your research, you may want to alter your original position or hypothesis, or research in a slightly different direction.

Assessing the Credibility of Information Sources

Understanding and evaluating the work of others is an important part of research. Think about how many messages, opinions, and pieces of information you hear and see every day. When you do research, you may access information from the Internet, textbooks, magazines, chat lines, television, radio, and through many other forms of communication.

Is all of this information "correct"? Are all of these information sources "reliable"? How do we know what to believe and what not to believe? Often science, or the appearance of science, is used to convince us that claims are true. Sometimes this method of reporting is used to encourage us to buy something or just to catch our interest. Even serious stories on scientific work are sometimes difficult to interpret.

To analyze information, you have to use your mind effectively and critically. When you encounter a "scientific" report in the media, analyze the report carefully, and see if you can identify the following:

- the type of investigation that is being reported
- the dependent and independent variables in any reported investigation
- the strengths and weaknesses in the design of the investigation

PERCS

A useful framework for evaluating the credibility of information gathered from different sources is PERCS (**Table 1**). This framework, developed at Central Park East Secondary School in New York City, NY, uses a series of questions to critically assess information and arguments concerning an issue. These questions can help you to evaluate the information you have collected.

Table 1	The PERCS Checklist
Perspective	From whose viewpoint are we seeing or reading or hearing? From what angle or perspective?
Evidence	How do we know what we know? What's the evidence and how reliable is it?
Relevance	So what? What does it matter? What does it all mean? Who cares?
Connections	How are things, events, or people connected to each other? What is the cause and what is the effect? How do they "fit" together?
Supposition	What if...? Could things be otherwise? What are or were the alternatives? Suppose things were different.

J Internet Research

The world wide web's accessibility and ease of use has led to an amazing increase in the amount of information available to us. However, as a research tool, the Web lacks the quality assurance that editors provide with print publications. In other words, anybody can post just about anything on the Web, without any proof of authenticity.

There is a huge variety of information on the Internet (facts, opinions, stories, interpretations, statistics) created for many purposes (to inform, to persuade, to sell, to present a viewpoint, and to create or change an attitude or belief). For each of these various kinds and purposes, information exists on many levels of quality or reliability: from very good to very bad with every shade in between. Given this variability, it is crucial that you critically evaluate the material you find.

Search Strategy

Before you begin searching the Internet you should think about the information you are searching for. What is your topic? What are the key concepts in your question? What words would best describe your subject? Try to be as precise as possible. Are there other ways that you can express these key concepts? When you have answered these questions, you will have a list of search terms to start with. Be willing to add to and subtract from your list as you evaluate what you have found to see if it is relevant and useful. (Later we will explore how to evaluate sources.)

Table 2 shows three primary ways of searching the Internet for documents and web pages.

Table 2   **Ways of Searching the Internet**

Search engine	Meta search engine	Subject gateway (or directory)	E-mail, discussion lists, databases
Searches using keywords that describe the subject you are looking for	Enables you to search across many search engines at once	Provides an organized list of web pages, divided into subject areas. Some gateways are general and cover material on many subjects.	Puts you in touch with individuals who are interested in your research topic
AltaVista Canada www.altavista.ca	InferenceFind www.infind.com/	About.com www.about.com	
Lycos Canada www.lycos.ca	MetaCrawler www.go2net.com/index.html	Looksmart www.looksmart.com	
Excite Canada www.excite.ca	SavvySearch www.savvysearch.com	Yahoo www.yahoo.com	
Google www.google.com		Librarians' Index http://lii.org/	
Go Network http://infoseek.go.com/		Infomine http://infomine.ucr.edu/	
HotBot www.hotbot.com		WWW VirtualLibrary http://vlib.org/overview.html	
Webcrawler www.webcrawler.com		SciCentral www.scicentral.com/index.html	

Search Engines

Search engines are automated programs that create an index of web pages in the Internet. When you use a search engine you are not actually searching the Internet, you are searching through this index. The larger search engines currently index over 100 million web pages each, but no search engine indexes every single web page. Most search engines look through, and index, all the words in the web pages they find. When you type some words in a search engine, it searches through its index to find web pages that contain as many of those words as it can. Search engines try to rank the pages so that the most relevant results are shown first. Most search engines provide online help/search tips. Always look at these to find tips for better searching.

Use a search engine to look for a specific web site or web page, information about a specific company or organization, or a specific subject. A very general subject search will probably produce too many results to be useful.

There are several reasons why you might not find what you are looking for. Although search engines update their indexes frequently, it can take several months for the engine to crawl the Web to find new web pages. If the page you are looking for is new it might not be indexed yet.

You will probably have a favourite search engine, but if you do not find what you are looking for try using another. Many web pages are only indexed in a couple of search engines. If you are not having much success, you could try using a meta search engine.

Meta Search Engines

Meta search engines allow you to search across several search engines at the same time. They take your search and run it in several search engine indexes. They will only return the top few results (usually between six and ten) from each search engine.

Use a meta search engine to look for a specific web site or web page, information about a specific company or organization, or a specific subject. If you do not find what you are looking for, try searching individual search engines. For general subject searching it might be better to use a subject gateway.

Subject Gateways

Subject gateways are directories of web resources on particular subjects. Usually the gateways are compiled by subject experts and may be published by professional societies, universities, or libraries. They contain particularly useful and important resources, possibly including databases and electronic journals.

Use a subject gateway when you want resources in a particular subject area. Although subject gateways contain far fewer resources than search engines, the resources have usually been selected and evaluated by subject experts so they are often useful places to start.

E-mail, Discussion Lists, and Databases

Although there are directories (or lists) of e-mail addresses on the Internet, which can be searched free of charge, none of them is comprehensive. Just because you do not find a person's e-mail address in the directories does not necessarily mean that the address doesn't exist. If you know the organization for which someone works, try its home page to see if an internal directory is available.

E-mail discussion lists are an extremely useful resource for researchers. They enable you to communicate with, and ask questions of, other people who are interested in similar topics. When you send an e-mail message to an e-mail discussion list, it is forwarded to all of the people who are members of that particular list. Many lists maintain archives of past discussions.

There are different types of discussion lists. An open list is open to anyone and the messages are forwarded automatically without human intervention. A closed list is available only to certain people, such as employees of a company. A moderated list is monitored by a person, often known as the list owner, who decides whether or not to forward the messages to other members.

There are many free databases of reference material on the Internet. A useful directory to them is http://www.isleuth.com/, which allows you to search multiple databases simultaneously for maximum results.

Search Results

Once you have done a search you will be confronted with a list of web pages, and a number (often very high) of "matches" for your search. This can seem daunting at first, but do not be put off. The most relevant pages should appear at the top of the list. There is often some information to help you decide which pages to look at in detail. You can always refine your search to reduce the number of "matches" you receive. There are several ways of refining or improving your search.

- Use more search terms to get fewer, more relevant records.
- Use fewer search terms to get more records.
- Search for phrases (words next to each other in the order you specified) by enclosing search terms in quotation marks (e.g., "robert menzies").
- Choose search engines that allow you to refine your search results (e.g., AltaVista).
- Limit your searches to Canadian sites by using local search engines, or limit your searches to sites with .ca at the end of their domain name.
- Use Boolean operators: + (an essential term) and - (a term that should be excluded).

Every page on the Web has a unique address or URL (Universal Resource Locator). Looking at the URL can help you decide whether or not a page is useful. The URL sometimes tells you the name of the organization hosting the site and can give a clue that you are viewing a personal page (often indicated by a ~ symbol in the URL). Some organizations are likely to provide more reliable information than others. The address includes a domain name, which also contains clues to the organization hosting the web page (**Table 3**). For example, the URL www.cmc.ec.gc.ca/cmc/images/Media/Cancola.jpeg is a page showing a weather map of Canada. "ec.gc.ca" is the domain name for Environment Canada — probably a fairly reliable source.

Table 3	Some Organization Codes
com or co	commercial
edu or ac	educational
org	nonprofit organizations
net	networking providers
mil	military
gov	government
int	international organizations

Evaluating Your Sources

Anyone with access to a server can put material on the Web; there are almost no controls on what people choose to write and publish. It is your job as a researcher to evaluate what you find in order to determine whether it suits your needs. As a result, web pages should be viewed with even more caution than most print material.

Use the following questions to determine the quality of a web resource. The greater number of questions answered "yes," the more likely that the source is of high quality.

Authority: Is it clear who is sponsoring the creation and maintenance of the page? Does the site seem to be permanent or part of a permanent organization? Is there information available describing the purpose of the sponsoring organization? Is there a way of verifying the legitimacy of the page's sponsor? For instance, is a phone number or address available to contact for more information? Is it clear who developed and wrote the material? Are that person's qualifications for writing on this topic stated?

Accuracy: Are the sources for factual information given so they can be verified? Is it clear who has the responsibility for the accuracy of the information presented? If statistical data are presented in graphs or charts, are they labelled clearly?

Objectivity: Is the page, and the information included, provided as a public service? Does it present a balance of views? If there is advertising on the page, is it clearly separated from the informational content?

Currency: Are there dates on the page to indicate when the page was written, first placed online, and last revised or edited? Are there any other indications that the material is updated frequently? If the information is published in print in different editions, is it clear what edition the page is from? If the material is from a work that is out of print, has an effort been made to update the material?

Coverage: Is there an indication that the page has been completed and is not still under construction? If there is a print equivalent to the web page, is there clear indication of whether the entire work or only a portion of it is available on the Web?

K Planning an Investigation

K1 Types of Inquiry

Scientists use an inquiry process to find answers to their questions. This process is also referred to as the scientific method. There are several kinds of scientific methods. The two kinds you are most likely to use are correlational studies and controlled experiments.

The purpose of scientific inquiry determines the kind of inquiry used.

- When the purpose of the inquiry is to *test* a suspected relationship (hypothesis) between two different variables, but a controlled experiment is not possible, then a correlational inquiry is conducted.
- When the purpose of the inquiry is to *create* a scientific concept, then we ask a general question, such as "What is the relationship among acceleration, change in velocity, and time?" and conduct a controlled experiment.
- If the purpose of the inquiry is to *test* a scientific concept, then we ask a very specific question, such as "What is the acceleration caused by a 2.0-N force acting on a 1.0-kg mass?" and conduct a controlled experiment.

Scientific work generally moves along a continuum from creating a hypothesis to testing the hypothesis to using the hypothesis. Of course, the hypothesis becomes less tentative and more certain if/when it passes the test of making verified predictions. At this point the hypothesis is no longer called a hypothesis: it is called an accepted concept.

Correlational Studies

Is there any truth to the saying "Red sky at night: sailor's delight. Red sky in the morning: sailor's warning"? In attempting to answer questions like this, there is no way we can manipulate or control the variables. We cannot make the sky red! Nor can we control all other variables concerning the environment and the weather. We would need to collect evidence and carry out a correlational study. In a correlational study, a scientist tries to determine whether a variable is affecting another variable without purposely changing or controlling any of the variables. Instead, variables are allowed to change naturally.

You are probably already quite familiar with correlational studies. They are frequently summarized in newspapers, under headlines like "Chemical X Suspected in Heart Disease" or "Vegetable Y Protects Against Cancer." Next time you are reading a newspaper, try to decide which articles would be classified as correlational studies.

It is often difficult to isolate cause and effect in correlational studies. Any two variables can be compared. It is important for the scientist to assess whether a reasonable link is possible. As an extreme example, one could graph the annual iceberg sightings from St. John's, Newfoundland, against the frequency of taxi accidents in Hamilton, Ontario, and discover that the years of highest iceberg count correspond to the years of the greatest number of taxi accidents. Could you expect to predict the frequency of accidents in the future by the number of icebergs sighted from St. John's? This kind of correlation is likely to be a coincidence.

Correlational inquiry requires very large sample numbers and many replications (repeated studies) in order to increase the certainty of the results. When reading media reports of correlational studies, remember to critique the design based upon these two important criteria.

The flow chart in **Figure 1** outlines the components that are important in designing a correlational study. By following this format, investigators can do science without doing experiments or fieldwork. They can use databases prepared by other researchers to find relationships between two or more variables. Of course, they may also make their own observations and measurements through fieldwork, interviews, and surveys. You can use this flow chart as a checklist to make sure you use all the steps necessary in completing a valid and reliable correlational study.

1 Choose a topic that interests or puzzles you. Determine what kind of study you will carry out, and whether you are going to replicate or revise a previous study or create a new one. Indicate your decisions in a statement of the **purpose**.

2 Ask a **question** about the relationship between two chosen variables.

3 Develop a **hypothesis** describing the relationship between the variables.

4 Write a **design** for the study. Decide how the evidence will be gathered. Will you be using existing databases or will you be gathering your own evidence through measuring, interviewing, or surveying? You will not be controlling variables, but you should atttempt to list other variables that may be relevant.

5 Write a procedure that you will follow to gather **evidence** and that could be followed by others to replicate your study. Indicate how your sample and sample size are chosen and how your measurements are done.

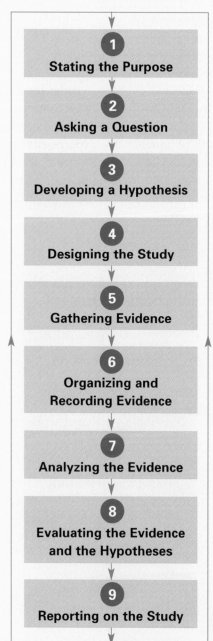

6 Create appropriate tables in which to record and, perhaps, analyze your **evidence**.

7 Use the evidence to calculate new values or to create graphs showing the relationship (if any) between the variables. Devise and write a hypothesis (tentative concept) by **analyzing** the evidence gathered.

8 **Evaluate** the evidence and hypotheses. The evaluation involves two steps — evaluating the evidence gathered in the study and evaluating the hypotheses stated in steps 3 and 7. Evaluate the design, materials, and procedure to determine the degree of confidence in the evidence. You can then compare the initial hypothesis with the hypothesis generated from your evidence. If the hypotheses are different, make a decision as to which hypothesis is best supported. Include your reasons.

9 Write or present your **report** on the study. Suggest the need for replication of this study or the need for different studies.

Figure 1
Conducting a correlational study

Controlled Experiments

A controlled experiment is a test in which one variable (something that can change or vary in your experiment) is purposely and steadily changed to find out its effect (if any) on a second variable. All other variables are purposely controlled. The ability to manipulate and control variables makes the study different from a correlational study. For instance, you may observe that there are more aquatic plants growing in a lake at the end of the summer, and ask yourself "Why?" Various answers might suggest themselves. Perhaps you think that aquatic plants are more abundant in the summer because they grow better in warmer water. This is your

hypothesis. From your hypothesis, you can make a specific prediction that you can test through a controlled experiment, for instance: "Aquatic plants grow faster in water at 16°C than at 6°C."

In a controlled experiment to test this hypothesis, you need to control, or keep constant, all other possible causes of the effect. You might conduct an experiment on five identical samples of lake water containing aquatic plants, ensuring that all growing conditions — such as volume of water, nutrients, and light — are the same. You would then change one condition — the temperature of the water — and measure the growth results over a period of time.

These different conditions in an experiment are called **variables**. There are three types of variables:

- **Independent variables** are those conditions that you manipulate. In our example, the water temperature is the independent variable.
- **Dependent variables** are what you measure to indicate a change (or lack of it) as you manipulate the independent variables. The growth of aquatic plants, possibly measured by height or mass, is our dependent variable.
- **Controlled variables** are all the factors that you keep the same. In a controlled experiment all

known possible causes of the result except one are controlled (kept constant). In our example there are many factors that are kept the same (e.g., volume of water, nutrients, and light) in order for the results of the experiment on aquatic plant growth to be valid.

The common components for controlled experiments are outlined in the flow chart in **Figure 2**. Even though the sequence is linearly presented, there are normally many cycles through the steps during the actual experiment.

1 Once you have decided that a controlled experiment is the best scientific method for your investigation, decide whether you are going to create a concept or whether you are going to test a concept. Indicate your decision in a statement of the **purpose**.

2 Ask a **question** about the relationship between an independent variable and a dependent variable (K2 page 673).

3 Depending on your question, you may create a **hypothesis** and a **prediction**, or just a prediction (K3 page 673).

4 A **design** describes what evidence you will gather, and how (K4 page 674). Your design can be expanded to include a procedure (K6 page 676) and any recording instruments you will need (K7 page 676).

5 Decide on the degree of reliability, precision, and accuracy your measuring instruments will need and list and gather the **materials** you need (K5 page 674).

6 Follow your procedure and **gather evidence**.

7 **Record your evidence and observations** (M page 679).

8 **Analyze** your evidence to find the relationship between the independent and dependent variables and your answer to the question (N page 681).

9 **Evaluation** involves two steps — evaluating the evidence gathered in the study and evaluating the prediction/hypotheses (O page 686).

10 Write or present a **report** on the study, including comments on the need for further study (Q page 691).

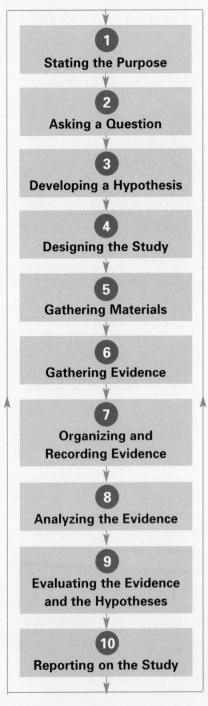

1 **Stating the Purpose**
2 **Asking a Question**
3 **Developing a Hypothesis**
4 **Designing the Study**
5 **Gathering Materials**
6 **Gathering Evidence**
7 **Organizing and Recording Evidence**
8 **Analyzing the Evidence**
9 **Evaluating the Evidence and the Hypotheses**
10 **Reporting on the Study**

Figure 2
Processes in controlled experiments

K2 Asking the Question

Inquiry normally begins with curiosity. The purpose of the inquiry is to create or test an idea (concept). Our experience and observations of the world often lead us to ask questions that interest us or express an idea that can be tested. To be classified as scientific the idea must be testable and the question must be answerable.

For example, you have probably been warned to be particularly careful when working with concentrated acids and bases. Why? Are concentrated solutions more dangerous than dilute solutions? Do they react more? Do they react to produce more of the products?

Each of these questions is the basis for a sound scientific investigation. However, not every question can be answered through scientific inquiry: some are too general. Learning to express ideas that can be tested or ask questions that can be answered by inquiry takes time and is a fundamental skill in scientific inquiry.

Let's look at each of the above questions in turn, to see if it could be answered through scientific inquiry:

- *Why be careful when working with concentrated acids and bases?* This question is too vague to be investigated scientifically.
- *Are concentrated solutions more dangerous than dilute solutions?* Now we are getting closer: we are comparing concentrated solutions with dilute ones. We still do not know exactly which acids and bases we are referring to, though, and we will need a working definition of "dangerous" in order to answer this question.
- *Do concentrated solutions react more?* The question is being narrowed further: all we need now is a way of measuring how much a substance reacts. We could look into its rate of reaction, the amount of products that result, or the amount of heat produced. We will also need to specify what the acids and bases are reacting with.
- *Do they react to produce more of the products?* Now we know we are looking at the products of the reaction: this is a measurable quantity.

A scientific question is often about cause-and-effect relationships. These questions often take the form: "What causes the change in [a variable]?" and "What are the effects on [a variable] if we change [another variable]?" As you know, a variable is something that can change or be changed in an investigation.

The one variable in the experiment that you purposely change is called the independent variable. For instance, decreasing the concentration of an acid is something you manipulate: you are changing the independent variable. The variable that shows an effect (for example, the mass of product produced) is called the dependent variable because it "depends" on the independent variable.

A scientific question that asks what happens to a dependent variable when we change the independent variable is a question we can answer by scientific inquiry.

K3 Developing the Prediction and Hypothesis

A tentative answer or reason why one variable affects another in a certain way is called a hypothesis. A **hypothesis** is a tentative concept and can range in certainty from an educated guess by an individual to a concept that is widely accepted in the scientific community. All hypotheses are concepts. Definitions, generalizations, laws, and theories are the other forms of scientific concepts.

If we ask a **general question** in an experiment, then we choose or create a hypothesis to answer the general question (see **Table 1**). In this case there is **no prediction**, because the prediction would be the same as the hypothesis. After the experiment, we create a generalization from the evidence gathered. In the Evaluation section of the lab report, we compare the initial hypothesis in the Hypothesis section to the generalization we created in the Analysis section. If the hypothesis and the experimental generalization are the same (or similar), then we judge the hypothesis to be acceptable.

Table 1 **General Questions and Hypotheses**

Question	Hypothesis (no prediction)
1. What is the relationship between mass and acceleration due to gravity?	The acceleration due to gravity is not affected by the mass of the object being dropped.
2. What is the relationship of wind to a pressure system going through?	The wind is clockwise around a high-pressure system and counterclockwise around a low-pressure system.
3. What do plants need to grow?	Plants need water and sunlight.
4. What is the relationship between the mass of reactants and the mass of products in a chemical reaction?	The mass of reactants and the mass of products in a chemical reaction are the same.

If a **specific question** is asked in the Question section of an investigation, then a prediction may be generated from a hypothesis. Usually the hypothesis is a general statement and the **prediction** is a specific consequence (**Table 2**). For example, if a metal generally reacts with a compound to produce a new metal and a new compound, then a specific consequence is that copper reacting with silver nitrate will produce silver and a copper nitrate.

Predictions and hypotheses go hand in hand. The hypothesis is how we explain a prediction — the reasoning/concept behind the prediction. The prediction is what we test through our experiment. And, if the evidence gathered verifies the prediction, we can have more confidence that our hypothesis is acceptable. If the evidence gathered falsifies the prediction, then we judge the hypothesis to be unacceptable to the scientific community.

Predict an answer to your initial specific question. This is your prediction. Try to explain why you might expect that answer. This is your hypothesis.

Table 2   Sample Hypotheses and Predictions

Hypothesis if (this possible cause-effect relationship)	Prediction then (this logical consequence)
1. If the work done on an object is generally the force times the distance,	then a force of 2 N acting through a distance of 5 m is predicted to do 10 N•m of work.
2. If the maple leaves have turned from green to red in the fall during the past 15 years,	then the leaves will turn from green to red this fall.
3. If the time of sunrise has changed by 16 min in the last seven days,	then the time of sunrise will change by 32 min in the next two weeks.

(K4) Creating the Design

An experimental design is a general procedure by which you plan to manipulate one variable (the independent variable), measure the response on another variable (the dependent variable), and, if possible, control all other variables.

Write your experimental design in a one- to three-sentence paragraph. The design is the general

plan that you are going to follow to answer the question asked. List all diagnostic tests, variables, and controls. See the examples in **Table 3**.

Table 3   Questions and Designs

Question	Design
What is the speed of the skateboard that you are riding?	The speed of the skateboard that you are riding is determined by squirting water at the dry ground every one second. The independent variable is the time; the dependent variable is the distance travelled; and controlled variables are the number and force of your pushes to get going. Evidence is collected three times.
What are the products of the reaction between sodium and water?	A very small piece of sodium metal is added to distilled water. The water is tested with red and blue litmus before and after the reaction. Any gas generated is tested with a flame. A flame test is conducted on the water before and after the reaction.
What is the effect of acid rain on the number and kind of soil organisms?	Soil is collected from the school yard and added to a mesh in an extraction apparatus. Vinegar is added to 16 similar soil samples. Distilled water is added to 16 similar samples. Organisms that come through the mesh are counted and classified. The independent variable is the pH and the dependent variable is the number and kind of organisms. Temperature and light conditions are controlled.

(K5) Selecting Materials

You can do many science investigations using everyday materials and equipment, such as plastic cups, straws, and water bottles. In addition, you may need to use more specialized pieces of equipment. Some of these are illustrated in **Figure 3**.

Decide what materials and apparatus you will need to perform your experiment. Again, keep safety in mind: choose the safest materials and equipment possible, and decide whether any particular safety equipment, such as goggles, bike helmets, or rubber gloves, should be worn. For more information on safety, see (B) Safety in the Laboratory (p. 658).

Figure 3

Common laboratory equipment

beaker tongs

slide

cover slip

graduated cylinder

test-tube holder

pestle

medicine dropper

test tube

mortar

retort stand

funnel

thermometer

ring clamp

beaker

spot plate

filter paper

overflow can

tweezers

stirring rod

evaporating dish

test-tube rack

crucible tongs

electronic balance

hot plate

petri dish

Erlenmeyer flask

(K6) Writing the Procedure

Write a procedure that describes how you will conduct your experiment. These are the detailed steps of the experimental design. Anyone who is interested in learning about your experiment needs to be able to understand how it was performed so that it can be replicated (repeated). Therefore, it is important that you be able to write an experimental procedure clearly, concisely, and accurately. The procedure should be divided into numbered steps, with only one instruction for each step. For example, the first three (and the last) steps of a procedure could look like this:

Procedure

1. Wear safety goggles, a protective apron, and rubber gloves.

2. Set up the experiment as shown in the diagram.

3. Measure the temperature of the water to +0.2°C every 5 min.
⋮
8. Return materials to the storage cabinet.

Your first step should refer to any safety precautions that must be observed. You might find that drawing a labelled diagram, illustrating your procedure or apparatus, clarifies your instructions. The last step in your procedure should relate to the cleanup of the area, including any necessary waste disposal or recycling.

(K7) Preparing Tables of Evidence

Create tables for recording your evidence. This is an important step, as it helps to clarify your thinking about your variables, numbers of trials, number of observations, and so on. It will also help you organize and analyze your evidence. If you are recording variables, they are generally used as the headings for the columns, as shown in **Tables 4** and **5**.

Table 4 The Iodine Clock Reaction

Trial	Temp. (°C)	Volume of solution A (mL)	Volume of solution B (mL)	Volume of water added to B (mL)	Time (s)
1	22.6	5	5	0	9.64
2	22.6	5	5	2	12.78
3	22.6	5	5	5	21.54

Table 5 Speeds on a Bicycle

Time (s)	Speed (m/s)
0.0	0.0
10.0	2.0
20.0	4.1
30.0	5.8
40.0	8.2
50.0	10.1

The following checklist will help you in constructing effective tables.
- Give each table a descriptive, yet concise, title.
- List the dependent variable(s) (the effect) in the last column of the table.
- List the independent variable (the cause) in the next to last column of the table.
- List the controlled variables, if appropriate, in the initial columns of the table. These are often optional columns.
- Be sure to include the units of measurement with each variable in the header at the top of the column, but not inside the table.

Prepare your table as part of your pre-lab work. The design, procedure, and table of evidence must work together. There is a logical consistency among them.

ⓛ Conducting the Experiment

L1 Using Timing Devices

Timing devices mentioned in this course vary greatly in their cost, availability, portability, reliability, accuracy, and precision. Different devices are appropriate for different tasks.

A **stopwatch** is a small hand-held device that measures the passage of time. It is turned on and off by an observer as an event occurs. It may be digital (giving its reading as numbers on a screen) or analogue (with hands that point to numbers around the face). Digital stopwatches usually give a reading to tenths or hundredths of a second. The accuracy of the measurement depends on the reaction time of the operator, although the "starting" and "stopping" error from reaction time may cancel out. Stopwatches are most useful for timing events that take more than a few seconds, and most can take only one measurement at a time.

A **ticker timer** is a small mechanical device that makes a series of dots in a strip of paper (**Figure 4**). The dots are made at equal time intervals, so the distance between the dots depends on the speed at which the paper tape is pulled through the ticker timer. On newer models you can adjust the time between dots (the period) by means of a knob or dial near the top of the ticker timer. The distance

between adjacent dots represents the distance travelled by the attached object in that interval of time. This is a very useful instrument for measuring the speed of objects travelling for short distances in a straight line.

An **air table** is a smooth horizontal surface on which an air puck rests (see **Figure 5**). It can be set to make dots at a chosen period of time on a piece of paper. The position of those marks depends on the position of the air puck at that time. The air table has an advantage over the ticker timer because there is less friction between the puck and the table than between the ticker timer and its paper tape. It is a very useful device for carrying out investigations into motion where friction would be a problem or where the motion is not in a straight line.

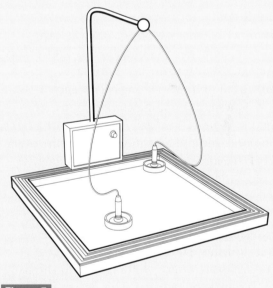

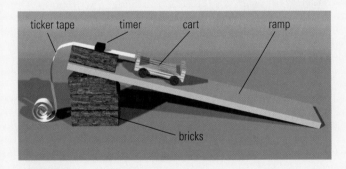

ticker tape   timer   cart   ramp

bricks

Figure 4

A ticker timer

Figure 5

An air table

A **stroboscope** is a device that lets you see a moving object for a very short length of time, several times a second. There are several kinds. The simplest is a mechanical device, such as a spinning disk, with viewing slits cut in it. If you look through the slits at a moving object, you will only see parts of the movement. More modern stroboscopes are basically electric lights that flash on and off with a set period combined with a camera. Just like the ticker timer and air table, we obtain a series of positions (like the dots) that shows the distance travelled after a certain time period. The photograph is like a scale drawing from which the actual distances must be calculated. This experimental setup is most often used for "real-world" situations involving motion, such as running animals, falling drops of water, or thrown balls.

An **ultrasonic probe** is a fairly recent technology in schools, involving a small instrument that emits ultrasonic pulses, and then detects the reflection of these pulses off a nearby object. The time difference between sending and receiving the pulse is converted (using the speed of sound) to a distance. The pulses are sent out and detected many times a second, so the probe can calculate the movement of the object. Some probes have small screens incorporated; others can be connected to desktop computers. Either way, the object's motion can be displayed as a graph of position versus time: a really neat way of "seeing" motion.

A **photogate** is a type of switch attached to a timer. In the laboratory, photogates are used to measure times for moving objects such as carts along a track, falling bodies, pendulums, and sliders on an air track. Outside the laboratory it is frequently used to time sporting events such as ski races and equestrian jumping competitions. At either end of the race is a "gate" consisting of a light source on one side and a light detector on the other side. When the athlete crosses the starting gate, he or she interrupts the beam of light. The sensor detects this interruption and starts the timer. At the end of the race the timer is stopped in the same way. This can give extremely precise times, to hundredths or thousandths of a second, over extensive distances: a very useful feature for high-level professional competition. This design is different in that the distance is kept constant (between the gates), while the total time is measured by the photogate(s).

Video analysis on a computer is a new technology for measuring distance and time. A video is taken of an event involving motion. The digitized video is then played back through the computer in equal intervals of time and the position of the object is marked with the mouse at the end of each time interval. The computer program generates a table of distance and time and will even calculate and graph the speed and the acceleration versus time. Computerized video analysis is suitable for analyzing complex motion like golf swings, dance, and car crashes.

For all of these technologies, time and/or distance are measured for the purpose of determining the speed (and perhaps the acceleration) of the object in motion. The technology chosen depends on the cost, availability, portability, reliability, accuracy, and precision.

(L2) Using a Mass Balance

To measure mass you must use some type of balance or scale. There are several types of balances available. Which one you choose will depend on availability, how heavy the object is, and the required accuracy. If you are measuring masses under 610 g then you will most likely use a triple-beam balance (**Figure 6**). If you are required to measure with a high degree of accuracy (for example, to measure chemicals or to calculate density), you may use an electronic balance. Electronic balances are more accurate, measuring to 0.01 g, whereas a triple-beam balance can only measure accurately to the nearest 1 g. If the object to be measured is over 610 g, you will need to use an apparatus with a larger range, such as a bathroom scale or an equal-arm balance.

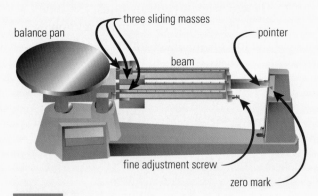

Figure 6
A triple-beam balance

A Triple-Beam Balance

To find the mass of an object:

1. Make sure the balance is on a level surface and that there is nothing on the balance pan.

2. Bring all three sliding masses to the zero point at the left of the beam. Make sure the two larger masses are placed into the notches at the beginning of the beam.

3. If the pointer does not line up with the zero mark, adjust the fine adjustment screw which is either at the far left side of the balance or near the left-hand side of the beams.

4. Place the object you want to measure in the centre of your balance pan.

5. Move the largest sliding mass along the beam notch by notch until it is just too heavy (making the balance beam drop below the mark at the end). Then place it one notch to the left. Make sure that the mass is securely set into the notch.

6. Repeat step 5 with the middle sliding mass.

7. Carefully slide the smallest mass until the pointer is centred on the mark. You may want to use a pencil to make the movements more gradual.

8. The mass of the object is the sum of the readings shown by the positions of the three sliding masses.

To measure a required amount of a substance:

1. Place the container (such as a watch glass, piece of paper, or small beaker) on the balance and record its mass. Add to this figure the required mass of your substance. Record the total.

2. With the container still on the balance, move the sliding masses to the total mass calculated in step 1.

3. Slowly add the substance into the container, being careful not to spill any directly onto the pan. Watch the pointer as it moves down, until it reaches the centre zero mark. You now have the correct amount of substance.

An Electronic or Digital Balance

To find the mass of an object:

1. Turn on the balance and wait until the display reads zero.

2. Place the object in the centre and read the number of grams directly.

To find the mass of a substance held in a container:

1. Turn on the balance and wait until the display reads zero.

2. Place the empty container on the centre of the electronic balance pan. Press the "Tare" or "ReZero" button. The display will now read 0 g.

3. Remove the container, fill it with the substance to be measured, and place it back on the centre of the balance pan. The display will then register the mass of the substance (without the mass of the container).

Observing and Recording

Obtaining Evidence

The evidence gathered in an experiment is often described as the ultimate authority in science. With this in mind you must gather and communicate your qualitative (non-numerical) and quantitative (numerical) evidence clearly and accurately. Although the kind of observations are dictated by the question asked at the beginning of the investigation, both qualitative and quantitative evidence is often gathered. Do not make the mistake of forgetting to record qualitative evidence when you are gathering quantitative evidence.

If a table of evidence is appropriate for your experimental design, use it to organize your observations and measurements. (See (N1) Interpreting Tables of Evidence.)

(M1) Qualitative Evidence

An observation is information that you get through your senses. You observe that a rose is red and has a sweet scent. You may also note that it has sharp thorns on its stem. When people describe the qualities of objects and events, the observations are qualitative. The colour of the rose, the fragrance of the flower, and the sharpness of the thorns are all qualitative observations. As you record the results of your investigations, include observations you made that you could not measure.

Recording Qualitative Evidence

Qualitative evidence can be recorded using words or pictures. If you have a camera available, particularly if you are doing field work and making many observations, this would be an appropriate tool. Often, however, a camera is either unavailable or inappropriate, so you may have to draw your observations.

When doing scientific drawings, your aim is to clearly represent what you see.
- Use a sharp H or HB pencil, and have an eraser and a ruler on hand.
- Draw large, on unlined white paper.
- Use single lines to represent the outlines or shapes of the objects.
- As accurately as possible, draw to scale: try to represent the relative sizes of objects.
- Draw only what you see, not what you think you should be able to see.
- Include labels, and make them as detailed as possible. Write the labels off to the side, and indicate what they refer to with a ruled line.

(M2) Quantitative Observations

Observations that are based on measurements or counting provide quantitative data, since they deal with quantities of things. The length of a rose's stem, the number of petals, and the number of leaves are quantitative observations.

Problems in Measurement

Many people believe that all measurements are reliable (consistent over many trials), precise (to as many decimal places as possible), and accurate (representing the actual value). But there are many things that can go wrong when measuring.

- There may be limitations that make the instrument or its use unreliable (inconsistent).

- The investigator may make a mistake or fail to follow the correct techniques when reading the measurement to the available precision (number of decimal places).

- The instrument may be faulty. Another similar instrument may give different readings. This indicates a problem with the accuracy of the instrument.

When measuring the temperature of a liquid, for instance, it is important to keep the depth of the thermometer at the mark set by the manufacturer and the bulb of the thermometer away from the bottom and sides of the container. If you are heating a liquid with the thermometer simply sitting in the container with its bulb at the bottom, you will be measuring the temperature of the bottom of the container, not the temperature of the liquid. There are similar concerns with most measurements.

To be sure that you have measured correctly, repeat your measurement at least three times. If your measurements appear to be reliable, calculate the mean and use that value. To be more certain about the accuracy, repeat the measurements with a different instrument.

Taking (Estimating) Measurements

All measurements are our best estimates of the actual value. The measuring instrument and the skill of the investigator determine the certainty and precision of the measurement. The usual rule is to make a measurement that estimates between the smallest divisions on the scale of the instrument. If the divisions are fairly far apart (greater than 1 mm), then the estimation should be to one-tenth ($\pm$ 0.1) of a division (e.g., 34.3 mL, 13.8 mL, and 87.1 mL). If the divisions are closer together (about 1 mm), then the estimation should be to two-tenths ($\pm$ 0.2) of a division (e.g., 12.6°C, 11.2°C, and 35.8°C). If the divisions are very close together, then the estimation should be to five-tenths ($\pm$ 0.5) of a division (e.g., 13.0 s, 33.5 s, and 42.0 s). Experienced observers can quickly tell what the precision of the instrument should be.

Check your expertise in making the best estimate for each of the following measurements (**Figure 7**). Estimate between the smallest divisions.

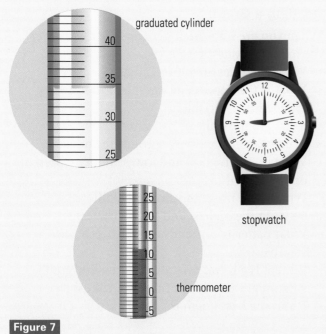

Figure 7
The graduated cylinder contains 34.3 mL of liquid; the thermometer is measuring a temperature of 12.6°C; and the stopwatch shows a time of 13.0 s.

Using a Protractor

A protractor, like other measuring devices, must be used correctly to obtain reliable, precise, and accurate measurements. Use the following rules.

1. Place the protractor with its origin at the apex (point) of an angle.

2. Rotate the protractor so its *x*-axis (0 to 180° line) covers one of the lines of the angle.

3. Read the angle to the nearest 0.1, 0.2, or 0.5 part of a degree, as appropriate for the size of the spacing between the lines marked on the scale (Figure 8).

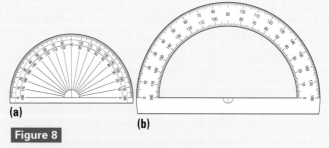

(a)

(b)

Figure 8
Different protractors can give different precision.
(a) A small protractor gives a reading to the nearest 0.5°: 23.5°.
(b) A larger instrument gives a more precise reading: 47.2°.

4. Record the angle to a decimal fraction of a degree.

Failure to do the measurement in the same way each time reduces the *reliability* of the measurement. Failure to read the scale to a fraction of a degree reduces the *precision* of the measurement. Using a protractor that is warped or whose markings are not visible and sharp reduces the *accuracy* of the measurement. If you practise making measurements with a protractor, your skill in making other measurements will increase.

Ⓝ Analyzing Results

Ⓝ1 Interpreting Tables of Evidence

Tables of evidence, although useful for organizing your observations, are not generally the final product of an investigation. You can almost always extract more information from your tables by studying your qualitative and quantitative observations and, when appropriate, plotting graphs of one variable against another to make better sense of quantitative data from your tables. For more information, see Ⓥ Graphing (p. 699). These visual representations make it much easier to identify patterns and trends.

Studying your evidence will also enable you to identify obvious errors. Any observation that is clearly very different from the others should be very carefully checked, and possibly discarded from your analysis. For example, in an investigation involving the growth rate of five identical plants, if one of the plants dies (therefore does not grow at all) you obviously would not consider that plant in your analysis.

(N2) Interpreting Graphs

A graph is an easy way to see whether a relationship or pattern exists between two or more variables. It also allows you to see more precisely what the relationship is, so it can be accurately described in words and by mathematics. Graphs will also help you decide whether the data support your hypothesis. Looking at the data in a graph may even lead you to a new hypothesis. For tips on drawing graphs, see (V2) Constructing a Line Graph (p. 700).

Figure 9 is a point-and-line graph that shows the data from **Table 6**. The graph shows the relationship between the two variables as a fairly straight line. It could be described by saying that the distance travelled by the deer steadily increased as the time increased. This is a simple direct relationship between time and distance and is made much more apparent by the graph than by the table.

Table 6	A Running White-Tailed Deer
Time (s)	Distance (m)
0	0
1.0	13
2.0	25
3.0	40
4.0	51
5.0	66
6.0	78

Reading a Graph

When you are interpreting a graph, try to answer the following questions:
- What variables are represented?
- What is the dependent variable? What is the independent variable?
- What are the units of measurement?
- Are two or more sample groups included?
- What do the highest and lowest values represent on the graph?
- What is the range of values (the difference between the highest and lowest values).
- What patterns or trends exist between the variables?
- If there is a linear relationship in a line graph, what might the slope of the line tell us?
- Is this the best graph for the data?

Using Graphs for Predicting

If a graph shows a regular pattern, you can use it to make predictions. For example, you could use the graph in **Figure 9** to predict how far the deer might run in 8.0 s. To do this, you would extrapolate the graph (extend it beyond the measured points) assuming the observed trend would continue.

Use your common sense when extrapolating, however. Sometimes a pattern extends only over a certain range. For example, if you extrapolated the graph of the running deer to 600 s (or 10 min), the deer would have covered 7800 m, or 7.8 km. Eventually, the deer is going to get tired!

A Running White-Tailed Deer

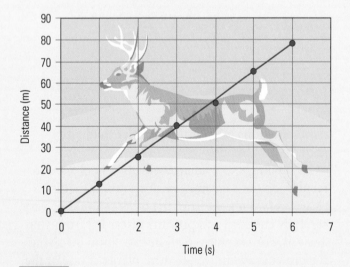

Figure 9

N3 Interpreting and Creating Weather Maps

There are two types of weather maps: "news maps" and "meteorological maps." The weather maps you typically see on television, the Internet, and in newspapers (news maps) are simplified versions of the meteorological maps used by professionals to forecast the weather.

News Maps

Weather maps in the various media are not all drawn the same. Some maps are in colour; some are black and white. Some state the actual temperatures; others give temperature ranges, using colour scales. Most include high- and low-pressure systems, precipitation, and cold, warm, and occluded fronts; some show lines of equal atmospheric pressure (called isobars) and the jet stream (**Figure 10**).

Several patterns will help you interpret news weather maps.

- In North America, weather systems tend to move from west to east.
- Low-pressure systems tend to bring stormy, unstable weather; their counterclockwise rotation allows wind directions to be forecast.
- High-pressure systems tend to bring clear, stable weather; they rotate clockwise.
- The symbols for fronts point in the direction in which the front is moving.
- The closer the isobars are, the greater the pressure gradient and, therefore, the greater the wind speeds.
- The upper-atmosphere jet stream influences weather at ground level.

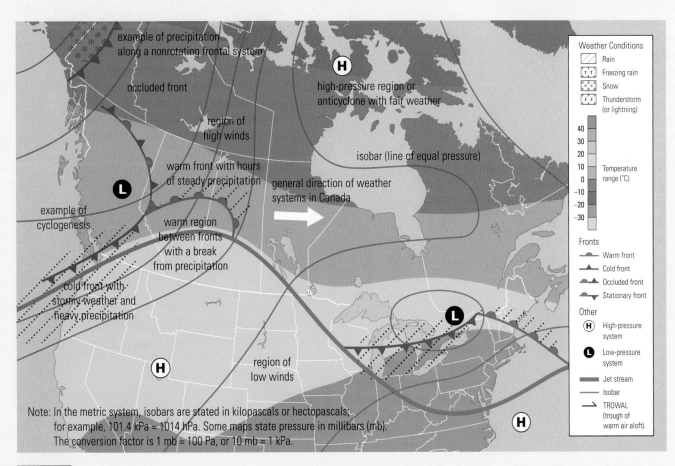

Figure 10

News weather map for much of North America

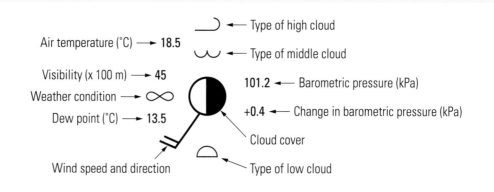

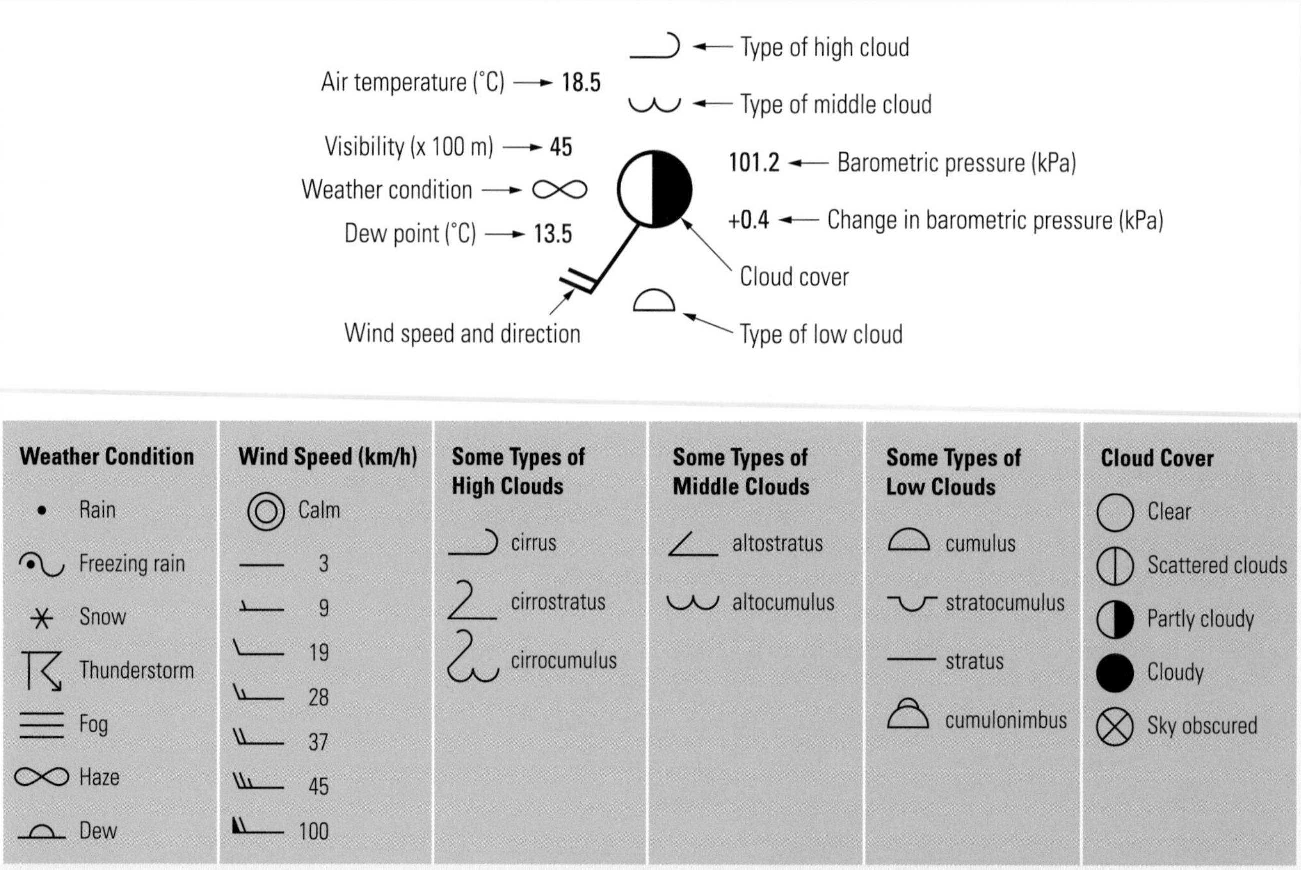

Air temperature (°C) → **18.5**

Visibility (x 100 m) → **45**

Weather condition → ∞

Dew point (°C) → **13.5**

Wind speed and direction

Type of high cloud

Type of middle cloud

101.2 ← Barometric pressure (kPa)

+0.4 ← Change in barometric pressure (kPa)

Cloud cover

Type of low cloud

Weather Condition	Wind Speed (km/h)	Some Types of High Clouds	Some Types of Middle Clouds	Some Types of Low Clouds	Cloud Cover
• Rain	◎ Calm	⌡ cirrus	∠ altostratus	⌒ cumulus	◯ Clear
⌒ Freezing rain	— 3	� cirrostratus	⌣ altocumulus	⌄ stratocumulus	◐ Scattered clouds
✳ Snow	⌐ 9	⌢ cirrocumulus		— stratus	◑ Partly cloudy
📈 Thunderstorm	⌐ 19			⌂ cumulonimbus	● Cloudy
≡ Fog	⌐ 28				⊗ Sky obscured
∞ Haze	⌐ 37				
⌒ Dew	⌐ 45				
	⌐ 100				

Figure 11

Each weather station shares the variables shown here with meteorologists around the world. The symbols help meteorologists tell at a glance what the conditions are for that location.

Meteorological Maps

Each weather station reports several variables regularly in a graphic summary called a station model. **Figure 11** shows a typical set of data on a station model, and **Figure 12** shows part of a meteorological map. After interpreting the data on these maps, meteorologists create the most likely forecast.

The following will help you interpret and create meteorological maps:

- The data on a map are all recorded at the same time.
- The symbol for wind direction indicates that the wind is blowing in the direction of the line, toward the circle indicating cloud cover. Remember, however, that wind direction is given

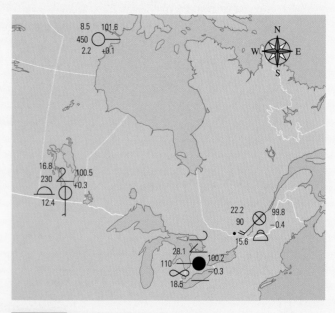

Figure 12

Some station models are shown on this meteorological map. Use the symbols in Figure 11 to interpret the data in each model.

as the direction from which the wind is coming (**Figure 13**).

- Visibility can be determined using a series of landmarks and a large-scale map. Visibility is the distance to the farthest landmark that can be seen.

Figure 13

Wind speed symbol indicating 50% cloud cover with a strong southwest wind

(N4) Answering the Question

As you know, scientific questions can be either general or specific. The graphic organizer in **Figure 14** shows you in which sections to present the answer.

Notice that, in the examples in **Table 7**, our calculations and graphs are very much a part of the Analysis. This is where we communicate any manipulation of the evidence, even if it is just reorganized into a new table. Other times we may use the evidence directly to calculate the answer or to create a graph from which we can obtain a generalization or a specific calculated answer.

Not all calculations are done in the Analysis. Sometimes calculations are done in the Prediction section. Remember that the calculation in the Prediction is based upon what information you have *before starting* the investigation. The calculation in the Analysis is based upon the evidence gathered *during* the investigation. One calculation that does not go into the Analysis is the percentage error calculation. This calculation is done to evaluate either the prediction or the experimental design and as such belongs in the Evaluation section of the lab report.

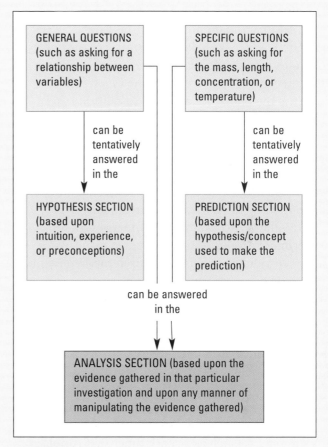

Figure 14

Where to answer the question

Table 7   **Examples of Answers to the Question**

Pre-lab			Post-lab	
Question Type	**Section**	**Example**	**Section**	**Example of an Answer**
General	Hypothesis	Based upon my experience, the acceleration of an object is inversely proportional to the mass of the object. My reasoning …	Analysis	According to the evidence gathered in this investigation, the acceleration of an object is inversely proportional to the mass of the object. My reasoning is …
Specific	Prediction	According to Newton's Second Law, the acceleration of the puck from the launcher on the air table is 0.34 m/s^2. The reasoning behind this prediction is based upon using Newton's Second Law to calculate the acceleration from the unbalanced force acting on the puck and the mass of the puck …	Analysis	According to the evidence gathered in this investigation and the slope of the velocity-time graph, the acceleration of the puck on the air table is 0.32 m/s^2. The table showing the calculations and the velocity-time graph, along with the calculation of slope, are presented below…

⓪ Evaluating

⓪1 Accuracy

Imagine a car driving along a street where the police have set up a radar gun to monitor vehicle speeds (**Figure 15**). The speedometer in the car indicates 65 km/h while, at the same time, the police are measuring 74.8 km/h. Which one is correct? Because the police are required to calibrate their radar guns using a scientifically valid procedure, the police reading is the authority that is legally accepted as correct. The car's speedometer is not accurate because it does not agree with the accepted value. This is not surprising because speedometers are not made to be accurate instruments.

   In science, **accuracy** is a comparison of an experimental value with an accepted value. An accepted value may be a recognized measurement, using the best equipment and procedures, or may be a value predicted from a hypothesis or accepted theory, law, or generalization. Accuracy is used in two different ways in science:

- To test an experimental design, procedure, skills, or equipment. No measurements can be exact because there are no perfect instruments. Every instrument has some limitations. In addition, there may be other errors in setting up equipment (such as a spark timer that is not level) and reading measurements (not reading at eye level and or not reading directly in front of the scale). In this case, the accuracy provides information necessary to evaluate the quality or performance of the design, equipment, procedure, or skill.

- To test scientific concepts. The accuracy of the experimental result either lends support to the concept or creates doubt in the concept. Scientists usually try to devise experiments to falsify (overthrow or prove wrong) existing concepts, and perhaps win a Nobel Prize!

Percentage Error

The simplest way to express accuracy mathematically is as a **percentage error** — the absolute value of the difference between experimental and accepted values expressed as a percentage of the accepted value.

$$\% \text{ error } = \left| \frac{\text{experimental value} - \text{accepted value}}{\text{accepted value}} \right| \times 100$$

The absolute value symbols (| … |) mean that we are interested only in the difference between the two values, and not the sign. In other words, ignore the negative sign in cases where the experimental value is less than the accepted value. In **Figure 15**, the speed measured by the police is the accepted value. The car's speedometer reading is the experimental value. What is the percentage error of the car's speedometer?

$$\% \text{ error } = \left| \frac{65 \, \frac{\text{km}}{\text{h}} - 74.8 \, \frac{\text{km}}{\text{h}}}{74.8 \, \frac{\text{km}}{\text{h}}} \right| \times 100 = 13\%$$

The car's speedometer has a percentage error of 13%.

   When you evaluate an experiment, you will need to judge whether the percentage error you obtain is reasonable, considering various sources of error or uncertainty.

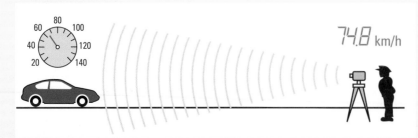

Figure 15

The speed indicated by a car's speedometer is not always accurate.

02 Evaluating the Evidence

How good is the evidence from an experiment? The answer to this question is important because we need good-quality evidence before we can evaluate the prediction and hypothesis. If the evidence is poor or unreliable, we can still usefully evaluate it to identify possible improvements when the experiment is repeated. The sources of error in the design, materials, procedure, and skills employed in the experiment determine the quality of the evidence (not the percentage error). To judge the evidence properly we must evaluate each source of error, looking for flaws and possible improvements. If there appear to be no sources of error, we could say something like "the procedure was very good because it produced sufficient and reliable evidence."

- Are there any flaws in the **design**? To answer this question, look at the plan, variables, and control. The plan should produce an answer to the question. Check to see if all controlled variables were considered. If applicable, a control (or control group) should be used for comparison.
- Were the **materials** of suitable quality to do the experiment? Check the list of materials used and evidence obtained. Look for poor evidence caused by the materials. Perhaps the evidence could be more precise if better equipment were used, or more evidence could be collected if the measurements were automated (for example, by using computer sensors). Note that any measurement made is a source of some error because no instrument is perfect.
- Did the steps of the **procedure** produce sufficient evidence? Check the evidence and analysis sections to see if all required evidence was obtained. Whenever possible, the procedure should include repetitions (trials) to produce more reliable evidence.
- Did you, or the investigator, have suitable **skills** to use the equipment? Check the evidence section and look for the precision of the measurements and the agreement among different trial results. Low precision or variable trial results may indicate that the investigator needs to improve measurement or manipulation skills.

Once you have identified possible errors or uncertainties in each part of the experiment listed above, you should make an overall judgment about the quality of the evidence (such as low, medium, or high quality). The evidence must be of reasonable quality in order to proceed with confidence to the evaluation of the prediction and hypothesis.

03 Evaluating the Prediction and Hypothesis

We evaluate the prediction by comparing the experimental result from the analysis to the predicted result. If these results are quantitative, we can show their accuracy by calculating the percentage error. (See 01 Accuracy, p. 686.) The percentage error is used only to judge the prediction, not the quality of the evidence. There should be a reasonable agreement between the two results for us to say that the prediction is verified. Reasonable means that we can explain any differences between the two results by normal or expected sources of error (identified when the evidence was evaluated). Generally, if the percentage error is less than about 10% then, based on the evidence gathered in this experiment, we can say that the prediction is verified. This rule will work for most experiments using equipment usually found in a high school. If the percentage error is clearly larger than expected (much greater than 10%), then we say that the prediction is falsified (or found false) for this experiment. If the percentage error is only slightly larger than expected, you may say that the results are inconclusive, and neither support nor falsify your prediction. In all cases, it is always best to repeat the experiment or check with other investigators who have done the same experiment.

The prediction was based on some reasoning from a concept such as a hypothesis or accepted theory, law, or generalization. A prediction that is verified means that the concept is likely acceptable. If the prediction is falsified then the concept is at best very questionable and may need to be rejected. In all cases additional experiments can be planned to test the same concept (or a new one). An inconclusive prediction means that no conclusion can be made about the concept until further experiments are done.

(04) Suggesting Further Experiments

Work in science does not end with a single experiment. Sometimes other investigators repeat the experiment to see if the evidence is reproducible. A good example of this process is an announcement of the discovery of a new element. Before the discovery is considered legitimate in the scientific community, other investigators have to repeat the experiment and verify the evidence. More commonly, the analysis and evaluation of one experiment can be used to create new, related experiments. If you are asked to suggest further experiments, the list below may give you some ideas.

- Review the evaluation of the evidence. You may suggest repeating the experiment using:
  - a new or improved design that is better in terms of controls or efficiency, or fixes any flaws that were noted
  - better equipment to make more precise measurements
  - a revised procedure to collect more evidence in cases of insufficient evidence
  - better skills in manipulating the equipment to make the measurements more reliable
- Review the design of the experiment and focus on the variables. Can a controlled variable become the independent variable in another experiment? Can the dependent variable be changed or measured in a different way?
- Review the concept (hypothesis or accepted theory, law, or generalization) and the evaluation of the concept. If it was acceptable then it may be tested in different experiments. Consider the implications of the concept and look for new ways to test it. If a hypothesis was rejected, then suggest a new hypothesis that would lead to new experiments to test its validity.

Communication Skills

In your future career, whether or not you work in the science field, you will probably be required to write a report of some kind. Your company may require a report on a current situation in your organization. They might ask you to write a report encouraging a certain type of action or determining what you think the competition will do. If you are involved in the law profession, you may have to write arguments intended to convince people that your position is the correct one. These arguments are especially important when the correct answer is not obvious, as in environmental issues.

One form of technical report writing — lab reports — evolves as you go through school. The report you will be expected to write in Grade 12 will be more demanding than the one written in Grade 10. If your professional career is science-based, you may have to write scientific papers: the professional's version of a lab report. Also similar to a lab report are research papers. You may have done these when you have worked on a research project in the library.

There are other methods of communication, besides traditionally written reports. One way of presenting information is to give an oral presentation to an audience. Many people find this very difficult, but there are ways to make it much easier. In our changing world there are always new types of communication, such as the world wide web. Web pages need to be prepared carefully to have the best effect. An additional problem with web pages is that the technology that is used to prepare them is changing very quickly, so they need to be updated periodically.

Whatever your method of communication, you have to get your message across to your audience clearly and concisely. To avoid confusion, there are some conventions used in scientific communications. Practise using these conventions, and you will find it easier to understand them in other people's work.

(P) SI Units

The international community of scientists and many countries, including Canada, have agreed on a system of measurement called **SI**, from *Système international d'unités*. In this system, all physical quantities can be expressed as some combination of seven fundamental SI units, called base units (**Table 1**).

Table 1	The Seven SI Base Units	
Quantity name	**Unit name**	**Unit symbol**
length	metre	m
mass	kilogram	kg[i]
time	second	s
electric current	ampere	A
temperature	kelvin	K[ii]
amount of substance	mole	mol
light intensity	candela	cd

[i] The kilogram is the only base unit that contains a prefix.

[ii] Although the base unit for temperature (T) is kelvin (K), the common temperature (t) unit is degree Celsius (°C).

For example, the speed of an object is a distance (length) divided by a time and has units of metres per second (m/s). Other common quantities and their units are shown in **Table 2**.

An important feature of SI is the use of a common set of prefixes to conveniently express small or large sizes of any quantity. SI prefixes (**Table 3**) act as multipliers or factors to increase or reduce the size, in multiples of ten. The most common prefixes change the size in multiples of a thousand (10^3 or 10^{-3}), except for the "centi" in centimetre.

Converting Units

SI prefixes are also used to create conversion factors (ratios) to convert to larger or smaller values of a unit. For example,

$$1 \text{ km} = 1 \times 10^3 \text{ m} = 1000 \text{ m}; \text{ therefore,}$$

$$\frac{1 \text{ km}}{1000 \text{ m}} = \frac{1000 \text{ m}}{1 \text{ km}} = 1$$

Multiplying by a conversion factor is like multiplying by one. This does not change the size of the quantity, only the unit in which it is expressed. The following example shows a common conversion of a distance from metres to kilometres.

$$d = 1256 \cancel{\text{m}} \times \frac{\text{km}}{1000 \cancel{\text{m}}} = 1.256 \text{ km}$$

Notice how the initial units "m" cancel (divide to give 1), leaving "km" as the new unit. You should always choose the form of the conversion factor that cancels the original unit. When creating a conversion factor for prefixes that represent fractions of a unit, you may find it easier to avoid fractions and use only integers. For example,

$$1 \text{ mm} = 1 \times 10^{-3} \text{ m} = \frac{1}{1000} \text{ m}; \text{ which means}$$

$$1000 \text{ mm} = 1 \text{ m}$$

Therefore, convenient conversion factors to convert between millimetres and metres are

$$\frac{1000 \text{ mm}}{1 \text{ m}} \text{ or } \frac{1 \text{ m}}{1000 \text{ mm}}$$

Conversion factors can be used for any unit equality, such as 1 h = 60 min and 1 min = 60 s. Sometimes, a set of conversion factors are combined to convert several units in one calculation step. For example, here is a useful conversion factor to convert a speed from metres per second to kilometres per hour.

$$v = 1 \frac{\cancel{\text{m}}}{\cancel{\text{s}}} \times \frac{1 \text{ km}}{1000 \cancel{\text{m}}} \times \frac{60 \cancel{\text{s}}}{1 \cancel{\text{min}}} \times \frac{60 \cancel{\text{min}}}{1 \text{ h}} = 3.6 \frac{\text{km}}{\text{h}}$$

Table 2   **Common Quantities and Units**

Quantity name	Quantity symbol	Unit name	Unit symbol
distance	d	metre	m
area	A	square metre	m^2
volume	V	cubic metre	m^3
		litre	L
speed	v	metre per second	m/s
acceleration	a	metre per second per second	m/s^2
concentration	c	gram per litre	g/L
temperature	t	degree Celsius	°C
pressure	p	pascal	Pa
heat	q	joule	J
energy	E	joule	J
power	P	watt	W

Table 3   **Common SI Prefixes**

Prefix	Symbol	Factor by which the unit is multiplied	Example
giga	G	$10^9 = 1\,000\,000\,000$	10^9 m = 1 Gm
mega	M	$10^6 = 1\,000\,000$	10^6 m = 1 Mm
kilo	k	$10^3 = 1\,000$	10^3 m = 1 km
		$10^0 = 1$	
centi	c	$10^{-2} = 0.01$	10^{-2} m = 1 cm
milli	m	$10^{-3} = 0.001$	10^{-3} m = 1 mm
micro	μ	$10^{-6} = 0.000\,001$	10^{-6} m = 1 mμ
nano	n	$10^{-9} = 0.000\,000\,001$	10^{-9} m = 1 nm

Lab Reports

It is important that scientists keep records of their plans and results, and share their findings. In order to have their investigations repeated and tested, scientists generally share their work by publishing papers describing the details of their design, procedure, evidence, analysis, and evaluation.

All investigators use a similar format in their lab books or final reports, although the headings and order may vary slightly. Your lab book or report should reflect the process of scientific inquiry that you used in the investigation and should be based on the following headings. See **Figure 1** for a sample lab report.

2.2 Classes of Chemical Elements
May 11, 2000

By: Mary S. and Jarad M.

Purpose
The purpose of this investigation is to test a classification of chemical elements.

Question
What are the classes (types) of chemical elements represented by aluminum, carbon, iron, nitrogen, sulfur, and zinc?

Prediction/Hypothesis
According to my experience, some of the elements are metals (aluminum and iron) but some are not, so there should be two classes of chemical elements.

Design
Each of the elements listed is observed carefully and the appearance, flexibility, magnetism, and electrical conductivity are recorded. The elements are the independent variable and the properties are the dependent variable. Controlled variables are the shape and size of the elements.

Materials
- safety goggles and apron
- magnet
- small piece of steel wool
- conductivity apparatus
- sample strips of aluminum, carbon, iron, and zinc
- sample piece of sulfur
- sample of nitrogen in a covered test tube

Procedure
1. Put on your lab apron and safety goggles.
2. Use the piece of steel wool to clean a small area of one sample.
3. Observe and record the appearance.
4. Try bending the sample and record whether the sample bends or breaks.
5. Bring the magnet near the sample. Note and record any effect.
6. Touch the electrical leads of the conductivity apparatus to opposite ends of the sample and record the movement of the needle on the meter. For nitrogen, insert the leads through the plastic covering on the test tube.
7. Return all materials to storage and wash hands.

Evidence
Properties of Chemical Elements

Element	Appearance	Flexibility	Magnetism	Electrical conductivity
aluminum	shiny, silvery solid	bends	no effect	needle moves to full scale
carbon	dull, black solid	breaks	no effect	needle moves most of the scale
iron	shiny, silvery solid	bends	attracted to magnet	needle moves to full scale
zinc	shiny, silvery solid	bends	no effect	needle moves to full scale
sulfur	dull, yellow solid	breaks	no effect	no movement of needle
nitrogen	colourless gas	n/a	not observable	no movement of needle

---

Figure 1

A sample lab report

Analysis

- Aluminum, iron, and zinc have similar properties and can be grouped together as metals.
- Nitrogen and sulfur look different from each other, but are obviously not metals and could form a different group of elements.
- Carbon is difficult to classify. It does not look like a metal, is not flexible like a metal, but does conduct electricity.

According to the evidence collected in this experiment, there are at least two and maybe three classes of elements — metals, nonmetals, and maybe a class in between.

Evaluation

The design is judged to be adequate because most of the observed properties were useful in answering the Question and there were no obvious flaws in this design.

The materials could be improved by having a strip of sulfur like the other solids.

The procedure was generally satisfactory to answer the question and no special skills were required. However, the quantity of evidence is too limited. Many more elements should be tested.

Some possible sources of error and uncertainty include: the effect of the magnet may be too small to be noticeable; the conductivity should be tested on a cleaned area; and the purity of the samples was unknown. I am not completely confident in the evidence.

The prediction is verified for now because it generally agrees with evidence collected. The hypothesis, based on previous experience of materials that are commonly used, appears acceptable because the prediction was verified.

Title: At the beginning of your lab report, write the number and title of your investigation (from the text). Include the date of the investigation and the names of your lab partners.

Purpose: State the purpose of your investigation. Why this investigation?

Question: This is the specific question that you were attempting to answer in the investigation. If it is appropriate, state the question in terms of independent and dependent variables.

Prediction and Hypothesis: The prediction is the answer you expected before the investigation, based on your reasoning or explanation (called the hypothesis) or based on a concept that you have studied.

Design: A brief general overview (one to three sentences) of what was done. If your investigation involved independent, dependent, and controlled variables, list them. Identify any control or control group that was used in the investigation.

Materials: A detailed list of all materials used, including sizes and quantities where appropriate. Be sure to include safety equipment. Draw a diagram to show a complicated setup of apparatus.

Procedure: List the steps you took in your procedure.

Evidence: This includes all qualitative and quantitative observations that you made. Be as precise as possible when describing quantitative observations, include any unexpected observations, and present your evidence in a form that is easily understood. If you only have a few observations, this could be a list; for controlled experiments or many observations, present them in a table.

Analysis: Interpret and present the evidence in the form of tables, graphs, or illustrations, each with a title. Include any calculations, the results of which can be shown in a table. Make statements about any patterns or trends you observed. Conclude the analysis with a statement answering the experimental question.

Evaluation: The evaluation is your judgment about the quality of evidence obtained and about the validity of the prediction and hypothesis. This section can be divided into two parts:
- Were you able to obtain suitable evidence to answer the question?
- Were the prediction and hypothesis supported or rejected by the results?

ⓇWriting for Specific Audiences

In the working world, individuals and companies often require detailed information on a particular topic to help them to make informed decisions. There are many kinds of scientific writing, for many different purposes and many different audiences. Before beginning, consider the purpose of your writing: are you presenting facts, laying choices before your readers, or trying to convert them to your way of thinking? Know who your audience is. Think about how much time they will be willing to spend reading your article, and how much they already know about the subject.

Your report should be helpful and easy to read. If your work is widely read and accepted, the chances increase that more people will trust your word. This tends to lead to better career positions and opportunities!

Before you submit a report of any kind, read it through and ask yourself "Is this appropriate to publish?" If you have doubts about the authenticity of your sources or the truth of your statements, or if a named person may be damaged by your writing, consider a rewrite. Once your report is published, it cannot be taken back.

Research reports are the most detailed and "scientific," so they are addressed in detail below. Other kinds of reports and articles vary slightly from this arrangement, as shown.

Research Reports

Research reports are less rigidly structured than lab reports but still need to be very clearly laid out. Your aim is to present factual information in an unbiased way.

- Start by writing an outline. Decide what your topic's main points are, and note your findings for each point. Plan an introduction for the beginning and a wrap-up for the end.
- The introduction or first section is the most important. It is your chance to make the interesting aspects of your research immediately known to your readers. In one page (or less), summarize what you have discovered about a given topic: the most important issues and your conclusions about them.

- Have a section (with a number and a title) for each main point. Readers will then be able to find a particular subject easily.
- Write carefully and concisely. People do not have the time to read pages of unnecessary information.
- You may be communicating quite advanced scientific or technical knowledge. Know your audience. Prepare a report that your readers can understand, without "talking down" to them. If possible, find out how much background knowledge they are likely to have. If it is only a small amount you will have to teach your readers about these topics. Use examples that are not too simple, but are easy to remember and convey the required principle.
- Follow conventions for scientific communication, although you may also have to "translate" some of these for a nonscientific audience.
- Unless you have been asked for your opinion on an issue, try to keep to the facts. If you make any extrapolations or assumptions, give reasons why you feel these are valid.
- In your final section, summarize your findings and what they mean, and briefly suggest aspects that could be researched further.
- Credit your sources in a complete list of references.

Issue Reports

Public and government decisions are rarely made purely on scientific fact. They are usually based on a combination of interpretations of those facts. When you are preparing an issue report, look at the issue from as many perspectives as possible. (For more information, see Ⓓ Identifying Alternatives/ Positions, p. 662.) Who will be affected by this issue? Issues are controversial because there are various points of view. Try to consider and address as many of them as possible. Bear in mind that major societal changes are unlikely to take place overnight, so try to keep your recommendations reasonable. For example, your issue might be increased cigarette smoking by young people. One possible solution is a government ban on the sale of cigarettes. But how attractive would that solution be to government?

Such solutions must be supported by a description of a process that would make the solution likely.

Position Papers

When planning a position paper (sometimes called an advocacy letter), you may either start with a position on an issue, and then conduct research to support your position, or start by researching a particular topic and then decide on a position in light of your research.

State your position in the beginning of your article and then support it with the results of your research. You do not have to balance your paper with contrary views, but you should be aware of other positions on the issue, and try to refute their arguments. However, it is very discourteous to insult those holding opposing views. Support your arguments with evidence, reasoning, and logic.

Letters to the Editor

A letter to the editor of a newspaper or magazine is typically a shorter version of a position paper. Space is expensive and, since you are not paying for it, the publisher will usually not print long articles. You must write concisely (keep it to a couple of paragraphs), but possibly in a humorous or ironic manner. It is not necessary to back up every point you make with scientific facts, but do indicate that there is some evidence to support your position. Be aware of the tone of the publication to which you are writing; each one has a slightly different approach. Do your research by reading the editorial page of your target newspapers; note the style of the letters they print.

Magazine Articles

Magazine articles are usually written in response to a request from the editor. Only rarely do magazines publish unsolicited articles, and they only publish articles of interest to their readers.

When writing for a magazine, know the readers well. Are they experts in the field, or have they little or no background knowledge? Should the article be an in-depth, thoughtful discourse, well supported by scientific evidence, or a lighter, more general piece? The editor will generally tell you how long the article should be, and how the illustrations will be prepared. There is no point in writing more than you are asked for: it will be cut!

Whatever the tone of the article, though, try not to stray from the truth, and be prepared to support your statements if you are challenged.

Environmental Impact Reports

Environmental impact reports are a relatively new type of report. Until fairly recently, the environment was not a consideration when developments were planned. Today we must consider, study, and explain the implications of any intended actions, such as constructing an oil pipeline in northern Alberta or building subdivisions on the Oak Ridges Moraine in southern Ontario. Sometimes governments conduct environmental impact assessments to investigate an issue more completely. What laws should they enact? What should be the penalties? It is never easy to predict the effect of a change on the environment: every ecosystem is unique and may react in an unexpected way to a change. Putting out forest fires seems like a good idea, but many tree species require periodic fires to open their fire-resistant cones or clear a space for them to grow. There is an environmental impact to almost everything.

Carrying out an environmental impact assessment is a rather daunting task. It begins with exhaustive research into the existing environment, including both biotic and abiotic factors. The research may extend to other, similar areas, where a comparable development has already taken place. What were the effects? To what extent can these findings be applied to the current site? Studies may be commissioned from various sources: geologists may be called upon to predict how the change would affect the stability of the area; hydrologists may be questioned about the water table; botanists could contribute information about how the plant life would change; toxicologists might warn of potentially dangerous substances. All this information must then be drawn together and presented in a coherent report.

There is no one format to follow when writing environmental impact reports, but there are a few elements that you must always include:
- a definition of the scope of the questions being researched (What are the boundaries of the questions you are trying to answer?);
- a description of how the data were collected;

- a presentation of the evidence and how it was analyzed;
- conclusions, with specific reference to those questions that could not be answered;
- long-term implications (which may be highly speculative); and
- suggestions for further research.

Figure 2

(S) Oral Presentations

You may be asked to make oral presentations for a variety of purposes. You could present results, take part in a debate, or role-play a situation. All of these would have different formats, but they all have something in common: you are communicating information to others using mainly your voice. Of course, your body language will also be important, and you may support your oral presentation with visual materials, but the primary means of communication is the spoken word.

Many people find this a very stressful method of communication: they feel exposed and alone, may be worried about forgetting what to say, and may get flustered and confused. These are very natural reactions that even experienced speakers have to overcome. There are some fairly simple general guidelines that will help to lower your stress level, improve your presentation, and help you convey your message to your audience, whatever type of oral presentation you are preparing.
- Plan your oral presentation well in advance.
- Find out how long you are expected to speak.
- Prepare a point-form "speech" on cue cards or a computer-based presentation. It is best not to read your speech, nor to memorize every word. Try to work from the points on your cue cards, and expand on them.

- Practise your presentation to make sure that it fits into the allowed time. If you get stuck, use your notes or props as a guide.
- Make sure that your "props" (objects, posters, slides for overhead projection, etc.) are ready and in good working order.
- If you are nervous, take some slow deep breaths to calm yourself.
- When you are speaking, keep your head up and do not talk too fast. Your audience must be able to hear what you have to say.

Presenting Results

This is a very factual type of oral presentation, which must be clear and to the point. Make sure you answer the following questions as you prepare and present your speech:
- What was the purpose of your investigation?
- Why was the topic interesting?
- What question were you trying to answer?
- What were your predictions and/or hypothesis?
- How did you carry out your investigation?
- What were your major results?
- Were there any problems or sources of error or bias that might cause you to question your results/findings?
- What conclusion did you reach?
- How might your findings help others?

- On the basis of your results, is there another investigation that could be done?

Debating

A debate is basically a structured form of argument, with some people presenting for the proposition, and others presenting against. Depending on the form of the debate, there may be an opportunity for you to present your own position, listen to the opposition's position, and then present a rebuttal: a brief argument as to why their position is not the correct one. Some debates begin and end with a vote. Your aim is to win the audience over to your way of thinking. You may be asked to debate either from your own personal point of view, or from the perspective of another character (similar to a role-play).

- Research your topic thoroughly, keeping notes as you go.
- Pick four or five major points to support your position, with examples. Write them out in point form.
- Present your arguments clearly and logically, within the allowed time limit.
- Listen closely to the opposition's presentations. If necessary, make notes to remind you which points you want to address in your rebuttal. If you have researched really thoroughly, you may find yourself familiar with some of the opposition's arguments and be able to answer them with evidence of your own.
- Make your presentation as persuasive as possible, while at all times showing respect for the opposition. While you can question the authenticity of their evidence, never resort to name-calling or rudeness.

Role-Playing

This allows a lot more freedom, as you are usually expected to take on a "character," and try to present an opinion, position, or decision from that person's perspective. The purpose of your speech is both to convey information and to sway the audience over to your character's way of thinking. Follow these steps as you prepare for and present your role-play.

- Research your topic and your character thoroughly, so you can give compelling reasons for your character's position.
- Organize the results of your research in a way that supports your character's position.
- Incorporate personal examples from your character's life, to account for your perspective.
- As you make your presentation, it is more fun for the audience (and more convincing) if you stay "in character" and use the first person ("I" and "my") as much as possible.

Electronic Communication

Electronic communication is becoming part of everyday life. From "overhead" presentations to web pages, electronics can help us communicate quickly to a wide audience. Used properly, technology can also make our communications look very slick and professional. The various technologies take practice however. Do not expect instant results at your first attempt.

When using high-tech methods of communication, be careful not to get carried away with the technology. Just as if you were writing a research report by hand, your thoughts must be clearly stated, well organized, and clearly presented, with supporting arguments and evidence. It is always a good idea to have someone not involved in your project check out your presentation before "going public" with it.

Creating a Presentation Using Overheads

There are several software programs (such as Microsoft PowerPoint) that allow you to create, write, edit, and illustrate a series of slides that can be projected onto a screen. You can even add a sound track, including music, sound effects, and your recorded voice, to your presentation. Write your slides as point-form notes, limit yourself to no more than 10 lines of text on each slide, and make the words large enough to be easily read by the audience.

Creating a Web Page

A web page is a way of communicating with anyone in the world who has access to the world wide web. Every page has its own unique address (URL) and may include graphics, sounds, animations, videos, and links to other web pages, in addition to regular text. Computer technology and software are changing so quickly that any detailed instructions would soon be out of date, but the following general points may help.

To create and "publish" a web page, you need
- a well-written article input into an electronic format
- a computer capable of running an HTML authoring tool (such as Microsoft FrontPage, Dreamweaver, or Adobe GoLine, that has design templates), software that can edit images and graphics, and a modem
- an Internet Service Provider (ISP)

All information on the Web is a series of documents formatted using a special "language" such as Hypertext Markup Language (HTML). You have to convert your article to that language using the authoring tool.

If you want to make your web site effective, you must be willing to invest the time and energy to create interesting page layouts and exciting graphics. When people leave your site, they remember the graphics and the page layout as well as the entire organization of the site. They remember how easy or difficult it was to get the information they wanted. This ease is determined by the speed, clarity, simplicity, and consistency of your presentation.

There are many programs available (such as Flash and Shockwave) that allow you to create amazing animation and special effects, and others that allow you to modify your own digitized photos. Remember that graphical elements on a web page use a lot of memory and can make your page slow to download.

Be aware of copyright restrictions when using images downloaded from other sources. Simply using type effectively in a graphic format can help make your web page stand out from the others, and may be much more readable than one cluttered up with fancy graphics.

You can add hypertext links to your page, to lead the reader to more information on other web pages. Your authoring tool will show you how to make links to other URLs. Always check that the links work.

You will be able to receive feedback from readers if you place your e-mail address at the bottom of your web page.

Do not give out any personal information about yourself (home address, phone number, etc.). The Web can be an exciting place to explore, but it is also dangerous to give out personal information to complete strangers.

A final word: now you know how easy it is for you to prepare your own web page, you can see how easy it is for other people. Material you read on the Internet comes from a variety of sources, from the totally ill-informed to the expert. Bear this in mind as you read! (For more information see Ⓙ Internet Research, p. 667.)

Math Skills

(U) Using the Calculator

A calculator is a very useful device that makes calculations easier, faster, and probably more accurate. However, like any other electronic instrument, you need to learn how to use it. These guidelines and instructions apply to a basic scientific calculator. If your calculator is different, such as a graphing calculator, some of the instructions and operations may use different keys or sequences: check the manual.

General Points

- Most calculators follow the usual mathematical rules for order of operations— multiplication/division before addition/subtraction. For example, if you are calculating y using y = mx + b, you can enter the values of m times x plus b in one sequence. The calculator will "know" that m and x must be multiplied first before b is added.
- Calculators do not keep track of significant digits. For example, 12.0 is the same as 12 for a calculator.
- Some calculator keys such as $\boxed{+/-}$, $\boxed{\frac{1}{x}}$, $\boxed{x^2}$ (and its 2nd function, $\boxed{\sqrt{x}}$) apply the operation only to the value in the display regardless of other operations in progress. This means you can quickly change the sign of the number, convert to the reciprocal, square the number, or find the square root while inputting a sequence of calculations.
- Do not clear all numbers from the calculator until you are completely finished with a question: the result of one calculation can be reused to start the next one.
- All scientific calculators have at least one memory location where you can store a number ($\boxed{M+}$ and $\boxed{STO}$ are the common keys) and recall it later (usually with $\boxed{MR}$ or $\boxed{RCL}$). Use it to avoid reentering many digits.

Multiplication and Division

- Division is the inverse of multiplication. This means that dividing by a number is the equivalent to multiplying by the inverse of the same number. For example,

$$\frac{12 \text{ km}}{0.75 \text{ h}} \text{ is the same as } 12 \text{ km} \times \frac{1}{0.75 \text{ h}} \text{ and equals } 16 \frac{\text{km}}{\text{h}}$$

This is particularly useful when you want to divide by a number that is currently in the display of your calculator. For example, you have just finished converting 45 min to 0.75 h in your calculator and now you want to calculate the speed.

Display: 0.75

Press: $\boxed{\frac{1}{x}}$ $\boxed{\times}$ $\boxed{1}$ $\boxed{2}$ $=$

New Display: 16

- Parentheses, (and), are useful to force the calculator to perform the operation(s) inside the parentheses first, before continuing with the calculation. The calculation of the slope of a line is a good example.

$$\text{slope} = \frac{\Delta d}{\Delta t} = \frac{(15.2 - 4.1) \text{ m}}{(6.5 - 3.6) \text{ s}} = 3.8 \frac{\text{m}}{\text{s}}$$

If you do not use the parentheses on your calculator, you will have to calculate the numerator and denominator separately and then divide. If you simply enter all of the numbers and operations without parentheses, you will get an incorrect answer.

Scientific Notation

Scientific notation is one method of expressing either a large or small value as a number between 1 and 10 multiplied by a power of 10. In most examples, scientific notation is an alternative to the use of SI prefixes, which is the recommended method (**Table 1**). However, either format can be used when a value needs to be rounded to the correct number of significant digits.

Table 1	Some Examples of Different Number Formats	
Regular Notation	Scientific Notation	SI Prefix Notation
1205 g	1.205×10^3 g	1.205 kg
0.0004 m	4×10^{-4} m	0.4 mm

On many calculators, scientific notation is entered using a special key, labelled EXP or EE. This key includes "× 10" from the scientific notation and you need to enter only the exponent. For example, to enter

7.5×10^4 press   7 . 5 EXP 4

3.6×10^{-3} press   3 . 6 EXP +/− 3

All mathematical operations can be carried out with numbers in scientific notation just like numbers in the regular format.

Ⓥ Graphing

Ⓥ1 Types of Graphs

There are many types of graphs that you can use when organizing your data. You need to identify which type of graph is best for your data before you start drawing it. Three of the most useful kinds are bar graphs, circle (pie) graphs, and point-and-line graphs.

Bar Graphs

When at least one of the variables is qualitative, use a bar graph. For example, a bar graph would be a good way to present the data collected from a study of the math marks of students (quantitative) who listened to different kinds of music (qualitative) while doing their math homework. In this kind of graph, each bar stands for a different category, in this case a type of music.

Circle Graphs

Circle graphs and bar graphs are used for similar types of data. If your quantitative variable can be changed to a percentage of a total quantity, then a circle graph is useful. For example, if you surveyed a class to find the students' favourite type of music, you could make a circle graph. In a circle graph, each piece stands for a different category (e.g., the kind of music preferred), and the size of the piece tells the percentage of the total that belongs in the category (e.g., the percentage of students who prefer a particular kind of music).

Point-and-Line Graphs

When both variables are quantitative, use a point-and-line graph (**Figure 1**). **Table 2** clearly shows that both time and distance are quantitative variables.

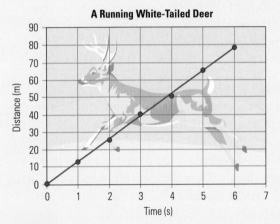

A Running White-Tailed Deer

Figure 1

Graph of a running deer

Table 2	A Running White-Tailed Deer
Time (s)	Distance (m)
0	0
1.0	13
2.0	25
3.0	40
4.0	51
5.0	66
6.0	78

V2 Constructing a Line Graph

Let's see how the data in **Table 1** are used to produce a graph.

1. Use graph paper and construct your graph on a grid. The horizontal edge on the bottom of this grid is called the x-axis and the vertical edge on the left is called the y-axis. Don't be too thrifty with graph paper — a larger graph is easier to interpret.

2. Decide which variable goes on which axis, and label each axis, including the units of measurement. The independent variable is generally plotted along the x-axis, and the dependent variable along the y-axis. The exception to this is when you plot distance or speed against time: regardless of which is the independent or dependent variable, always plot time on the x-axis. This convention ensures that the slope of the graph always represents speed (from a distance-time graph) or acceleration (from a speed-time graph).

3. Determine the range of values for each variable. The range is the difference between the largest and smallest value. For the times in the table, the maximum is 6.0 s, and the minimum is 0 s, so the range is: 6.0 s – 0 s = 6.0 s. For the distance travelled by the deer, the range is 78 m – 0 m = 78 m. Graphs often include a little extra length on each axis, so they appear less cramped.

4. Choose a scale for each axis. This will depend on how much space you have, and the range of values for each axis. Each line on the grid usually increases steadily in value by a convenient number, such as 1, 2, 5, 10, 50, or 100. In **Figure 1** we have chosen to use one line for each second on the x-axis, and one line for each 10 m on the y-axis.

5. Plot the points. Start with the first pair of values from the data table, 0 s and 0 m. This is, of course, the origin of the graph, but not all graphs start at the origin. The second point is at 1.0 s and 13 m. Place the point where an imaginary line starting at 1.0 s on the x-axis meets an imaginary line starting at 13 m on the y-axis.

6. After all the points are plotted, and if it is possible, draw a line through the points to show the relationship between the variables. It is unusual for all the points to lie exactly on a line. Small errors in each measurement tend to move the points slightly away from the perfect line. You must draw a line that comes closest to most of the points. This is called the line of best fit — a smooth line that passes through or between the points so that there are about the same number of points on each side of the line. The line of best fit may be a straight line or a curved line.

7. Title your graph.

V3 Calculating Slopes

If the line of best fit is a straight line, this is an indication that there is a simple relationship between the two variables. You can represent this linear (or straight-line) relationship with a mathematical equation that looks like this

$$y = mx + b$$

where y is the dependent variable (on the y-axis), x is the independent variable (on the x-axis), m is the slope (or steepness) of the line, and b is the y-intercept (the point where the line crosses the y-axis). Perhaps the most important of these is the slope of the line. To find the slope, choose two points on the line (x_1, y_1) and (x_2, y_2). (Note that these are not data points: just two imaginary points on the line you have drawn.) The slope is equal to

$$m = \frac{\text{rise}}{\text{run}} = \frac{y_2 - y_1}{x_2 - x_1}$$

For our graph (**Figure 2**), we could choose the two points (1.5, 19.5) and (5.5, 71.5). We can now calculate the slope:

$$m = \frac{y_2 - y_1}{x_2 - x_1}$$
$$= \frac{85 - 20 \text{ m}}{6.5 - 1.5 \text{ s}}$$
$$= \frac{65 \text{ m}}{5 \text{ s}}$$
$$= 13 \text{ m/s}$$

A Running White-Tailed Deer

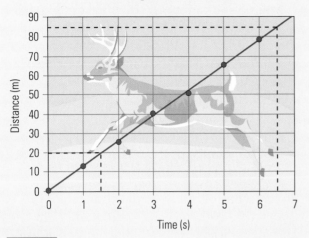

Figure 2

A positive slope

The slope of the line is 13 m/s. This is a positive number, indicating a direct relationship. A negative slope (if the line were angled as in **Figure 3**) would give a negative number, indicating an inverse relationship.

Bailey Finishes the Race

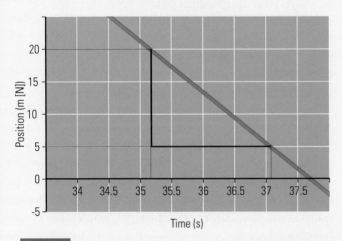

Figure 3

The slope of this line is -7.9 m/s [N].

If the line of best fit is a curved line, its slope cannot be described by a single value. In fact, the slope changes at every point along the line. We can estimate the slope of the line at various points along the curve by drawing tangents to the curve (**Figure 4**). A tangent is a straight line that touches a curve at only one point. On a graph, the tangent represents the slope of the curve at that point.

Drawing a tangent by hand is not easy and rarely gives a very accurate result. (You can reduce the error considerably by using a graphing

The Motion of an Accelerating Object

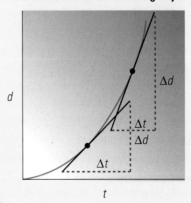

Figure 4

A curved line on a distance–time graph indicates acceleration.

calculator to draw the graph and the tangent.) However, drawing it by hand is a useful exercise and helps you to understand how the slope of a curve changes.

1. When drawing a tangent, you will have the most success if the curve has been drawn very smoothly, using a sharp pencil.

2. Put your (still sharp) pencil on the curve, at the point for which you want to find the slope. Hold the pencil in place firmly.

3. Place a ruler on the outside of the curve, touching your pencil, and adjust the ruler until the curve appears to sit symmetrically on the ruler, like the bottom of a basketball on a tabletop.

4. Hold the ruler firmly and draw a long line along it, with the tangent ending on grid lines on the graph.

(V4) Using Computers for Graphing

There are many useful computer programs that can help with the graphing process. For example, Microsoft Excel is a powerful spreadsheet/graphing program that allows us to construct point-and-line, bar, and circle graphs among others. In addition, such programs can use statistical analysis to compute the line of best fit.

The instructions given below guide you through the use of a spreadsheet program such as Excel. The aim is to produce a best-fit line graph for a table of values for an independent and a dependent variable.

This is the most common type of graph for scientific applications.

1. Start the spreadsheet program. Enter the data with the values for *x* in the A column (**Table 3**), starting in cell A2, and the values for *y* in the B column, starting in cell B2.

Table 3	Sample Data	
x-variable (unit)	*y*-variable (unit)
0.50	0.46
1.00	0.85
1.50	1.51
2.00	1.89
2.50	2.36

2. To draw the graph:
   - Highlight the two columns containing your data (A2...B6). From the toolbar, select the button for creating graphs. The cursor may change to a symbol, which allows you to "click and drag" to choose the size of your graph.

- A series of choices will now be presented to you, so you can specify what kind of graph you want to create. A scatter graph is most appropriate for our data.
- Click in the "Title" box and type the title of the graph.
- Click in "Value (X)" box and type the label and units for the *x*-axis.
- Click in the "Value (Y)" box and type the label and units for the *y*-axis.
- Click the "Finish" button.

3. To add a line of best fit, point your cursor to one of the highlighted data points and right click once. Select the "Trendline" option. Make sure that the "Linear" box is highlighted under Type.

4. If you want to know the slope or y-intercept, click on the "Options" tab and select the box beside "Display Equation on Chart." (This will put the values for $y = mx + b$ on the graph so that you will have the slope and *y*-intercept value.)

5. Save your spreadsheet before your close the program.

(W) Calculating

(W1) Calculation Rules

There are two types of initial quantities that are used in science — exact values and measurements. Quantities that have exact values include defined quantities such as those obtained from SI prefix definitions (e.g., 1 km = 1000 m) and from other definitions (e.g., 1 h = 60 min). Counted values such as 5 beakers or 10 cells are also exact values. All exact values are considered to be completely certain with an infinite number of significant digits. In other words, 1 km is exactly 1000 m, not 999.9 m or 1000.2 m. The same principle applies to counted objects. For example, 5 beakers could not be 4.9 or 5.1 beakers; it is exactly 5 beakers.

However, every measurement has some uncertainty or error. No measurement is exact. This uncertainty depends on the limitations of the particular measuring instrument used and the technological skill of the person making the measurement. When making a measurement, you should look at eye level directly in front of the scale and record all certain digits plus one digit estimated between the lines of the smallest division on the scale. For example, a 100-mL graduated cylinder has fairly widely spaced divisions marked every 1 mL. You should measure and record one decimal place in the volume (e.g., 56.4 mL or 78.0 mL).

Precision is the place value of the last estimated digit. This will usually be the number of decimal places (**Table 4**).

Table 4 Precision and Certainty

Example	Precision (# of decimal places)	Certainty (# of significant digits)
120.50 mm	2	5
0.9 mL	1	1
84.6 mL	1	3
2502 g	0	4

Certainty is communicated by the number of significant digits in the measurement and includes all certain digits plus the one estimated digit. When counting significant digits, count all digits except leading zeroes in decimal fractions (**Table 4**).

To obtain the best possible measurement, you should use the most precise instrument (greatest number of decimal places) and the largest convenient sample size (greatest number of digits).

Rounding a Calculated Answer

After measurements are made, they are often used in calculations to determine other quantities. We will assume that all quantities given in examples and questions are measured quantities, except those that are exact by definition. After you have finished a calculation and determined the digits allowed in the answer (see rules below), then you may need to round the final answer. There are several methods of rounding, but we will use the simplest rule:

If the digit after the one to be retained is a 5 or greater, then round up.

For example, rounded to 1 decimal place, 26.446 m becomes 26.4 m, and rounded to 2 significant digits, 17.53 kg becomes 18 kg.

When rounding after an addition or subtraction calculation, use the **addition/subtraction rule**:

Round the answer to the same number of decimal places as the measured value with the fewest number of decimal places.

For example,

9.3 m + 0.45 m + 110 m = 120 m

In other words, the answer cannot be more precise than the least precise value.

When rounding after a multiplication or division, use the **multiplication/division rule**:

Round the answer to the same number of significant digits as the measured value with the fewest number of significant digits.

For example, $m = \dfrac{1.15\text{ g}}{\cancel{cm^3}} \times 16\ \cancel{cm^3} = 18\text{ g}$

$\Delta t = 1.25\ \cancel{h} \times \dfrac{60\text{ min}}{1\ \cancel{h}} = 75.0\text{ min}$

In the second example, 60 min/h is an exact quantity with an infinite number of significant digits. Therefore, the number of significant digits in the final answer is based only on the measured value of 1.25 h.

In other words, the answer cannot be more certain than the least certain value.

Scientific Notation

Scientists sometimes work with very large or very small numbers. Because we do not want to spend the better part of our day writing out zeros, it is convenient to use a mathematical abbreviation known as scientific notation. To convert to scientific notation, simply count the number of places you have to move the decimal point to yield a value between 1 and 10. This counted number is the exponent. The exponent is positive if the original number is greater than 10, and negative if the original number is less than 10. The scientific notation for 150 000 000 000 is 1.50×10^{11} m. Likewise, 0.000 000 000 050 can be written as 5.0×10^{-11} m.

(W2) Calculating a Mean

There are many statistical methods of analyzing experimental evidence. One of the most common and important is calculating an arithmetic mean, or simply a **mean**. The mean of a set of values is the sum of all reasonable values divided by the total number of values. (This is also commonly known as the average of a set of values, but this term is not recommended because it is too vague and open to different interpretations.)

Suppose you measure the root growth at the tip of five seedlings. Your measurements after three days are: 1.7 mm, 1.6 mm, 1.8 mm, 0.4 mm, and 1.6 mm. What is the mean root growth? Inspection of the measurements shows that the 0.4 mm measurement clearly does not fit with the rest.

Perhaps this seedling was infected with a fungus or some other problem occurred. You should not include this result in your mean, but leave it in your evidence table so everyone can see the decision that you made. Using only the reasonable values,

$$\text{mean root growth} = \frac{1.7 \text{ mm} + 1.6 \text{ mm} + 1.8 \text{ mm} + 1.6 \text{ mm}}{4}$$

$$= 1.7 \text{ mm}$$

Means are used in all areas of science because multiple measurements or trials increase the reliability of the results.

(W3) Working with Equations

Algebra is a set of rules and procedures for working with mathematical equations. In general, you will work with one equation that contains one unknown quantity. To solve for this unknown you need to isolate it on one side of the equal sign. To accomplish this requires three logical rules:

1. *The same quantity can be added or subtracted from both sides of the equation without changing the equality.*
   The following examples illustrate this rule.

$$100 \text{ m} = 100 \text{ m} \qquad\qquad x + b = y$$
$$100 \text{ m} - 5 \text{ m} = 100 \text{ m} - 5 \text{ m} \qquad x + b - b = y - b$$
$$95 \text{ m} = 95 \text{ m} \qquad\qquad x = y - b$$

The example on the left shows the application of this rule using quantities with numbers and units. The rule works equally well with quantity symbols. In the example on the right, we want to isolate x.

2. *The same quantity can be multiplied or divided on both sides of the equation without changing the equality.*

$$120 \text{ m} = 120 \text{ m} \qquad\qquad v = \frac{d}{t}$$
$$\frac{120 \text{ m}}{8.0 \text{ s}} = \frac{120 \text{ m}}{8.0 \text{ s}} \qquad\qquad v \times t = \frac{d}{t} \times t$$
$$\frac{15 \text{ m}}{\text{s}} = \frac{15 \text{ m}}{\text{s}} \qquad\qquad vt = d \text{ or } d = vt$$

The following examples illustrate this rule.
   The example on the left shows the use of this rule with known quantities. We use the same rule with an equation containing quantity symbols to isolate one of the quantities. If we want to solve for d in the example on the right, we multiply both sides by t. Notice that t divided by t gives 1.

Multiplying or dividing any quantity by 1 does not change the quantity; therefore, $d \times 1 = d$.

3. *The same power (e.g., square or square root) can be applied to both sides of the equation without changing the equality.*
   The following examples illustrate this rule.

$$25 \text{ s}^2 = 25 \text{ s}^2 \qquad\qquad b^2 = A$$
$$\sqrt{25 \text{ s}^2} = \sqrt{25 \text{ s}^2} \qquad\qquad \sqrt{b^2} = \sqrt{A}$$
$$5.0 \text{ s} = 5.0 \text{ s} \qquad\qquad b = \sqrt{A}$$

If several of the rules listed above are required to isolate an unknown quantity, then you should apply rule 1 first, whenever possible, and then apply rule 2. In general, rule 3 should be used last.

Fractions

One example of a fraction that is common, and sometimes creates difficulties, is a fraction that also contains a fractional denominator. For example, what is six divided by one-half; $\frac{6}{\frac{1}{2}}$? The answer is 12, not 3.

$$\frac{6}{\frac{1}{2}} = \frac{6 \times \frac{2}{1}}{\frac{1}{2} \times \frac{2}{1}} = 6 \times \frac{2}{1} = 12 \quad \text{(Dividing a quantity by 1 does not change the quantity.)}$$

If there is a fraction in the denominator, then, to reduce the denominator to 1, you should multiply both numerator and denominator by the reciprocal of the denominator. Notice that this means the *answer can always be obtained by multiplying the numerator by the reciprocal of the original denominator.* You are likely to see this situation when simplifying the units to calculate time in a motion calculation. For example, if a distance in kilometres is divided by a speed in kilometres per hour, the units will simplify to hours by multiplying by the reciprocal, hours per kilometre.

$$\frac{\text{km}}{\frac{\text{km}}{\text{h}}} = \text{km} \times \frac{\text{h}}{\text{km}} = \text{h}$$

Working Together

Scientific discoveries are almost always made by teams of people working together. Scientists share ideas, help each other design experiments and studies, analyze each other's observations, and evaluate each other's investigations. Group work is necessary and usually more productive than working alone.

There will be a number of times throughout the year when your teacher asks you to work with one or more of your classmates. You may be brainstorming and sharing ideas, working on an activity, doing research, or designing an experiment. Whatever the situation, there are a few rules that will help you and your classmates to be members of an efficient and effective team.

General Rules for Effective Team Work

- Keep an open mind and be accepting of all ideas: the more the better.
- Value the efforts of every member, and encourage all members to participate to the best of their abilities.
- Divide the various tasks among all group members. Choose a role on the team that is best suited to your particular strengths.
- Work collaboratively: take turns, encourage, listen, clarify, give help, and trust each other.
- Remember that the success of the team is everyone's responsibility. Every member needs to be able to demonstrate what the team has learned and support the team's final decision.

Exchanging Information Orally

You will be involved in a number of different activities during your science course. These activities help you express your ideas and learn about new ones. They are all governed by the rules for effective teamwork. Here are three of the more successful techniques.

- In a **think–pair–share activity** you and your partner are given a problem. Each of you develops a response (usually within a time limit). You then share your ideas to resolve the problem with each other. You may also be asked to share your resolutions with a larger group or the class.

- In a **jigsaw activity** you are an active member in two teams: your home team and your expert team. Each member of the home team chooses or is assigned to a particular area of research. Each home team member then meets with an expert team in which everyone is working on the same area of research. In your expert team you may work together to come up with answers to questions around your area of research. Once you have accomplished your task as a team, you return to your home team where it is your responsibility to teach what you have learned to the members of your home team. Each person on the home team will do the same thing. The rules of teamwork are very important with the jigsaw, so try to keep them in mind as you work with your expert and home teams.

- A **round table activity** can be used to give your team an opportunity to review what they know. A group is given a pen, paper, and a question or questions. Pass the pen and paper around and take turns writing one line of the solution. You can pass on your turn if you wish. Keep working until the solution is complete. Check to ensure that everyone understands the solution. Finally, review the steps to the solution with the team.

Investigations and Activities

This kind of work is most effectively accomplished by small groups. Make sure everyone in the group understands and agrees to his/her tasks. If possible, take turns doing the various tasks. At all times keep safety in mind and be aware of where other members of your group are. Remember that, as well as being responsible for your group, you are also responsible for your own learning. Make your own observations during investigations to compare with those of other members of your group. Think of it as quality control! Whether you are designing a balloon car, collecting weather data, or creating an inventory of the species living in your schoolyard, every suggestion is important and every group member has something to contribute.

Explore an Issue

When there is research to be done, a group of people can get the work done much more quickly than an individual if each member knows exactly what to look for. To avoid duplication, divide the topic into several areas and assign one to each person. It is essential to keep records of your sources, whether they be book titles or web sites, in case other group members want to follow up on your initial research.

- Decide on the format for exchanging information: will you exchange photocopies of notes, share computer printouts of web pages, or give brief oral presentations?
- When the time comes for you to share your findings, reach some conclusions, and take a position, allow every member of the group to contribute. Make decisions together, by compromise and consensus.
- Preparing for the final stage — communicating your position — should also be a team effort.

Decide on an appropriate way to share the workload.

- Last but not least, every group member should be given credit and take responsibility for the team's work. You should all be proud of what you have produced!

Evaluating Your Group's Work

If you are asked to consider the effectiveness of your teamwork, consider the following questions.

1. What were the *strengths* of your teamwork?
2. What were the *weaknesses* of your teamwork?
3. What *opportunities* were provided by working with your team?
4. What possible *challenges* did you see with respect to your teamwork?
5. How would you ensure that the team functions better next time?

Graphic Organizers

When you are describing situations, issues, or events, it is sometimes helpful to record your ideas so that you can see them and compare them with those of other people. Instead of putting your ideas in sentences, they can be made into graphic organizers. A familiar example of a graphic organizer is a data table that is used to record experimental observations. These visual representations of ideas indicate your understanding of a topic and can take many forms.

The PMI Chart

Plus	Minus	Interesting

Figure 1
A PMI chart

Purpose: To examine both sides of an issue.

Directions: Record notes on positive aspects of the topic or issue in the P (Plus) column; record notes on negative aspects in the M (Minus) column; record notes on interesting or controversial questions in the I (Interesting) column.

The KWL Chart

Know	Want to Know	Learned

Figure 2
A KWL chart

Purpose: To help you identify prior knowledge and experience, and to reflect on learning.

Directions: Before you begin a new concept, lesson, or unit, list what you **know** about a topic in the **K** column and what you **want to know** in the **W** column. After studying the new topic, list what you **learned** in the **L** column.

The Venn Diagram

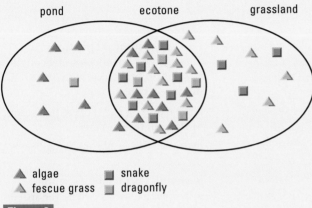

algae
fescue grass
snake
dragonfly

A Venn diagram

Purpose: To show similarities and differences in two or more concepts.

Directions: List the unique traits of each concept in the appropriate circles, but not in the overlapping section. Write all similarities or likenesses between the two concepts in the overlapping section of the circles.

The Fish Bone Diagram

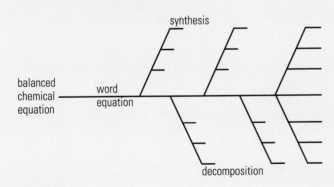

Figure 4

A fish bone diagram

Purpose: To identify separate causes and effects.

Directions: In the head of the fish, identify the effect, topic, or result. At the end of each major bone, identify the major subtopics or categories.

On the minor bones that attach to each major bone, add detail about the subtopics or possible causes of each effect or result.

The Concept Map

Purpose: To show connections between ideas and concepts, using words or visuals.

Directions: Put the central idea in the middle of a sheet of paper. Organize the ideas most closely related to each other in the same area around the centre. Draw arrows between the ideas that are related. On each arrow, write a short description of how the terms are related to each other. Expand and add ideas or relationships as you think of them.

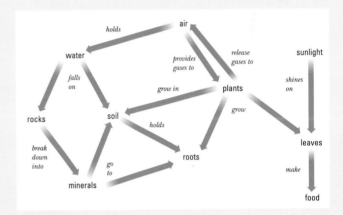

Figure 5

A concept map using words

Figure 6

A concept map using visuals

Glossary

A

abiotic: factor in an ecosystem created by non-living agents, for example, amount of sunlight, temperature, and strength and direction of wind

acceleration: the rate of change in speed (a scalar quantity) or velocity (a vector quantity); $a = \frac{\Delta v}{\Delta t}$ or $\vec{a} = \frac{\Delta \vec{v}}{\Delta t}$

acceleration due to gravity: the change in velocity of a falling object (ignoring friction), each second; a vector quantity

accuracy: a comparison of an experimental value with an accepted value; usually expressed as a percentage error

acid: a substance that tastes sour, turns blue litmus paper red, reacts with some metals to produce hydrogen gas, is a good conductor of electricity in solution, and reacts with a base to produce a salt and water

acid deposition: a term used to describe the falling of acids from the atmosphere to the ground, whether dissolved in precipitation or as solids

acid precipitation: a form of acid deposition in which acids are dissolved in rain, fog, dew, or snow; this precipitation has a pH of less than 5.6 (the pH of normal rainwater)

acidic oxide: a nonmetal oxide that reacts in water to form an acid

active layer: in the tundra, a layer of soil above the permafrost that thaws in summer; this soil permits the uptake of water and minerals by plant roots

advection: the horizontal transfer of energy by the movement of particles in a fluid

advisory: an alert from Environment Canada that means that severe weather is predicted for your area; an advisory is more serious than a watch

air mass: a large body of air in which the temperature and moisture content at a specific altitude are fairly uniform

albedo: a measurement of the percentage of light that an object reflects; the higher the albedo, the greater the object's ability to reflect sunlight

alkali metals: elements in the far left column of the periodic table; also called Group 1 elements

alkaline: a substance that may also be described as basic

alkaline earth metals: elements in the second column from the left of the periodic table; also called Group 2 elements

altitude: the height above sea level, usually measured in metres or kilometres; also called elevation

antacid: a mild base that can neutralize acid

anticyclone: a high-pressure system that rotates clockwise in the Northern Hemisphere and counterclockwise in the Southern Hemisphere

antioxidant: a substance that acts as a preservative by slowing down the rate of oxidation of molecules in food, particularly fats

area under the line: the size of the space between the graph line and the x-axis; (of a speed–time graph) a way of calculating distance; (of a velocity–time graph) a way of calculating displacement

artificial ecosystem: an ecosystem that is planned and maintained by humans, for example, a park, a farm, or a garden

atmosphere: the blanket of air and moisture that surrounds Earth

atmospheric pressure: the pressure the air exerts as gravity pulls it toward the centre of the Earth; it is greatest at sea level and decreases at higher altitudes

autotroph: an organism that uses energy and raw materials to make its own food, whether from photosynthesis or some other form of chemical synthesis; a producer

average acceleration: the acceleration of an object measured over a fairly large time interval

average speed: the total distance divided by the total time for a trip or other extended time period

average velocity: the resultant displacement divided by the total time from start to finish; the overall rate of change of position

B

base: a substance that tastes bitter, feels slippery, turns red litmus paper blue, is a good conductor of electricity in solution, and reacts with an acid to produce a salt and water

basic oxide: a metal oxide that reacts in water to form a base

bedrock: a layer of rock, lying below the soil

Bernoulli's principle: a scientific principle that states: where the speed of a fluid is high, the pressure is low, and where the speed of a fluid is low, the pressure is high; named after Swiss scientist Daniel Bernoulli (1700–1782)

bioamplification: a process that results in increasing concentrations of a toxin in the bodies of consumers at each succeeding trophic level

biodiversity: the number of species in an ecosystem, and the variety within those species

biomass: a pyramid-shaped measure of the mass of the dry matter contained in a group of living things, whether of a species, a class of species, or all of the organisms within an ecosystem

biome: a collection of ecosystems that are similar or related to each other in that the dominant form of plant life is the same; for example, the boreal forest biome is dominated by coniferous trees

biotic: a factor in an ecosystem created by the presence and roles of other living things

biotic potential: the maximum number of offspring that a species could produce, if resources were unlimited

blizzard: a severe storm with winds of 55 km/h or greater, low temperatures, and blowing snow that reduces visibility to 0.2 km or less

BOD (biological oxygen demand): a measure of the amount of dissolved oxygen needed by decomposers (bacteria) to break down the organic matter in a sample of water over a five-day period at 20°C; used to indicate the amount of organic matter in a water sample

Bohr diagram: a diagram used to represent the arrangement of electrons for an element; the electrons are drawn in a series of concentric circles around the nucleus

boreal forest: a biome dominated by coniferous trees; the most extensive biome in Canada; its biodiversity can be high or moderate, precipitation may be moderate or high, temperatures vary, and soil is often thin and slightly acidic

C

carbon cycle: the matter cycle in which, through the processes of photosynthesis, digestion, cellular respiration, decomposition, and combustion, carbon atoms move from an inorganic form in the air, water, or soil, to an organic form in living things, and then back to an inorganic form; all organic compounds contain carbon

carnivore: an animal that feeds on other animals

carrying capacity: the maximum population of a species that can be supported indefinitely by an ecosystem

catalyst: a substance that increases the rate of a chemical reaction without being consumed by the reaction

catalytic converter: a device in an automobile that converts polluting exhaust gases into safer molecules

cellular respiration: the process by which most living things generate useful energy, by combining sugars and oxygen to produce carbon dioxide and water

certainty: an expression of the level of confidence in a value; communicated by a number of significant digits

certainty rule: "When multiplying and/or dividing, the answer has the same number of significant digits as the original value with the fewest number of significant digits."

chemical change: the alteration of a substance into one or more different substances with different properties; also called a chemical reaction

chemical equation: a written representation of a chemical reaction using chemical formulas for reactants and products

chemical family: a group of elements in the same vertical column of the periodic table that tend to have similar physical and chemical properties

chemical property: the characteristic behaviour that occurs when a substance interacts with another to become a new substance

chemical test: a distinctive chemical reaction that can be used to identify an unknown substance

chemistry: the study of matter, its properties, and its changes or transformations

clear-cutting: forest harvesting in which all of the trees in an area are cut for use as timber or to make pulp for paper

climate: weather conditions of an area averaged over many years

closed population: a population in which only natality and mortality (not emigration and immigration) are acting

cloud seeding: the process of adding tiny particles (of dry ice or silver iodide) to clouds to control the formation of rain droplets and ice crystals; cloud seeding is used to reduce the chance of hailstones or increase the chance of rain

coastal zone: the area extending out from the high-tide line of an ocean or sea to the edge of the continental shelf; the coastal zone usually contains more nutrients, and so has higher biodiversity, than the oceanic zone

coefficient: a number written in front of a chemical symbol or formula; indicates the number of atoms or molecules of that substance

cold front: the leading edge of a cold air mass

coliform bacteria: a microorganism that occurs naturally in the intestines of humans and many other animals; the presence of this form of bacteria can be used as an indicator of the presence of more dangerous bacteria

collision model: a model of the rate of a reaction showing how the rate is proportional to the number of collisions of reactant molecules

combination reaction: the combination of smaller atoms and/or molecules into larger molecules; also called a synthesis reaction

combining capacity: the number of electrons an atom can gain, lose, or share to form an ionic compound (or a stable molecule)

combustion: the chemical reaction that occurs when a substance reacts very quickly with oxygen to release energy

community: the collection of all the populations of all the species in an ecosystem; all of the organisms in an ecosystem

compound: a pure substance that contains two or more different elements in a fixed proportion

concentrated solution: a solution that contains a large amount of solute compared to solvent

conduction: the transfer of energy through the collision of particles

constant acceleration: a rate of change in speed or velocity that does not change during the acceleration; also called uniform acceleration

constant speed: travelling the same distance over successive equal time intervals; also called uniform motion

constant velocity: motion in which both the direction and speed remain unchanged

consumer: a heterotroph; an organism that must eat producers or other consumers to survive

convection: the verticle transfer of energy by the movement of particles in a fluid

convective clouds: clouds formed from convection, that is, when air near the ground absorbs energy from heated surfaces (oceans, lakes, asphalt, concrete, dirt), becomes warmer and less dense, and rises in the atmosphere; most clouds are convective

Coriolis effect: the apparent change of direction of a moving object in a rotating system, named after French mathematician Gaspard G. de Coriolis (1792–1843); in weather systems, the Coriolis effect is caused by Earth's counterclockwise rotation

covalent bond: a bond formed by two or more nonmetal atoms sharing one or more pairs of electrons

cumulus clouds: clouds with a billowing, rounded shape; usually indicate unstable weather

cyclogenesis: the process of creating a cyclone

cyclone: a low-pressure, swirling air mass; winds in a cyclonic storm move counterclockwise in the Northern Hemisphere and clockwise in the Southern Hemisphere

D

decomposer: an organism that feeds on detritus, in the process releasing nutrients to the soil and water, where they can be used by other organisms

decomposition reaction: a chemical reaction in which a compound is broken down into elements or smaller compounds

defining equation: the definition of a quantity expressed in quantity symbols, e.g.,

$$\vec{v} = \frac{\vec{d}}{t}$$

denitrification: the process, performed by some soil bacteria, in which nitrates are converted to nitrites, and then to nitrogen gas; part of the nitrogen cycle

density-dependent factor: a factor in an ecosystem that affects a population, and that increases or decreases its effect based on the density of the population, for example, food supply, territory, and some forms of disease

density-independent factor: a factor that affects a population in a manner that does not vary according to the density of the population it is acting on, for example, fire and flood

detritus: waste from plants and animals, including their dead remains

dew: forms when the air cools and the water vapour it contains condenses on a cool surface near the ground

dew point: the temperature at which dew forms; dew forms when the air reaches the saturation temperature, i.e., when the relative humidity is 100%

dilute solution: a solution that contains a small amount of solute compared to solvent

displacement: a change in position; a vector quantity; the area under the line on a velocity–time graph

distance: length of path travelled; a scalar quantity (SI unit: metre)

double displacement reaction: a chemical reaction that occurs when elements in different compounds displace each other or exchange places to form two new compounds

drought: a long period with much less rainfall than average; some areas can experience both droughts and floods

E

ecological niche: the place or role of a species within an ecosystem; everything an organism does to survive and reproduce, including its place in the food web, its habitat, its breeding area, and the time of day that it is most active

ecology: the study of the interaction of living things with each other and with the abiotic (non-living) factors in their environment

ecosystem: in an area defined by an ecologist, the set of relationships between populations of species and between those populations and the abiotic (non-living) factors in their environment

ecotone: a transition area between two ecosystems that includes members of the community of both ecosystems

El Niño: a shift in the ocean currents, temperatures (water becomes warmer), and atmospheric conditions in the tropical Pacific Ocean; during El Niño, the warmer than normal water temperatures off the west coast of South America have a chain reaction effect, devastating plant and bird life and the local fishing industry

electrolyte: a substance that can conduct electricity when it dissolves in water

electromagnetic spectrum: the set of waves that can travel through empty space at the speed of light

electron: a negatively charged particle that moves around the nucleus of an atom at different energy levels, or orbits

element: a pure substance that cannot be broken down into a simpler substance

emigration: the number of individuals of a species moving out of an existing population

empirical knowledge: knowledge gained through observation or measurement

endangered: a species that is close to extinction

endothermic: a chemical reaction that absorbs heat (energy) from the surroundings

enzyme: a protein that controls the rate of chemical reactions in the body; also known as a biological catalyst

epilimnion: the upper level of a lake, which warms up in summer

eutrophic: a term used to describe a lake that contains more dissolved nutrients than an oligotrophic lake; such lakes are generally shallow and warm, and the water is often murky

exothermic: a chemical reaction that releases heat (energy) to the surroundings

extinct: a species that no longer exists anywhere on Earth

extirpated: a species that no longer exists in one part of its range

eye: the centre of a hurricane; in the eye of a hurricane the winds are fairly calm, the pressure is low, and the sky above is clear

eye wall: the part of a hurricane where the swirling winds and volume of rainfall are the greatest; the eye wall is at the outer edges of the eye

F

fertilizer: a material used to restore nutrients to plants, usually for the purpose of increasing production from farmland and in gardens

flood: extra water from rain, rivers, or oceans over land that is already saturated and cannot hold any more water; there are two types of floods: flash floods and broadside floods

food chain: a step-by-step sequence linking organisms that feed on each other, starting with a food source, such as a producer or detritus, and continuing with a sequence of consumers

food spoilage: natural breakdown of food that occurs over time

food web: a pictorial representation of the feeding relationships among organisms in an ecosystem

fossil fuel: a fuel (coal, oil, gasoline, or natural gas) formed over millions of years as organic materials decayed and were changed by heat and pressure under the surface of the Earth

front: the leading edge of a moving air mass; air masses with different properties don't blend easily, so a boundary, or front, develops as they meet

frontal clouds: clouds that form where the front of a large moving mass of air meets another air mass of a different temperature

G

glucose: a sugar; one of the products of photosynthesis

grassland: a biome dominated by grasses, it is found in Canada at approximately the same latitude as deciduous forests, but in areas where average precipitation is lower; its biodiversity is moderate, precipitation is low to moderate, temperatures are moderate, and soil is thick and very fertile

greenhouse effect: the process by which gases build up energy in the form of warmth in the atmosphere by absorbing long-wavelength (infrared) radiation from Earth's surface; this effect is named after how an actual greenhouse works

greenhouse gases: the gases in the atmosphere that absorb or reflect infrared radiation, for example, water vapour, carbon dioxide, and oxygen

ground water: the water found in the soil or rock layers of the Earth's crust; may flow out on to the surface (as it does at springs) or into bodies of surface water

H

habitat: the conditions required for the survival of a species

hail: a solid form of water created in cumulonimbus clouds high in the troposphere

halogens: elements in the second column from the right of the periodic table; also called Group 17 elements

heat capacity: the measure of how much heat a substance requires to increase its temperature or how much heat it releases as its temperature decreases

heat sink: any object or material that absorbs energy and becomes warmer; the atmosphere and oceans are examples of heat sinks

heat wave: a period of more than three days at or above 32°C

herbivore: an animal that eats plants

heterotroph: an organism that is incapable of making its own food, and so must feed on other organisms to gain energy

humidity: a measure of the amount of water vapour in the atmosphere; the more water vapour in the atmosphere, the more humid it becomes

humus: the organic component of soil, made up mostly of decomposing plants

hurricane: a severe cyclone that occurs in the western Atlantic Ocean, the Caribbean Sea, the Gulf of Mexico, or the eastern Pacific Ocean; if the winds in a cyclonic storm exceed 119 km/h, the storm is officially classified as a hurricane

hydrate: a solid compound that contains water molecules as part of the solid crystalline structure

hydrocarbon: a compound composed of hydrogen and carbon

hydrosphere: all of Earth's water, both fresh and salt, liquid and ice; the hydrosphere makes up around 70% of Earth's surface

hypolimnion: the lower level of a lake, which remains cool even in summer

I

ice storm: a storm in which rain freezes on contact with the surfaces it touches, forming a coat of ice; ice storms generally last for a few hours

immigration: the number of individuals of a species moving into an existing population

incomplete combustion: the chemical reaction that occurs when there is not enough oxygen available for complete combustion; the incomplete

combustion of a hydrocarbon produces carbon monoxide, carbon, carbon dioxide, and water

indicator: a substance that turns a different colour in acids and bases

inhibitor: an antioxidant that slows down chemical reactions; used as a preservative in food

inorganic: compounds that do not contain a combination of carbon and hydrogen atoms; carbon dioxide, water, and ammonia are all inorganic

instantaneous speed: the speed of an object at a particular instant

instantaneous velocity: the change in position over an extremely short period of time; a tangent to the curve on a position–time graph

intertidal zone: the area of the coastal zone of an ocean or sea that is defined by low and high tide

ion: an atom that has become charged by gaining or losing one or more electrons

ionic charge: the numerical value of the electric charge of an ion

ionic compound: a compound consisting of positive and negative ions

J

jet stream: high-speed winds in the upper troposphere, often around the mid-latitudes

L

La Niña: a shift to cooler than average water temperatures and atmospheric conditions in the tropical Pacific Ocean; this effect is opposite to El Niño

land breeze: a thermal, or wind, that forms over water near the shore and flows from the land toward the water

Law of Conservation of Mass: a scientific law that states that the total mass of the reactants in a chemical reaction is always equal to the total mass of the products

law of the minimum: the nutrient in least supply is the one that limits growth

law of tolerance: states that an organism can survive within (tolerate) a certain range of an abiotic factor; above and below this limit it can not survive; the greater this range of tolerance, the greater the organism's ability to survive

leaching: a process in which nutrients such as organic matter and minerals are dissolved in percolating water and carried into lower layers of soil or bedrock

limnetic zone: the area of the open lake, beyond the littoral zone, where there is enough light for free-floating organisms, such as algae, to carry out photosynthesis

litter: the upper layer of soil, made up mostly of partially decomposed leaves or grasses

littoral zone: the area extending out from the shore of a lake to the point where plants rooted in the bottom of the lake can no longer be found

M

matter: anything that has mass and takes up space

metal oxide: the substance formed when a metal reacts in oxygen; a metal oxide, also called a basic oxide, reacts in water to form a base

meteorologist: a person who works in the field of meteorology

meteorology: the study of the atmosphere and weather forecasting; the science of weather

microclimate: a set of atmospheric conditions near Earth's surface at a particular location, for example, the centre of a forest

molecular compound: a compound formed by the combination of two or more atoms held together with covalent bonds

monsoons: seasonal winds that bring heavy rains in one season and dry air in its other season

mortality: the number of individuals of a species that die in an ecosystem in one year

N

natality: the number of offspring of a species born in an ecosystem in one year

natural ecosystem: an ecosystem that is neither planned nor maintained by humans; an ecosystem in which

organisms are free to interact and change their interactions without human interference

natural product: a product that is obtained from natural sources, such as animals, plants, or minerals

neritic zone: the area of the coastal zone of an ocean or sea where photosynthesis can occur (i.e., to a depth of about 200 m), lying between the low-tide mark and the edge of the continental shelf

neutralization: a chemical reaction between an acid and a base that produces a salt and water

neutron: a neutral particle found in the nucleus of an atom

nitrogen cycle: a matter cycle in which, through the processes of nitrogen fixation, synthesis, decomposition, and denitrification, nitrogen atoms move from nitrogen gas in the atmosphere, to inorganic form in the soil, to organic form in living things, and then back to inorganic form in the soil and nitrogen gas in the atmosphere; organic compounds that contain nitrogen include amino acids (and therefore proteins) and DNA

nitrogen fixation: two processes in which atmospheric or dissolved nitrogen is converted into nitrate ions; part of the nitrogen cycle; both lightning and some soil bacteria can fix nitrogen

noble gases: the elements in the far right column of the periodic table; also known as Group 18 elements

nonmetal oxide: the substance formed when a nonmetal reacts in oxygen; a nonmetal oxide, also called an acidic oxide, reacts in water to form an acid

nutrient: any chemical that is essential to living things; nutrients are cycled through ecosystems and geological processes

O

occluded front: the front that forms when a cold front catches up to and overtakes a warm front; the warm air is lifted above the surface of Earth and cut off, or occluded, from the cooler air below and the storm weakens

oligotrophic: a term used to describe a lake that is deep, cold, and low in dissolved nutrients; the water of such lakes is usually clear

omnivore: an animal that eats both plants and animals

open population: a population in which natality, mortality, immigration, and emigration are all acting

organic: compounds that contain atoms of both carbon and hydrogen; many organic compounds also contain oxygen and nitrogen atoms; sugars, fats, and proteins are all organic

organic compound: a molecular compound that contains carbon

orographic clouds: clouds that form when air moves up a mountain, expands at the lower pressure, and cools

oxyacid: a compound formed when hydrogen combines with a polyatomic ion that contains oxygen

ozone: a gas that consists of three oxygen atoms (O_3); in the upper atmosphere ozone absorbs ultraviolet (UV) radiation, which is harmful to us

ozone hole: an extended area in the upper atmosphere where the ozone concentration is abnormally low

P

peat: slowly decomposing plant matter; created in low-oxygen environments such as bogs; peat may be transformed, through geologic processes, into coal

percolation: the process in which ground water, pulled by gravity, flows downward through the soil

periodic table: a structured arrangement of elements; elements with similar chemical and physical properties are in the same column

permafrost: in the tundra, a layer of soil that remains frozen, even in summer

pest: an organism that people consider harmful or inconvenient in a particular situation, such as weeds and some insects, fungi, and rodents

pesticide: a chemical designed to kill pests; pesticides are often used to protect species that are beneficial to humans from a competitor or predator that is less useful

pH scale: a numerical scale, ranging from 0 to 14, used to measure how acidic or basic a solution is

photosynthesis: the process by which green plants and some other organisms use sunlight energy, carbon dioxide, and water to produce carbohydrates (sugars) and oxygen

physical change: a change in the size or form of a substance, which does not change the chemical properties of the substance

physical property: a characteristic or description of a substance (including the state of matter at room temperature, hardness, melting and boiling points, odour, solubility, and colour) that can be used to identify it

plankton: a term used to describe small organisms found in lakes and oceans; the term includes heterotrophic plankton (usually invertebrate animals) and autotrophic plankton (such as algae)

plastics: polymers that are shaped by flow at some point in their manufacture

pollutant: a chemical in the air that causes harm to living things or to the environment

polyatomic ion: a group of atoms that tend to stay together and carry an overall ionic charge

polymers: long-chain molecules formed when hundreds of smaller molecules link together

population: all of the members of a species living in the same ecosystem or habitat

position: the straight-line distance and direction from a reference point; a vector quantity

position–time graph: a graph in which position is plotted on the y-axis and time on the x-axis

positive test: a test for a substance that clearly indicates the substance is present

precipitate: a solid formed from two solutions

precipitation: water that reaches the ground in either liquid or solid form, for example, rain, snow, freezing rain, and dew; it is the stage in the water cycle that follows condensation, freezing, or sublimation

precision: the place value of the last digit obtained from a measurement or calculation; indicated by the number of decimal places

precision rule: "When adding and/or subtracting values, the answer has the same number of decimal places as the original value with the fewest number of decimal places."

pressure gradient: a measure of the amount the atmospheric pressure changes across a certain distance; can be vertical or horizontal

prevailing winds: winds that affect large areas, for example, the trade winds, mid-latitude westerlies, and the jet stream

primary consumer: in a food chain or food web, an organism that relies on autotrophs directly for its source of energy; organisms at the second trophic level

producer: an autotroph; an organism that uses photosynthesis or another form of chemical synthesis to make food

product: the substance produced in a chemical reaction

profundal zone: the region beneath the limnetic zone of a lake, where there is not enough light to carry out photosynthesis

proton: a positively charged particle that is found in the nucleus of an atom

psychrometer: an instrument used to determine the relative humidity in the atmosphere; the most common psychrometer uses a wet-bulb and a dry-bulb thermometer

pure substance: a substance that contains only one kind of particle

Q

quantity symbols: italic letters used to represent quantities in scientific equations, e.g., t, d, v

R

radiation: the transfer of energy by means of waves that do not require a medium

rate of reaction: the speed at which a reaction occurs

reactant: the starting material in a chemical reaction

reference point: the point from which position is measured; usually the origin or starting point

relative humidity: the measure of the amount of water vapour actually in the air as a percentage of the maximum amount of water vapour the air can hold at that temperature

resultant displacement: vector sum of two or more displacements; a single displacement that has the same effect as all of the individual displacements; a vector quantity

rounding: reducing the results of a calculation to the appropriate number of significant digits or decimal places

S

salt: a combination of positive and negative ions; formed by the reaction of an acid and a base

saturation: when a substance reaches saturation, this means that, at a particular temperature, the substance is holding the maximum amount of water vapour (e.g., in air) or a material (e.g., in a solution) possible

scalar quantity: a quantity that involves only size, but not direction

scientific law: a general statement that sums up the conclusions of many experiments

sea breeze: a thermal, or wind, that forms near a sea, an ocean, or a lake and flows from the water toward the land

secondary consumer: in a food chain or food web, an organism that relies on primary consumers for its principal source of energy; organisms at the third trophic level

selective cutting: forest harvesting in which only certain species or sizes of trees are removed from an area for use as timber or to make pulp for paper

SI: *Système international d'unités* or the International System of Units

significant digits: an indication of the certainty of a measurement; the number of certain digits, plus one estimated digit, in a measurement

single displacement reaction: a chemical reaction in which one element displaces, or replaces, another element in a compound

skeleton equation: a representation of a chemical reaction in which the formulas of the reactants are connected to the formulas of the products by an arrow

slope of the line: on a graph, represents the steepness of the line; the relationship between the two variables:
$$\text{slope} = \frac{\text{rise}}{\text{run}} = \frac{y_2 - y_1}{x_2 - x_1}$$

smog: a type of air pollution resulting from emissions from vehicles and industries that burn fossil fuels; greenhouse gases also contribute to smog (from the words "smoke" and "fog")

stationary front: an unmoving front between a warm air mass and a cold air mass; usually means stable weather until the air masses begin to move

storm surge: a huge volume of water that is piled up by the winds of a severe storm and pushed onto the shore; can cause serious damage and flooding because of the sheer volume of water

stratus clouds: clouds with a flattened, layered shape; usually indicate stable weather

subsoil: a layer of soil, below the topsoil, that usually contains many stones and only small amounts of organic matter

surface area: the amount of area of a sample of matter that is visible and able to react

surface water: water in lakes, ponds, rivers, and streams

sustainable system: a system that survives, functions, and is renewed over time; a system in which people can continue to live and flourish for many generations

sustainable yield: the maximum amount of fish, whether of a species or of all species, that can be harvested in a year from a body of water and that can be replaced through natural processes in the course of that year

synthesis reaction: a chemical reaction in which two or more elements or compounds combine to form a single compound; also called a combination reaction

synthetic: artificially made materials that have been manufactured in the chemical industry

T

tangent: a straight line that just touches a curve at one point; used to find the slope of a curve on a graph

temperate deciduous forest: a biome dominated by deciduous trees — birch and maple in the north, oak and beech in the south; this biome is limited to the area south of the boreal forest in Eastern and Central Canada; its biodiversity is high, precipitation is moderate, temperatures are moderate, and soil is mostly thick and fertile

temperature gradient: the change of temperature of the atmosphere at different altitudes

temperature inversion: forms when a warm layer of air in a high-pressure system moves in and pushes down on cooler air; when this happens at the lower altitudes, the cooler air mass is trapped near the ground, and it cannot rise as it becomes heated, thereby keeping the air near the ground humid and often polluted

theoretical knowledge: knowledge that we cannot observe, but that explains the world around us

thermal: a rising current of warm air, caused by convection; a wind

thermocline: a narrow zone in a lake between the epilimnion and the hypolimnion in which the temperature drops rapidly from warm to cold

thermodynamics: the scientific study of energy transformations, described by laws; the first law states that although energy can be transformed from one form to another, it cannot be created or destroyed; the second law states that during any energy transformation, some of the energy is converted into a form, mostly heat, that cannot be used (i.e., each time energy is transformed in a system, some of that energy is lost from the system)

threatened: a species that is likely to become endangered if factors that make it vulnerable are not reversed

thunderstorm: a storm with lightning, thunder, heavy rain, and sometimes hail

time: duration between two events (SI unit: second)

titration: a method used to analyze a solution by measuring the amount of a solution needed to completely react with another solution; in acid-base reactions, an acid is added to a base until neutralization is complete

topsoil: a layer of soil, below the litter, made up of small particles of rock, usually mixed with relatively large amounts of decaying plant and animal matter

tornado: a severe component of a thunderstorm in which a rotating funnel cloud extends from the base of the cumulonimbus clouds to the ground

trophic level: a way of categorizing living things according to how they gain their energy; the first trophic level contains autotrophs, and each higher level contains heterotrophs

tropical cyclone: a severe cyclone that develops in the Indian Ocean and the area around Australia; typhoons and tropical cyclones can be more severe than hurricanes because they are fuelled by the warm waters of the huge Pacific and Indian oceans

tropopause: the layer in the atmosphere where the troposphere ends and before the stratosphere begins

troposphere: the atmospheric layer closest to Earth's surface, up to an altitude of about 12 km, but less near the poles; responsible for most of our weather systems

tundra: the huge treeless region, between the northern limits of Canada's tree line and the permanently ice-covered area in the Arctic; it is dominated by lichens and small plants such as moss, sedge, and short grasses; its biodiversity and average precipitation and temperatures are all low, and its soil is thin and low in fertility

typhoon: a severe cyclone that develops in the northwestern Pacific Ocean or the China Sea

U

universal indicator: a substance that turns different colours in solutions with different pH values

uniform motion: constant speed or constant velocity

UV index: a scale that reveals how much time in the Sun on a specific day would cause sunburn

V

valence: the combining capacity of an element

valence shell: the outer electron shell of an atom; the electrons in this shell are called valence electrons

vector: a line segment representing the size and direction of a vector quantity

vector diagram: a combination of several vectors, usually added "head-to-tail," to show the resultant vector, such as the resultant displacement

vector quantity: a quantity that includes a direction, such as position

velocity: speed in a stated direction; displacement divided by time interval; a vector quantity

velocity–time graph: a graph in which velocity is plotted on the y-axis and time on the x-axis

vulnerable: a species that is not in imminent danger of extinction, but that is at risk because of low or declining numbers at the fringe of its range, or in some restricted area

W

warm front: the leading edge of a warm air mass

warning: an alert from Environment Canada that means that extreme weather may be occurring or that it is highly likely to arrive somewhere in your area; this is the most serious weather alert

watch: an alert from Environment Canada that means that extreme weather could occur in your area

water pollution: any change, whether physical or chemical, that is introduced to surface water or ground water

water table: the boundary, found either in the soil or in bedrock, between the area where ground water is percolating down and a layer that is saturated with water

weather: the conditions outside considered from day to day; compare with climate

weather balloon: a helium-filled balloon used to gather weather-related data as it rises in the atmosphere; different types of weather balloons gather different data

weather dynamics: the study of how the motion of water and air causes weather patterns; air pressure and ocean currents are two examples of weather dynamics

weather satellite: a spacecraft that orbits Earth, regularly obtaining images and gathering data related to weather; information gathered by weather satellites is relayed to weather stations on the ground

weather system: a set of temperature, wind, pressure, and moisture conditions, for a certain region, that moves as a unit for a period of days

wind chill factor: a measure of the cooling effect of wind on a body; the effect of wind in the winter can be dangerous

word equation: a representation of a chemical reaction

Index

Credits

Unit 1: Sustaining Ecosystems

Unit 2: Chemical Processes

p. 177 © Steve Strickland/Visuals Unlimited; p. 178 © Kevin Fleming/CORBIS; p. 179 © Arthur Strange/VALAN PHOTOS; p. 181 Dave Starrett; p. 183 courtesy Lynn Walker; p. 184 top left © Lester V. Bergman/CORBIS, top centre © John Fowler/VALAN PHOTOS, top right © Lester V. Bergman/CORBIS, bottom left © Charles O'Rear/CORBIS, bottom centre © Rich Treptow/Visuals Unlimited, bottom right © Lester V. Bergman/CORBIS; p.188 top Jeremy Jones, bottom from left to right © Jeannie R. Kemp/VALAN PHOTOS, © J. A. Wilkinson/VALAN PHOTOS, last two © John Fowler/VALAN PHOTOS; p. 191 Jeremy Jones; p. 199 © Jerry Mason/Science Photo Library; p. 200 Dave Starrett; p. 201 left © Charles D. Winters/Photo Researchers, right © Phillip Norton/VALAN PHOTOS; p. 202 top © John Borden/Visuals Unlimited, middle © Randy Faris/CORBIS, bottom © Chinch Gryniewicz; Ecoscene/CORBIS; p. 205 top © David Muench/CORBIS, bottom © Lowell Georgia/CORBIS; p. 206 top and bottom © Joseph Sohm; ChromoSohm Inc./CORBIS; p. 208 top © Richard Hamilton Smith/CORBIS, upper middle left © Dave G. Hauser/CORBIS, upper middle right © James L. Amos/CORBIS, lower middle © Bettman Archive/CORBIS, bottom © AFP/CORBIS; p. 209 top © Ken Redding/CORBIS, bottom Dave Starrett; p. 210 © top Anne Goodes, bottom © Tiziana and Gianni Baldizzone/CORBIS; p. 215 Anne Goodes.

Chapter 6: p. 216 left and right Yoav Levy/Phototake/PictureQuest; pp. 218–221 Dave Starrett; p. 222 top © Jonathan Blair/CORBIS, bottom © Sergio Dorantes/CORBIS; p. 223 © Pat J. Groves; Ecoscene/CORBIS; pp. 224–225 Dave Starrett; p. 227 © Darrell Gulin/CORBIS; p. 230 top Dave Starrett, bottom © George Hall/CORBIS; p. 231 © Lionel Bourque/VALAN PHOTOS; p. 232 Dave Starrett; p. 233 © CORBIS; p. 234 top Dave Starrett, bottom Canadian Press/ Darrell Cake; p. 235 PhotoDisc; pp. 236–238 Dave Starrett; pp. 240–245 Dave Starrett; p. 248 © Michael Pole/CORBIS; p. 250 Courtesy Ann Tran; p. 252 © J. A. Wilkinson/VALAN PHOTOS; p. 253 © Paul A. Souders/CORBIS.

Chapter 7: p. 254© Tom Bean/CORBIS; p. 256 Dave Starrett; p. 258 ©Charles D. Winters/Photo Researchers Inc.; p. 259 Dave Starrett; p. 260 top Dave Starrett, bottom © Tom Bean/CORBIS; p. 261 © Dean Conger/CORBIS; p. 262 top and bottom left and centre Dave Starrett, bottom right © Paul A. Souders/CORBIS; p. 263 © Roger Wood/CORBIS; p. 265 top © James L. Amos/CORBIS, bottom left and right © Uwe Walz/CORBIS; p. 266 © Bettman Archive/CORBIS; p. 267 © Tim Wright/CORBIS; p. 268 © Charles D. Winters/Photo Researchers Inc.; p. 270 top © James L. Amos/CORBIS, bottom NASA/Photo Researchers Inc.; p. 271 Dave Starrett; p. 272 Dave Starrett; p. 273 Richard Megna/Fundamental Photographs; p.277 Dave Starett; p. 278 top © Danny Lehman/CORBIS, bottom Dave Starrett; p. 279 top © Luis Rosendo/FPG, middle and bottom Dave Starrett; p. 280 Dave Starrett; p. 281 top © Raymond Gehman/CORBIS, bottom © Jane Torrance/VALAN PHOTOS; pp. 282–283 Dave Starrett; p. 284 courtesy Mark Argent; p. 286 Dave Starrett.

Chapter 8: pp. 288–289 © Gary W. Carter/Visuals Unlimited; pp. 290–291 Dave Starrett; p. 293 © John Fowler/VALAN

PHOTOS; p. 294 Dave Starrett; p. 297 © D. S. Kerr/Visuals Unlimited; p. 298 Dave Starrett; p. 303 Dave Starrett; p. 305 Jeremy Jones; p. 306 top © R. Moller/VALAN PHOTOS, bottom © James L. Amos/CORBIS; p. 307 Jeremy Jones; p. 308 © Rob Simpson/Visuals Unlimited; p. 310 © Joe McDonald/Visuals Unlimited; p. 311 left and right © V. Wilkinson/VALAN PHOTOS; p. 312 © John D. Cunningham/Visuals Unlimited; pp. 315–316 Dave Starrett; p. 317 top © Simon Fraser/Science Photo Library, bottom © Owen Franken/CORBIS; p. 318 left © Betz, Science VU/Visuals Unlimited, right PhotoDisc; p. 319–321 Dave Starrett; p. 322 © Ed Eckstein/CORBIS, bottom © Ted Spiegel/CORBIS; p. 324 courtesy Bruce Kosugi; p. 326 © Mark E. Gibson/Visuals Unlimited; p. 327 Dave Starrett; p. 328 left PhotoDisc, right © Blow-Up/TCL; p. 329 © David Noton/TCL; p. 331 Anne Goodes and Monica Kompter.

Unit 3: Motion

Unit Opener (pp. 334–335) © Raymond Gehman/CORBIS; p. 336 left © Phillip Norton/VALAN PHOTOS, right Dave Buston/Canadian Press; p. 337 left © Phil Schermeister/CORBIS, right Associated Press AP/Rick Stevens; p. 338 Canadian Press; p. 339 top and middle © Bettman Archive/CORBIS, bottom Anne Goodes.

Chapter 9: p. 340 top main © Ronald Royer/Science Photo Library, top inset © Science Photo Library, bottom © IMBRL/Visuals Unlimited; p. 341 Dave Starrett; p. 342 top ©LT4/SpectrumStock, bottom © Armand Trottier/La Presse; p. 344 courtesy AECL Photographic Dept.; p. 345 © L. S. Stepanowicz/Visuals Unlimited; p. 347 NASA/JPL; p. 350 NASA/HST; p. 351 Peter Menzel/Stock, Boston/PictureQuest; p. 352 Dave Starrett; p. 355 top Jose Azel/Picture Quest; p. 356 courtesy Via Rail Canada; p. 357 courtesy Janna Van Kessel; p. 358 Associated Press AP/Fabrice Coffrini; p. 359 Associated Press/REMOTE MANIPULATOR SYSTEM; p. courtesy 360 Hans Van Kessel; p. 366 Suzanne Bird/Canadian Press; p. 369 top Boréal, bottom © George Lepp/CORBIS; p. 372 top and bottom Boréal; p. 374 courtesy Marilyn Reynolds; p. 376 top Associated Press/Trevor Collins, bottom © CORBIS.

Chapter 10: p. 378 left © NASA/CORBIS, right © V. Wilkinson/VALAN PHOTOS; p. 379 left © Telegraph Colour Library/FPG, right © John Sohlden/Visuals Unlimited; p. 380 top © Tim Hauf/Visuals Unlimited, bottom-Richard Thom/Visuals Unlimited; p. 381 © Kevin Collins/Visuals Unlimited; p. 384 © Francis Lepine/VALAN PHOTOS; p. 385 Frank Gunn/Canadian Press; p. 386 top © Ken Chernus/FPG, bottom Tom Hanson/Canadian Press; p. 387 top © Al Harvey/TNbct, bottom © Staffan Widstrand/CORBIS; p. 388 Kevin Frayer/ Canadian Press; p. 389 © CORBIS; p. 394 top © Bob Anderson/ Masterfile, bottom Boréal; p. 396 © top Kennon Cooke/VALAN PHOTOS, bottom left and right courtesy of Automotive Journalists Association of Canada; p. 401 © Joe McDonald/ Visuals Unlimited; p. 404 top © Richard T. Nowitz/CORBIS, bottom Associated Press/Andy Newman; pp. 406–407 top courtesy Honda/Acura, left courtesy Mitsubishi, right courtesy Volkswagon; p. 408 courtesy Volker Nolte; p. 411 Paul Chiasson/Canadian Press.

Chapter 11: p. 420 © Nik Wheeler/CORBIS; p. 426 top Jacques Boissinot/Canadian Press, bottom PhotoDisc; p. 430 top Paul Chiasson/Canadian Press, middle Jacques Boissinot/Canadian Press, bottom © Mike King/CORBIS; p. 437 courtesy Ricardo Browne; p. 438 top © Bob Gurr/ VALAN PHOTOS, bottom Courtesy Canadian Peregrine Foundation Project Release; p. 440 top Associated Press/ Shizuo Kambayashi, bottom © Tom Wilson/Masterfile; p. 441 courtesy Air Canada.

Chapter 12: pp. 444–445 left © Jay Dickman/CORBIS, right © Cassy Cohen/PhotoEdit/PictureQuest; p. 446 © Ray Richardson/Animals Animals; p. 454 Jeff McIntosh/Canadian Press; p. 456 left Kevin Frayer/Canadian Press, right © CORBIS; p. 458 top Alessandro Trovati/Canadian Press, bottom Brian Smith/Stock, Boston/PictureQuest; p. 462 © David Nunuk/ First Light; p. 467 top Anne Goodes; p. 474 top courtesy of Paramount Parks, bottom Associated Press/ Amy Sancetta; p. 475 Scala/Art Resource, NY; p. 475 bottom NASA p. 477 © First Light; p. 479 © Jim Sugar Photography/CORBIS; p. 480 © Tom Sanders/Masterfile; p. 482 top and bottom © Bettman Archive/CORBIS; p. 484 courtesy Kirsty Watson; p. 488 left Scala/Art Resource, NY, right © Bettman Archive/CORBIS; p. 489 © Rommel/Masterfile; p. 490 Dave Starrett; p. 491 Associated Press/Brian Cassey; p. 492 © Paul A. Souders/ CORBIS; p. 493 Frank Gunn/Canadian Press.

Unit 4: Weather Dynamics

Unit Opener (pp. 494–495) A&J Verkaik/SkyArt; p. 496 left NASA, right © Mark Gibson/CORBIS; p. 497 left © Phillip Norton/VALAN PHOTOS, right Environment Canada; p. 498 Associated Press/Itsuo Inouye; p. 499 top © Link/Visuals Unlimited, middle © Francis Lepine/VALAN PHOTOS, bottom © Ray Nelson/Phototake/PictureQuest.

Chapter 13: p. 500 © CORBIS; p. 502 © Kennon Cooke/ VALAN PHOTOS; p. 510 Dave Starrett; p. 513 © Mark Burnett/Science Photo Library; pp. 514–515 Dave Starrett; p. 520 Associated Press/Fabrice Coffrini; p. 522 © Bob Gurr/ VALAN PHOTOS; p. 523 © VCG/FPG; p. 528 Associated Press/AFP; p. 530 © Ian Davis-Young/VALAN PHOTOS; p. 532 ©Eastcott/Momatiuk/VALAN PHOTOS; p. 538 courtesy of Sangeeta Sharma; p. 541 clockwise from top left © John Fowler/ VALAN PHOTOS, © J. A. Wilkinson/ VALAN PHOTOS, © Ian Davis-Young/VALAN PHOTOS, © Bob Gurr/VALAN PHOTOS.

Chapter 14: p. 542 © David Parker/Science Photo Library; pp. 544–545 Dave Starrett; p. 548 Environment Canada/GOES I-M; p. 553 © main Eastcott/Momatiuk/VALAN PHOTOS, inset © Barbara K. Hesse/Visuals Unlimited; p. 555 left A&J Verkaik/SkyArt, right © Neal Solomon/Visuals Unlimited; p. 556 © Pat O'Hara/CORBIS; p. 559 © Tom Bean/CORBIS; p. 562 Boréal; p. 564 top © Carl Purcell/CORBIS, bottom Willy Waterton/Canadian Press; p. 565 top © Don Loveridge/VALAN PHOTOS, middle and bottom © Alan J. Hirsch; p. 567 top

© Andrew Menzel/Masterfile, bottom © CORBIS; p. 568 top © David R. Frazier/Photo Researchers Inc., bottom Environment Canada; p. 569 clockwise from top left © Jerry Mason/Science Photo Library, © Gilles Delisle/VALAN PHOTOS, © Carol Havens/CORBIS, © R. Moller/VALAN PHOTOS, © Sam Ogden/Science Photo Library; p. 570 Dan Roitner/ SpectrumStock; p. 572 Associated Press/Drew Wilson; p. 574 courtesy of Sarah Wong; p. 576 © Paul Seheult; Eye Ubiquitous/CORBIS; p. 577 top © Mark L Stephenson/ CORBIS, bottom © Val Wilkinson/VALAN PHOTOS.

Chapter 15: p. 578 © Jim Zuckerman/CORBIS; p. 584 J. T. Lewis/Welland Tribune/Canadian Press; p. 585 © Jim Zuckerman/ CORBIS; p. 587 Environment Canada; p. 589 top Tom Hanson/ Canadian Press, bottom Jacques Boissinot/Canadian Press; p. 590 top Tom Hanson/Canadian Press, bottom Canadian Press; p. 591 John Eastcott/YVA Momatiuk/VALAN PHOTOS; p. 592 © Michel Julien/VALAN PHOTOS; p. 594 Canadian Press; p. 595 Associated Press/Amy E. Cohen; p. 596 Associated Press, p. 598 SpectrumStock; p. 599 Kevin Frayer/Canadian Press; pp. 600 Kingston Whig-Standard/Canadian Press; p. 601 Robert Galbraith/Canadian Press; p. 602 main Tom Hanson/ Canadian Press, inset Ryan Remiorz/Canadian Press; p. 604 © David Schmidt/Masterfile; p. 606 © Visuals Unlimited; p. 608 Peter Power/Canadian Press; p. 610 courtesy Sarah Wong and The Weather Network; p. 612 ©CNES/Photo Researchers; p. 613 NASA/GSFC/SeaWiFs/Science Visualization Studio; p. 615 Jeff Greenberg/SpectrumStock; p. 616 courtesy Patrick Auger; p. 618 Dave Starrett; p. 619 top Associated Press, bottom Environment Canada.

Chapter 16: p. 620 ©Reuters Newsmedia/CORBIS; p. 622 © Stephen J. Krasemann/VALAN PHOTOS; p. 627 © NASA/GSFC/Science Photo Library; p. 629 courtesy Thien Nguyen; p. 630 © Steve Raymer/CORBIS; p. 632 Reuters/Jason Reed/Archive Photos; p. 633 top courtesy of Mountain Equipment Co-Op, bottom © Alan J. Hirsch; p. 637 top © Joe McDonald/Visuals Unlimited, middle © J. R. Page/VALAN PHOTOS, bottom © Yogi, Inc./CORBIS; p. 639 ©Reuters Newsmedia/CORBIS; p. 643 main and inset Dr. R. Schemenauer; p. 648 Associated Press; p. 650 left © Dan Roitner/Spectrum Stock, right Joseph Schuyler/Stock, Boston, PictureQuest; p. 653 NASA/LBJ Space Centre; p. 654 © Alan J. Hirsch.

Skills Handbook

Unit Opener (pp. 656–657) © Phil Schermeister/CORBIS; pp. 659–660 Dave Starrett; p. 665 © David Young-Wolff/ PhotoEdit; p. 695 © Michael Newma/PhotoEdit.

Career Profile Writing Credits:

Maureen de Sousa (Brian Swaile, Karin Banerd, Sarah Wong); Peggy Ferguson (Mary Bishop, Clynt King, Ann Tran, Mark Argent); Todd Mercer (Lynn Walker, Bruce Kosugi, Marilyn Reynolds, Volker Nolte, Ricardo Browne, Kirsti Watson); Matthew Roberts (Sangeeta Sharma, Patrick Auger, Thien Nguyen).

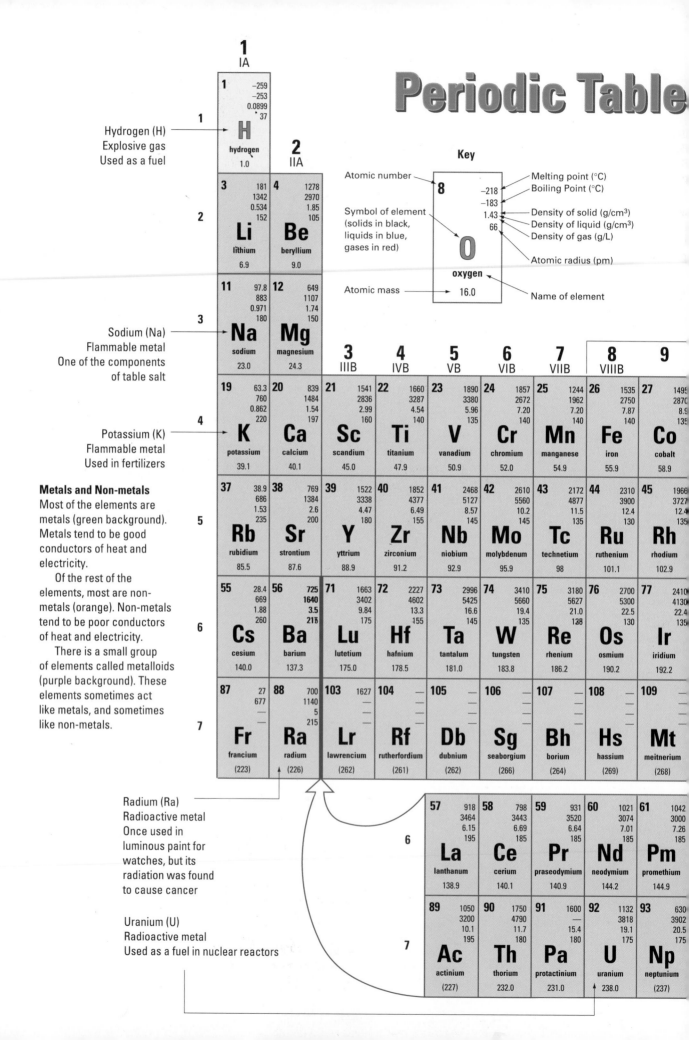

Periodic Table

Key

- Atomic number → 8
- Symbol of element (solids in black, liquids in blue, gases in red) → O
- Atomic mass → 16.0
- Melting point (°C) → −218
- Boiling Point (°C) → −183
- Density of solid (g/cm³) → 1.43
- Density of liquid (g/cm³)
- Density of gas (g/L) → 66
- Atomic radius (pm)
- Name of element → oxygen

Hydrogen (H)
Explosive gas
Used as a fuel

Sodium (Na)
Flammable metal
One of the components of table salt

Potassium (K)
Flammable metal
Used in fertilizers

Metals and Non-metals
Most of the elements are metals (green background). Metals tend to be good conductors of heat and electricity.
Of the rest of the elements, most are non-metals (orange). Non-metals tend to be poor conductors of heat and electricity.
There is a small group of elements called metalloids (purple background). These elements sometimes act like metals, and sometimes like non-metals.

Radium (Ra)
Radioactive metal
Once used in luminous paint for watches, but its radiation was found to cause cancer

Uranium (U)
Radioactive metal
Used as a fuel in nuclear reactors

Group headings: 1 IA, 2 IIA, 3 IIIB, 4 IVB, 5 VB, 6 VIB, 7 VIIB, 8 VIIIB, 9

Each element cell lists (top to bottom in the data column): melting point (°C), boiling point (°C), density, atomic radius (pm); then atomic number, symbol, name, atomic mass.

No.	Symbol	Name	Melting pt	Boiling pt	Density	Atomic radius	Atomic mass
1	H	hydrogen	−259	−253	0.0899	37	1.0
3	Li	lithium	181	1342	0.534	152	6.9
4	Be	beryllium	1278	2970	1.85	105	9.0
11	Na	sodium	97.8	883	0.971	180	23.0
12	Mg	magnesium	649	1107	1.74	150	24.3
19	K	potassium	63.3	760	0.862	220	39.1
20	Ca	calcium	839	1484	1.54	197	40.1
21	Sc	scandium	1541	2836	2.99	160	45.0
22	Ti	titanium	1660	3287	4.54	140	47.9
23	V	vanadium	1890	3380	5.96	135	50.9
24	Cr	chromium	1857	2672	7.20	140	52.0
25	Mn	manganese	1244	1962	7.20	140	54.9
26	Fe	iron	1535	2750	7.87	140	55.9
27	Co	cobalt	1495	2870	8.9	135	58.9
37	Rb	rubidium	38.9	686	1.53	235	85.5
38	Sr	strontium	769	1384	2.6	200	87.6
39	Y	yttrium	1522	3338	4.47	180	88.9
40	Zr	zirconium	1852	4377	6.49	155	91.2
41	Nb	niobium	2468	5127	8.57	145	92.9
42	Mo	molybdenum	2610	5560	10.2	145	95.9
43	Tc	technetium	2172	4877	11.5	135	98
44	Ru	ruthenium	2310	3900	12.4	130	101.1
45	Rh	rhodium	1966	3727	12.4	135	102.9
55	Cs	cesium	28.4	669	1.88	260	140.0
56	Ba	barium	725	1640	3.5	215	137.3
71	Lu	lutetium	1663	3402	9.84	175	175.0
72	Hf	hafnium	2227	4602	13.3	155	178.5
73	Ta	tantalum	2996	5425	16.6	145	181.0
74	W	tungsten	3410	5660	19.4	135	183.8
75	Re	rhenium	3180	5627	21.0	135	186.2
76	Os	osmium	2700	5300	22.5	130	190.2
77	Ir	iridium	2410	4130	22.4	135	192.2
87	Fr	francium	27	677	—	—	(223)
88	Ra	radium	700	1140	5	215	(226)
103	Lr	lawrencium	1627	—	—	—	(262)
104	Rf	rutherfordium	—	—	—	—	(261)
105	Db	dubnium	—	—	—	—	(262)
106	Sg	seaborgium	—	—	—	—	(266)
107	Bh	borium	—	—	—	—	(264)
108	Hs	hassium	—	—	—	—	(269)
109	Mt	meitnerium	—	—	—	—	(268)
57	La	lanthanum	918	3464	6.15	195	138.9
58	Ce	cerium	798	3443	6.69	185	140.1
59	Pr	praseodymium	931	3520	6.64	185	140.9
60	Nd	neodymium	1021	3074	7.01	185	144.2
61	Pm	promethium	1042	3000	7.26	185	144.9
89	Ac	actinium	1050	3200	10.1	195	(227)
90	Th	thorium	1750	4790	11.7	180	232.0
91	Pa	protactinium	1600	—	15.4	180	231.0
92	U	uranium	1132	3818	19.1	175	238.0
93	Np	neptunium	630	3902	20.5	175	(237)

of the Elements

Oxygen (O)
Reactive gas
Product of
photosynthesis

Silicon (Si)
Metalloid
Used in computer
chips

Aluminum (Al)
Low-density metal
Used in aircraft parts,
cooking foil

	18 VIIIA
	2 −272 / −269 / 0.179 / 31 **He** helium 4.0

1

Helium (He)
Low-density, unreactive gas
Used to fill blimps, balloons

13 IIIA	14 IVA	15 VA	16 VIA	17 VIIA
5 2300 / 2550 / 2.34 / 85 **B** boron 10.8	6 3550 / 4827 / 2.26 / 70 **C** carbon 12.0	7 −210 / −196 / 1.25 / 65 **N** nitrogen 14.0	8 −218 / −183 / 1.43 / 66 **O** oxygen 16.0	9 −220 / −188 / 1.70 / 50 **F** fluorine 19.0

+3   +4   −3   −2   −1

	10 −249 / −246 / 0.900 / 38 **Ne** neon 20.2

2

Neon (Ne)
Unreactive gas
Used in electric discharge
tubes ("neon lights")

| 13   660 / 2467 / 2.70 / 125 **Al** aluminum 27.0 | 14   1410 / 2355 / 2.33 / 110 **Si** silicon 28.1 | 15   44.1 / 280 / 1.82 / 100 **P** phosphorus 31.0 | 16   113 / 445 / 2.07 / 100 **S** sulfur 32.1 | 17   −101 / −34.6 / 3.21 / 100 **Cl** chlorine 35.5 | 18   −189 / −186 / 1.78 / 71 **Ar** argon 39.9 |

3

Reactivity
Elements tend to be more
reactive the farther they
are from the centre of the
table, and the closer they
are to the bottom left and
upper right. Gold (Au) is
so unreactive that it can
be kept in elemental form
fairly easily. On the other
hand, fluorine (F)
is almost never found in
pure elemental form
because it is so reactive.

10	11 IB	12 IIB

| 28   1455 / 2730 / 8.90 / 135 **Ni** nickel 58.7 | 29   1083 / 2567 / 8.92 / 135 **Cu** copper 63.5 | 30   420 / 907 / 7.14 / 135 **Zn** zinc 65.4 | 31   29.8 / 2403 / 5.90 / 130 **Ga** gallium 69.7 | 32   937 / 2830 / 5.35 / 125 **Ge** germanium 72.6 | 33   817 / 613 / 5.73 / 115 **As** arsenic 74.9 | 34   217 / 684 / 4.81 / 115 **Se** selenium 79.0 | 35   −7.2 / 58.8 / 3.12 / 115 **Br** bromine 79.9 | 36   −157 / −152 / 3.74 / 88 **Kr** krypton 83.8 |

4

| 46   1554 / 2970 / 12.0 / 140 **Pd** palladium 106.4 | 47   962 / 2212 / 10.5 / 160 **Ag** silver 107.9 | 48   321 / 765 / 8.64 / 155 **Cd** cadmium 112.4 | 49   157 / 2080 / 7.30 / 155 **In** indium 114.8 | 50   232 / 2270 / 7.31 / 145 **Sn** tin 118.7 | 51   631 / 1750 / 6.68 / 145 **Sb** antimony 121.8 | 52   450 / 990 / 6.2 / 140 **Te** tellurium 127.6 | 53   114 / 184 / 4.93 / 140 **I** iodine 126.9 | 54   −112 / −107 / 5.89 / 108 **Xe** xenon 131.3 |

5

| 78   1772 / 3827 / 21.5 / 135 **Pt** platinum 195.1 | 79   1064 / 2808 / 19.3 / 135 **Au** gold 197.0 | 80   −39.0 / 357 / 13.5 / 150 **Hg** mercury 200.6 | 81   304 / 1457 / 11.85 / 190 **Tl** thallium 204.4 | 82   328 / 1740 / 11.3 / 180 **Pb** lead 207.2 | 83   271 / 1560 / 9.80 / 160 **Bi** bismuth 209.0 | 84   254 / 962 / 9.40 / 190 **Po** polonium (210) | 85   302 / 337 / — / — **At** astatine (210) | 86   −71 / −61.8 / 9.73 / 120 **Rn** radon (222) |

6

Noble Gases
The gases in the column
at the far right of the
table are very unreactive.
As a result, they are
found in nature mostly as
gases made up of single
atoms. Because of this
refusal to react, helium
(He), neon (N), and the
others (blue background)
are called the noble gases.

| 110   — / — / — / — **Uun** ununnilium (269) | 111   — / — / — / — **Uuu** unununium (272) | 112   — / — / — / — **Uub** ununbium (277) | 113 | 114   — / — / — / — **Uuq** ununquadrium (289) |

7

| 62   1074 / 1794 / 7.52 / 185 **Sm** samarium 150.4 | 63   822 / 1527 / 5.24 / 185 **Eu** europium 152.0 | 64   1313 / 3273 / 7.90 / 180 **Gd** gadolinium 157.3 | 65   1356 / 3230 / 8.23 / 175 **Tb** terbium 158.9 | 66   1412 / 2567 / 8.55 / 175 **Dy** dysprosium 162.5 | 67   1474 / 2700 / 8.80 / 175 **Ho** holmium 164.9 | 68   1529 / 2868 / 9.07 / 175 **Er** erbium 167.3 | 69   1545 / 1950 / 9.32 / 175 **Tm** thulium 168.9 | 70   819 / 1196 / 6.97 / 175 **Yb** ytterbium 173.0 |

6

| 94   64 / 3232 / 19.8 / 175 **Pu** plutonium (244) | 95   994 / 2607 / 13.7 / 175 **Am** americium (243) | 96   1340 / 3110 / 13.5 / — **Cm** curium (247) | 97   986 / — / 14 / — **Bk** berkelium (247) | 98   900 / — / — / — **Cf** californium (251) | 99   860 / — / — / — **Es** einsteinium (252) | 100   1527 / — / — / — **Fm** fermium (257) | 101   1021 / 3074 / — / — **Md** mendelevium (258) | 102   863 / — / — / — **No** nobelium (259) |

7